24th EUROPEAN SYMPOSIUM ON COMPUTER AIDED PROCESS ENGINEERING

COMPUTER-AIDED CHEMICAL ENGINEERING, 33

24th EUROPEAN SYMPOSIUM ON COMPUTER AIDED PROCESS ENGINEERING

PART – B

Edited by

Jiří Jaromír Klemeš
University of Pannonia, HU

Petar Sabev Varbanov
University of Pannonia, HU

Peng Yen Liew
University of Pannonia, HU

ELSEVIER

Amsterdam – Boston – Heidelberg – London – New York – Oxford
Paris – San Diego – San Francisco – Singapore – Sydney – Tokyo

Elsevier
Radarweg 29, PO Box 211, 1000 AE Amsterdam, The Netherlands
The Boulevard, Langford Lane, Kidlington, Oxford OX5 1GB, UK

First edition 2014

British Library Cataloguing in Publication Data
A catalogue record for this book is available from the British Library

Library of Congress Cataloging-in-Publication Data
A catalog record for this book is available from the Library of Congress

ISBN (Part B): 978-0-444-63455-9
ISBN (Set): 978-0-444-63434-4
ISSN: 1570-7946

For information on all Elsevier publications
visit our web site at store.elsevier.com

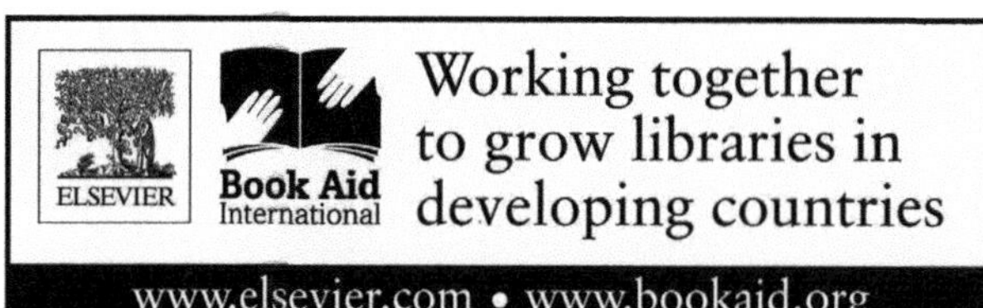

Contents

Sustainability and Life Cycle Analysis *(continued)*

Design and Optimisation

Efficient Energy Integrated Solutions for Manufacturing Industries (EFENIS)

Jiří Jaromír Klemeš, Petar Sabev Varbanov and Peng Yen Liew (Editors)
Proceedings of the 24th European Symposium on Computer Aided Process Engineering – ESCAPE 24
June 15-18, 2014, Budapest, Hungary.

Knowledge Management Framework for Assessing Environmental Impact in the Enterprise

Elisabet Capón-García[a*], Edrisi Muñoz[b], José M. Laínez-Aguirre[c], Antonio Espuña[d], Luis Puigjaner[d], Konrad Hungerbühler[a]

[a] *Department of Chemistry and Applied Biosciences, ETH Zürich, Wolfgang-Pauli-Str. 10, 8093 Zürich, Switzerland*
[b] *Centro de Investigación en Matemáticas A.C., Jalisco S/N, Mineral y Valenciana 36240, Guanajuato, Mexico*
[c] *School of Chemical Engineering, Purdue University, West Lafayette, IN, USA*
[d] *Department of Chemical Engineering, Universitat Politècnica de Catalunya, Av. Diagonal, 647, E08028 Barcelona, Spain*
elisabet.capon@chem.ethz.ch

Abstract

Since enterprises are highly involved systems, decision-making becomes a highly challenging task, and decision process is usually separated in several levels. Nevertheless, such levels are closely related, since they share data and information. Therefore, effective integration among the different hierarchical levels, by means of tools improving information sharing and communication, may play a crucial role for the enhanced enterprise operation, and consequently for fulfilling the enterprise's goals. Ontologies stand for an excellent choice for building complex models maintaining a high level of flexibility, re-usability, usability and easiness of maintenance. This work proposes the re-use of an ontological model for the integrated enterprises structure in order to include the environmental assessment function. The ontological framework facilitates integration among the different decision levels, and works as the mechanism for information and knowledge sharing for multiple applications. An example related to the waste-to-energy problem in the industry illustrates the opportunity for providing decision makers with new technologies to assess and evaluate the plant performance.

Keywords: Environmental Impact, Knowledge Management, Enterprise Wide Optimization, Intelligent Systems

1. Introduction

Nowadays, operational functions in enterprises have become crucial to remain competitive and offer a better service to customers. Some of these functions also aim to respond rapidly to the continuously changing market conditions and gain quick time-to-market and operational flexibility. Moreover, enterprises are increasingly committed to decrease the environmental impact of their activities due to stricter regulations. These activities, such as production, marketing, sales, human resources and logistics, usually interact with each other and share a large amount of data and information. Therefore, the consideration of environmental aspects within the enterprise is a highly challenging task. What is more, those functions and activities within enterprises consist of multiple business and process units of different time and space scales working together. Thus, the organization and management of the different scales and levels within such complex systems is crucial to understand, analyse, synchronize and improve their operations.

It is clear the need for infrastructures that continuously and coherently support for fast and reliable decision-making activities related to the production process, is now of paramount importance (Venkatasubramanian et al., 2006). This need is more evident when we consider recent activity in the fields of data warehousing, online analytical processing (OLAP), data mining and Web based DSS, followed by the treatment of collaborative support systems and optimization-based decision support.

The effective integration of the environmental issues within the enterprise structure may be achieved using tools improving information sharing and communication. In this sense, knowledge management technologies have proved to be highly promising for supporting this integration task. Therefore, the representation of the life cycle assessment within a knowledge management model will provide decision makers a framework to assess and evaluate the environmental impact of the enterprise activities.

Regarding the application of knowledge representation to environmental issues, Kraines et al. (2006) present a framework for expert knowledge sharing and discovery for integrated environmental assessment of technologies and processes associated with industrial ecology. They present a prototype software consisting of an upper ontology, logical inference reasoners and a multiagent system, which deals with industrial ecology focusing on human activities and industrial impacts on the environment. Industrial ecology concentrates on the mass and energy flows between and within the industrial systems and ecosystems aiming to contribute to the efforts of controlling and reducing the impacts that the use of those flows generates. A Life Cycle Assessment Ontology has been proposed by Brascher et al. (2007), including the domain represented by the ISO 14040 resulting in an ontology containing the four phases of the LCA. However, such ontology has natural language limitations, it contains a total of 132 terms, but the other properties of the ontology such as number of properties, classes or axioms are not specified. Davis et al. (2009) show how a agent based simulation can be used to explore the impacts of different CO_2 tax policies. They use an ontology to generically structure the data needed by the agents to trade and evaluate the environmental impacts of their decisions. The environmental burdens considered by this approach were restricted to those related to global warming.

Despite the aforementioned ontological approaches, none of them exploits the potential of combining the environmental issues within an integrated enterprise model. The aim of this work is to provide process analytical models with the necessary data and information related to the life cycle assessment, in order to optimize and evaluate them from an environmental perspective thus supporting decision-making. The scope of these decisions encompasses the operational, tactical and strategic levels. Therefore, a semantic model approach representing an integrated enterprise framework and considering the environmental system representation within the different enterprise decision levels is proposed. As a result, more environmentally conscious supply chains and production processes can be obtained.

2. Methodology

The proposed ontology supports different activities by stream lining information and data integration by means of an integrated model which captures the activities developed along the different levels of the enterprise structure resulting in an integrated decision making framework. The ontology provides the shared and common do main structures required for these mantic integration of information sources, resulting in a competitive advantage.

The developed ontology uses as base model a previous enterprise conceptualization presented by Muñoz et al. (2011) which supports the different enterprise levels, resulting in an integrated decision making framework. Additional model classes, properties and axioms have been created to include the environmental functionalities. As a result, the environmental assessment model is described and integrated with the enterprise model. Extended reference of the integrated enterprise ontology can be found in the original paper by Muñoz et al. (2011).

The environmental domain is represented based on the life-cycle assessment (LCA) methodology standardized in the ISO 1404X series (ISO14001) for setting an environmental management system (EMS). Moreover, the LCA has been selected for the assessment of the environmental performance of the enterprise functions, since it avoids shifting burdens from part of the product supply chain to another, which would eventually lead to larger environmental damages. The implementation of the LCA for a given process or product requires data associated with process environmental interventions (e.g. raw material consumption, uncontrolled emissions and waste generation). This set of data is organized in a life cycle inventory (LCI) which is the basis for the environmental impact calculation, as specified in the ISO 1404X series. The results of the LCI are classified into impact categories which can be located at any point in the cause-effect chain (Jolliet et al., 2003).

Information from the different hierarchical levels is needed to improve and assess overall process and environmental performance. The supply chain management decisions are related to the facilities location, production capacity and resources allocation, distribution flows and inventory policies. Therefore, the flow of materials, information and economic resources along the wide enterprise structure are modeled as well as the restrictions regarding mass balances, capacity and technological constraints, such as product recipes, product sequencing, unstable and perishable materials, economic limitations, suppliers' capacity and market demand among others. In fact, waste generation, fugitive emissions and raw material, transportation tasks or utility consumption are the key components of the LCIs. Therefore, the life cycle inventory is comprised in the original model of the enterprise ontology project Muñoz et al. (2011). As a result, the part of the environmental domain to be represented in the updated ontology concerns the environmental management system and the environmental metrics, since balance flows are already contained in the enterprise domain. This integration in the decision making system requires the information system to be robust.

The environmental performance of the management system analyzed is calculated using different environmental performance indicators, which are broadly classified in mid point and end point categories (Figure 1). The assessment of these indicators is based on the resources consumption (energetic, raw material, human, etc.) and pollutants generation of products and processes.

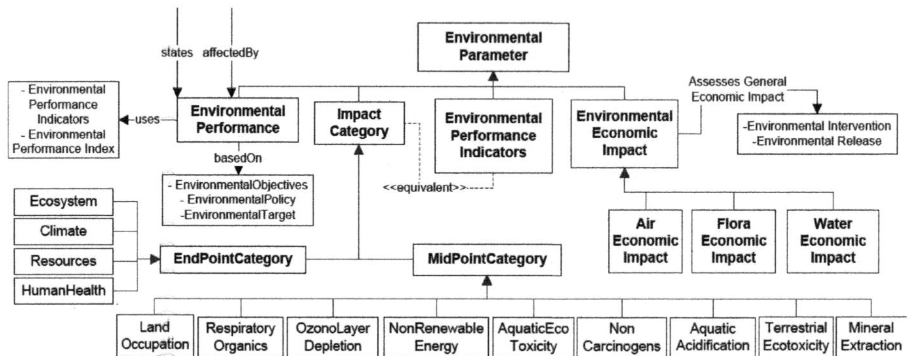

Figure 1. UML representation of a part of the environmental semantic model.

The methodology adopted in this work regarding the ontology development consists of the continuous improvement cycle presented in Muñoz (2011). Since the new ontological model is based on a previous one Muñoz et al. (2011), the ontology is the result of the re-planning and revisiting of the different phases of the continuous improvement cycle.

In order to exploit the full potential of the ontological model, for connecting transactional and analytical systems, Java has been used as a high-level programming language, because it provides a good versatility, efficiency and security. The code was built using the platform NetBeans IDE 7.0. The application of the ontological model for the environmental performance assessment takes place within the different enterprise decision layers, which are integrated by means of the enterprise ontology project. In this particular work, decision-making concerns the operational and strategic levels. The operation of the framework consists of retrieving the environmental mid-point categories related to the functional units and elements in the LCA assessment by querying to SIMAPRO using the Java code, the values for the ontologies instances that require environmental assessment. Once such values are obtained, they are stored in the ontology. Next, when the optimization model needs the data for formulating the problem, such information is retrieved from the ontology as well.

Once strategic and operational decisions are taken by the appropriate analytical system the actual solution is also represented within the ontology. The proposed ontology is intended to promote transversal process-oriented management, to enable crossover among the different functionality silos in which businesses have typically been structured. Such structures can recognize the existing trade-offs and impacts of the available alternatives at the different information aggregation levels, and discard non-significant effects, through retuning the decision-making/optimization model according to the current enterprise status. Furthermore, the benefits for the environmental performance assessment from having an integrated enterprise model is clear, since the life cycle inventory is automatically included within the latter model structure.

The dimension of the final ontological model consists of 276 classes, 67 restrictions, and 224 object properties stemming from the enterprise model itself, and 108 classes, 34 restrictions, and 74 object properties characterizing the environmental management domain. These components make the ontology reasoning and its use possible. The reasoning time for the consistency of the model and classes is 1.062 and 0.281 CPU s respectively in an Intel-Core 2 at 2.83GHz in a successful compilation. In addition, transactional systems related to data management are represented by databases (MySQL databases) linked to the different parts of the ontological model. This results in an improved way to manage these databases since they are better structured and can be adequately mined by the potential users.

3. Case study

An example related to the waste-to-energy problem in the industry has been studied since it stands as an opportunity for providing decision makers with new technologies to assess and evaluate the plant performance. The framework supports the information management based on a semantic representation of a waste treatment plant, namely its operational and logistics functions, and assessing the potential of energy generation and savings. It is demonstrated that the ontological framework can adapt and recognize the different elements found through the hierarchical levels associated with the enterprise functions and relate them to their environmental impact. The semantic model is the core of the knowledge based system, whose interface is beyond the scope of this work.

The main concern in that plant is to optimize decisions related to waste stream management in order to increase the economic yield and reduce the environmental impact of its operation. Since there is a huge number of waste streams with different properties, such as air demand and heat of combustion, the management at different levels of the treatment is not a trivial task, and information should be stored and managed efficiently. The waste treatment plant treats 50 different waste streams stemming from 50 independent external storage tanks located close to the production processes of different enterprises in the same site. Such streams are lead to one of the 28 available tanks in the industrial waste treatment plant, which store the waste streams previously to the waste treatment units. There are three different industrial waste treatment units in the waste treatment plant, namely two similar constructed incinerators with different capacities and a burner.

The instantiation of this example results in 1,220 instances, and the time for checking their consistency with the reasoner is 1.745 CPU s in a successful compilation. Figure 2 contains an extract of the instantiation of the problem, and illustrates the semantic relationships among the elements of the supply chain structure.

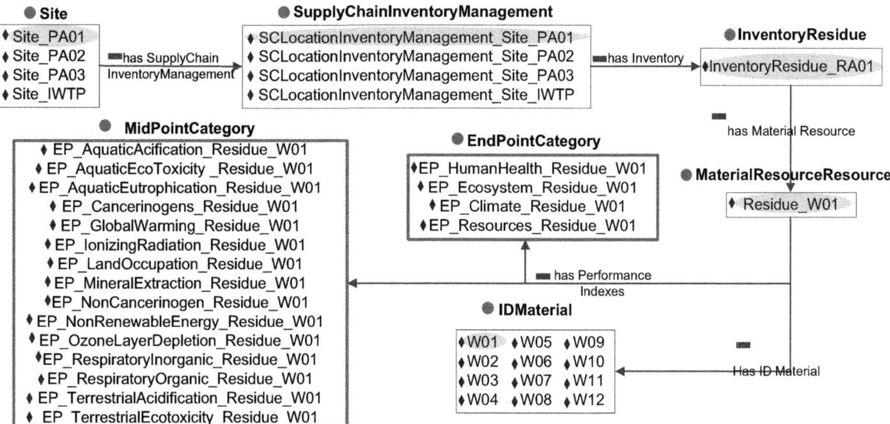

Figure 2. Extract of the ontology instantiation for the case study.

Specifically, for the "Site_PA01", the "SCInventoryManagement" has the property "hasInventory", which relates it to "InventoryResidue_RA01". The "InventoryResidue" has the property "hasMaterialResource", which in this case belongs to the class "Residue". Therefore, the instance "Residue_W01" of "Residue" has the property "hasEnvironmentalImpactIndexes", which directly connects the environmental impact of the residue resources to the computed mid and end point categories. In the figure, the classes are represented in bold on top of the boxes, the properties are written on the arrows relating classes and the instances are listed in the boxes.

4. Conclusions

This ontological framework allows assessing the environmental performance of the enterprises by communicating environmental life cycle data to analytical models. This ontology enhances the way for achieving a successful enterprise decision-making supporting tool, which adapts and recognizes the different elements found through the hierarchy models that are associated with the whole supply chain. Moreover, a general semantic framework is proposed, which is able to model any enterprise particular case and its environmental implications, proving its re-usability. As a whole, the main contributions of this framework and the model behind are re-usability, usability, higher efficiency in communication and coordination procedures within the enterprise in order to assess its environmental issues. This work represents a step forward to support the integration of different software tools applicable to the management of plant database information, resulting into an enhancement of the entire process management structure for aiding the automatic design and operation of more sustainable enterprises.

Acknowledgements

Authors would like to acknowledge the Spanish Ministerio de Economía y Competitividad and the European Regional Development Fund for supporting the present research by projects EHMAN (DPI2009-09386) and SIGERA (DPI2012-37154-C02-01). Thus, financial support received from CIMAT México is fully acknowledged.

References

M. Brascher, F. Monteiro, A. Silva, 2007, Life cycle assessment ontology, Proceedings of the 8th Conference of the International Society for Knowledge Organization, 169 – 177.

C. Davis, I. Nikolic, G.P.J. Dijkema, 2009, Integration of life cycle assessment into agent-based modeling, Journal of Industrial Ecology, 13, 306–325.

ISO14001, 2004, Environmental Management Systems - requirements with Guidance for Use, Technical report, ISO, Canada.

O. Jolliet, M. Margni, R. Charles, S. Humbert, J. Payet, G. Rebitzer, R. Rosenbaum, 2003, Impact 2002þ: a new life cycle impact assessment methodology, Int. Journal of LCA, 8, 324 – 330.

S. Kraines, R. Batres, B. Kemper, K. Michihisa, V. Wolowski, 2006, Internet-based integrated environmental assessment, part ii: Semantic searching based on ontologies and agent systems for knowledge discovery, Journal of Industrial Ecology, 10, 37 – 60.

E. Muñoz, 2011, Knowledge management tool for integrated decision-making in industries, PhD Thesis, Universitat Politècnica de Catalunya, Barcelona, Spain.

E. Muñoz, E. Capón-García, J. Lainez, A. Espuña, L. Puigjaner, 2011, Ontological framework for the enterprise from a process perspective, Proceedings of the International Conference on Knowledge Engineering and Ontology Development, 538 – 546.

V. Venkatasubramanian, C. Zhao, G. Joglekar, A. Jain, L. Hailemariam, P. Suresh, P. Akkisetty, K. Morris, G. Reklaitis, 2006, Ontological informatics infrastructure for pharmaceutical product development and manufacturing, Comput. Chem. Eng., 30, 1482 – 1496.

Jiří Jaromír Klemeš, Petar Sabev Varbanov and Peng Yen Liew (Editors)
Proceedings of the 24th European Symposium on Computer Aided Process Engineering – ESCAPE 24
June 15-18, 2014, Budapest, Hungary.

Design Methodology of Biomass Utilization System Considering Impacts on Petroleum Refining Industry

Baharuddin Maghfuri,[a*] Hirokazu Sugiyama,[a] Yasunori Kikuchi,[b] Masahiko Hirao[a]

[a]*Department of Chemical System Engineering, The University of Tokyo, 7-3-1, Hongo, Bunkyo-ku, Tokyo 113-8656, Japan*
[b]*Presidential Endowed Chair for "Platinum Society", Organization for Interdisciplinary Research Project, The University of Tokyo, 7-3-1, Hongo, Bunkyo-ku, Tokyo 113-0033, Japan*
baharuddin@pse.t.u-tokyo.ac.jp

Abstract

Biomass utilization systems are gaining attentions of governments, researchers and companies. However, in conventional researches, impacts of introducing biomass on the existing systems are not considered. This study proposes a novel design methodology of biomass utilization systems which incorporates impacts on the existing petroleum refining industry into consideration. A simulation model has been developed in order to quantify changes of material flows in refineries due to introduction of biomass. This model enables to evaluate alternatives of biomass utilization system in terms of crude oil consumption and refinery processes throughput at regional as well as global levels. The method was demonstrated through a case study on the selection of biomass conversion technology. The results revealed several undiscovered features, which have become first possible by extending the evaluation boundary. Such features include sensitivity of the selection to the net crude oil reduction and also to the throughput of refinery processes, especially crude distillation and cracking units.

Keywords: system design, scenario analysis, refinery, bio-products, optimization

1. Introduction

Recently, utilization of biomass offers promising alternatives to satisfy energy and material demands while reducing fossil fuel dependency. To utilize biomass, systems illustrated in Fig. 1 which include life cycle stages of bio-products, need to be designed. During the design of biomass utilization systems (BUS), several decisions are to be made, for example the selection of conversion technology, utilization scale, and target of products to be substituted.

Several studies have proposed methods to select biomass conversion pathways and to decide production scale of BUS by evaluating economic and environmental performance (You et al., 2012). In these studies, evaluation is limited to the BUS itself, and the impacts of introducing bio-products on the existing systems such as petroleum refining industry (PRI) are not considered. Recently, Andersen et al. (2013) and Tong et al. (2014) integrated BUS design with the regional PRI in order to quantify flow changes in the process. However, impacts on PRI outside the region have not been investigated in the existing studies.

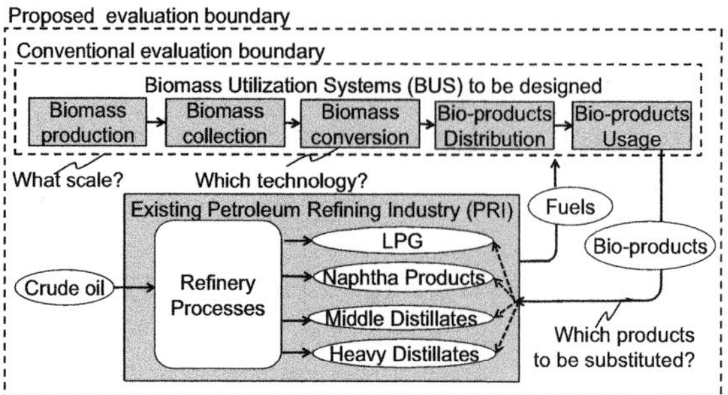

Figure 1. Biomass utilization system (BUS) and evaluation boundary proposed in this study

Introduction of bio-products into market adds supply of certain products, be it fuels or materials (Tong et al., 2014). Changes of supply consequently give impacts on production in PRI. Furthermore, petroleum refineries have important characteristics that need to be addressed, i.e., the system has one input and multiple outputs as shown in Fig. 1. Besides, PRI in certain regions is interconnected with other regions. These characteristics do not always guarantee that reducing one petroleum product by substituting it with a bio-product would lead to effective reduction of crude oil. To ensure the benefits of biomass utilization, it is necessary to consider impacts on the material flows in the existing PRI when designing BUS.

2. Proposed Design Methodology

We propose a novel BUS design methodology which consists of four steps.

2.1. Specification of design objectives and scope

First, design objectives are defined such as minimizing worldwide crude oil consumption. Regarding the scope of design, several information is need to be obtained, including potential of biomass feedstock, available conversion technologies.

2.2. Analysis of material and energy flows of the design alternatives of BUS

Each alternative differs from each other in terms of decision variables, e.g. biomass source location, biomass conversion technology, production scale or target petroleum products for substitution. This second step produces information on the yield of bio-products and the amount of fuels needed for the BUS, such as biomass cultivation, transportation, conversion, and bio-products distribution.

2.3. Analysis of impacts on PRI

PRI is a complicated global network consisting of raw materials supply, petroleum refining and product distribution. Consequently, impacts of BUS implementation in certain region are not limited to refineries in the region utilizing biomass but also to other regions. Therefore, a model which represents worldwide PRI needs to be created. PRI is considered as a multi-site refinery network of petroleum refineries covering main geographical regions: Asia-Pacific, Russia and Central Asia, Europe, Africa, Middle East, North America and South America. Each region is represented by one petroleum refinery with different petroleum product supply and demand, product price, and refining capacity. Crude oil and products exchanges between regions are also included in the model. Statistical data issued by US EIA (2013) is used as model parameters. A linear programming formulation shown in the following equations is used to optimize the flow rate of raw materials, products, the throughput of refineries and inter-regional transfer, by maximizing net margin of the entire system. The model is developed and solved using commercial refinery simulator Aspen PIMS™ version 7.3.

$$\text{maximize} \sum_{pr\in PR}\sum_{i\in I} PrPrice_{pr,i}\, D_{pr,i} - \sum_{cr\in CR}\sum_{i\in I} CrCost_{cr,i} S_{cr,i} \\ - \sum_{cm\in CR\cup PR}\sum_{i\in I}\sum_{i'\in I} TrCost_{pr,i,i'} Trans_{cm,i,i'} \\ - \sum_{i\in I}\left(FixCost_i\right) - \sum_{i\in I}\sum_{k\in K} CapCost_k \Delta Cap_{k,i} \tag{1}$$

Subject to:

- Supply and demand constraints in region *i* based on the statistical data in 2010.

$$D_{pr,i} = Dmd_{pr,i,2010} \tag{2}$$

$$S_{cr,i} \le 1.2Sup_{cr,i,2010} \tag{3}$$

- Inter-region transfer of raw material *cr* and product *pr* from refineries in region *i* to demand in region *i'*.

$$\sum_{i'\in I}\sum_{k\in K} F_{cr,k,i,i'} - S_{cr,i} = 0 \tag{4}$$

$$LoBnd_{cr,k,i,i'} \le \sum_{i'\in I}\sum_{k\in K} F_{cr,k,i,i'} \le UpBnd_{cr,k,i,i'} \tag{5}$$

$$\sum_{i\in I} Trans_{pr,i,i'} - D_{pr,i'} = 0 \tag{6}$$

$$LoBnd_{pr,i,i'} \le \sum_{i\in I} Trans_{pr,i,i'} \le UpBnd_{pr,i,i'} \tag{7}$$

- Capacity constraints of process *k* in refineries in region *i*.

$$Cap_{k,i} \le UpBnd_{k,i,2010} \tag{8}$$

- Material and energy balances, quality constraints of raw materials, and final products in typical petroleum refinery processes.

Introduction of BUS alternatives into the system affects demand variable $D_{pr,i}$ and price $PrPrice_{pr,i}$ of certain petroleum products. Type and quantity of products affected by each BUS alternative are entered as input information into the calculation.

2.4. Selection of promising alternatives

For each BUS alternative, changes in crude oil consumption, petroleum products, and refinery throughput are evaluated and a set of alternatives that best meets the design objectives is selected by comparing results of each BUS alternative regarding how the alternatives change flows in PRI.

3. Case study

3.1. Settings

Applicability of the proposed methodology is demonstrated through a case study about biomass utilization in China and its impacts on PRI in China as well as in the rest of the world. Jiang et al. (2012) estimated the current available biomass crop residues as 253.7 Mton/y (4.57 EJ/y). Reduction of world's crude oil dependency is regarded as design objective. Table 1 summarizes the generated alternatives. Each alternative varies in biomass conversion technology, as selection of biomass conversion technology remains

Table 1. Generated alternatives of biomass utilization in China

BUS Alternative	1	2	3
Biomass utilization percentage and type of bio-products	50% to Ethanol + 50% to FT-Diesel	100% to Ethanol	100% to FT-Diesel
Petroleum product substitution	Gasoline + Diesel	Gasoline	Diesel
Biomass to product energy efficiency, η_{btp} (Huang and Zhang (2011))	0.50	0.51	0.51
Useful energy as bio-product [EJ/y]	2.28	2.33	2.31

one of the most important decision variables in the design of BUS. In addition, biomass utilization scale is also varied between 0 and the current available biomass.

To analyse impacts of implementing above alternatives, first, evaluation boundary is set to include PRI in China and other regions as mentioned in section 2.3. Changes of demand and price of certain petroleum products caused by the introduction of bio-products are then estimated. These changes can be obtained by solving an econometric model (Du and Hayes, 2009). However, in this study, because our primary focus was to investigate the impacts on the material and energy balances, price and demand are assumed to remain constant. Under such a condition, proportion of certain products derived from petroleum can be assumed to decrease. Also, because of another assumption that bio-products are prioritized to be used in China, the decrease of petroleum-derived products is set to occur only in China.

3.2. Results and discussion

3.2.1. Impacts on crude oil consumption

Fig. 2 shows the crude oil consumption in the whole world, China, and other regions for BUS alternative 1. Because of the similarity of results in other alternatives, only the result of alternative 1 is presented. The result indicates that each BUS alternative has potential to reduce world crude oil consumption in proportion with the amount of implemented bio-products. However, as mentioned in section 2.3, the objective function is net margin of the entire system, which implies that PRI in all regions need to cooperate each other in order to achieve the calculated amount of reduction. In Fig. 2, crude oil produced in China remains almost constant, and crude oil reduction occurs in other regions, due to lower price of crude oil in China.

For all alternatives, the slopes of world crude oil consumption are summarized in Table 2. It is observed that alternative 2 which converts biomass to ethanol through fermentation process gives a better result in reducing world crude oil consumption than other alternatives. This can be understood because in refineries, to produce gasoline, raw materials must pass processes with higher loss (FCC, coker) than to produce diesel. Therefore, reducing gasoline production leads to reduction of loss in these processes.

Table 2. Slope of world crude oil consumption for each BUS alternative

BUS Alternative	Slope m [10^7 m^3-crude/EJ-biomass]
1	-1.419
2	-1.457
3	-1.366

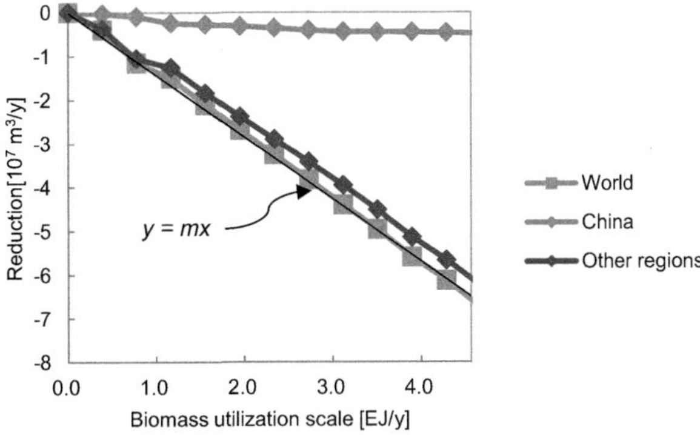

Figure 2. Crude oil consumption due to implementation of BUS alternative 3

3.2.2. Impacts on petroleum refining processes

Fig. 3 summarizes changes of process throughputs in PRI for all BUS alternatives. The result reveals that the throughputs of crude units decrease with the increase of biomass utilization scale. Each BUS alternative shows different changes of the throughputs of secondary processes. For example, results of alternative 2 indicates that in the refinery, cracking processes (FCC, hydrocracking, etc.) and naphtha upgrading processes (C4 isomerization, alkylation, naphtha hydrotreater) tend to decrease their throughputs. However, for middle distillate processes such as kerosene hydrotreater, distillate hydro treater, etc., the throughputs are observed to increase. This is because petroleum refineries need to reduce gasoline while production of middle and heavy products need to be maintained.

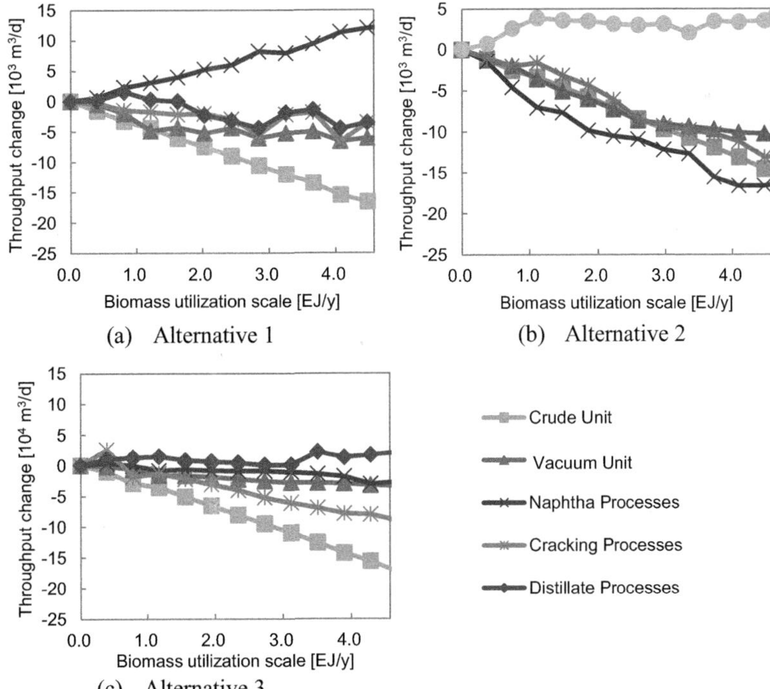

Figure 3. Changes in refinery process throughputs for each BUS alternative

A common characteristic of all alternatives is the decrease of cracking process throughputs. Nowadays, several studies claim that the cracking of heavy distillates and residues is a difficult process due to the content of heavy metals and sulfur which could poison catalysts (Rana et al., 2007). Although further evaluation is needed to decide more suitable materials to be cracked, this result suggests that utilizing biomass is a powerful candidate to replace the difficult upgrading of heavy oil.

4. Conclusions and future work

We presented a methodology for designing BUS considering impacts on PRI. The methodology incorporates quantitative analysis of material flow changes in PRI. Results of the case study indicate that substituting petroleum products by bio-products give significant impacts on PRI in terms of product flow rate, crude oil consumption and refining throughputs. This implies the necessity to include PRI in the evaluation boundary when designing BUS, especially in the selection of biomass conversion technology. For further development of the design methodology, evaluation scope of each alternative will be extended to cover various aspects such as environmental impacts. Moreover, comprehensive analysis of economic impacts of supply and demand changes will be incorporated.

References

F. E. Andersen, M. S. Díaz, I. E. Grossmann, 2013, Multiscale strategic planning model for the design of integrated ethanol and gasoline supply chain, AIChE J., 59,12, 4655–4672.

X. Du, D. J. Hayes, 2009, The impact of ethanol production on US and regional gasoline markets, Energy Policy, 37, 8, 3227-3234.

D. Jiang, D. Zhuang, J. Fu, Y. Huang, K. Wen, 2012, Bioenergy potential from crop residues in China: Availability and distribution, Renew. Sust. Energ. Rev., 16,3, 1377-1382.

M. S. Rana, V. Sámano, J. Ancheyta, J. A. I. Diaz, 2007, A review of recent advances on process technologies for upgrading of heavy oils and residua, Fuel, 86, 9, 1216-1231.

K. Tong, J. Gong, D. Yue, F. You, 2014, Stochastic programming approach to optimal design and operations of integrated hydrocarbon biofuel and petroleum supply chains, ACS Sustainable Chem. Eng., 2, 1, 49–61.

US Energy Information Administration (EIA), 2013, International Energy Statistics, <www.eia.gov/cfapps/ipdbproject/IEDIndex3.cfm> accessed on 07/11/2013.

F. You, L. Tao, D. J. Graziano, S. W. Snyder, 2012, Optimal design of sustainable cellulosic biofuel supply chains: Multiobjective optimization coupled with life cycle assessment and input–output analysis, AIChE Journal, 58, 4, 1157-1180.

Jiří Jaromír Klemeš, Petar Sabev Varbanov and Peng Yen Liew (Editors)
Proceedings of the 24th European Symposium on Computer Aided Process Engineering – ESCAPE 24
June 15-18, 2014, Budapest, Hungary.

Designing Energy Supply Chains with the P-graph Framework under Cost Constraints and Sustainability Considerations

Leisha Vance[a], Istvan Heckl[b], Botond Bertok[b], Heriberto Cabezas[a,b,*], Ferenc Friedler[b]

[a]*Office of Research and Development, U.S. Environmental Protection Agency, USA.*
[b]*Department of Computer Science and Systems Technology, University of Pannonia, Hungary.*
cabezas.heriberto@epa.gov

Abstract

A computer-aided methodology for designing sustainable supply chains is presented using the P-graph framework to develop supply chain structures which are analyzed using cost, the cost of producing electricity, and two sustainability metrics: ecological footprint and emergy. They represent environmental burden in terms of land use and energy resources. The P-graph framework provides a mathematically rigorous procedure for synthesizing optimal and alternative networks subject to profitability considering ecological footprint and emergy inputs. Emergy is a measure of energy used in transformations directly and indirectly to make a product or maintain a service, or in our case, energy production. Emergy and ecological footprint complement each other because they represent very different aspects of sustainability. The proposed methodology is demonstrated with a supply chain whichprovides electric power and heat to an agricultural region utilizing agricultural wastes as renewable resources. The results indicate that, compared to electricity from the grid and/or natural gas, renewable energy resources can yield cost reductions of up to 17 % as well as ecological footprint and emergy reductions. This allows the design of more sustainable supply chains that are both cost-effective and less environmentally damaging.

Keywords: P-graph, Emergy, Footprint, Supply Chain, Energy

1. Supply Chains, Process Networks and Sustainability

Supply chains are comprised of an optimized network of all providers involved in the creation, production and distribution of products and services to consumers in order to achieve maximum profits and minimize costs in terms of balancing supply and demand. Critical to successful supply chain design and management is the role of information flows, which is the deciding factor of successful business in today's competitive industry practices (Misra et al., 2010). Historically, supply chains were focused on maximizing profits, but more recently, there is a growing movement to incorporate sustainability by adding the minimization of environmental impact as a supply chain criterion.

Like a supply chain, the goal of a process network is to create a product or service from raw materials into an end product or service (Friedler et al., 1995), but instead of focusing on providers within the supply chain network, the focus is on technology and materials (Čuček et al., 2010). In process synthesis, the most advantageous network is determined based upon maximization of some desired objective, such as high profits or low environmental impact (Vance et al., 2012). The P-graph methodology was developed as an algorithmic (Varga et al., 1995) and computer aid (Bertok et al., 2013) for delineating the structures of PNS problems. While the P-Graph methodology has been applied to optimize regional energy supply chains (Lam et al., 2010), the current development integrates sustainability metrics for ecological evaluation, in contrasts to the more traditional approaches based on life-cycle assessment (You et al., 2012).

In the current contribution Ecological Footprint (EF) and Emergy Analysis (EA) measures the sustainability. EF assesses the amount of productive and assimilative land required to support a given population's resource consumption and remediate the corresponding wastes (Wackernagle and Rees, 1996). EA is an environmental accounting method that calculates the amount of solar energy required to produce products and services, or sustain regional systems (Odum, 1996). Emergy is roughly the sum of the thermodynamic work of all forms using solar, tidal, and geothermal energy in the creation and operation of products or services, or in our case, a supply chain. Conversion of input and output flows to solar equivalents (solar energy joules or seJ) is done by applying solar conversion factors known as solar transformities. The present work represents the next logical step in our efforts to develop a computer-aided methodology to design sustainable supply chains by utilizing the P-graph framework with two sustainability criteria and economic considerations. Previous work used EF criteria inputs to derive optimal networks for maximum profitability and sustainability (Vance et al., 2012). For this study, we include EA along with EF and economic criteria within the P-graph framework to demonstrate the use of multiple indicators in the design of sustainable supply chains. The cost of generating electricity is also considered, because electricity is generally more useful than heat.

Even though logistics are important in the design of optimal supply chains, for this work the supply chains will be evaluated based upon the energy conversion technologies, and the raw materials used as feedstocks for the heat and electricity generation processes. Feedstocks include renewable resources of corn silage, grass silage, wood and fossil fuel resources of natural gas and grid electricity (primarily natural gas- and nuclear-generated). Operating units include pelletizers, biogas plants and gas/biomass furnaces. We compare the different amounts of energy required to generate specific amounts of heat and electricity, and combine EA results with the EF results of the previous study.

2. Methodology

PNS Studio can build solution networks from scratch or modify existing models. Inputs include materials, material properties, operating units and numerical parameters such as flowrates, cost, etc. Modifications are internally evaluated within the program, and if a change is inappropriate with existing model parameters, a warning box appears. PNS Draw facilitates the graphical representation of a P-graph. In this way, a new tool has been developed which is capable of placing and connecting materials and operating units on acanvas. The result can then be exported into PNS Studio and displayed again in PNS Draw. PNS Studio and PNS Draw can be found on the web (PNS Studio and PNS Draw, 2014).

Using the methodology of Ewing et al. (2010), EFs were computed for each of the energy generation processes (Vance et al., 2012). For each process, the amount of cropland and forest land for feedstock production, and forest land for assimilation of CO_2 emission generated during feedstock production was determined (Vance et al., 2012). To equitably compare EFs of each process, the amount of feedstocks required to produce 1 MWh of primary energy (electricity or heat) was assessed (Vance et al., 2012). As per Ewing et al. (2010), all process EFs were normalized into global footprints by multiplying regionalized yield factors by relevant equivalence factors (Vance et al., 2012). EF is measured in global hectares (ha).

To calculate emergy, the unit emergy values (UEV) of Rugani et al. (2011) are adopted. This source gives emergy values in seJ per unit of mass, volume, or energy as appropriate for substances, products, and energies produced or generated by common processes and at various locations. The UEV are estimated by considering the detailed process by which aproduct was produced or the energy generated, including all of the energy transformations. Then the calculation involves multiplying the mass of a substance or the amount of energy by the appropriate UEV value which gives the conversion to solar energy joules (seJ).

3. Modeling Energy Supply Chains

In PNS, usually two classes of problems are considered: cost minimization and profit maximization. The former assumes the required amount of products has to be produced with the aim of minimum cost. In a profit maximization problem there are only potential products; the models produce products only if they are profitable.

This type of targetselection is adequate as long as cost is the only objective of the optimization. In assessing the EF within the P-graph methodology, the initial structure was transformed by adding a new material-type node (EF), which is the starting point for all units which contributed to EF feedstock generation process (Vance et al., 2012). If the footprint is attributed to a raw material or feedstock, an additional node must be included in the structure as an operating unit source. The modeling of Emergy within the P-graph methodology happens similarly to EF. A new material-type node (EM) must be added to the network, with connection from this new node to each process which contributes to emergy production. For the particular supply chain presented herein, it was assumed that the feedstocks has the dominant contribution to the emergy of the supply chain. The issue here is that the emergy used in building the supply chain structure represents a modest one-time investment, whereas the emergy associated with the feedstock of natural gas, corn silage, etc. represents an on-going investment of emergy. Over time, this on-going investment will greatly exceed the initial investment of emergy. The emergy values used in the calculation are given in Table 1 based on the UEVs of Rugani et al. (2011). These were matched to conditions in Hungary.

The UEV of corn straw was estimated by allocating the emergy at the farm of corn grown in the United States between the corn grain and the corn straw. Twenty-three metric tons of corn and corn straw were utilized a year, and that included 9 t of corn grain and 14 t of corn straw. From Rugani et al. (2011), the UEV of corn plus straw at the farm is 4.45E11 seJ/kg. Because corn grain and corn straw grow together as part of the same plant, it is assumed that UEV for the whole corn plant (UEV_{wcp}) is equal to the UEV of the corn grain (UEV_{cg}) which is itself equal to the UEV for corn straw (UEV_{cs}) or $UEV_{wcp} = UEV_{cg} = UEV_{cs} =$ 4.45E11 seJ/kg. This implies that there exists an emergybalance for corn at the farm, i.e. the total emergy of the whole corn plant corn is equal to that of the corn grain plus that of the corn straw. This can be formally expressed by,

$$UEV_{wcp}\left(\frac{sej}{kg}\right)m_{wcp}(kg) = UEV_{wcp}\left(\frac{seJ}{kg}\right)m_{cg}(kg) + UEV_{wcp}\left(\frac{seJ}{kg}\right)m_{cs}(kg) \quad (1)$$

where m_{wcp}, m_{cg}, and m_{cs} represent the mass of whole corn plant, corn grain, and corn straw equal to 23, 9, and 14 t. The emergy of each input flow to the supply chain is calculated by multiplying each mass or energy input to the supply chain by the corresponding UEV as shown in Table 1.

4. Case Study

Energy supply chains for a geographical district are synthesized while taking into account cost, ecological footprint and emergy. The case study in Vance et al. (2012) is extended, with emergy analysis added to the problem. The goal is to meet the heat and electricity requirement of 5,000 and 2,000 MWh/y. Conventional non-renewable methods are available, such as obtaining electricity from the grid, and heat from natural gas combustion, and this district also has some renewable energy sources available like corn silage, grass silage, corn cobs, and wood. Economic data were obtained from Luttenberger et al. (2008).Several energy conversion technologies such as those used in biogas plants, biogas CHP (combined heat and power) plants, gas burners, pelletizers, and furnaces are available, and appear as operating units.

5. Results

Twenty-three supply chain structures created to supply heat and electricity to a geographic region in Hungary from various energy and material feed stocks are displayed in Figure 1. Structures 1 to 21 produce 18.00 TJ of heat and 7.20 TJ of electricity/y. Structures 22 and 23 produce 18.00 TJ and 27.69 TJ of electricity/y, but with higher costs. Figure 1 gives a representation of the cost, cost of electricity production, ecological footprint and emergy for all the supply chain structures normalized to Structure 13 (our reference case). Structure 13 consumes natural gas and electricity from the Hungarian grid, and represents "business as usual", e.g. heat and electricity from a non-renewable hydrocarbon source and nuclear power. Note that cost, ecological footprint, and emergy are not highly correlated, and represent independent aspects of the supply chain. The cost and the cost of producing electricity are more correlated, but diverge from each other for structures 22 and 23.

From Figure 1, 5 structures (#2, #7, #10, #16, and #22) are improved both financially and environmentally compared to #13. Each one has different advantages and disadvantages; the choice can be specific to the locale and local

Table 1. Unit Emergy Values (UEVs) (Rugani et al., 2011).

Input	Quantity	Unit Emergy Value	Emergy	Data Location
Electricity	1 MWh	7.77E11 seJ/kWh	7.77E+14 seJ	Hungary (HU)
Corn Silage	12 t	7.55E10 seJ/kg	9.06E+14 seJ	Switzerland (CH)
Grass Silage	12 t	2.62E11 seJ/kg	3.14E+15 seJ	Switzerland (CH)
Natural Gas	91.9 m^3	2.12E12 seJ/m^3	1.95E+14 seJ	Europe (RER)
Wood	3 m^3	1.16E14 seJ/m^3	3.48E+14 seJ	Europe (RER)
Corn Straw	14 t	4.45E11 seJ/kg	6.23E+15 seJ	United States (US)

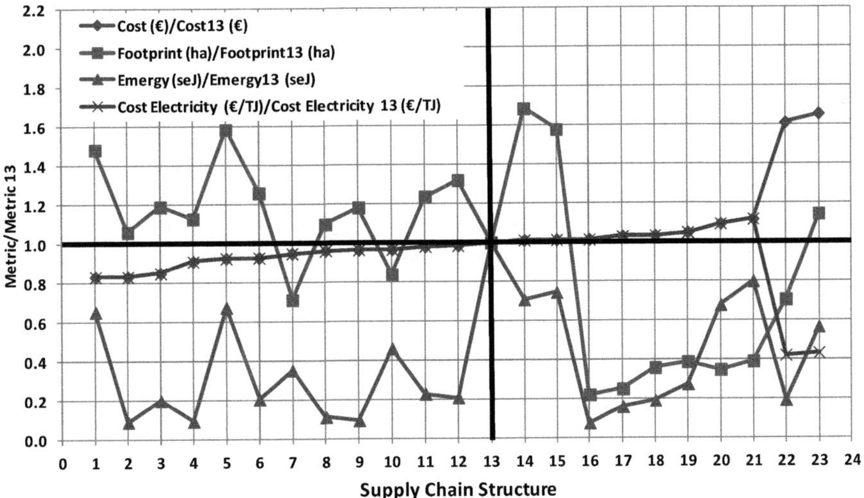

Figure 1. Twenty-three supply chain structures designed to produce electricity and heat are compared according to cost, ecological footprint, emergy input, and the cost of electricity with respect to supply chain structure 13 which uses natural gas and electricity from the grid. The thick vertical and horizontal lines represent reference supply chain structure 13.

economic and environmental circumstances. Structure #2 has a 17 % decrease in cost and cost of electricity, a 91 % decrease in emergy input, but an 8 % increase in footprint. Structure #7 has a 5 % decrease in cost and the cost of electricity, a 29 % decrease in EF, and 65 % decrease in emergy input. Structure #10 has a 3 % decrease in cost and the cost of electricity, a 16 % decrease in the ecological footprint, and 54 % decrease in the emergy input. This represents a supplementation to natural gas use. Structure #16 has a modest 2 % increase in cost and the cost of generating electricity, but a substantial 78 % decrease in ecological footprint and 93 % decrease in emergy input. Structure #22 has a 61 % increase in cost, but also a 58 % decrease in the cost of electricity. This is coupled with a substantial 28 % decrease in ecological footprint, and a very considerable 81 % decrease in emergy input. This structure would benefit an area where there is a strong market for electricity that can be sold at high enough prices to cover increased costs.

6. Conclusions

The 23 possible supply chains for case study are ranked by cost, i.e. the initial and operating financial investments, and the ecological footprint measuring productive land area needed, the emergy input gauging energy resources invested by the environment, and the cost of producing electricity, which can be a measure of profitability as electricity is often the primary product. The concept is that one should attempt to design supply chains that are, compared to current practice (#13), less costly, have a lower ecological footprint, require less emergy input, and have lower cost of producing electricity for cases where electricity dominates profitability. Together these criteria give a comprehensive but flexible assessment with respect to both business and sustainability aspects.

The economic considerations included in our analysis are limited to capital and operating costs, and profit normally considered in engineering economics. Obtaining hard cost data can prove difficult. For these analyses, the cost parameters from Luttenbergeret al. (2008) were applied and considered to be self-consistent and valid. We reiterate that the focus here is on the methodology, itself. The most important summary results are that: (1) it should be possible to find alternative supply chain structures to supply heat and electricity more economically than current practice, (2) this can be done utilizing renewable feedstock – often wastes like silage – or a mixture of non-renewable and renewable feedstock, (3) structures can be found that have lower impact on the environment at lower costs than currently operated, and (4) there may be opportunities to improve both profitability and environmental performance with careful process systems engineering.

Acknowledgments

The authors acknowledge help with economic data of the case study from Michael Narodoslawsky and his team at the Technical University of Graz. The research and its publication have been supported by project TÁMOP-4.2.2.A-11/1/KONV-2012-0072.

References

B. Bertok, M. Barany, F. Friedler, 2013, Generating and Analyzing Mathematical Programming Models of Conceptual Process Design by P-graph Software, Industrial and Engineering Chemistry Research, 52, 1, 166-171.

L. Čuček, H.L. Lam, J.J. Klemeš, P.S. Varbanov, Z. Kravanja,2010, Synthesis of Regional Networks for the Supply of Energy and Bioproducts, Clean Technologies and Environmental Policy, 12, 6, 635-645.

B. Ewing, A. Reed, A. Galli, J. Kitzes, M. Wackernagel, 2010, Calculation Methodology for the National Footprint Accounts, Global Footprint Network, Oakland, CA.

F. Friedler, J.B. Varga, L.T. Fan, 1995, Decision-Mapping: A Tool for Consistent and Complete Decisions in Process Synthesis, Chemical Engineering Science, 50, 1755-1768.

H.L. Lam, P.S. Varbanov, J.J. Klemeš, 2010, Optimisation of regional energy supply chains utilising renewables: P-graph approach, Computers and Chemical Engineering, 34, 5, 782-792.

C. Luttenberger, B. Birnstingl-Gottinger, K. Puchas, L. Riebenbauer, C. Krotscheck , E. Stubenschrott, Jauschnegg, M. Mandl, M. Lauer, M. Narodoslawsky, G. Gwehenberger, G. Komeos, 2008, Conceptual Models of Multifunctional Energy Centers in East Styria, Project Report, Graz, Austria (in German).

V. Misra, M.I. Khan, U.K. Singh, 2010, Supply Chain Management Systems: Architecture, Design and Vision, Journal of Strategic Innovation and Sustainability, 6, 4, 102-108.

H.T. Odum, 1996, Env. Accounting, Emergy and Decision Making, John Wiley, NY.

PNS Studio and PNS Draw, 2014, <www.p-graph.com>, accessed on 23/01/2014.

B. Rugani, M.A. Huijbregts, C. Mutel, S. Bastianoni, S. Hellweg, 2011, Solar energy demand (SED) of commodity life cycles, Environmental Science andTechnology, 45, 12, 5426-5433.

L. Vance, H. Cabezas, I. Heckl, B. Bertok, F. Friedler, 2012, Synthesis of Sustainable Energy Supply Chain by the P-Graph Framework, Ind. Eng. Chem. Res., 52, 1, 266-274.

J.B. Varga, F. Friedler, L.T. Fan, 1995, Parallelization of the Accelerated Branch-and-Bound Algorithm of Process Synthesis: Application in Total Flowsheet Synthesis, Acta Chimica Slovenica, 42, 15-20.

M. Wackernagel, W. Rees, 1996, Our Ecological Footprint, New Society Publishers, Gabriola Island, BC and Stony Creek, CT.

F. You, L. Tao, D.J. Graziano, S.W. Snyder, 2012. Optimal design of sustainable cellulosic biofuel supply chains: Multiobjective optimization coupled with life cycle assessment and input–output analysis, AIChE Journal, 58, 4, 1157-1180.

Jiří Jaromír Klemeš, Petar Sabev Varbanov and Peng Yen Liew (Editors)
Proceedings of the 24th European Symposium on Computer Aided Process Engineering – ESCAPE 24
June 15-18, 2014, Budapest, Hungary.

Multi-Objective Optimization of US Economy via Multi-Regional Input-Output Analysis

Janire Pascual González, Gonzalo. Guillén Gosálbez,* L. Jiménez Esteller

Departament d'Enginyeria Química, Universitat Rovira i Virgili, Av. Països Catalans 26, Tarragona 43007, Spain
gonzalo.guillen@urv.cat

Abstract

In recent years, new environmental policies have been developed to reduce the environmental impact of human activities. Designing these policies in an effective manner is challenging because it requires a detailed knowledge of the whole economic and environmental system and the way in which they interact with each other. To this end, environmentally extended multi-regional input-output tables (EEMRIO) have gained wider interest in the recent past. In this work, we perform a multi-objective optimization (MOO) on a multi-regional input-output (IO) table that covers 35 manufacturing sectors of 40 countries to identify the activities whose control and regulation can lead to larger reductions of global warming potential (GWP) at minimum decrease in gross domestic product (GDP). We have applied our tool to the economy of the United States in order to identify the best policies to be implemented in practice. Our approach provides valuable insight into how to reduce the environmental impact globally. By adopting this birds' eye view of a whole economy, it is possible to determine how the final demand (and the total production) of every sector in an economy should be modified so as to attaining given environmental goals while keeping the economic performance as high as possible.

Keywords: Input-Output Analysis, Public Policy, Sustainability

1. Introduction

CO_2 atmospheric concentration has increased drastically in the last four centuries with a marked increase each year. Hence, countries must face promptly the challenge of adapting their economies to meet the necessary environmental targets while at the same time remaining competitive in the market place. Policies like Kyoto Protocol were developed to this end, but they cannot guarantee the reduction of global emissions since they only focus on reducing the emissions of Annex B countries and overlook CO_2 emissions embodied in international trades. Although several efforts have been devoted to compute such emissions (Peters, 2008; Stevens, 2010), no systematic method has been proposed to devise specific measures to mitigate them. Furthermore, a successful environmental policy cannot be built ignoring the economical effort associated to its commitment.

In order to overcome such limitations we propose to obtain the guidelines for these policies by posing and solving an optimization problem embedding an EEMRIO model and considering both, economic and environmental objectives. EEMRIO models are typically used for predicting changes in all the sectors of an economy according to changes in the demand of a single (or several) sectors, but also allow for the assessment of the impact that the economic activity produces on the environment. Hence, these models are a valuable tool to attribute pollution or resources depletion to the final demand of a product or service following a consistent approach (Wiedmann, 2009). Our strategy combines multi-objective optimization and multi-regional input-output models within a single unified framework that allows identifying the activities whose control and regulation can lead to larger reductions of impact at a minimum decrease in gross domestic product (GDP).

We have applied our tool to the economy of the United States in order to identify the best policies to be implemented in practice for optimizing simultaneously the economic and environmental performance.

2. Mathematical Model

2.1. Input-Output (IO) Model

In its basic form, an input-output model consists of a system of linear equations, each of which describes the distribution of an industry's production throughout the economy (Miller and Blair, 2009). For an economy with $|i|$ sectors, the equations of an IO model can be expressed as follows:

$$X(i) = \sum_j a(i,j)X(j) + y(i) \qquad \forall i \tag{1}$$

where $X(i)$ is the total output in currency units (e.g. US$) of sector i, $a(i,j)$ are technological coefficients representing the amount (in US$) of output of sector i necessary to produce one dollar of output of sector j and $y(i)$ is the final demand (end user) of the sector i. The technological coefficients are calculated via Equation 2:

$$a(i,j) = \frac{x(i,j)}{X(j)} \qquad \forall i,j \tag{2}$$

where, $x(i,j)$ is the output of sector i acting like an input for sector j. Note that the IO assumes that there is a direct proportionality between the total outputs of sector j and the inputs that this sector acquires from its supplying sectors. Accepting this premise, the technological coefficients $a(i,j)$ can be considered constant. This is valid for a certain range, assuming that the technological conditions of the total production of an economy remain unchanged.

2.2. Multi-regional IO Model

In our approach, we are dealing with a multi-regional IO model that considers transactions of goods and services among several economic regions. Hence, the IO model presented before must be modified. Given an economy with $|r|$ regions and $|i|$ sectors in each region, the modified model can be expressed as follows:

$$X(i,r) = \sum_j \sum_{r'} X(j,r')a(i,j,r,r') + y(i,r) \qquad \forall i,r \tag{3}$$

where $X(i,r)$ is the total output in currency units (e.g. US$) of sector i in region r, $a(i,j,r,r')$ are technological coefficients representing the amount (in US$) of output of sector i of region r necessary to produce one dollar of output of sector j of region r' and $y(i,r)$ is the final demand (end user) of the sector i of region r. Technological coefficients are obtained by means of Equation 4:

$$a(i,j,r,r') = \frac{x(i,j,r,r')}{X(j,r')} \qquad \forall i,j,r,r' \tag{4}$$

where *x(i,j,r,r')* is the output of sector *i* of region *r* acting like an input for sector *j* of region *r'*. Taking this into account, we write the environmental equations as follows:

$$impact(i,k,r) = X(i,r)e(i,k,r) \qquad \forall i,r,k \tag{5}$$

$$IMPACT(k) = \sum_i \sum_r impact(i,k,r) = \sum_i \sum_r X(i,r)e(i,k,r) \qquad \forall k \tag{6}$$

where *impact(i,k,r)* is the environmental impact in category *k* (e.g. GWP-100) produced by sector *i* of region *r*, while *e(i,k,r)* is the environmental coefficient for sector *i* of region *r* (i.e., impact per monetary unit traded). Finally, *IMPACT(k)* is the total environmental impact in category *k* generated by all sectors of the economy in all regions.

2.3. Optimization problem based on linear programming.

We use the basic EEMRIO table to develop a multi-objective LP model that seeks to optimize simultaneously the economic and environmental performance of a whole economy. This LP will be applied to the economy of the United States (US) in order to identify those sectors whose demand should be modified for achieving a given environmental target while keeping the economic performance as high as possible. The approach presented gives rise to the following multi-objective LP formulation:

$$\begin{aligned} \min \quad & \left\{-\sum_i \sum_{r=US} X(i,r), IMPACT(k)\right\} \\ s.t. \quad & Equations\ 3,6 \\ & \underline{y_0(i,r)} \le y(i,r) \le \overline{y_0(i,r)} \qquad \forall i, r = US \end{aligned} \tag{7}$$

This multi-objective LP model seeks to optimize simultaneously the total amount of economic transactions in US (i.e., gross domestic product, GDP) and the associated impact at a global scale (i.e., across the world), subject to the standard equations of the input output tables, the environmental equation, and a flexible demand constraint. Thus, we minimize the total impact regardless of the place where this impact takes place. This avoids solutions in which the impact within a country is minimized by displacing the manufacturing tasks to other regions.

In this formulation the demand of every sector in US, *y(i,r=US)* is not a parameter but a variable constrained within realistic lower and upper bounds (i.e., 90% and 100% of the basic case, respectively). Hence, as oppose to standard IO tables where *y* is a parameter for all regions and sectors, we consider it as a variable for the sectors within the US. This provides the model with flexibility for leaving part of the demand unsatisfied, reflecting the situation that would arise when imposing taxes on a sector. Hence, the model provides as output the values of the demand that should be implemented so as to achieve a given environmental target while maximizing the economic performance. This solution can then be implemented in practice by imposing taxes on the sectors whose demand should be reduced.

Recall however that in general the solution to a MOO problem is not a single point but a set of alternatives known as the Pareto set. In order to obtain such set, or more precisely, some of its points, we must resort to a MOO optimization method. In this work, we use without loss of generality the so-called epsilon constraint method.

3. Numerical Results

We apply our approach to the economy of the US in order to identify the optimal changes that should be performed in the economy for reducing GWP. Specifically, we solve two case studies, each considering data from a different year (2000 and 2009).

3.1. Data source

We use in our calculations the World Input-Output Database (WIOD), which was originally developed to analyze the effects of globalization on trade patterns, environmental pressures, and socio-economic development across a wide set of countries (Timmer, 2012). WIOD describes the economic inputs and outputs in monetary terms of 35 manufacturing sectors covering 27 EU countries and 13 other major countries in the world for the period 1995 to 2009. In this work, we have used data from 2000 and 2009 to build the model for each case study.

3.2. Optimization

The multi-objective IO model described above, which features 5,742 variables and 4,308 constraints, was implemented in GAMS v23.7 and solved by means of the epsilon constraint method using CPLEX v12.3 as the solver. The CPU times vary between 36.29 and 36.53 CPU seconds depending on the instance addressed. Figure 1 shows the set of Pareto points obtained for the two case studies. The Pareto frontier, as expected from the LP nature of the model, is concave, with the slope increasing as we move to the left. Hence, as we go from the maximum GDP solution to the minimum impact one, greater reductions of GDP are required for a given reduction of impact.

Each point of the curve corresponds to a different macroeconomic alternative. In intermediate points, we can identify three groups of sectors: those with a demand hitting its upper bound, those with a demand hitting its lower bound, and only one sector with a demand lying between the lower and upper bound. Hence, an important result of the optimization concerns the number of sectors whose final demand is modified to reach a given environmental target (i.e., those belonging to the last two groups).

Similarly, the number of sectors cut (i.e., those whose total output *X(i,r)* is lower than in their base case) increases as we move from the maximum GDP solution (in which all sectors within the US fully cover the final demand), to the minimum impact one (in which all the demands in US hit the lower bound of 90%). This information is quite valuable for governments and public policy makers, as it pinpoints the sectors on which

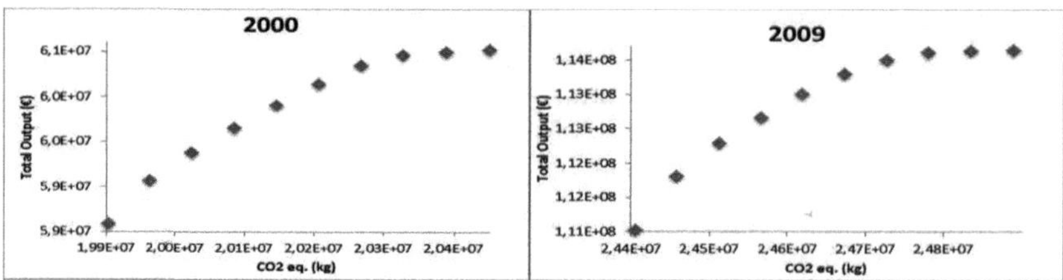

Figure. 1. Optimal solutions for GWP-100 for years 2000 and 2009.

we should act for attaining a given environmental target while maximizing at the same time the economic performance (considering the diminishing returns principle that governs this process). Recall that a sector i can be cut as a result of two effects: (i) a decrease in the corresponding demand $y(i,r)$ (this is only valid for sectors within the US since the demands in the remaining regions are parameters) and/or (ii) a decrease of the total output $X(j,r)$ of another sector j for which sector i is a supplier. Hence, the model has the flexibility to reflect how a decrease in the demands of sectors within the US affects the world-wide trades.

In Table 1 and Table 2, we display the ratio between the reduction in impact and GDP for every point of the Pareto frontier:

$$Ratio = \frac{impact\ reduction\ (\%)}{GDP\ reduction\ (\%)} \tag{8}$$

The values of this Ratio are consistent with the concave nature of the Pareto set. The Cut sectors indicates the number of productive sectors whose total output $X(i,r)$ is reduced (in comparison to the base case) to reach the corresponding environmental target.

In the maximum GDP solution, all the sectors fulfil the maximum demand. The minimum impact solution shows the lowest ratio (0.84), but allows for the largest reduction of GWP (of near 3 % in 2000, and 2 % in 2009) at the expense of reducing the GDP by 3.2 % and 2.3 %, and cutting 1,132 and 1,172 sectors, respectively. In contrast, intermediate Pareto points such as solution 5 show a higher ratio (1.47 in 2000, and 1.92 in 2009) with a high reduction of GWP (1.5 % in 2000, and 1.1 % in 2009) and only a GDP reduction of 1 % and 0.6 %, respectively.

A deeper analysis reveals that the largest reduction in GDP occurs in United States, followed by Canada and Mexico. This is because a large percentage of the GDP of these countries is associated with transactions with US. We also found that as we move from the maximum GDP to the minimum impact solution, the model cut first the sector Electricity, Gas and Water Supply (2.6 %), which shows a high ratio (defined as the quotient between the reductions of the impact and the total output of the corresponding sector i) . The model then starts cutting gradually an increasing number of sectors, until

Table 1. Optimal solutions found for the GWP-100 minimization for 2000.

2000	1	2	3	4	5	6	7	8	9	10
Impact reduction (%)	-2.67	-2.37	-2.08	-1.78	-1.48	-1.19	-0.89	-0.59	-0.30	0.0
GDP reduction (%)	-3.17	-2.39	-1.87	-1.42	-1.01	-0.63	-0.28	-0.09	-0.03	0.0
Ratio	0.84	0.99	1.11	1.26	1.47	1.90	3.15	6.32	10.01	-
Cut sectors	1132	901	843	754	708	671	537	249	28	-

Table 2. Optimal solutions found for the GWP-100 minimization for 2009.

2009	1	2	3	4	5	6	7	8	9	10
Impact reduction (%)	-1.94	-1.72	-1.51	-1.29	-1.08	-0.86	-0.65	-0.43	-0.22	0.0
GDP reduction (%)	-2.30	-1.61	-1.19	-0.87	-0.56	-0.30	-0.12	-0.03	-0.01	0.0
Ratio	0.84	1.07	1.27	1.49	1.92	2.86	5.21	15.91	15.91	-
Cut sectors	1172	904	664	664	590	426	260	10	5	-

it reaches the minimum impact solution, in which there are only three sectors with a reduction lower than 7 %: Private Households with Employed Persons (-2.01 % and -1.74 %), Water Transport (-4.92 % and -5.16 %), and Electrical and Optical Equipment (-6.65 % and -5.98 %), with the others showing a reduction close to 10 %.

Finally, analysing how the economic sectors change when we minimize the environmental impact, we note that the model cuts first sectors with a high ratio, being Air transport the most affected sector. The analysis of the minimum impact solution shows also that the top-five sectors affected by the demand's reduction are Health and Social Work, Retail Trade, Except of Motor Vehicles and Motorcycles; Repair of Household Goods, Renting of M&Eq and Other Business Activites, Financial Intermediation and Public Administration and Defence; Compulsory Social Security. This information might be used to design effective regulations to decrease the environmental impact globally.

4. Conclusions

We have presented here a detailed analysis on how to decrease the environmental impact of an economy by modifying its economic sectors. Our approach combines multi-objective optimization and multi-regional input-output models within a single unified framework that allows identifying the activities whose control and regulation can lead to larger reductions of impact at a minimum decrease in GDP. We have applied this tool to the economy of the US in order to identify the best policies to be implemented in practice for optimizing simultaneously the economic and environmental performance.

After applying the optimization algorithm, we find that taxes on US sectors aiming to control the emissions may have a large impact not only in US but also in Canada and Mexico, both of which with a high trade with US. The model also indicates which sectors are affected, thus helping policy makers to take the appropriate measures.

Acknowledgements

The authors wish to acknowledge the financial support received from the University Rovira i Virgili and from the Spanish Ministry of Education and Science (CTQ2012-37039 and DPI2012-37154).

References

G.P. Peters, E.G. Hertwich, 2008, CO2 embodied in international trade with implications for global climate policy, Environ Sci Technol, 42, 1401-1407.

J.D. Stevens, K. Caldera, 2010, Consumption-based accounting of CO2 emissions, PNAS, 107, 12, 5687-5692.

M. Timmer, A.A Erumban, R. Gouma, B. Los, U. Temurshoev, G.J. Vries, I. Arto, V.A.A Genty, F. Neuwahl, J.M. Rueda-Cantuche, A. Villanueva, J. Fracois, O. Pindyuk, J. Pöschl, R. Stehrer, 2012, The world input-output database (WIOD): Contents, sources and methods, version 0.9, <www.wiod.org/publications/papers/wiod10.pdf> accessed on 10/03/2014.

R. E. Miller, P. D. Blair, 2009, Input-output analysis: foundations and extensions, Second Edition, Cambridge University Press, UK.

T. A Wiedmann, 2009, Review of recent multi-regional input-output models used for consumption-based emissions and resource accounting, Ecol. Econ., 69, 211-222.

Jiří Jaromír Klemeš, Petar Sabev Varbanov and Peng Yen Liew (Editors)
Proceedings of the 24th European Symposium on Computer Aided Process Engineering – ESCAPE 24
June 15-18, 2014, Budapest, Hungary.

Techno-Economic, Sustainability & Environmental Impact Diagnosis (TESED) Framework

Carina L. Gargalo,[a,b] Ana Carvalho,[c] Henrique A. Matos,[a*] Rafiqul Gani,[b]

a CPQ/DEQ, Instituto Superior Técnico, Universidade de Lisboa, Av. Rovisco Pais, 1049-001 Lisboa, Portugal

b CAPEC, Department of Chemical and Biochemical Engineering, Technical University of Denmark, DK-2800 Lyngby, Denmark

c CEG-IST, Instituto Superior Técnico, Universidade de Lisboa, Avenida Rovisco Pais, 1049-001 Lisboa, Portugal

henrimatos@tecnico.ulisboa.pt

Abstract

Nowadays, companies are looking for new sustainable design alternatives that improve their original processes. To assess the best design alternative, economic aspects have been the preferred indicators. However, environmental and social concerns should also be included in the decision process so that truly sustainable design alternatives can be found. This work proposes a framework, called 'Techno-Economic Sustainability Environmental Impact Diagnosis' (TESED) that allows users to assess chemical/biochemical processes in a product oriented analysis. TESED is a systematic and generic approach that can be applied to any product/processes combination. Bioethanol production was the case-study selected to highlight the TESED framework. Two production processes using two different feedstocks, hardwood chips and cassava rhizome, have been analysed.

Keywords: TESED; Bioethanol; Retrofit; Sustainability

1. Techno-Economic Sustainability Environmental Impact Diagnosis Framework (TESED)

TESED is a generic and systematic framework to select the most sustainable process design of a target product. This framework employs a multi-level approach, where at the first level a set of possible processes, available to produce the target product, are analysed and more sustainable alternatives are generated for each process. At the end of this level, the new design alternatives, identified for each process, are assessed and the most sustainable is selected. At the second-level the most sustainable design alternatives defined in the first level are evaluated through a multi-criteria analysis, to determine the most sustainable process to produce the target product. The TESED framework is illustrated in Figure 1 and described in the text below.

1.1. Step 1 – Problem Definition

In the first step of the framework the problem should be described and identified. The target product should be selected for the framework analysis. Then a set of processes available to produce the target product should be selected. These processes are classified as the Base Case design, which are the designs already available in the market to produce the target product.

1.2. Step 2 – Data Collection

In this step the data required to classify all Base Case designs is collected. This data can be collected from the literature or from the actual plant. The data collection process is divided into two sub-steps: 2.1 Product data collection (chemical compounds properties such as density, enthalpy of vaporization, thermal capacity, etc.) and 2.2 Process data collection (reactions, published process simulation, stream composition, operating conditions).

1.3. Step 3 – Process Simulation

A rigorous simulation of the BaseCase design for each process is made in this step. Commercial simulators such as ASPEN or PRO II are used to simulate the Base Case designs. Through process simulation the remaining process data (mass and energy balances) required to perform the subsequent steps of the framework are obtained.

1.4. Step 4 – BaseCase Detailed Analysis

At this stage, a complete analysis of all Base Case designs, with respect to process bottlenecks and sustainability metrics (step 4.1), economic factors (step 4.2) and environmental impact (step 4.3) is performed. The sustainability analysis (step 4.1) is performed through SustainPro (Carvalho et al., 2013) software. SustainPro is a software tool, which employs a retrofit methodology to propose new sustainable design alternatives for a Base Case design, based on sustainability metrics. Moreover, this tool is also used to assess the proposed new design alternatives. Step 4.2 employs another computer-aided tool, ECON, (Carvalho et al., 2013) to perform a full economic evaluation. Two of the most important parameters obtained through this software are the operational and capital costs. The potential environmental impact of a certain chemical/biochemical plant design is also estimated following step 4.3, where LCSoft (a third computer aided tool) is applied (Carvalho et al., 2013). Several environmental impact categories are estimated based on a cradle-to-gate analysis (potential environmental impacts and carbon footprint). From this step the first analysis of the Base Case designs is obtained and a set of indicators and metrics are available to classify them.

1.5. Step 5 – Bottleneck Identification

Steps 1-4 provide a complete analysis on the Base Case design processes generating a good understanding of the process critical points with respect to sustainability issues, economic issues and environmental impacts. Through SustainPro and its systematic approach, the critical points of the process in terms of external dependence and natural resources consumption are identified. Next, based on the set of indicators obtained from SustainPro the bottlenecks with high potential for process improvements are identified. These critical points (step 4.1), are then verified through ECON (step 4.2) and LCSoft (step 4.3). The aforementioned tools are used as a cross-sectional approach integrating the current main areas of concern and identifying the set of indicators that represent the bottleneck. The bottlenecks that have the best chance for improvement are targeted for further study. In this way, the probability of achieving the desired (targeted) improvements in the sustainability, economics and environmental impacts of the process is increased.

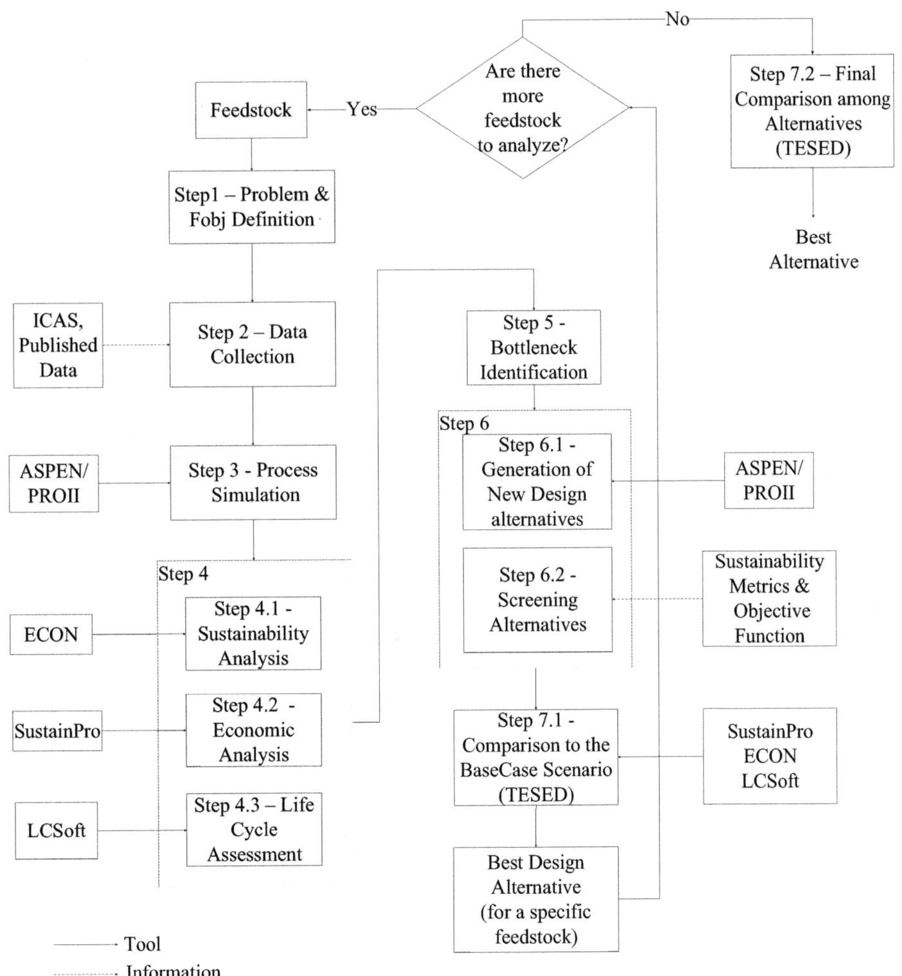

Figure 1. Flow-diagram of TESED framework.

1.6. Step 6 – Generation & Evaluation of new design alternatives

Step 6 is divided into two sub-steps: Step 6.1: here, a new design alternative to the Base Case design of a certain feedstock is generated, based on the bottlenecks identified in the previous step; Step 6.2: the New Design alternatives are compared and screened in terms of their sustainability metrics. It is important to note that after any change made in each Base Case design, for instance by either heat, mass or water integration, a new design alternative is generated. Therefore, the new design alternatives must be simulated again to allow comparison and screening of alternatives (Step 6.2). The most sustainable alternative is selected in Step 6.2 from all generated alternatives for a specific feedstock BaseCase design. The selection is performed through the application of sustainability metrics and the objective function introduced in step 1. The alternative that has the best values with respect to the design targets is selected for further analysis in the next step.

1.7. Step 7 – Comparison of different design alternatives and Final Decision

TESED proposes an option to compare several processes that produce a target product. Therefore, Step 7 is divided into two sub-steps: 7.1 and 7.2. In Step 7.1, the different best feasible alternatives from the step 6.2 are compared to Base Case design from each feedstock using SustainPro, ECON and LCSoft. In Step 7.2, the best alternative from Step 7.1 is selected, determining the most sustainable process design to produce the target product.

2. Case Study

In this paper the bioethanol production process is studied in detail. The main results obtained by employing the framework are presented.

2.1. Step 1

The assessment of different process designs to produce Bioethanol was identified as the objective of the study. Bioethanol was selected as the target product. The selected Base Case designs for the production of bioethanol are based on two feedstocks: hardwood chips and cassava rhizome.

2.2. Step 2 & Step 3

Data for the two Base Case designs (Alvarado-Morales et al., 2009; Mangnimit, 2013) were collected. Based on the data of the BaseCase designs (processes using hardwood chips and cassava rhizome) the two processes were simulated using PROII. The flowsheet of bioethanol produced from hardwood chips and cassava rhizome were built considering 99.95 % purity of the bioethanol product. The most important data needed for process assessment are schematically shown in Table 1 & 2.

2.3. Step 4.1

SustainPro has been applied and a list containing the most critical indicators in terms of mass, water and energy consumption was obtained.

For the hardwood chips process, the identified critical points are: 1) The excess of fresh water added to the system in the pre-treatment stage; 2) The excess of energy wasted in the output stream, since it has high energy content that can be integrated with a cold stream. For the cassava rhizome process, the two main critical points were identified:

Table 1. Mass balance of the bioethanol production BaseCase from hardwood chips

Hardwood Chips			
In	ton/day	Out	ton/day
Feedstock	3819	Ethanol	419
water	5152	Waste gases	1223
NH3	31.8	residue	32.3
Acid	1183	Waste water	8642
Z. mobilis	7.44		
Enzyme	106		
Lime	18		
Total in	10317	Total out	10317

Table 2. Mass balance of the bioethanol production BaseCase from cassava rhizome.

Cassava rhizome			
In	ton/day	Out	ton/day
Feedstock	807	Ethanol	121
HP+LP steam	93	Waste gases	126
NH3	0.08	residue	113
Acid	6	Waste water	546
Enzyme	1.1	$CaSO_4$	9
Corn steep Liquor	3.6		
Lime	4.4		
Total in	915	Total out	915

1) The fresh water that is being added to the process in the pre-treatment stage and then released as waste water; 2) The amount of solid residue that is being discarded as waste(mostly lignin), since it has economic value and it could be burned.

2.4. Step 4.2

A number of economic metrics were employed as criteria for comparison and were estimated using ECON. However, due to the limit of 6-pages per paper, only a few are presented here. Regarding bioethanol production from hardwood chips, the operational cost obtained was calculated as 0.520 $/kg of Ethanol and the process Internal Rate of Return (IRR) was 5 %. With respect to bioethanol production from cassava rhizome, the calculated operational cost was 0.258 $/kg of Ethanol and IRR was 25 %.

2.5. Step 4.3

Several environmental impact categories were predicted through LCSoft; nevertheless, due to the limit of space, only carbon footprint results are presented. Bioethanol produced from hardwood chips registered 5.91 kg CO_2 eq./kg of Ethanol and from cassava rhizome was found to be 5.92 kg CO_2 eq./kg of Ethanol.

2.6. Step 5

The critical points already identified by SustainPro were confirmed by the data obtained through ECON and LCSoft. To improve the identified process critical points and to increase the overall process sustainability, the major target was to decrease the amount of fresh water added to the system and the net energy input.

2.7. Step 6

For bioethanol production from hardwood chips, three different retrofit design alternatives were generated in order to overcome the identified bottlenecks (step 6.1) through heat integration (HC-A), water integration (HC-B) and a combination of heat and water integration (HC-C) were separately analyzed. For bioethanol production from cassava rhizome only the conjugated effect of water, energy co-production were tested (CR-A) (see Table 3). After screening (step 6.2), HC-C and CR-A were the retrofit options chosen with respect to bioethanol production from hardwood chips and cassava rhizome, respectively.

2.8. Step 7.1

In this step, both Base Cases were compared against the most sustainable alternative selected in step 6.2, and from that two designs come out.. Table 4 gives the performance criteria used for comparison of the two best alternatives: design-alternative HC-C for bioethanol production from hardwood chips and design-alternative CR-A for bioethanol production from cassava rhizome.

2.9. Step 7.2

According to Table 4, the best option with respect to the defined objectives of this study is bioethanol produced from cassava rhizome. Bioethanol production from cassava rhizome has improved water, raw materials and energy consumptions and the better economic factors, as well as larger operating profit. Likewise, with respect to environmental impact, the total carbon footprint of the processing plant has better values.

Table 3. Retrofit options generated

Hardwood chips			Cassava rhizome
HC-A	HC-B	HC-C	CR-A
heat integration	water integration	heat + water integration	Water recycle + energy co-production (steam/electricity by a turbo-generator)

Table 4. Summary of the most relevant comparison metrics obtained in Step 7.1.

	HARDWOOD CHIPS	CASSAVA RHIZOME
Alternative selected in Step 7.2	HC-C	CR-A
Raw Material usage (kg RM/kg EtOH)	8.96	3.103
Total Energy usage (GJ/kg of EtOH)	0.12	0.013
Net Fresh Water added(kg/kg of EtOH)	6.14	1.45
Total Utility Cost ($/kg of EtOH)	0.221	0.007
Operating Cost($/kg of EtOH)	0.48	0.111
Capital Cost ($/kg of EtOH)	0.69	0.65
Operating Profit ($/kg of EtOH)	0.19	0.46
Net Present Value	230	157
Internal Rate of Return (IRR)	8%	45%
Ethanol minimum selling Price ($/kg)	0.51	0.14
Total Carbon Footprint (kg CO_2/kg of EtOH)	5	4
Ozone Depletion Potential(CFC-11eq.)	6.31E-07	1.26E-10

3. Conclusion

A framework, which assesses the Techno-Economic, Sustainability and Environmental Impact Diagnosis (TESED) of chemical/biochemical processes for a target product production has been presented. TESED is not only a systematic way of generating more sustainable, economic and environmentally feasible options, but it also provides options to perform multi-criteria comparison of alternatives. Thereby enabling, the simultaneous comparison of different processes producing the same product. Currently TESED was used to test the production from different feedstock. Bioethanol produced from hardwood chips and cassava rhizome was the case study selected to highlight the application of the framework. Bioethanol produced from cassava rhizome was found to be a better option with respect to the multi-criteria set of metrics that were employed.

References

M. Alvarado-Morales, J. Terra, K. V. Gernaey, J. M. Woodley, R. Gani, 2009, Biorefining: Computer aided tools for sustainable design and analysis of bioethanol production, Chemical Engineering Research and Design, 87, 9, 1171–1183.

A. Carvalho, H. A. Matos, R. Gani, 2013, SustainPro—A tool for systematic process analysis, generation and evaluation of sustainable design alternatives, Computers and Chemical Engineering, 50, 8–27.

S. Mangnimit, P. Malakul, R. Gani, 2013, Sustainable process design of biofuels: bioethanol production from cassava rhizome, Proceedings of the 6th International Conference on Process Systems Engineering (PSE ASIA), Kuala Lumpur.

Jiří Jaromír Klemeš, Petar Sabev Varbanov and Peng Yen Liew (Editors)
Proceedings of the 24th European Symposium on Computer Aided Process Engineering – ESCAPE 24
June 15-18, 2014, Budapest, Hungary.

An Optimal Planning for the Reuse of Municipal Solid Waste Considering Economic, Environmental and Safety Objectives

José E. Santibañez-Aguilar,[a] Juan Martínez-Gómez,[a] José M. Ponce-Ortega,[a]* Fabricio Nápoles-Rivera,[a] Medardo Serna-González,[a] Mahmoud M. El-Halwagi[b]

[a]*Chemical Engineering Department; Universidad Michoacana de San Nicolás de Hidalgo, Morelia 58000, México.*

[b]*Chemical Engineering Department; Texas A&M University, College Station 77843, USA.*

jmponce@umich.mx

Abstract

Nowadays, the waste generation is a serious problem mainly in the countries with inefficient waste management systems. However, some waste can be reused as raw material for several products using a set of available technologies. In this context, several options to attack this problem have been implemented, but just a few alternatives consider the waste management as an integral part in the supply chain. This way, several technical, environmental and economic aspects have been taken into account for the assessment of the entire supply chain; although, the incorporation of safety criteria into the assessment of the supply chain focused in municipal solid waste have not been implemented in previous papers. Therefore, in this paper is proposed a mathematical programming model for the optimal planning of the reuse of municipal waste to maximize the economic benefits considering sustainability and safety criteria simultaneously. This methodology considers several phases: the separation of waste, distribution of waste to processing facilities, processing of waste to obtain useful products and distribution of products to consumers. Additionally, the safety criteria are based on the fatalities associated with the supply chain for the waste management. The problem is formulated as a multi-objective problem that considers three different objectives: the net annual profit, the amount of reused waste and the total fatalities generated with the considered risks. Results show that it is possible to implement a distributed processing system to reuse municipal waste in an economically attractive way. In addition, results can be used for governments to take decisions about the waste disposal and define the amount of waste that must be reused to obtain several products. It should be noted that results include the supply chain configuration. In addition, in future works this methodology can be extended to problems focused in supply chain design and retrofit simultaneously.

Keywords: Supply chain, Waste management, Risk assessment, Optimal planning.

1. Introduction

Nowadays, there is much interest in waste production, management and disposal. In this context, Abarca-Guerrero et al. (2013) defined the solid waste management as a challenge for the cities' authorities in developing countries, mainly due to the increasing generation of waste, the high costs associated to the waste management as well as a side effect of consumption and production.

It is important to note that the actions that have been implemented to solve this problem are focused only on one type of waste separately, without taking into account the interaction between the waste composition and distribution, and without considering the entire supply chain optimization as well as the economies of scale. Also, the distribution of waste, products and the design and selection of the processing facilities are crucial in yielding an adequate solution for the entire problem. Some works have been focused on the production of different products mainly energy from the municipal solid waste. In this context, Varbanov et al. (2012) introduced a new indicator called the Waste Energy Potential Utilization to indicate the impact of logistics and energy distribution during the municipal solid waste management.

Others works have been focused on modeling and optimizing the supply chains for the waste management. For example, Hung et al. (2007) presented a review for several models developed to support decision making in municipal solid waste management. Furthermore, the work by Morrissey and Browne (2004) revised the types of models that are currently being used in the area of municipal waste management, dividing these models in three categories: cost benefit analysis, based on life cycle assessment and based on multi-criteria decision making. In addition, Karmperis et al. (2013) revised the types of waste management models dividing them in the same categories than Morrissey and Browne (2004). Also, Santibañez-Aguilar et al. (2013) proposed a mathematical programming model for the optimal planning of the supply chain associated to the municipal solid waste management system to maximize the economic benefit while accounting for technical and environmental issues.

Besides, although the economic and environmental issues are certainly critical, the social aspect has been overlooked or just considered after design. In this regard, an additional way to consider the social aspect is through the risk assessment, which has not been considered simultaneously in the design phase of supply chains. In this context, El-Halwagi et al. (2013) proposed a new approach to explicitly take into account the risks associated with the supply chain of biorefineries while incorporating economic factors. In this way, the goal of the work is to present a mathematical programming model for the optimal planning associated to the reuse of municipal solid waste taking into account economic, environmental and safety issues simultaneously, also the model is based on a distributed system. The optimization model is able of selecting the processing technologies, consumers, cities producing waste, amount of recycled waste, products and location of processing facilities.

2. Problem Statement

The addressed problem considers several cities with a given municipal solid waste production, these waste can be utilized to obtain different useful products like energy, recycled materials, olefins, fuels, etc. However, the waste is stored in several disposition centers or dumps; these dumps can affect the population's safety in different ways, the first one is the fatalities associated for consuming polluted water, since the pollutant in the dump can be transported through leaching from the surface to shallow well that can serve as water source to the population. On the other hand, the risk associated the intoxication by the gas emissions caused by the burning of a given dump has been implemented; this risk is taken into account by the implementation of a gas dispersion model. One of the main considerations is that each city is divided in several grids named sites, each one of these sites have different waste production, population and may have processing plants and dumps, this division is accomplished because each dump can affect in different magnitude each one of the sites, since each sites is located at different distances from the dumps considered. The proposed methodology is shown in Figure 1, which also show the main components of the proposed superstructure.

3. Mathematical model

The proposed mathematical model is a mixed integer linear programming model and consists of several mass balances as well as constraints for product demands and waste availability. In addition, the model considers equations to obtain the cost of the integrated system; in addition, equations for the fatalities assessment are needed.

3.1. Mass balances, constraints and equations for risk assessment

The considered mass balances are associated to the splitters and mixers in the distribution of the waste from each site to each dump as well as the distribution of waste from dumps to processing facilities and the transportation of products from processing plants to sites. Additionally, the mass balances are carried out to determine the inventory of materials in the different locations (sites, dumps and processing plants). In addition, another mass balance is utilized to model the conversion of waste to products, this is done through black-box models, where only is necessary a conversion factor for a specific technology to obtain the products from the waste. Furthermore, several constraints have been proposed for modeling the supply chain based on municipal solid waste, these constraints account for the availability of waste, limits for transportation and processing, as well as, constraint in the demand that can be satisfied.

On the other hand, there is necessary to define the different types of risk associated to the waste management process. The first one is the risk for leaching, which depends on each shallow well (in each site is considered a shallow well) as well as each dump; in this case, a shallow well can be polluted for only a dump. In addition, each shallow well

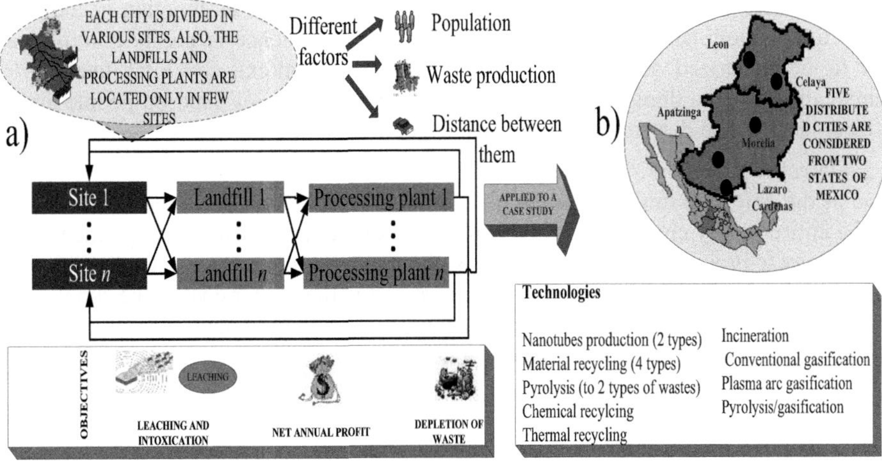

Figure 1. General representation of the solution approach. a) Superstructure for the supply chain based on municipal solid waste; b) Case study.

is associated to a given population. It is important to note that the fraction of fatalities for leaching is a function of the concentration in each shallow well, and this relation is given by a Probit curve; however, to represent this relation, the Probit curve is segmented in several linear relationships that determine the fraction of fatalities depending on the concentration level. Each linear relationship is associated to a binary variable.

To take into account the fatalities for intoxication when the dump is burning, it is necessary to define a dispersion gas model. This way, the Pasquill-Guilford model is a proper way to consider the dispersion of gases. According with the Pasquill Guilford model (see Eq. (1)), the concentration of gaseous pollutants depends on the emission rate of the source multiplied by a factor that depends on the position of the receptor respect to the emissary

$$C_{g,d,s}^{\substack{toxic\\concentration}} = Q_{g,d}\alpha_{d,s}^{dispersion}, \quad \forall g \in GAS\ POLLUTANT, d \in DUMPS, s \in SITES \tag{1}$$

where the factor $\alpha_{d,s}^{dispersion}$ depends on the position, and this is equal to an expression that depends on various parameters of the geographic region, allocation and the proposed scenario. This parameter is given in the following relationship.

$$\alpha_{d,s}^{dispersion} = \frac{\dfrac{1}{2\pi\sigma_{d,s}^{y}\sigma_{d,s}^{z}u}\exp\left[-\dfrac{1}{2}\left(\dfrac{y_{d,s}}{\sigma_{d,s}^{z}}\right)^{2}\right]}{\left\{\exp\left[-\dfrac{1}{2}\left(\dfrac{z_{d,s}\text{-}Hr_{d,s}}{\sigma_{d,s}^{z}}\right)^{2}\right]+\exp\left[-\dfrac{1}{2}\left(\dfrac{z_{d,s}\text{-}Hr_{d,s}}{\sigma_{d,s}^{z}}\right)^{2}\right]\right\}^{-1}}, \quad \forall d \in DUMPS, s \in SITES \tag{2}$$

The concentration for intoxication is useful to calculate the Probit value for the fatalities associated to intoxication when a dump is burned. This function can be linearized in similar way than the fatalities for leaching. It should be noticed that the exposition time for the risk analysis is 8 h since the considered risk is acute; although if the exposition is greater than 96 h the considered model would be invalid. In addition, it is necessary to propose others equations to obtain the probability of fatalities as function of the Probit value for the pollutant in the considered risk. The dependence is highly nonlinear and has to be linearized as the previous cases. In this context, the total fatalities for intoxication when a dump is burning depend on the number of exposed people and the affectation fraction determined by the gas dispersion model.

3.2. Objective functions

One of the objective functions is the net annual profit that considers the associated cost to the entire supply chain, this is, the capital and operational costs for implementing the technology to process the waste; as well as, the transportation cost for the distribution of raw materials and products, the separation cost that is the higher cost of the supply chain and the disposition cost that is normally paid by the government; this objective also considers the revenue for the selling of products.

$$\begin{aligned} Net\ Profit = {} & Revenue\ Sales - Operational\ Cost - Capital\ Cost \\ & - Transportation\ Cost - Separation\ Cost - Disposition\ Cost \end{aligned} \tag{3}$$

The second objective is given by the amount of consumed waste since this affects directly the environment by the huge quantity of generated waste.

$$\textit{Percentage of Consumed Wastes} = 100\left[\textit{Used Quantity of Waste} \,/\, \textit{Available Quantity of Waste}\right] \quad (4)$$

Finally, the third objective function is the total fatalities for the implementation of the waste management system, this function is defined as the fatalities caused by leaching plus the fatalities caused by intoxication for gas emissions.

$$\textit{Total Fatalities} = \textit{Fatalities Leaching in Shallow Well} + \textit{Fatalities Intoxication by Gaseosus Emissions} \quad (5)$$

4. Results

A case study for the central-west part of Mexico was considered. The proposed case study takes into account 11 types of waste, 14 processing technologies to obtain 13 products, as well as, five cities divided each one in 10 sites, considering that each city has 4 dumps and 2 processing facilities. The different technologies and the considered cities are shown in Figure 1b.

The solution approach is based on generating several Pareto curves taking into account only two objectives. The mathematical model was coded in the software GAMS and consists of 208,000 constraints, 134,000 continuous variables and 60,240 binary variables, taking an average of 0.76 s of CPU time in a processor i7-3720QM at 2.60GHz with 16GB of RAM for the solution of each point of the Pareto curves using the solver CPLEX. The first Pareto curve considers the maximization of the net annual profit and the maximization of the consumed amount of waste in cities without considering the risk, this curve has a similar behavior that the one reported by Santibañez-Aguilar et al. (2013). On the other hand, a second Pareto curve for the maximization of the profit and the minimization of the total fatalities was generated; in this last case the fatalities increase when the net profit increases (see Figure 2).

In addition, it should be noticed in the Pareto curve of Figure 2a that there is a significant change in the consumed waste respect to the fatalities (i.e., the change in the value of the fatalities can be until 96 %). Furthermore, results show different configurations depending which objective is prioritized. For example, if the economic

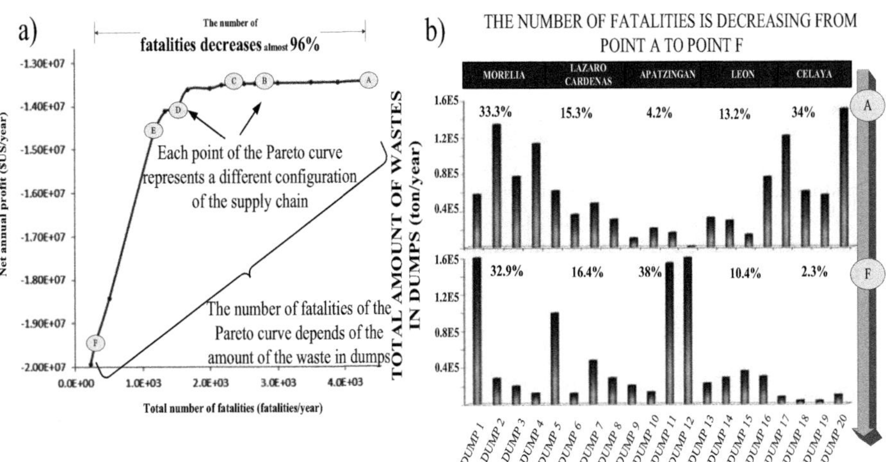

Figure 2. a) Pareto curve for the maximization of the net profit and minimization of fatalities. b) Distribution of waste for some solutions of the Pareto curve.

and environmental objectives are selected with around 46 % of consumed waste, seven types of waste are selected (aluminum, paper, clear glass, green glass, brown glass, polyethylene and polypropylene). In this context, the results show that the processing of waste should be accomplished in processing plants located in the cities of Morelia and Leon for the different waste, and the dumps are located in sites with a low density of population and in the boundary of the cities to avoid the dispersion of gases, because the fatalities for intoxication are greater than the fatalities for leaching for the case study considered.

5. Conclusions

This paper has presented a mathematical model for the optimal planning of a distributed system to treat municipal solid waste while considering economic, environmental and safety aspects simultaneously. The problem has been mathematically formulated as a multi-objective mixed integer linear programming problem. The model considers simultaneously the supply chain optimization for the products obtained from the municipal solid waste taking into account the risk assessment for activities that can produce fatalities when a given configuration for a waste management system is implemented. The application of the proposed methodology has been illustrated through a case study of a distributed waste management system in a central-west region of Mexico. In this regard, the model can be useful to consider the waste management in regions where the waste management is not developed or there is not an established way to control waste.

References

A.C. Karmperis, K. Aravossis, I.P. Tatsiopoulos, A. Sotirchos, 2013, Decision support models for solid waste management: Review and game-theoretic approaches, Waste Management, 33, 1290-1301

A.J. Morrissey, J. Browne, 2004, Waste management models and their application to sustainable waste management, Waste Management, 24, 3, 297-308

A.M. El-Halwagi, C. Rosas, J.M. Ponce-Ortega, A. Jiménez-Gutiérrez, M.S. Mannan, M.M. El-Halwagi, 2013, Multiobjective optimization of biorefineries with economic and safety objectives, AIChE Journal, 59, 7, 2427-2434

J.E. Santibañez-Aguilar, J.M. Ponce-Ortega, J.B. González-Campos, M. Serna-González, M.M. El-Halwagi, 2013, Optimal planning for the sustainable utilization of municipal solid waste, Waste Management, 33, 12, 2607-2622

L. Abarca-Guerrero, G. Maas, W. Hogland, 2013, Solid waste management challenges for cities in developing countries, Waste Management, 33, 1, 220-232

M.L. Hung, H.W. Ma, W.F. Yang, 2007, A novel sustainable decision making model for municipal solid waste management, Waste Management, 27, 2, 209-219

P.S. Varbanov, H.L. Lam, F. Friedler, J.J. Klemes, 2012, Energy Generation and Carbon Footprint of Waste to Energy: Centralised vs. Distributed Processing, Computer Aided Chemical Engineering, 31, 1402-1406

Jiří Jaromír Klemeš, Petar Sabev Varbanov and Peng Yen Liew (Editors)
Proceedings of the 24th European Symposium on Computer Aided Process Engineering – ESCAPE 24
June 15-18, 2014, Budapest, Hungary.

Life Cycle Assessment Based Process Design of CO_2 Capture Options

Laurence Tock*, François Maréchal

Industrial Process and Energy Systems Engineering, Ecole Polytechnique Fédérale de Lausanne, Station 9, CH-1015 Lausanne, Switzerland.
laurence.tock@epfl.ch

Abstract

In the perspective of mitigating climate change, CO_2 capture and storage (CCS) is considered as a promising option. To evaluate the environmental benefit of capturing CO_2 it is important to make a systematic comparison including the whole life cycle from the resource extraction to the final product (i.e. electricity). Especially when comparing natural gas, coal and biomass fed processes the supply chain differences have to be accounted for. Besides the benefit in terms of greenhouse gas emissions reduction, CCS induces an energy and cost penalty due to the CO_2 separation and compression. The trade-offs between environmental impacts, efficiency and costs are systematically assessed here by combining life cycle assessment (LCA) with flowsheeting, energy integration and economic evaluation in a multi-objective optimisation framework. Post- and pre-combustion CO_2 capture options for electricity generation processes, using fossil and renewable resources, are analysed, compared and optimised. Multi-objective optimisations are performed for various thermo-economic and environmental objectives to highlight the influence on the optimal process design and on the decision making.

Keywords: CO_2 capture, LCA, Multi-objective optimisation, Power plant

1. Introduction

Carbon capture and storage (CCS) is regarded as a promising measure to reduce the greenhouse gas emissions. For CO_2 capture in power plants three different concepts can be distinguished; post-, pre- and oxy-combustion. The competitiveness of these options depends on the power cycle, the resources, the capture technology and the economic scenario. Previous studies made for European (ZEP, 2011) and OECD countries (Finkenrath, 2011) have mainly focused on technology and economy, which is a crucial part but not sufficient for decision making with regard to sustainable development. Few comprehensive comparative evaluations of the environmental impact of CCS are available. The trade-off between the global warming potential (GWP) and other environmental impacts is revealed by Pehnt and Henkel (2009) for coal power plants and by Singh et al. (2011) for different CCS options in natural gas and coal power plants. The LCA analysis of Volkart et al. (2013) included biomass based CCS options and Viebahn et al. (2007) compared the impacts of CCS with the one of renewables. So far, only reduced multi-criteria assessments were applied to power plants with CCS. If comparisons are made, they are mostly made for a given process design. Multi-objective optimisation of the process design with regard to environmental objectives resulting from a rigorous life cycle assessment (LCA) such as presented by Bernier et al. (2010) is rarely performed.

Therefore, the objective of this paper is to systematically compare and optimise different CO_2 capture options taking into account energetic, economic and environmental considerations simultaneously. The process design is optimised in terms of operating conditions and energy integration. In Tock and Maréchal (2013) the systematic methodology for thermo-environomic modelling and optimisation presented by Gerber et al. (2011) has already been applied to assess the competitiveness of CO_2 capture options for natural gas (NG) and biomass (BM) fed power plants. In this optimisation it was focused on the minimisation of the energy penalty and of the local CO_2 emissions (i.e. maximisation of the captured CO_2). However, since there is a trade-off between GWP and other environmental impacts (i.e. resources depletion), different life cycle impact objectives will be considered here in order to reveal the influence on the optimal process design and on the decision making.

2. Methodology

With regard to CO_2 emissions mitigation, an assessment of the overall life cycle environmental impacts from the resource extraction along the production chain to the final product, including off-site emissions and construction emissions, is essential. Life cycle assessment (LCA) has been proven to be suitable for this scope. LCA is a well-established method, standardised in ISO 14040 & 14044. The four main stages of LCA are; the goal and scope definition, the life cycle inventory (LCI), the impact assessment (LCIA) and the interpretation. As shown by Gerber et al. (2011), life cycle assessment can be included in the thermo-economic modelling. For this purpose, the LCI is written as a function of the characteristics of the thermo-economic model (i.e. design variables, mass and energy balances, equipment size). The applied thermo-environomic optimisation approach, previously presented by Gassner and Maréchal (2009) combines flowsheeting and energy integration techniques with economic evaluation and life cycle assessment in a multi-objective optimisation framework. These method has been extended in Tock and Maréchal (2012) to combine flowsheets developed with different software. Here the different processes have been modelled with the conventional flowsheeting software Belsim Vali and Aspen Plus based on literature data for the operating conditions. To assess the trade-offs of the competing objectives an evolutionary algorithm described by Molyneaux et al. (2010) is applied in the optimisation.

The scope of this study being to evaluate power plants with CO_2 capture, 1 GJ_e of net electricity produced is chosen as a functional unit (FU=1 GJ_e). In the LCI phase every flow, crossing the system boundaries as an extraction or an emission, which is necessary to one of the unit processes, is identified and quantified based on the process layouts. The major process steps are resource extraction and transport, heat and power generation and CO_2 removal (Figure 1). The data available from the Ecoinvent database (Ecoinvent, 2013) are used to compute the different contributions of the unit processes. Different impact methods are compared to address the influence on greenhouse gas emissions, ecosystem, human health and resources. The IPCC 07 method calculates the global warming potential by using the characterisation factors of different gaseous emissions published by the International Panel on Climate Change in 2007 (IPCC). The global warming potential over 100 years is computed in terms of CO_2 equivalent emissions. It has to be noted that the GWP of fossil CO_2 emissions is standardised to 1, while for biogenic CO_2 emissions the GWP is considered as 0. Storage of fossil CO_2 accounts as zero to GWP, while storage of biogenic CO_2 leads to a GWP of -1. The negative balance is due to the fact that the released CO_2 was previously fixed in the plant as hydrocarbon by photosynthesis. In addition to the climate change impact (CC), the impacts on resources (Res), human health (HH) and ecosystem quality (EQ) are evaluated by the Impact 2002+ method (endpoint categories) and the damage-oriented Ecoindicator99-(h,a) method (hierarchist perspective, single score). In the Ecoindicator99 method climate change is accounted

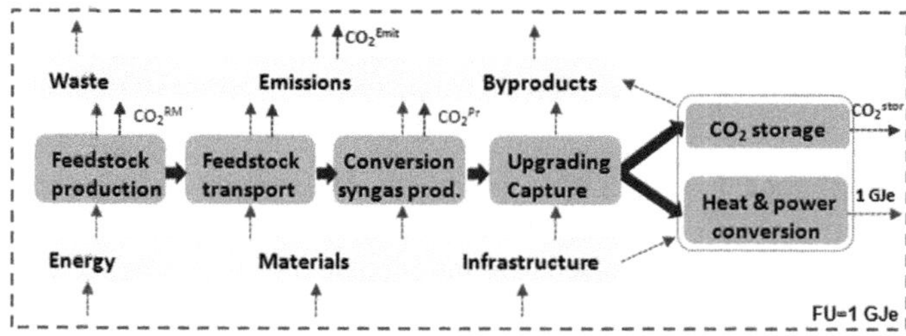

Figure 1. System's boundary for life cycle inventory of pre-combustion CO_2 capture processes.

in the human health impact aggregating also carcinogenic, ozone layer depletion and respiratory effects. The respective weighting factors are 40 % HH, 40 % EQ and 20 % Res.

3. Process description

Three representative CO_2 capture options are investigated: 1) Post-combustion CO_2 capture by chemical absorption with monoethanolamine applied to a natural gas combined cycle (NGCC) plant (582 $MW_{th,NG}$) (*NG post-*), 2) Pre-combustion CO_2 capture by physical absorption with Selexol in a natural gas fuelled power plant based on autothermal reforming (725 $MW_{th,NG}$) (*NG pre-*), 3) Pre-combustion CO_2 capture by physical absorption with Selexol in a biomass fired power plant based on fast internally circulating fluidised bed gasification (380 $MW_{th,NG}$) (*BM pre-*). The biomass plant's scale is limited by the biomass availability and the logistics of wood transport, as explained in Gerber et al. (2011). The biomass based process models have been described and analysed previously in Tock and Maréchal (2012a) and the one using natural gas as a resource in Tock and Maréchal (2012b). The performance is evaluated by the energy efficiency ε_{tot} defined by the ratio between the net electricity output and the resources energy input (lower heating value basis), the CO_2 capture rate η_{CO2} based on local CO_2 emissions, the life cycle GWP and the electricity production costs (COE), including annual capital investment, operation and maintenance costs and if indicated a carbon tax on local or life cycle CO_2 emissions (i.e. tax CO_2 local / LCA). The competitiveness is compared with a conventional NGCC plant (559 $MW_{th,NG}$) without CO_2 capture yielding an efficiency of 58.8 % (Table 1). The economic assumption are: operation 7,500 h/y, lifetime 25 y, interest rate 6 % and resource price 9.7 $\$/GJ_{res}$. Figure 2 illustrates the environmental impact of the base case CO_2 capture process options.

The benefit of CO_2 capture is clearly revealed with the IPCC and Impact 2002+ method. With a capture rate of 90 %, the GWP is reduced to 34 $kg_{CO2,eq}/GJ_e$ with post-combustion CO_2 capture compared to a conventional NGCC plant (120 $kg_{CO2,eq}/GJ_e$). Pre-combustion CO_2 capture (60 %) in biomass fed power plants leads even to a negative balance of -140 $kg_{CO2,eq}/GJ_e$ due to the advantage of capturing biogenic CO_2. However, with the Ecoindicator99 method, the overall impact of CO_2 capture in a NGCC plant is 3 % higher than without capture because of the depletion of fossil resources. Due to the energy demand for CO_2 capture and compression, the natural gas consumption is increased to produce 1GJ of electricity compared to a conventional NGCC having a higher productivity. In this method the resources impact overweights the climate change benefit (included in HH impact). For CO_2 capture in a biomass fed plant the overall impact is however lower. These results reveal the influence of the choice of the impact method on the CO_2 capture options performance evaluation and thus on the selection of the optimal process design.

4. Multi-objective optimisation

The decision variables for the optimisation are the process operating conditions (i.e. T & P of the process units, design of ab-and desorption columns, etc.) and the objectives are respectively:

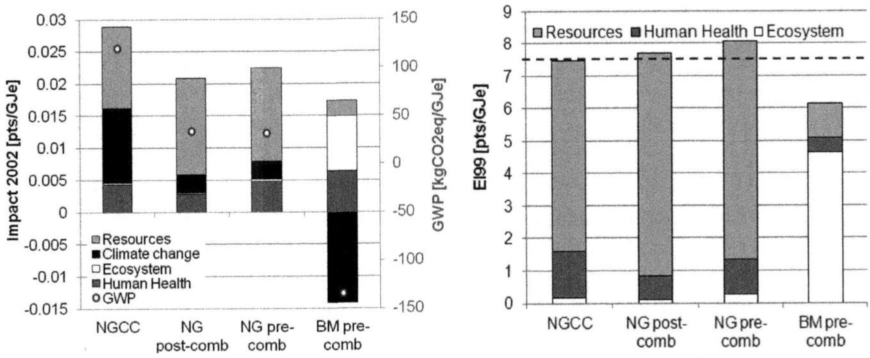

Figure 2. Environmental impacts comparison for base case CO_2 capture process designs.

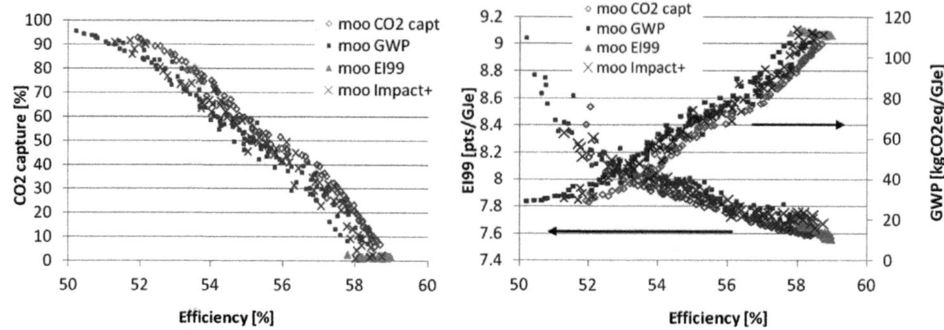

Figure 3. Influence of the objective function on the Pareto optimal solutions for the natural gas fed power plant with pre-combustion CO_2 capture.

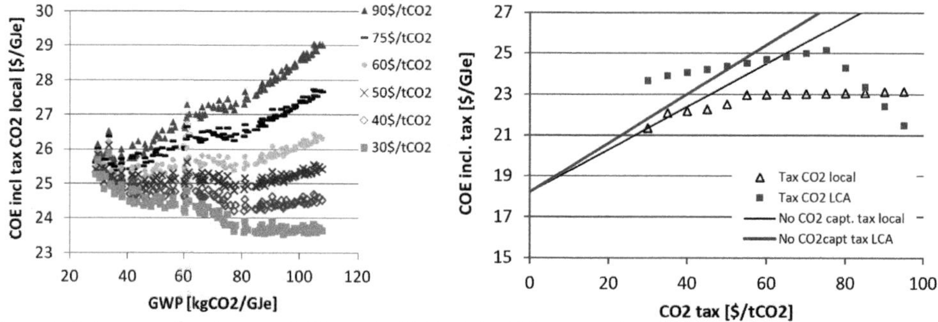

Figure 4. Influence of carbon tax (left) on the COE of the NG power plant with pre-combustion capture and (right) on the COE of the most economically competitive process (right).

- Moo CO_2 capt.: max ε_{tot}, max η_{CO2}
- Moo GWP: max ε_{tot}, min GWP $kg_{CO2,eq}/GJ_e$, min COE
- Moo EI99: max ε_{tot}, min total impact Ecoindicator99, min COE
- Moo Imp.: max ε_{tot}, min total impact Impact 2002+, min COE

The opposite behaviour between the Ecoindicator99 and GWP impact is clearly revealed in Figure 3 for the option of a natural gas fed plant with pre-combustion CO_2 capture. Optimising local CO_2 emissions or the GWP or the total impact assessed with the Impact 2002+ method leads to the same process designs. However, when minimising the Ecoindicator99 total impact, the optimisation leads to solutions with high efficiencies and low CO_2 capture rates (i.e. high emissions) because the increased impact on the resources overweights the decreased impact on the human health (incl. climate change) at high capture rates.

To evaluate the economic competitiveness of each process design generated by the optimisation and to support decision making, the impact of the introduction of a carbon tax on the local CO_2 emissions and on the whole life cycle CO_2 emissions is assessed. Figure 4 (right) reveals that for low CO_2 taxes process designs with high GWP (i.e. low η_{CO2}, high ε_{tot}) lead to the lowest COE, while for taxes higher than 50 $/$t_{CO2}$ process designs with low GWP become profitable. For a given carbon tax, the process design yielding the lowest COE (incl. tax) has been identified from all the generated Pareto optimal solutions and is illustrated in Figure 4 (left) highlighting also the break-even carbon tax for which the CO_2 capture becomes competitive compared to an NGCC plant. The slopes change is related to a switch of the optimal process design with CO_2 capture. The decrease in COE (incl. tax CO_2 LCA) after the maximum is due to a transition of the resource from natural gas to biomass. The performance results of the respective designs are reported in Figure 5 and Table 1.

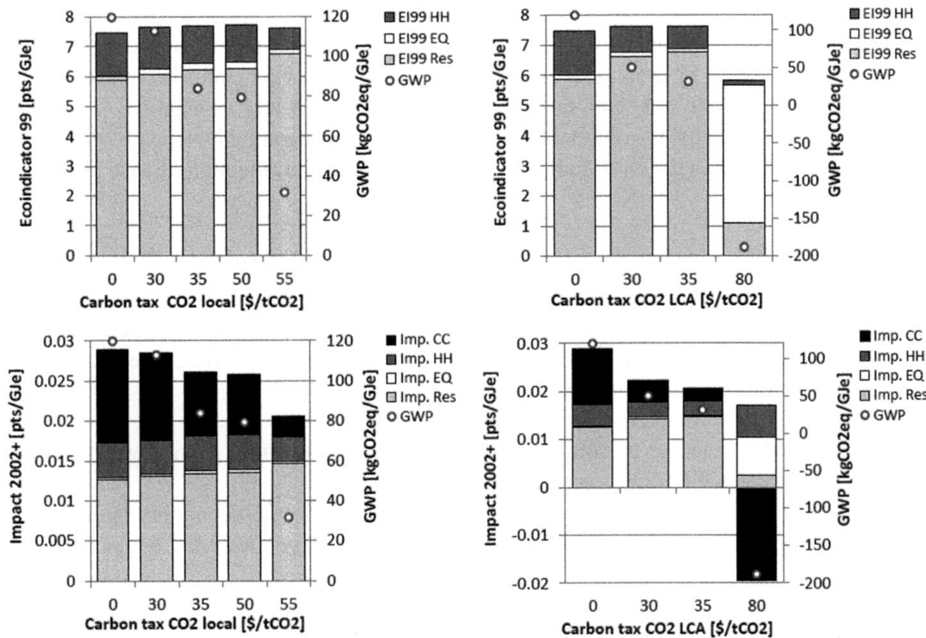

Figure 5. Environmental impact of the process designs with the lowest COE including a tax on the local CO_2 emissions (left) or on the life cyle CO_2 emissions (right) (Table 1).

Table 1. Performance of the optimal process designs yielding the lowest COE (Figure 5).

		tax local CO_2				tax LCA CO_2		
Process	NGCC	NG pre-	NG pre-	NG pre-	NG post-	NG post-	NG post-	BM pre-
Carbon tax [$/t_{CO2}$]	0	30	35	50	55	30	35	80
CO_2 capture rate [%]	0	1.2	33.6	38.8	83.9	76.6	83.9	71.9
Efficiency [%]	58.8	58.2	56.8	56.5	50.6	51.6	50.5	39.3
COE incl. tax [$/GJ$_e$]	18.3	21.3	22.1	22.5	23.0	23.7	23.9	24.9

With a tax up to 50 $/$t_{CO2}$ on the local CO_2 emissions, pre-combustion designs with capture rates up to 38 % are competitive, while post-combustion capture with high capture rates becomes interesting for taxes above 55 $/$t_{CO2}$. Figure 5 (left) shows the reduction of the climate change impact with the increasing tax, leading to a lower overall environmental impact evaluated with the Impact 2002+ and IPCC method and a slightly higher one with the Ecoindicator99 due to the resources impact as previously explained. If a tax is introduced on the life cycle CO_2 high capture rates (80 % post-combustion) inducing a climate change impact reduction (Figure 5 right) become already competitive for low taxes 30-75 $/$t_{CO2}$, while for higher taxes biomass processes emerge due to the environmental benefit of capturing biogenic CO_2. These results illustrate the influence of the introduction of a carbon tax on the process design.

5. Conclusion

Different CO_2 capture options using natural gas and biomass resources are systematically compared and optimised in terms of energetic, economic and environmental considerations. By including LCA impacts as an objective in the multi-objective optimisation it is highlighted how the environmental objective influences the decision making. Different impact methods are compared to address the influence on greenhouse gas emissions, ecosystem, human health and resources. With the Ecoindicator99-(h,a) method the environmental impact of power plants with CO_2 capture appears to be worse than without capture because of the larger resources depletion impact, related to the energy penalty, over-weighting the climate change benefit aggregated in the human health impact. When the climate change impact is accounted in a separate impact category as in the Impact 2002+ and the IPCC method, CO_2 capture shows a clear environmental benefit. The introduction of a carbon tax favours power plants with CO_2 capture. For a tax on the local CO_2 over 50 $\$/t_{CO2}$ natural gas power plants with 80 % post-combustion capture are the most competitive and allow to reduce the GWP by around 75 % to 31 $kg_{CO2,eq}/GJ_e$. Biomass plants become competitive with a tax on the life cycle CO_2 emissions around 80 $\$/t_{CO2}$ and lead to a negative GWP of -187 $kg_{CO2,eq}/GJ_e$. Consequently, the optimal CO_2 capture process design highly depends on the chosen impact method to evaluate the environmental impact and on the introduction of a carbon tax.

References

Aspen Tech, Aspen Plus V7.2, <www.aspentech.com>, Accessed 20/10/2013.

Belsim SA., Vali, http://www.belsim.com/, Accessed 20/10/2013.

E. Bernier, F. Maréchal, R. Samson, 2010, Multi-objective design optimization of a natural gas-combined cycle with carbon dioxide capture in a life cycle perspective, Energy, 35 , 1121-1128.

Ecoinvent, v2.2, http://www.ecoinvent.ch/, Accessed 30/10/2013.

M. Finkenrath, 2011, Cost and Performance of Carbon Dioxide Capture from Power Generation, Report, International Energy Agency, Paris, France.

M. Gassner, F. Maréchal, 2009, Methodology for the optimal thermo-economic, multi-objective design of thermochemical fuel production from biomass, Computers & Chemical Engineering, 33, 769-781.

L. Gerber, M. Gassner, F. Maréchal, 2011, Systematic integration of LCA in process systems design: Application to combined fuel and electricity production from lignocellulosic biomass, Computers & Chemical Engineering, 35, 1265 - 1280.

ISO, 2006a, Environmental management - Life Cycle Assessment - Principles and framework, International standard, ISO 14040.

ISO, 2006b, Environmental management - Life Cycle Assessment - Requirements and guidelines, International standard, ISO 14044.

A. Molyneaux, G. Leyland, D. Favrat, 2010, Environomic multi-objective optimisation of a district heating network considering centralized and decentralized heat pumps, Energy, 35, 751-758.

M. Pehnt, J. Henkel, 2009, Life cycle assessment of carbon dioxide capture and storage from lignite power plants, International Journal of Greenhouse Gas Control, 3, 49-66.

B. Singh, A.H. Strø mman, E.G. Hertwich, 2011, Comparative life cycle environmental assessment of CCS technologies, International Journal of Greenhouse Gas Control, 5, 911-921.

L. Tock, F. Maréchal, 2012a, Co-production of hydrogen and electricity from lignocellulosic biomass: Process design and thermo-economic optimization, Energy, 45, 339 - 349.

L. Tock, F. Maréchal, 2012b, H2 processes with CO2 mitigation: Thermo-economic modeling and process integration. International Journal of Hydrogen Energy, 37, 11785-11795.

L. Tock, F. Maréchal, 2012, Platform development for studying integrated energy conversion processes: Application to a power plant process with CO2 capture, Computer-aided Chemical Engineering, 31, 1015-1019.

L. Tock, F. Maréchal, 2013, Process engineering method for systematically comparing CO2 capture options, Computer Aided Chemical Engineering, 32, 367 -372.

P. Viebahn, J. Nitsch, M. Fischedick, A. Esken, D. Schüwer, N. Supersberger, U. Zuberbühler, O. Edenhofer, 2007, Comparison of carbon capture and storage with renewable energy technologies regarding structural, economic, and ecological aspects in Germany, International Journal of Greenhouse Gas Control, 1, 121-133.

K. Volkart, C. Bauer, C. Boulet, 2013, Life cycle assessment of carbon capture and storage in power generation and industry in Europe, International Journal of Greenhouse Gas Control, 16, 91-106.

ZEP, 2011, The costs of CO2 capture, transport and storage - Post-demonstration CCS in the EU, Report, European Technology Platform, Brussels, Belgium.

Jiří Jaromír Klemeš, Petar Sabev Varbanov and Peng Yen Liew (Editors)
Proceedings of the 24th European Symposium on Computer Aided Process Engineering – ESCAPE 24
June 15-18, 2014, Budapest, Hungary.

Development of a Life Cycle Assessment Model for the Analysis of the Energy, Water and Food Nexus

Tareq Al-Ansari[a,*], Anna Korre[a], Zhenggang Nie[a], Nilay Shah[b]

[a]Department of Earth Science and Engineering, [b]Department of Chemical Engineering, Imperial College London, SW7 2AZ, London, UK
t.al-ansari11@imperial.ac.uk

Abstract

There is a growing momentum to analyse the broader interdependencies of the energy, water and food systems rather than evaluating them in isolation. For instance, when analysing a food system, it is necessary to consider it in terms of its agriculture, water and energy characteristics using a suitable robust sustainability assessment methodology. The objective of this paper is to integrate energy, water and food (EWF) systems in one resource model described by a series of sub-systems; the agriculture sub-system includes the production and application of fertilizers and the raising of livestock. The water sub-system is represented by reverse osmosis for the production of water. The energy sub-systems consider fossil fuel in the form of combined cycle natural gas based energy production and solar renewable energy. Life Cycle Assessment (LCA) is used to evaluate impacts on the natural environment by considering the material flows from the sub-systems on a range of impact categories in addition to calculating resource consumption. It is shown that the food sub-system produces the largest emissions, followed by fossil fuel powered desalination for irrigation. The use of renewable energy has a significant land footprint however, it reduces overall emissions significantly.

Keywords: Energy, Water, Food, Nexus, LCA

1. Introduction

Energy utilisation represents about 65 % of global anthropogenic greenhouse gas emissions, resulting in significant increases in the global levels of CO_2, CH_4 and N_2O. The world's population, estimated to be six thousand million currently, is appropriating 54 % of the accessible fresh water reserves which will be further strained with variations in temperature from climate change and increasing population. Projections show that feeding the world population of nine thousand million in 2050 would require a 70 % increase in agricultural production. This would require a significant input of resources such as energy, water and mineral fertilizers producing a large environmental footprint. Evidently, energy, water and food (EWF) are; rapidly growing in demand, have different regional availability and have strong interdependencies with the environment. The objective of this paper is to present a sustainability assessment model currently under development by the authors which integrates EWF systems in one resource model. The integrated EWF modelling tool is designed to estimate the performance of the nexus at an appropriate scale and resolution by identifying and quantifying the impact of given food production scenarios on terrestrial and marine eco-systems from a life cycle perspective. The approach to nexus analysis can be very complex and is dependent on the resource that is being examined. As such, the tool should be modular which will ensure that complex systems are accurately represented and analysed. This approach makes sure that the technical, spatial and temporal differences that exist between different systems and unit operation effects can be accounted for by modifying appropriate parameters of the component unit processes.

The model under development aims to answer a fundamental question concerning the environmental burden of the provision of food in water-scarce countries and establish how this burden can be reduced. For this reason, Qatar is chosen as a test site. Qatar is an arid country that suffers from a severe lack of natural water resources. Annual freshwater extraction from aquifers is four times the rate of natural recharge of 50 Mm^3/y. The depletion is driven by agriculture which only accounts for 8 % of domestic consumption, and is leading to greater salination of aquifer water. Consequently, fossil fuel powered desalination provides more than 99 % of Qatar's water demand providing up to 539 Mm^3/y. In 2012 Qatar's electricity generating capacity reached 9,000 MW and is expected to rise with increasing population growth. The total arable land in the countries representing the Gulf Cooperation Council (GCC) is in the order of 1.7 % and as a result imports at least 80 % of its food requirements. Furthermore, the total food imports will have to increase to accommodate the increasing population estimated at 14.3 % per year.

2. Life Cycle Assessment model development

Life Cycle Assessment as a methodological tool involves the compilation and evaluation of the inputs, outputs and potential environmental impacts of a product, process or system throughout its entire life. The four main stages of LCA according to ISO 14040 are: the goal and scope definition; the life cycle inventory analysis (LCI); the impact assessment (LCIA); and the interpretation of the results. Impact categories (e.g. global warming, acidification, and human toxicity, etc.), category indicators, and characterisation factors are defined and inventory data are assigned to categories via the characterisation factors. LCA provides the methodological framework for the EWF system model developed and is used to evaluate the performance of alternative options. Similar work by Morales-Mendoza et al. (2012) uses process simulation models to optimise engineering processes while incorporating environmental considerations.

The EWF nexus consists of a series of sub-system LCI models that are developed to quantify material flows, natural resource and energy consumption at component unit process level. The LCI models are built using a combination of mass balance models, literature emission factors and engineering calculations which are validated using published literature and industry data. The flexible structure of the LCI database, provided through modularisation, enables the practitioner to choose component unit processes so that different technological options can be considered without the need for redesign or loss of information. The nexus modelling system presented here has adopted a food perspective with the objective of evaluating the impact when raising domestic production. The rationale behind the crop profile choice, which includes greenhouse, open field vegetables and fruits, is not the subject of this study. Three scenarios all of which serve to deliver the same functional unit are evaluated. The baseline scenario uses fossil fuel to power the whole system. The second scenario integrates solar photovoltaic (PV) to power the desalination plants. The third scenario uses solar PV to power desalination plants and fertilizer production facilities including the water requirement to manufacture the fertilizer. Energy requirements for pumping and distribution of water, food processing facilities, irrigation and administrative buildings and the embodied energy of equipment are not considered for simplicity. Emissions associated with the

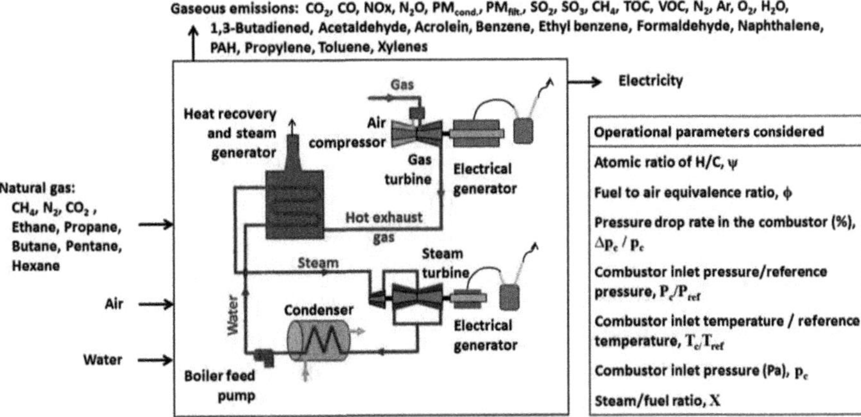

Figure 1. CCGT LCI model unit processes, inputs and outputs

import of crops outside the crop profile consumed domestically were not considered. With regards to land footprint calculations, land occupation for desalination facilities, power plants and fertilizer production facilities were not considered. Finally, waste water treatment and reclaim has not been considered in this study as it is assumed that in Qatar there are social barriers which prevent the use of treated water for food crops.

2.1. Energy sub-system

Energy is the main driver of the EWF nexus system. The analysis presented here only considers the mechanical energy which is delivered through electricity generation rather than thermal energy in the form of steam. As such, the LCA models developed for natural gas and solar PV power systems are used. The combined cycle gas turbine (CCGT) model developed by Ibrahim and Rahman (2012) based on a Brayton cycle based topping cycle and Rankine cycle bottoming cycle was used to determine the power output of a turbine for any given composition of natural gas. The model assumes a fuel to air equivalence ratio at 0.85 and calculates a total thermal efficiency in the range of 50-60 % in line with predicted values. Furthermore, the LCA model developed by Korre et al. (2012) which can be used to evaluate the performance of various CCGT power generation plant configurations has been integrated with the thermal efficiency calculations in order to complete the LCI database with a spectrum of emissions from power generation (Figure 1). This study considers on-grid PV applications and the procedure described by the RET screen photovoltaic model (RETScreen, 2004). The life cycle emissions for solar PV are also considered (Fthenakis, 2011). The functional unit for the calculations is a 100 MW using monocrystalline-silicon PV modules with an embodied energy of 31,244 GJ/MW photovoltaic power plant and a 30 y lifetime (Ito et al., 2008). The indirect natural gas requirement, energy and emissions associated with the PV module manufacture are calculated using the CCGT sub-system model.

2.2. Water sub-system

With increasing water demand in isolation to power and improved anti-fouling/scaling membranes, the use of Reverse Osmosis (RO) is increasing. Furthermore, the specific energy requirement of RO systems is significantly lower than other desalination technology options. For instance thermal desalting systems such as Multi-Stage Flash consume specific mechanical equivalent energy of about 4 kWh/$m^3$of desalinated water, and heat energy in the range of 20 kWh/m^3, whilst RO desalting systems reduce the total energy requirement to 4-6 kWh/m^3 (Darwish and Al-Najem, 2000). Therefore,

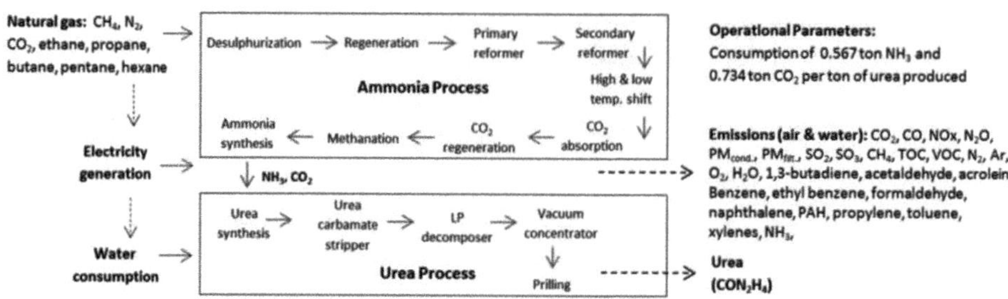

Figure 2. Ammonia and urea processes LCI model, inputs and outputs

thermal desalination technologies have not been considered here. A one stage pass RO model that calculates the energy requirement per m^3 of desalinated water for the salinity characteristics of any intake of seawater was developed (Wilf and Awerbuch, 2007). The energy requirement is calculated using the net driving pressure (NDP). It is the driving force through a semi-permeable membrane which is defined as the fraction of the applied pressure in excess of the average osmotic pressure of the feed and any pressure losses within the system. Darwish and Al-Najem (2000) considered an extra a 20 % energy consumption which accounts for seawater supply, seawater boost and chemical dosing pumps. Furthermore, a Pelton wheel energy recovery device with 65 % efficiency was integrated. With seawater data for a coast in Qatar used as input data into the RO model, the specific energy consumption calculated is 4.5 kWh/m^3.

2.3. Food sub-system

The food nexus element encompasses fertilizer production and agriculture practices such as fertilizer application and the raising of livestock. For this study the production and application of urea is considered in the quantification of emissions. Individual models which integrate mass balance calculations with plant data and emission factors were developed to calculate the emissions and resource consumption for ammonia and urea production. The electricity requirement encompasses the power required to drive the process and to convert water into steam. Regarding the GHG emissions from fertilizer application, updated emission factors from the work of Brentrup and Pallière (2008) are utilised. The emissions include; urea hydrolysis (the release of CO_2 after application, equivalent to the CO_2 fixed during production), direct N_2O from use, indirect N_2O via NH_3, indirect N_2O via NO_3 and CO_2 from liming. Methane and nitrous oxide (CH_4, N_2O) emissions from manure management both contribute to global warming, whilst volatilization of ammonia (NH_3) contributes to acidification. The quantification of the GHG fluxes for all emission sources follow the IPCC (2006) tier 1 guidelines which include; methane emissions from enteric fermentation and manure management direct and indirect N_2O emissions from manure management.

2.4. Water requirement for energy and food production

The water requirement for food is driven by irrigation requirement and fertilizer production. It is assumed that the water requirement is supplied from desalination facilities. The water requirement for fertilizer production which encompasses process water and steam was based on plant data from a local producer. Water consumption in thermoelectric generation systems is used to drive a steam turbine and for cooling purposes to condense the steam. The source of water varies for different regions depending on the availability of fresh water. For the purposes of this study it is assumed that the water utilisation factors for a closed loop CCGT power plant and PV (negligible) are based on Mielke et al. (2010).

3. Assessment of the environmental impact of Qatar's energy, water, food future requirements

Besides the baseline LCA impact categories, the local environmental impact from brine discharge on the Arabian Gulf can be integrated into the LCA model (Zhou et al., 2012). The methodology integrates both the high demand chemical by chemical approach with the low data but less accurate whole effluent approach in what is known as the group by group approach. This approach calculates the average aquatic ETP impact as the sum of impacts generated by acknowledged groups of influential chemicals. With respect to the regional impact, there is great uncertainty regarding the effect brine discharge has on the overall salinity of the Arabian Gulf which houses over 50 % of the world's desalination capability. The predictive capability regarding this issue is limited. The mathematical model developed by Purnama et al. (2005) is one example of how salinity in the Arabian Gulf has been analysed to date. The case study presented here considers an increase in Qatar's domestic food production from the current 8 % to 40 % using a particular crop profile by the year 2025.

The results from this study indicate that the largest GWP originates from the food nexus element where the emissions of CH_4 and N_2O are large occupying 71 % of the total share in baseline scenario and almost the complete share in the total PV scenario, where all fossil fuel emissions are eliminated. The GWP can be reduced with the introduction of solar PV; however, since the majority of emissions originate from non-energy related emissions from the food sector, they cannot be eliminated by solar PV alone. The introduction of solar PV entails a significant land investment. The lower limit only considers the area of the modules and the upper limit uses the typical size of a single 100 MW solar power plant as a standard multiplied by the number of plants required. The energy and emission payback period for the manufacture of the PV module is 3 years. Finally, a larger amount of natural gas is required to manufacture urea than to power a system driven by CCGT. Even though PV will eliminate the use of natural gas for power generation, a replacement of mineral fertilizers is necessary to ensure complete sustainability of the system and conservation of resources.

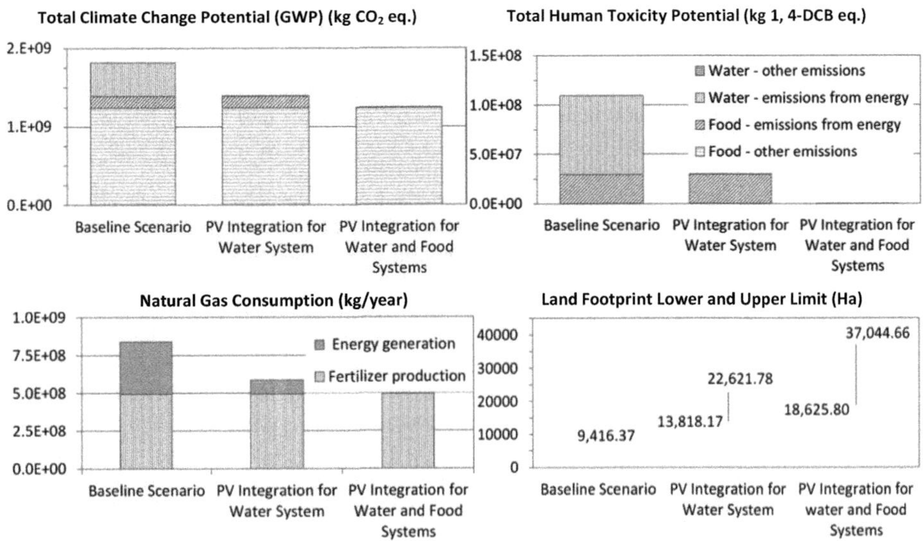

Figure 3. LCA results for different scenarios supporting Qatar's domestic food production

The reverse osmosis driven food system can increase the aquatic ecotoxicity impact by approximately 125 million PAF m^3/d. Considering the regional effects of desalination, the advection-diffusion model predicts that the maximum salinity of the Arabian Gulf will rise. The contribution of the food system RO to the overall trend is approximately 0.5 %. However, when evaluating real data from ROPME (regional organization for the protection of the marine environment) and historical data dating from 1923-2006, it doubtful that the evidence supports significant differences in salinity within the Arabian Gulf. Furthermore, important factors including seasonal or latitudinal salinity variations, atmospheric mixing forces and coastal currents are not considered, and the oceanographic circulation systems of the Arabian Gulf are too complex to be simply represented through a 1-D model. Additional uncertainties regarding the boundary condition (fixed salinity at the Strait of Hormuz) and the water volumes crossing the Hormuz weaken the modelling assumptions. Therefore, it is stipulated that although the model cannot provide conclusive prediction on the salinity evolution of the Arabian Gulf, it can be used sensibly to compare systems states or scenarios.

References

F. Brentrup, C. Pallière, 2008, GHG emissions and energy efficiency in european nitrogen fertiliser production and use, International Fertiliser Society Conference, Cambridge,UK,1-25.

M. Darwish, N. Al-Najem, 2000, Energy consumption by multi-stage flash and reverse osmosis desalters, Applied Thermal Engineering, 20, 399-416.

V. Fthenakis, H.C. Kim, R. Frischknecht, M. Raugei, P. Sinha, M. Stucki, 2011, Life cycle inventories and life cycle assessment of photovoltaic systems, International Energy Agency (IEA) PVPS Task 12, Report T12-02, New York, USA.

T.K. Ibrahim, M. Rahman, 2012, Effect of compression ratio on performance of combined cycle gas turbine, International Journal of Energy Engineering, 2, 9-14.

IPCC, 2006, 2006 IPCC Guidelines for National Greenhouse Gas Inventories, the National Greenhouse Gas Inventories Programme, H.S. Eggleston, L.Buendia, K.Miwa, T. Ngara, K. Tanabe (eds), Institute for Global Environmental Strategies, Japan.

M.Ito, K. Kato, K. Komoto, T. Kichimi, K. Kurokawa, 2008, A comparative study on cost and life-cycle analysis for 100 MW very large-scale PV (Vls-Pv) systems in deserts using M-Si, A-Si, CdTe, and Cis Modules, Progress in Photovoltaics:Research and Applications,16,17-30.

A. Korre, Z. Nie, S. Durucan, 2012, Life cycle assessment of the natural gas supply chain and power generation options with CO_2 capture and storage: Assessment of Qatar natural gas production, LNG transport and power generation in the UK, Sustainable Technologies, Systems and Policies 2012, CCS Workshop:11, DOI:10.5339/stsp.2012.ccs.11.

E. Mielke, D.A. Laura, V. Narayanamurti, 2010, Water Consumption of Energy Resource Extraction, Processing, and Conversion, Belfer Center for Science and International Affairs, Harvard Kennedy School, Cambridge, MA, United States.

L.F. Morales-Mendoza, C. Azzaro-Pantel, J.-P. Belaud, L. Pibouleau, S. Domenech, 2012, An integrated approach combining process simulation and life cycle assessment for eco-efficient process design, Computer Aided Chemical Engineering, 30, 142-146.

A. Purnama, H.H. Al-Barwani, R. Smith, 2005, Calculating the environmental cost of seawater desalination in the Arabian marginal seas, Desalination, 185, 79-86.

Retscreen, 2004, Clean Project Analysis: RET Screen Engineering & Cases Textbook, Photovoltaic Project Analysis, CANMET Energy Technology Centre, Varennes, Canada.

M. Wilf, L. Awerbuch, 2007, The Guidebook of Membrane Desalination Technology: Reverse Osmosis, Nanofiltration and Hybrid Systems, Process, Design, Applications and Economics, Balaban Desalination Publications –Membranes (Technology), 55-64,USA.

J. Zhou, V.W.-C. Chang, A.G Fane, 2012, An improved life cycle impact assessment (LCIA) approach for assessing aquatic eco-toxic impact of brine disposal from seawater desalination plants, Desalination, 308, 233-241.

Jiří Jaromír Klemeš, Petar Sabev Varbanov and Peng Yen Liew (Editors)
Proceedings of the 24th European Symposium on Computer Aided Process Engineering – ESCAPE 24
June 15-18, 2014, Budapest, Hungary.

Simulation of Carbon Dioxide Capture Using Ionic Liquid 1-Ethyl-3-methylimidazolium Acetate

Koon Khonkaen[a], Kitipat Siemanond[a,b], Amr Henni[c,]*

[a]The Petroleum and Petrochemical College Chulalongkorn University, 254 Chula Soi 12, Wangmai, Pathumwan, Bangkok 10330, Thailand.

[b]Center of Excellence on Petrochemical and Materials Technology, Chulalongkorn University, Phyathai Rd, Chula Soi 12, Pathumwan, Bangkok 10330, Thailand

[c]Faculty of Engineering and Applied Science, 3737 Wascana Parkway Regina, Saskatchewan, S4S 0A2, Canada.

amr.henni@uregina.ca

Abstract

A major greenhouse gas that contributes to global warming effect is carbon dioxide (CO_2), which is mainly generated from coal power plant. Aqueous amines scrubbing technology such as monoethanolamine (MEA)-scrubbing system is currently considered the most feasible technology that can be used to capture CO_2 using absorption and stripping configuration. However, the main drawback of MEA-based system is high energy requirement during solvent regeneration. Retrofitting this unit to an existing power plant would lower the energy output and the cost of electricity would be increased accordingly, which does not respond to the target of the Department of Energy to remove 90 % of CO_2 from post-combustion flue gas with no more than 35 % increase in the cost of electricity. Among the emerging innovative technologies to overcome the energy intensive problem of the MEA-scrubbing system, ionic liquids (ILs) are considered potential solvent for green CO_2 capture technology with the benefit of cost reduction. One promising ionic liquid namely 1-Ethyl-3-methylimidazolium Acetate ([emim][Ac]) strongly (chemically) absorbs CO_2 with the heat of absorption equals -38 kJ/mol CO_2, which is much lower than MEA. This is the first clue of being more energy efficiency of this IL. In this study, the CO_2 capture processes are simulated to capture 90 % of CO_2 from post-combustion flue gas using conventional-MEA and IL ([emim][Ac]) based on the flue gas from a 180 MWe coal burning power plant. The energy consumption and investment cost of both processes are compared to determine the potential of this IL. The results show lower energy requirement of IL-based process compared to MEA-based process by 13.5 %, but the investment cost of IL-based process doubles compared to MEA-based process.

Keywords: post combustion CO_2 capture, MEA scrubbing process, CO_2 solubility in ionic liquids.

1. Introduction

The rapid growth of population, industry and agriculture causes the rapid growth of greenhouse gases (GHGs) emission, which CO_2 is a major greenhouse gas. The global CO_2 emission had increased around 40 % from the year 1990 to 2008 (20.9 to 29.4 Gt). Currently the power sector is responsible for 41 % of total CO_2 emission, followed by transportation (23 %), industry sector (10 %), and others. The CO_2 emission in the power sector is related to fuel combustion to generate electricity or heat. The biggest share of fuel combustion in the year 2008 is coal by 43 %, while the contribution of oil and gas is 37 % and 20 %. Therefore, CO_2 capture process is primarily needed to capture CO_2 from the power plant flue gas. There are three main combustion technologies for fuel-combustion, including post-combustion, pre-combustion and oxyfuel-combustion. These three processes have different characteristics, yielding different conditions for CO_2 capture. In this study, the focus will be on post-combustion technology, which is widely used at traditional fossil-fuel-fired power stations to produce electricity. To capture CO_2 at low partial pressure (7-16 mol %) like post-combustion flue gas, chemical absorption is needed. Aqueous amines scrubbing technology such as monoethanolamine (MEA)-based system is currently considered the most feasible technology that can be used to capture CO_2 from post-combustion flue gas due to its maturity, stable operation, good reactivity, high absorption capacity and the low cost of MEA. However, the capture of CO_2 with MEA involves a chemical reaction with a large enthalpy of absorption (-88.91 kJ/mol CO_2). Consequently, a large amount of heat is required to release the captured CO_2 in the regeneration step. Retrofitting this unit to an existing power plant, would lower the energy output of the plant approximately 25-40 %. Accordingly the price of electricity would increase, which does not respond to the target of the Department of Energy to remove 90 % of CO_2 from post-combustion flue gas with no more than a 35 % increase in the cost of electricity. The high cost of CO_2 removal of MEA-scrubbing process (50 to 150 \$/t CO_2) also causes this process to be unattractive for large scale operation, although much lower costs (30-35 \$/t CO_2) were recently reported by Tollefson (2011). Besides the energy penalty, the MEA-based system suffers a number of other drawbacks such as high volatility, tendency to degradation (above 393 K), and equipment corrosion. These drawbacks cause a solvent loss and contamination to the environment. Among the emerging technologies to replace the conventional MEA-based system, a special class of absorption materials, namely ionic liquids (ILs) with properties of high CO_2 solubility, non-volatility, high thermal stability, and tunability of structure and properties, are considered potential solvent for green CO_2 capture technology with the benefit of cost reduction. Blenchard et al (1999) were the first to observe that significant amount of CO_2 could be dissolved in imidazolium-based ionic liquids (ILs). Their study initiated an explosion of scientific research on CO_2 absorption with ILs, leading to a rapid growth of the literature on this specific topic. Researches on ILs for CO_2 capture (measurement of CO_2 solubility in ILs) have been done in laboratories for almost ten years; a few process simulations using IL for CO_2 capture have also been done. However, only one process simulation of an IL-based scrubber compared to a MEA-based process has appeared in the literature (Shiflett and Yokozeki, 2010). To provide another option, one promising ionic liquid namely 1-Ethyl-3-methylimidazolium Acetate has been taken to this study due to its possibility to capture CO_2 (chemical absorption behavior) with lower energy consumption compared to MEA-based process. In this study, flow sheets of both scrubbing processes (MEA and IL) for post-combustion CO_2 capture are simulated and optimized using a commercial simulation program (Aspen Plus). Then, the energy consumption of both processes is compared. To ascertain the potential of economic benefits of the IL-based process, the investment cost is calculated and compared to the MEA-based process. Results show lower energy requirement of IL-based process by 13.5 % compared to MEA-based process, but the investment cost of IL-based process doubles compared to MEA-based process.

2. MEA-based scrubbing system

The CO_2 capture units in this thesis are simulated to capture CO_2 based on the flue gas from 180 MWe coal burning power plant (flue gas flow rate 32 t/h, gas composition 84 % N_2, 12 % CO_2, and 4 % water vapor per standard volume). The MEA CO_2 capture unit is designed to meet the target of 90 % capture capacity with 98 % purity of CO_2 by using 25 wt. % MEA. The process flow diagram of CO_2 capture unit (absorber/stripper configuration) is displayed in Figure 1. The flue gas goes through the scrubber to cool down the temperature to 319 K with the pressure near atmospheric pressure (115.1 kPa) that is appropriate to the absorber. The flue gas enters the bottom of the absorber, and the lean MEA (25 wt. %) with a CO_2 loading of 0.2 mol CO_2/mol MEA enters the top of the column, at pressure 135.8 kPa and 308 K. The number of stages for the absorber column in this study is 25 to achieve a rich amine loading of 0.36 mol CO_2/mol MEA and 90 % recovery. Vent gas from the top of absorber consists of CO_2 less than 0.02 vol %. The rich amine from the bottom of the absorber goes to the rich amine pump to increase the pressure to 239.2 kPa. Then it goes to rich/lean heat exchanger with a temperature approach 5 K to exchange the duty with the hot stream that comes out the stripper column. The rich amine is heated by the stripper pre-heater to the temperature close to the stripper operating temperature (389.4 K) and enters at the top of the stripper column. In this study, the stripper has 24 stages. In the stripper, the rich solution flow downward against the hot stream from the re-boiler. CO_2 is thereby stripped off from the solvent with purity of 98.2 %. The lean solution from the bottom of the stripper is then recycled back to the top of the absorber to complete the loop.

$$\text{Loading} = \frac{[CO_2]+[HCO_3^-]+[CO_3^{2-}]+[MEACOO^-]}{[MEA]+[MEA^+]+[MEACOO^-]} \tag{1}$$

Loading is an important parameter that affects the energy performance of MEA-based system, referring to mol of CO_2 carrying species over mol of MEA carrying species as displayed in Eq.(1). The MEA-based system is optimized to minimize energy consumption by varying MEA mass flow rate and MEA loading. In this study, the MEA mass flow rate and loading of the solution that minimize the energy consumption are 41.78 kg/s and 0.2, respectively.

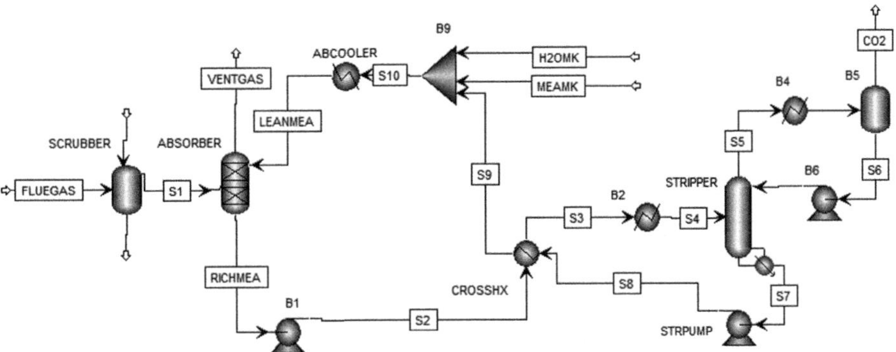

Figure 1. Process flow diagram of MEA-based scrubbing system.

3. IL-based scrubbing system

Ionic liquids are salts in the liquid state (melting point generally below 100 °C), composed of cation and anion. Most of them are determined as physical absorbent (conventional ILs) that cannot capture CO_2 at low partial pressure (post-combustion). To overcome this problem, researchers appealed to the amine chemistry by arguing that including an amine moiety to conventional ILs (amine-functionalised ILs) could greatly improve CO_2 absorption capacity. However, the presence of amine group in the structure causes the enthalpy of reaction to remain high in this type of ILs. For example, the enthalpy of reaction with CO_2 of ionic liquid [P66614][Pro] is at -80 kJ/mol that is nearly the value of MEA at -85 kJ/mol. One promising ionic liquid namely [emim][Ac] shows an unusual phase behaviour that is different from the other conventional ILs. Shiflett and Yokozeli (2009) reported that at low CO_2 concentration (less than 20 mol %), the binary system of (CO_2 + [emim][Ac]) has hardly any vapor pressure, reflecting the strongly (chemically) absorbed CO_2 into [emim][Ac] and with the benefit of low enthalpy of absorption (-38 kJ/mol CO_2). When doing the simulation using Aspen Plus, the properties parameters of selected components will be automatically retrieved. Since the databases of Aspen Plus do not provide any pure component data for [emim][Ac], the direct input information and data regression mode in Aspen Plus are essentially employed. For the critical properties of ILs, the so-called group contribution method, "modified Lyndersen-Joback-Reid" method is used to estimate the critical properties of IL (Valderama et al, 2007), since the ILs start to decompose at the temperature near their normal boiling point. For the temperature dependent properties, the parameters of nine property models that are shown in Figure 2 (CPIGDP, DHVLDP, etc) are regressed based on the reported properties of [emim][Ac] available in the literature. The IL-based system involves the mixture system, which is composed of the solubility of gases in IL (N_2 and CO_2 in [emim][Ac]) and solubility of liquid in liquid ([emim][Ac] in water). The binary interaction parameters of Non-Random Two Liquid (NRTL) are used to calculate the activity coefficient of the binary system ([emim][Ac] + water) and Henry's constant model is used to calculate the Henry's constant of N_2 and CO_2 in [emim][Ac]. Both binary interaction parameters and parameters of Henry's constant model are taken from the regression of the experimental data (PTX-diagram) reported in the literature. The reaction data of [emim][Ac] with CO_2 are taken from the literature for equilibrium calculation.

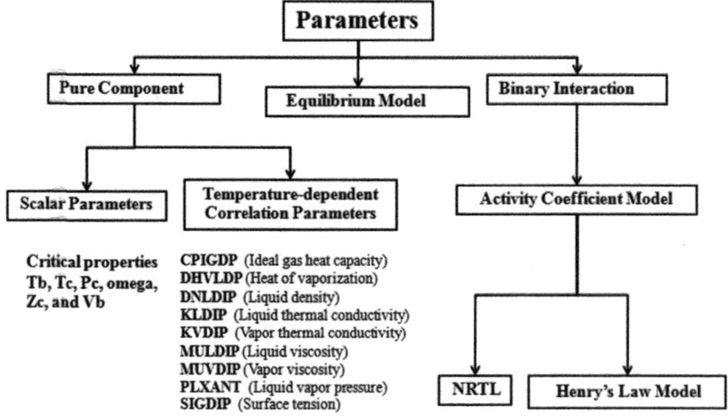

Figure 2. Flowchart of defining ionic liquid into Aspen Plus.

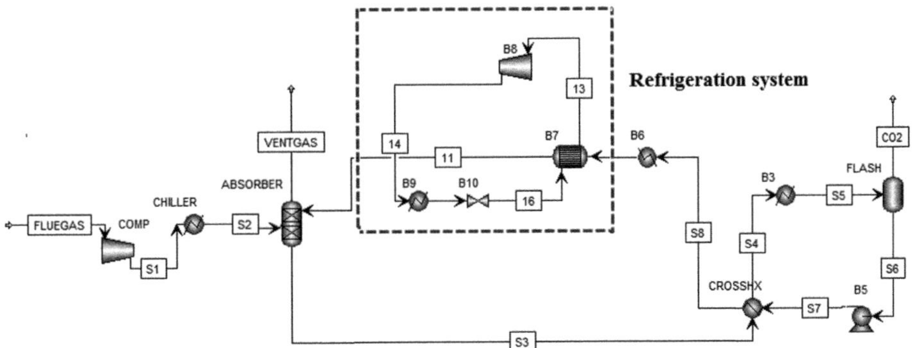

Figure 3. Process flow diagram of IL-based scrubbing system.

Based on all of these parameters, a process simulation of IL [emim][Ac] can be carried out to meet the same target of MEA-based system. The flow diagram of IL process is shown in Figure 3. The plant is similar to the one used by (Shifflet et al, 2010). Due to the low capacity, the absorber is operated under pressure at 618 kPa to improve the solubility of CO_2. The absorber pressure and IL flow rate are optimized to minimize the energy consumption and meet the same target with MEA process. CO_2 is chemically absorbed by [emim][Ac]. Regeneration process is different from MEA by using flash technique instead of stripper column (Aspen Plus RCSTR). IL-rich solution is regenerated by decreasing the pressure to the atmospheric pressure and increasing temperature to about 353 K. IL-lean solution is pumped back and cooled down to 271K using refrigeration and then recycled back to the top of the absorber. Table 1 shows the process specification of MEA and IL process. The results show that the energy requirement of MEA and IL-based process are 10,069 kW and 8,710 kW. This indicates that IL-based process has lower energy consumption by 13.51 %. To ascertain the economic benefit, capital cost is figured out using the percentage of delivered equipment cost method. In this method, the cost of equipment has been estimated, from online cost estimator and the estimated cost has been converted to the year 2012.

Table 1. Process specification of MEA and IL-based process

	MEA			IL		
	T (K)	P (kPa)	m(kg/s)	T (K)	P (kPa)	m(kg/s)
Absorber						
Flue gas	320.00	115.10	9.03	313.00	790.80	8.54
Vent gas	328.00	101.30	7.63	281.00	618.00	6.92
Absorbent inlet	309.00	135.80	41.78	272.00	790.80	47.98
Absorbent outlet	325.00	101.30	43.19	250.00	618.00	49.60
Stripper/Flash						
CO_2 outlet	302.00	101.30	1.64	354.00	101.30	1.62
Absorbent inlet	363.00	239.20	43.19	332.00	618.00	49.60
Absorbent outlet	390.00	173.00	41.55	354.00	101.30	47.98

Table 2. Scrubbing performance and cost of MEA and IL-based process

	MEA	IL
CO2		
Capacity (tons/year)	50,758.00	50,749.00
Recovery (%)	90.03	90.01
Purity (%)	98.18	99.26
Utilities		
Steam (kg/s)	5.05	1.85
Cooling water (kg/s)	226.33	150.06
Energy		
Steam (kW)	10,061.00	3,738.00
Electricity (kW)	8.57	4,972.00
Total (kW)	10,069.00	8,710.00
Total capital investment (M $)	18,656,329.00	34,455,621.00

The raw materials (absorbent cost) are also included in the investment cost due to the high cost of IL, which is approximately 10 times higher than MEA. IL-based process has almost twice as much investment cost compared to MEA-based process due to its high cost of additional equipment (compressor and refrigeration system).

4. Conclusion

This study focuses on the comparison of the energy requirement and capital investment cost between conventional MEA and IL-based process using ionic liquid [emim][Ac] for post-combustion carbon dioxide capture process, based on the flue gas from coal burning power plant 180 MWe. The results show lower energy requirement by 13.5 % of IL-based compared to MEA. However, the investment cost of IL-based process doubles due to the high cost of its additional equipment. In order to ascertain the preferable economic benefit of IL-based process over conventional MEA-based process, the economic evaluation should be done to determine the trade-off between energy consumption cost and investment cost of both processes.

Acknowledgement

Koon Khonkaen gratefully acknowledges the financial support from PETROMAT and Chulalongkorn University, and sincerely thanks Asst. Prof. Dr. Kitipat Siemanond and Asst. Prof. Dr. Amr Henni for their academic assistance.

References

M.B. Shiflett, D.W. Drew, R.A. Cantini, A. Yokozeki, 2010, Carbon Dioxide Capture Using Ionic Liquid 1-Butyl-3-methylimidazolium Acetate, Energy and Fuels, 24, 5781-5789

M.B. Shiflett, A. Yokozeki, 2009, Phase Behavior of Carbon Dioxide in Ionic Liquids: [emim][Acetate], [emim][Trifluoroacetate], and [emim][Acetate] + [emim][Trifluoroacetate] Mixtures, Chemical Engineering, 54, 108-114

J. Tollefson, 2011, Low cost carbon capture project sparks interest, Nature, 469, 276-277

J.O. Valderama , P.A. Robles, 2007, Critical Properties, Normal Boiling Temperature, and Acentric Factors of Fifty Ionic Liquids, Industrials and Engineering Chemistry Research, 46, 1338-1344

Jiří Jaromír Klemeš, Petar Sabev Varbanov and Peng Yen Liew (Editors)
Proceedings of the 24th European Symposium on Computer Aided Process Engineering – ESCAPE 24
June 15-18, 2014, Budapest, Hungary.

Biofuels from Residues of the Tequila Industry of Mexico

Pascual Eduardo Murillo-Alvarado,[a]* Jose María Ponce-Ortega,[a] Agustin Jaime Castro-Montoya,[a] Medardo Serna-González,[a] Mahmoud M. El-Halwagi[b]

[a]Department of Chemical Engineering, Universidad Michoacana de San Nicolas de Hidalgo, Morelia, Michoacan, Mexico.
[b]Department of Chemical Engineering, Texas A&M University, College Station, TX, USA.
uno_ok@hotmail.com

Abstract

One of the most important industries in Mexico is the one associated to the tequila production; where several agave residues are produced (agave is the plant used to make tequila), these residues are lignocellulosic matter that can be used to produce bioethanol. The agave residues are obtained in the harvesting sites located in several states of Mexico and from the tequila factories that are mainly located in two places in Mexico. Therefore, this paper presents an optimization framework for designing a supply chain for the bioethanol production from residues of agave bagasse obtained in the tequila processing in Mexico; where central and distributed bioethanol processing plants are considered. The bioethanol production process in the central and distributed plants is modeled according to conversion factors for the different processing steps obtained from experimental data. Results show that the bioethanol production from agave bagasse is a feasible way for obtaining biofuels. For the current situation, the results show that is possible to satisfy around 10 % of the total demand of bioethanol of Mexico. Finally, no numerical complications were observed during the application of the proposed approach, which is general and can be applied to different biomass types and biofuels.

Keywords: Agave, Tequila Industry, Bioethanol, Supply Chain, Optimization.

1. Introduction

The agave is a perennial arid plant that consists of thin sheets around a plant head, whose main elements are fibers, sugars, minerals and water. Juice with high concentration of fructose and other vitamin properties is naturally produced in the center of the plant head. This way, a large number of products can be obtained from agave as honey water, paper, textiles, liquors and tequila. During the processing of agave to yield tequila several lignocellulosic residues from the agave are produced; these residues correspond to the sheets that are obtained in the cultivation areas because these are not used for the tequila processing, and also there are other lignocellulosic residues obtained in the factories associated to the tequila processing from the plant heads after the fermentation process. It should be noted that the agave is mainly cultivated in the central-west part of Mexico (in the states of Jalisco, Guanajuato and Michoacán), and most of the factories associated to the tequila are located also in this region. These lignocellulosic residues can be used as raw material to produce several products, including bioethanol. In this way, Alex-Marvin et al. (2012) presented an optimization study focusing on the net present value of five types of lignocellulosic biomass for ethanol production. To promote the sustainable use of this residue as raw material for bioethanol production, recent works are focused on developing a systematic approach for optimizing the entire supply chain, this way Mele et al. (2011) presented a systematic optimization approach for designing and planning supply chains for the sugar cane industry involving economic and environmental aspects. Therefore, this work proposes a mathematical programming model for the sustainable optimization for the supply chain management associated to the bioethanol production from the residues of agave from the tequila processing in Mexico and the optimal location of central and distributed plants. The optimization formulation considers the entire supply chain considering several objectives (economic, environmental and social issues) to promote sustainability (Santibañez-Aguilar et al., 2011).

2. Superstructure

The optimization method is based on the representation shown schematically in Figure 1, which shows the most important harvesting areas of agave in Mexico. These harvesting sites produce agave that can be separated in leaves and plant heads, where the leaves are transported to processing facilities and the plant heads are distributed to the tequila industries. In addition, it is possible to obtain bagasse as waste from the tequila industries; this waste can be transported to bioethanol processing facilities, the produced bioethanol can be transported to different consumption regions located in the main cities of Mexico. The proposed superstructure is show in Figure 2, which shows the steps required to transform biomass to bioethanol, also it presents the equipment required inside the distributed and central processing plants. The difference between central and distributed plants is the bioethanol production capacity and the associated costs due to the location in industrialized and no industrialized places, respectively.

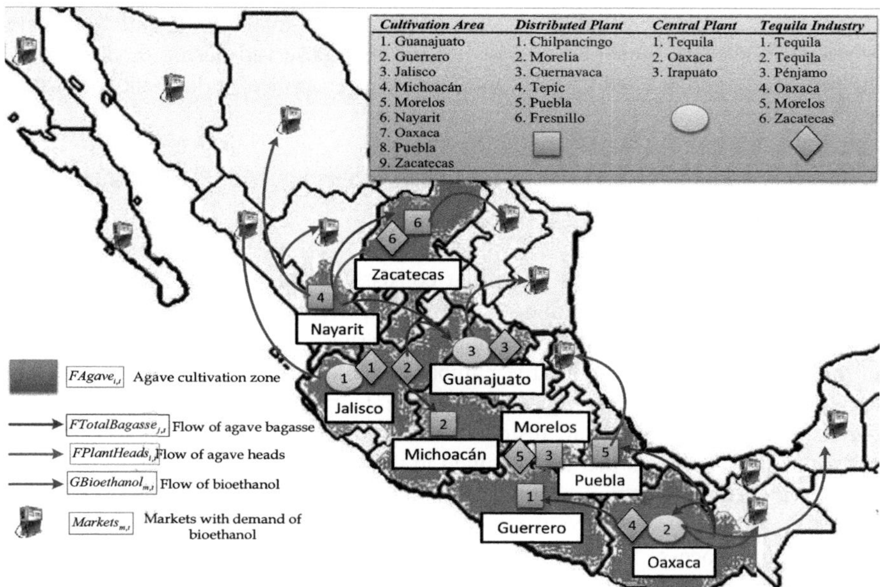

Figure 1. Schematic representation of the addressed problem for the supply chain of bioethanol production in Mexico from agave bagasse.

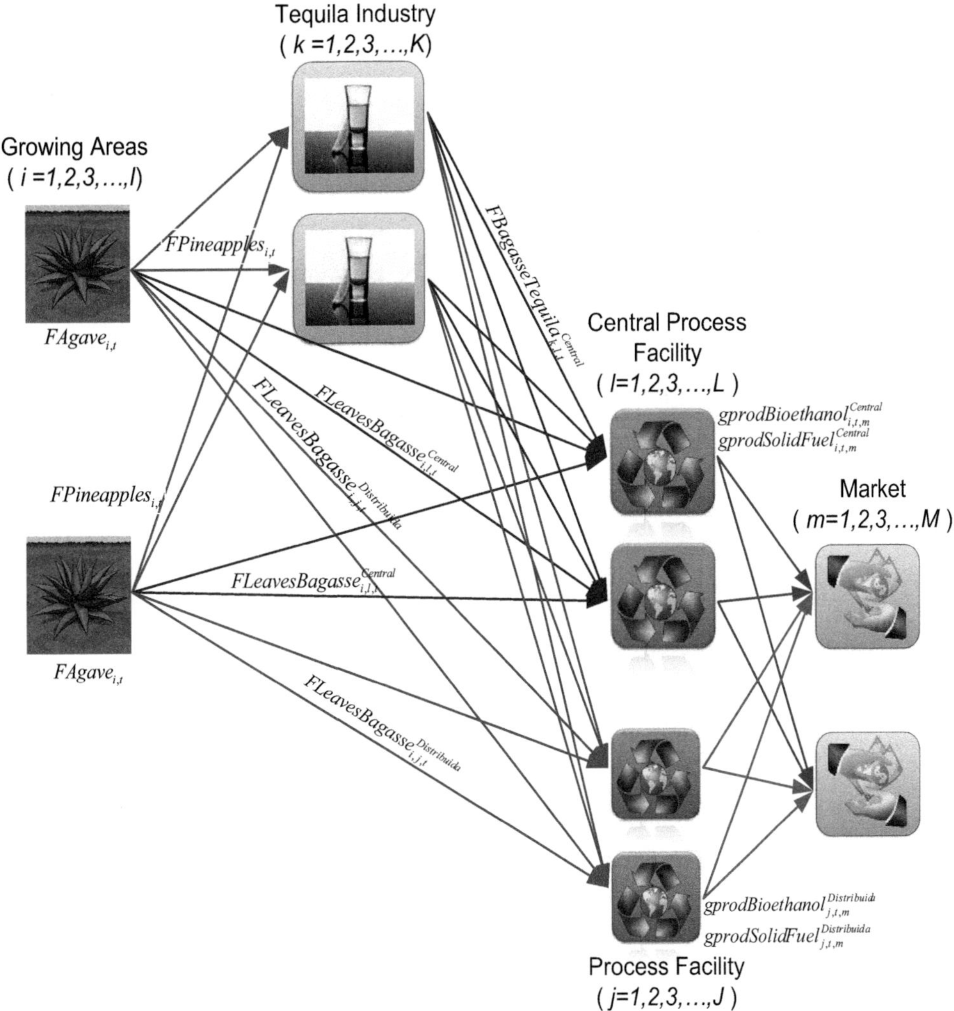

Figure 2. Superstructure for bagasse distribution.

3. Optimization Formulation

The mathematical model is based on Figures 2 and 3. The following sets are used: i represents a set for harvesting areas, j is an index used to define the distributed process plants, l is used to represents the central process plants, the sites for the industries for tequila production are associated to the index k, locations where products (bioethanol and solid fuel) are consumed are defined by the index m, finally the time periods are identified by the index t. The proposed model consists of the following relationships.

- Mass balance in cultivation areas. Eq.(1) represents the mass balance in the agave growing areas i in the time period t, this balance is applied to determine the agave available for the case study in Mexico.

$$FAgave_{i,t} \leq FAgave_{i,t}^{MAX}, \forall i \in I, t \in T \tag{1}$$

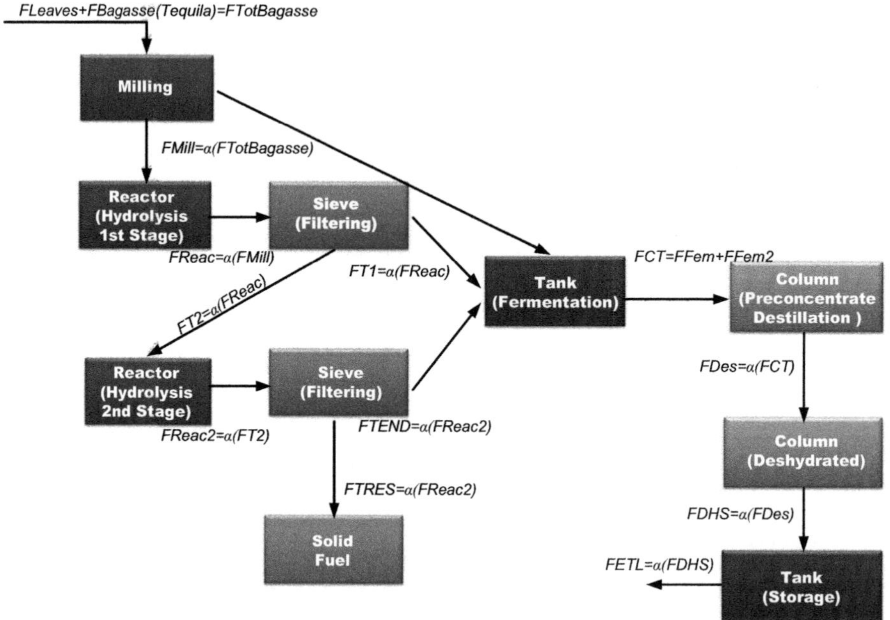

Figure 3. Agave processing to yield bioethanol.

- Agave plant heads. Eq.(2) determines the total flow of agave plant heads in the cultivation areas i over the time period t, these plant heads are the raw materials for the tequila production.

$$FAgave_{i,t} \cdot zAH_i = FHeads_{i,t}, \forall i \in I, t \in T \tag{2}$$

- Agave stalks. The main wastes in the agave cultivation areas are the stalks that represent about 40 percent of the agave plant. Eq.(3) determines the total stalk flow that is the most important raw material for the bioethanol production.

$$FAgave_{i,t} \cdot zAL_i = FTotalLeavesBagasse_{i,t}, \forall i \in I, t \in T \tag{3}$$

- Mass balance in tequila industry. Eq.(4) represents the total plant head flow that receives the tequila industry.

$$FHeads_{i,t} = \sum_{k \in K} FHeads_{i,k,t}^{TequilaIndustry}, \forall i \in I, t \in T \tag{4}$$

- Mass balance in central and distributed plants. Eqs.(5) and (6) represent the mass balance of agave waste obtained in the cultivation areas for the agave stalks and the waste from the tequila industry, the total flow of bagasse in sent to the central and distributed plant to obtain bioethanol.

$$FTotalBag_{j,t}^{Distributed} = \sum_{k \in K} FBagTequila_{k,j,t}^{Distributed} + \sum_{i \in I} FLeavesBag_{i,j,t}^{Distributed}, \forall j \in J, t \in T \tag{5}$$

$$FTotalBag_{l,t}^{Central} = \sum_{k \in K} FBagTequila_{k,l,t}^{Central} + \sum_{l \in L} FLeavesBag_{i,l,t}^{Central}, \forall l \in L, t \in T \tag{6}$$

- Total bioethanol obtained. Eqs.(7) to (9) represent the totalbioethanol flow obtained in central and distributed processing plants. The bioethanol obtained is according with the process detailed in Figure 3, the total bioethanol obtained can be sent to the markets*m*.

$$FprodBioethanol_{j,t}^{Distributed} = \sum_{m \in M} gBioethanol_{j,m,t}^{Distributed}, \forall j \in J, t \in T \tag{7}$$

$$FprodBioethanol_{l,t}^{Central} = \sum_{m \in M} gBioethanol_{l,m,t}^{Central}, \forall l \in L, t \in T \tag{8}$$

$$\sum_{j \in J} gBioethanol_{j,m,t}^{Distributed} + \sum_{l \in L} gBioethanol_{i,m,t}^{Central} = GBioethanol_{m,t}, \forall m \in M, t \in T \tag{9}$$

- Capital and operating costs. Eq.(10) determines the cost of the distributed and central processing plants, the operating costs are calculated with a unitary cost times the flow of each step, and the capital costs are modeled according with the disjunction shown in Eq.(10), where the Boolean variable Y_l defines the installation of each plant.

$$\begin{bmatrix} Y_j^{Distributed} \\ FTotalBagasseCAP_j^{Distributed^{MIN}} \leq FTotalBagasseCAP_j^{Distributed} \\ FTotalBagasseCAP_j^{Distributed} \leq FTotalBagasseCAP_j^{Distributed^{MAX}} \\ CDist_j^{Mill} = CFixDist_j^{Mill} + CVarDist_j^{Mill} \cdot FFTotalBagasseCAP_j^{Distributed} \\ CDist_j^{Reactor} = CFixDist_j^{Reactor} + CVarDist_j^{Reactor} \cdot FMillCAP_j^{Distributed} \\ CDist_j^{Reactor2} = CFixDist_j^{Reactor2} + CVarDist_j^{Reactor2} \cdot Ffiltered2CAP_j^{Distributed} \\ CDist_j^{Sieve} = CFixDist_j^{Sieve} + CVarDist_j^{Sieve} \cdot FReactorCAP_j^{Distributed} \\ CDist_j^{Sieve2} = CFixDist_j^{Sieve2} + CVarDist_j^{Sieve2} \cdot FReactor2CAP_j^{Distributed} \\ CDist_j^{Tank} = CFixDist_j^{Tank} + CVarDist_j^{Tank} \cdot FFiermentationCAP_j^{Distributed} \\ CDist_j^{Column} = CFixDist_j^{Column} + CVarDist_j^{Column} \cdot FColumn1CAP_j^{Distributed} \\ CDist_j^{Column2} = CFixDist_j^{Column2} + CVarDist_j^{Column2} \cdot FColumn2CAP_j^{Distributed} \\ CDist_j^{TankA} = CFixDist_j^{TankA} + CVarDist_j^{TankA} \cdot FStockCAP_j^{Distributed} \end{bmatrix} \vee \begin{bmatrix} \neg Y_j^{Distributed} \\ FTotalBaggaseCAP_j^{Distributed} = 0 \\ CDist_j^{Mill} = 0 \\ CDist_j^{Reactor} = 0 \\ CDist_j^{Reactor2} = 0 \\ CDist_j^{Sieve} = 0 \\ CDist_j^{Sieve2} = 0 \\ CDist_j^{Tank} = 0 \\ CDist_j^{Column} = 0 \\ CDist_j^{Column2} = 0 \\ CDist_j^{TankA} = 0 \end{bmatrix}, \forall j \in J \tag{10}$$

- Objective function. Eqs.(11) to (13) show the terms involved in the objective function, the first term is the total cost that represents the cost of installation and transportation, the second term is the sales for the obtained products, and finally is the profit that is the objective function to maximize.

$$TotCost = \begin{pmatrix} CostDist^{OP} + CostDist^{CAP} + CostCent^{OP} + CostCent^{CAP} + CostTranspLeaves^{Dist} \\ +CostTranspLeaves^{Central} + CostTranspBagasse_{Teq}^{Dist} + CostTranspBagasse_{Teq}^{Central} \\ +CostTranspProdBioethanol + CostTranspProdBioethanol \end{pmatrix} \tag{11}$$

$$TotSales = \left(\sum_{m \in M} \sum_{t \in T} GBioethanol_{m,t} \cdot \beta_m^{Bioethanol} H_{M_t} + \sum_{m \in M} \sum_{t \in T} GSolidFuel_{m,t} \cdot \beta_m^{SolidFuel} \right) \tag{12}$$

$$PROFIT = TotSales - TotCost \tag{13}$$

4. Results

The optimization model was coded in the software GAMS, where the solver DICOPT was used to solve different scenarios for the considered case study. The proposed optimization formulation is applied to a case study of Mexico shown in Figure 3; this figure shows the main cultivation areas, the possible locations for the central and distributed processing plants, and the most important tequila industries, the bioethanol obtained is sent to markets that represent the main cities of Mexico. Several scenarios are identified and discussed as follows.

Scenario A (Best economic Solution with a constraint for the bioethanol demand): The optimal solution for Scenario A determines the installation of two central processing plants (Central 1 at the city of Tequila in the State of Jalisco; and Central 2 at the city of Oaxaca in the State of Oaxaca), and no distributed processing plants were selected.
The optimal distribution presents a total annual profit of 1.5337×10^8 USD/y; where the sales and costs are 3.72646×10^8 USD/y and 2.1927×10^8 USD/y, respectively. In the bioethanol production, the agave waste is used as solid fuel, adding an important monetary value; this waste provides 2.1645×10^6 USD/y to the total sales.

Scenario B (Solution without constraint for the demand of bioethanol in the markets): In this scenario, the mathematical model is solved without constraints for demands in markets. The optimal solution selects the installation of the central processing facilities 1, 2 and 3. In this Scenario B, the demand is not limited to satisfy all markets; for this reason, in the optimal solution the plants send bioethanol to the nearest markets. The obtained profit is 1.8541×10^8 USD/y for the given configuration of the supply chain. The solution of the proposed optimization approach shows that with the current lignocellulose materials from the agave only 2 % of the biogasoline demanded in Mexico can be obtained, and the satisfied markets correspond to the regions near to the cultivation areas.

5. Conclusions

This paper has presented a study for the optimal planning of the sustainable use of agave residues obtained in the tequila production in Mexico and the results show that the bioethanol production from agave bagasse is a feasible way for obtaining biofuels, considering that this is obtained from the wastes of the tequila industry, and these are not used for other economic activity. With the bioethanol obtained, in some specific cities is possible to satisfy about 40 % and 50 % of the demanded bioethanol in some seasons of the year, and with a considerable obtained profit for processing this residue from the tequila industry. But generally the total demand satisfied is about 10 % considering a mix with oil 10-90 that means 10 % of bioethanol and 90 % of oil.

References

J.E. Santibañez-Aguilar, J.B. González-Campos, J.M. Ponce-Ortega, M. Serna-González, M. M. El-Halwagi, 2011, Optimal Planning of a Biomass Conversion System Considering Economic and Environmental Aspects, Industrial and Engineering Chemistry Research, 50,14, 8558-8570.

F. D. Mele, A. M. Kostin, G. Guillen-Gonsalbez, L. Jimenez, 2011, Multiobjetive Model for More Sustainable Fuel Supply Chains. A case Study of the Sugar Cane Industry in Argentina, Industrial and Engineering Chemistry Research, 50, 9, 4939-4958.

W. Alex-Marvin, L. D. Schmidt, S. Benjaafar, D. G. Tiffany, P. Daoutidis, 2012, Economic Optimization of a Lignocellulosic Biomass-to-ethanol Supply Chain, Chemical Engineering Science, 67, 1, 68-79.

Jiří Jaromír Klemeš, Petar Sabev Varbanov and Peng Yen Liew (Editors)
Proceedings of the 24th European Symposium on Computer Aided Process Engineering – ESCAPE 24
June 15-18, 2014, Budapest, Hungary.

Sustainable Water Management in Cities

Ma. Guadalupe Rojas-Torres[a], Fabricio Nápoles-Rivera[a]*, Merdardo Serna-González[a], Mahmoud M. El-Halwagi[b], José María Ponce-Ortega[a]

[a]*Chemical Engineering Department, Universidad Michoacana de San Nicolás de Hidalgo, Morelia Michoacán, 58060, México.*

[b]*Chemical Engineering Department, Texas A&M University, College Station, TX, 77843, USA.*

fnapoles@umich.mx

Abstract

A multi annual model for the optimal planning and scheduling of water storage and distribution in a macroscopic system is presented. The model considers natural resources such as superficial and subterranean water bodies, whereas the alternative water resources are harvested rainwater and reclaimed wastewater. Due to the seasonal nature of precipitation, it is considered that storage devices can be constructed in specific locations in the city and then used to satisfy the different demands of the system. The proposed model overcomes previously reported methodologies by considering important aspects such as population growth, time value of money and the expected change in the precipitation patterns due to climate change. A case study for a Mexican city was solved. Results show that the implementation of alternative water sources in the multi annual water management problem in a macroscopic system might increase the revenue up to 22.9 % respect the current operation and that the alternative water sources have the potential to satisfy up to 25.2 % of the agricultural, domestic and industrial demands in the city during the time span of the project, reducing the overexploitation of natural water bodies.

Keywords: Sustainable water use; Water integration; Resource conservation; Optimization.

1. Introduction

Several efforts for the use of harvested water and reclaimed water have been made in order to reduce natural sources depletion. Li et al. (2010) found that the rainwater collection and the use of treated grey water might be enough to satisfy 94 % of the domestic water demand in Ireland, which is the main use in this country, accounting for 60 % of the total water demand; they stressed out the key importance of the government to establish incentives that promote the use of no conventional sources of water. Domènech and Saurí (2011) made a comparative study for using rainwater in single and multifamily buildings; they found that using a relatively small storage tank could be enough to satisfy the toilet flushing demand. In addition, rainwater could be used for toilet flushing, gardening and laundry, achieving reductions up to 37 L/capita/day in a single-family house. The main limitation for implementing this technology resides in the high payback period, especially in single-family houses but with proper subsidies and regulations, local governments might promote its use. Domènech et al. (2012) studied the use of rainwater in developing countries; they showed the importance of implementing good practices in the maintenance of the collection systems to ensure the quality of the water. Recently, Nápoles-Rivera et al. (2013) presented a mathematical programming model for the optimal allocation of water in a macroscopic system considering rainwater harvesting and water reclamation as an option to minimize the natural resources depletion. None of the previously reported methodologies (applied to microscopic or macroscopic systems) has taken into account important factors associated to the multiannual planning and scheduling such as population and demands growth, change in precipitation patterns and time value of money. Thus, in this work a multiannual storage and distribution scheduling for a macroscopic system considering all these aspects is presented.

2. Mathematical model

The mathematical model is based on the superstructure shown in Figure 1. Natural water sources are sent to a main either for domestic, agricultural or industrial purposes. In these facilities, the water is treated in order to be sent to the final users. In the proposed model, rainwater harvesting is considered; where the rainwater can be collected and stored in four types of storage devices, which are storage tanks and artificial ponds for domestic and agricultural uses, and storage tanks and artificial ponds for industrial uses. Rainwater can be used for any purpose, whereas reclaimed water can be used only for agricultural uses. The mathematical model is given as follows.

2.1. Equations for selecting installation of storage tanks or artificial ponds

For a given type of device, a set of constraints are required. If the storage device exists, then a binary variable (for example $z_{l,t}^{s}$) is equal to one and a storage device is installed in location l at time t (for storage tanks used for domestic and/or agricultural purposes); else, the binary variable is zero and the device is not installed, thus the associate installation cost will be zero. The capacity of the storage devices must be within specific limits, which are enforced only if the device exists. This is done with the following equations.

For domestic and agricultural uses:

$$\sum_{t} z_{l,t}^{s} \leq 1, \qquad \forall l \tag{1}$$

$$S_{l,t'} \leq \delta_{l}^{s,\max} \sum_{t=1}^{t=t'} z_{l,t}^{s}, \qquad \forall l, \forall t, \forall t', \forall t' \leq t \tag{2}$$

$$s_{l,t'}^{in} \leq \delta_{l}^{s,\max} \sum_{t=1}^{t=t'} z_{l,t}^{s}, \qquad \forall l, \forall t, \forall t', \forall t' \leq t \tag{3}$$

$$K_{Fl} = \sum_{t} K_{Fl,t} \cdot \sum_{t} VP_{l,t} \cdot z_{l,t}^{s}, \qquad \forall l \tag{4}$$

$$\sum_{t} z_{n,t}^{a} \leq 1, \qquad \forall n \tag{5}$$

$$A_{n,t'} \leq \delta_{n}^{a,\max} \sum_{t=1}^{t=t'} z_{n,t}^{a}, \qquad \forall n, \forall t, \forall t', \forall t' \leq t \tag{6}$$

$$a_{n,t'}^{in} \leq \delta_{n}^{a,\max} \sum_{t=1}^{t=t'} z_{n,t}^{a}, \qquad \forall n, \forall t, \forall t', \forall t' \leq t \tag{7}$$

$$K_{Fn} = \sum_{t} K_{Fn,t} \cdot \sum_{t} VP_{n,t} \cdot z_{n,t}^{a} \qquad \forall n \tag{8}$$

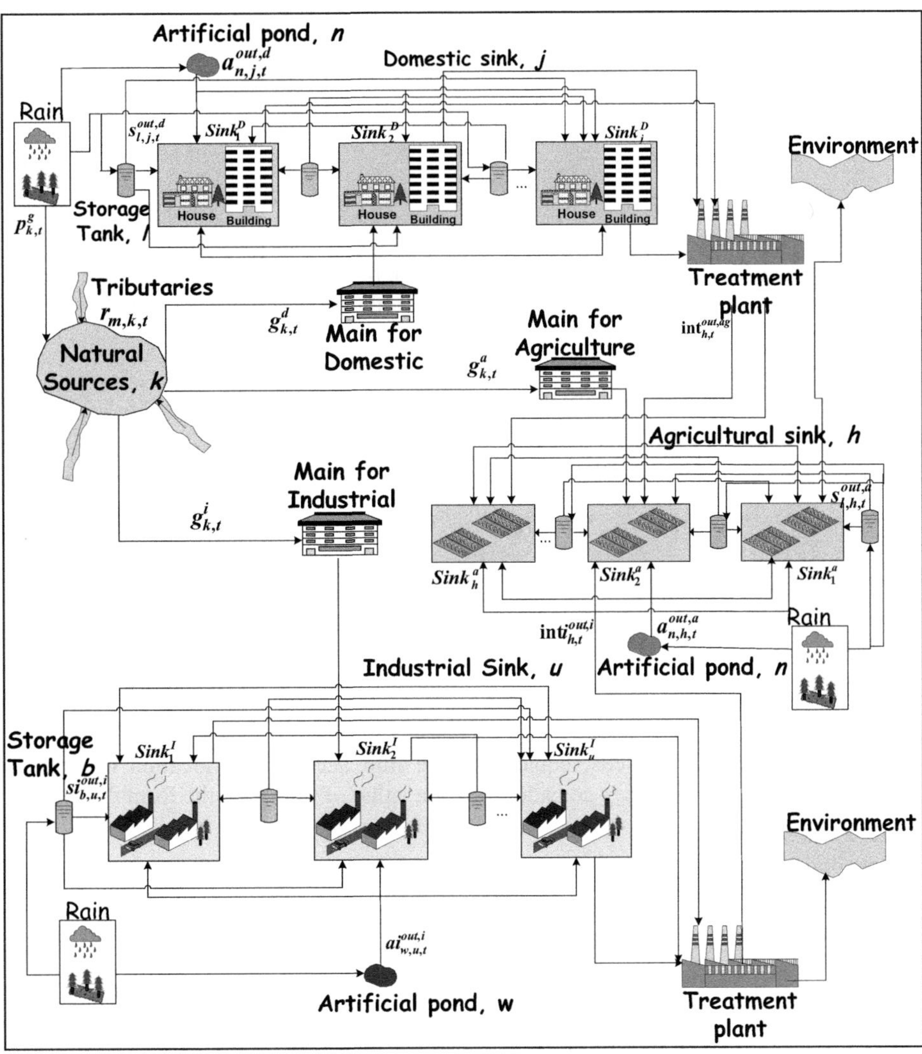

Figure 1. Proposed superstructure for water distribution at macroscopic level.

For industrial users:

$$\sum_{t} z_{b,t}^{si} \leq 1, \qquad \forall b \tag{9}$$

$$SI_{b,t'} \leq \delta_b^{si,\max} \sum_{t=1}^{t=t'} z_{b,t}^{si}, \qquad \forall b, \forall t, \forall t', \forall t' \leq t \tag{10}$$

$$si_{b,t'}^{in} \leq \delta_b^{si,\max} \sum_{t=1}^{t=t'} z_{b,t}^{si}, \qquad \forall b, \forall t, \forall t', \forall t' \leq t \tag{11}$$

$$K_{Fb} = \sum_{t} K_{Fb,t} \cdot \sum_{t} VP_{b,t} \cdot z_{b,t}^{si}, \qquad \forall b \tag{12}$$

$$\sum_{t} z_{w,t}^{ai} \leq 1, \qquad \forall w \tag{13}$$

$$AI_{w,t'} \leq \delta_w^{ai,\max} \sum_{t=1}^{t=t'} z_{w,t}^{ai}, \qquad \forall w, \forall t, \forall t', \forall t' \leq t \tag{14}$$

$$ai_{w,t'}^{in} \leq \delta_w^{ai,\max} \sum_{t=1}^{t=t'} z_{w,t}^{ai}, \qquad \forall w, \forall t, \forall t', \forall t' \leq t \tag{15}$$

$$K_{Fw} = \sum_t K_{Fw,t} \cdot \sum_t VP_{w,t} \cdot z_{w,t}^{ai}, \qquad \forall w \tag{16}$$

If the storage device exists, then its cost must be considered. In this work the cost functions take into account the fixed and variable installation costs for the different users.

For domestic and agricultural users:

$$Cost_{l,t}^{s} = K_{Fl}\left[A + B\left(S_l^{\max}\right)^{\alpha}\right], \qquad l \in L, t \in T \tag{17}$$

$$Cost_{n,t}^{a} = K_{Fn}\left[C + D\left(A_n^{\max}\right)^{\alpha}\right], \qquad n \in N, t \in T \tag{18}$$

For industrial users:

$$Cost_{b,t}^{si} = K_{Fb}\left[A + B\left(SI_b^{\max}\right)^{\alpha}\right], \qquad b \in B, t \in T \tag{19}$$

$$Cost_{w,t}^{ai} = K_{Fw}\left[C + D\left(AI_w^{\max}\right)^{\alpha}\right], \qquad w \in W, t \in T \tag{20}$$

Notice that the previous cost equations take into account the location and time of installation and this way they consider the time value of money in the formulation.

2.2. Mass balances

Mass balances are required in the mixing and splitting points of the network; these balances are time dependent and have the form:

$$Inlet = Accumulation + Outlet + Losses \tag{21}$$

Only the storage devices allow accumulation (natural reservoirs like deep wells and dams, and also artificial devices like storage tanks and artificial ponds), while losses can occur in different nodes of the network due to leakage, evaporation or consumption.

2.3. Objective Function

The objective function consists in maximizing the net profit expressed as follows:

$$TAR = contributions - treatment\ cost - storage\ cost - piping\ cost \tag{22}$$

3. Case Study

The city of Morelia, Michoacán, Mexico was selected as a case study for the scheduling of water storage and distribution. According to data from CONAGUA (National Council of Water-Mexico), the water consumption in Morelia was 90,168,374.77 m^3/y for public uses, 21,348,208 m^3/y for agricultural uses and 26,005,188 m^3/y for industrial uses (CONAGUA, 2011). This yields an annual consumption of 137,521,771 m^3/y. The city is divided in five areas: Center (CE), North-East (NE), North-West (NW), South-East (SE) and South-West (SW). The monthly precipitation in Morelia in the period of 1951-2010, according to the Meteorological National System (SMN, 2010), was taken as reference for projecting for the time span of the project, considering that rainfall is expected to decrease 6 % by 2030 (CONAGUA-SMN, 2011).

4. Results

The proposed model was coded in the software GAMS (Brooke et al., 2013). The problem consists of 53,473 constrains, 6,864 discrete variables, and 89,257 continuous variables. The model is a Mixed Integer Non-Linear Programming (MINLP) problem and it was solved with the solver DICOPT on a computer with an Intel Core i7 Processor 2.20 GHz with 8 GB of RAM, where the solution of each scenario was obtained in an average of 216,000 s. Figure 2 shows the water storage and distribution scheme when water harvesting and water reclamation is considered.

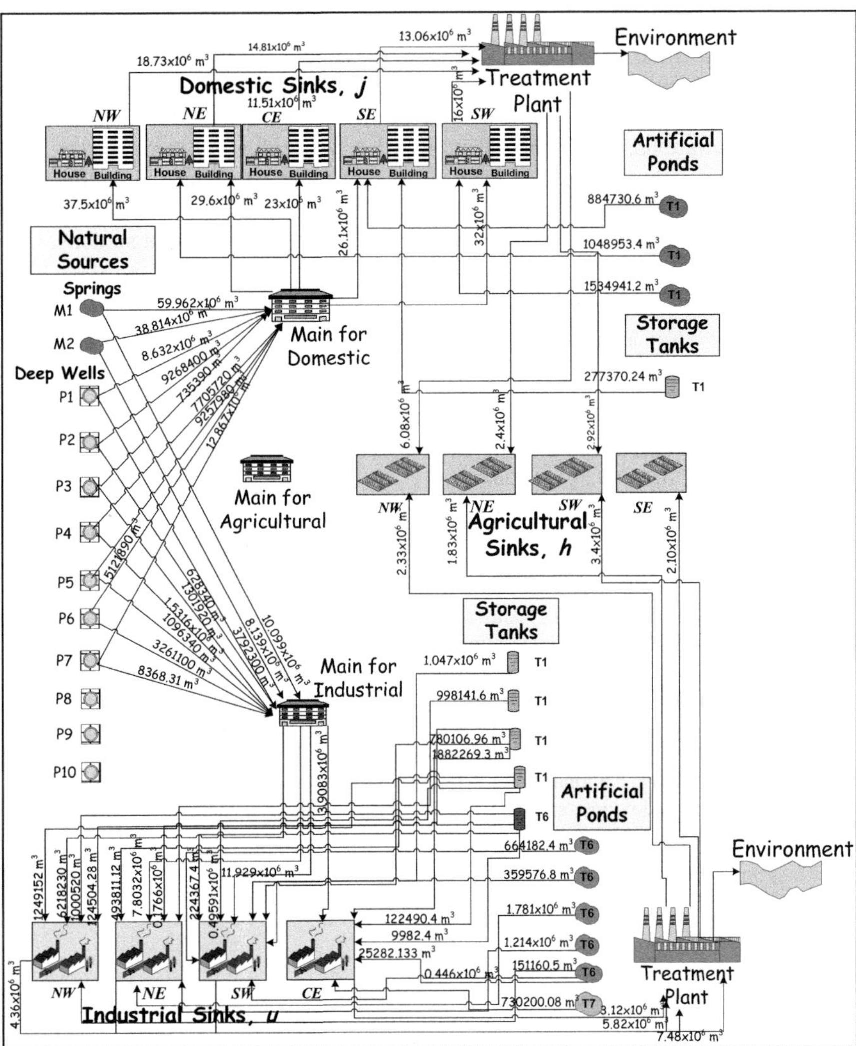

Figure 2. Results of water distribution in Morelia city.

In the first year, three artificial ponds and one storage tank are installed for domestic and agricultural sinks, in addition, for industrial sinks it is necessary to install five artificial ponds in the sixth year and one artificial pond in the seventh year, furthermore five storage tanks are required for industrial users, four are installed during the first year and one in the sixth year. The reclaimed water provides all the required water for agricultural purposes in the last year. The total water obtained from alternative water sources is 38.8x10^6 m^3, which represents 18.4 % of the total demand of the last year. Reclaimed water contributes with 12.5 % of the total demand during the time of project, and in the same way the harvested rainwater provides 12.7 % of the total demand. This means that alternative water sources have the potential to satisfy up to 25.2 % of the water demands in the city. This helps to reduce the pressure over the natural water bodies, with a profit of \$1.403x10^9 at the end of the project.

5. Conclusions

A case study for the Morelia city was presented. In the case, rainwater harvesting by itself has the potential to provide more than 20 % of the water demands, however the change in the precipitation patterns cannot be accurately predicted and long drought periods could make it an unreliable source, because when both harvested rainwater and reclaimed water are used simultaneously, they have potential to reduce the consumption of natural water sources up to a 25.2 %. Furthermore, the implementation of water reclamation can effectively complement the use of harvested rainwater providing enough water for agricultural activities in the city even during drought seasons.

6. References

CONAGUA, 2011, National Water Commission, Water Statistics in Mexico, <www.conagua.gob.mx/CONAGUA07/Publicaciones/Publicaciones/SGP-1-11-EAM2011.PDF>, Accessed on 01/06/2013.

L. Domènech, H. Heijnen, D. Saurí, 2012, Rainwater harvesting for human consumption and livelihood improvement in rural Nepal: benefits and risks, Water and Environment Journal, DOI:10.1111/j.1747-6593.2011.00305.

L. Domènech, D. Saurí, 2011, A comparative appraisal of the use of rainwater harvesting in single and multi-family buildings of the Metropolitan Area of Barcelona (Spain): social experience, drinking water savings and economic costs, Journal of Cleaner Production, 19, 6-7, 598-608.

Z. Li, F. Boyle, A. Reynolds, 2010, Rainwater harvesting and greywater treatment systems for domestic application in Ireland, Desalination, 260, 1-3, 1-8.

F. Nápoles-Rivera, M. Serna-González, M.M. El-Halwagi, J.M. Ponce-Ortega, 2013, Sustainable water management for macroscopic systems, Journal of Cleaner Production, 47, 102-117.

SMN, National Meteorological System, Climatologic Averages 1951-2010, <www.cm.colpos.mx/meteoro/progde/norm/n5110/> Accessed on 01/07/2013.

CONAGUA-SMN, 2011, National Water Commission- National Meteorological System, Weather Report in Mexico, <smn.cna.gob.mx/climatologia/analisis/reporte/Anual2011.pdf>, Accessed on 01/06/2013.

Jiří Jaromír Klemeš, Petar Sabev Varbanov and Peng Yen Liew (Editors)
Proceedings of the 24th European Symposium on Computer Aided Process Engineering – ESCAPE 24
June 15-18, 2014, Budapest, Hungary.

Functional-unit-based Life Cycle Optimization for Design of Sustainable Product Systems with Application on Biofuel Supply Chains

Dajun Yue, Fengqi You*

Northwestern University, 2145 Sheridan Rd., Evanston, IL, 60201, USA
you@northwestern.edu

Abstract

We propose a life cycle optimization framework for sustainable design of hydrocarbon supply chains considering economic and environmental criteria that are based on the concept of "functional unit". With the functional-unit-based objective functions, we develop a biofuel supply chain system that is both cost-effective and environmentally sustainable. The ε-constraint method is applied for multi-objective optimization and a series of Pareto-optimal solutions are obtained which reveal the tradeoff between economic and environmental performances. Due to the introduction of functional-unit-based objectives, the resulting model is formulated as a mixed integer linear fractional program (MILFP), which can be challenging for global optimization. Therefore, we further introduce two tailored MILFP methods, namely parametric algorithm and reformulation-linearization method for the efficient solution. The model and solution methods are illustrated by the spatially explicit optimization of a potential county-level hydrocarbon biofuel supply chain in the state of Illinois.

Keywords: Biofuel supply chain, functional unit, life cycle optimization, sustainable product system.

1. Introduction

Biomass-derived liquid transportation fuels are considered the most promising near-term solution to climate change and the country's heavy dependence on imported oil (Lin et al., 2014). As the biorefinery technologies are increasingly mature, the design and development of corresponding biomass-to-biofuel supply chains are desired (Avami, 2013). When addressing the design of a biomass-to-biofuel supply chains, one ought to take into account the environmental sustainability issues in addition to the economic consideration (Grossmann and Guillén-Gosálbez, 2010). Many relevant works tended to minimize the total cost and total environmental impact of a supply chain (Sharma et al., 2013). Whereas, minimizing the unit cost and unit environmental impact associated with per functional unit of the products would result in a product system that is more cost-effective in the competing marketplace and greener in the sense of environmental sustainability (Yue et al., 2013b).

The above bi-criterion optimization problem can be tackled with multi-objective optimization techniques to obtain a series of Pareto-optimal solutions. Whereas, incorporating the functional-unit-based criteria in the optimization model would lead to a set of mixed integer linear fractional programming (MILFP) problems, which is a special class of nonconvex mixed-integer nonlinear programs (MINLPs). Hence, the global optimization of resulting MILFP problems can be challenging due to the combinatorial nature and pseudoconvexity of the objective function (Floudas, 1999). In addressing these challenges, the major contributions of this work include:

- Novel functional-unit-based life cycle optimization (LCO) modeling framework for the design of hydrocarbon biofuel supply chains.
- Functional-unit-based economic and environmental optimization objectives and efficient solution strategies for the resulting MILFP problems.

2. Life cycle optimization framework

Life cycle assessment (LCA) methodology is widely employed to evaluate the life cycle environmental impact of a product system (Azapagic and Clift, 1999). However, LCA cannot automatically generate alternatives and identify the optimal one. Hence, to overcome the drawbacks, we propose a novel LCO framework in this paper, which organically integrates the classical four-step LCA methodology with multi-objective optimization techniques (Gebreslassie et al., 2012), as shown in Figure 1. The "functional unit" is defined in the goal and scope definition phase, which is a key element of LCA . The functional unit provides a reference to which the system's inputs and outputs can be related, and a logical basis for comparing the sustainability performance of different products. A general formula for the calculation of the total amount of functional unit is given by, $qt^T = \sum_i \lambda_i \cdot qt_i$, where qt^T stands for the total amount of functional unit, qt_i is the amount of product i and λ_i is the quantity of functional unit possessed by a unit of product i .

3. Problem statement

In this work, we study the sustainable design of a potential hydrocarbon biofuel supply chain network in the state of Illinois. A spatially explicit model at county-level resolution is employed. The superstructure of the supply chain is given in Figure 2. Three types of biomass feedstock are considered, namely crop residues, energy crops, and wood residues. Two types of biomass-derived liquid transportation fuel products are considered, namely gasoline and diesel. Two types of conversion pathways are considered, which are centralized and distributed, respectively. The centralized pathway consists of two integrated conversion methods, which are gasification with Fischer-Tropsch (FT) synthesis and fast pyrolysis followed by hydroprocessing. In contrast, the distributed pathway first converts the biomass feedstock to intermediate products (e.g., bio-oil and bioslurry) at preconversion facilities and then upgrades them into liquid fuel products at upgrading facilities. Two preconversion technologies are considered, namely rotating cone reactor pyrolysis and fluidized bed reactor pyrolysis. Two upgrading technologies are considered, namely hydroprocessing and gasification with FT synthesis. The candidate sites are shown in Figure 5(a).

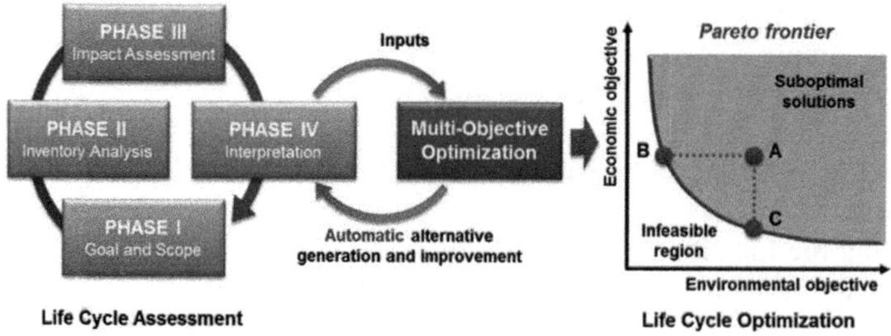

Figure 1. Life cycle optimzation framework

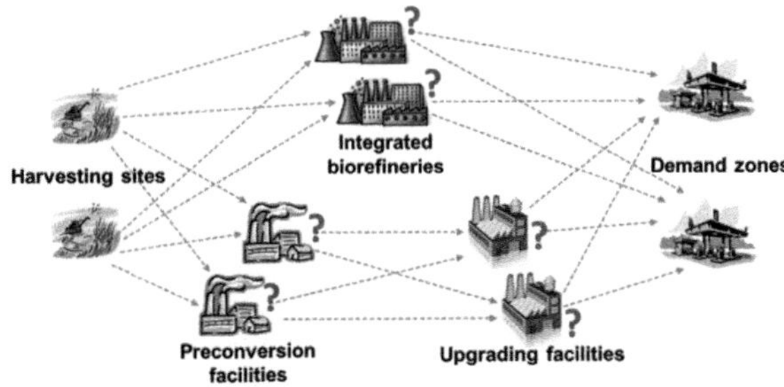

Figure 2. Superstructure of hydrocarbon biofuel supply chain

Most importantly, we define gasoline equivalent gallon (GEG) as the functional unit, which is the amount of alternative fuel it takes to equal to the energy content of one liquid gallon of gasoline. Therefore, the economic objective is to minimize the unit cost per GEG, (including annualized capital costs and annual operation costs) while the environmental objective is to minimize the unit life cycle greenhouse gas (GHG) emission (including CO_2, CH_4, NO_X, etc.) per GEG. The decision variables in the biofuel supply chain optimization involve facility location, technology selection, capital investment, production operation and logistics management. The goal of this work is to determine the optimal decision profile simultaneously under both economic and environmental considerations.

4. Model formulation

The life cycle optimization model employed in this work is modified from You and Wang, (2011). A brief model formulation is given below.

$$\min ftc = \frac{C_{capital} + C_{acquisition} + C_{distribution} + C_{production} + C_{transportation} - C_{incentive}}{\sum_i \lambda_i \cdot qt_i} \tag{1}$$

$$\min fte = \frac{E_{acquisition} + E_{distribution} + E_{production} + E_{transportation} - E_{sequestration}}{\sum_i \lambda_i \cdot qt_i} \tag{2}$$

s.t. biomass feedstock availability, material balance relationship,
conversion facility capacity, transportation link capacity,
cost and emission related constraints, etc.

The constraints are assumed all linear equations. The only nonlinear terms in the model are the economic and environmental objectives. In addition, the numerator and denominator of Eqs.(1 - 2) are both linear equations. Therefore, the problem is formulated into a bi-criterion MILFP model.

5. Solution strategy

5.1. ε-constraint method

Due to its efficiency and simplicity, the ε-constraint method is widely used to obtain Pareto-optimal solutions for multi-objective optimization problems. We convert the environmental objective in the original problem into the ε-constraint while leaving the economic objective. The resulting problem is a single-objective MILFP (P1), which is a special class of nonconvex MINLP. In order to globally optimize the MILFP problem (P1) efficiently, we present two tailored MILFP algorithms in the following sections.

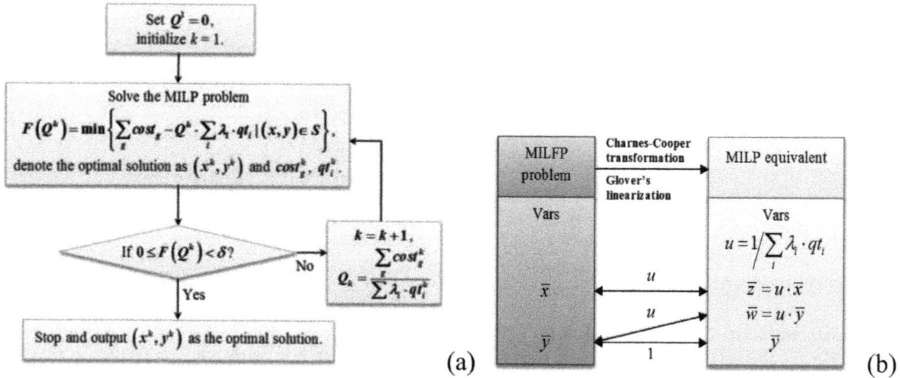

Figure 3. Solution strategies. (a) flowchart of the parametric algorithm. (b) one-to-one mapping of the reformulation-linearization method.

5.2. Tailored MILFP methods

The parametric algorithm relies on the solution of a sequence of MILP sub-problems iteratively to obtain the global optimal solution of the original MILFP problem (You et al., 2009). The flowchart of the parametric algorithm is given in Figure 3(a). Another alternative, the reformulation-linearization method, transforms the original MILFP problem into its exact equivalent MILP problem (Yue et al., 2013). The reformulation-linearization method is based on the integration of Charnes-Cooper transformation and Glover's linearization scheme. An important property of the reformulated equivalent MILP problem is that there is a one-to-one correlation between the reformulated variables and variables in the original formulation as shown in Figure 3(b).

6. Results and discussion

We derive the approximated Pareto curve by investigating 10 instances of the aforementioned bi-criterion optimization model using the proposed solution approaches. The results are presented in Figure 4. Point A corresponds to the most environmentally sustainable solution, with the lowest GHG emission of 10.66 kg CO_2-eq./GEG but the highest unit cost of \$4.63 /GEG. In contrast, point C corresponds to the most economical solution, with the highest GHG emission of 23.82 kg CO_2-eq./GEG but the lowest unit cost of \$3.58 /GEG. Considering the tradeoffs between the economic and environmental criteria, we identify a "good choice" solution (point B) with the GHG emission of 12.12 kg CO_2-eq./GEG and the unit cost of \$ 4.10 /GEG, which significantly reduces the cost with a small sacrifice in the GHG emission. Though all these solutions are Pareto-optimal, solutions on the left emphasize more on reducing the environmental impact and green manufacturing, while the solutions on the right tend to pursue a more cost-effective product system.

The Pareto-optimal supply chain profile corresponding to the most environmentally sustainable solution (Env), the "good choice" solution (GC), and the most economically sustainable solution (Eco) are illustrated in Figure 5b, 5c and 5d, respectively. The results indicate the trend that the more distributed the biofuel supply chain configuration is, the more cost-effective the product system will be while the centralized pathway is favored if a strict emission regulation is imposed. Also, we note that the optimal selection of conversion technologies is influenced by the capacity levels of the facilities.

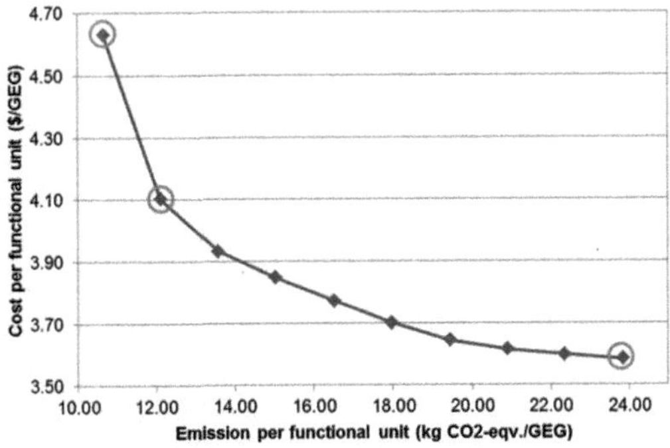

Figure 4. Pareto curve showing tradeoff between economic and environmental performances

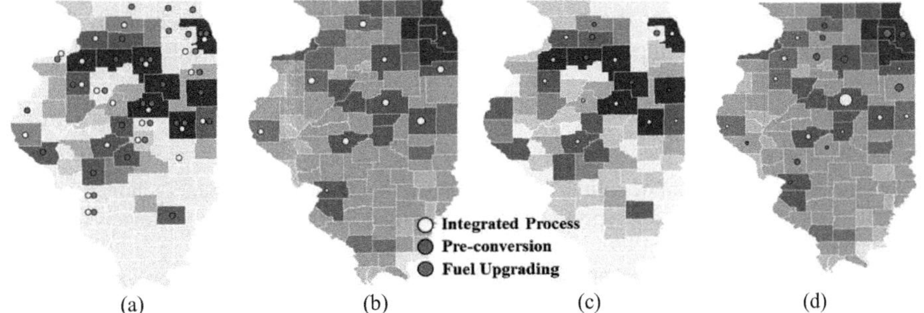

Figure 5. Optimal designs for the hydrocarbon biofuel supply chain (a) Candidate plants with potential harvesting sites as background. (b) The most environmentally sustainable biofuel supply chain profile with population distribution as background. (c) The "good choice" solution with biomass resources distribution as background. (d) The most economical biofuel supply chain profile with population distribution as background.

To illustrate the effectiveness of the proposed solution approaches, we also present the computational results in this section to compare the proposed tailored MILFP algorithms with the general-purposed MINLP ones. The original MILFP model consists of 244 discrete variables, 131,351 continuous variables and 30,826 constraints. The solution reports for the three selected instances are summarized in Table 1, where the rows correspond to different solution methods and the columns correspond to the most environmental, good-choice and most economically sustainable instance, respectively. Overall, the parametric algorithm exhibits the best computation performance among all the investigated solution methods, both in terms of computation efficiency and solution quality, thus is most recommended for the global optimization of MILFP models encountered in the LCO framework for sustainable design of biofuel supply chains.

Table 1. Computation time (CPUs) using different solution methods

Solution method	Env	GC	Eco
BARON 12	5,276.7	7,200*	7,200*
SBB	7,200*	7,200*	7,200*
DICOPT	3.7	31.8	406.3
R-L	80.8	125.1	215.4
Parametric	1.5	20.0	244.3

* indicates that no solution or merely suboptimal solutions were returned in 2 hours.

7. Conclusions

We employed two functional-unit-based economic and environmental objectives, respectively, to achieve a biofuel supply chain design that is both cost-competitive and environmentally friendly. The bi-criterion optimization problem was coped with using the ε-constraint method. The MILFP problems resulted from the introduction of functional-unit-based objectives were globally optimized using tailored MILFP approaches, namely parametric algorithm and reformulation-linearization method in an efficient manner. A potential hydrocarbon biofuel supply chain at county-level resolution in the state of Illinois was studied to illustrate the tradeoff between economic and environmental performances. The results indicated that the most environmentally sustainable design can be achieved with a unit cost of $ 4.63 /GEG and GHG emission of 10.66 kg CO_2-eq./GEG for the biomass-derived gasoline and diesel, while the most economical design leads to a unit cost of $3.58 /GEG and GHG emission of 23.82 kg CO_2-eq./GEG. In addition, the proposed tailored MILFP methods were proved to be much more efficient compared to the general-purpose MINLP solvers and global optimizer.

References

A. Avami, 2013, Assessment of optimal biofuel supply chain planning in Iran: Technical, economic, and agricultural perspectives, Renewable and Sustainable Energy Reviews, 26, 761-768.

A. Azapagic, R. Clift, 1999, The application of life cycle assessment to process optimisation, Computers and Chemical Engineering, 23, 1509-1526.

C. A. Floudas, 1999, Deterministic global optimization: theory, methods and applications, Kluwer Academic Publishers, Boston, US.

B. H. Gebreslassie, Y. Yao, F. You, 2012, Design under uncertainty of hydrocarbon biorefinery supply chains: Multiobjective stochastic programming models, decomposition algorithm, and a Comparison between CVaR and downside risk, AIChE Journal, 58, 2155-2179.

I. E. Grossmann, G. Guillén-Gosálbez, 2010, Scope for the application of mathematical programming techniques in the synthesis and planning of sustainable processes, Computers and Chemical Engineering, 34, 1365-1376.

T. Lin, L. F. Rodríguez, Y. N. Shastri, A. C. Hansen, K. C. Ting, 2014, Integrated strategic and tactical biomass–biofuel supply chain optimization, Bioresource Technology, 156, 256-266.

B. Sharma, R. G. Ingalls, C. L. Jones, A. Khanchi, 2013, Biomass supply chain design and analysis: Basis, overview, modeling, challenges, and future, Renewable and Sustainable Energy Reviews, 24, 608-627.

F. Q. You, P. M. Castro, I. E. Grossmann, 2009, Dinkelbach's Algorithm as An Efficient Method to Solve A Class of MINLP Models for Large-Scale Cyclic Scheduling Problems, Computers and Chemical Engineering, 33, 1879-1889.

F. Q. You, B. Wang, 2011, Life Cycle Optimization of Biomass-to-Liquid Supply Chains with Distributed-Centralized Processing Networks, Industrial and Engineering Chemistry Research, 50, 10102-10127.

D. Yue, G. Guillén-Gosálbez, F. You, 2013a, Global optimization of large-scale mixed-integer linear fractional programming problems: A reformulation-linearization method and process scheduling applications, AIChE Journal, 59, 4255-4272.

D. Yue, M. A. Kim, F. You, 2013b, Design of Sustainable Product Systems and Supply Chains with Life Cycle Optimization Based on Functional Unit: General Modeling Framework, Mixed-Integer Nonlinear Programming Algorithms and Case Study on Hydrocarbon Biofuels, ACS Sustainable Chemistry and Engineering, 1, 1003-1014.

Jiří Jaromír Klemeš, Petar Sabev Varbanov and Peng Yen Liew (Editors)
Proceedings of the 24th European Symposium on Computer Aided Process Engineering – ESCAPE 24
June 15-18, 2014, Budapest, Hungary.

GHG Emissions Minimization at the Macroeconomic Level via a Multi-objective Optimization/Input-output Approach: A Case Study of the EU-25 Economy

Daniel Cortés-Borda[a], Antonio Ruiz-Hernández[a], Gonzalo Guillén-Gosálbez[a]*, Maria Llop[b], Roger Guimerà[a], Marta Sales-Pardo[a]

[a]*Departament d'Enginyeria Química, Universitat Rovira i Virgili, Av. Països Catalans 26, 43007 Tarragona, Spain.*
[b]*Centre de Recerca en Economia Industrial i Economia Pública (CREIP), Universitat Rovira i Virgili, Av. Universitat 1, 43204 Reus, Spain.*
gonzalo.guillen@urv.cat

Abstract

We investigate the issue of how to mitigate global warming by performing changes in an economy. We use of a systematic tool that combines linear programming, environmentally extended input-output models and life cycle assessment. The problem of identifying economic sectors that mainly contribute to global warming is posed in mathematical terms as a bi-criteria linear program that seeks to optimize the total output and the life cycle CO_2 emissions simultaneously. We applied this approach to the European economy, finding possible to reduce the global warming potential in higher proportion than the economic output by regulating specific sectors.

Keywords: Input-output analysis, global warming mitigation, multi-objective optimization, linear programming.

1. Main Text

CO_2 atmospheric concentration and global warming has become increasingly evident. A large body of literature has studied different alternatives to mitigate global warming from an engineering point of view, however, at the macroeconomic scale has received less attention so far. Input-output (IO) models (Leontief, 1936) establish connections among sectors and nations according to their production/consumption flows. The environmentally extended input-output (EEIO) models are suitable to assess the environmental impact of an economy by adding impact-intensity vectors.

EEIO models have been used to assess the greenhouse gas (GHG) emissions as a function of the demand (Duarte et al., 2013), the CO_2 emissions of specific sectors/regions (Cellura et al., 2013), trade-embodied CO_2 emissions (Su, 2014) and various toxic emissions and environmental indicators (Qiang et al., 2013). Some studies have gone further by using EEIO models to formulate punctual changes (Fleskens et al., 2013) and study the effect of environmental policies (Barrett and Scott, 2012) in the economy.

Most of the existing studies are based on "what if?". They explore the consequences of a set of scenarios defined beforehand, restricting the analysis to a given number of alternatives (that could be sub-optimal solutions), which hinders developing effective environmental policies. A possible manner to overcome this limitation consists of integrating systematic optimization tools with EEIO models. In particular, linear programming (LP) is well suited for minimizing the environmental impact of processes and has been already coupled with IO analyses for solving environmental problems (Lin, 2011).

In this work, we explore the benefits of coupling EEIO models with multi-objective optimization (MOO) by applying this approach to the minimization of the GHG emissions of the European Union (EU-25) economy. The EEIO model is based on a Comprehensive Environmental Data Archive—EU25 ($CEDA_{EU25}$) database (Huppes et al., 2006), which considers 487 sectors for the EU-25 economy in 2006. Numerical results show that, by regulating some specific sectors, it is possible to attain significant reduction in global warming potential (GWP) at a comparatively smaller drop in the total output.

2. Problem statement

The problem under study is stated as follows. We are given the IO data of the EU-25 economy in 2006 and the associated environmental impact. We assume that the final demand of each sector can range within lower and upper bounds defined beforehand (in practice the demand could be lowered by imposing taxes to the corresponding final consumer products). The goal is to identify the economic sectors that should be regulated in order to minimize the environmental impact while maximizing the total output. Since a trade-off will naturally exist between both objectives, the solution of the problem will consist of a set of Pareto optimal points (see details in Ehrgott, 2005).

3. Mathematical formulation

We describe next a model that aims to identify the best changes to be performed in an economy so as to reduce the environmental impact while keeping the total output as high as possible. We first review the fundamentals of EEIO models, and then present the multi-objective LP problem. An EEIO model, in its basic form, consists of a system of linear equations, each of which describes the distribution of the production of an economic sector among the remaining sectors of the economy (Miller and Blair, 2009). For an economy with n sectors, the basic equations of the input output model can be expressed in compact form as follows:

$$X_i = a_{i,j} \cdot X_j + y_i \qquad (1)$$

Where X_i is the total output of sector i and y_i is the final demand of sector i, both expressed in currency units (e.g. Euros). Parameter $a_{i,j}$ denotes the output of sector i required to produce one unit of output in sector j. This coefficient is given as follows:

$$a_{i,j} = \frac{x_{i,j}}{X_i} \qquad (2)$$

Where $x_{i,j}$ is the portion of the output of sector i acting like an input for sector j. Hence, IO models assume a direct proportionality between the total output of a sector and the inputs that this sector acquires from its supplying sectors. Under this premise, the technical coefficients $a_{i,j}$ can be considered constant in a given time period (assuming that the technological conditions remain unchanged). IO analyses can be adequately modified to include environmental aspects along with economic information. To this end, we consider the pollution intensity (PI) defined by a column vector with a consistent sector disaggregation representing the environmental load per Euro of output for each sector. Here we focus on the global warming potential (GWP) measured in a 100-year period, which is the GWP-100 indicator. Then the GWP per sector is given by:

$$GWP_i = X_i \cdot PI_i \tag{3}$$

And the total GWP is obtained as follows:

$$Total\_GWP = \sum_i GWP_i \tag{4}$$

Regarding the optimization problem, we aim to simultaneously maximize the output and minimize the impact of the EU-25's economy. For such purpose, we leave the final demand as a free variable that can vary within lower and upper bounds. Our mathematical formulation takes therefore the form of the following LP model:

$$min\left\{-\sum_i X_i, GWP\right\}$$

S.t:

$$X_i = a_{i,j} \cdot X_j + y_i \quad \forall\, i$$
$$GWP_i = X_i \cdot PI_i \quad \forall i$$
$$\underline{y_i} \le y_i \le \overline{y_i}$$

By defining the demand as a variable (constrained within realistic lower and upper bounds represented by $\underline{y_i}$ and $\overline{y_i}$), we provide the model with enough flexibility as it can leave part of it unsatisfied, reflecting the situation that would arise when environmental policies result in reductions of consumption by final consumers.

We expect to find a trade-off between the total output and the GWP. The solution of the problem is given by a set of Pareto optimal points, each achieving a unique combination of economic output and GWP. We apply the epsilon-constraint method, which is based on solving a series of single objective sub-problems, where one criterion is kept as main objective while the others are transferred to auxiliary constraints that impose limits on them (Bérubé et al., 2009). Our multi-objective was implemented in the modelling system GAMS and solved with CPLEX 12.

4. Results

We solved the LP problem containing 976 variables and 489 constraints in GAMS, using CPLEX 12 on an Intel(R)Core(TM) Duo CPU with 3.00 GHz and 3.25 GB of RAM. We obtained a Pareto front of 10 points, with a solution time (per iteration) in the range of 0.14 to 0.157 CPU seconds. In the extreme point corresponding to the maximum output, the demand of all the sectors hit the upper bound; while in the one of minimum impact, the demand of all the sectors reaches the lower bound. Note that the demand of each sector ranges between a lower bound (90 % of the current demand), and an upper bound (the current demand). By observing in wider detail the sectors that are restricted in each intermediate Pareto point, we can get valuable insight on the main sources of impact. The identification of sectors whose regulation leads to major GHG savings at marginal decreases in economic performance might help to establish effective environmental policies. Figure 1 shows the Pareto front trading-off the GWP-100 and the total output. The Pareto solutions are labelled from 1 to 10, being 1 the minimum impact solution and 10 the maximum output solution. Since the model is linear, the Pareto front is concave, and the slope increases when moving to the left, requiring greater reductions of output in order to achieve the same GWP reduction.

Particularly, as we reduce the environmental impact, the number of sectors that are regulated increases. Table 1 shows, for each Pareto point, the number of sectors that are regulated along with the ratio between the variations of the total output and GWP-100. This can be interpreted as an elasticity-output of the reduction in emissions. A high value in this elasticity indicates a high sensibility of the emissions under a decrease in output.

The model identifies first the sectors that reduce the impact the most for a given drop in total output. Once such sector hits the lower bound; the algorithm proceeds in the same manner with the following sectors until the environmental target imposed by the epsilon constraint is identified. The sector that is being reduced when the algorithm meets the epsilon target is not decreased any further, so its demand finally falls between its upper and lower bounds. Hence, in each Pareto point, we find sectors whose demand is reduced to the lower bound, those whose demand hit the upper bound and only one of them with a demand between its upper and lower bound.

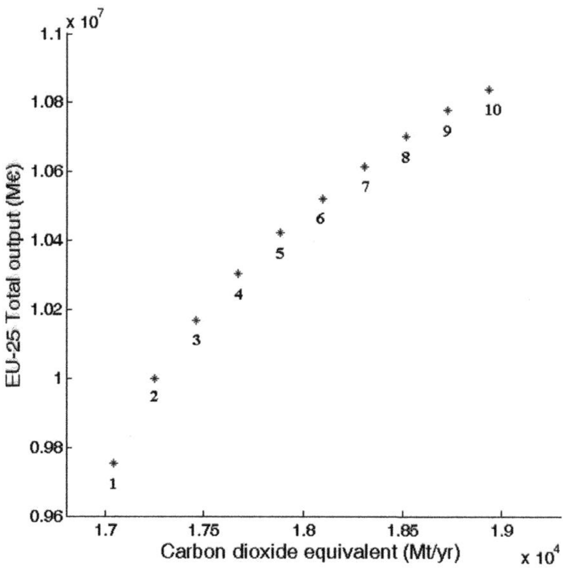

Figure 1. Pareto front for GWP-100 vs. the EU-25's total output in the year 2006

Table 1. Optimal solutions found for the GWP-100 minimization

	Pareto points									
	1	2	3	4	5	6	7	8	9	10
GWP reduction (%)	10.0	8.9	7.8	6.7	5.6	4.4	3.3	2.2	1.1	0.0
Output reduction (%)	10.0	7.7	6.2	4.9	3.8	2.9	2.0	1.2	0.5	0.0
Elasticity-output	1.00	1.15	1.26	1.36	1.46	1.53	1.63	1.79	2.07	-
Number of capped sectors	282	214	175	116	88	46	43	21	11	-

Table 2. Affected activities final demand reduction for Pareto optimal solution 9.

Sector	$\frac{y(i) - y_0(i)}{y_0(i)}$
Household cooking equipment	-10.0 %
Household refrigerators and freezers	-10.0 %
Household laundry equipment	-10.0 %
Electric housewares and fans	-10.0 %
Electric lamp bulbs and tubes	-10.0 %
Household audio and video equipment	-10.0 %
Chemical and fertilizer minerals	-10.0 %
Sausages and other prepared meat products	-9.6 %
Nonwoven fabrics	-10.0 %
Fabricated textile products, n.e.c.	-10.0 %
Boot and shoe cut stock and findings	-10.0 %

An important outcome from the optimization problem concerns the number of sectors whose final demand is restricted to reach a given environmental target in each Pareto point. This information is valuable for governments and public policy makers, as it pinpoints the sectors to be firstly regulated to attain significant environmental benefits. As observed, solution 9 shows the highest elasticity-output (2.07), allowing to reduce 1.1 % of GWP at the expense of a drop in the output of 0.5 %. In this solution, only 11 sectors are restricted. Table 2 provides detailed information on the sectors that are capped in the Pareto point 9, and the extent to which their demand should be reduced with respect to the original one.

Among the sectors that are regulated in solution 9, we find both industrial sectors and domestic activities. Domestic activities appear in first place since reducing the energy consumption in households does not harm the European economy as much as it would affect reducing the energy expenditure of the industrial sector. Regarding the restricted industrial sectors, we observe that their economic contribution to the European economy is low in comparison to their associated GWP.

5. Conclusions

We provide details on how the European economy should proceed to optimally reduce the GWP without significantly compromising the economy. Through a detailed sector-by-sector analysis we identify the sectors leading to major environmental savings with the least economic impact. Numerical results showed that, with the existing technology and the current international trade network; the GWP could be lowered in greater proportion than the economic output, by adequately restricting the demand of certain sectors. In particular, the GWP-100 can be lowered by 1.1 % with an output reduction of 0.5 %; this restricting 10 % of the final demand in 11 out of 487 sectors. We found that the economic activities that should firstly be restricted are those that are producing GHG with low economic contribution the to the EU-25's total output. Some minor changes in the basic consuming habits in households could lead to significant environmental savings without modifying the overall economic structure of the EU-25. We conclude that the multi-objective environmental and economic optimization of IO-

LCA models are powerful tools that could contribute to develop effective environmental policies by pinpointing sectors embedded in intricate trading networks, to be firstly regulated in order to attain specific environmental savings.

The scope of this study limits to illustrate the use of our methodology; hence our results are rather indicative, since we are considering that all the sectors are able to reduce 10 % of the original demand. However, we are aware that not all sectors are especially "elastic" and reducing the demand in 10% could be in practice impossible. Other aspects out of the scope of our study are the possible changes in consumers' behaviour in terms of sector substitution processes in final consumption.

Acknowledgements

The authors acknowledge the following institutions: Spanish Ministry of Education and Science (CTQ2012-37039-C02 and DPI2012-37154-C02-02), James S. McDonell Foundation Research Award, European Union (PIRG-GA-277166 and PIRG-GA-2010-268342), Spanish Ministry of Economy and Competitiveness (FIS2010-18639), Spanish Ministry of Culture (ECO2010-17728) and the Catalan Government (SGR2009-322 and "Xarxa de Referencia d'R+D+I en Economia Aplicada").

References

J. Barrett, K. Scott, 2012, Link between climate change mitigation and resource efficiency: A UK case study, Glob Environ Change, 22, 299–307.

J.F. Bérubé, M. Gendreau, J.Y. Potvin, 2009, An exact epsilon-constraint method for bi-objective combinatorial optimization problems: Application to the Traveling Salesman Problem with Profits, Eur J of Oper Res, 194, 39-50.

M. Cellura, F. Guarino, S. Longo, M. Mistretta, A. Orioli, The role of the building sector for reducing energy consumption and greenhouse gases: An Italian case study, Ren Energy, 60, 586-97.

R. Duarte, A. Mainar, J. Sánchez-Chóliz, 2013, The role of consumption patterns, demand and technological factors on the recen evolution of CO_2 emissions in a group of advanced economies, Ecol Econ, 96, 1-13.

M. Ehrgott, 2005, Multicriteria optimization, 2nd ed, Springer, Berlin, Germany.

L. Fleskens, D. Nainggolan, M. Termansen, K. Hubacek, M. S. Reed, 2013, Regional consequences of the way land users respond to future water availability in Murcia, Spain, Reg Environ Change, 13, 3, 615-32.

G. Huppes, A. de Koning, S. Suh, R. Heijungs, L. van Oers, P. Nielsen, J.B. Guinée, 2006, Environmental impacts of consumption in the European union: High-resolution input-output tables with detailed environmental extensions, J Ind Ecol, 10, 3, 129-46.

W.W.Leontief, 1936, Quantitative Input-Output Relations in the Economic System of the United States, Rev Econ Statistics, 18, 105-25.

C.Lin, 2011, Identifying lowest-emission choices and environmental Pareto frontiers for wastewater treatment, J Ind Ecol, 15, 367-80.

R.E. Miller, P.D. Blair, 2009, Input-output analysis: foundations and extentions, 2nd ed, Cambridge University press, New York, United States.

T. Qiang, D. Yu, A. Zhang, H. Gao, Z. Li, Z. Liu, W. Chen, Z. Han, 2013, Life cycle assessment on polylactide-based wood plastic composites toughened with polyhydroxyalkanoates, J Clean Prod, 66, 139-145.

B. Su, B.W. Ang, 2014, Input-output analysis of CO_2 emissions embodied in trade: A multi-region model for China, Appl Energy, 114, 377-84.

Jiří Jaromír Klemeš, Petar Sabev Varbanov and Peng Yen Liew (Editors)
Proceedings of the 24th European Symposium on Computer Aided Process Engineering – ESCAPE 24
June 15-18, 2014, Budapest, Hungary.

Handling of Uncertainty in Life Cycle Inventory by Correlated Multivariate Lognormal Distributions: Application to the Design of Supply Chain Networks

Juan A. Reyes-Labarta[a], Raquel Salcedo-Díaz[a], Rubén Ruiz-Femenia[a], Gonzalo Guillén-Gosálbez[b*], Jose A. Caballero[a]

[a]*Department of Chemical Engineering, University of Alicante. Ap. Correos 99, E-03080, Alicante. Spain.*

[b]*Departament d'Enginyeria Química, Universitat Rovira i Virgili, Tarragona E-43007, Spain.*

gonzalo.guillen@urv.cat

Abstract

In this work, we analyze the effect of incorporating life cycle inventory (LCI) uncertainty on the multi-objective optimization of chemical supply chains (SC) considering simultaneously their economic and environmental performance. To this end, we present a stochastic multi-scenario mixed-integer linear programming (MILP) coupled with a two-step transformation scenario generation algorithm with the unique feature of providing scenarios where the LCI random variables are correlated and each one of them has the desired lognormal marginal distribution. The environmental performance is quantified following life cycle assessment (LCA) principles, which are represented in the model formulation through standard algebraic equations. The capabilities of our approach are illustrated through a case study of a petrochemical supply chain. We show that the stochastic solution improves the economic performance of the SC in comparison with the deterministic one at any level of the environmental impact, and moreover the correlation among environmental burdens provides more realistic scenarios for the decision making process.

Keywords: lognormal distribution, life cycle assessment, multi-objective optimization, sustainable supply chain, risk management.

1. Introduction

Environmental databases coupled with mathematical programming techniques have enhanced tremendously the quantitative assessment of the environmental performance of process system engineering designs. The databases offer detailed information with a huge list of environmental burdens for each source of environmental impact in the system (e.g., utilities, raw materials or transport). Nevertheless, the values listed in the environmental database should be used with caution because their value cannot be considered as perfectly known. As the environmental assessment relies on these values, incorporating uncertainty through stochastic optimization guarantees a better performance of the system in comparison with the behavior exhibited for the same system but designed with deterministic optimization, which assumes nominal values for the uncertain parameters thus neglecting their variability (Grossmann and Guillén-Gosálbez, 2010). A case where is especially important the incorporation of uncertainty, is the design of a supply chain. Ruiz-Femenia et al. (2013), studied the effect of the demand uncertainty in the optimal design of a petrochemical supply chain considering simultaneously their economic and environmental performance. There are also studies incorporating uncertainty in the price of the CO_2 emissions rights in the design of a supply chain, located in a region where carbon trading is promoted by the government(Ruiz-Femenia et al., 2012).

To handle uncertainty, a Monte Carlo simulation can be performed. One of the decisions for a Monte Carlo simulation is the choice of probability distributions for the random variables. Selecting a distribution for each individual variable is often straightforward, but deciding what dependencies should exist among the variables is not obvious. However, there is a scarcity of information on which to base the dependence among environmental burdens. Therefore, it is useful to investigate with different correlating combinations among the environmental burdens emissions, gathered in the life cycle inventory (LCI), in order to determine how the model faces uncertainty, which is described with a set of realistic scenarios from a correlated distribution.

In this work, we explore the effect of the uncertainty in the life cycle inventory (LCI) for the optimal design of a supply chain (SC) considering simultaneously its economic and environmental performance, which is quantified following life cycle assessment (LCA) principles that consider the greenhouse gas (GHG) emissions released in all the echelons of the SC.

2. Methodology

We model the uncertainty in the LCI by a set of scenarios, generated by Monte Carlo sampling. Using the lognormal distribution, which is the default distribution for Ecoinvent database (Goedkoop et al., 1998), we implement a two-step transformation algorithm to generate the scenarios from a correlated multivariate random distribution function with the desired lognormal marginal distribution for each environmental burden in the LCI. Given are the mean expected value, the geometric standard deviation of each burden and the correlation matrix (whose entries range from -1 to 1, and 0 means no correlation). The geometric standard deviation is calculated from the uncertainty factors in conjunction with the pedigree matrix (Frischknecht et al., 2005). With these three inputs we compute the covariance matrix, whose diagonal elements contain the variances for each variable, while the off-diagonal elements contain the covariance among variables. Then, we use the probability density function of a multivariate normal distribution to generate a certain number of scenarios. Thus, a statistical dependence among each pair of variables is created, following each variable a normal marginal distribution (Figure 1a).Then we apply the 2 step algorithm:

Step 1: Apply a transformation separately to each random variable (i.e., environmental burden) using the normal cumulative distribution function with the corresponding expected mean and standard deviation. This transformation results in a correlated distribution with uniform marginal distribution on the interval (0,1) (Figure 1b).

Step 2: Transform each random variable (i.e., each burden) applying the inverse cumulative distribution function of a lognormal distribution (which is the desired marginal distribution). This transformation creates correlated random variables whose marginal distributions are exactly the lognormal distribution (Figure 1c).

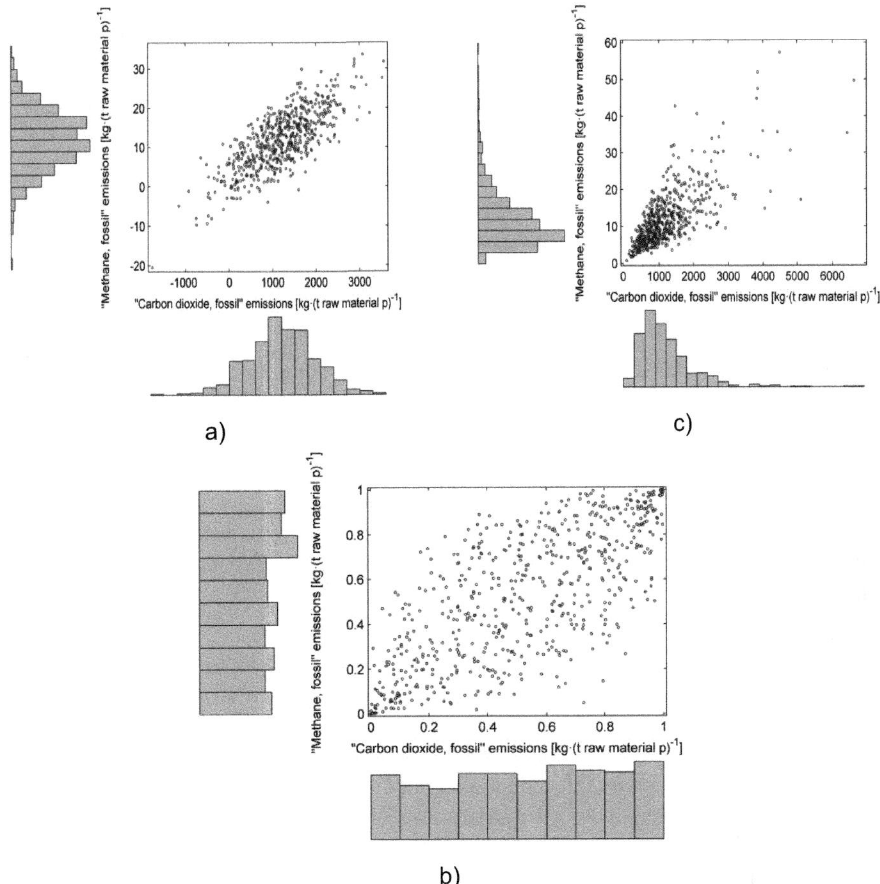

Figure 1. Correlated bivariate distributions with marginal: a) normal; b) uniform; c) lognormal distributions for two environmental burdens in the life cycle inventory, carbon dioxide and methane, for one kg of the raw material propylene.

3. Mathematical model

The MILP formulation is based on that introduced by Guillén-Gosálbez and Grossmann (2009) for the case of petrochemical SC. It includes binary variables to represent the occurrence of the capacity expansion of manufacturing technology i at plant j in time period t $\left(X_{ijt}^{PL}\right)$, the capacity expansion of warehouse k in time period $t\left(X_{kt}^{WH}\right)$, and the establishment of transportation links between plant j and warehouse k in time period $t\left(Y_{jkt}^{PL}\right)$, whereas continuous ones denote the transportation flows, capacity expansions, storage inventories and production rates.

The model includes three main blocks of equations: mass balances, capacity constraints and objective functions. A brief outline of each of these sets of equations is next given.

3.1. Mass balance equations

The mass balance must be satisfied for each node embedded in the network. Thus, for each plant j and chemical p, the purchases in period $t\left(PU_{jpt}\right)$ plus the amount produced must equal the amount transported from the plant to the warehouses $\left(Q_{jkpt}^{PL}\right)$ plus the amount consumed:

$$PU_{jpt} + \sum_{i \in OUT(p)} W_{ijpt} = \sum_{k} Q_{jkpt}^{PL} + \sum_{i \in IN(p)} W_{ijpt} \qquad \forall j,p,t \tag{1}$$

3.2. Capacity constraints

Plant and warehouses capacity expansions are bounded between upper and lower limits, using the binary variables $\left(X_{ijt}^{PL}\right)$ and $\left(X_{kt}^{WH}\right)$ to allow or prevent the expansion. Analogously, regarding the transportation flows, a zero value of the binary variable $\left(Y_{jkt}^{PL}\right)$ prevents the flow of materials between the corresponding nodes, whereas a value of one allows the materials flow within some lower and upper bounds.

3.3. Objective functions

3.3.1. Economic performance

The economic objective is represented by the net present value (NPV), which is calculated as the summation of the discounted cash flows (CFt) generated in each of the time periods t in which the time horizon is divided.

3.3.2. Environmental performance

The environmental performance of the SC is assessed according to the principles of Life Cycle Assessment (LCA) using the global warming potential (GWP) indicator as described by the IPCC 2007 (Intergovernmental Panel on Climate Change) (Hischier R., 2010). The probability of meeting unfavorable scenarios is controlled by adding the worst case (WC) environmental impact as an additional objective to be minimized. The worst case is determined from the maximum GWP attained over all the scenarios as follows:

$$GWP_s \leq WC \qquad \forall s \tag{2}$$

3.4. Solution method

The solution to this problem is given by a set of Pareto alternatives representing the optimal trade-off between the two objectives. In this work, these Pareto solutions are determined via the ε-constraint method (Ehrgott, 2005), which entails solving a set of instances of the single-objective NPV for different values of the auxiliary parameter e, where the lower and upper limits within which the epsilon parameter must fall are obtained from the optimization of each separate scalar objective.

4. Case study

We consider the first example introduced by Guillén-Gosálbez and Grossmann (2009). This problem addresses the optimal retrofit of an existing SC established in Europe. There are 6 different technologies available to manufacture 6 main products in 2 plants, 2 warehouses and 4 final markets.

5. Results and discussion

The algorithm to construct the correlated multivariate distributions is implemented in MATLAB and provides the set of scenarios required by the GAMS optimization solver. Data is transferred to GAMS using the GDX facilities. The ε-constraint multi-objective optimization model was implemented in GAMS and solved to global optimality with CPLEX 12.5.1.0.The Life Cycle Inventory data for the raw materials, utilities used and transportation tasks have been taken from ecoinvent database (Hischier R., 2010). The optimization results have been post-processed with Matlab® using the GDXMRW suit of utilities to export/import data between GAMS and Matlab®.

The results obtained shows how the correlation among environmental burdens affects the solution. To illustrate our results we present, as an example, one of the correlations studied. Among the three sources of environmental impact (raw materials, transport and utilities) considered in the supply chain design, raw materials exhibit the highest contribution to the GWP indicator. For the particular SC studied in this work, the most consumed raw material in the available technologies is propylene. Therefore, for illustration purposes, we investigate how the correlation among the burdens in the LCI of the raw material propylene, influences the stochastic design of the SC. For the calculation of the GWP in each scenario, the LCI considers 35 burdens, among which we correlated the two of them whose emissions provide the highest quantity of CO_2 equivalent, while for the remaining burdens no correlation has been assumed. The two burdens with the highest contribution to the GWP for the raw material propylene are: carbon dioxide, fossil and methane, fossil. To further highlight the importance of using a stochastic model, we compared the solutions produced by the deterministic and stochastic approaches. Note that the deterministic model can be easily obtained from the stochastic one by defining only one single scenario which corresponds to the mean value of the uncertain parameter. Hence, we first solved the deterministic MILP maximizing the NPV and minimizing the WC of the GWP, thereby generating a set of SC designs and associated planning decisions. Then we incorporated the uncertain parameter and maximized the NPV and minimized the WC with the structural continuous and binary variables fixed to the values provided by the deterministic model. As seen in Figure 2, the stochastic solution dominates the deterministic design when we consider the two dimensional space given by the NPV and worst case.

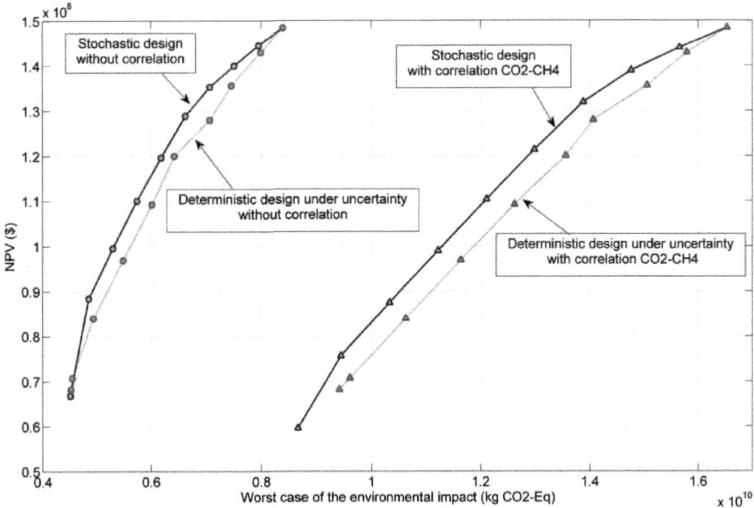

Figure 2. Pareto set of solutions for the deterministic and stochastic design with no burden correlation and correlating the two contaminants with more contribution to the GWP.

Figure 2 also compares the solutions obtained when no correlation is applied for the design of the SC and when a correlation factor of 0.9 is applied to the selected burdens. The Pareto curves obtained considering correlation among LCI burdens are shifted to the right with respect to the Pareto curves without correlation. Hence, the latter curves represent too optimistic solutions, due to the fact that a non correlated uncertainty causes unrealistic scenarios where the contribution of a burden in the total environmental impact, is compensated by other burdens.

6. Conclusions

The results show how the incorporation of the correlation among the LCI entries that comprises the GWP, influences on the solution design of the supply chain. It has been proved that incorporating uncertainty in the LCI facilitates the decision-making process, providing a robust solution when burden emissions uncertainty reveals with different values from those nominal ones gathered in the environmental database.

Acknowledgements

The authors wish to acknowledge support from the Spanish Ministry of Science and Innovation (CTQ2012-37039-C02-02).

References

M. Ehrgott, 2005, Multicriteria optimization, Berlin, New York, Springer.

R. Frischknecht, N. Jungbluth, H.-J. Althaus, G. Doka, R. Dones, T. Heck, S. Hellweg, R. Hischier, T. Nemecek, G. Rebitzer, M. Spielmann, 2005. The ecoinvent Database: Overview and Methodological Framework, The International Journal of Life Cycle Assessment, 10, 3-9.

M. Goedkoop, P. Hofstetter, R. Müller-Wenk, R. Spriemsma, 1998, The ECO-indicator 98 explained. The International Journal of Life Cycle Assessment, 3, 352-360.

I. E. Grossmann, G. Guillén-Gosálbez, 2010, Scope for the application of mathematical programming techniques in the synthesis and planning of sustainable processes, Computers and Chemical Engineering, 34, 1365-1376.

G. Guillén-Gosálbez, I. Grossmann, 2009, Optimal design and planning of sustainable chemical supply chains under uncertainty, AIChE Journal, 55, 99-121.

W. B. Hischier R., , H.-J. Althaus, C. Bauer, G. Doka, R. Dones, R. Frischknecht, S. Hellweg, S. Humbert, N. Jungbluth, T. Köllner, Y. Loerincik, M. Margni, T. Nemecek, 2010, Implementation of Life Cycle Impact Assessment Methods, Final report ecoinvent v2.2., Swiss Centre for Life Cycle Inventories, Dübendorf, CH.

R. Ruiz-Femenia, G. Guillén-Gosálbez, L. Jiménez, J. A. Caballero, 2013, Multi-objective optimization of environmentally conscious chemical supply chains under demand uncertainty, Chemical Engineering Science, 95, 1-11.

R. Ruiz-Femenia, R. Salcedo-Díaz, G. Guillén-Gosálbez, J. A. Caballero, L. Jiménez, 2012, Incorporating CO_2 emission trading in the optimal design and planning of chemical supply chain networks under uncertainty, Computer Aided Chemical Engineering, 30, 127-131.

Jiří Jaromír Klemeš, Petar Sabev Varbanov and Peng Yen Liew (Editors)
Proceedings of the 24th European Symposium on Computer Aided Process Engineering – ESCAPE 24
June 15-18, 2014, Budapest, Hungary.

Assessment of Hydrogen Production Systems based on Natural Gas Conversion with Carbon Capture and Storage

Calin-Cristian Cormos,* Letitia Petrescu, Ana-Maria Cormos

Babes – Bolyai University, Faculty of Chemistry and Chemical Engineering
11 Arany Janos, RO-400028, Cluj – Napoca, Romania
cormos@chem.ubbcluj.ro

Abstract

Introduction of hydrogen in the energy system, as a new energy carrier complementary to electricity, is exciting much interest not only for heat and power generation applications, but also for transport and petro-chemical sectors. In transition to a low carbon economy, Carbon Capture and Storage (CCS) technologies represent another way to reduce CO_2 emissions. Hydrogen can be produced from various feedstocks, the most important being based on fossil fuels (natural gas and coal). This paper investigates the techno-economic and environmental aspects of hydrogen production based on natural gas reforming conversion with and without carbon capture. As CO_2 capture options, gas - liquid absorption and chemical looping were evaluated. The evaluated plant concepts generate 300 MW_{th} hydrogen (based on hydrogen LHV) with purity higher than 99.95 % (vol.), suitable to be used both in petro-chemical applications as well as for Proton Exchange Membrane (PEM) fuel cells for mobile applications. For the designs with CCS, the carbon capture rate is about 70 % for absorption-based scheme while for chemical looping-based system is >99 %. Special emphasis is put in the paper on the assessment of various plant configurations and process integration issues using CAPE techniques. The mass and energy balances have been used furthermore for techno-economic and environmental impact assessments.

Keywords: Hydrogen production; Natural gas reforming; Carbon Capture and Storage (CCS); Chemical looping.

1. Introduction

Hydrogen is considered to be a promising clean energy carrier for the future. One of the main advantage of using hydrogen as a new energy carrier represents the negligible greenhouse gas emissions at the point of usage. Considering these aspects, hydrogen has a special place in deployment of large scale industrial applications for transition to low carbon economy (European Commission, 2007). Another important trend in developing low carbon technologies is Carbon Capture and Storage (CCS). The energy intensive processes (e.g. power generation, cement manufacture, chemical and petro-chemical applications etc.) using fossil fuels need to be fundamentally restructured for implementing reliable carbon capture technologies (Metz et al., 2005). Combining hydrogen production based on fossil fuels with carbon capture is one of the major research topics in developing innovative energy conversion processes. The most evaluated hydrogen production methods are based on fossil fuels particularly on natural gas conversion. Gasification of coal and biomass can also be used for H_2 production, a detailed analysis of these systems has been performed by Muresan et al. (2013).

This paper tackles the research gap of techno-economic and environmental assessments for hydrogen production based on natural gas, highlighting the main advantages of innovative chemical looping conversion. As illustrative examples, steam reforming and autothermal reforming of natural gas were evaluated without and with carbon capture. The configurations without carbon capture are currently the state of the art technology in the field (Abânades et al., 2013). The first evaluated carbon capture configuration is based on pre-combustion capture using an alkanolamine system (Methyl-DiEthanol-Amine - MDEA). The second high efficient carbon capture option evaluated in the paper is based on direct natural gas chemical looping system using iron oxide (ilmenite) as oxygen carrier (Adanez et al., 2012). Chemical looping systems implies the usage of several independent reactors (Cormos, 2012): the first reactor (called fuel reactor) is for natural gas conversion to CO_2 and water based on oxygen carrier reduction, the second reactor (steam reactor) is for oxygen carrier partial oxidation with steam to produce hydrogen and the third reactor (air reactor) is for total reoxidation of the oxygen carrier with air. The reactions involved in an iron-based looping system are:

Fuel reactor:

$$4Fe_2O_3 + 3CH_4 \rightarrow 8Fe + 6H_2O + 3CO_2 \qquad \Delta H = 274.5\, kJ/mol \qquad (1)$$

Steam reactor:

$$3Fe + 4H_2O \rightarrow Fe_3O_4 + 4H_2 \qquad \Delta H = -32.09\, kJ/mol \qquad (2)$$

Air reactor:

$$4Fe_3O_4 + O_2 \rightarrow 6Fe_2O_3 \qquad \Delta H = -478.81\, kJ/mol \qquad (3)$$

The above mentioned CO_2 capture options were evaluated in pre-combustion capture configuration. The plant concepts are generating about 300 MW_{th} hydrogen.

2. Plant configurations and main design assumptions

The first hydrogen production method is natural gas reforming with pre-combustion capture using MDEA-based gas-liquid absorption. Three reforming technologies were assessed: conventional steam reforming (noted as Case 1a); oxygen authothermal reforming (Case 2) and air autothermal reforming (Case 3). The conceptual design of conventional steam reforming with carbon capture (Case 1b) is presented in Figure 1.

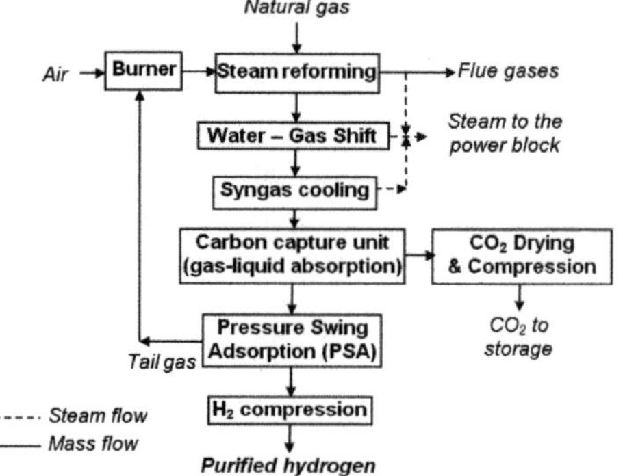

Figure 1. Hydrogen production based on natural gas reforming with pre-combustion capture using gas-liquid absorption (MDEA)

The second hydrogen production method is based on chemical looping using ilmenite ($FeTiO_3$) as oxygen carrier (Case 4). The conceptual design is presented in Figure 2. As presented in Figure 2 compared to Figure 1, the chemical looping system implies a significant reduction in plant complexity with positive influence on carbon capture energy and cost penalties. The main disadvantages are reactive gas-solid systems (implying circulating fluidised beds) and high steam duty, see Eq.(2). All plant concepts were modeled and simulated to produce the mass and energy balances for performance assessment. The main plants sub-systems and correspondent design assumptions are presented in Table 1, e.g. CO_2 specification proposed by De Visser et al. (2008).

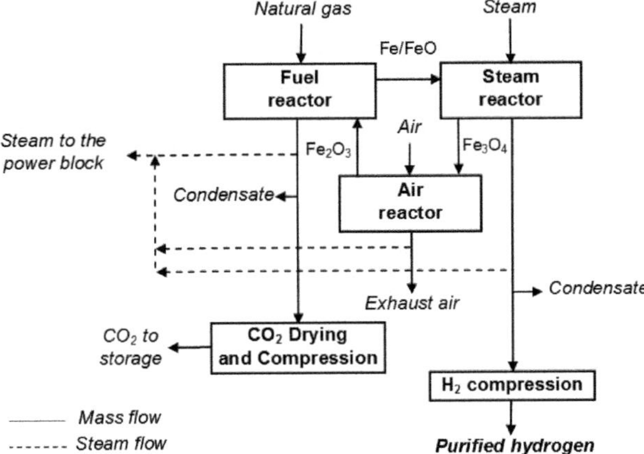

Figure 2. Hydrogen production based on chemical looping natural gas conversion

Table 1. Main design assumptions

Unit	Parameters
Natural gas desulphurisation (all cases)	Temperature: 350 °C Adsorbent: zinc oxide (ZnO)
Air separation unit (Case 2)	Oxygen purity: 95 % (vol.) Power consumption: 225 kWh/t O_2
Natural gas reformer (Cases 1 - 3)	Pressure: 30 bar Outlet temperature: 900 °C Burner configuration: Cases 1a and 1b Autothermal configuration: oxygen (Case 2), air (Case 3)
Chemical looping unit (Case 4)	Chemical looping agent: ilmenite ($FeTiO_3$) Fuel reactor parameters: 30 bar / 700 - 750 °C Steam reactor parameters: 28 bar / 700 - 800 °C Air reactor parameters: 26 bar / 850 - 1000 °C Gibbs free energy minimization model for both reactors Pressure drop fuel and steam reactors: 1 bar / reactor CL unit fully thermally integrated with the rest of the plant
CO_2 compression and drying	Delivery pressure: 120 bar Compressor efficiency: 85 % Solvent used for CO_2 drying: TEG (Tri-ethylene-glycol) Captured CO_2 quality specification (vol. %): >95 % CO_2; <2000 ppm CO; <500 ppm H_2O; <100 ppm H_2S
H_2 compression (all cases)	Delivery pressure: 60 bar Compressor efficiency: 85 %
Heat recovery steam generation (HRSG), steam cycle and power block	Steam pressure levels: 34 bar / 3 bar Steam turbine isoentropic efficiency: 85 % Steam wetness ex. steam turbine: max. 10 %
Heat exchangers	$\Delta T_{min.}$ = 10 °C Pressure drop: 1 - 2 % of inlet pressure

3. Results and discussions

All hydrogen production options with and without CCS were modeled and simulated using ChemCAD. Simulation of various plant concepts generated all data necessary to assess the techno-economic and environmental performances. The designs were optimized by performing heat and power integration using pinch technique as presented by Smith (2005) for maximization of power generation. Steam flows generated in reforming island and chemical looping reactors were integrated in the steam cycle of the power block. As an illustrative example for Case 4, Hot and Cold Composite Curves (HCC and CCC) for chemical looping reactors are presented in Figure 3.

The mass and energy balances, resulted from simulation, were furthemore used to calculate the overall plant performance indicators. The technical performance indicators for evaluated hydrogen production case studies without carbon capture (Cases 1a, 2 and 3) and with carbon capture (Cases 1b and 4) are reported in Table 2.

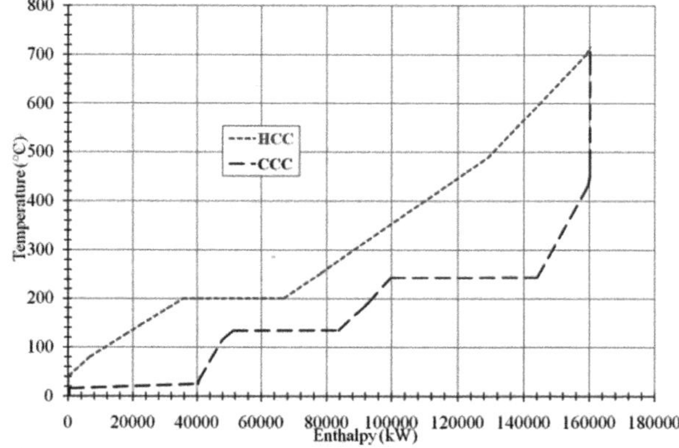

Figure 3. Composite curves for iron-based chemical looping plant (Case 4)

Table 2. Key technical performance indicators

Main Plant Data	Units	Case 1a	Case 2	Case 3	Case 1b	Case 4
Natural gas flowrate	t/h	31.37	34.11	32.98	31.37	30.63
Natural gas LHV	MJ/kg			46.7346		
Feedstock thermal energy (A)	MW_{th}	407.26	442.93	428.24	407.26	397.66
Steam turbine output	MW_e	16.03	31.45	28.69	11.32	9.45
Expander output	MW_e	0.99	1.26	2.94	0.37	8.08
Gross power output (B)	MW_e	17.02	32.71	31.63	11.69	17.53
Hydrogen output (C)	MW_{th}	300.00	300.00	300.00	300.00	300.00
Air Separation Unit (ASU)	MW_e	0.00	8.62	17.90	0.00	0.00
CO_2 capture & compression		0.00	0.00	0.00	4.23	1.98
Hydrogen compression	MW_e	4.18	4.18	4.18	4.18	3.97
Power island	MW_e	2.08	2.36	2.29	2.08	2.04
Ancillary consumption (D)	MW_e	6.26	15.16	24.37	10.49	7.99
Net power output (E = B - D)	MW_e	10.76	17.55	7.26	1.20	9.54
Net power efficiency (E/A * 100)	%	2.64	3.96	1.69	0.29	2.39
Hydrogen efficiency (C/A * 100)	%	73.66	67.73	70.05	73.66	75.44
Cumulative energy efficiency	%	76.30	71.69	71.74	73.95	77.83
Carbon capture rate	%	0.00	0.00	0.00	70.00	99.25
CO_2 specific emissions (H_2+power)	kg/MWh	267.39	284.59	284.37	82.78	1.94

As can be noticed from Table 2, the introduction of pre-combustion carbon capture step using an alkanolamine (MDEA) implies an energy penalty for gas-liquid absorption case (Case 1b) due to the heat requirement for solvent regeneration (about 0.77 MJ/kg CO_2). This value is significantly lower compared to post-combustion case (about 3 MJ/kg CO_2), underlining the advantages of pre-combustion capture scheme. Carbon capture rate is limited to 70 % due to unreformed methane which is not captured by the chemical solvent, and is finally used in the burner. Autothermal reforming technologies (Cases 2 and 3) were not analysed in carbon capture configuration due to lower energy efficiencies compared to conventional steam reforming (Case 1a).

Chemical looping case (Case 4) shows superior energy efficiency compared to all other cases (even in comparison with the cases without carbon capture). This fact underlines the primary advantage of looping systems in delivering high energy conversion efficiencies. Another significant advantage lays in almost total decarbonisation rate (>99 %). As main conclusion, in terms of technical evaluations, chemical looping case shows higher energy efficiency and CO_2 capture rate, in addition the plant configuration is also drastically reduced compared to reforming cases.

The next evaluation step was concerning the economic parameters (e.g. capital cost, operation & maintenance costs). For estimation of capital cost, the plants were divided into basic sub-systems (e.g. reformer island, syngas processing unit, carbon capture unit, power block etc.), equipment costs being estimated as a power law of capacity (Cormos et al., 2013). The operation & maintenance (O&M) costs were divided in fixed and variable. The summary of economic parameters is presented in Table 3.

As can be noticed, the carbon capture feature implies a significant capital cost penalty: about 45 % for gas-liquid absorption design (Case 1b) and about 42 % for chemical looping design (Case 4). In terms of O&M cost, the gas-liquid absorption design (Case 1b) has lower fixed and variable costs compared to chemical looping case, which is mainly due to spent oxygen carrier make-up. Comparing the reforming technologies, conventional steam reforming shows lower capital and O&M cost in comparison with the other two autothermal cases. Comparing the economic parameters of natural gas-based hydrogen production to coal or biomass gasification (Muresan et al., 2013), one can notice advantages of natural gas cases. Table 4 presents the normalised mass and energy inputs and outputs per unit of energy for Case 1a vs. Case 1b. These data show the environmental benefit of CCS case despite the increased resource consumptions.

Table 3. Key economic performance indicators

Main Plant Data	Units	Case 1a	Case 2	Case 3	Case 1b	Case 4
Hydrogen output	MW_{th}	300.00	300.00	300.00	300.00	300.00
Net power output	MW_e	10.76	17.55	7.26	1.20	9.54
Total installed cost (ex. contingency)	MM €	109.23	137.46	132.89	153.69	155.11
Total investment cost	MM €	131.07	164.96	159.46	184.43	186.13
Specific investment cost per kW net	€ / kW	421.79	519.46	518.98	612.31	601.33
Total fixed O&M cost (year)	MM €	7.71	8.15	8.14	8.19	8.51
Total fixed O&M cost (kWh)	€/kWh	0.0033	0.0034	0.0035	0.00363	0.0036
Total variable O&M cost (year)	MM €	55.66	60.48	58.51	56.20	61.71
Total variable O&M cost (kWh)	€/kWh	0.0238	0.0254	0.0253	0.0248	0.0265
Total fixed and variable costs (year)	MM €	63.37	68.64	66.65	64.39	70.22
Total fixed and variable costs (kWh)	€/kWh	0.0271	0.0288	0.0289	0.0285	0.0302

Table 4. Normalised mass and energy balances

Input	Units	Value	Output	Units	Value
Hydrogen production by steam reforming without CCS (Case 1a)					
Natural gas	kg	100.94	Hydrogen + net power	MWh	1.00
Air	kg	631.30	Captured CO_2	kg	0.00
BFW & CW	kg	17092.28	Flue gases	kg	855.03
Thermal energy (NG)	MWh_{th}	1.31	BFW & CW	kg	16940.47
			Thermal energy (CW)	MWh_{th}	0.19
Hydrogen production by steam reforming with CCS (Case 1b)					
Natural gas	kg	104.15	Hydrogen + net power	MWh	1.00
Air	kg	651.34	Captured CO_2	kg	193.00
BFW & CW	kg	23275.56	Flue gases	kg	882.17
Thermal energy (NG)	MWh_{th}	1.35	BFW & CW	kg	23118.93
			Thermal energy (CW)	MWh_{th}	0.27

4. Conclusions

This paper evaluates the techno-economic and environmental performances of hydrogen production based on natural gas conversion with and without carbon capture. The analysis demonstrates that chemical looping technology is very promising option to increase overall energy efficiency (~3.9 net energy efficiency percentage points) as well as a reduced cost penalty (2 % lower specific investment cost) for carbon capture with an almost total decarbonisation rate (>99 % vs. 70 % for MDEA-based option).

Acknowledgement

This work was supported by Romanian – Swiss Research Programme, project no. IZERZ0_141976/1 (13RO-CH/RSRP/2013): "Advanced thermo-chemical looping cycles for the poly-generation of decarbonised energy vectors: Material synthesis and characterisation, process modelling and life cycle analysis".

References

A. Abánades, C. Rubbia, C. Salmieri, 2013, Thermal cracking of methane into Hydrogen for a CO_2-free utilization of natural gas, International Journal of Hydrogen Energy, 38, 8491-8496.

J. Adanez, A. Abad, F. Garcia-Labiano, P. Gayan, L.F. de Diego, 2012, Progress in chemical-looping combustion and reforming technologies, Progress in Energy and Combustion Science, 38, 215-282.

C.C. Cormos, E. Vatopoulos, E. Tzimas, 2013, Assessment of the consumption of water and construction materials in state-of-the-art fossil fuel power generation technologies involving CO_2 capture, Energy, 51, 37-49.

C.C. Cormos, 2012, Evaluation of syngas-based chemical looping applications for hydrogen and power co-generation with CCS, International Journal of Hydrogen Energy, 37, 13371-13386.

E. De Visser, C. Hendriks, M. Barrio, M.J. Mølnvik, G. De Koeijer, S. Liljemark, Y. Le Gallo, 2008. Dynamis CO_2 quality recommendations, International Journal of Greenhouse Gas Control, 2, 478-484.

European Commission, 2007, A European strategic energy technology plan (SET Plan) - Towards a low carbon future, COM(2007) 723 final, Brussels, Belgium.

B. Metz, O. Davidson, H. Coninck, M. Loos, L. Meyer, 2005, Special report: Carbon Dioxide Capture and Storage, Intergovernmental Panel on Climate Change (IPCC), Cambridge University Press, UK.

M. Muresan, C.C. Cormos, P.S. Agachi, 2013, Techno-economical assessment of coal and biomass gasification-based hydrogen production supply chain system, Chemical Engineering Research and Design, 91, 1527-1541.

R. Smith, 2005, Chemical processes: Design and integration, Wiley, West Sussex, England.

Jiří Jaromír Klemeš, Petar Sabev Varbanov and Peng Yen Liew (Editors)
Proceedings of the 24th European Symposium on Computer Aided Process Engineering – ESCAPE 24
June 15-18, 2014, Budapest, Hungary.

Comparative Analysis between Coal-to-Olefins with CCS and Methanol-to-Olefins

Zihao Mai, Dong Xiang, Xiuxi Li, Yu Qian*

School of Chemical Engineering, State Key Lab of Pulp and Paper Engineering South China University of Technology, Guangzhou 510640, P.R. China ceyuqian@scut.edu.cn

Abstract

Development of the coal-to-olefins (CTO) is favourable in the context of increasingly severe oil supply shortage in China. However, it suffers the problem of high CO_2 emissions. CTO processes therefore face increasing challenges from another alternative process, methanol-to-olefins (MTO). This paper models the CTO process with CCS, conducts a techno-economic comparison between the CTO process with CCS and MTO. The CTO process with CCS is slightly less thermodynamically efficient than the conventional CTO process. The corresponding mitigation cost of the process is 150 RMB/t, which is roughly equivalent to the current carbon tax. In comparison to the MTO process, the CTO process with CCS is competitive in product cost when considering carbon tax.

Keywords: Olefins, Coal-to-olefins, Methanol-to-olefins, CCS.

1. Introduction

In China, olefins are very important to development of chemical processing industry and national economy. Currently, coal accounts for 75.1 % of the national total energy supply, oil for 15.2 %, and natural gas for 2.8 % (NBS, 2012). Thus, developing coal-based olefins is critical to sustainable development of chemical processing industry. However, CTO is characteristic of high CO_2 emission. In recent years, carbon capture and storage (CCS) technology has received increasing attention (Markewitz et al., 2012). Introduction of CCS is usually at the cost of decreasing energetic and economic performance (Pettinau et al., 2013). For example, the CO_2 avoidance cost is about 250-330 RMB/t for most Chinese coal-based power plants, which is much higher than the current carbon price (Yi et al., 2012). The penalties brought by the CCS on chemical processes is, however, lower than those on power generation (Mantripragada et al., 2011). It is thus necessary to assess the impact of CCS on the whole performance of CTO processes.

Planning a sound development roadmap for alternative olefins production requires a broad and comprehensive assessment. There have been a number of techno-economic analyses of CTO processes (Xiang et al., 2013). Besides, some experts favor methanol-to-olefins (MTO) processes since its low investment and environmental impact. Which production route should be developed for olefins? We answer this question by the techno-economic comparison of the CTO process with CCS and the MTO process in this paper.

2. Methodology

2.1. CTO with CCS process

As a base of techno-economic analysis, major units of a CTO process are modeled, including air separation unit (ASU), coal gasification unit (CG), acid gas removal unit (AGR), carbon capture and storage unit (CCS), water gas shift unit (WGS), methanol synthesis unit (MS), and methanol-to-olefins unit (MTO), as shown in Figure 1. For a plant with given capacity and specified operating conditions, the model calculates all mass and energy flows. Coal and water are gasified with the oxygen agent from the ASU, to produce syngas in the CG. The hot syngas is quenched in a radiant cooler and a convection condenser, where heat is recovered to generate steam. The syngas is then fed into the WGS to increase the ratio of H_2/CO for the methanol synthesis. The crude methanol solution is concentrated to 90 % (molar fraction) before fed into the MTO unit. DMTO technique was used to synthesize olefins at the condition of 763 K and 0.22 MPa. Methanol is converted into product gas in MTO reactor. The hot product gas is purified in the quenching tower and the alkaline tower. After then, ethylene and propylene are extracted by the front-end depropanization separation technique. Details of the simulation referred to the author's previous work (Xiang et al., 2014).

The CCS includes carbon capture, compression, transportation, and storage, as shown in Figure 2. The crude syngas from the gasifer consists of impurities such as ash and acid gases. It is necessary to remove these impurities before methanol synthesis. We employed Rectisol method in this paper. The syngas from the WGS is fed into the water scrubber to remove ammonia and fly ash. After flash dehydration, it is fed into the bottom of the acid gas absorber and absorbed by top-down low temperature methanol, which is obtained from the regeneration tower and cooled through multistage cooling to 223 K. The upper part of the absorber mainly removes CO_2 while the lower part removes sulfur containing compounds. Without CO_2 capture process, CO_2 is separated

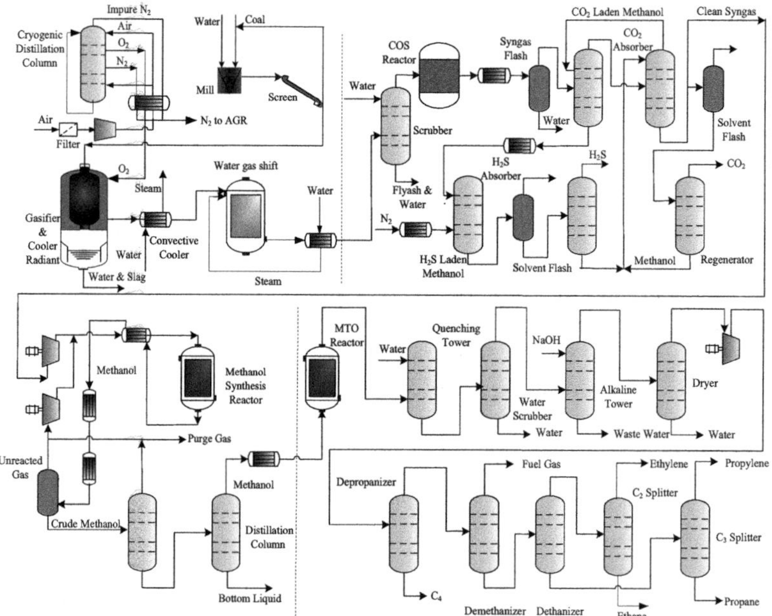

Figure. 1. Process flow diagram of the CTO process

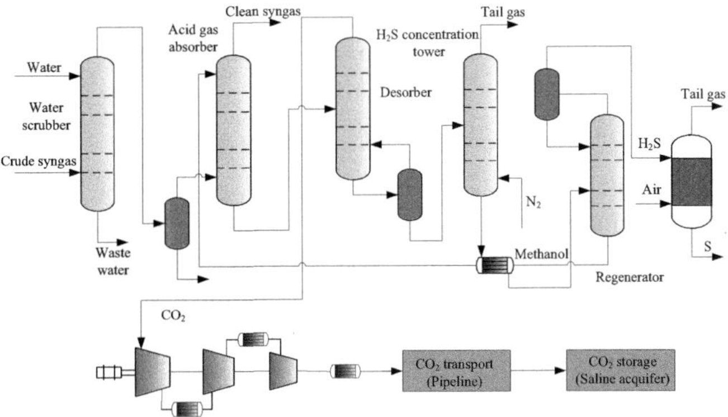

Figure 2. Process flow diagram of the CCS process

and exhausted to environment by using N_2 as the purge gas. In this case, the exhausted gas is a mixture of N_2 and CO_2. For CO_2 capture process, a desorber and a companying flash are introduced to purify CO_2 to the high concentration of about 98 %. The capture rate of CO_2 could be increased by changing the temperature and pressure of the flash. The H_2S separated from methanol regenerator is placed into CLAUS conversion process for sulfur recovery (Yang et al., 2012).

For modeling, RadFrac model was used to simulate the acid gas absorber, the desorber, the H_2S concentration tower, and the regenerator. Flash model and Compr model were adopted for simulating flashes and compressors, respectively. PSRK was selected as the thermodynamic method. The described CCS referred to the CCS demonstration of coal-to-liquid process installed by Shenhua group in Ordos, China (Li et al., 2011). Different from this CCS, we use pipeline to transport CO_2 in our model. Purified CO2 is firstly compressed to 15 MPa, and then carried to injection wells 20 km away, last injected into the saline aquifer 2 km underground for geological storage.

2.2. Techno-economic model

In this section, we mainly analyze the CTO process with CCS and MTO from technical and economic points of view. A few indexes are selected involving energy efficiency, capital investment, and product cost.

The energy efficiency is defined as the product energy generated by all input energy. The energy of coal, methanol, and olefins is calculated based on their lower heating values. The all input energy involves both the energy of feedstock and utilities.

The economic indexes, capital investment of CTO with CCS and MTO, was calculated according to the references (Dahowski et al., 2014; Xiang et al., 2014). In this paper, the capital investment was updated to 2012 prices by using the Chemical Engineering Plant Cost Index (Ng et al., 2013). The currency exchange rate between US$ and RMB was 6.2 in 2012. For calculation of the product cost, we made some assumptions. The consumption of raw materials and utilities was determined according to simulation results. Their corresponding costs were calculated on the basis of the average prices of 2012 in China (Xiang et al., 2014). Operating labor cost was calculated referring to Han's work (Xiang et al, 2013). A straight-line method was adopted to calculate the depreciation cost under the assumption of 20 y life time and 4 % salvage value. CO_2 TS&M cost was calculated by the work of Mantripragada and Rubin (2010). The rest part of product cost was calculated according to the ratio to product cost (Xiang et al., 2014). The product cost is defined as the sum of the above components as shown in Eq. (1).

$$PC = C_R + C_U + C_{O\&M} + C_D + C_{POC} + C_{AC} + C_{DSC} + C_{TS\&M} \quad (1)$$

where PC is the product cost, C_R is the raw material cost, C_U is the utilities cost, $C_{O\&M}$ is the operating & maintenance cost, C_D is the depreciation cost, C_{POC} is the plant overhead cost, C_{AC} is the administrative cost, C_{DSC} is the distribution and selling cost, $C_{TS\&M}$ is the cost of CO_2 transportation, sequestration, and monitoring.

3. Results and discussion

3.1. Energy efficiency analysis

The CTO plant with CCS and the MTO plant producing the same 0.7 Mt/y olefins were simulated in Aspen Plus, which produce all process data needed to assess the techno-economic and environmental performance of cases studied. The mass and energy data of these plants is shown in Table 1. Producing 0.7 Mt/y of olefins needs about 1.8 Mt/y methanol for the MTO plant and 2.87 Mt/y coal for the CTO plant. The resulting CO_2 emissions of the CTO plant are close to 4.05 Mt/y. With shorter conversion route, the energy efficiency of the MTO plant is around 80.10 %, much higher than that of the CTO plant which is only 35.69 %, which is roughly equivalent to traditional CTO plant.

3.2. Economic analysis

The breakdown of total capital investment of CTO with CCS and MTO shown in Fig. 3. It is seen that additional investment for CCS makes the total capital investment increase from 2.52×10^4 RMB/t/y to 2.69×10^4 RMB/t/y. While the total capital investment of MTO is less than half of CTO with CCS.

On the other hand, the product cost of MTO and CTO plants are calculated and shown in Figure 4. For the CTO plant, most of capital is expended on purchasing coal, accounting for 39.5 % of the product cost. The second largest is the cost for utilities, about 24.8% of the product cost. The total capital investment is involved in the product cost as the form of depreciation, amounting to 16.8 % of the product cost, which is the next major contributor to product cost. By introducing the CCS process, 80 % of CO_2 is mitigated. However, there is additional cost required for CCS energy use, geological sequestration, and monitoring. The product cost of the MTO plant is about 7,896 RMB/t, which is much higher than that of the CTO plant with CCS (7,131 RMB/t).

Table 1. Mass and energy results from the techno-economic model for CTO with CCS and MTO

Item	MTO	CTO without CCS	CTO with CCS
Input			
Coal (Mt/y) / (MW LHV)[a]	—	2.87/2800.24	2.87/2800.24
Methanol (Mt/y) / (MW LHV)[b]	1.80/1250	—	—
Electricity (MW)	36.61	146.21	187.58
Steam (MW)	123.98	212.75	212.75
Total energy input (MW)	1410.59	3159.20	3200.57
Output			
Ethylene (Mt/y) / (MW LHV)[b]	0.32/522.22	0.32/522.22	0.32/522.22
Propylene (Mt/y) / (MW LHV)[b]	0.28/456.94	0.28/456.94	0.28/456.94
$C_4^=$ (Mt/y) / (MW LHV)[b]	0.10/163.19	0.10/163.19	0.10/163.19
Product energy (MW LHV)	1142.35	1142.35	1142.35
CO_2 emissions (Mt/y)	Negligible	4.05	0.69
Energy efficiency (%, LHV basis)	80.10	36.16	35.69

[a] The LHV is based on (Hu et al., 2014). [b] The LHV is based on (Ren and Patel, 2009).

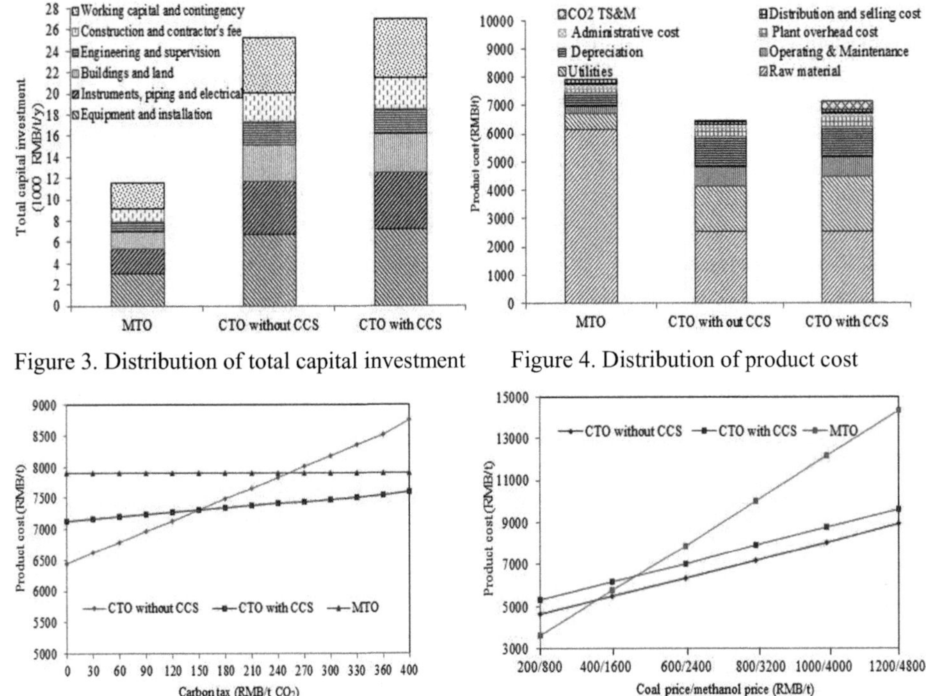

Figure 3. Distribution of total capital investment

Figure 4. Distribution of product cost

Figure 5. Effect of carbon tax on product cost

Figure 6. Effect of prices of feedstock on product cost

The methanol cost is the biggest part, amounting to 78.1 %, followed by the utilities cost of 6.7 % and depreciation cost of 6.0 %. The effect of increasing carbon tax on the product cost is shown in Figure 5. It is obvious that when carbon tax exceeds 250 RMB/t the product cost of the CTO plant without CCS is higher than that of the MTO plant, while the product cost of the CTO plant with CCS is much lower than that of the MTO plant when carbon tax is as high as 400 RMB/t. For the CTO plant with CCS, the break-even carbon tax between CTO plants with and without CCS is about 150 RMB/t, roughly equivalent to the current carbon price. Thus, the CTO plant with CCS could be firstly built to demonstrate the potential application of CCS technologies. The effect of feedstock price on product cost of the MTO plant is about 2 times that of the CTO plants with and without CCS, as shown in Figure 6. This means that the product cost of the MTO plant is highly affected by feedstock price and that for CTO plants the influence is relatively small. Although MTO plants have advantages of low capital investment and low environmental impact, their economic performances are easily intervened by methanol price. In other words, MTO plants have less anti-risk capability of market fluctuation than CTO plants in China.

4. Conclusions

Techno-economic performance of the CTO process with CCS was analyzed in this paper. It was also compared with the MTO process. The performance results indicate that the CTO plant with CCS is slightly less thermodynamically efficient than the conventional CTO plant without CCS. Compared to the CTO plant, the total capital investment increases by 6 %, from 2.52×10^4 RMB/t/y to 2.69×10^4 RMB/t/y, and the product cost rises nearly 11 %, from 6,442 RMB/t to 7,131 RMB/t. On the other hand, the product cost of the MTO plant is 7,896 RMB/t, which is much higher that of the CTO plant with CCS even in the context of carbon tax as high as 400 RMB/t. Although the MTO plant has low capital investment and CO_2 emissions, its economic performance is susceptible to fluctuation of market price. In a word, developing CTO processes with CCS is important to the sustainable development of olefins industry in China from the perspectives of resource reserve, economic performance, and environmental protection.

Acknowledgements

This work is supported from the National Science & Technology Support Plan (2012BAK13B02), the Natural Science Foundation of China (No. 21306056, 21176089, 21376091), Guangdong Natural Science Foundation Team Project (S2011030001366), and the Fundamental Research Funds for the Central Universities (No. 2013ZP0010).

References

A. Pettinau, F. Ferrara, C. Amorino, 2013, Combustion vs. gasification for a demonstration CCS (carbon capture and storage) project in Italy: a techno-economic analysis, Energy, 50, 160-9.

D. Xiang, L.J. Peng, S. Yang, Y. Qian, 2013, A review of oil and coal resource processes for olefins production, Chem. Ind. Eng. Prog., 32, 5, 959-970.

D. Xiang, Y. Qian, Y. Man, S. Yang, 2014, Techno-economic analysis of the coal-to-olefins process in comparison with the oil-to-olefins process, Appl. Energy, 113, 639-647.

H.C. Mantripragada, E.S. Rubin, 2011, Techno-economic evaluation of coal-to-liquids (CTL) plants with carbon capture and sequestration, Energy Policy, 39, 2808-2816.

K.S. Ng, N. Zhang, J. Sadhukhan, 2013, Techno-economic analysis of polygeneration systems with carbon capture and storage and CO_2 reuse, Chem. Eng. J., 219, 96-108.

National Bureau of Statistics (NBS), 2011, China energy statistics yearbook, China Stat. Press, Beijing (in Chinese).

P. Markewitz, W. Kuckshinrichs, W. Leitner, J. Linssen, P. Zapp, R. Bongartz, A. Schreiber, T.E. Müller, 2012, Worldwide innovations in the development of carbon capture technologies and the utilization of CO_2, Energy Environ., Sci., 5, 7281-7305.

Q. Yi, B. Lu, J. Feng, Y. Wu, W. Li, 2012, Evaluation of newly designed polygeneration system with CO_2 recycle, Energy Fuel, 26, 1459-1469.

S. Yang, Q. Yang, H. Li, X. Jin, X. Li, Y. Qian, 2012, An integrated framework for modeling, synthesis, analysis, and optimization of coal gasification-based energy and chemical processes, Ind. Eng. Chem. Res., 51, 15763-15777.

T. Ren, M.K. Patel, 2009, Basic petrochemicals from natural gas, coal and biomass: energy use and CO_2 emissions, Resour. Conser. Recycl., 53, 513-528.

X. Hu, A. Li, H. Cheng, D. Xin, D. Zhang, B. Zheng, 2008, General principles of the comprehensive energy consumption calculation, China Stand. Press, Beijing.

Z. Li, D. Zhang, L. Ma, W. Logan, W. Ni, 2011, The necessity of and policy suggestions for implementing a limited number of large scale, fully integrated CCS demonstrations in China, Energy Policy, 39, 5347-5355.

Jiří Jaromír Klemeš, Petar Sabev Varbanov and Peng Yen Liew (Editors)
Proceedings of the 24th European Symposium on Computer Aided Process Engineering – ESCAPE 24
June 15-18, 2014, Budapest, Hungary.

Biomass Characteristics Index: A Numerical Approach in Palm Bio-Energy Estimation

Jiang Ping Tang,[a] Hon Loong Lam,[a*] Mustafa Kamal Abdul Aziz,[b] Noor Azian Morad[b]

[a]*Centre of Excellance for Green Technologies, University of Nottingham Malaysia Campus, Jalan Broga, 43500 Semenyih, Selangor, Malaysia*
[b]*Centre of Lipid Engineering and Applied Research, Universiti Teknologi Malaysia, 81310 UTM Johor Bahru, Malaysia*
HonLoong.Lam@notthingham.edu.my

Abstract

In order to give a clear insight of the energy output estimation from the biomass, a comprehensive study on the physical properties of the biomass: bulk density and moisture content is crucial. A Biomass Characteristics Index (BCI) is proposed to represent the relationship between bulk density and moisture content. A numerical framework is developed to determine the BCI. This index is used to estimate the biomass bulk density and moisture content before the calorific value calculation. The classification of biomass according to its specific BCI can forecast the related bulk density and moisture content. Therefore, it reduces the hassle and time constraint to get those values through conventional empirical method. This will increase the overall biomass operational management efficiency.

Keywords: Biomass characteristics; Energy output estimation framework; Physical properties; Bulk density; Moisture content; Calorific value

1. Introduction

Moisture content and bulk density have been studied separately depends on the application area, either the pre-treatment process or end product (mostly is pellet). The focus of the research is target on the performance of final product rather than the raw biomass itself. There is no integration on both properties to indicate the initial biomass appearance and shape before the biomass pre-treatment stage. Raw biomass form has essential information that determines the handling, transportation and storage issues (Lam et al., 2013). This information can be feed into biomass supply chain for the purpose of optimized resource planning (Lam et al., 2011). A well planned supply chain design plays an important role to achieve the efficiency in cost and energy utilization (Klemeš et al., 2013).

Aquisition of bulk density and moisture content are obtained through empirical methods such as the British Standard (Standards Policy and Strategy Committee, 2010). Results from those methods may varied from sample to sample and limit by handling procedures. There is no standard or reference value of bulk density and moisture content for one particular biomass such as empty fruit bunch (EFB). In certain analysis, either one of the characteristics - bulk density, moisture content or component breakdown of biomass is involved. This shows the lack of overall coverage of the material's physical. In Chevenan et al. (2010) paper, the characterisation of bulk density is focused on switch grass, wheat straw and corn stover and each gives a different relationships model. Lack of generalized characterisation on various biomass impacts on the time constraint and reduces the efficiency in biomass management design and process.

In this paper, Biomass Characteristics Index is proposed to correlate the physical appearance of biomass to its properties, bulk density and moisture content. Numerical method will be used to perform Biomass Characteristics Index calculation. The introduction of the methodology is discussed in details on the following section.

2. Methodology

2.1. Relationships between bulk density and moisture content

There is a relationship between bulk density and the moisture content of biomass. The more moisture in a biomass material, the larger volume it has. Therefore, the biomass has a lower bulk density. Sims (2005) provided intuitive formulae for this study,

$$Bulk\ Density\ (\frac{kg}{m^3}) = \frac{13{,}600}{(100 - \%m.c.w.b.)} \tag{1}$$

However from his study, this is only applicable for wood chips. In order to provide a generalize characteristics for biomass; this formulae can be enhanced by getting a constant value of k for various types of biomass to replace the value of 13,600. The new modified formulae is,

$$Bulk\ Density\ (\frac{kg}{m^3}) = \frac{\kappa}{(100 - \%m.c.w.b.)} \tag{2}$$

In this study, this constant k is a reference index for various appearance shapes of biomass and is proposed as Biomass Characteristics Index (BCI).

2.2. BCI calculation

A systematic numerical approach proposes:

1. To obtain a series of BCI, a complete biomass database is needed. Various forms of biomass bulk densities and moisture contents are constructed to provide a comprehensive coverage on various appearance shapes of biomass.
2. From the above database, BCI can be obtained by using the bulk density and moisture content values into this formulae,

$$BCI = Bulk\ Density \times (100 - \%m.c.w.b.) \tag{3}$$

3. After the whole set of BCI is obtained, a graph is plotted to obtain the relationships between BCI and bulk density. From the graph, best fitted line is drawn. A new regression equation is obtained through the fit.

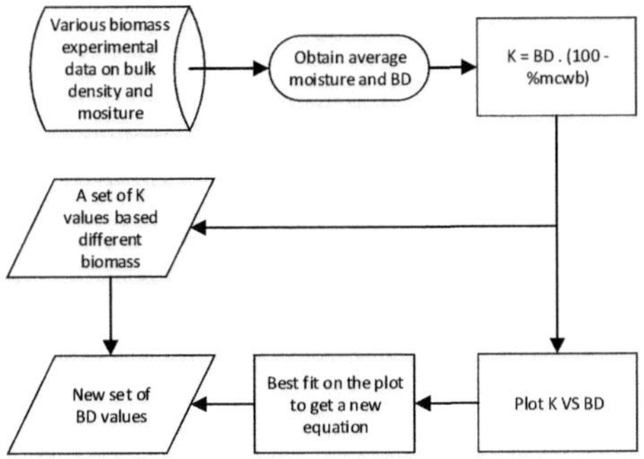

Figure 1. Flow chart of BCI calculation

3. Case study

A case study is demonstrated on a set of different appearance shapes biomass. The database includes most of the common found biomass and few types of oil palm biomass.

Table 1(a). Biomass characteristics.

Biomass Types	Min Moisture (%)	Max Moisture (%)	Average Moisture (%)	Min Bulk Density (kg/m^3)	Max Bulk Density (kg/m^3)	Average Bulk Density (kg/m^3)	BCI
Green wood chips	40.00	50.00	45.00	280	410	345	18,975
Empty Fruit Bunch	15.00	65.00	40.00	160	550	355	21,300
Green wood chunks	40.00	50.00	45.00	350	530	440	24,200
Mesocarp Oily Fiber	30.00	N/A	30.00	N/A	N/A	305	21,350
Fresh Fruit Bunch	40.00	N/A	40.00	N/A	N/A	480	28,800
Green sawdust	40.00	50.00	45.00	420	640	530	29,150
Straw bales	7.00	14.00	10.50	200	500	350	31,325

Table 2(b). Biomass characteristics (continued)

Biomass Types	Min Moisture (%)	Max Moisture (%)	Average Moisture (%)	Min Bulk Density (kg/m^3)	Max Bulk Density (kg/m^3)	Average Bulk Density (kg/m^3)	BCI
Green round wood	40.00	50.00	45.00	510	720	615	33,825
Ash	0.00	N/A	0.00	N/A	N/A	437	43,700
Sterilized Fruit	30.00	N/A	30.00	N/A	N/A	660	46,200
Fruitlets	30.00	N/A	30.00	N/A	N/A	680	47,600
Wood pellets	7.00	14.00	10.50	500	700	600	53,700
Press expelled cake	12.00	N/A	12.00	N/A	N/A	650	57,200
Palm Nuts	12.00	N/A	12.00	N/A	N/A	653	57,464
Cracked mixture	12.00	N/A	12.00	N/A	N/A	653	57,464
Dry EFB Cut Fiber	10.00	N/A	10.00	N/A	N/A	710	63,900
Shell	12.00	N/A	12.00	N/A	N/A	750	66,000
Coal	6.00	10.00	8.00	700	800	750	69,000
Wood briquettes	7.00	14.00	10.50	900	1,100	1,000	89,500

Table 1 shows the related bulk density and moisture content for all the common available types of biomass. Average value of bulk density and moisture content are calculated for the proposed BCI Eq.(3). The calculated BCI values are based from average bulk density and moisture content. As discussed in section 2, the values of BCI from Table 1 are calculated using Eq.(3).

By using the BCI values and average bulk densities, a graph is plotted to show the relationships. Figure 2 shows the linear regression fit on the plotted data. The best fit linear regression equation is y=90977x-6115.1 with R-squared value of 0.8675.

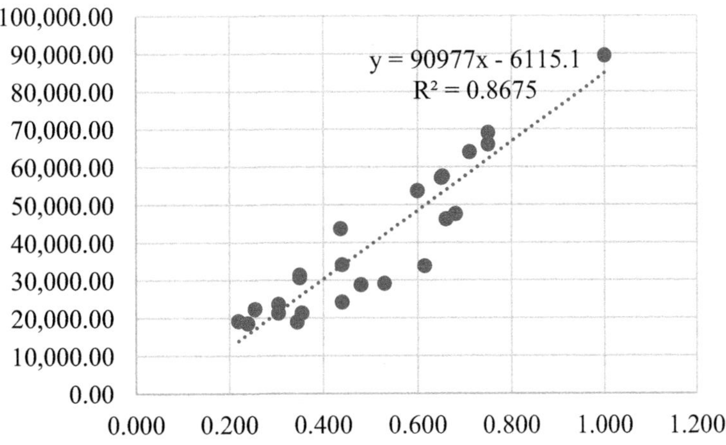

Figure 2. BCI vs average bulk density

4. Analysis

The validity of BCI can be verified through comparison between the calculated data and collected data. From Table 2, the error differences are relatively small. The highest differences are observed on empty fruit bunch (EFB) and fresh fruit bunch (FFB) which are 327 and 196. This is mainly due to the nature of these two materials, which have a large range of moisture content.

Table 3. Comparison of collected and BCI forecast bulk density

Oil Palm Biomass	Collected data (kg/m^3)	Forecast from BCI (kg/m^3)	Difference (kg/m^3)
Empty Fruit Bunch	628	301	327
Mesocarp Oily Fiber	257	302	45
Fresh Fruit Bunch	580	384	196
Ash	550	548	2
Sterilized Fruit	640	575	65
Fruitlets	640	590	50
Press expelled cake	550	696	146
Palm Nuts	653	699	46
Cracked mixture	535	699	164
Shell	650	793	143

5. Conclusion

A numerical framework of BCI is developed to represent the appearance and shapes of different biomass materials. By referring to the correct BCI of biomass material, forecast bulk density and moisture contents are obtained without running any time consuming empirical method. These values are critical to the amount of biomass fuel being transfer and the generated output power from the plant. Thus, it improves the overall biomass management process design and development. An efficient design means more output, less waste.

Acknowledgement

The financial supports from Long Term Research Grant Scheme, University of Nottingham Early Career Research and Knowledge Transfer Award (A2RHL6), and Universiti Putra Malaysia Institute of Advanced Technology are gratefully acknowledged.

References

N. Chevanan, A. R. Womaca, V.S.P. Bitra, C. Igathinathane, Y.T. Yang, P.I. Miu, S. Sokhansanj, 2010, Bulk density and compaction behavior of knife mill chopped switchgrass, wheat straw, and corn stover, Bioresource Technology, 101, 207-214.

J.J. Klemeš, P.S. Varbanov, Z. Kravanja, 2013, Recent developments in Process Integration, Chemical Engineering Research and Design, 91, 2037-2053.

H.L. Lam, P.S. Varbanov, J.J. Klemeš, 2011, Regional renewable energy and resource planning, Applied Energy, 88, 545-550.

H.L. Lam, W.P.Q. Ng, R.T.L. Ng, E.H. Ng, M.K. Abdul Aziz, D.K.S. Ng, 2013, Green strategy for sustainable waste-to-energy supply chain, Energy, 57, 4-16.

R.E.H. Sims, 2005, The Brilliance of Bioenergy: In Business and in Practice, James & James (Science Publishers) Ltd., London, UK.

Standards Policy and Strategy Committee, 2010, Solid biofuels — Determination of bulk density, British Standard, London, UK.

Jiří Jaromír Klemeš, Petar Sabev Varbanov and Peng Yen Liew (Editors)
Proceedings of the 24th European Symposium on Computer Aided Process Engineering – ESCAPE 24
June 15-18, 2014, Budapest, Hungary.

Plant-wide Process Improvement in Cooperation of Mathematical Optimization using the MIPT Algorithm in ChemCAD™

Hilke-Marie Lorenz[a,*], Daniel Otte[a], Daniel Staak[b], Jens-Uwe Repke[a],

[a]*TU Bergakademie Freiberg, Institute of Thermal, Environmental and Natural Products Process Engineering, Leipziger Strasse 28, 09599 Freiberg, Germany*

[b]*Lonza Group, Rottenstrasse 6, 3930 Visp, Switzerland*

hilke-marie.lorenz@tun.tu-freiberg.de

Abstract

This paper presents a systematic approach for the improvement of existing complex processes in chemical industry in order to increase their efficiency. As a result, modifications of process configurations are developed. Due to their implementation several internal stream compositions may be changed. In order to guarantee all demanded product specifications, new operating points need to be found. Hence, a method based on the global optimization algorithm MIPT has been developed in Matlab™. The process simulation software ChemCAD™ has been linked to Matlab™ in order to solve the optimization problem. The developed method is applied to a complex example process. The influence of changing feed composition on several process variables is pointed out.

Keywords: optimization, simulation, process synthesis, MINLP, multicomponent mixtures

1. Introduction

Due to an increasing energy demand and the shortage of fossil resources, sustainable and efficient processes in the chemical industry become more and more important. In the design of new processes, efficiency and sustainability criteria become established, whereas the improvement and the continuous development of existing industrial processes offer a high potential to increase the efficiency. Since it is still a major challenge to make changes in an operating process plant, in particular when the process comprises a large number of components and internal recycle streams, effective process analysis and optimization is crucial.

For plant-wide process synthesis and optimization several methods are described in literature. Mathematical algorithms are commonly used in contrast to heuristic rules. A superstructure generation of process alternatives can be adapted to process synthesis (Hostrup et. al, 1999). Optimization tasks can be formulated as MINLP-problems (Biegler and Grossmann, 2004) whereas multi-objective optimization problems can be solved with pareto optimization (Bortz et al., 2014). But often, especially for problems with a certain complexity in an industrial relevant size, these methods cannot be used (Chakraborty and Linninger, 2002). Furthermore, a toolbox to evaluate process alternatives in the early stage using superstructure optimization is presented by Steimel et al. (2013). Due to the maximal computation time for the optimization, the processes is limited in complexity.

A heuristic-mathematical approach has been developed for the improvement of existing complex processes in the chemical industry. The integration of modifications in the entire process using mathematical optimization is described in this paper. The MIPT (Molecular inspired parallel tempering) algorithm (Ochoa et al., 2010) is used for the optimization. This method will be applied to a complex example process.

2. Approach for plant-wide process improvement

The formulated approach for the plant-wide improvement of existing processes can be divided into five steps (Figure 1). The first step covers the formulation of the optimization goal for the entire process. This goal can be either an economic or a process specific goal. The second step comprises the analysis and the complete understanding of the entire process. Collecting existing process data and component properties gains this understanding. Component and mass balances need to be closed. The third step covers the interpretation of the process analysis to identify the optimization potential. Therefore, bottlenecks and operation problems, as well as process units where the optimization goal can be achieved need to be identified. Typical indications for that are blurred separation splits, contaminated waste or recycle streams. At this stage, the detailed knowledge of the thermodynamic behavior of the multicomponent streams is crucial. In the fourth step, the development of process modifications is accomplished. Necessary improvement aims for all identified bottlenecks and weak points in the process need to be formulated. Sub-processes consisting of several unit-operations need to be defined in which the respective problems can be solved. This can be done with mathematical optimization methods or, if necessary, new unit-operations need to be developed and integrated to the existing process. The fifth and last step covers the implementation of the process modifications into the existing process. The effect on the entire process in particular has to be considered, what will be discussed in the paper.

Since often, there is a huge number of internal recycle streams, the compositions of the streams can change considerably due to the process modifications. The accomplishment of the goals in accordance with the fixed specifications of all outlet streams (product and waste streams) regarding the modified process structure is a mandatory task in this part. As a result, new operating points need to be found to fulfill all demanded specifications. This task can be formulated as a MINLP-problem.

3. Optimization method

A mathematical optimization is carried out to consider the necessary modifications of the process configurations according to changed feed composition (Step 5). Therefore a Matlab^{TM} based optimization toolbox, including the used global optimization MIPT algorithm, is linked to the flowsheet simulator ChemCAD^{TM}, where the model of the process is implemented. In this chapter the MIPT algorithm will be described and the developed method will be presented.

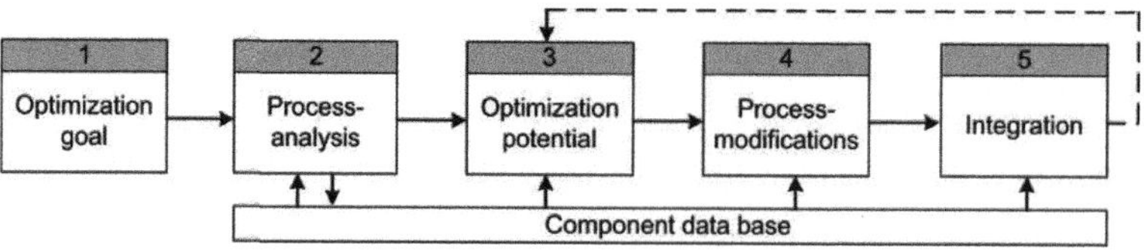

Figure 1. The five step plant-wide process improvement.

3.1. MIPT algorithm

The MIPT algorithm (Ochoa et al., 2010) is based on the stochastical parallel tempering (PT) (Earl and Deem, 2005). In contrast to PT, MIPT varies the friction force for tempering instead of changing the temperature of the replica. Furthermore, MIPT is using a two-molecule system that imitates the behavior of charged molecules in a solution for searching the global optimum. Due to the strong repulsive force explorer molecules are searching in the whole area for the global optimum. The local refinement is simulated with the lower friction force of the so called refiner molecules. It should be noted that on the one hand a high amount of molecules is increasing the possibility to find the global optimum but on the other hand the computation time is increasing. The classification of molecules is in accord with the higher and lower temperature classification of the PT. Ochoa et al. (2010) demonstrated that the MIPT algorithm is promising an enhanced performance for global optimization compared to other widely used algorithms. This robust algorithm is also able to find the global optimum for highly integrated and complex systems with a reasonable number of function evaluations. Therefore the MIPT algorithm is used in this work for solving the complex optimization problem

3.2. Integration of Matlab^{TM} based algorithm into ChemCAD^{TM}

The MIPT optimization algorithm is programmed in a Matlab^{TM} toolbox. A data connection is realized to connect this toolbox to the flowsheet simulation. In this case the communication is carried out on a Component Object Model (COM) interface. COM is a Microsoft^{TM} standard platform for sharing contents between programs. MS Excel^{TM} acts as a carrier of information and for the control of ChemCAD^{TM}. All in all it is possible to interact with ChemCAD^{TM} directly from Matlab^{TM}. The necessary functions are integrated in the problem statement of the MIPT toolbox that enables Matlab^{TM} to interact with ChemCAD^{TM} at every new required calculation of the objective function value. The data transfer from Matlab^{TM} to ChemCAD^{TM} and back to Matlab^{TM} via MS Excel^{TM} takes 6 seconds which is fast in comparison to the time needed for complex simulations (>3 minutes, 3.1 GHz Processor, 4 GB RAM, Matlab^{TM} 2013a).

4. Case Study

As mentioned before, the composition of internal streams can change considerably due to the integration of necessary process modifications elaborated in the fifth step of the presented approach. In this chapter the procedure for the improvement of new operating points is demonstrated on an example process using the MIPT optimization. The flowsheet can be seen in Figure 2. A multicomponent feed stream is separated in four distillation columns and an extraction column into its components.

4.1. Process description

The feed contains cyclohexane, benzene, toluene and o-xylene. Water and acetone are added as extraction solvents. In the first and second column (C1 and C2) the high boiling components (o-xylene (3) and toluene (6)) are removed as bottom products. Subsequently, benzene (9) and cyclohexane (12) are captured as distillate fraction. Benzene and cyclohexane are forming an azeotrope and have close boiling points. Benzene is separated from cyclohexane in C3 by adding acetone (7) which forms an azeotrope with cyclohexane at around 70 wt.-% acetone. Finally, cyclohexane is removed from acetone in an extraction stage (E1) by adding water (14) as a solvent. Stream 11 contains water, acetone and traces of cyclohexane and is separated at column C5. The solvents acetone (13) and water (14) are recycled.

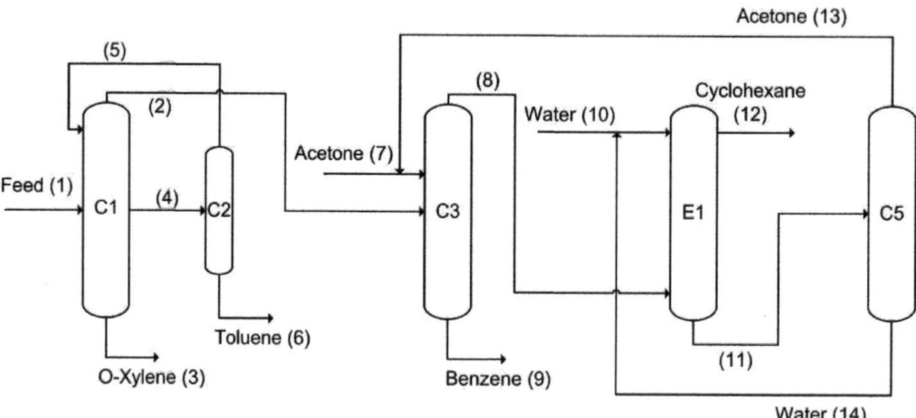

Figure 2. Separation process for case study.

4.2. Optimization Problem

The optimization problem is formulated as an objective function F_{obj} and several constrains. For the investigated process, the energy demand has to be minimized (Eq.(1)).

$$F_{obj} = \frac{\dot{Q}_{C1} + \dot{Q}_{C2} + \dot{Q}_{C3} + \dot{Q}_{C5}}{\dot{m}_{o-Xylene} + \dot{m}_{Toluene} + \dot{m}_{Benzene} + \dot{m}_{Cyclohexane}} \tag{1}$$

The constraints are characterized as minimum product concentrations of 90 wt.-% and minimum product yield of 80 wt.-% to ensure a high economic potential for this separation process. The previously described connection between Matlab^{TM} and ChemCAD^{TM} is used to accomplish a sensitivity study using an own Matlab^{TM} toolbox with the aim to detect the variables with the highest influence on the objective function with the purpose to decrease the optimization time. The decision variables which are characterized, as process variables (reboiler duty $\dot{Q}$, mass flow $\dot{m}$ and reflux ratio R) are presented in Table 3. Furthermore, design variables (e.g. feed stage) are not considered as decision variables for optimization because of a small influence on the objective function value. The number of column stages is set to a fixed value because existing plants are considered.

4.3. Benchmark configuration and optimization of new operation points

The specifications of the separation units used in the simulation are shown in Table 1. The benchmark (BM) feed composition depicts the original status. Case I and II represent the changed composition due to modifications in previous process units. Table 2 gives an overview of the three different feed specifications. The feed stream of Case I has a higher o-xylene and a lower benzene and toluene amount compared to the benchmark case. Case II considers more cyclohexene and toluene, less o-xylene and benzene in the feed stream. The properties of the mixture are calculated with the ChemCAD^{TM} properties database. The NRTL method is used to consider the real thermodynamic behavior of the mixture.

Table 1. Process specifications (All units have a top pressure of 1 bar).

Unit number	C1	C2	C3	E1	C4
Stages	50	20	30	15	15
Feed stage	1 + 35	8	13	1 + 15	10
Side Product stage	25	-	-	-	-

Table 2. Feed specifications.

Component	Unit	BM	Case I	Case II
Benzene	$kg \cdot h^{-1}$	50	30	30
Cyclohexane	$kg \cdot h^{-1}$	20	20	60
Toluene	$kg \cdot h^{-1}1$	50	20	60
o-Xylene	$kg \cdot h^{-1}$	50	100	20

5. Results and Discussion

The results obtained for the optimized values of the decision variables for the three investigated cases are shown in Table 3. It can be seen that the changing feed composition has a small influence on some decision variables, e.g. R_{C2} or R_{C5} but there is a large influence on other variables, like on the flow rates of the solvents. The evolution of the objective function versus function iterations (not presented here) shows that there is a strong decrease in the objective function in the beginning of the optimization which can be explained by a fast scan of the global problem done by the explorer molecules of the MIPT algorithm. Because of a narrow search range it is difficult for the explorer molecules to encounter better function values. There is a high amount of function evaluations which are generating an infeasible result (one or more constraints are not satisfied). However, the explorer molecules are able to leave local optima and find the global optimum. The resulting energy consumption for the separation process for the benchmark configuration is 8.19 $MJ \cdot kg^{-1}$. For Case I (8.48 $MJ \cdot kg^{-1}$) and for Case II (19.99 $MJ \cdot kg^{-1}$) a higher energy demand is necessary to separate the feed into its components. This difference can be explained with the higher consumption of water and acetone to accomplish the separation of cyclohexane. Furthermore, the concentration of each product stream for the relevant product is higher

Table 3. Decisions variables with optimized values for three different feed compositions.

		lower bound			upper bound			optimized value		
Variable	Unit	B	CI	CII	BM	CI	CII	BM	CI	CII
$\dot{m}_4$	$kg \cdot h^{-1}$	100	200	150	320	450	450	281.9	350.8	349.0
R_{C1}	mol/mo	1	10	1	20	25	20	12.0	16.9	12.0
$\dot{Q}_{C1}$	$MJ \cdot h^{-1}$	10	150	200	500	350	500	286.9	234.5	350.7
R_{C2}	mol/mo	0.1	0.5	0.1	5	3	5	1.0	0.9	1.0
$\dot{Q}_{C2}$	$MJ \cdot h^{-1}$	10	150	100	400	350	400	178.2	235.2	213.7
R_{C3}	mol/mo	1	5	1	20	15	20	8.7	9.0	8.0
$\dot{Q}_{C3}$	$MJ \cdot h^{-1}$	100	400	1,000	1,000	700	2,500	553.1	574.4	1591.
R_{C5}	mol/mo	1	1	1	10	10	20	5.1	5.0	5.0
$\dot{Q}_{C5}$	$MJ \cdot h^{-1}$	300	300	500	400	450	2,000	345.8	348.4	1,095
$\dot{m}_7$	$kg \cdot h^{-1}$	50	50	100	180	200	500	100.2	99.5	299.8
$\dot{m}_{10}$	$kg \cdot h^{-1}$	30	30	100	150	200	500	71	69.9	301.4

Table 4. Product streams and energy consumption for the optimized objective function value.

Variable	Unit	Benchmark	Case I	Case II
$\dot{m}_{o-Xylene}$	$kg{\cdot}h^{-1}$	49.85	100	19.99
$x_{o-Xylene}$	kg/kg	0.999	0.992	0.965
$\dot{m}_{Toluene}$	$kg{\cdot}h^{-1}$	49.91	19.21	59.06
$x_{Toluene}$	kg/kg	0.995	0.914	0.997
$\dot{m}_{Benzene}$	$kg{\cdot}h^{-1}$	49.88	28.50	29.95
$x_{Benzene}$	kg/kg	0.917	0.913	0.950
$\dot{m}_{Cyclohexane}$	$kg{\cdot}h^{-1}$	16.91	16.49	53.62
$x_{Cyclohexane}$	kg/kg	0.999	0.999	0.999
$\sum\dot{Q}_{reboiler}$	$MJ{\cdot}h^{-1}$	1,364	1,392	3,251
F_{obj}	$MJ{\cdot}kg^{-1}$	8.19	8.48	19.99

than the demanded specifications (Table 4). These results show the influence of modifications in the process on the following units.

6. Conclusions and outlook

A systematic approach for the plant-wide improvement of existing complex processes has been presented. With this approach, effective modifications to increase the efficiency of the entire process can be obtained. A tool to optimize the following units has been developed for the determination of the new operating point. The MIPT optimization algorithm has been implemented in MATLAB™ and connected to the simulation tool ChemCAD™. This method was applied on a complex process example. Process decision variables have been pointed out in a sensitivity study. The influence of changing feed composition on process parameters has been investigated. For some variables a significant influence on the feed composition can be seen. In the future work this method will be developed for the improvement of an existing process in chemical industry containing more than 15 unit operations and up to 30 components.

References

L. T. Biegler, I. E. Grossmann, 2004, Retrospective on optimization, Computers and Chemical Engineering, 28, 8, 1169-1192

M. Bortz, J. Burger, N. Aspiron, S. Blagov, R. Böttcher, U. Nowak, A. Scheithauer, R. Welke, K.-H. Küfer, H. Hasse, 2014, Multi-criteria optimization in chemical process design and decision support by navigation on Pareto sets, Computer and Chemical Engineering, 60, 354-363

D. Earl, M. Deem, 2005, Parallel tempering: Theory, applications and new perspective, Physical Chemistry Chemical Physics, 7, 23, 3910-3916

A. Chakraborty, A. Linninger, 2002, Plant-Wide Waste management. 1. Synthesis and Multiobjective Design, Industrial and Engineering Chemistry Research, 41, 18, 4591-4604

M. Hostrup, P. M. Harper, R. Gani, 1999, Design of environmentally benign processes: Integration of solvent design and separation process synthesis, Computers and Chemical Engineering, 23, 10, 1395–1414

J. Steimel, M. Harrmann, G. Schembecker, S. Engell, 2013, Model-based conceptual design and optimization tool support for the early stage development of chemical processes under uncertainty, Computers and Chemical Engineering, 59, 63-73

S. Ochoa, G. Wozny, J.-U. Repke, 2010, A New Algorithm for Global Optimization: Molecular-Inspired Parallel Tempering, Computers and Chemical Engineering, 34, 12, 2072-2084

Jiří Jaromír Klemeš, Petar Sabev Varbanov and Peng Yen Liew (Editors)
Proceedings of the 24th European Symposium on Computer Aided Process Engineering – ESCAPE 24
June 15-18, 2014, Budapest, Hungary.

Modelling and Prediction of Renewable Energy Generation by Pressure Retarded Osmosis

Endre Nagy[a*], László Hajba[a], Zsolt Prettl[a]

[a]*University of Pannonia , Egyetem u. 10., Veszprém 8200, Hungary*
nagy@mukki.richem.hu

Abstract

A more general mass transport model of pressure retarded osmosis has been developed and will be presented in this lecture. Essential of this model is that it does not have any simplifications and/or neglects for description of the mass transport process. It takes into account the effect of the external boundary layers on both sides of the membrane, the dense and the sponge layers of an asymmetric membrane used, applying the diffusive-convective mass transport equation for every sub-layer except of the skin/dense layer of the membrane. A widely applied, “diffusive” transport equation was used for the dense layer, for the salt transport through it. Accordingly this model enables the user to calculate the membrane performance under all possible operating conditions. Thus, it can be used to optimize the operating conditions in order to get efficient energy generation unit. The energy density obtained by means of the presented and the literature model have been compared in the paper and showed the process performance under different conditions.

Keywords: energy generation, pressure retarded osmosis, mathematical description, diffusive-convective model.

1. Introduction

Osmotically-driven membrane processes, such as forward osmosis (FO) and pressure retarded osmosis (PRO) could be of strategic importance in application of several fields as electricity production (Chung et al., 2012), food production (Jiao et al., 2004), desalination (Achilli et al., 2009), in the coming decades. These processes operate on the principle of osmotic transport of water across a semi-permeable membrane from a low salinity feed solution (e.g. fresh water, river water) into a high salinity brine/draw solution (e.g. see water, brine water) (Kim and Elimelech, 2013). The draw solution side is pressurized to obtain power by depressurizing the portion of water permeated through the membrane from the low salinity solution in case of PRO process. The performance of both processes strongly depends on the internal concentration polarization (ICP) caused by the porous sponge layer of an asymmetric membrane and external polarization layers (ECP) building up in the fluid boundary layers on both sides of membrane. Several papers discuss roles of the polarization layers on the membrane performance. The exact prediction of the osmotic transmembrane pressure difference is also an important task in order to get the correct value of the water flux. McCutcheon and Elimelech (2006) have developed a model which takes into account the external mass transfer resistance on the higher concentration side of the membrane. Silvester et al. (2012) analyzed the effect of the cylindrical coordinate on the membrane performance. Recently, Kim and Elimelech (2013) published a diffusion-convection model. These models neglect both the effect of the salt permeability and the mass transfer resistance of fluid boundary layer on the permeate side. Accordingly this model is strictly valid when there is not salt transport, i.e. it is fully rejected by the membrane.

The aim of this work is to develop a new, more general mass transport model which can describe the transport process without any neglect or simplification, taking into account all mass transfer resistances of a PRO process, namely that of the external boundaries, the skin and the sponge layers of an asymmetric membrane independently of their effect on the process performance. Then the water transport rates and power densities of the literature and presented models will be compared to each other in order to demonstrate the superiority of the model equations developed.

2. Theory

The solute flow should be expressed for all sub-layer affecting the salt and thus, the water flux. These sub-layers are the skin- and the sponge layer of an asymmetric membrane used for energy generation as well as the external mass transfer resistances caused by the fluid polarization layer. The diffusive-convective mass flow equation is used for description of the mass transport. The differential mass balance equation and its solution is described in section 5 of Nagy (2011) in details. The only exception is the dense/skin layer where the widely accepted transport expression is used.

2.1. Mass transport through sub-layers

The mass transport in the four sub-layers, namely the concentration polarization layers on both sides of membrane, the dense layer and the sponge layer, assuming an asymmetric membrane, should be given in order to be able to predict the concentration distribution and the interface concentrations during FO or PRO processes. Thus, the simplified differential solute mass balance equation for the boundary layer can be given, in the case of PRO in dimensionless space coordinate ($Y = y/\delta$), as follows:

$$\frac{d^2C}{dY^2} = -\frac{\upsilon}{k}\frac{dC}{dY} \equiv -Pe\frac{dC}{dY} \tag{1}$$

Instead of the well-known Pe number ($Pe = v/k \equiv J_w/k$), the expression of J_w/k is used in this paper following the wide spreading practice in the literature. The value of k denotes the diffusive mass transfer coefficient in the boundary layer. The negative sign of the convective term expresses that the water flux is of reverse direction to that of the solute compound. Let us introduce the generally applied notation, namely, J_w ($J_w \equiv v$), for the convective water velocity, perpendicular to the membrane interface and directed to the bulk fluid phase. After solution of Eq. (1), one can get as (Nagy, 2011):

$$C = Ae^{-(J_w/k)Y} + B \tag{2}$$

where parameters of A and B are integration constants. Their values should be obtained by means of suitable boundary conditions as e.g.:

$$Y=0 \quad \text{then} \quad C=C_b \quad and \quad Y=1 \quad \text{then} \quad C=C_m \tag{3}$$

See Figure 1 for denotes and the concentration distribution. Determining the integration constants by means of the boundary conditions, the concentration distribution will be as:

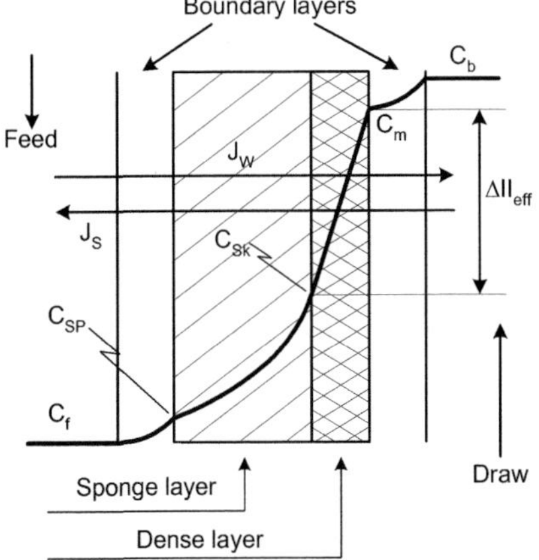

Figure 1. Schematic illustration of the mass transfer sub-layers, the concentration profiles and notation of pressure retarded osmosis

$$C = \frac{(C_m - C_b)e^{(J_w/k)}}{1-e^{(J_w/k)}} e^{-(J_w/k)y} + \frac{C_b - C_m e^{(J_w/k)}}{1-e^{(J_w/k)}} \tag{4}$$

Let us express the solute transfer rate, i.e. the sum of its diffusive and convective flows:

$$-J_s = \frac{D}{\delta}\frac{dC}{dy} - \upsilon C \tag{5}$$

According to the above definition, the salt flux has negative sign because the direction of salt flow is opposite to that of water flow. The salt mass transfer rate, through the boundary layer in direction of the membrane layer, can then be expressed, using Eqs. (4) and (5), as:

$$J_s = -\frac{J_w}{1-e^{(J_w/k)}}\left(C_b - C_m e^{(J_w/k_d)}\right) = \beta_d\left(C_b - C_m e^{(J_w/k_d)}\right) \tag{6}$$

The mass transfer rate for the boundary layer on the permeate side of the membrane:

$$J_s = -\frac{J_w}{1-e^{(J_w/k_f)}}\left(C_{sp} - C_f e^{(J_w/k_f)}\right) = \beta_f\left(C_{sp} - C_f e^{(J_w/k_f)}\right) \tag{7}$$

The mass transfer rate for the dense layer (Lee et al., 1981)

$$J_s = -B(C_m - C_{sk}) \tag{8}$$

The mass transfer rate for the sponge layer:

$$\mathrm{J_s} = -\frac{\mathrm{J_w}}{1-\mathrm{e}^{(\mathrm{J_w K})}}\left(\mathrm{C_{sk}} - \mathrm{C_{sp}e}^{(\mathrm{J_w K})}\right) = \beta_{\mathrm{sp}}\left(\mathrm{C_{sk}} - \mathrm{C_{sp}e}^{(\mathrm{J_w K})}\right) \tag{9}$$

2.2. Application resistance-in-series model for expression of the overall salt flux

The mass transfer rates have been defined for all sub-layers, namely for the two boundary layers [Eqs. (6) and (7)] and for the dense layer [Eq. (8)] as well as for the sponge layer [(Eq. (9)]. The overall mass transfer rate can be obtained by the equality of these expressions, as:

$$J_s = \beta_{ov}\left\{C_b - C_f^{\left(J_w\left[1/k_f + 1/k_d + K\right]\right)}\right\} \tag{10}$$

where

$$\frac{1}{\beta_{ov}} = \frac{1}{\beta_d} + \left(\frac{1}{\beta_{sp}} + \frac{e^{(J_w K)}}{\beta_f} - \frac{1}{B}\right) e^{(J_w / k_d)} \tag{11}$$

Values of β_d, β_{sp} and β_f are defined in Eqs. (6), (7) and (9), respectively. The salt transfer rate can simply be calculated if one knows the parameters involved in this equation. But an unknown value is also involved in the above expression, namely the water flux, J_w. Its value should be predicted in order to be able to calculate the overall solute transfer rate. Let us look at in the following section how the water transfer rate can be obtained.

2.3. Water flux with IPC and ECP

There are several opportunities for expression the internal concentrations, namely C_m/C_b and C_{sk}/C_b, applying the transfer rates given by Eqs. (6-9). Looking the more simple method, the C_m value can be obtained by means of Eq. (6) and (10). Applying the equality of this two salt transfer rates, the value of C_m can be obtained as:

$$\frac{C_m}{C_b} = \left\{1 - \frac{\beta_{ov}\left(1 - e^{J_w/k_d}\right)}{J_w e^{J_w/k_d}}\left(1 - \frac{C_f}{C_b} e^{J_w\left(K + 1/k_d + 1/k_f\right)}\right)\right\} e^{\left(-J_w/k_d\right)} \tag{12}$$

The overall mass transfer coefficient, β_{ov}, is given by Eq. (11). Similarly, the value of C_{sk} should be determined by means of the overall and the partial mass transfer rates. Thus, expressing the partial mass transfer rate by means of Eqs. (6) and (8) and taking into account its equality to the overall one [Eq. (10)], the value of C_{sk} will be as:

$$\frac{C_{sk}}{C_b} = \left\{1 - \frac{\beta_{ov}}{\beta^*}\left(1 - \frac{C_f}{C_b} e^{J_w\left(1/k_d + 1/k_f + K\right)}\right)\right\} e^{-J_w/k_d} \tag{13}$$

where β^* is a partial mass transfer coefficient as:

$$\frac{1}{\beta^*} = \frac{1 - e^{J_w/k_d}}{J_w} - \frac{e^{J_w/k_d}}{B} \tag{14}$$

For example introducing the widely applied approach, namely $(C_m - C_{sk})/C_b = (\pi_m - \pi_{sk})/\pi_b$, one can we get the following approach of the water flux:

$$J_w = A\left[\pi_b\left(\frac{C_m}{C_b} - \frac{C_{sk}}{C_b}\right) - \Delta P\right] \tag{15}$$

The water flux can be determined by means of Eq. (14) by iteration method, taking into account the values of C_m and C_{sk} obtained by means of Eqs. (12) and (13). The widely used model of McCutcheon and Elimelech (2006), taken into account the EPC in the draw solution, is as:

$$J_w = A\left(\pi_b e^{(-J_w/k_d)} - \pi_f e^{J_w K}\right) - A\Delta P \tag{16}$$

3. Results and discussion

The model developed takes into account the effect of every single sub-layer on the transport of compounds accordingly it serves the interface concentrations under all mass transfer conditions. It can apply under all mass transport conditions independently of the parameter values, as water permeability coefficient A, salt permeability coefficient, B, mass resistivity coefficient, K, mass transfer coefficients, k_d, k_f, fluid concentrations, C_f, C_b, hydraulic pressure difference, ΔP (see Figure 1). In order to get the optimum operating parameters, the effect of every parameter should be taken into account. In this paper two typical figures will be shown to illustrate the effect of the membrane properties. The effect of important membrane parameters are illustrated in Figure 2. The average water permeability coefficient of the industrial osmosis membranes is ranged about 2-5 x 10^{-7} m/s atm. This figure illustrates the water flux strongly depends on both the A value and the B resistivity coefficient. The external mass transfer coefficients are rather high, thus they have lesser extent of the process. If one can decrease the value of K than the water flux can essentially be increased. Figure 3 illustrates the change of energy density. Difference between them is more than 20 %. The model results are excellently agreed with the measured ones (not shown here). The model enable the user to predict at which parameter values can be maximized the membrane performance. To reach it the C_{sk} value should be zero.

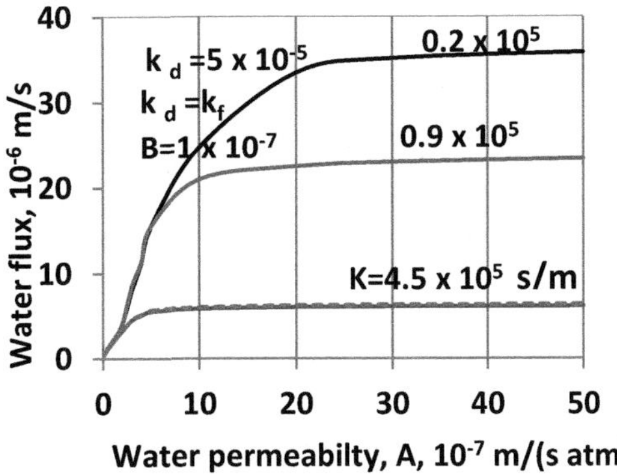

Figure 2. Water flux vs. water permeability coefficient at different mass transfer resistivity of the sponge layer (C_f=2.5; g/L, π_f=2.1 atm; C_b=58.5 g/L; π_b=49.2 atm; k_d=k_f=5 x 10^{-5} m/s; B=1 x 10^{-7} m/s)

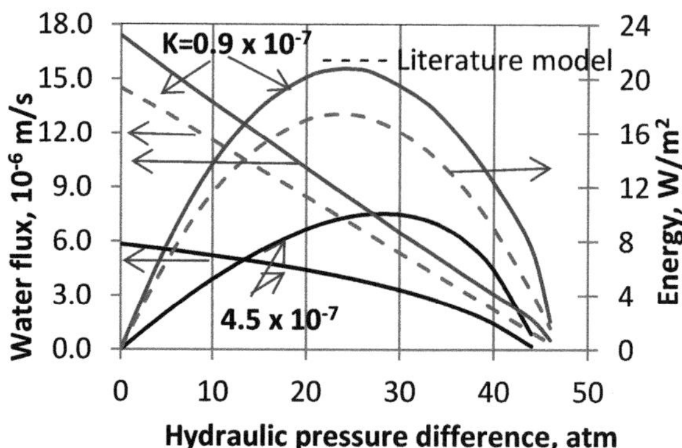

Figure 3. Energy density as a function of ΔP (parameter values as in Figure 2)

4. Conclusions

A general and exact model has been developed which enables the user to predict the process performance under all operating and mass transport conditions. This model takes into account the mass transfer resistance of all mass transport layers, namely the external ones on both sides of membrane, the dense and the sponge membrane layers. Thus, it makes possible to predict the membrane performance under any operating transport conditions. The energy generation may firstly be improved by decreasing the resistance of the sponge layer and increasing the value of water permeability coefficient. On the other hand, the salt rejection of the dense layer should be as high as possible. It can easily be predicted the optimum operating conditions by the model presented.

Acknowledgement

The National Development Agency grant TÁMOP-4.2.2/A-11/1/KONV-2012-0072 and the IRSES ZSE Project of FP7 (Contract No.: PIRSES-GA-2011-294987) greatly acknowledged for the financial support.

References

A. Achilli, T.Y. Cath, A.E. Childress, 2009, Power generation with pressure retarded osmosis: An experimental and theoretical investigation, J. Membr. Sci., 343,42-52.

B. Jiao, A. Cassano, E. Drioli, 2004, Recent advances on membrane processes for the concentration of fruit juices: a review, J. Food Eng., 63, 201-206.

T.S. Chung, X. Li, R.C. Ong, Q. Ge, H. Wang, G. Han, 2012. Emerging forward osmosis technologies and challenges ahead for clean water and clean energy, Current Opinion in Chem. Eng. 1, 246-257.

J.R. McCutcheon, M. Elimelech, 2006, Influence of concentrative and dilutive internal concentration polarization on flux behavior in forward osmosis, J. Membr. Sci., 197,237-247.

Y. C. Kim, M. Elimelech, 2013, Potential of osmotic power generation by pressure retarded osmosis using seawater as feed solution: Analysis and experiments, J. Membr. Sci., 429, 330-337.

E. Nagy, 2012, Basic equation of mass transport through a membrane layer, Elsevier, Amsterdam, The Nederlands.

E. Sivertsen, T. Holt, W. Thelin, G. Brekke, 2012. Modelling mass transport in hollow fibre membrane used for pressure retarded osmosis, J. Membr. Sci., 417-418, 69-79.

Jiří Jaromír Klemeš, Petar Sabev Varbanov and Peng Yen Liew (Editors)
Proceedings of the 24th European Symposium on Computer Aided Process Engineering – ESCAPE 24
June 15-18, 2014, Budapest, Hungary.

Process for Synthesis of Biodiesel from Used Cooking Oil: Feasibility and Experimental Studies

Raj Patel[a*], Karen Dawson[a,b], Richard Butterfield[a], Amir Khan[a], Bilal Ahada[a], Harvey Arellano-Garcia[a]

[a]*School of Engineering, University of Bradford, West Yorkshire, UK*
[b]*Clarkson University, Potsdam, NY, USA*
R.Patel@Bradford.ac.uk

Abstract

Biodiesel has turned out to be an integral part of the discussion of renewable energy sources and has diverse advantages in terms of its flexibility and applicability. Considering the characteristics of the transesterification reaction, a laboratory-scale system has been developed in this work. Waste Vegetable Oil (WVO), mainly sunflower oil, from local sources has been used and the transesterification carried out using methanol in the presence of sodium hydroxide catalyst. Characterisation of the biodiesel produced has been carried out using a number of different techniques including rheology, calorimetry, and gas liquid chromatography. The main factors affecting the % yield of biodiesel are temperature, catalyst, and alcohol to triglyceride ratio. Thus, experimental work has been carried out so as to study the rate and yield of the reaction as a function of those factors. A model has also been developed to validate the experimental data and this should help in increasing the efficiency of these processes and reducing the energy input. Moreover, the novel use of ultrasound as a method of measuring progression of the reaction is correlated with in-situ pH monitoring of the reaction process.

Keywords: Biodiesel, Ultrasound, Transesterification

1. Introduction

With the current global drive to reduce the reliance on fossil fuels, in particular that used as automotive fuel; the search for alternate and renewable sources of fuel is now more prevalent than ever. One of the most commonly cited and researched being biodiesel; a liquid fuel derived from virgin vegetable oils or waste frying oils that have undergone a transesterification reaction with an alcohol, typically methanol, in the presence of a sodium or potassium hydroxide catalyst as reported by the works of Pelly (2003), Demirbas (2005), Ferdous et al. (2012). There is a plethora of oils that have the ability to be used in the manufacturing. A non-inclusive list is shown below Marchetti et al. (2005) and Ma and Hanna (1999) e.g. Babassu, Coconut, Corn, Cottonseed, Crambe, Lard, Palm oil, Palm, Peanut, Rapeseed, Soybean, Sunflower, Tallow, Canola oil. Each of the oil is differentiated by the amount and location of double bonds on the triglyceride. There are seven major types of fatty acids – lauric, myristic, palmitic, stearic, oleic, linoleic, and linolenic Marchetti et al. (2005). The properties of the fatty acids affect the properties of the finalized product—biodiesel.

Reaction kinetics have been extensively studied and the rate constants determined for various oils The kinetics for Soyabean oil was reported in the works of Noureddini and

Zhu (1997), Feedman et al. (1986), and Mahajan et al. (2006). The kinetics for Palm oil was reported by Darnoko and Cheryan (2000), and the kinetics for Sesame oil was reported by Ferdous et al. (2012). A study by Benavides and Diweka (2012a) and continued in Benavides and Diweka (2012b) describes a batch reactor model for the optimal control of the production of biodiesel within a batch reactor, using deterministic and then stochastic control and based upon the reaction kinetics determined by Noureddini and Zhu (1997). This study is developed further by Benavides and Diweka (2013) in an effort to accommodate the possible variability in available feedstock and optimise biodiesel production using various performance indices. There is however, little experimental data in the literature.

Moreover, there are many ways to characterize the final biodiesel product such as viscosity, cold flow (i.e. cloud point, pour point, freezing point), density, acid number, lubricity and discussed extensively by Knothe (2005), Demirbas (2005), Demirbas (2003), Singh and Padhi (2009), Akers et al. (2006), Mahajan et al. (2006a), US DOE (2005). These characterization methods are typically offline measurements that cannot be performed in-situ and therefore give little indication about the reactive process. A recent study by Clark et al. (2013) demonstrated that pH could be used to monitor the progress of the transesterification reaction in-situ and provide real time monitoring of biodiesel production in pure canola oil. The study suggested that the measured pH change is related to the dilution of OH- ions as the oil is converted to products, and not from the depletion of OH- ions due to the reaction. As the reaction proceeds there is a noticeable change in viscosity of the biodiesel compared to the starting vegetable oil. Ultrasound measurements can thus be used to monitor such changes, as the ultrasound wave will pass through the lower viscosity biodiesel much faster than in the higher viscosity untreated oil. Such measurements have only been made offline with WVO and the biodiesel and the results are promising. If the ultrasound measurements could be correlated to other in situ measurements of conversion, such as pH, this would provide a novel and none invasive technique to monitor progress of the transesterification reaction.

This work shows that pH has been used to continuously monitor the progression of the reaction in pure and waste vegetable oil in situ. The pH measurements are correlated with reaction conversion and fitted to a kinetic model using the gPROMs software. Ultrasound measurements, also taken continuously in-situ are correlated with the pH measurements and hence the reaction conversion.

2. Methods

2.1. Reaction Kinetics & Modelling

Biodiesel can be produced using a transesterification process whereby a triglyceride (vegetable oil) is reacted with either methanol or ethanol. The reaction also uses a base catalyst usually sodium hydroxide or potassium hydroxide to aid the reaction process. The process involves reacting triglyceride with methanol to produce methyl ester (Biodiesel) and a by-product, glycerol. In the study by Noureddini and Zhu, (1997) the reaction is considered to consist of three stepwise and reversible reactions, where triglycerides (TG) are converted to diglycerides (DG), digylcerides to monoglycerides (MG), and monoglycerides into glycerol, as presented in Eqs. (1)-(4)

$$\mathbf{TG + CH_3OH \overset{k1,k2}{\Longleftrightarrow} DG + R_1COOCH_3} \tag{1}$$

$$DG + CH_3OH \overset{k3,k4}{\Longleftrightarrow} MG + R_2COOCH_3 \tag{2}$$

$$MG + CH_3OH \overset{k5,k6}{\Longleftrightarrow} GL + R_3COOCH_3 \tag{3}$$

The overall reaction is denoted as:

$$TG + 3CH_3OH \leftrightarrow GL + 3RCOOCH_3 \tag{4}$$

The mathematical model for the biodiesel production in a batch reactor is governed by the following Ordinary Differential Equations, Eqs. (5)-(7), which have been derived from the mass balance of a batch reactor and first presented by Noureddini and Zhu, (1997).

$$\frac{dC_{TG}}{dt} = -k_1 C_{TG} C_A + k_2 C_{DG} C_E \tag{5}$$

$$\frac{dC_{DG}}{dt} = -k_1 C_{TG} C_A + k_2 C_{DG} C_E - k_3 C_{DG} C_A + k_4 C_{MG} C_E \tag{6}$$

$$\frac{dC_{MG}}{dt} = k_3 C_{DG} C_A + k_4 C_{MG} C_E - k_5 C_{MG} C_A + k_6 C_{GE} C_E \tag{7}$$

$$\frac{dC_E}{dt} = k_1 C_{TG} C_A - k_2 C_{DG} C_E + k_3 C_{DG} C_A - k_4 C_{MG} C_E + k_5 C_{MG} C_A - k_6 C_{GL} C_E \tag{8}$$

$$\frac{dC_A}{dt} = -\frac{dC_E}{dt} \tag{9}$$

$$\frac{dC_{GL}}{dt} = k_5 C_{MG} C_A - k_6 C_{GL} C_E \tag{10}$$

Where C_{TG}, C_{DG}, C_{MG}, C_E, C_A, C_{GL}, are concentrations of triglycerides, digylcerides, mono glycerides, methyl ester, methanol and glycerol, respectively. The reaction rate constants, k_i, can be expressed by the Arrhenius equation and the constants are presented by Noureddini and Zhu, (1997). The above ODEs will be used to model our system using the gPROMS software, which is appropriate for this type of modelling. The change in concentration of the various components, during the reaction, will be calculated from data obtained via the pH and ultrasound measurements techniques.

2.2. Experimental equipment

Methanol, Isopropyl alcohol, Potassium Hydroxide (KOH), Sodium Hydroxide (NaOH), distilled water, food grade vegetable oil, and waste vegetable oil (WVO) are being used in this conversion process. A Pyrex 2 L jacketed reactor is used with an overhead stirrer to ensure good mixing. Constant temperature is maintained using a Grant GD120 circulating water bath which pumps the water through the reactor jacket. A DrDAQ data logger connected via USB to a PC is used to monitor and record the process temperature and the pH of the mixture. Ultrasound probes (multicomp - transceivers , centre frequency 200 kHz, 19mm in diameter, directivity ± 7 degree, distance of detection 0.1 m to 2 m, operating temperature range -20 to +80 °C) are used to measure the time taken for the sound waves to travel through the reaction mixture and hence their velocities. Figure 1 shows a schematic diagram of the set-up used. At present the ultrasound probes are placed inside the reactor vessel. As the reaction proceeds, the viscosity of the mixture decreases and the ultrasound wave velocity is expected to increase. This change in velocity of the ultrasound waves can be used to determine the concentration of the reactants and the products. Later on, the probes will be placed on the outside of the vessel making it a non-intrusive measurement technique. The effect of the vessel wall will be a constant factor and can thus be accounted for.

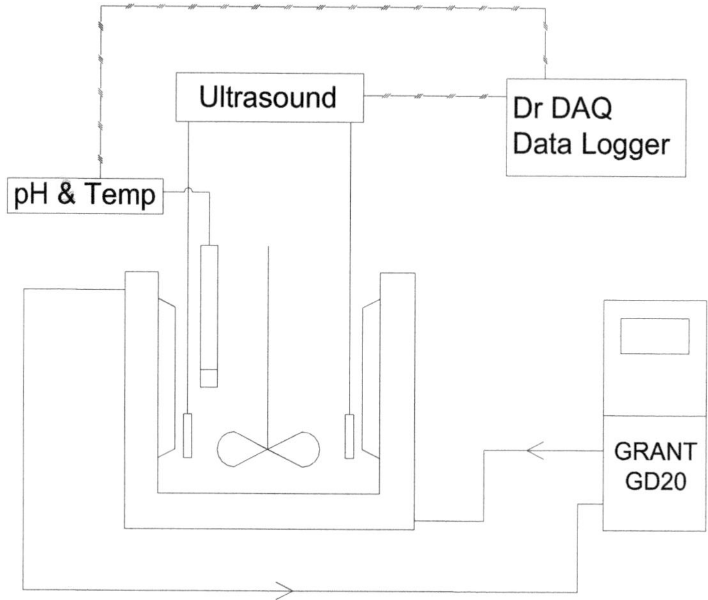

Figure 1: Diagram of the experimental set-up

2.3. Reaction conditions

A sample from each vegetable oil used undergoes a titration as described by Pelly, (2003) to determine the required amount of Potassium Hydroxide (or Sodium Hydroxide) to be used. The amount of methanol used is 20 % by mass of the vegetable oil undergoing reaction, as described by Pelly, (2003). The transesterification of the oil is conducted under the following conditions: 800 rpm stirring, atmospheric pressure and at three different temperatures of 25 °C, 35 °C and 45 °C. The WVO and alcohol are mixed in stoichiometric proportions and are thermally conditioned at the reaction temperature before being charged into the reactor.

2.4. Experimental procedure

Half of the methanol required for the reaction is mixed with the oil. This was to establish small droplets of methanol dispersed within the oil to increase the contact surface area and hence rate of reaction. The required KOH is then dissolved within the remainder of the methanol. The reaction is initiated by adding the mixture to the 2 L reactor and the pH recorded over time for at least 60 minutes. The time taken for the ultrasound waves to travel between the transmitter and receiver is also measured and at 1 Hz frequency. The glycering is separated from the oil by decanting and the oil washed with water. The water-oil mixture is then allowed to settle to form two layers. These are then separated to give the final biodiesel product. Characterisation of the biodiesel, although not a topic for discussion here, is also carried out to measure properties such as rheology and calorific value. Between each run, the reactor is cleaned thoroughly with acetone and allowed to dry.

3. Results & Discussion

Initial ultrasound measurements with the WVO and Biodiesel have shown propagation velocities of 1,606 m/s and 1,873 m/s respectively showing a substantial difference between the two. These are the two extremes and measurements of pH and ultrasound velocities during the reaction will be measured to calibrate fully the latter technique. This will provide a non-intrusive technique for monitoring the change in concentration of the components in the system as a function of the operating parameters i.e temperature, type of catalyst and the mole ratio of the reactants. The efficiencies of the reaction process can then be evaluated in terms of the reaction rate and the yield.

4. Conclusion

In this ongoing study, initial measurements of biodiesel concentration using ultrasound have been made and there is a clear difference in the propagation velocities as the viscosity of the oil decreases. A detailed study of ultrasound and pH measurements during the reaction will enable us to monitor the concentrations and hence the rate of the reactions. Data on reaction rates make it possible to calculate the efficiency of the process as a function of operating parameters. Modelling of the reaction process is conducted to corroborate experimental data and enable scale up studies to be carried out. Finally, the use of ultrasound to measure reaction rates is a novel technique and to our knowledge has not been reported elsewhere.

References

S.M. Akers, J.L. Conkle, S.N. Thomas, K.B. Rider, 2006, Determination of the Heat of Combustion of Biodiesel Using Bomb Calorimetry, Journal of Chemical Education, 83, 2, 260-263.

P.T. Benavides, U. Diwekar, 2012a, Optimal control of biodiesel production in a batch reactor, Part I: Deterministic control. Fuel, 94, 211-217.

P.T. Benavides, U. Diwekar, 2012b, Optimal control of biodiesel production in a batch reactor, Part II: Stochastic control. Fuel, 94, 218-226.

P.T. Benavides, U. Diwekar, 2013, Studying various optimal problems in biodiesel production in a batch reactor under uncertainty. Fuel, 103, 585-592.

W.M. Clark, N.J. Medeiros, D.J. Boyd, J.R. Snell, 2013, Biodiesel transesterification kinetics monitored by pH measurement, Bioresource Technology, 136, 771-774.

D. Darnoko, M. Cheryan, 2000, Kinetics of Palm Oil Transesterification in a Batch Reactor, Journal of American Oil Chemist Society, 77, 12, 1263-1267.

A. Demirbas, 2003, Biodiesel Fuels from Vegetable Oils via Catalytic and Non-Catalytic Supercritical Alcohol Transesterifications and Other Methods: A Survey, Energy Conversion and Management, 44, 2093-2109.

A. Demirbas, 2005, Biodiesel Production from Vegetable Oils via Catalytic and Non-Catalytic Supercritical Methanol Transesterification Methods, Progress in Energy and Combustion Science, 31, 466-487.

K. Ferdous, M.R. Uddin, M.R. Khan, M.A. Islam, 2012, Biodiesel from Sesame Oil: Base Catalyzed Transesterification, International Journal of Engineering and Technology, 1, 4, 420-431.

B. Freedman, , R.O. Butterfield, E.H. Pryde, 1986, Transesterification Kinetics of Soybean Oil, Journal of the American Oil Chemists' Society, 63, 10, 1375-1380.

G. Knothe, 2005, Dependence of Biodiesel Fuel Properties on the Structure of Fatty Acid Alkyl Esters. Fuel Processing Technology, 86, 1059-1070.

F. Ma, M.A. Hanna, 1999, Biodiesel Production: A Review, Bioresource Technology, 70, 1-15.

S. Mahajan, S.K. Konar, D.G.B. Boocock, 2006a, Determining the Acid Number of Biodiesel. Journal of the American Oil Chemists' Society, 83, 6, 567-570.

S. Mahajan, S.K. Konar, D.G.B. Boocock, 2006b, Standard Biodiesel from Soybean Oil by a Single Chemical Reaction, Journal of the American Oil Chemists' Society, 83, 7, 641-644.

J.M. Marchetti, V.U. Miguel, A.F. Errazu, 2005, Possible Methods for Biodiesel Production, Renewable and Sustainable Energy Reviews, 11, 1300-1311.

H. Noureddini, D. Zhu, 1997, Kinetic of Transesterification of Soybean Oil, Journal of American Oil Chemistry Society, 74, 11, 1457-1463

M. Pelly, 2003, Biodiesel From Used Kitchen Grease or Waste Vegetable Oil, <www.journeytoforever.org/biodiesel_mike.html>, accessed on 15/03/2014.

R.K. Singh, S.K. Padhi, 2009, Characterization of jatropha oil for the preparation of biodiesel. Natural product radiance, 8, 2, 127-132.

U.S Department of Energy, 2005, Characterization of biodiesel oxidation and oxidation products, CRC Project No. AVFL-2b.

Jiří Jaromír Klemeš, Petar Sabev Varbanov and Peng Yen Liew (Editors)
Proceedings of the 24th European Symposium on Computer Aided Process Engineering – ESCAPE 24
June 15-18, 2014, Budapest, Hungary.

Simulation and Optimization of Biofilm Activated Sludge Process for the Biological Treatment of Effluents from Cellulose and Viscose Industry

Marta Revilla, Javier Viguri, Berta Galán*

University of Cantabria, Department of Chemistry and Process and Resources Engineering, Avda. Los Castros s/n. 39005, Santander, (Spain)
berta.galan@unican.es

Abstract

The BAS (Biofilm Activated Sludge) process is comprised of MBBR (Moving Bed Biofilm Reactor) pre-treatment followed by conventional AS (activated sludge) which presents several advantages in comparison with conventional wastewaters technologies. In this study the BAS process is used for the treatment of wastewaters coming from a viscose and cellulose industry. Initially, the process is simulated using a wastewater process simulator BioWin under the three different scenarios and the experimental results are compared with the simulated results. Later on, the optimization of the process is carried out by the minimization of the operation cost since the nutrient dosage of N and P can be reduced until the COD percentage removal is affected. Finally, the introduction of urban waters together with the industrial wastewaters is studied to minimize the costs of the addition of chemicals nutrients.

Keywords: BAS, biofilm, activated sludge, MBBR, urban wastewaters.

1. Introduction

The AS process is one of the most commonly used systems for biological treatment of pulp and paper industry effluents. The effluent to be treated is fed to one or more aeration basins, in which bacteria and other microorganisms, the activated sludge, are used to convert organic matter of the influent (inlet stream) into carbon dioxide, water and new microbial biomass. The mixture of treated effluent (outlet stream) and activated sludge goes to a clarifier, in which the sludge is separated from the effluent by settling (Welander, 2002). The main disadvantage of the AS process is the low settling of the sludge called "bulking" (Kocerba, 2013) produced by nutrient deficiency or when in the biological reactors there is not enough biodegradable organic matter; as a consequence the F/M (food/microorganism) is low leading to growth of filamentous bacteria and overproduction of extracellular polymers (EPS) (Rankin et al., 2007). To solve this problem the pre-treatment of high organic load (Abdul et al., 2012) with biofilm formation systems (Kaindl, 2010) is an alternative to control the phenomenon of "bulking".

The BAS (Biofilm Activated Sludge) process is comprised of MBBR (Moving Bed Biofilm Reactor) pre-treatment followed by conventional AS (activated sludge) which presents several advantages in comparison with conventional AS process. The wastewater from the pulp industry and viscose is deficient in nutrients required for optimal growth of microorganisms. Recent research has shown that BAS process under nutrient deficiency is very efficient for the pulp and paper industry (Welander, 2002) to improve the characteristics of settling sludge, significantly reduce sludge production and nutrient dosage lowering the cost of operation (Zalakain and Manterola, 2011). BAS process requires a minimum quantity of N and P nutrients, therefore the dosage of them is necessary. UW (urban waters), containing high amount of N and P, can be also treated by the MBBR reactors called HYBAS process (Zalakain et al., 2008). The mixing of urban and industrial viscose and cellulose wastewaters is considered in this work to reduce the costs of the addition of chemicals nutrients.

2. The wastewater treatment plant for the pulp and viscose industry

The WWTP (wastewater treatment plant) for a pulp and viscose industry was designed in two phases (Figure 1). The phase I consists two MBBR reactors in series followed by a clarification stage. This phase I (scenario I) treats pulp and viscose wastewaters and runs for nine months continuously and requires with high dosage of nutrients to get high COD removal efficiency. Later, at phase II, activated sludge reactor (AS) was added resulting in the BAS process. In phase II, recirculation sludge from the clarifier to the activated sludge reactor is necessary to maintain a constant concentration of microorganisms in the reactor. In both phases, there is a purge of sludge from the system. The phase II operation runs for nine months: first five months with pulp and viscose wastewaters (scenario II) and the last four months pulp wastewaters (scenario III). Phase II requires lower nutrients dosage than Phase I (Paice, 2008). The characteristics of the biological reactors are described in the Table 1. Influent wastewater was characterized by TSS (total suspended solids), COD (chemical oxygen demand) and flow rate. Table 2 shows the characterization of the influent in each proposed scenario. These data are expressed using a reference value, QR (reference flow), TSSR (reference suspended solids) and CODR (chemical oxygen demand reference). The second part of this works includes the treatment of urban wastewater together with the industrial wastewaters. The WWTP was designed for a maximum flow of 1.57·QR, therefore the maximum flow permitted of the UW is 0.51·QR in the scenario II and 1.06·QR in the scenario III.

The main characterization of common urban water is 430 mg/L of COD, 25 mg/L of N-NH_4^+ and 7 mg/L of P (Tchobanoglous et al. 1995).

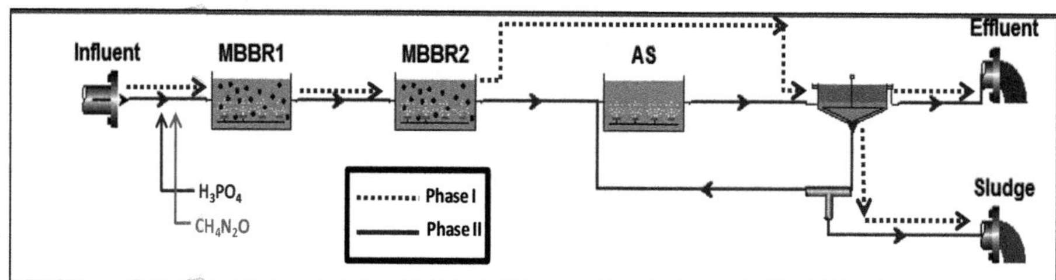

Figure 1. Flowsheet of the wastewater plant of a pulp and viscose industry.

Table 1. Characteristics of the biological reactor.

Operation conditions	MBBR $_{1\ and\ 2}$	AS
Filling percentage of carriers	10 %	-
Specific area (carrier)	900 m^2/m^3	-
Thickness (carrier)	3 mm	-
Volume (reactor)	5,331 m^3	47,000 m^3
Dissolved oxygen (reactor)	2-3 mg/L	2-3 mg/L

Table 2. Characterizacion of the influent in each proposed scenario.

	Flow(m^3/d)	TSS(mg/L)	COD(mg/L)
Scenario I	1.07·QR	1.55·TSSR	5.83·CODR
Scenario II	1.06·QR	1.00·TSSR	5.21·CODR
Scenario III	0.51·QR	0.61·TSSR	5.37·CODR

Table 3. Kinetic and stoichiometric parameters introduced in the BioWin.

$MBBR_{1\ and\ 2}$	AS	Parameter description
Y=0.5 mg/mg	Y=0.5 mg/mg	Y, true growth yield.
Ks= 10 mg/L	Ks= 5 mg/L	Ks, half-velocity constant.
Kd= 0.1 d^{-1}	Kd= 0.68 d^{-1}	Kd, specific decay rate.
Umax=5 d^{-1}	Umax= 3 d^{-1}	Umax, maximum specific growth rate.
Df =0.8 cm^2/d	-	Df, molecular diffusion of substrate in biofilm.

The simulations of the wastewaters plant were accomplished with a specific software for wastewater treatment called BioWin. This software uses the ASM2d mathematical model from the International Association on Water Quality to describe the biological processes in the reactors and substrate diffusion model through the layers of the biofilm. It is necessary to introduce the characteristics of the inlet stream and the kinetic and stoichiometric parameters of the model. In this study, the parameters from Rittmann and McCarty (1980a; 1980b) were considered (Table 3).

3. Results

3.1. Simulation results

Initially, the characteristics of the outlet stream were compared in Figure 2. Figure 2a shows the characteristics of the effluent for scenario I, II and III obtained by simulation and the real experimental data. In relation with the COD of the outlet stream an average deviation of 5.3 %, 3.2 % and 0.9 % is obtained for a period of 9 months in the scenario I, for a period of 5 months in the scenario II and for a period of 4 months in the scenario III respectively. Taking into account the low values of the average deviation it is confirmed that the parameters and the model used are valid for representing the cellulose and/or viscose wastewater treatment plant.

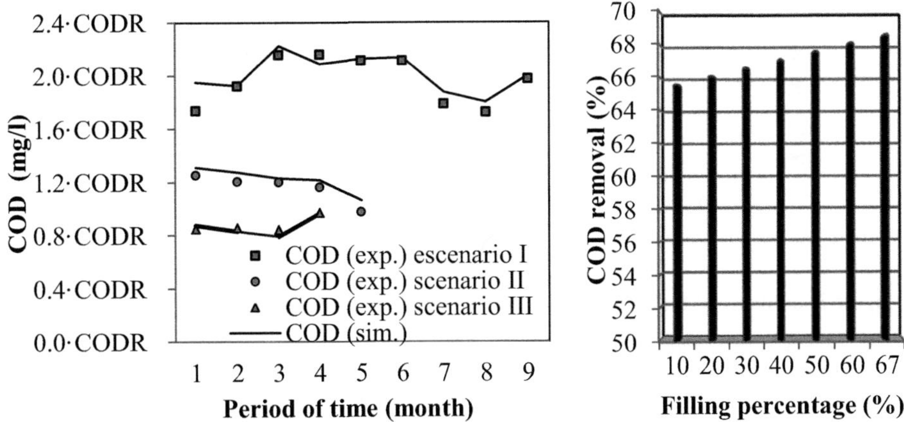

Figure 2. Simulations of the WWTP. (a) Experimental and simulated values of COD in the effluent.

Later, the influence of the percentage of carriers filling rates and specific surfaces for the same type of influent is simulated. It is observed in Figure 2b that increasing the percentage of carriers filling from 10 % to 67 % (Qiqi et al., 2012) increases the COD removal percentage by 3.5 %. Besides, by simulation it is observed that increasing the surface area of the carrier from 900 m^2/m^3 to 1,200 m^2/m^3 increases the COD removal percentage by 4 %.

3.2. Optimization of the process

The second part of this study is the optimization of the wastewater plant based on the simulation results. The objective function is the minimization of the operation costs of the plant (Hegazy et al., 2013). The operating costs include the energy consumption, the sludge treatment cost and the chemicals consumption cost. Roughly, the energy consumed is basically the energy required by the biological reactors aerators to maintain aerobic conditions, in the scenario II representing 22 % of the total cost of operation and 35 % in the scenario III. The treatment of excess sludge generated in plant is a 3 % in the scenario II and 2 % in the scenario III. Chemical consumption comprises the use of sodium hydroxide to increase the pH of the influent, antifoam to prevent foam in biological reactors, phosphoric acid and urea as nutrients and finally flocculants for dewatering sludge. The consumption of chemicals in the scenario II represents 75 % of the total costs and 62 % in the scenario III. The dosage sodium hydroxide, antifoam and the flocculants are fixed by the inlet wastewater conditions. However, the dosage of nutrients is studied to minimize the cost of the process without affecting the percentage removal of COD.

Firstly, the influence of reduction of nutrients (N and P) in the percentage of removed COD is analyzed at Figure 3. It is observed that low nutrient reduction does not decrease the percentage of removed COD, however when dosage of nutrients is reduced 17 % or higher in the scenario II, the COD removal decreases deeply. For scenario III, 21 % of nutrient dosage can be reduced maintaining the rate constant COD removal.

As a result of the reduction of nutrients, the operating costs due to the reduction of nutrient dosage decreases 2.5 %-1.6 % for scenario II and III respectively.

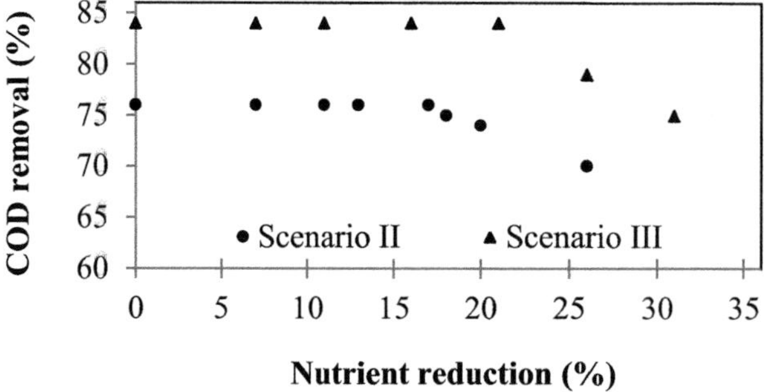

Figure 3. Influence of the reduction of nutrients on the COD removal.

Table 4. Characterizacion of the influent fixed by the mixture of urban waters and industrials.

	Flow (m^3/d)	COD (mg/L)	N (mg/L)	P (mg/L)
Sc II + UW	1.06·QR+0.51·QR(UW)	3.84·CODR	0.875·NR	0.6·PR
Sc III + UW	0.51·QR+1.06·QR(UW)	2.42·CODR	1.750·NR	1.4·PR

Secondly, the treatment of the urban waters is considered together with the industrial wastewaters in the WWTP since the urban wastewaters contains the nutrients that are necessary to incorporate in the industrial wastewater. The characterization of the inlet stream when the maximum flow rate of UW is considered is presented in Table 4. The presence of the nutrients (N and P) coming from the urban wastewaters is also presented.

The results obtained for both scenarios II and III shows that if the maximum flow of UW is treated, the amount of P in the outlet stream exceeds legal limits of P for the disposal of wastewaters at public fields (91/271/CEE). Therefore, a new restriction related to the maximum concentration of P in the outlet stream is added. The results with this new restriction are shown in Figure 4. It is observed in the scenario II that a flow rate of 0.39·QR of UW is required to get a COD removal percentage of 75 %. However, higher flow rate of UW are not possible since the concentration of P in the outlet stream would be higher than the legislation limits. At this optimal flow rate the inlet concentration of N (0.64·NR) form the urban waters is low and extra-urea must be dosaged. Figure 4b shows the quantity of urea that must be added to obtain 75 % efficiency of COD removal.

In the scenario III (Figure 4a), flow rate of 0.16·QR is the optimal UW flow rate since the concentration of P in the outlet stream satisfies the European legislation and obtains a removal efficiency COD of 83.7 %. As in the scenario II, in the scenario III the concentration of N from the UW, is not sufficient to achieve maximum COD removal efficiency and therefore urea has to be dosed. Figure 4b shows the quantity of urea that must to be added: 0.84·NR. For both scenarios, the optimal urban flow rate incorporated with the industrial wastewater is around 25 % of the total inlet flow rate.

The decrease in operating costs associated to the reduction of nutrient dosage is finally obtained: in the scenario II the reduction of cost is 12.3 % and in the scenario III is 5.5 % compared to the optimal conditions in scenario II and III without UW respectively. Further reductions of WWTP cost can be obtained if it is considered that the flow rate of UW may represent income for the industry. These considerations will be investigated in the near future works.

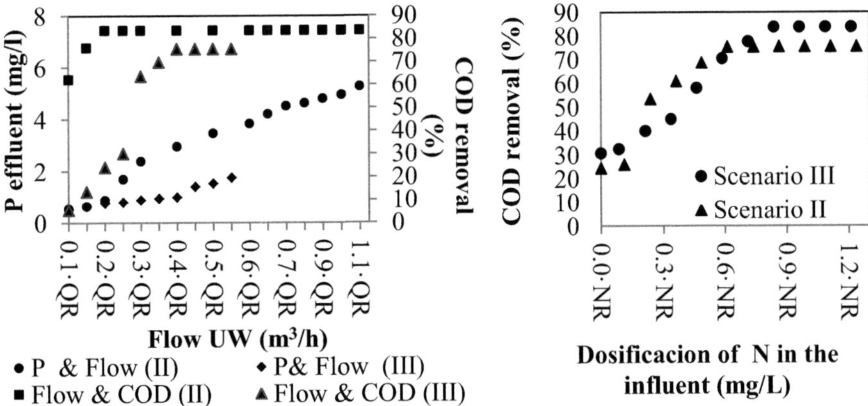

Figure 4. Simulations in the scenario II and III. (a) Influence of UW flow rate over the P concentration in the effluent and over the COD removal efficiency of the process. (b) Influence of the quantity of N added in the influent over the COD removal efficiency of the process.

4. Conclusions

The paper presents the optimization of a wastewater real plant for the treatment of viscose and pulp industry wastewaters by using BioWin software. First of all, the simulation of the process is analysed and the experimental results are compared with the simulated results. It is observed that the difference between the simulated and the experimental results of COD removal percentage is less than 8 %. Secondly, the optimization of the operation cost of the process is carried out by means of the nutrients dosage reductions. It is observed that the nutrient dosage can be reduced among 17 %-21 % in comparison to the dose of nutrients in industrial installation and the operating costs of the WWTP decrease around 2.5 %-1.6 %. In addition, the introduction of urban waters together with the industrial wastewater is optimized using the minimization of the costs as the objective function: in the scenario II the reduction of cost is 12.3 % and in the scenario III is 5.5 % compared to the optimal conditions in scenario II and III without UW respectively.

References

M. A. Abdul, H. Hmeed, M. Inam, F. Abtan, H. Irzooqi, 2012, Wastewater Treatment in Baghdad City Using Moving Bed Biofilm Reactor (MBBR) Technology, Engineering and Technology Journal, 30, 9, 1550-1561.

Directiva del consejo de 21 de Mayo de 1991 sobre el tratamiento de las aguas residuales urbanas. (91/271/CEE)

B. Hegazy, H. Fouad, A. Kamel, 2013, Moving bed biofilm reactor with activated sludge for treating paper industrial wastewater, International Journal of Academic Research, 5, 4, 155-160.

N. Kaindl, 2010, Upgrading of an activated sludge wastewater treatment plant by adding a moving bed biofilm reactor as pretreatment and ozonation followed by biofiltration for enhanced COD reduction: design and operation experience, Water Science and Technology, 62, 11, 2710-2729.

W. Kocerba, E. Fiałkowska, A. Pajdak, B. Klimek, E. Kowalska, A. Drzewicki, H. Salvadó, J. Fyda, 2013, The use of rotifers for limiting filamentous bacteria Type 021N, a bacteria causing activated sludge bulking, Water Science and Technology, 67, 7, 1557-1563.

G. Tchobanoglous, F. Burton, D. Stensel, 1995, Ingeniería de Aguas Residuales, Tratamiento, vertido y reutilización, 3rd ed, Madrid, Metcalf and Eddy, McGraw Hill.

M. Paice, 2008, Water use and effluent treatment in canadian high yieldpulp mills, TAPPI Press, Engineering, Pulping and Environmental Conference Proceedings, Portland, OR, United States, 3, 1506-1547.

Y. Qiqi, H. Qiang, T. Husham, H.T. Ibrahim, 2012, Review on Moving Bed Biofilm Processes, Pakistan Journal of Nutrition, 11, 9, 706-713.

A. Rankin, M. Van Aert, T.Welander, A. Malmqvist, 2007, Low sludge yield Bio-film Activated Sludge (BAS) Upgrade– Quesnel River Pulp Co., Tappi Journal, 6, 5, 17-22.

B.E. Rittmann, P.L. McCarty, 1980a, Model of steady-state-biofilm kinetics, Biotechnology Bioengineering, 22, 11, 2343-2357.

B.E. Rittmann, P.L. McCarty,1980b, Evaluation of steady-state-biofilm kinetics, Biotechnology Bioengineering, 22, 11, 2359-2373.

T. Welander, L. Olsson, C. Fasth 2002, Nutrient-limited biofilm pretreatment: an efficient way to upgrade activated sludge plants, Tappi Journal, 1, 4, 20-26.

G. Zalakain, A. Larrea, J. Malfeito, J. Albizuri, L. Larrrea, 2008, Proceso híbrido con lecho móvil HYBAS, una eficaz alternativa para la remodelación de EDAR urbanas existentes, Tecnología del agua, 294, 54-62.

G. Zalakain, G.Manterola, 2011, Tratamiento biológico de la EDAR de Sniace mediante el proceso BAS, Tecnología del agua, 335, 2-8.

Jiří Jaromír Klemeš, Petar Sabev Varbanov and Peng Yen Liew (Editors)
Proceedings of the 24th European Symposium on Computer Aided Process Engineering – ESCAPE 24
June 15-18, 2014, Budapest, Hungary.

Technical and Economic Analysis of Chemical Looping Combustion with Humid Air Turbine Power Cycle

Akeem Olaleye[a,b], Meihong Wang[a,b,*]

[a]*Process and Energy Systems Engineering Group, School of Engineering, University of Hull, Cottingham Road, Hull HU6 7RX, United Kingdom*

[b]*Process Systems Engineering Group, School of Engineering, Cranfield University, Cranfield, MK43 0AL, United Kingdom*

Meihong.Wang@hull.ac.uk

Abstract

Chemical looping combustion (CLC) is an innovative concept that offers potentially attractive option to capture CO_2 with appreciably lower thermal efficiency penalties when compared to the tradition approaches. This paper presents process simulation, technical and economic analysis of the CLC integrated with humid air turbine (HAT) cycle for natural gas-fired power plant with CO_2 capture. Aspen Plus® process simulator and Aspen Process Economic Analyzer® were employed for technical and economic analysis of the CLC-HAT and conventional HAT cycle.The analysis shows the CLC-HAT cycle has a thermal efficiency of 57 % at oxidizing temperature of 1,200 °C and reducer inlet temperature of 530 °C. The economic evaluation performed shows that a 50 MW_{th} CLC-HAT plant with a projected lifetime of 30 y has a payback period of 6 y compared to 7 y for conventional HAT cycle. This indicates that CLC-HAT cycle is commercially viable with respect to CO_2 capture cost.

Keywords: Chemical Looping Combustion (CLC), Humid Air Turbine (HAT), Economic Analysis, Process simulation.

1. Introduction

Chemical looping combustion (CLC) is an innovative concept that offers potentially

$$(a + b/4)\ MeO + C_aH_b \rightarrow (a + b/4)\ Me + aCO_2 + b/2H_2O \quad (1)$$

attractive option to capture CO_2 with appreciably lower thermal efficiency penalty when compared to the tradition carbon capture approaches (i.e. pre-, post-, and oxy-combustion). CLC is characterized by indirect fuel combustion because the air and fuel are never in direct contact. The fuel conversion is achieved in two sub-reactions (oxidation and reduction) and with oxygen carrier particle as the chemical intermediates. In the reduction stage, the oxygen carrier particle is reduced by the fuel, yielding CO_2 and H_2O. This is depicted in Eq.(1) for a gaseous fuel (Fan, 2010). This fuel conversion step could either be exothermic or endothermic depending upon the type of oxygen carrier and fuel used. The reduced metal is then sent to the oxidizer where combustion occurs with air. The reduced metal is regenerated to its initial oxidation state as shown in Eq. (2) (Fan, 2010).

$$Me + Air \rightarrow MeO\ +\ Oxygen\text{-}depleted\ Air\ +\ Heat \quad (2)$$

The oxidation step being exothermic produces an enormous amount of heat which is used to generate electricity; also the fact that both the fuel and the air conversion process occur in different reactors leads to the production of a CO_2 stream from the reducer that has only H_2O as the other component, hence it may be easily separated from the mixture. CLC can be applied to both gaseous (natural gas) and solid fuels (coal). The most common metals used as oxygen carrier include Fe, Ni, and Cu. A number of promising oxygen carriers have been found, of which $NiO/NiAl_2O_4$ is perhaps the most promising (Mattison et al., 2011). NiO/Ni oxygen carrier particle together with $NiAl_2O_4$ as inert support material was used in this study.

The CLC system can be integrated into different power cycles, and analysed at different operating conditions. A number of articles have been published on the integration of CLC into power cycles. The major focus of such studies has been thermal efficiency improvement (Peltola et al., 2013), exergy analysis (Ishida and Jin, 1994), and comparative studies with equivalent conventional power cycles (Brandvoll and Bolland, 2004). In this study, the CLC system is integrated into a HAT cycle. Ishida and Jin (1994), presented exergetic analysis of CLC-HAT cycle, Brandvoll and Bolland (2004) extended the work of Ishida and Jin (1994) to include comparative analysis of the exergy of conventional combustion. This study extended the work Brandvoll and Bolland (2004) to include economic analysis of both conventional HAT and CLC-HAT cycle.

2. Process Simulation and Economic Analysis

The CLC system, the conventional HAT cycle power plant and the CLC-HAT process were each simulated in Aspen Plus®. Dual circulating fluidized bed (DCFB) reactors have been recognized as the best combination of reactors for both the oxidation and reduction reactions of the CLC system for good contact between the solid carriers and the gas for long-term operation (Lyngfelt et al., 2001). In this study, each of the DCFB were simulated as two regions: (i) dense lower region, based on Gibb's free energy minimization, hence RGIBBS reactor unit in Aspen Plus® was used, (ii) the dilute upper region, based on completely well mixed condition and RSTOIC reactor unit in Aspen Plus® was used. The reaction kinetics and fluid dispersion velocities were not considered.

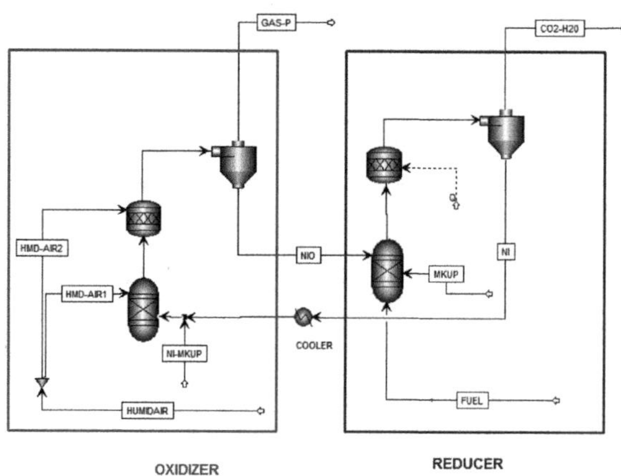

Figure 1. Simulation of DCFB for CLC system in Aspen plus®

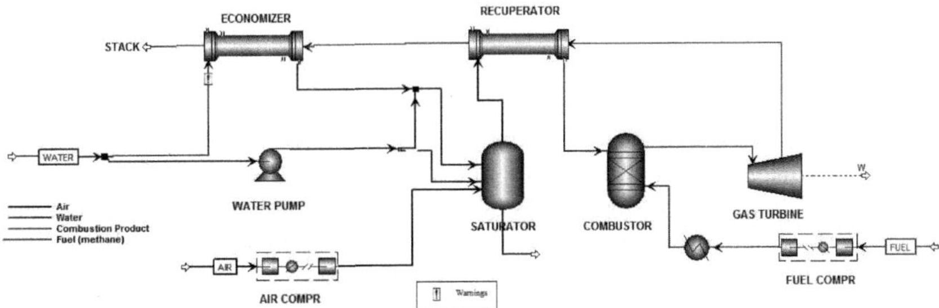

Figure 2. Simulation of conventional HAT Cycle in Aspen Plus®

The HAT cycle is an improvement to the combined cycles for its high thermal efficiency. In this cycle, air is compressed in a multistage compressor and intercooled with water, it is then admitted into the saturator where hot water is allowed to evaporate and mix with air. The humidified air is then pre-heated in the recuperator by the exhaust gas from the turbine before it is sent into the combustion unit. The heat recovery is completed with the economizer used to heat water, using the hot exhaust gas from the turbine before being purged in the stack stream. The conventional HAT process simulation is largely based on the parameters of the final reports on advanced fossil fuel power system comparative study by NETL (Parsons and Shelton, 2002). The HAT cycle power plant used in this study is a simplified model as shown in Figure 2.

The process flow diagram of the CLC-HAT process is shown in Figure 3. The oxidation reaction is exothermic, producing an exhaust gas stream (G-OX) at 1,200 °C which is passed into turbine GT-1 to generate electricity, pre-heat the humidified air in the HEX-3, and further cooled in HEX-4 and HEX-5 by releasing heat to the process water. The H_2O vapour is then condensed in condenser (GT1-COND) and recovered for re-use.
The exhaust gas stream (mainly N_2 and water vapour) is also condensed in GT2-COND. The product gas discharged from the reducer (stream G-RED) is mainly CO_2 and H_2O vapour. This exhaust gas is used to drive the gas turbine GT-2 to generate electricity. It is subsequently cooled by releasing heat to CH_4 and process water. CO_2 and water vapour are condensed.

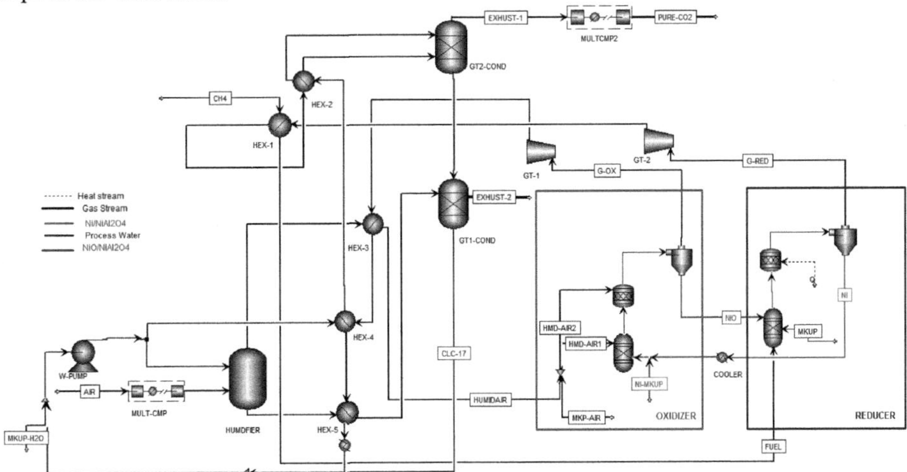

Figure 3. Simulation of CLC-HAT Power Cycle in Aspen Plus®

CO_2 at 70 ^0C and 1.1 bar is captured and compressed to a pressure of 150 bar for sequestration. The simulation in Aspen Plus® was validated by comparing the results of this study with the work of Brandvoll and Bolland (2004).

The economic analysis of both conventional and CLC-HAT power cycles were based on Aspen Economic Analyser®. It is not intended to obtain absolute power generation costs from this evaluation as the results of this work may not accurately reflect the final cost of constructing the plants, but it is a useful method for establishing economic viability of a process and comparing competing processes.

3. Results and Discussions

For this study, the mass flow rate of the humid air and the fuel were 49.8 kg/s and 1 kg/s respectively. The $NiO/NiAl_2O_4$and $Ni/NiAl_2O_4$ carrier flowrates were 32.6 kg/s and 37.05 kg/s in the oxidizer and reducer respectively. The operating pressures in both reactors were approximately 20 bar. Table 1 shows the simulation results (compared with a reference case for the CLC-HAT cycle) based on the key performance indicators in the power plants. The results show that the thermal efficiency of the CLC-HAT power plant is 57.1 % and is approximately 2 % lower than the conventional HAT power plant (without CO_2 capture) due to the energy used in the CLC reactors. This is in agreement with the results obtained from the reference case by Brandvoll and Bolland (2004).The economic analysis is largely based on the Aspen Plus® process simulation input parameters, flow conditions, and the simulation results. The two HAT power cycles were compared based on some key economic indicators (Table 2).

Table 1. Summary of Simulation Results (after Brandvoll and Bolland, 2004)

Parameters	Reference Case	Conventional HAT	CLC-HAT
Power from Gas Turbine (MW_{th})	50.0	43.64	49.02
Compressor work (MW_{th})	22.0	14.14	20.47
Net Power Output (MW_{th})	28.0	29.50	28.55
Net Plant Efficiency (% LHV)	55.9	59.0	57.1
Energy penalty	3.62	-	3.39
Efficiency penalty (%)	2.1	-	1.9

Table 2. Economic indicators for the Conventional HAT and the CLC-HAT cycles

Economic Indicators	Conventional HAT	CLC-HAT
Plant generation capacity (MW_{th})	29.50	28.55
Total capital investment (£)	29,271,400	51,999,270
Total operating cost (£/y)	7,934,559	9,104,170
Payback period (y)	7.03	6.14
Profitability index (PI)	1.42	1.60
Net present value (NPV) (£)	94,162,100	104,240,000
Internal Rate of Return (%)	26.83	37.87
Capital Requirement (£/kW)	584	1,040

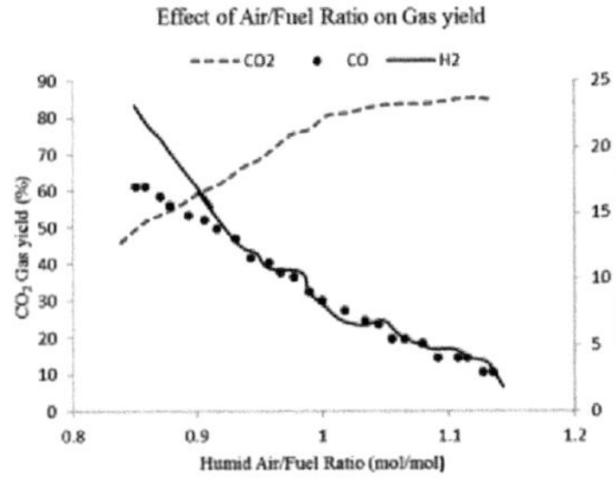

Figure 4. Effect of humid air/fuel ratio

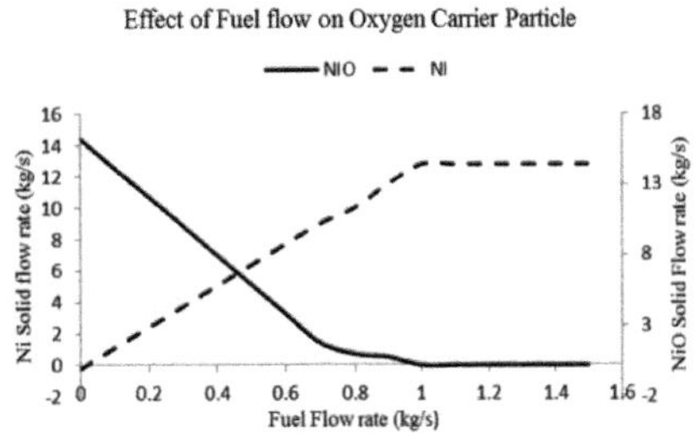

Figure 5. Effect of fuel flow

The following sub-sections discuss the effect of some key process variables on the performance of the CLC-HAT power plant.

3.1. Effect of Humidified Air/Fuel Ratio

The effect of the humid air/fuel molar ratio on the product distribution in the fuel reactor was considered in this case study. Figure 4 shows the gas products CO_2, H_2 and CO concentrations at the reducer outlet. It is observed that increasing the humid air/fuel ratio between 0.8 – 1.2 has effect on the amount of CO and H_2 that are produced alongside the main product, CO_2 (obtained after H_2O condensation). Increasing the air/fuel ratio leads to an increase in CO_2 concentration. However, H_2 and CO reduces as the air/fuel ratio increases. A humid air/fuel ratio of 1.1 was used in the study.

3.2. Effect of fuel flow on Ni solid Product

The effect of the fuel flow rate on the solids product is shown in Figure 5. Increasing the fuel flow rate in the reducer, results in a corresponding increase in the flow rate of Ni to be used in the oxidation reaction. However, Figure 5 shows that NiO conversion in the fuel reactor is limited by the stoichiometric fuel flow (1 kg/s) available for reduction process. Increasing the flow rate of the fuel after this point does not influence the NiO conversion.

3.3. Effects of Fuel(CH_4) Inlet Temperature on Thermal Efficiency

At the given fuel flow and outlet conditions, reducing the fuel inlet temperature means more of the heat from the fuel pre-heat exchanger can be available to the air pre-heat exchanger, thereby increasing the inlet temperature of the oxidizer. In terms of mass flows, the amount of fuel intake in the process is much lower than the air flow requirement in the system. Consequently, little effect is observed on the overall plant thermal efficiency, for example in Figure 6, an efficiency increase of 0.2 % is observed

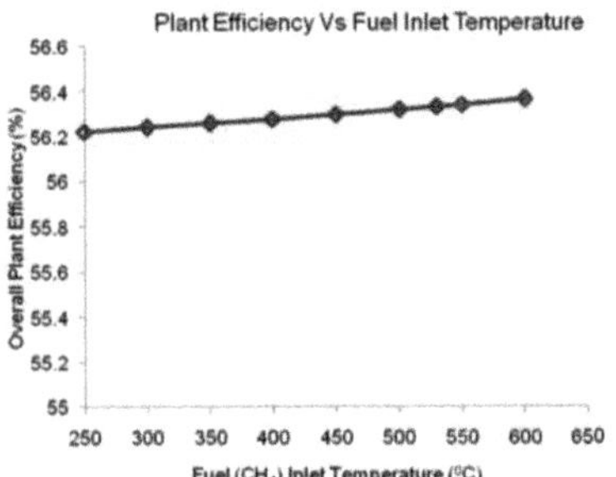

Figure 6. Effect of fuel inlet temperature

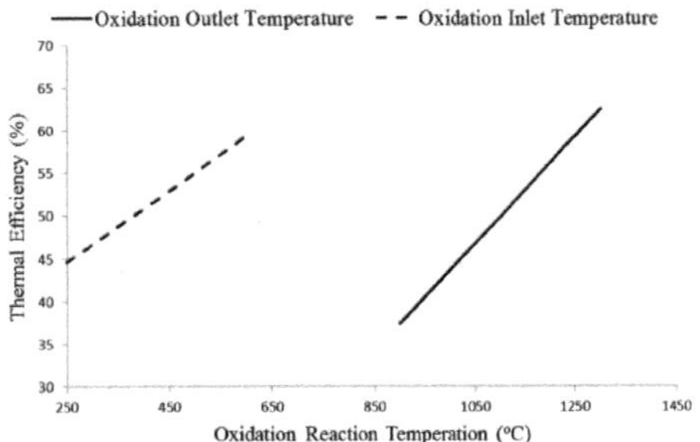

Figure 7. Effect of inlet and outlet oxidizer temperature

over a temperature range of (250-600 °C). Hence, maximum temperature allowable by ΔT_{min} required in the exchanger was used in the simulation.

3.4. Effects of Inlet & Outlet Temperature of Oxidizer on Plant Thermal Efficiency

The saturated-air temperature at oxidizer inlet determines the saturated-air flow rate through the unit at a given outlet temperature and heat exchanger duty. An increase in the overall efficiency is observed due to a relatively larger increment in the gas turbine output. From Figure 7, assuming constant fuel input, an increase in the air inlet temperature results in a proportional increase in the outlet temperature of the oxidizer, and the plant thermal efficiency.

4. Conclusions

A process simulation and economic analysis for CLC-HAT power plant was performed. The CLC system with HAT principle shows an efficiency of 57 % at oxidizing temperature of 1,200 °C and reducer inlet temperature of 530 °C, and a very low penalty point among other CCS options integrated into the power cycles. The sensitivity analysis showed that the overall thermal efficiency of the plant is greatly influenced by the air inlet temperature to the oxidation reactor and its exhaust temperature. The efficiency penalty and thermal energy penalty were found to be very low at a value of 2 % and 3.4 % respectively for the 50 MW_{th} plant. The economic evaluation shows that the 50 MW_{th} plant with a projected lifetime of 30 y has a payback period of 7 y, and a total capital investment of £ 29.2 million for the conventional HAT cycle; and 6 y, and a total capital investment of £ 52 million for the CLC-HAT cycle. The profitability index of 1.6 for the CLC-HAT cycle as against 1.3 for conventional HAT cycle also affirms the long term superiority of the CLC-HAT process in combating CO_2 emission over conventional combustion.

5. Acknowledgements

This work was financially supported by PTDF, Nigeria.

References

P. Peltola, J. Ritvanen, T. Tynjala, 2013, Model-based evaluation of a chemical looping combustion plant for energy generation at a pre-commercial scale of 100 MW_{th} Energy Conversion and Management, 76, 323-331.

O. Brandvoll, O. Bolland, 2004, Inherent CO_2 Capture using Chemical Looping Combustion in a Natural Gas Fired Power Cycle, ASME Journal for Engineering for Gas Turbines and Power, 126, 316-321.

L-S. Fan, 2010, Chemical Looping Systems for Fossil Energy Conversions, John Wiley and Sons, New Jersey, USA.

M. Ishida, H. Jin, 1994, A New Advanced Power-Generation System using Chemical-Looping Combustion, Energy, 19, 4, 415-422.

T. Mattison, E. Jerndal, C. Linderholm, 2011, Reactivity of a spray-dried $NiO/NiAl_2O_4$ oxygen carrier for chemical-looping combustion, Chemical Engineering Science, 66, 4636-4644.

A. Lyngfelt, B. Leckner, T. Mattisson, 2001, A Fluidized-Bed Combustion Process with Inherent CO_2 Separation; Application of Chemical-Looping Combustion, Chemical Engineering Science, 56, 3101-3113.

E.L. Parsons, W.W. Shelton, 2002, Advanced Fossil Power Systems Comparison Study, National Energy Technology Laboratory USDOE Final Report, Pittsburgh, PA.

Jiří Jaromír Klemeš, Petar Sabev Varbanov and Peng Yen Liew (Editors)
Proceedings of the 24th European Symposium on Computer Aided Process Engineering – ESCAPE 24
June 15-18, 2014, Budapest, Hungary.

Can Exergy be a Useful Tool for the Dairy Industry?

Mohammed T. Munir, Wei Yu, Brent R. Young*

Industrial Information and Control Centre (I^2C^2),
The University of Auckland, 20 Symonds Street, Auckland 1010, NewZealand
b.young@auckland.ac.nz

Abstract

Dairy processing is regarded as being one of the most energy intensive industries in countries where primary production dominates the economy. In the New Zealand economy, dairy processing energy consumption typically accounts for about 15 % of the total energy consumption of the industrial sector. An annual spend of NZ$2 – 3 million on energy is typical for a medium to large dairy processing (milk powder) site and these energy costs are a significant incentive to reduce total energy usage. This paper proposes the use of the thermodynamic concept exergy as a potential tool for improving the energy efficiency of the dairy industry. Although exergy analysis has been proposed for process optimisation in other industries, applications are rare in dairy processing. Therefore exergy analysis was applied as a case study to a milk powder production plant typical of New Zealand. The aim was to show that the concept of exergy has a great potential to be used as a useful diagnostic tool for analysing and optimising dairy processes in terms of exergy or energy efficiency. It was found that the exergy efficiency for dairy processing (i.e. milk powder plant) unit operations ranges from 36 – 99 % with higher exergy losses observed in the evaporators and drier than in other unit operations, and opportunities for exergy efficiency were subsequently identified.

Keywords: dairy processing, exergy analysis, energy efficiency

1. Introduction

The dairy industry is the 5th most energy intensive industry after petroleum, chemical, pulp and paper, and iron and steel industries (G. Bylund, 2003). Along with these other industries, the dairy industry is also concerned to minimize its energy usage to minimize production cost and to play its role in the global efforts to control the global environment, e.g. (von Keyserlingk et al., 2013). Several studies and results have shown that the processing of a billion litres (BL) of milk consumes 300 – 500 GWh of energy. Most of the energy consumed by the dairy industry (≈ 60 – 75 %) is used for heating and steam generation via boilers. The remaining energy (≈ 25 – 40 %) is used for different unit operations and building demands (e.g. HVAC).Fossil fuels (e.g. coal, gas and oil) are the dominant energy sources in the dairy industry (Brush et al., 2011). Figure 1 shows energy use by energy type in New Zealand's dairy industry, which is main industry focus of this manuscript.

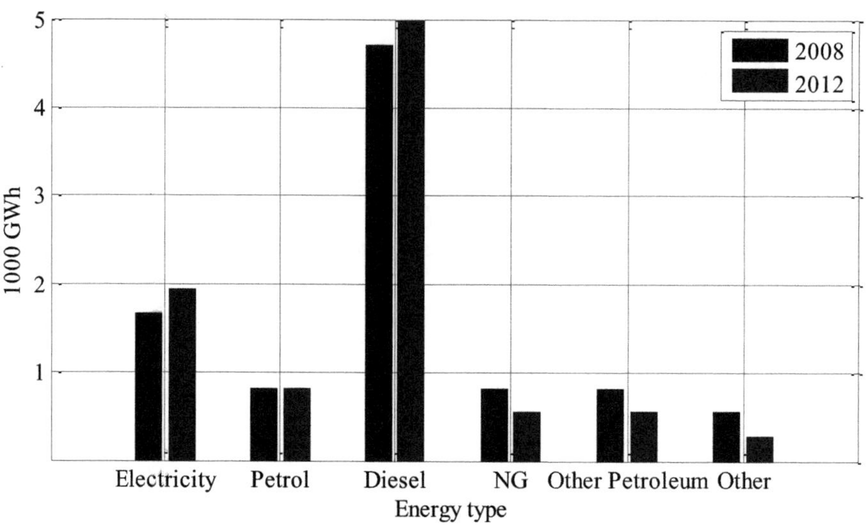

Figure 1. Energy use by energy type in NZ's dairy industry

There are a variety of technologies which have been proposed for reducing energy and fossil fuel use in dairy processing industry, namely: 1) renewable energy use, 2) energy conservation, and 3) energy efficiency/exergy efficiency.

Improving energy efficiency is a potential candidate to minimize energy usage in dairy processing. New equipment or renovated old equipment with higher energy efficiency is introduced in dairy processing plants to save energy. Increased energy efficiency of dairy processing plant is cost effective and profitable with reduced greenhouse gas emissions. In literature, reported applications of energy efficiency in dairy industry are not frequently found. However, there are a couple of examples e.g. (Tomasula et al., 2013). The application of energy efficiency improvement also has the many challenges of renewable energy technologies (RETs) and energy conservation applications.

In literature it is rare to find a significant contribution of improved energy efficiency. Other potential challenges and obstacles include, 1) less attention paid to innovation than production, 2) major capital investments, 3) other priorities, 4) role of energy companies, 4) preference to proven old technologies over new risky technologies, and 5) short term financial horizons. Finally, a major drawback of energy efficiency analysis is that it does not truly represent equipment efficiency because it is based on the 1st law of thermodynamics. It does not take the quality of energy into account in its loss and performance calculations. This means energy efficiency analyses are therefore often misleading.

A complete and better understanding of efficiency is attained when a more comprehensive thermodynamic view is taken into account, using the quality of energy (i.e. exergy or 2nd law of thermodynamics) in conjunction with the quantity of energy (i.e. energy or 1st law of thermodynamics). However, an energy efficiency analysis provides the relative magnitude of energy losses and should also be done in conjunction with exergy analysis.

In the chemical and petrochemical industries, extensive applications of the exergy concept and exergy analysis can be found, e.g. (Aghbashlo et al., 2013). Recent literature also has some more exergy related case studies that have been done on food manufacturing processes, e.g. (Aghbashlo et al., 2013), but it is very rare to find a reported application of exergy analysis to the dairy manufacturing process. It might be due to fact that dairy products are complex in nature and the non-availability of dairy components in component libraries make them hard to model in commercial process simulators.

The specific objective of this paper is to propose the use of an exergy analysis tool for the dairy industry. Exergy analysis was also applied to a milk powder production plant typical to New Zealand as a case study, in an attempt to illustrate potential merits of exergy analysis for the dairy industry.

2. Materials and Methods

In thermodynamics, efficiency is one of the most frequently used terms to indicate how well energy is converted into useful work. Generally it is defined as the ratio of desired output to required input. Energy efficiency (i.e. ratio of output energy to input energy) is primarily based on the 1st law of thermodynamics. It helps to understand the system's behaviour to some extent and provides the relative magnitude of energy losses, but does not include the usability of the converted energy. In other words it only considers the quantity of energy but not the quality level of the converted energy in its analysis.

In contrast to energy efficiency, exergy efficiency (i.e. ratio of output exergy to input exergy) is based on combing the 1st and 2nd laws of thermodynamics. It includes the quality level of the converted energy, and thereby determines the true magnitudes of energy losses, their causes and locations. Exergy analysis of a process and/or the individual units making up the overall process is performed using their exergetic efficiencies.

For an exergy analysis, the exergy value of every material stream coming into and going out of the considered process is required. There are different methods for the exergy calculation available in literature, e.g. (Hinderink et al., 1996). In this work we used the exergy calculator developed by Munir et al.(2012) for exergy calculation of material streams for three major reasons: 1) it is based on a recent commercial process simulator with the most up to date thermodynamic data; 2) calculations using thermodynamic data are relatively easy to perform in a commercial process simulator; and 3) it divides the total exergy of the material stream into its three main components (physical exergy, chemical exergy and exergy change due to mixing) which is helpful to identify the major component responsible for the total exergy destruction of a material stream. The exergy calculator was built in the VMGSim commercial simulator.

3. Case Study

Here we consider a milk powder production plant typical to New Zealand as a case study. In this case study, as shown in Figure 2, milk is converted to a milk powder to reduce the bulk for storage, transport and enhance storage life by removing water or water activity.

3.1. Process description, model and simulation

A milk powder production plant involves several units as shown in Figure 2. Milk from dairy farms is stored in large milk silos at ≈ 4 °C until used for processing. The milk then goes to a centrifuge to separate the cream (≈ 88 % fat on dry basis) and skim milk (≈ 1.5 % fat on dry basis) fractions. The skim milk stream is then sent to mixers and then to the pasteurizer after adjusting its fat content. During pasteurization, skim milk is heated to 72 °C, and cream is heated to 80 °C for 15 sec to kill the major strains of pathogenic microorganisms. The milk is then preheated to a temperature of between 75 – 125 °C before entering into the evaporator train. In the evaporator, skim milk is concentrated from 9 – 9.5 % w/w to 45 – 50 % w/w total solids under vacuum at temperatures between 40 – 70 °C. The concentrated milk from the evaporator leaves at a temperature between 40 – 58 °C with ≈ 85 % of water removed from the milk. The spray drier then atomizes the milk concentrate arriving inside its large chamber. Hot air at a temperature of 180 – 245 °C comes in contact with this atomized milk in a co-current flow pattern producing fine milk powder(G. Bylund, 2003).

The milk powder production plant was modelled using the commercial process simulator VMGSim developed by Virtual Materials Group Inc. (VMG). Before developing the model of the milk powder production plant, the "pseudo" milk mixture (with hypothetical components) was developed due to the absence of dairy product components (e.g. milk fat, protein) in the component libraries of commercial process simulators. The reader is referred to a research article recently published for further details on the "pseudo" milk mixture, and dairy plant modelling in VMGSim (Zhang et al., 2013).

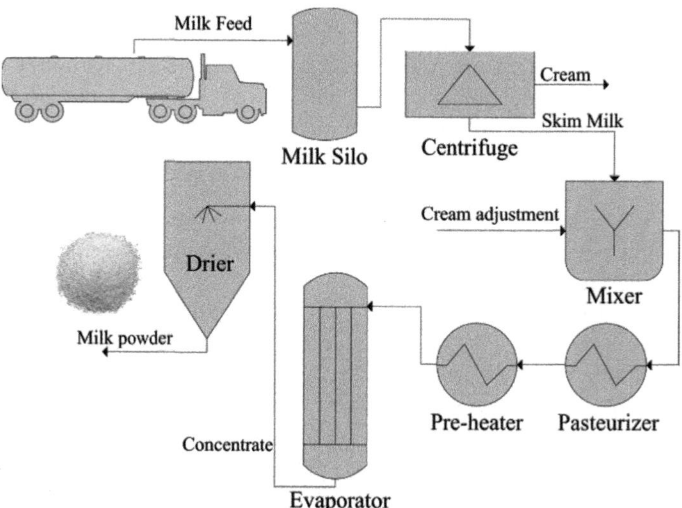

Figure 2. Milk powder manufacturing process schematic

Table 1.Case study milk powder process exergy flows

Unit	Total Exergy In, kW	Total Exergy Out, kW	Exergy efficiency (η) (as a fraction)
Milk Silo	23,068	23,061	0.99
Centrifuge	24,552	23,789	0.97
Pasteurizer	26,313	24,453	0.93
Pre-heater	23,153	23,009	0.99
Evaporator	24,314	21,283	0.87
Drier	85,632	30,828	0.36

4. Results and Discussion

The exergy flow and exergy efficiency values obtained for the milk powder plant unit operations are summarized in Table 1. This table presents total exergy in and out for each of the main process unit operations.

The exergy values shown in Table 1 along with the exergy efficiencies of the individual units were needed to do an exergy analysis. Table 1shows the units where the exergy losses are more significant. From the exergy analysis of the milk powder manufacturing process, it can be seen that the units where the most exergy is lost are the evaporator (3,031 kW exergy destroyed) and dryer (54,804 kW exergy destroyed). The exergy losses are insignificant in all other units except the pasteurizer (1,860 kW exergy destroyed).

This information could be considered during early process design stages for new milk powder manufacturing plants and for optimizing existing plants. A detailed analysis within the evaporator and dryer is required that can lead to the exact locations inside them where exergy is being destroyed and where process improvement or optimization can be performed. To make the exergy analysis presented above more useful for practicing engineers and to optimize the unit performance, the effect of the process parameters of the inlet and outlet streams on the exergy efficiency of the unit needs to be investigated.

5. Conclusions

This paper has discussed the use of exergy analysis as a tool for the dairy industry. Exergy appears to be a useful tool in addressing compensation for increased energy usage and dependence on fossil fuels in the dairy processing industry. An illustrative case study of milk powder production plant was used to highlight the importance of exergy efficiency utilization. Exergy analysis of the milk powder production plant revealed that most of exergy is destroyed in the evaporator and dryer. These results may be helpful to design and optimize the performance of different unit operations in the dairy industry.

References

M. Aghbashlo, H. Mobli, S. Rafiee, A. Madadlou, 2013, A review on exergy analysis of drying processes and systems, Renewable and Sustainable Energy Reviews, 22, 1-22.

A. Brush, E. Masanet, E. Worrell, 2011, Energy Efficiency Improvement and Cost Saving Opportunities for the Dairy Processing Industry Lawrence Berkeley National Laboratory, Berkeley, CA 94720.

G. Bylund, 2003, Dairy processing handbook, S-221 86 Lund, Sweden, Tetra Pak Processing Systems AB.

A. P. Hinderink, F. P. J. M. Kerkhof, A. B. K. Lie, J. De Swaan Arons, H. J. Van Der Kooi, 1996, Exergy analysis with a flowsheeting simulator—I. Theory; calculating exergies of material streams, Chemical Engineering Science, 51, 20, 4693-4700.

M. T. Munir, W. Yu, B. R. Young, 2012, Determination of Plantwide Control Loop Configuration and Eco-efficiency, Plantwide Control, 441-457.

P. M. Tomasula, W. C. F. Yee, A. J. McAloon, D. W. Nutter, L. M. Bonnaillie, 2013, Computer simulation of energy use, greenhouse gas emissions, and process economics of the fluid milk process, Journal of Dairy Science, 96, 5, 3350-3368.

M. A. G. von Keyserlingk, N. P. Martin, E. Kebreab, K. F. Knowlton, R. J. Grant, M. Stephenson, C. J. Sniffen, J. P. Harner Iii, A. D. Wright, S. I. Smith, 2013, Invited review: Sustainability of the US dairy industry, Journal of Dairy Science, 96, 9, 5405-5425.

Y. Zhang, M. T. Munir, W. Yu, B. R. Young, 2013, Development of hypothetical components for milk process simulation using a commercial process simulator, Journal of Food Engineering, 121, 87 - 93.

Jiří Jaromír Klemeš, Petar Sabev Varbanov and Peng Yen Liew (Editors)
Proceedings of the 24th European Symposium on Computer Aided Process Engineering – ESCAPE 24
June 15-18, 2014, Budapest, Hungary.

Optimum Sizing of PV-CAES Configurations for the Electrification of Remote Consumers

D. Zafirakis[a], K. Kavadias[a], Emilia M. Kondili[b], John K. Kaldellis[a*]

[a]*Soft Energy Applications and Environemntal Protection Lab*
[b]*Optimisation of Production Systems Laboratory, TEI of Piraeus, Greece*
jkald@teipir.gr

Abstract

Acknowledging the increased levels of energy dependence of remote communities, relying almost exclusively on oil imports to cover their electricity needs, an alternative solution is currently proposed. Based on the scenario of natural gas introduction in island grids, development of a sizing algorithm for photovoltaic (PV)-based compressed air energy storage (CAES) systems is undertaken. To this end, a novel dual-mode CAES configuration is studied considering also areas of different quality solar potential, belonging to the broader region of the Aegean Sea. According to the results obtained, such configurations could provide high levels of energy autonomy under minimum natural gas consumption, even in areas of relatively low quality solar potential that in the case of the Aegean Sea corresponds to 1,300 kWh/m^2.a.

Keywords: energy storage, gas turbine, natural gas, solar energy.

1. Introduction

Increased interest is recently noted in the concept of distributed generation (DG) (Ai et al., 2014; Bernardon et al., 2014), with renewable energy sources (RES) technologies called to play a critical role. At the same time, there are several remote areas across the globe that rely on electricity grids of small scale (micro-grids), normally employing oil-fired power generation solutions (Kaldellis and Zafirakis, 2007a). On the other hand, in many of these regions one may encounter medium to high quality RES potential that encourages installation of solutions such as wind power and photovoltaics (PVs) (Kaldellis and Zafirakis, 2012). In this context, there are various energy storage technologies, either more mature or emerging (Kaldellis and Zafirakis, 2007b), that may interact with the primary RES energy source. Among the various solutions existing, grown interest is recently noted in compressed air energy storage (CAES). Acknowledging the fact that although CAES is considered as bulk storage it may equally well be downscaled so as to serve small-medium size applications, the current research study investigates the solution of an integrated PV-CAES solution used to serve remote communities. More precisely, a sizing methodology is developed, investigating the levels of energy autonomy offered to the remote community each time examined on the one hand and the annual fuel consumption required on the other. On top of that, two different system versions are studied; i.e. the conventional CAES cycle and the dual-mode CAES (DMCAES) cycle (Zafirakis and Chalvatzis, 2014; Zafirakis and Kaldellis, 2009; 2010), where the system may allow shift to the Brayton cycle when energy stores are not sufficient to cover energy demand.

2. The PV-DM CAES solution

Emphasizing on the need to achieve high levels of load demand satisfaction using non-oversized CAES configurations, an alternative CAES solution is currently proposed. More precisely, the solution of a DMCAES plant is currently adopted. Such a plant has the ability to switch its operation from the CAES mode to the traditional gas-turbine cycle with the addition of a second compression system and the help of a clutch that may allow connection between the gas-turbine and the compressor. To this end, the proposed solution (see also Figure 1) comprises of the following components:

- A PV park comprising of a number of PV panels (see also Figure 2 for the PV panel curves), with total capacity "$N_{PV\text{-}t}$".
- A CAES motor of rated power "N_m", used to exploit any PV energy surplus and feed the compressor under an efficiency of "η_m".
- A multi-stage compressor, used in the CAES cycle to compress ambient air into the air cavern/tank, under a given pressure ratio "r_c". Similar to the case of the motor, the compressor power "$N_{cr\text{-}CAES}$" is determined in relation to the maximum PV energy surplus appearing during daytime, i.e. "N_{PV}-N_d", taking also into account any energy losses induced by the motor, with "N_{PV}" representing the mean hourly PV park power output and "N_d" standing for the mean hourly load demand.
- A second compression system, operated in the case of the DM cycle execution, i.e. when energy deficit appears and the combined PV-CAES system is not able to cover it, with its rated power being "$N_{cr\text{-}dual}$" and its pressure ratio being "r'_c".
- A storage cavern or tank of maximum volume storage "V_{ss}" and maximum depth of discharge "DOD_L", determined by the ratio of $[(r_c\text{-}r_t)\cdot r_c^{-1}]$, where "$r_t$" is the pressure ratio of the gas-turbine employed.
- A combustion chamber where the required amount of compressed air is burned with natural gas for the production of gases, that will then be used to operate the gas-turbine under a maximum permitted temperature of "T_{cc}".
- A natural gas tank, used for the storage of fuel, with the latter being determined by the respective calorific value "H_u".
- A gas-turbine of power output "$N_{gt\text{-}f}$", determined after considering the maximum appearing deficit in the case of both the CAES "N_{def}" and the DM "N'_{def}" cycle, that is connected to an electrical generator responsible for the delivery of electrical energy to the demand side.

In this regard, the main problem variables currently taken into account include the PV capacity and storage volume, while the main problem inputs require detailed solar irradiance and ambient temperature-pressure measurements along with the hourly electricity load demand of the system under investigation. At the same time, the technical characteristics of the main system components are also required (see also Table 1), while to simulate operation of similar systems, a sizing algorithm has been developed (see also Fig. 3 and (Zafirakis and Kaldellis, 2010) for the DMCAES governing equations). In this context, the operation scenarios of the proposed configuration include the following:

- In case that PV energy production is sufficient to cover energy demand, solar energy is fed directly to the local consumption and any appearing energy surplus is used to compress air inside the cavern/tank, provided that the latter is not full.

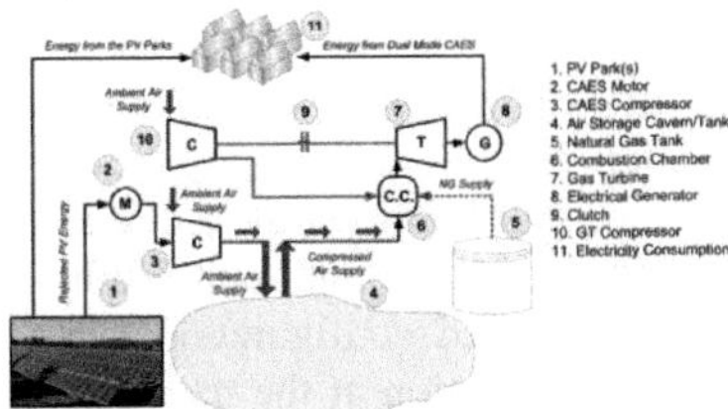

Figure 1. The proposed PV-DMCAES system.

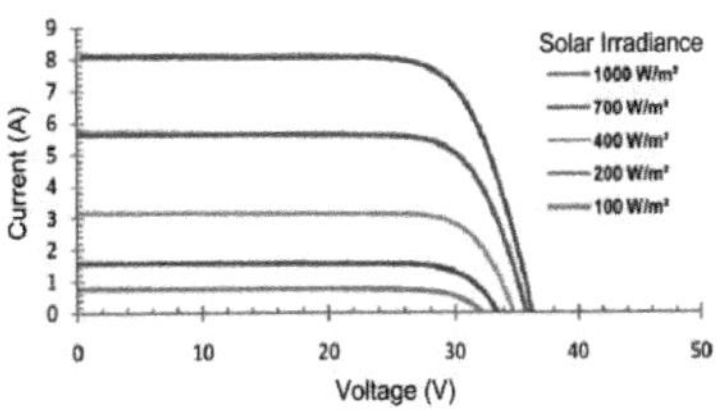

Figure 2. Current-voltage curves of a commercial PV panel under standard day conditions.

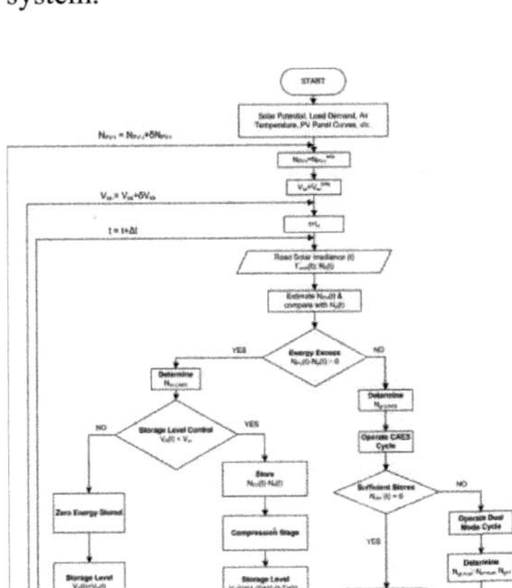

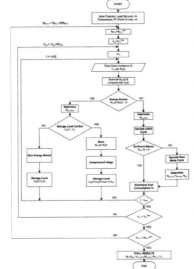

Figure 3. The PV-DMCAES sizing algorithm.

Table 1: CAES Characteristics

Parameter	Value
Compressor isentropic efficiency	0.85
Gas turbine isentropic efficiency	0.88
Compressor mechanical efficiency	0.98
Gas turbine mechanical efficiency	0.98
Motor efficiency "η_M"	0.98
Electrical generator efficiency "η_{gen}"	0.98
Storage temperature (K)	300
CAES compressor pressure ratio "r_c"	75
DMCAES compressor pressure ratio "r'_c"	32
Gas turbine pressure ratio "r_t"	30
Specific heat capacity of air (J/kg/K)	1,004.5
Specific heat capacity of gases (J/kg/K)	1105
Air to fuel ratio	4
Air mass for stoich. combustion (kg/kg_{NG})	15
Gas turb. maximum operating temp. (K)	1,200
Air constant (J/kg/K)	287
Calorific value of natural gas "H_u" (MJ/kg)	47

- In case that PV energy production is not sufficient to cover the load demand, the required amount of compressed air and fuel are used to operate the gas-turbine.
- In case that both PV energy and energy stores are not able to cover load demand, the appearing energy deficit is covered by the DM system, i.e. the gas-turbine is clutched to the DM compressor, under a different heat rate in comparison to CAES.

As a result, given a PV capacity value, the hours of load rejection per year are recorded under a fixed storage volume, while to obtain minimum hours of rejection the storage capacity is gradually increased within a predefined range of variation. Furthermore, in the case that energy autonomy is not achieved, the PV park capacity is also increased, up to the point that 100 % energy autonomy is obtained on the basis of using the PV-CAES solution. At the same time however, results obtained also include the complementary energy (fuel consumption) required by the DMCAES cycle in case that 100 % energy autonomy is not achieved by the original PV-CAES system.

3. Area of interest – Case study

For the application of the proposed solution, the area of the Aegean Sea has been selected as case study. The specific region is located on the east-side of the Greek mainland and comprises of hundreds of scattered islands. Furthermore, the entire area is favored by high quality solar potential (PPC, 1986) (ranging between 1,300 kWh/m^2.a to 1,800 kWh/m^2.a) that stimulates application of solar-based configurations. In this context, by acknowledging the need to increase RES contribution at the national level (e.g. target of 40 % of the national gross electricity consumption covered by RES by 2020) (Kalampalikas and Pilavachi, 2010) and the fact that up till now non-interconnected island regions of the Aegean Sea rely heavily on oil imports that entail high electricity production costs and strong environmental considerations (Kaldellis and Zafirakis, 2007a), the scenario of introducing RES power and natural gas comes with multiple benefits, facilitating at the same time application of RES-based CAES schemes. In this regard, the proposed solution is accordingly applied to two different solar potential areas, capturing the entire range of solar potential variation in the Greek territory. In this context, the annual solar potential of the two representative areas corresponds to 1,365 kWh/m^2.a and 1,760 kWh/m^2.a respectively. At the same time, a typical, average ambient temperature profile is adopted, being representative of the mild climate met in the island region of Aegean. Furthermore, the hourly load demand profile of a typical small-medium scale island for an entire year is given in Fig. 4, with the peak load demand reaching 2 MW and the respective minimum load demand dropping to 400 kW, while the annual energy demand exceeds 7.5 GWh.

4. Application Results

Results obtained from the application of the proposed algorithm are given in the following figures, considering also variation of the PV park capacity as well as of the employed storage volume (i.e. N_{PV-t} = 2-15 MW, V_{ss} = 1,000 - 20,000 m^3). The energy autonomy levels achieved by the proposed solution are first examined. More precisely, in Figs. 5-6 the solution of a PV-CAES scheme is investigated. According to the results, parallel increase of PV power and storage volume is gradually reducing hourly load rejections. In this context, the selected range of variation of input parameters fails to produce energy autonomous PV-CAES configurations for the low solar potential. On the other hand, PV park capacity of 15 MW along with the maximum storage volume of 20,000 m^3 leads to a total of only 105 h of load rejection per year. At the same time, critical PV capacity (i.e. the PV capacity that leads to 100 % energy autonomy) is found to decrease as the solar potential quality improves. On top of that, as it may be seen, storage volume of V_{ss}=1,000 m^3 is unable to support energy autonomous configurations,

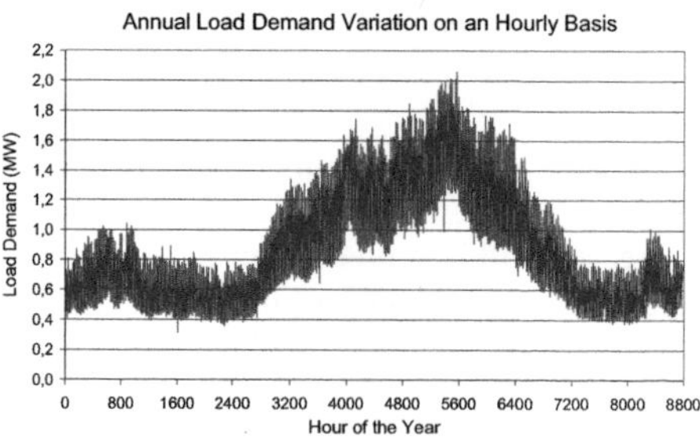

Figure 4. Load demand variation of the typical island

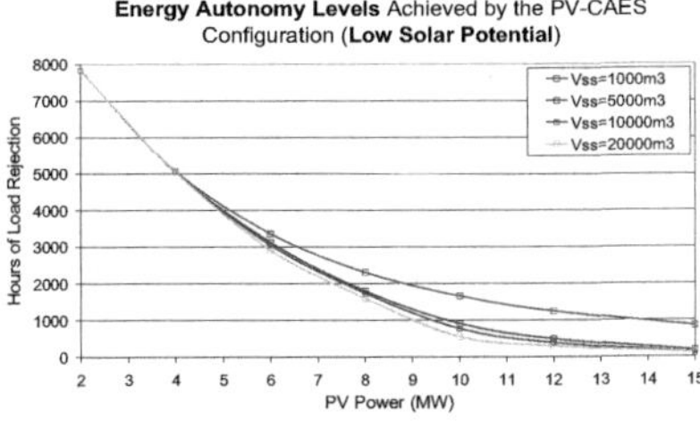

Figure 5. Energy autonomy achieved by the PV-CAES system (low solar potential).

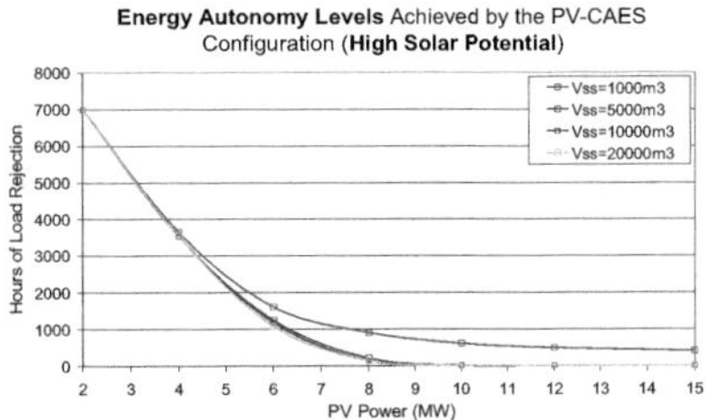

Figure 6. Energy autonomy achieved by the PV-CAES system (medium solar potential).

independently of the PV park capacity and the solar potential each time investigated. Besides, what is also critical to note is that according to the figures, employment of storage volume that is larger than 5,000 m^3 entails minimum increase of energy autonomy levels for all cases examined. Next, in Figs. 7-8, the total natural gas consumption is presented for the same configurations, considering also contribution of the DM cycle. As one may see from the figures, low PV capacity implies that contribution of the DM cycle is more important, and thus total fuel consumption increases considerably. Accordingly, influence of the local solar potential gradually fades out, as the capacity of the PV park increases and thus DM operation minimizes, eventually leading to similar numbers concerning the total fuel consumption regardless of the solar potential quality (i.e. in the order of 400-450 t/y of natural gas). As one may see, contribution of the DM cycle reduces with the increase of the PV capacity and is as expected zeroed once 100 % energy autonomy is achieved (encountered only in the cases of high solar potential). The above conclusions are better demonstrated in the following set of figures, i.e. Figs. 9-10.

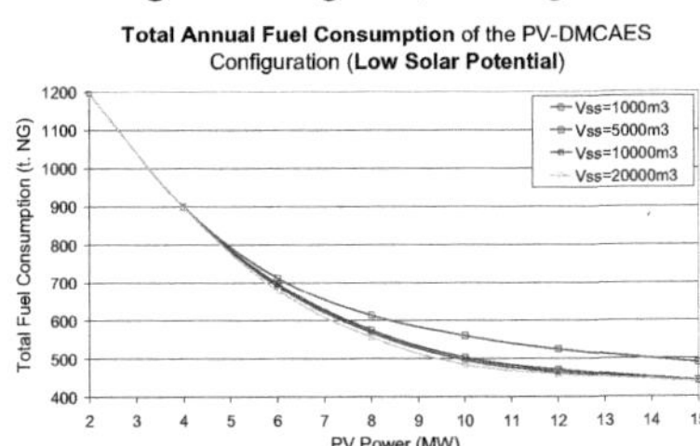

Figure 7. Total fuel consumption (low solar potential).

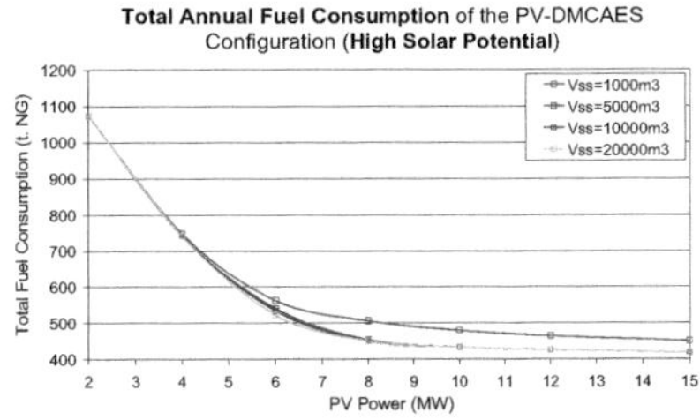

Figure. 8. Total fuel consumption (high solar potential).

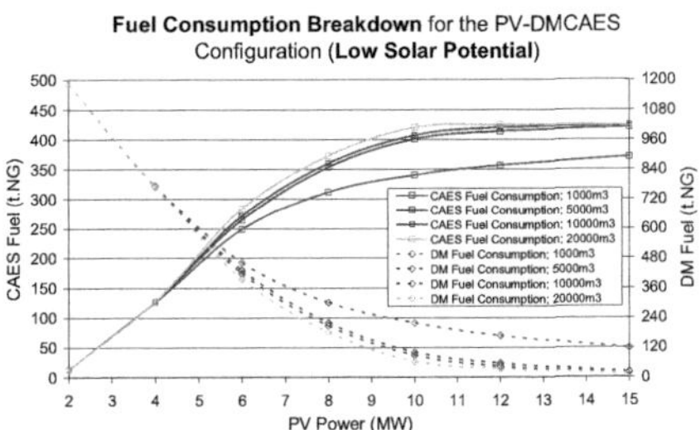

Figure 9. Fuel consumption breakdown (low solar potential).

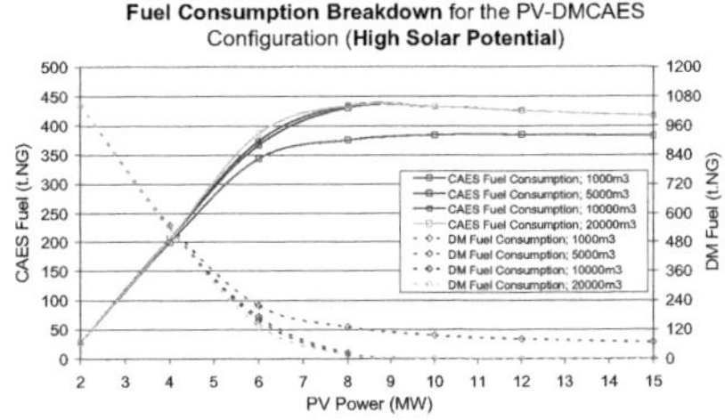

Figure 10. Fuel consumption breakdown (medium solar potential).

5. Conclusions

Based on the development of an appropriate sizing algorithm, the solution of DMCAES combined with PV power was currently examined for isolated island regions expecting introduction of natural gas in the forthcoming years. To this end, the area of the Aegean Sea was selected as case study, with two different quality solar potential areas used in order to capture the entire range of solar variation across the Archipelagos. According to the results obtained, influence of the local solar potential implies significant difference in terms of both energy autonomy achieved and fuel consumption required, that is however becoming inconsiderable once PV power increases to extreme values, i.e. above 10 MW.

Furthermore, according to the results, employment of storage larger than 5,000 m^3 implies no actual benefit for the system performance, with 1,000 m^3 on the other hand failing to provide energy autonomy even for the highest PV capacity examined. Overall, according to the results of this study, appreciable quality of solar potential across the entire Greek territory is found to stimulate similar projects not only for the island territory, but also for the Greek mainland, where use of CAES configurations coupled with considerable PV power could serve night-time peak loads and thus relieve the main grid from the operation of strictly thermal-based peak power units.

Acknowledgement

This study was supported by the European Union and the Greek General Secretariat for Research and Technology under the Greek-French Bilateral Collaboration Program and specifically under the project entitled "NAPOLEON".

References

Q. Ai, X. Wang, X. He, 2014, The impact of large-scale distributed generation on power grid and microgrids, Renew. Energ., 62, 417-423.

D.P. Bernardon, A.P.C. Mello, L.L. Pfitscher, L.N. Canha, A.R. Abaide, A.A.B. Ferreira, 2014, Real-time reconfiguration of distribution network with distributed generation, Electr. Pow. Syst. Res., 107, 59-67.

J.K. Kaldellis, D. Zafirakis, 2007a, Present situation and future prospects of electricity generation in Aegean Archipelago islands, Energ. Policy, 35, 9, 4623-4639.

J.K. Kaldellis, D. Zafirakis, 2012, Optimum sizing of stand-alone wind-photovoltaic hybrid systems for representative wind and solar potential cases of the Greek territory, J. Wind Eng. Ind. Aerod., 107-108, 169-178.

J.K. Kaldellis, D. Zafirakis, 2007b, Optimum energy storage techniques for the improvement of renewable energy sources-based electricity generation economic efficiency, Energy, 32, 12, 2295-2305.

D. Zafirakis, K.J. Chalvatzis, 2014, Wind energy and natural gas-based energy storage to promote energy security and lower emissions in island regions, Fuel, 115, 203-219.

D. Zafirakis, J.K. Kaldellis, 2009, Economic evaluation of the dual mode CAES solution for increased wind energy contribution in autonomous island networks, Energ. Policy, 37, 5, 1958-1969.

D. Zafirakis, J.K. Kaldellis, 2010, Autonomous dual-mode CAES systems for maximum wind energy contribution in remote island networks, Energ. Convers. Manage., 51, 11, 2150-2161.

Public Power Corporation (PPC), 1986, Solar Irradiance Measurements for Greece 1980–1985, 1st ed., PPC, Athens.

N.G. Kalampalikas, P.A. Pilavachi, 2010, A model for the development of a power production system in Greece, Part II: Where RES meet EU targets, Energ. Policy, 38, 11, 6514–6528.

Jiří Jaromír Klemeš, Petar Sabev Varbanov and Peng Yen Liew (Editors)
Proceedings of the 24th European Symposium on Computer Aided Process Engineering – ESCAPE 24
June 15-18, 2014, Budapest, Hungary.

Energy Management of a Hybrid Controlled Process with Renewable Sources

Lucas Nieto Degliuomini[b], Martin Cunningham[c], Facundo Ferreyra[c], Patricio A. Luppi[b,c], Marta S. Basualdo[a,b,c*]

[a]*Computer Aided Process Engineering Group (CAPEG) Technological National,University Faculty of Rosario (UTN-FRRo) Zeballos 1341, S2000BQA, Rosario, Argentina*
[b]*French Argentine International Center for Information and Systems Sciences (CIFASIS - CONICET - UNR – AMU) 27 de Febrero 210 bis, S2000EZP, Rosario, Argentina*
[c]*FCEIyA-UNR Pellegrini 250- Rosario, Argentina*
basualdo@cifasis-conicet.gov.ar

Abstract

This work focuses on the multivariable control of a hydrogen production plant from bio-ethanol to feed a fuel cell and solar energy power generation system. The concept of combining bio-ethanol with solar energy to vehicular applications is new. A central power bus structure to receive and give the power generation is proposed. So the designed Energy Management Strategies (EMS) must act at every instant to achieve the most efficient way to handle the available energy sources. Some assumptions are adopted for defining the conceptual engineering of an integrated dynamic model of this system. It includes solar subsystem, the bio ethanol processor system (BPS), as well as a battery bank and supercapacitors to best satisfy the electric motor power demand. Several simulations are carried out to illustrate the applicability and effectiveness of the proposed design and strategies. The solar profile and standard driving cycles for Rosario city in Argentine are considered for the tests. In addition, the hydrogen quality for the fuel cell is guaranteed by improving the base conventional control strategy with Model Predictive Control.

Keywords: Hybrid solar-fuel cell vehicle, Predictive control , Energy management

1. Introduction

The progressive transition to Fuel Cell Hybrid Electric Vehicles (FCHEV) is essential to help on solving the problems derived from the fossil fuel dependence. It is common to add Energy Storage Systems (ESS) on vehicles propelled by fuel cells. Hybridization can bring significant benefits: the improvement of transient power demand, the ability to absorb the energy from regenerative braking and the opportunities for optimization of the vehicle efficiency. The coordination among the various power sources requires a high level of control in the vehicle. Proton Exchange Membrane Fuel Cell (PEM-FC), fed by hydrogen, is considered the best option for mobile applications due to its compactness, modularity, low temperature working point, higher conversion efficiencies and low emissions of pollutants and noise. Some previous interesting works about the control problem of PEMFC (Zenith and Skogestad, 2009; Woo and Benziger, 2007) can be found in the literature. In this work the PEMFC control is considered in the context of the overall hybrid system. An onboard processing system to produce hydrogen from bio-ethanol, is a great replacement, given that it is much safer to manipulate, and the current refuelling infrastructure is able to handle it.

This paper is based in the work presented by Nieto Degliuomini et al., 2012; which proposed a decentralized PI control structure with six loops through the implementation of a generalized methodology for plant-wide control. All the control loops present a suitable dynamic behaviour. Nevertheless, the transient response of the CO concentration at the feeding of the PEM-FC is unable to achieve the CO specification. Hence, in this work a model predictive control (MPC) strategy is proposed for replacing only the critical loop related to CO concentration. Based on the study of the relative gain array (RGA) presented at Rullo et al, 2014; the most interactive loops in the plant are identified and become candidates for substitution with a predictive functional control (PFC). In addition, the design of the energy management strategy (EMS) integrated to the enhanced base control structure with PFC on the BPS are presented in order to satisfy the power load requirements of the vehicle. To improve the efficiency of the proposed system, the inclusion of batteries bank (BB) and super-capacitors (SC) is done. Dynamic simulations of the hybrid system are presented, considering the solar subsystem with an isolation and temperature profile from the city of Rosario, Argentine. The vehicle load profile is generated assuming standardized driving cycles adapted for the same city.

2. System Description

In this section the modelling of the integrated energy generation system is explained. The solar module comprises a PhotoVoltaic (PV) panel, which surface corresponds to the rooftop of the vehicle connected to the dc bus via a dc/dc converter, which controls the operation point of the PV panel. The main assumptions for doing the calculations for the PV panel were taken from Feroldi et al. (2013). The dc bus collects the energy generated by both sources and delivers it to the BPS if it is necessary and to the BB and SC. Its voltage is imposed by the BB which comprises lead-acid batteries connected in a series/parallel array. The lead-acid BB may be modelled as a voltage source connected in series with a resistance and a capacitance. A part of the energy generated is used to fulfill the thermal requirements of the BPS which is helpful to reduce the biofuel consumption. The BPS was modeled by using mass and energy balances, chemical equilibrium, thermodynamic models and feasible heat transfer conditions. The BPS consists of an Ethanol Steam Reforming (ESR) plug flow reactor, where most of the conversion of ethanol to H_2 is made. There are three reactors that configure the cleaning system of carbon monoxide (CO). These are two Water Gas Shift (WGS) and the third is a Preferential Oxidation of Carbon monoxide (CO-PrOx) reactor, where oxidation of CO into CO_2 is made. Ethanol and vaporized water are mixed and then supplied to the ESR, to produce ethanol decomposition according to the reaction: $CH_3CH_2OH+3.H_2O \leftrightarrow 6.H_2+2.CO_2$ .The topology of the hybrid system under consideration is depicted in Fig. 1. The overall reaction is endothermic, and in this work the heat requirement can be supplied mainly by the electric heater or by using fresh ethanol in the burner. This last option is only considered when there is no other source available. The transfer of heat is achieved passing the hot gases through the jacket of the ESR. More details about the BPS are given at Nieto Degliuomini et al. (2012).

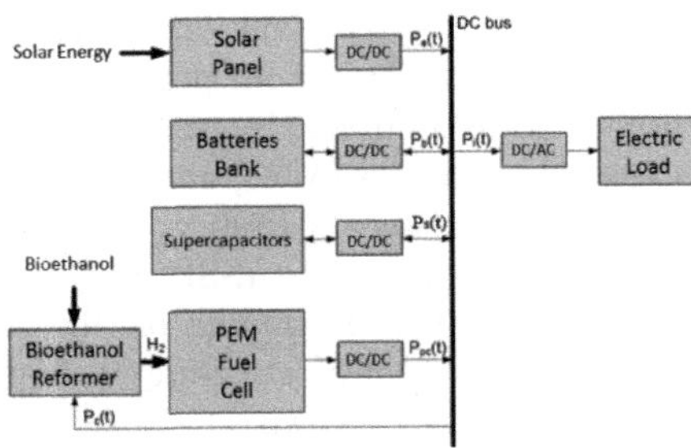

Figure 1. Hybrid energy generation system

3. Model Predictive Control Strategy

In this section PFC strategy is proposed to maintain the CO levels within the desired range and to improve the general closed loop dynamic behavior. The main control objectives of the BPS together with the designed base decentralized control structure were presented in Nieto Degliuomini et al. (2012). It includes for the BPS the list of variables given in Table 1. In section 5 the comparisons are given taking into account the previous results obtained with this multivariable control structure.

Table 1. Variables considered in the BPS

Measured		Manipulated		Disturbances	
y_1	ESR exit temperature	u_1	Water to ESR inlet	d_1	Ethanol purity
y_2	Jacket exit gases temp.	u_2	Exchanged heat	d_2	Stack current
y_3	Burner exit temperature	u_3	Ethanol to Burner		
y_4	Burner entering molar flow	u_4	Oxygen to Burner		
y_5	Molar ratio H_2O/Ethanol	u_5	Oxygen to CO-PrOx		
y_6	HTS exit temperature	u_6	CM voltage		
y_7	LTS exit temperature	u_7	ESR exit flow(*)		
y_8	CO-PrOx exit temperature	u_8	HTS exit flow(*)		
y_9	Molar ratio O_2/CO	u_9	LTS exit flow(*)		
y_{10}	Burner exit molar flow	u_{10}	CO-PrOx exit flow(*)		
y_{11}	CO-PrOx CO exit conc.	u_{11}	Bio-ethanol flow(*)		
y_{12}	Net Power				
y_{13}	Oxygen excess				
y_{14}	Stack voltage				
y_{15}	ESR pressure(*)				
y_{16}	HTS pressure(*)				
y_{17}	LTS pressure(*)				
y_{18}	CO-PrOx pressure(*)				
y_{19}	H_2 production rate(*)				

(*) indicates the stabilizing control loops.

Table 2. RGA for the BPS

	u_1	u_3	u_3	u_4	u_5	u_6
y_1	0.0001	**0.9908**	0.0074	0.0014	0.0004	0.0000
y_3	0.0242	0.0012	**0.8882**	0.0844	0.0020	0.0000
y_8	0.3953	0.0011	0.0143	0.0108	**0.5796**	-0.0011
y_9	**0.5776**	0.0005	0.0004	0.0027	0.4187	0.0000
y_{10}	0.0031	0.0064	0.0897	**0.9008**	0.0000	0.0000
y_{13}	-0.0003	0.0000	0.0000	0.0000	-0.0007	**1.0011**

The methodology begins by stabilizing the plant with five control loops indicated with "*" at Table 1. The most critical variables are the pressures in each reactor (ESR, HTS, LTS, Co-Prox). These pressures are controlled by manipulating each reactor's exit flow. As can be seen, six manipulated variables (MVs) are available (u_1-u_6). The selection of controlled variables is done by choosing six from y_1 to y_{14}. The search is driven such that minimizing the sum of square deviations (SSE_{yr}) of the non controlled variables when set points changes or disturbances impact on the overall plant. Under this assumption the final decentralized control structure is found by implementing the Relative Gain Array (RGA) analysis shown at Table 2, which recommends the following six control loops: 1, y_9 - u_1; 2, y_1 - u_2; 3, y_3 - u_3; 4, y_{10} - u_4; 5, y_8 - u_5 and 6, y_{13} - u_6. However, with this control structure large transient values of CO-PrOx CO exit concentration (y_{11}) occur. In the next section, PFC technology is considered as good option to satisfy the CO requirements for the PEM-FC.

3.1. Predictive Functional Control

The PFC option is recommended to be considered when one loop presents troubles which affect the overall plant behavior. From Table 2 can be detected that loops 1 and 5 present certain degree of interaction. In Figure 2 can be seen that with PI control y_{11} presents sudden change in the CO concentration. It is particularly influenced by the loop 5 dynamic. Then, the PFC algorithm will be used instead of PI on loop 5. The PFC algorithm is implemented as a Toolbox of MATLAB, developed based on the theoretical concepts given by Richalet and O'Donovan, 2009. In Figure 2 the dynamic responses of the CO-PrOx CO exit concentrations are compared for both control structures (PI and PFC) showing the great benefit produced by PFC implementation.

4. Energy Management Strategy

Basically, the EMS is designed considering the total generation from solar source, the fuel cell and regenerative braking. The total demand is given by the required load from the electrical motor of the vehicle, plus the required power to recharge the BB and SC together with the electrical heater. Note that the operation can be maintained as long as the energy available in the entire system is sufficient to satisfy the load requirements. If this limit is surpassed, the load must be disconnected to recharge batteries and avoid damages. In addition, given the opposite situation, if the battery reaches a maximum safety level of charge, the generators must be disconnected and the storage system alone

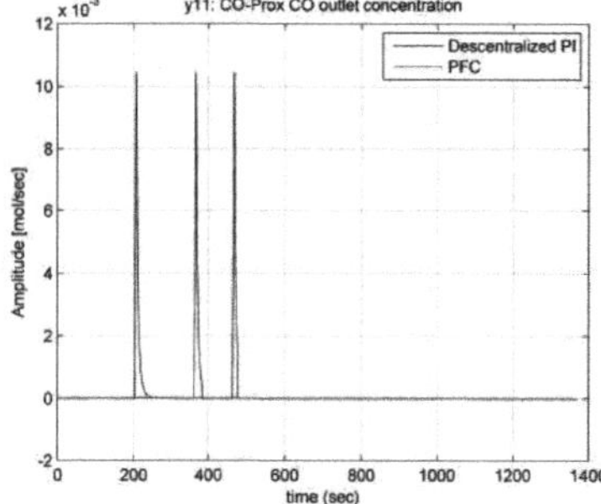

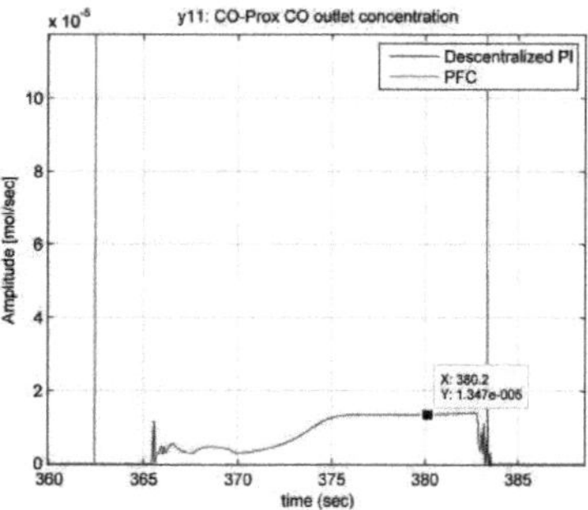

Figure 2. Dynamic responses of CO-PROx exit CO concentration with both controllers must supply the power, to avoid overcharging, and consequent reduction of life-span

The core of the EMS lies in considering the operation of the fuel cell in two different pseudo-static points. Two operating points are chosen for the FC: 8 kW, because it presents a good trade-off between the FC efficiency and 10kw, because it is the maximum capacity of the FC. As long as the load requirements do not surpass the available power for a long period, a good performance can be achieved by using the FC at 8 kW. This policy demonstrated to give a substantial reduction in the consumed bioethanol. As can be seen in Figure 2, the strategy begins determining the operating point for the FC which depends of the total required power. The usage of batteries and the operation time for the FC at one point are also considered, to prevent malfunctions (overpressures or oxygen starvation) in the FC due to fast dynamics. When the operating point is chosen, the EMS makes a final calculation of Net Power, and the SC power. Once the two previous steps are fulfilled, the EMS behaves as a state-machine with four different states. In the state machine concept, the system makes a transition from one state (mode) to another, provided that specific condition is true and defines the change. The description of the four states created and their respective triggering conditions are listed below:

- State 1: if the Net Power is positive and the BB's SoC (State of Charge) is lower than the maximum, it means that the system has power to spare. Accordingly, the BB and SC are charged, and the cell is operated at the chosen operating point.
- State 2: if the Net Power is positive, but the BB's SoC is larger than the limit, the fuel cell is operated at the chosen point, but nor the BB neither the SC are charged. They are both disconnected
- State 3: if the Net Power is negative, it means that an extra power is required besides the fuel cell, the solar panel and the regenerative braking. As a result, the BB is discharged, and the SC contributes if the power given by the BB is not enough. This helps prevent lack of power due to fast demands.
- State 4: If the BB's SoC becomes lower than the minimum (it also means the SC are already fully depleted), then the system enters in an 'emergency state mode'. The fuel cell operates at 10kw, the electrical heater is turned off, and the BB is charged with a reserved fraction of the fuel cell's power (prioritizing the recharge over the performance).

5. Results

In Figure 3 are presented the load requirements of power corresponding to the most exigent standardized driving cycle, the Urban Dynamometer Driving Schedule (UDDS) and the generated power by the hybrid system, fuel cell, batteries and supercapacitors . The system was tested too against two other different driving cycles, Federal Test Procedure and New European Driving Cycle. For all the cases, the ethanol consumption was decreased in over 30 % with the hybridization, compared with the system without energy storage and/or renewable energy sources.

6. Conclusions

A novel integrated system for obtaining power from bio-ethanol and solar energy sources for vehicles application was presented. The BPS to produce H_2 rich synthesis gas, and feeds the PEM-FC converts the energy vector into useful power. The PFC strategy enhanced the original decentralized control structure to guarantee PEM-FC hydrogen quality. The principal objective of providing the heat required by the H_2 production plant mainly by electrical source, through the operation of photovoltaic arrays is achieved. The solar panel is sized to fit in the available surface of the rooftop

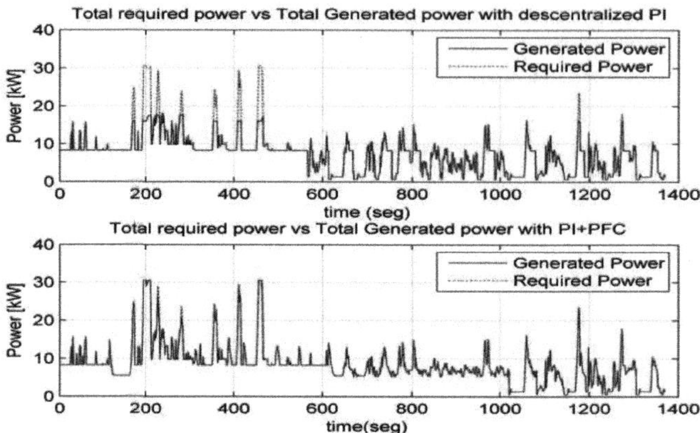

Figure 3. Dynamic responses of the required and generated power on the system

of the vehicle. To distribute the power, a structure with a central power bus is besought, so the EMS must act in every instant, integrating in the most efficient way, the available energy sources. This new topology works properly for the proposed scenarios and the EES is capable of switching between energy sources, or using the BB or SC in the right situations. By means of this ESS, it is possible to keep the fuel cell working in high efficiency zones, without neglecting the variations of the energy requirements. Therefore, the power distribution maintains the subsystems operating in good efficiency zones, and keeps the battery charge in a safety zone. Future works will include the development of a supervisory control for the plant-wide problem based on real time optimization techniques.

Acknowledgements

The authors want to acknowledge the financial support from CONICET, ANPCyT , UNR-FCEIA and UTN-FRRo.

References

D. Feroldi, L. Nieto Degliuomini, M. Basualdo, 2013, Energy management of a hybrid system based on wind-solar power sources and bioethanol, Chemical Engineering Research and Design, DOI: 10.1016/j.cherd.2013.03.007.

L. Nieto Degliuomini, D. Zumoffen, M. Basualdo, 2012, Plant-wide control design for fuel processor system with PEMFC, International Journal of Hydrogen Energy, 37, 19, 14801 – 14811.

J. Richalet, D. O'Donovan, 2009, Predictive Functional Control – Principles and Industrial Applications, Springer, London, UK.

P. Rullo, L. Nieto Degliuomini, M. Garcıa, M. Basualdo, 2014, Model predictive control to ensure high quality hydrogen production for fuel cells, DOI:10.1016/j.ijhydene.2013.12.069

C. Woo, J Benziger, 2007, PEM fuel cell current regulation by fuel feed control, Chemical Engineering Science, 62, 4, 957-968

F. Zenith, S. Skogestad, 2009, Control of the mass and energy dynamics of polybenzimidazole-membrane fuel cells, Journal of Process Control, 19, 3, 415-432.

Jiří Jaromír Klemeš, Petar Sabev Varbanov and Peng Yen Liew (Editors)
Proceedings of the 24th European Symposium on Computer Aided Process Engineering – ESCAPE 24
June 15-18, 2014, Budapest, Hungary.

Kinetic Modelling of Copper and Zinc Dissolution from Brass Obtained from Waste Electrical and Electronic Equipment

Ioana A. Popescu[a,*], Tamás Varga[b], Árpád Imre-Lucaci[a], Tibor Chován[b], Petru Ilea[a],

[a] *"Babeş-Bolyai" University, Faculty of Chemistry and Chemical Engineering, Department of Chemical Engineering, 11 Arany Janos Street, RO-400028 Cluj-Napoca, Romania*
[b] *University of Pannonia, Department of Process Engineering, 10 Egyetem Street, H-8200 Veszprém, Hungary*
alipopescu@yahoo.com

Abstract

The leaching kinetics of copper and zinc from brass was investigated in sodium persulfate solution. The factors affecting the performance and efficiency of the leaching process, such as leaching time, acid concentration and temperature were separately investigated. The obtained results revealed that copper and zinc are successfully dissolved in a persulfate environment, especially for high temperature (60 °C) and oxidant concentration (0.3 M $Na_2S_2O_8$ solution). To define the exact geometry changes that appear a shrinking core model can be used. With the determination of pre-exponential constants, activation energies and reaction orders, the concentration and temperature dependence can be examined. The identified kinetic model can be used for describing similar processes involving dissolution of metals or alloys.

Keywords: brass, copper and zinc leaching, kinetic modelling, shrinking core model

1. Introduction

The current trend of industrialization and technological innovation continues to accelerate the replacement of electrical and electronic equipment, resulting in an increase of waste electric and electronic equipment (WEEE). Recycling of WEEE is important not only to reduce the amount of waste requiring treatment, but also to promote the recovery of valuable materials, such as copper and zinc (Fogarasi et al., 2013). Leaching process to recover and recycle metals from wastes of brass which contain copper, zinc and lead using different leaching agents including sulfuric acid, ammonia, hydrochloric acid, cyanide and acetic acid has been studied extensively (Le et al., 2011). Compared with acid as leaching agent a potential alternative to the environmental benign process is alkaline leaching where persulfate is used as a leaching agent (Liu et al., 2011). The dissolution of copper and zinc from brass using a persulfate solution has not yet been reported.

The present study aims to analyze the dissolution kinetics of copper and zinc from brass in persulfate environment. The first step involves testing individually the efficiency of sodium persulfate in the dissolution process of copper (Popescu et al., 2013) and zinc. We propose a new kinetic model that adequately describes the geometric changes that appear in the leaching process of the two investigated metals.

2. Experimental

2.1. Material

The materials used in the leaching process derive from waste electrical and electronic equipment (WEEE); shape, size, weight and composition were chosen to highlight specific components of the dissolution kinetics. The first set of experiments aimed at investigating the usage of $Na_2S_2O_8$ in copper dissolution. The material used in these experiments was metallic copper wire with a purity of 99.99 %. The utilized cylindrical copper samples had a weight of approximately 2 g and a length ranging between 2.9 and 3.4 cm, with a diameter of 0.3 cm (Popescu et al., 2013). For the study of zinc dissolution in persulfate environment a rectangular block of zinc was chosen. These experiments aimed at highlighting the leaching degree of zinc at the surface of the block. Five facets of the block were varnished and one facet has been left untouched to interact with the persulfate solution, since the zinc block sinks to the bottom of the reactor. The weight of samples used ranged between 3.2 and 5 g, with an area of interaction varying from 1.62 to 1.98 cm^2. The material used for copper and zinc dissolution from brass is a cylindrical rod of brass. The composition of the alloy (60 % copper and 40 % zinc) was determined by complete dissolution of the metal in nitric acid and analysis of the components was performed using an atomic absorption spectrometer. Weight and length of the samples ranged between 3.6 and 5.6 g, 1.4 and 2 cm, with a diameter of 0.6 cm.

2.2. Leaching process

The leaching experiments were performed in a 150 mL isothermal stirred batch reactor. The reactor was equipped with a thermometer and a mechanical stirrer. The temperature was kept constant using an electric thermostat. 100 mL of $Na_2S_2O_8$ solution was added to the reactor. When the desired stirring speed and reaction temperature were reached, the solid sample was added into the reactor. 1 mL of sample solution was withdrawn at specific time intervals for analysing the concentration of copper/zinc by an atomic absorption spectrometer (AAS). Metals (Cu and Zn) or brass samples remained after the leaching process were dried and weighed after each experiment.

3. Results and discussions

The global reactions describing the leaching process of copper and zinc using sodium persulfate as an oxidizing agent are presented in Eq.(1) and Eq.(2). The same reactions have been proposed for the dissolution process of zinc and copper from brass.

$$Zn + Na_2S_2O_8 \rightarrow ZnSO_4 + Na_2SO_4 \tag{1}$$

$$Cu + Na_2S_2O_8 \rightarrow CuSO_4 + Na_2SO_4 \tag{2}$$

The experiments were conducted to separately investigate the performance and efficiency of the $Na_2S_2O_8$ solution in the leaching of samples on copper and zinc and brass respectively. The effect of temperature, concentrations of sodium persulfate and leaching time were determined on the rate of the process steps. Specific kinetic parameters were identified for each set of experiments. Quantities of dissolved copper and zinc that resulted after 2 h of dissolution time have been centralized in Table 1. The complete experimental results for copper leaching from brass are presented in Figure 1.

3.1. Effect of temperature

The effect of temperature on the dissolution of copper and zinc was investigated for 30, 45 and 60 °C, while the rest of the parameters were kept constant. It can be observed

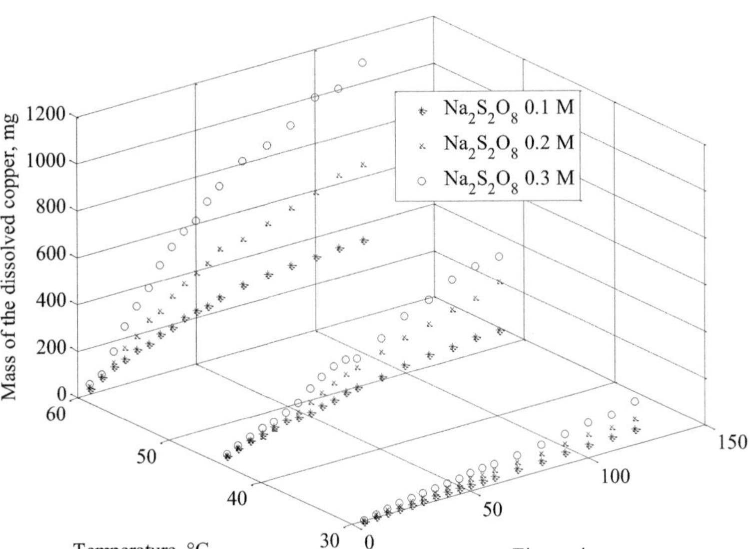

Figure 1. Evolution of dissolved copper mass from brass depending on temperature and duration of dissolution for different concentrations of sodium persulfate

that the extraction of copper increases with the increase of leaching time at different temperatures. The copper and zinc dissolution rate is greatly affected by temperature. A temperature increase from 30 to 45 °C at 0.2 M $Na_2S_2O_8$ concentration results in an increase in the amount of dissolved copper by 14.9 % and 3.1 % increase in zinc, after 2 h of leaching time. The same increase in temperature results in a rise of 9 % of dissolved copper (Figure 1) and 8 % dissolved zinc for the process of brass leaching.

3.2. The effect of concentration

Effect of $Na_2S_2O_8$ solution concentration was investigated for values of 0.1, 0.2 and 0.3 M for an interval of 120 min of leaching time. The amount of dissolved copper and zinc increases with the rise of sodium persulfate concentration. If we take in consideration only the experiments that targeted copper dissolution in persulfate environmental, the results show an increase in the amount for dissolution rate in the range of 60-168 mg/cm^2/h (Table 1). For the study regarding zinc dissolution we obtain similar results if

Table 1. Dissolution rate (mg/cm^2/h) for different experimental conditions

$Na_2S_2O_8$	T	Copper			Copper from brass			Zinc			Zinc from brass		
mole/L	°C	mg	cm^2	mg/cm^2/h	mg	cm^2	mg/cm^2/h	mg	cm^2	mg/cm^2/h	mg	cm^2	mg/cm^2/h
	30	161	3.2	25	65	3.2	10	120	1.2	50	41	3.2	6
0.1	45	368	3.0	61	219	3.8	29	399	2	100	137	3.8	18
	60	518	3.1	85	330	4.5	37	663	1.6	205	186	4.5	21
	30	317	3.1	52	110	4.0	14	802	1.9	206	72	4.0	9
0.2	45	622	3.2	96	425	4.1	51	938	1.8	249	254	4.1	31
	60	1,017	3.3	152	654	4.3	75	1,152	2	288	348	4.3	40
	30	400	2.9	70	184	4.3	21	1,212	1.8	337	95	4.3	11
0.3	45	861	3.2	136	534	3.7	71	1,340	1.9	338	331	3.7	44
	60	1,550	3.2	238	1,090	5.1	107	1,510	1.6	458	619	5.1	61

we disregard the concentration of 0.1 M of sodium persulfate. The dissolution process of copper and zinc from brass (40 % zinc, 60 % copper) indicates an increase of dissolution rate in the range of 27-86 mg/cm^2/h for copper, respectively 15-50 mg/cm^2/h for zinc (Table 1).

4. Kinetic modelling

Two kinds of models can be found in the literature which is developed to describe the dissolution process. The first group contains very complex models, which can describe the change of the surface very precisely in micro scale (Ouden et al., 2013). The other group contains simplified shrinking core models in which the simplifications usually based on that assumption that the dissolution process is under reaction control (Ahmed et al., 2012). In this work we proposed a model which describes the dissolution process on macro scale and calculates with the change in the surface of the solid due to the dissolution process.

Since the dissolution of solids is a mass transport process via the interaction surfaces between the solid and liquid phases, the rate of the dissolution process is hardly depend on the size of that surface. Hence, such a model, which can describe the dissolution process, should calculate the changes of the interaction surface. We investigated two kinds of solid geometry as we introduced earlier in Chapter 2.1. In both cases we proposed that the dissolved volumes in each direction of the investigated geometry are proportional to the surface of the solid in that direction. In the pure zinc dissolution experiments the block has only one facet where the mass transport process can take place. Hence, due to the shrinking, only the height (h) of the block changes. We assumed that the reactor is well mixed so the reaction mixture around the block is homogenous. The change in the height of the block can easily be calculated with the following expression:

$$dh/dt = \frac{dm/dt}{\rho_{Zn} \cdot l \cdot w}, \tag{3}$$

where the l is the length, w is the width of the block. The change in the total mass of the solid is calculated with the following equation:

$$dm/dt = -A \cdot r \cdot M_{Zn}, \tag{4}$$

where A is the surface where the mass transport process takes place, r is the dissolution rate of the zinc and M_{Zn} is the molecular mass of the zinc. To calculate the dissolution rate an Arrhenius type correlation is applied:

$$r = k_{0,r} \cdot e^{-Ea_r/RT} \cdot \left(c_{Zn^{2+}}^{sat.} - c_{Zn^{2+}}\right)^{n_r}, \tag{5}$$

where are three unknown parameters $k_{0,r}$ – preexponential factor, Ea_r – activation energy, n_r – reaction order. The saturated Zn^{2+} ion concentration ($c_{Zn^{2+}}^{sat.}$) is determined at each temperature and reagent concentration based on measurements. The actual Zn^{2+} ion concentration changes due to dissolution process:

$$dc_{Zn^{2+}}/dt = A \cdot r/V = -dc_{S_2O_8^{2-}}/dt \tag{6}$$

As the Zn^{2+} ion concentration increases the $S_2O_8^{2-}$ ion concentration decreases with the same rate. As it can be seen in Figure 2. the measured dissolved zinc mass show an interesting characteristic. If we applied mild conditions during the experiments (low temperature and reagent concentration) there is an inflection point on the profile which means there must be another process next to reaction step which controls in these periods. It can be the increase of the interfacial area due to the formation of a porous layer on the solid. We supposed this increase is the function of the temperature, the reagent concentration, and of course the surface of the block (A_g) which can be calculated from the sizes:

$$dA/dt = k_{0,A} \cdot e^{-Ea_A/RT} \cdot \left(n_A \cdot A_g - A\right) \cdot c_{S_2O_8^{2-}} \tag{7}$$

where three more unknown parameters $k_{0,A}$, Ea_A, n_A are applied. The last parameter determines what the maximal surface in the formed porous layer is. The introduced model was implemented in MATLAB and solved with Runge-Kutta method. The model error is calculated as the sum of square error in case of all the nine experiments (see Figure 2). The proposed model describes the dissolution of zinc block with acceptable precision. The identified model parameters are: $k_{0,r} = 1.4 \cdot 10^{-3}\ m^3 m^{-2} s^{-1}$, $Ea_r = 0.1\ J\ mol^{-1}$, $n_r = 0.646\ 1$, $k_{0,A} = 1.98\ m^3\ mol^{-1} s^{-1}$, $Ea_A = 3.5 \cdot 10^4\ J\ mol^{-1}$, $n_A = 0.466\ 1$.

In the brass experiment the investigated geometry is cylindrical (diameter – d, length – l). The geometry can change its size in both ways proportional to the material transport area on that direction:

$$dl/dt = \frac{4 \cdot dm/dt}{\rho_{brass} \cdot \left(1 + 2l/d\right) \cdot d^2 \pi} \tag{8}$$

$$dd/dt = d - d^{0.5} \cdot \left(l - dl/dt\right)^{-0.5} \cdot \left(d \cdot l - d \cdot dl/dt - 2 \cdot l \cdot dl/dt\right)^{0.5} \tag{9}$$

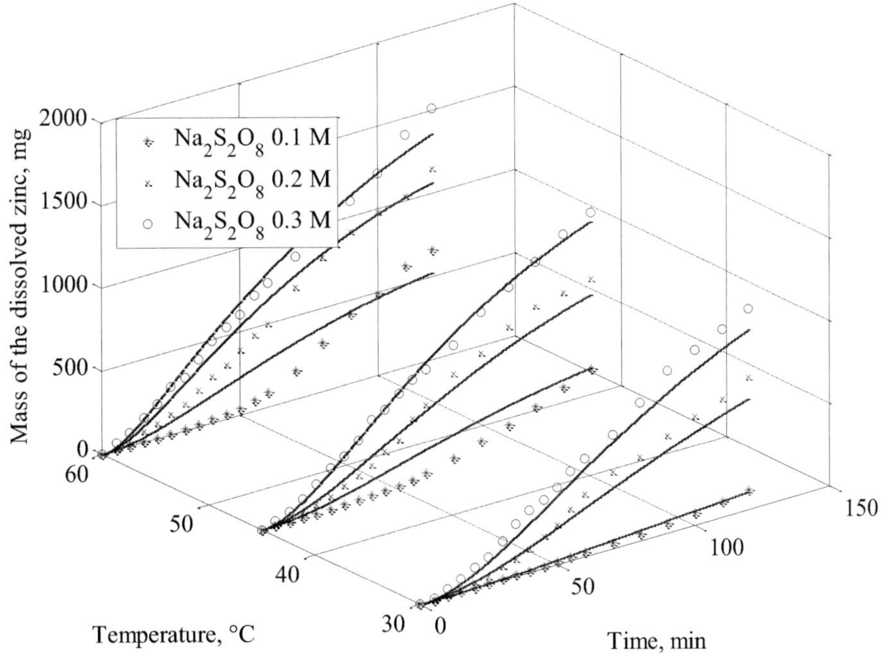

Figure 2. The measured (markers) and the calculated (continuous line) dissolved zinc mass at different experimental conditions

The component mass balance is based on the proposed reaction mechanism given by Eq.(1) and Eq.(2) and the rates of the reactions calculates with the following equations:

$$r_i = k_{0i} \cdot e^{-Ea_i/RT} \cdot \left(c_{S_2O_8^{2-}}\right)^{n_i} \tag{10}$$

where i represents the number of the reaction (i.e. if $i=1$ the expression gives the rate of Eq.(1)). In this case the model error is calculated based on the difference of the measured and calculated dissolved mass profiles of zinc and copper. The proposed model has better fit to the measurements than in case the dissolution of pure zinc. The identified model parameters are: $k_{0,1} = 1.97 \cdot 10^3\ m^3 m^{-2} s^{-1}$, $Ea_1 = 6.51 \cdot 10^4\ J\ mol^{-1}$, $n_1 = 2.106\ 1$, $k_{0,2} = 4.21 \cdot 10^3\ m^3\ m^3 m^{-2} s^{-1}$, $Ea_2 = 5.22 \cdot 10^4\ J\ mol^{-1}$, $n_2 = 1.136\ 1$.

5. Conclusions

Experimental study and the modelling of the dissolution of copper and zinc respectively brass (40 % zinc, 60 % copper) were investigated in sodium persufate solution. The formation of a porous layer was identified during the dissolution process of pure zinc block. This porous layer increases the interfacial area between the two phases and also increases the rate of the dissolution process. The mathematical model of the proposed mechanism was developed and tested. The dissolution process of zinc and copper from brass was also investigated and the unknown kinetic parameters were identified.

Acknowledgements

This work was supported by the Romanian-Hungarian Bilateral Program under project no. 673/2013, TET_12-RO-1-2013-0017 and by the European Union and the State of Hungary, co-financed by the European Social Fund in the framework of TÁMOP-4.2.2/A-11/1/KONV-2012-0071 project. Tamás Varga's research activity in this work was supported by the European Union and the State of Hungary, co-financed by the European Social Fund in the framework of TÁMOP-4.2.4.A/ 2-11/1-2012-0001 'National Excellence Program'.

References

I.M. Ahmed, A.A. Nayl, J.A. Daoud, 2012, Leaching and recovery of zinc and copper from brass slag by sulfuric acid, Journal of Saudi Chemical Society, DOI: 10.1016/j.jscs.2012.11.003.

H.L. Le, J. Jeong, J.C. Lee, B.D. Pandey, J.M. Yoo, T.H. Huyunh, 2011, Hydrometallurgical Process for Copper Recovery from Waste Printed Circuit Boards (PCBs), Mineral Processing & Extractive Metall. Rev, 32, 90–104.

Z. Liu, Z. Yin, H. Hu, Q. Chen, 2012, Leaching kinetics of low-grade copper ore containing calcium-magnesium, carbonate in ammonia-ammonium sulfate solution with persulfate, Trans. Nonferrous Met. Soc., 22, 2822-2830.

Sz. Fogarasi, F. Imre-Lucaci, P. Ilea, Á. Imre-Lucaci, 2013, The environmental assessment of two new copper recovery processes from Waste Printed Circuit Boards, Journal of Cleaner Production 54,264-269.

I.A. Popescu, A. Egedy, Sz. Fogarasi, T. Varga, P. Ilea, 2013, Kinetic modelling and optimisation of copper leaching process from waste electrical and electronic equipments, Romanian International Conference on Chemistry and Chemical Engineering 18, Sinaia, Romania.

D. den Ouden, A. Segal, F.J. Vermolen, L. Zhao, C. Vuik, J. Sietsma, 2013, Application of the level-set method to a mixed-mode driven Stefan problem in 2D and 3D, Computing, 95, 8553-8572.

H. Yang, J. Liu, J. Yang, 2011, Leaching copper from shredded particles of waste printed circuit boards, Journal of Hazardous Materials, 187, 393–400.

Jiří Jaromír Klemeš, Petar Sabev Varbanov and Peng Yen Liew (Editors)
Proceedings of the 24th European Symposium on Computer Aided Process Engineering – ESCAPE 24
June 15-18, 2014, Budapest, Hungary.

Flood Prevention in Jijia Catchment Using Control Structures Based on Hydraulic Modelling

Mihai L. Mogoş-Kirner*, Mircea V. Cristea, Paul Ş. Agachi

Faculty of Chemistry and Chemical Engineering, Babeş-Bolyai University, Arany János Street, 11, Cluj-Napoca, Romania
mihaimogos@chem.ubbcluj.ro

Abstract

The present paper aims at modelling the catchment of Jijia River, situated in eastern Romania, and designing control structures for the reservoirs' inventories by manipulating their outflow gates. The model includes the main river, several main tributaries and five reservoirs. A simplified graph-like conceptual model is used as the backbone for the description of the real catchment. The Saint Venant equations are used to simulate water flow in the river basin. They are associated to equations for mass balance of water accumulation in the reservoirs. The model for the Jijia catchment is created using hydrodynamic equations. Real data of the reservoirs and river reaches is used to fit the model. Using adequate traditional and advanced control techniques, the outflow of each reservoir is manipulated in such a way to maintain the water level to a safe value and minimize the likelihood of flood occurrence in the downstream river reach.

Keywords: catchment, flood prevention, Saint Venant model, PI control, MPC control.

1. Introduction

The unpredictable weather has always been a problem for mankind because of its chaotic nature. Floods are natural phenomena, part of the Earth's hydrologic cycle, that cannot be avoided and have become main factors of social and economic losses in the world. This year, in Europe, they caused damages of more than 4,500 million EUR. In Romania, 45,000 houses have been damaged and a total cost of 1,500 million EUR was paid for the 2,005 floods.

These damages can be reduced with a system that prevents such disasters by implementing pro-acting measures. For a general catchment, the preventing system must be based on a process model (hydraulic and/or hydrologic) of the catchment, a specific control technology and a control system structure. One of the simplest ideas in flood prevention, although not always easily put in practice, is pre-releasing a certain amount of water from the reservoir based on the forecasted inflow as presented by Chou et al. (2013). Regarding hydraulic modelling, Freed (1985) describes some hydraulic models while Huang et al. (2007) discuss the effectiveness of a polder system. Saleh et al. (2013) analyze the performance of a hydrodynamic model based on the Saint Venant equations and come up with interesting results. Scattolini (2009) proposes a classification for decentralized, distributed and hierarchical control architectures involving large scale systems which could be applied to vast spatially spread watersheds. Proportional-Integral (PI) controllers have also been used for open channel flow and level control. Litrico et al. (2003) discuss the control of an irrigation canal based on the Saint Venant model, Weyer (2002) analyzes a decentralized PI control for an open channel system with overshot gates while YiZi et al. (2011) employ PI controllers on a south-to-north water transfer project using as a flow model a linearized form of the full 1D Saint Venant model. Breckpot et al. (2013) apply the Model Predictive Control (MPC) technique to flood control in the Demer river system, Delgoda et al. (2013) develop a new MPC method called Adaptive Multi Model Predictive Control to be used with multiple inflow models and Chiang et al. (2013) create a simplified conceptual model from a detailed hydrodynamic model to be used for real-time flood control using as a case study the same Demer river.

The paper presents the Jijia catchment, the developed hydraulic model for the water flow in the river bed together with the water mass balance in the reservoirs and the system behavior under PI and MPC control.

2. Jijia catchment description

Jijia River is a tributary of Prut River the confluence being situated at the border with Moldova. There are 4 important tributaries, 3 flowing from the right side of Jijia, namely Sitna, Miletin and Jijioara, and 1 from the left, this being Ibăneasa. Floods are almost a yearly threat for the people residing in the area. The flash floods produced on the steep slopes of Jijia's tributaries are very frequent. Thus, reservoirs were built for mitigating flood events and also as a water supply for the population. The total length of the river is 275 km with an average bed slope of about 1 ‰. The hydrographic network is formed of 144 streams having a catchment area of 5,757 km^2 and total length of 2,181 km. Over 80 % of the watercourses have a non-permanent flow, but, regardless of that, high levels of precipitation, especially in the spring, combined with bed slopes as high as 13 ‰ in some regions and large deforestated areas give birth to a rapidly increasing water level. This causes severe floods in the populated downstream zones. Table 1 and 2 provide data for Jijia catchment. The only non-permanent reservoir is Câmpeni.

Table 1. Jijia tributaries data

Tributary	Jijia river reach (km)	Confluence position	Tributary length (km)	Tributary catchment area (km^2)	(%) of Jijia catchment
Ibăneasa	55	left	43	189	3.28
Sitna	118	right	78	943	16.38
Miletin	167	right	90	675	11.72
Jijioara	173	right	34	237	4.12

Table 2. Catchment reservoirs data

Reservoir	River	River reach (km)	Total water volume (Mm^3)	Normal retention level (m)
Ezer	Jijia	16.2	10.33	3.18
Cătămărăşti	Sitna	17	17.95	10.4
Suliţa-Dracşani	Sitna	60	26.2	3.2
Câmpeni	Miletin	44.2	11.5	-
Hălceni	Miletin	80	42.8	7.5

3. Model development

The most utilized model for open channel flow is the Saint Venant model. It is a derivation of the Navier-Stokes model for fluid motion. It comprises 2 equations, one for the mass balance (Eq. 1) and one for the momentum balance (Eq. 2). Together, they describe the water flow through the channel. The equations are written for 1 spatial dimension (1D).

$$\frac{\partial Q}{\partial x} + \frac{\partial A}{\partial t} = q_x \tag{1}$$

$$\frac{1}{g}\frac{\partial v}{\partial t} + \frac{v}{g}\frac{\partial v}{\partial x} + \frac{\partial h}{\partial x} - J_0 = -J_e \tag{2}$$

The simulation model makes use of a simplified version of the Saint Venant equations named the kinematic wave model (Eqs. 3 and 4) together with a total mass balance equation (Eq. 5), which models the water accumulation in the reservoirs.

$$\frac{\partial h}{\partial t} + \frac{\partial Q}{\partial x} = \frac{q_x}{B} \tag{3}$$

$$Q = \left(\frac{J_0^{1/2}}{n}\right)\left(\frac{A^{5/3}}{P^{2/3}}\right) \tag{4}$$

$$\frac{dV}{dt} = Q_i - Q_e \tag{5}$$

The structure of the model is represented in Figure 1.

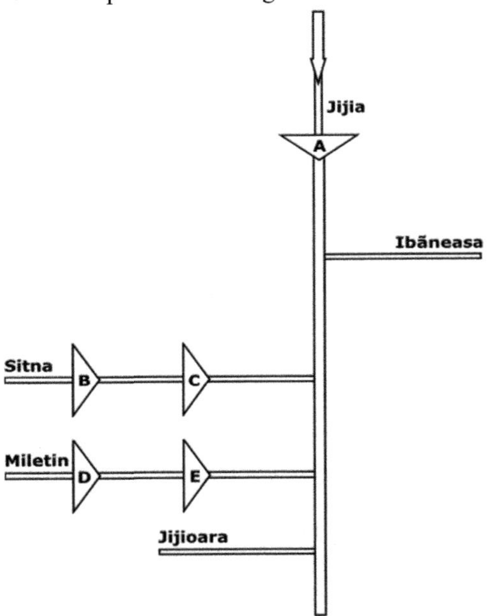

Figure 1. Catchment simplified model

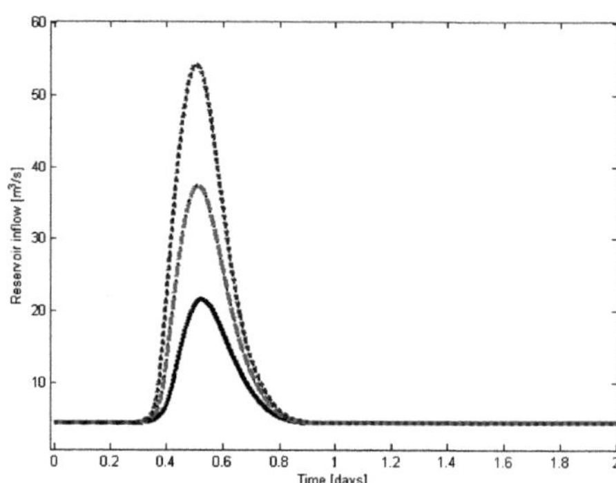

Figure 2. Reservoir inflows for the three flooding cases

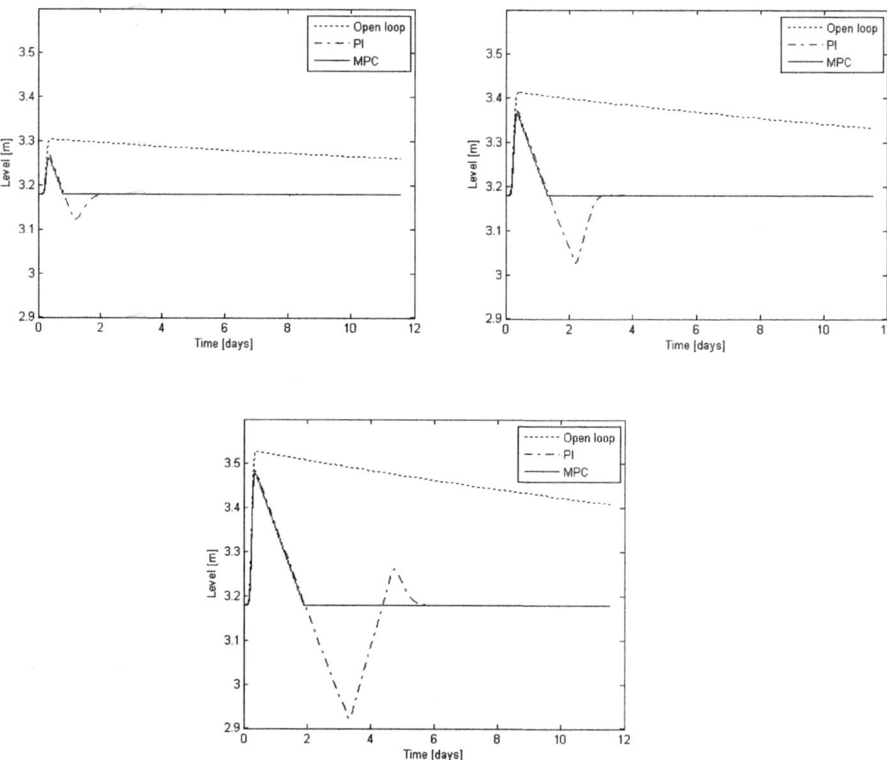

Figure 3. Reservoir level for the three flooding cases

The reservoirs are as they follow: A – Ezer, B – Cătămărăşti, C – Suliţa-Dracşani, D – Câmpeni and E – Hălceni. The system in this case is a distributed parameter one. For the simulation, the space resolution of 50 m was considered. A total of about 9,000 equations form the complete model. The geometry of the river bed is assumed of rectangular shape, with both width and longitudinal slope being considered constant. The lateral bank inflow is being neglected. The model was fitted with real field data of the streams under study and the characteristic details of each reservoir. Capacity curves of each reservoir were also estimated using on-site measured level-volume data.

4. Simulation results

Three scenarios were tested on Ezer reservoir in which different magnitude flood waves were simulated. The controlled variable was the water level h of the reservoir. In all cases, the manipulated variable was the opening c of the bottom gate which, practically, modified directly the outflow Q_e.

The inflow for the 3 flooding cases is presented in the Figure 2. Figure 3 presents the comparison between the PI and the MPC control results. In the case of a small size flood wave (approximately 12 h long, with an increase in the upstream water depth of about 2 m and a rise in inflow of about 18 m^3/s), the level returns to the setpoint relatively fast, in 1 day in the MPC case and in 2 days in the PI case, while for a medium flood wave (approximately 12 h long, with an increase in the upstream water depth of about 3.5 m and a rise in inflow of about 33 m^3/s), the MPC controller brings the level to the setpoint in 1.5 days and the PI controller in about 3 days. As for the case of the high flood wave (approximately 12 h long, with an increase in upstream water depth of about 5 m and a rise in inflow of about 50 m^3/s), the difference between the 2 controllers is more than obvious, the MPC controller succeeding to bring the level to the setpoint in 2 days while for the PI controller the period being 6 days.

One of the reasons behind the overall large return time is the small surface area of the bottom gate (and associated magnitude of the outflow) compared to the quantity of water needed to be evacuated. This, in turn, leads to the saturation of the PI controller output signal. The control system is, therefore, limited in its actions. The weight of the manipulated variable change from the MPC optimization index was tuned to provide short return time to the setpoint and to prevent the override of the maximum allowed change in time of the level (to preserve the banks integrity). Constraints on the maximum allowed level, associated with the minimum and maximum values of the outflow have been embedded in the MPC controller. This design step of the model-based control system will be followed by the development of the regulations for the operation of the reservoir system and by its integration with the existing weather forecast system, in order to fully benefit from the MPC inherent prediction capability. Validation will be performed as a follow-up of these previous steps.

5. Conclusions

A mathematical model for part of the Jijia river catchment was elaborated based on the mass and momentum balance equations of the Saint Venant 1D kinematic wave model and the reservoir mass balance. The results of the simulated scenarios show that PI control has satisfactory ability for regulating the water level in the reservoir. This control has favourable effects on diminishing the amplitude of the downstream propagated flooding wave, but, depending on the specific conditions, such as the properties of the flood wave and the characteristics of the system (surface area of bottom gate or flood attenuation capacity) it may partially fail to bring back the level to the setpoint in a reasonable period of time.

The MPC control has better results and is a more appropriate choice than the PI control as the overshoot and the integral square error are diminished. The controller prediction capability and systematic handling of the constraints are highly appreciated and offer optimal solutions for flooding control in exceptional situations. The flood prevention system using MPC control will be also extended for counteracting the accidental pollution that may appear in association or independently with the flood event and working as an integrated control structure.

Acknowledgement

The authors gratefully acknowledge the financial support provided by the Romanian National University Research Council through grant no. PN-II-PT-PCCA-2011-3.2-0344:"Pro-active operation of cascade reservoirs in extreme conditions (floods and droughts) using Comprehensive Decision Support Systems (CDSS). Case study: Jijia catchment (e-Lac)".

Nomenclature

Q, Q_i, Q_e - water flow, m^3/s
A - flow area, m^2
P - wetted perimeter, m
h - water level, m
v - water velocity, m/s
q_x - lateral inflow, $m^3/s/m$
B - channel width, m
J_0 - river bed slope, m/km
J_e - energy slope, m/km
g - gravitational acceleration, m/s^2
n - Manning coefficient, -
V - reservoir volume, m^3
x - length, m
t - time, s

References

M. Breckpot, O. M. Agudelo, P. Meert, P. Willems, B. De Moor, 2013, Flood control of the Demer by using Model Predictive Control, Control Engineering Practice, 21, 1776–1787.

P-K. Chiang, P. Willems, 2013, Model Conceptualization Procedure for River (Flood) Hydraulic Computations: Case Study of the Demer River, Belgium, Water Resources Management, 27, 4277–4289.

D. K. Delgoda, S. K. Salem, M. N. Halgamuge, H. Malano, 2013, Multiple Model Predictive Flood Control in Regulated River Systems with Uncertain Inflows, Water Resources Management, 27, 765–790.

F. N-F. Chou, C-W. Wu, 2013, Expected shortage based pre-release strategy for reservoir flood control, Journal of Hydrology, 497, 1–14.

D. L. Freed, 1985, Chapter 14, Hydrological forecasting (Series: Landscape Systems), John Wiley and Sons Ltd., Bury St Edmunds, UK.

S. Huang, J. Rauberg, H. Apel, M. Disse, K.-E. Lindenschmidt, 2007, The effectiveness of polder systems on peak discharge capping of floods along the middle reaches of the Elbe River in Germany, Hydrology and Earth System Sciences, 11, 1391-1401.

X. Litrico, V. Fromion, J.-P. Baume, M. Rijo, 2003, Modelling and PI control of an irrigation canal, European Control Conference, Cambridge, UK.

M. Mercangöz, J. Doyle, 2007, Distributed model predictive control of an experimental four-tank system, Journal of Process Control, 17, 297-308.

F. Saleh, A. Ducharne, N. Flipo, L. Oudin, E. Ledoux, 2013, Impact of river bed morphology on discharge and water levels simulated by a 1D Saint-Venant hydraulic model at regional scale, Journal of Hydrology, 476, 169-177.

R. Scatollini, 2009, Architectures for distributed and hierarchical Model Predictive Control – A review, Journal of Process Control, 19, 723-731.

S. YiZi, L. RongHua, L. TieJian, Z. Cheng, W. GuangQian, 2011, Transient flow control for an artificial open channel based on finite difference method, Science China Technological Sciences, 54, 4, 781–792.

E. Weyer, 2002, Decentralised PI control of an open water channel, Proceedings of the 15th IFAC World Congress, Barcelona, Spain, Volume R, 95-100.

Jiří Jaromír Klemeš, Petar Sabev Varbanov and Peng Yen Liew (Editors)
Proceedings of the 24th European Symposium on Computer Aided Process Engineering – ESCAPE 24
June 15-18, 2014, Budapest, Hungary.

INES – Interface between Experiments and Simulation

Norbert Asprion,[a,*] Regina Benfer,[a] Sergej Blagov,[a] Roger Böttcher,[a] Michael Bortz,[b] Richard Welke,[b] Jakob Burger,[c] Erik von Harbou,[c] Karl-Heinz Küfer,[b] Hans Hasse[c]

[a]*BASF SE, Carl-Boschstr. 38, 67063 Ludwigshafen, Germany*
[b]*Fraunhofer Institute for Industrial Mathematics ITWM, Fraunhofer-Platz 1, 67663 Kaiserslautern, Germany*
[c]*Laboratory of Engineering Thermodynamics, University of Kaiserslautern, Erwin-Schrödinger-Str. 44, 67663 Kaiserslautern, Germany*
norbert.asprion@basf.com

Abstract

The development of chemical processes is usually based on both experiments (often in pilot plants), and process simulation. Design of experiments, data evaluation and reconciliation, model development and validation are essential steps in this procedure. Different tools and approaches are available for each of these tasks but in the process developer's workflow, they are usually not supported in an integrated way. Therefore, in the project INES, on which this paper reports, a new interface between experiments and simulation for process design was created, and integrated in a tool box which comprehensively supports process design. It contains modules for data selection and reconciliation, sensitivity analysis, and model validation and –adjustment. Methods from the literature are suitably combined to support the overall goal. The chosen methods, their combination and implementation are described and examples are given which demonstrate the benefits of the new interactive tool in the process development workflow.

Keywords: Modelling, Data selection, Sensitivity, Uncertainty, Design of Experiments.

1. Introduction

Often simulation models are used to represent a known good operation point and for the investigation of impacts of different parameters and for optimization in a closer surrounding of this operating point. Since new methods and computational speed allow a more rigorous exploration of the whole design space there is the necessity of high quality simulation models applicable in this range. Therefore the modelling process is a decisive factor for the reliability of simulation and optimization results. Although the necessary steps for the creation of good simulation models are known (see for example Gani et al., 2012), there is to our knowledge no commercial tool available supporting of the modelling process in all steps. Either tools exist covering only single aspects or methods are only available in an academic environment sometimes overstraining the "normal" process designers. The goal of the project "INES – Interface between Experiments and Simulation" is therefore to implement successful and tuned methods into a "user-friendly", interactive interface supporting the process designer in his workflow. The project INES focuses on the development of steady state flowsheet simulation models based on plant data (either from mini-, pilot or production plants).

There is the chance to reduce costly experimental effort in the development of the model and to reduce risks in the process design due to insufficient model quality.

It is assumed as a starting point for the support of the modelling process that a first simulation model already exists, since the planning of plants is usually based on such simulation results. The project INES aims to support the process developer in the following tasks: Data selection, model sensitivity analysis, validation and adjustment as well as in design of experiments. The development is based on the BASF in-house simulation tool CHEMASIM since here the integration into the workflow is easy due to the accessibility of the source code and possibility to integrate the new supporting tools in BASF's process net tool box so as to efficiently support the process design workflow at BASF. The experience gained in this project is in its fundamental aspects generic and independent of the choice of the process simulator or the company's environment.

2. Data selection and reconciliation

Usually a large number of experimental data from plants is available and might be used for the validation or development of simulation models. But identification of good data is today still often handwork. As a consequence in model development typically only a limited amount of data is used, selected very often by intuition and experience alone. Support of this selection process facilitates this modelling step.

Process information management systems (PIMS) like InfoPlus.21 (ASPEN) or the PI (OSIsoft) system for example facilitate the selection of operating data for model validation and improvement. They are often used within BASF and therefore interfaces to these systems are established. Since for smaller lab or mini plant scale sometimes Excel is still used to store the operating data or parts like analytical data are in some cases provided in Excel, the use of interfaces to both Excel and PIMS will be implemented and might also be used simultaneously.

The data selection starts with the analysis of time series for a selected time period. Plotting operating data of selected measurement tags vs. time helps to identify interesting operating conditions. Methods for segmentation known from the literature (e.g. Fukuda et al., 2004) are available to generate a preselection of different steady state regions. For larger processes it will be hard to check each tag and to identify a common time period where all tags show steady state behaviour. Therefore only a limited number of tags for the selection of the time period will be used but with indication of the steady state quality of the remaining. Outlier detection like for example described in Buzzi-Ferraris and Manenti (2011) is one essential step in this preselection task. For the different selected steady state periods averaged data together with standard deviations should be stored for the following steps: data reconciliation, model validation and/or adjustment.

For subsequent steps a link between measurement tags and streams from simulation has to be provided. So the first step is then a mapping of measurement tags to streams and unit operations of the simulation. Furthermore in the data selection step the flowsheet of the simulation can already be used for a process monitoring very similar to a process control system showing relevant data in the flowsheet with the ability to investigate trends and for example first checks of mass balances for selected control volumes, which might help to identify gross errors.

The selected data sets can be used further in a first data reconciliation step. Here as the only assumption the validity of mass balances is used. It is also possible to include component balances, which in case of reactions have to include reasonable stoichiometry of the reactions. Data reconciliation requires redundancy in measurements which usually is given, albeit the redundancy for mini plants is generally much higher than for production plants. To determine redundancy, analysis of the topology of the process is necessary and can be taken from the simulation. From the previously mapping of tags with streams it is possible to use graph theory to identify redundant and observable measurements and to set up the data reconciliation problem (see e.g. Narasimhan and Jordache, 1999).

3. Sensitivity analysis

Sensitivity analysis is important in model development, validation and optimization. A simulation model is influenced by several different parameters as shown in Figure 1. There are process parameters including design parameters like numbers of theoretical stages of columns or operating parameters like for example a pressure. These process parameters specify the necessary input of the simulation, when a certain model for physico-chemical properties (incl. thermodynamic, physical property and reaction models) is chosen. These physico-chemical property models also contain model parameters for pure components e.g. for the vapor pressure or for binary mixtures like interaction parameters for Gibbs excess enthalpy models or equation of states and reaction parameters like kinetic constants or equilibrium constants. Additionally for the evaluation methods, like for example cost estimation, evaluation parameters for example information about raw material costs, etc. are needed.

A sensitivity analysis can be used in different contexts, hence different methods to apply such an analysis are required. For the investigation of uncertainties local sensitivity measures might be used. Here uncertainties of process parameters but also from model parameters will be investigated. The use of uncertainties in model parameters (e.g. reflected by confidence intervals) is somehow abstract, therefore we implement

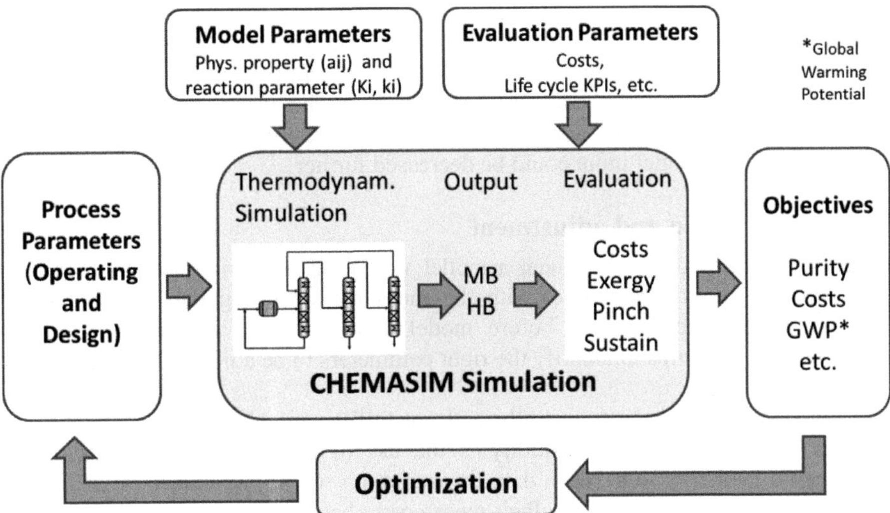

Figure 1. Parameters influencing simulation and optimization objectives

methods which rather use uncertainties in direct measurable or derived experimental data. We rather would specify the uncertainty of limiting activity coefficients in a binary system than in the interaction parameters of a Gibbs excess enthalpy model to investigate sensitivities.

In a previous project (for a brief overview refer to Asprion et al. 2011, for a more detailed description to Bortz et al. 2014) multi-objective optimization with a decision support system was developed and integrated into the simulation tool CHEMASIM. The impact of uncertainties in the optimization results is now studied in INES and the results are included in the decision support system. This will enhance the system by adding information on confidence intervals of the optimization. It will also enable identifying where a reduction of uncertainties is necessary or beneficial.

Another use case for sensitivity analysis is the investigation of the impact of parameters prior to an adjustment: Here rather global sensitivity metrics are necessary to apply since the parameter ranges might be large. Sensitivity analysis in this context helps to focus on the most sensitive parameters for the model adjustment, avoids over-fitting and reduces the effort of model adjustment. Here methods like elementary effect analysis and factorial design from the literature are tested (e.g. Saltelli et al. 2008). Besides the first order effects of a parameter it is highly valuable to be aware of the total effect since there might be interactions with others: Saltelli et al. (2010) investigated different estimators for the total sensitivity index. Successful candidates will be implemented.

Sensitivity analysis might also be used prior to an optimization (single or multi-objective) of the simulation model. It might be used either to identify the sensitive optimization parameters or to investigate the impact of uncertainties of parameters on the result of the optimization already mentioned above.

One of our key new methods is the concept of interactive sensitivity analysis, which offers an interactive visual representation of the sensitivities not only of a single, but of a large set of operating points. A schematic view is given in Figure 2. A user-defined set of operating points have been recalculated before, together with efficient samplings of the uncertain parameters. Thus it is possible to navigate the operating points and visualizing in real time the corresponding sensitivities. Furthermore, by restricting the uncertainty intervals, a direct feedback is obtained how the uncertainties in the objective functions would decrease if – for example by further experimental measurements – the uncertainties in the model input could be decreased further.

4. Model validation and adjustment

Before doing any model adjustment a model validation step will show how good the agreement of the existing model with the measured operating data is. So the data selection is an important step before model validation and as already mentioned sensitivity analysis helps to identify the right parameters to be adjusted.

The data sets from the plant generally will not fulfill model restrictions like the mass balances for instance. One possibility is the use of reconciled data for the model validation— another is to perform data reconciliation within the model validation. The integration of data reconciliation albeit more costly has several advantages: Within the simulator a non-linear programming solver is used to find a solution of the least squares problem (or similar robust objective functions) and allows incorporating constraints for the mass flows like non-negativity. Data reconciliation with the simulation model takes some thermodynamic restrictions of the model into account which are not included in the data reconciliation solely based on mass balances. Furthermore the incorporation of component mass balances in systems with reactions is easy, since all information about the stoichiometry is already included in the simulation model.

The goal is to determine the capability of the model describing several different operating points. Here in general one master simulation (or a small number of masters in case of plant modifications) should be used as a basis for the comparison between operating data and simulation.

Some of the process parameters usually are not known for example the number of theoretical stages of a column used in the investigation. Another example is reflux rates which also often remain unknown. Therefore for some parameters either best guesses have to be used or they can be used for a model adjustment. Before adjusting these parameters, a sensitivity analysis will give an idea about the variances in some data of the operating points (see Figure 2).

The classical approach for a model adjustment is to minimize the sum of the least squares, but is usually very sensitive to outliers. Methods for robust optimization will help to get reliable parameters.

5. Design of experiments

The knowledge of the sensitivities of the simulation model helps to determine process parameters (operating and design parameters) where different case-dependent objectives are fulfilled. The overall goal of the design of experiments is to reach the objectives of the experiments with a low number of investigations. The first step therefore is to define the objectives of the experiments. For example are these experiments used to maximize yield and product purity or to estimate unknown parameters?

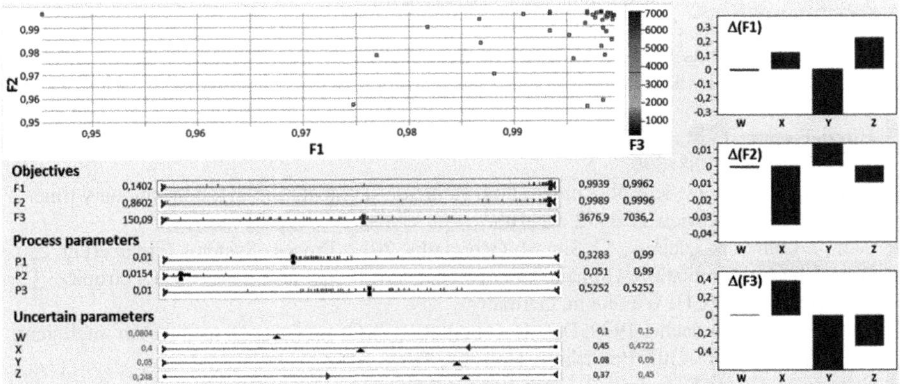

Figure 2. Schematic view of interactive sensitivity analysis support tool. The objectives together with sensitivity measures Δ are given as well as the corresponding process parameters and the uncertain parameters entering the simulation. By navigating on the objectives or process parameters the corresponding sensitivities are updated online.

In model-based design of plant experiments multi-objective optimization helps to investigate the trade-offs of different objectives of the experiments. For example, process conditions where the yield of a reaction is at its maximum must not be the best selection for estimating reliable reaction parameters. In this case the decision support tool might help to identify a good compromise by taking into account the robustness of an operating point as an objective function.

6. Conclusions

The need for optimized processes requires high quality simulation models. There is a lack of a tool supporting model development in the process designer's workflow. The project INES was started to remedy these deficiencies and to develop an interactive interface to support the modeling based on plant data. The systematic modelling support can reduce time and costs in process development and lead to improved quality of simulation models for scale-up and optimization and, in the end, to an improved quality of the new process.

Specific potential benefits of the project include reduced mini plant time and costs, reduced production costs by reliable optimization, less risk in process design (less delays and costs), reduced time-to-market and relief of highly trained personnel from time consuming elementary tasks so that they can focus creative competences within the project or become available for other tasks.

Acknowledgement

We are grateful for valuable contributions in the project by Oliver Hirth, Stefan Höser, Jako Nieuwoudt, Tobias Keller, Michael Rieger (BASF), Martin Kaul (University of Kaiserslautern), Jan Schwientek, Maksym Berezhnyi (Fraunhofer ITWM).

References

N. Asprion, S. Blagov, O. Ryll, R. Welke, A. Winterfeld, A. Dittel, M. Bortz, K.-H. Küfer, J. Burger, A. Scheithauer, H. Hasse, 2011, Pareto-Navigation in Chemical Engineering, Computer Aided Chemical Engineering, 29, 422-426.

M. Bortz, J. Burger, N. Asprion, S. Blagov, R. Böttcher, U. Nowak, A. Scheithauer, R. Welke, K.-H. Küfer, H. Hasse, 2014, Multicriteria optimization in chemical process design and decision support by navigation on Pareto sets, Computers and Chemical Engineering, 60, 354–363.

G. Buzzi-Ferraris, F. Manenti, 2011, Outlier detection in large data sets, Computers and Chemical Engineering, 35, 388–390.

K. Fukuda, H.E.Stanley, L.A.N. Amral, 2004, Heuristic segmentation of a nonstationary time series, Physical Review E, 69, 2, 021108.

R. Gani, I. Cameron, Lucia A., G. Sin, M. Georgiadis, 2012, Process Systems Engineering, 2. Modeling and Simulation, Ullmann's Encyclopedia of Industrial Chemistry, Electronic Release, Wiley-VCH, Weinheim, Germany.

S. Narasimhan, S. Jordache, 1999, Data Reconciliation & Gross Error Detection, An intelligent use of process data, Gulf-Publishing, Houston, Texas, USA.

A. Saltelli, M. Ratto, T. Andres, F. Campolongo, J. Cariboni, D. Gatelli, M. Saisana, S. Tarantola, 2008, Global Sensitivity Analysis, The Primer, John Wiley & Sons, Chichester, England.

A. Saltelli, P. Annoni , I. Azzini, F. Campolongo, M. Ratto, S. Tarantola, 2010, Variance based sensitivity analysis of model output. Design and estimator for the total sensitivity index,Computer Physics Communications, 181, 259–270.

Jiří Jaromír Klemeš, Petar Sabev Varbanov and Peng Yen Liew (Editors)
Proceedings of the 24th European Symposium on Computer Aided Process Engineering – ESCAPE 24
June 15-18, 2014, Budapest, Hungary.

Dynamic Flux Balance Analysis in Cyanobacteria for Ethanol Production with Simultaneous Optimization Approaches

Claudio Delpino[a], Vanina Estrada[a], Juan Laglecia[a], Rebeca Vidal, Francisco Florencio[b], Miguel Garcia Guerrero[b], M. Soledad Diaz[a*]

[a]Planta Piloto de Ingeniería Química (PLAPIQUI), CONICET-Universidad Nacional del Sur, Camino La Carrindanga Km 7,Bahía Blanca 8000, Argentina
[b]Instituto de Bioquímica Vegetal y Fotosíntesis (IBVF), CSIC-Universidad de Sevilla, Av. Americo Vespucio 49, Sevilla E-41092 España
sdiaz@plapiqui.edu.ar

Abstract

In this work we address dynamic optimization of ethanol production by Dynamic Flux Balance Analysis in an engineered cyanobacterium with autotrophic growth (i.e., using CO_2 as substrate). The photobioreactor optimization model is integrated to the metabolic network one by replacing the inner problem by its first order optimality conditions. Complementarity constraints that arise associated to the optimality conditions are efficiently handled with a penalty function formulation. Numerical results suggest the possibility to activate the ethanol production pathway after 20 h in the batch run to enhance ethanol production.

Keywords: dynamic flux balance, bioethanol, cyanobacteria, dynamic optimization

1. Introduction

Considerable effort is being devoted to obtain third generation biofuels from algae. Algal biofuels constitute sustainable alternatives, as they uptake carbon dioxide as the carbon source, have higher yields than other terrestrial biomass feedstock, and can be grown with non-fresh water sources without requiring high-value arable land. Their photoautotrophic growth also enables capture of industrial carbon dioxide emissions to reduce greenhouse gasses pollution. In particular, cyanobacteria are an abundant and diverse group of ancient autotrophic prokaryotes that perform oxygenic photosynthesis. Optimizing photosynthetic organisms for biotechnological purposes will therefore require a systems understanding of photosynthetic processes (Nogales et al., 2012).

During the last decade, a few authors have addressed the study and design of metabolic networks by dynamic flux balance analysis (DFBA). In this approach, a bilievel optimization problem is formulated with the dynamic bioreactor model at the outer optimization level and the metabolic network linear model as the inner level. Raghunathan et al. (2003) addressed data reconciliation and parameter estimation in metabolic flux balance models by formulating this type of bilevel optimization problem and reformulating it as a single level one by replacing the inner LP by its optimality conditions; they solved the resulting NLP with an interior point method. Gadkar et al. (2005) proposed DFBA for glycerol and ethanol production from E. coli, solving the bilevel optimization problem in Matlab. Laiglecia et al. (2013) have carried out parameter estimation for ethanol producing cyanobacteria by reformulating the bilevel problem as a single level one.

In this work we address dynamic flux balance analysis, to optimize ethanol production from the same genetically modified cyanobacteria. The control variables of the dynamic optimization problem are batch temperature, light intensity and phosphate concentration in the culture medium. The model includes two major components: (a) a dynamic model with mass balances for biomass, ethanol, nitrate, phosphate, internal nitrogen and phosphorus (Laiglecia et al., 2013), and (b) a steady state metabolic Linear Programming (LP) model of the central carbon metabolism. The biomass equation includes limiting functions for light, temperature and nutrients, kinetics of growth inhibition by ethanol toxicity and the decrease in the available light by biomass concentration increase. Numerical results suggest activating the ethanol production pathway 20 h after the beginning of the batch run to increase ethanol production in around 26 %.

2. System Description

We address the enhancement of ethanol production by a mutant strain of the cyanobacterium Synechocystis sp. PCC 6803 obtained by Vidal (2009). This modified strain harbors the heterologous genes pdc and adhII from the ethanolgenic bacterium Zymomonas mobilis, to create an ethanol production pathway. The pdc and adhII genes encode, respectively, the enzymes pyruvate decarboxylase (pdc), which catalyzes the non-oxidative decarboxylation of piruvate (PYR) to produce acetaldehyde (ACAL) and CO2, and alcohol dehydrogenase II (adhII), which participates in the reduction of acetaldehyde to ethanol. The new pathways are as follows:

pdc:	pyruvate decarboxylase	$PYR \rightarrow ACAL + CO_2$
adh:	alcohol dehydrogenase isoenzyme IV	$ACAL + NADH \leftrightarrow ETH + NAD$

In previous work, Deng and Coleman (1999) inserted these heterologous genes in Synechococcus sp. strain PCC 7942; Dexter and Fu (2009) inserted these genes in Synechocystis PCC 6803 under the control of the constitutive promoters from the rbcLS and psbAII genes. In this paper, we work with the cyanobacterium Synechocystis sp. PCC 6803 strain obtained by Vidal (2009), in which these genes have been introduced under the control of the gene petE promoter. Expressing the operon pdc-adhII under the control of this promoter, which is induced by copper, allows the induction of the ethanol system production when this is required or, otherwise, kept inactive.

3. Dynamic Flux Balance Analysis

Much research has been devoted to modeling of metabolic networks during the last two decades. The most popular approaches are based on the pseudo steady state assumption for the metabolic network, which is supported by the fact that intracellular, enzyme catalysed reactions have a relaxation time of milliseconds, which is very fast as compared to the relaxation time of cellular growth, normally on the order of hours. Within these approaches, Flux Balance Analysis (FBA) is a genome-scale constraint-based modeling approach for metabolic networks, where steady state mass balances corresponding to metabolic fluxes (reactions) around each node (metabolite) are formulated, rendering an underdetermined systems of linear equations. In FBA, a linear programming problem (LP) is formulated where the objective function is the maximization of the growth rate. Solving the LP problem gives the metabolic flux distribution of the cell. However, this approach allows a static description of the metabolic network, which is appropriate for continuous cultures, but does not account for regulation and does not provide description of dynamic properties. In this sense, Dynamic Flux Balance Analysis allows modeling the interaction between the cellular metabolism and the environment, by keeping a linear model that describes intracellular reactions and dynamic equations for extracellular reactions. The LP problem for the metabolic network is embedded within an outer optimization model that takes into account dynamic mass balances for main substrates, products and biomass at the bioreactor level, allowing the inclusion of kinetic expressions and resulting into a bilevel optimization problem. It is a case of spatial and temporal multiscale problem, which we reformulate as a single level optimization problem by replacing the inner optimization problem by its first order optimality conditions (Karush Kuhn Tucker, KKT, conditions), as detailed in Section 6.

4. Bilevel optimization problem

In the outer optimization problem, we formulate dynamic mass balances for biomass, nutrients and ethanol at the batch photobioreactor level. We also include mass balances for internal phosphorus and nitrogen to model the storage of the main nutrients, which are described in Laiglecia et al. (2013), as well as the model parameters. The net growth rate (μ) is calculated affecting the maximum growth rate (v^*_{growth}), which is the objective function for the inner optimization problem, by limiting functions for ethanol concentration (E) and temperature (T) as follows:

$$\mu = v^*_{growth} f(T) f(E) \tag{1}$$

$$f(E) = \frac{1}{1 + \frac{E}{KI}} \tag{2}$$

$$f(T) = \frac{T}{T_{opt}} exp\left(1 - \frac{T}{T_{opt}}\right) \tag{3}$$

The objective is to maximize ethanol concentration along the time horizon, re-written as minimization of the square difference between ethanol concentration (*E*) and a desired value (*Esp*), for a better performance of the optimization algorithm, as follows:

$$min \int_0^{tf} (E - Esp)^2 dt \tag{4}$$

The internal metabolism is represented by an LP problem that maximizes biomass growth rate (v^*_{growth}) subject to a linear homogeneous system for the internal metabolic fluxes. The metabolic network model includes 50 metabolites and 57 metabolic reactions which represent the central carbon metabolism of *Synechocystis* that comprises the Calvin cycle (CO_2 fixation), Krebs and pentose phosphate cycles, glycolysis, pyruvate metabolism and transport system. The model also includes the reactions presented in Section 2, corresponding to the heterologous genes *pdc* and *adh*. The intracellular and extracellular models are linked by biomass growth rate (v^*_{growth}), absorbed photon flux (v_{APF}) and phosphorus uptake rate by the microorganism (v_{PO_4}). The model includes a limiting function for the light uptake, *f*(*I*), that takes into account the decrease of light availability (*I*) by biomass accumulation in the reactor. The phosphate uptake incorporates a kinetic expression *f(N)* depending on both external (*Pmax, Pmin*) and internal phosphorus concentration (*PI*). Bounds over these fluxes (Eqs. 5-6) represent additional constraints for the outer problem, being v^*_{APF} and v^*_{PO4} , fixed upper bounds.

$$v_{APF} \leq v^*_{APF} f(I) \tag{5}$$

$$v_{PO_4} \leq v^*_{PO_4} f(N) \tag{6}$$

$$f(N) = \frac{PI - P_{min}}{P_{max} - P_{min}} \tag{7}$$

$$f(I) = \frac{I_o}{I_{opt}} exp\left(1 - \frac{I_o}{I_{opt}}\right) \tag{8}$$

$$I_o = \frac{1 - exp(K_{ext}\, p\, X)}{(K_{ext}\, p\, X)} \tag{9}$$

5. Solution strategy

The reformulation of the previously described bilevel optimization problem into a single level one is carried out by replacing the inner optimization problem (intracellular model) by its first order optimality conditions (KKT), as follows:

$$\nabla v_{growth}(v) + A^T\lambda + \mu^U - \mu^L = 0 \tag{10}$$

$$Av = 0 \tag{11}$$

$$v - v^U + s^U = 0 \tag{12}$$

$$-v + v^L + s^L = 0 \tag{13}$$

$$\mu^U \perp s^U \tag{14}$$

$$\mu^L \perp s^L \tag{15}$$

$$s^U, s^L, \mu^U, \mu^L \geq 0 \tag{16}$$

where metabolic flux lower and upper bounds are converted into equalities by adding positive slack variables s^U, s^L, respectively. Kuhn Tucker multipliers for the nonnegativity condition on slack variables are μ^U, μ^L, respectively. The single level dynamic optimization problem is solved by a simultaneous optimization approach, in which state and control variables are approximated by piecewise polynomials over finite elements. Differential and algebraic equations are discretized over these finite elements, rendering a large scale nonlinear programming problem (NLP).

6. Discussion of results

In previous work, we have carried out fermentations with the genetic engineered strain Synechocystis sp. PCC 6803, which was cultivated in BG-11 medium at 30 °C under continuous light (100 μE m-2 s-1) and air bubbling enriched with 1 % CO2, which is considered as a CO2 rich medium. Liquid batch cultures were performed by duplicate for wild type and ethanol mutant strains for 73 hours from the beginning of the exponential growth phase of growth. Biomass was estimated by OD, Chlorophyll a concentration and total organic carbon. Experimental data from the fermentations have been used to estimate main parameters for the extracellular model (Laiglecia et al., 2013). In this work, we carry out dynamic optimizations to maximize ethanol production, while maximizing cell growth in the inner intracellular model. The discretized NLP is formulated in GAMS (Brooke et al., 2012) using an automatic reformulation of complementarity constraints (14), (15) with the penalty formulation provided by the NLPEC meta-solver, and solving the resulting NLP with CONOPT3. Control variables are bioreactor temperature (T), light intensity (I) and phosphate feed flowrate (which is considered negligible as compared to tank volume). We have considered the addition of phosphate to increase ethanol production because the pdc catalyzed reaction (for acetaldehyde production from pyruvate) is decreased to negligible values after 40 hours (see Fig. 1) in simulations related to experimental conditions. The problem has 58,351 variables and 88,483 constraints when discretizing with 73 finite elements and two collocation points. The CPU time is 297 s. Figures 1 to 4 show DFBA results and their comparison with simulations for the described fermentation experiments.

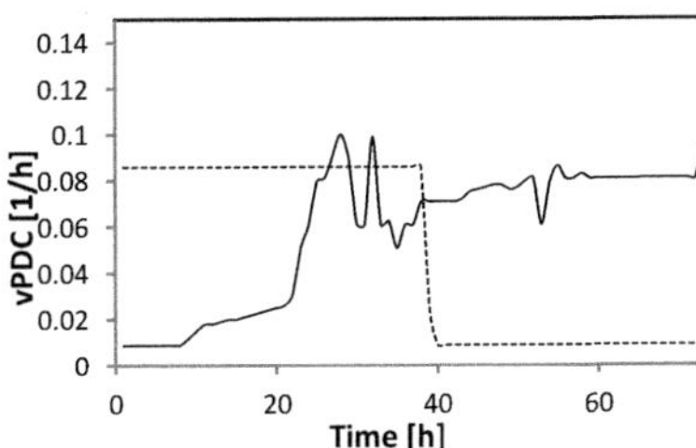

Figure 1. Reaction rates for the intracellular pdc catalyzed reaction. (·····) Parameter estimation simulation (—) Optimal profile

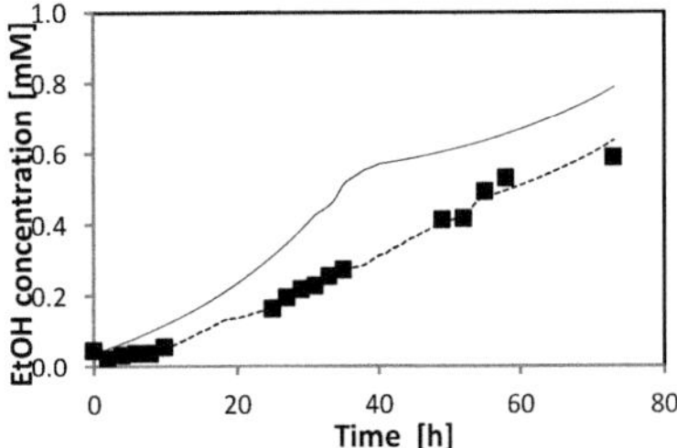

Figure 2. Extracellular ethanol concentration profiles. (■) Experimental data (·····) Parameter Estimation simulation (—) Optimal profile

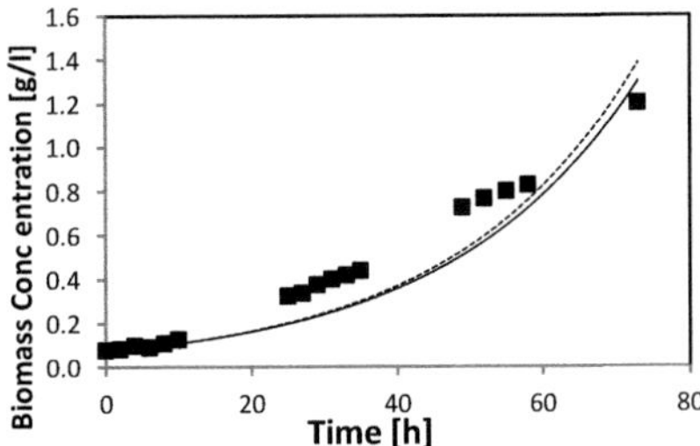

Figure 3. Biomass concentration. (■) Experimental data (·····) Parameter estimation simulation (—) Optimal profile

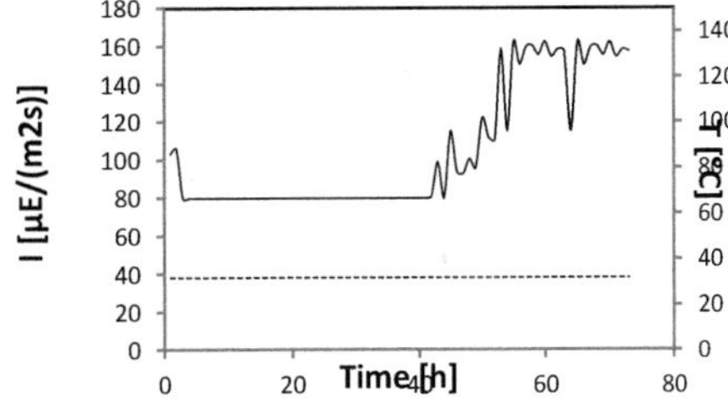

Figure 4. Control Variables for the Optimization problem. (·····) Temperature (—) Irradiation

Experimental work has been carried out using the genetic modified strain, and activating the Pet promoter from the very beginning of the runs (with copper); i.e., enabling ethanol production path throughout the entire time horizon. However, numerical results obtained with DFBA suggest modifications in the metabolic network during the fermentation, with the consequent increase in ethanol production. Figure 1 shows the pdc catalyzed reaction (for acetaldehyde production and hence ethanol production, from pyruvate) in both the experimental conditions and after optimization. It can be seen that this pathway in the optimized network should be activated after 20 hours of fermentation, with the consequent increase in ethanol production. Extracellular metabolite concentrations for ethanol are shown in Figure 2. It can be seen that during the analyzed time horizon ethanol concentration is increased 26 % with respect to the simulated values. Figure 3 shows experimental, simulated and optimal values for biomass concentration profiles; it can be noted that ethanol production increase does not affect biomass growth, as it has been previously shown in experiments carried out by Vidal (2009). Figure 4 shows optimal profiles for batch temperature, which is kept constant at 32 ^{o}C and light intensity, which is constant at 80 μE/(m2.s) up to 40 h and increases to double its value by the end of the fermentation. In this last case, the irregular shape could be due to the fully discretization approach.

7. Conclusions

In this work we have integrated a photobioreactor model with a metabolic network for an engineered cyanobacterium for ethanol production by reformulating the bilevel problem replacing the inner optimization problem by its KKT conditions. Numerical results suggest possible modifications to the metabolic network during the runs to enhance ethanol production, using CO_2 as substrate for fermentations.

References

A. Brooke, D. Kendrick, A. Meeraus, R. Raman, 2012, GAMS, A User Guide.

J. Laiglecia, V. Estrada, R. Vidal Vidal, J. Florencio, M. García Guerrero, M.S. Diaz, 2013, Dynamic flux balance analysis of a genetic engineered cyanobacterium for ethanol production. Parameter estimation, Chemical Engineering Transactions, 32, 955-960.

M. Deng, J. Coleman, 1999, Ethanol synthesis by genetic engineering in cyanobacteria, Applied and Environmental Microbiology, 65, 2, 523-528.

J. Dexter, P. Fu, 2009, Metabolic engineering of cyanobacteria for ethanol production. Energy and Environmental Sciences, 2, 857-864.

K. Gadkar, F. Doyle III, J. Edwards, R. Mahadevan, 2005, Estimating optimal profiles of genetic alterations using constraint-based models. Biotechnology and Bioengineering, 89, 243–251.

K. Höffner, S. Hatwood, P. Barton, 2012, A reliable simulator for dynamic flux balance analysis, Biotechnol Bioeng., 110, 792-802.

J. Nogales, S. Gudmundsson, E. Knight, B. Palsson, I. Thiele, 2011, Detailing the optimality of photosynthesis in cyanobacteria through systems biology analysis, PNAS, 109, 2678-2683.

C. Paulo, J. Di Maggio, V. Estrada, M.S Diaz, 2011, Optimizing cyanobacteria metabolic network for ethanol production, Computer Aided Chemical Engineering, 29, 1366-1370.

A. Raghunathan, J. Perez-Correa, L. Biegler, 2003, Data Reconciliation and Parameter Estimation in Flux-Balance Analysis, Biotechnology and Bioengineering, 84, 700–709.

R. Vidal Vidal, 2009, Producción fotosintética de etanol por la cianobacteria Synechocystis sp. PCC 6803, PhD. Thesis, Universidad de Sevilla, Sevilla, Spain.

Jiří Jaromír Klemeš, Petar Sabev Varbanov and Peng Yen Liew (Editors)
Proceedings of the 24th European Symposium on Computer Aided Process Engineering – ESCAPE 24
June 15-18, 2014, Budapest, Hungary.

Postulating Compartmental Models Using a Flexible Approach

José M. Laínez-Aguirre*, Gary E. Blau, Gintaras V. Reklaitis

School of Chemical Engineering, Purdue University, West Lafayette, IN 47907, USA
jlainez@purdue.edu

Abstract

In this work an optimization framework is presented to support the model builder in postulating compartmental models that plausibly describe data that is obtained during experimentation. In the proposed approach, one specifies a priori the maximum number of compartments and the type of flows (e.g., zero order, first order, second order rate flows) to contemplate. With this input, the mathematical model follows a "flexible" approach, which inherently considers all feasible flows between any pair of compartments. The model activates those flows/compartments that provide the optimal fit for a given set of experimental data. A regularized log-likelihood function is formulated as performance metric in order to handle parameter over-fitting. To deal with the resulting set of differential equations orthogonal collocation on finite elements is employed. A case study related to the pharmacokinetics of an oncological agent is reported to demonstrate the advantages and limitations of the proposed approach. Numerical results show that the proposed approach can provide 33 % smaller mean prediction errors in comparison with a compartmental model previously suggested in the literature that employs a larger number of parameters.

Keywords: Compartmental modeling, Model building, NLP.

1. Introduction

Compartment models are usually employed to represent transport of material in systems such as chemical reactions, biological processes and ecological interactions. They consist of a collection of compartments that are inter-linked by material flows of different order. One of the tasks of compartmental model building is to postulate models that are capable of describing experimental data obtained from the system under study. This model building exercise is typically carried out in a sequential/iterative fashion. It begins with experimentation and then data analysis follows in order to evaluate and improve the candidate models. This cycle is repeated until a suitable model is found (Blau et al., 2008). Depending on the complexity of the system under study, finding appropriate models to postulate can be a difficult undertaking.

Recently, some applications of approaches from Computer Aided Process Engineering to physiology and clinical medicine make use of compartmental analysis. For example, Sresht et al. (2011) employ a compartmental model to study the side effects of cisplatin therapy. Pavurala and Achenie (2013) present compartmental models in the study of drug release, absorption and transit in order to test hypothesis regarding drug delivery mechanisms. The problem of identifying whole-body physiologically based pharmacokinetic (PBPK) models and estimating their respective parameters has been addressed by Mosât et al. (2013). PBPK models are usually comprised of a collection of interlinked compartmental sub-models representing the organs of interest. The authors recognize that identifying the appropriate model still remains a relevant scientific challenge. In this work, we propose an optimization framework that can address this challenge by supporting the model builder in elucidating plausible compartmental models.

2. The mathematical model

The proposed approach is similar to the material balances presented by Laínez et al. (2009) for the design of supply chains. The underlying idea is to inherently consider all possible flows between any pair of compartments. However, not only zero order but other different types of flows may be considered in compartmental modeling. Accordingly, the different types of flows that are taken into account are represented by set s in this model. Figure 1 shows a schematic representation of two compartments i and i'. The model "flexibility" is provided by variable $k^T_{sii'}$ which is the rate of transfer of flow type s delivered from compartment i to compartment i'.

The optimization model is comprised of three groups of equations, namely, (a) the mass balances, (b) the predictions, and (c) the log-likelihood equation. They are briefly explained next.

2.1. Mass balances.

The structure for material balances is expressed in Eq. (1) which states that the rate of change of the material amount in compartment i must equal the difference between (a) the input transfers, which include flows from an external source (k_i^o) and from other compartments i' ($k_{si'i}^T$), and (b) the transfers made from compartment i to other compartments i' ($k_{sii'}^T$). The elimination of material from compartment i can be contemplated as a transfer from compartment i to a dummy compartment i'. The dummy compartment is represented by the unitary set $\overline{I}$. Also note that each type of flow rate s has a pair of associated parameters $e1_s$ and $e2_s$. They denote the power to which the material amount in the origin and destination compartment is to be raised in the mass balance equation. In that manner, for instance, $e1_s$ is equal to 1 and $e2_s$ takes a value of 0 for a first order rate transfer from compartment i to compartment i'.

$$\frac{\mathrm{d}A_i(t)}{\mathrm{d}t} = k_i^o + \sum_s \sum_{i' \neq i} k_{si'i}^T A_{i'}^{e1_s} A_i^{e2_s} - \sum_s \sum_{i' \neq i} k_{sii'}^T A_i^{e1_s} A_{i'}^{e2_s} \quad \forall\, i \notin \overline{I} \tag{1}$$

2.2. Predictions.

The predictions are computed using the generic Eq. (2). Here, $\hat{\mathbf{y}}$ is the vector of predicted values for the experimental observations, while f is a function relating the amount of material in the compartments to the predicted values.

$$\hat{\mathbf{y}}(\mathbf{t}) = f(A_1(\mathbf{t}), \ldots, A_I(\mathbf{t})) \tag{2}$$

2.3. The regularized log-likelihood function.

Assuming that the experimental error is a zero-mean Gaussian process with covariance matrix **V**, the log-likelihood function can be expressed as the first term in the right hand side of Eq. (3). The covariance matrix **V** can be represented as a constant diagonal matrix for homoscedastic errors; while, correlation functions can be used when heteroscedasticity is considered (Rasmussen and Williams, 2006). In order to control the over-fitting phenomenon, a regularization term has been added to the log-likelihood

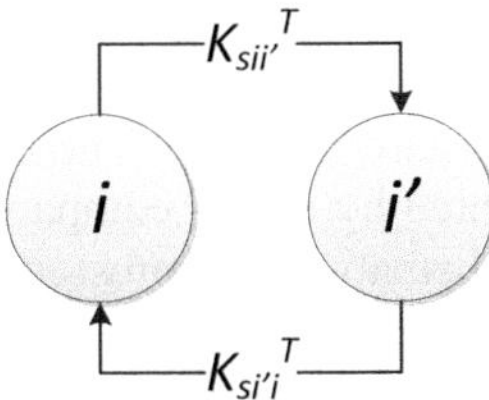

Figure 1. Schematic representation of the flexible compartmental model

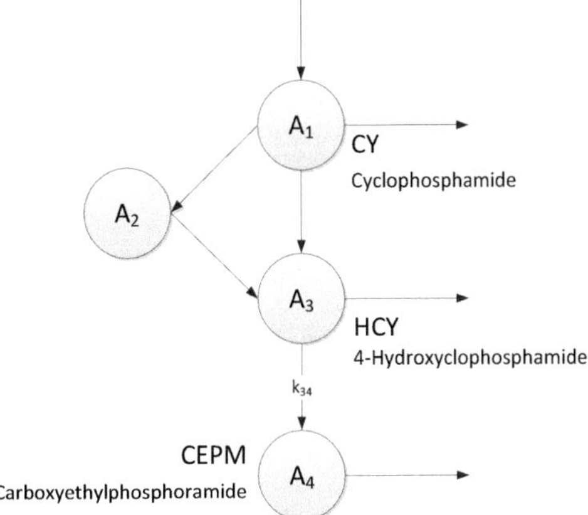

Figure 2. Schematic representation of the previously suggested compartmental model

function. The parameter α dictates the relative importance of the penalty term in the fitting metric (*OF*).

$$OF = \ln\left(\mathrm{N}\ ([y_1,\ldots,y_n] | [\hat{y}_1,\ldots,\hat{y}_n], \mathbf{V})\right) + \alpha \sum_s \sum_{i=i'} \left(k_{sii'}^T\right)^2 \tag{3}$$

The "flexible" compartmental model whose objective function is to minimize a regularized log-likelihood can then be mathematically posed as follows:

$$\begin{aligned} &\max_{\aleph}\ OF \\ &\text{subject to Eqs. (1) - (3)} \\ &\aleph \in \mathrm{R} \end{aligned}$$

where the set $\aleph$ denotes the model continuous variables. One of the key features of this optimization model is that it determines which of the compartments and linking flows are activated in order to best fit the experimental data. In order to deal with the resulting set of differential equations in the optimization, orthogonal collocation on finite elements is employed (Cuthrell and Biegler, 1987).

3. Case study: cyclophosphamide pharmacokinetics

The model presented in the previous section consists of a general system of differential mass balance equations and thus covers a wide range of potential applications. Nevertheless in this work to demonstrate the capabilities of the proposed approach, a case study related to the pharmacokinetics of an oncological therapeutic agent,

Cyclophosphamide (CY), is reported. CY has a complex metabolism leading to its conversion to two important metabolites: hydroxycyclophosphamide (HCY) and carboxyethylphosphoramide mustard (CEPM). The most relevant pathways of the drug metabolism have been represented by a four compartment model (Hassan et al., 1999) as depicted in Figure 2 and mathematically expressed as follows:

$$
\begin{aligned}
&\frac{d\hat{A}_1(t)}{dt} = -\frac{CL_{non}}{V_{cy}}\hat{A}_1(t) - \frac{CL_{ind}}{V_{cy}}\hat{A}_1(t)\hat{A}_2(t) \\
&\frac{d\hat{A}_2(t)}{dt} = k_{enz}\left(1 + \frac{\frac{E_{max}}{V_{cy}}\hat{A}_1(t)}{EC_{50} + \frac{\hat{A}_1(t)}{V_{cy}}}\right) - k_{enz}\hat{A}_2(t) \\
&\frac{d\hat{A}_3(t)}{dt} = \frac{CL_{ind}}{V_{cy}}\hat{A}_1(t)\hat{A}_2(t) - k_{hcy}\hat{A}_3(t) - k_{34}\hat{A}_3(t) \\
&\frac{d\hat{A}_4(t)}{dt} = k_{34}\hat{A}_3(t) - k_{cepm}\hat{A}_4(t) \\
&\hat{A}_1(0) = 0; \hat{A}_2(0) = 1; \hat{A}_3(0) = 0; \hat{A}_4(0) = 0
\end{aligned}
\tag{4}
$$

However, there is evidence in previous studies (Salinger et al., 2006; Laínez-Aguirre et al., 2013) that this model is not adequate to describe the time course of at least one of the metabolites concentration. Experimental data from the clinical study published by Salinger et al. (2006) is used to postulate an improved model by using the proposed "flexible" approach. The optimization will suggest the number of compartments, the corresponding links among them and their associated estimated parameters such that the best fit to the experimental data is provided. In Salinger's study HCY and CEPM concentrations were quantified after and during the administration of two CY infusions separated by 24 h. We take into account in the optimization model a maximum of four potential compartments and one dummy compartment for the elimination processes. They could be sharing material via the three different kinds of flows listed in Table 1. The model was implemented in GAMS and consist of a Nonlinear Program (NLP) with 879 equations and 787 continuous variables. The total CPU time for its solution was 37.6 s using the solver CONOPT3 on an Intel i7 at 2.67 GHz computer.

The solution obtained with the flexible compartmental model is shown in Figure 3 and described in Eq. (5). Note that the resulting optimal solution suggests that only three compartments and six material flows are activated. This leads to a total of eight parameters, including the volume of distribution for CEPM and HCY, that are estimated during the optimization. By contrast, the four compartment model proposed by Hassan et al. (1999) requires the estimation of eleven parameters.

Table 1. Type of flows considered in the optimization model

Type (s)	$e1_s$	$e2_s$
1	1	0
2	1	1
3	2	0

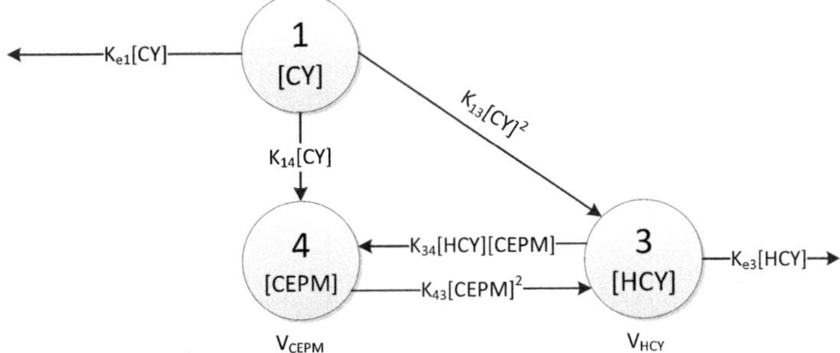

Figure 3. Schematic representation of the solution obtained with the flexible compartmental model

$$
\begin{aligned}
\frac{d\hat{A}_1(t)}{dt} &= -k_{13}\hat{A}_1^{\,2} - k_{14}\hat{A}_1 - k_{e1}\hat{A}_1 \\
\frac{d\hat{A}_3(t)}{dt} &= k_{13}\hat{A}^2 + k_{43}\hat{A}_4^{\,2} - k_{34}\hat{A}_3\hat{A}_4 - k_{e3}\hat{A}_3 \\
\frac{d\hat{A}_4(t)}{dt} &= k_{14}\hat{A}_1 + k_{34}\hat{A}_3\hat{A}_4 - k_{43}\hat{A}_4^{\,2}
\end{aligned}
\tag{5}
$$

$\hat{A}_1(0) = 0; \hat{A}_3(0) = 0; \hat{A}_4(0) = 0$

The mean square prediction error for the model suggested by Hassan et al. (1999) is 2.98 $\mu mol^2/L^2$; while the numerical results show that the proposed three-compartment model results in a mean square prediction error equal to 2.00 $\mu mol^2/L^2$. This constitutes a reduction of 32.6 % in the mean square prediction error. Figure 4 shows the prediction vs. observation plot for the two compartmental models. As can be observed, the HCY concentrations predicted using the model proposed by the "flexible" approach reduces the departures from the 45 line in comparison with the Hassan's model. In fact, the mean square prediction error is reduced from 4.67 $\mu mol^2/L^2$ to 2.58 $\mu mol^2/L^2$ for HCY by using the model proposed in this work.

4. Conclusions

The proposed optimization framework allows evaluating and discriminating simultaneously a significant number of potential compartmental models in a straight-forward manner. Thus, this superstructure type of model offers a tool that can assist the model builder in considering alternatives that may not be very intuitive yet which can provide gains in terms of fitting adequacy.

A Mixed Integer NLP and a bi-objective optimization are under investigation to provide a better control of over-parameterization and to permit the quantitative assessment of the existing trade-off between model complexity (i.e., number of estimated parameters and compartments) and fitting adequacy. In addition, strategies to reduce the computational complexity are required to accommodate models that may be comprised of a high number of potential compartments and interlinks.

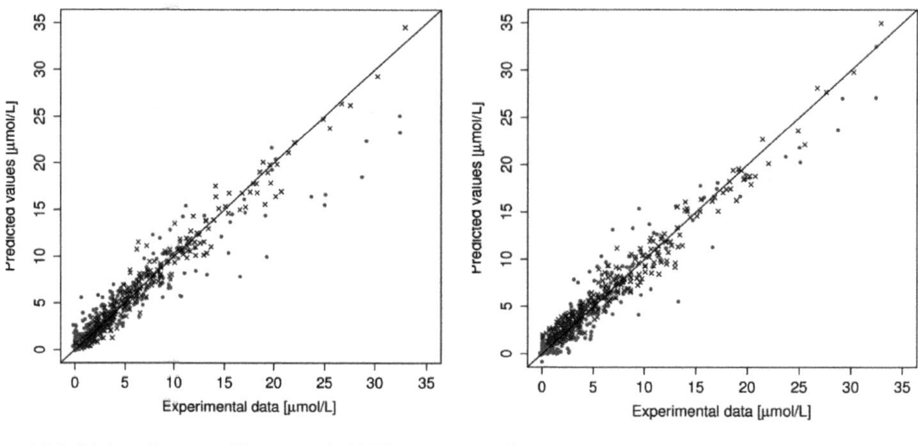

a) Model from literature (Hassan et al., 1999)

b) Model obtained using the flexible approach

Figure 4. Comparison of the experimental data with the model predictions. HCY and CEPM are represented by dots and 'x's, respectively.

Acknowledgement

Support from the United States National Science Foundation (Grant NSF-CBET-0941302) is gratefully acknowledged.

References

G. Blau, M. Lasinski, S. Orcun, S.H. Hsu, J. Caruthers, N. Delgass, V. Venkatasubramanian, 2008, High Fidelity Mathematical Model Building with Experimental Data: A Bayesian Approach, Computers and Chemical Engineering, 32,971-989.

J.E. Cuthrell, L.T. Biegler, 1987, On the optimization of differential-algebraic process systems, AICHE Journal, 33, 1259-1270.

M. Hassan, U. Svensson, P. Ljungman, B. Björkstrand, H. Olsson, M. Bielenstein, M. Abdel-Rehim, C. Nilsson, M. Johansson, M.O. Karlsson, 1999, A mechanism-based pharmacokinetic-enzyme model for cyclophosphamide autoinduction in breast cancer patients, British Journal of Clinical Pharmacology, 48, 1365-2125.

J.M. Laínez-Aguirre, S. Orcun, J.F. Pekny, G.V. Reklaitis, A. Suvannasankha, C. Fausel, E.J. Anaissie, G.E. Blau, 2013, Comparison of an assumption-free Bayesian approach with Optimal Sampling Schedule to a maximum a posteriori Approach for Personalizing Cyclophosphamide Dosing, Pharmacotherapy, DOI: 10.1002/phar.1346.

J.M. Laínez, G. Kopanos, A. Espuña, L. Puigjaner, 2009, Flexible design-planning of supply chain networks, AIChE Journal, 55, 1736-1753.

A. Mošat, E. Lueshen, M. Heitzig, C. Hall, A.Linninger, G. Sin, R. Gani, First principles pharmacokinetic modeling: A quantitative study on Cyclosporin, Computers and Chemical Engineering, 54, 97-110.

N. Pavurala, L. Achenie, A mechanistic approach for modeling oral drug delivery, Computers and Chemical Engineering, 57, 196-206.

C.E. Rasmussen, C.K.I. Williams, 2006, Gaussian Processes for Machine Learning, Cambridge, Massachusetts, MIT Press.

D.H. Salinger, J.S. McCune, A.G. Ren, D.D. Shen, J.T. Slattery, B. Phillips, G.B. McDonald, P. Vicini, 2006, Real-time Dose Adjustment of Cyclophosphamide in a Preparative Regimen for Hematopoietic Cell Transplant: A Bayesian Pharmacokinetic Approach, Clinical Cancer Research, 12, 4888-4898.

V. Sresht, J.R. Bellare, S.K. Gupta, 2011, Modeling the Cytotoxicity of Cisplatin, Industrial & Engineering Chemistry Research, 50, 12872-12880.

Jiří Jaromír Klemeš, Petar Sabev Varbanov and Peng Yen Liew (Editors)
Proceedings of the 24th European Symposium on Computer Aided Process Engineering – ESCAPE 24
June 15-18, 2014, Budapest, Hungary.

Optimization of Entrainer Feeding in Batch Extractive Distillation

Laszlo Hegely, Peter Lang*

Budapest University of Technology and Economics, Department of Building Services and Process Engineering, H-1521 Budapest, Muegyetem rkp. 3-5.
lang@mail.bme.hu

Abstract

The separation of a multicomponent azeotropic industrial waste solvent mixture by batch distillation (BD) and batch extractive distillation (BED) is studied. From a mixture methanol-THF-water-toluene methanol must be recovered in high purity. The optimization of both processes is performed by a genetic algorithm (GA) coupled with a professional flow-sheet simulator performing the dynamic simulation. The optimization variables are the reflux ratios of the operation steps, the location, flow rate and duration of entrainer (water) feeding. The objective function to be maximized is the profit.

Keywords: batch distillation, extractive distillation, entrainer, optimization, genetic algorithm.

1. Introduction

Batch distillation (BD) is frequently applied for the separation pharmaceutical waste solvent mixtures. These mixtures often contain several components forming azeotropes with each other, rendering the recovery of the main component more difficult, or even infeasible. In these cases a special (e.g. extractive) distillation method must be applied. In batch extractive distillation (BED, Yatim et al., 1993), an entrainer (E) is fed continuously into the column, changing the relative volatilities favourably.

The usual application of BED is to extract pollutants of moderate concentration from the main component to be recovered. However the entrainer may reduce the volatility of the main component, which is then extracted from beside the pollutants of low concentration forming minimum azeotropes with it. These pollutants can be removed in fore-cuts. It is possible to reduce the loss of the main component with the fore-cuts by BED. However, the high amount of E fed renders the separation of the main component from it more difficult and the application of BED can be even uneconomical.

E-feeding can be started after the start-up of the column, or during the heating-up, as early as the vapour reaches the location of the feed, as suggested by Lang et al. (2006). Lang et al. (2012) proposed a new BED operational policy, where E-feeding is applied only during the heating-up. The new BED policy was studied by Hegely et al. (2013) for the separation of a waste solvent mixture of a pharmaceutical plant containing methanol (A), tetrahydrofuran (B), water (C) and toluene (D), from which methanol must be recovered in a purity of 99.5 mass%. The entrainer is water. The new BED policy was compared with BD and the traditional policy of BED by laboratory and industrial-size experiments. The best results were obtained by the new BED policy. In this study neither the BD nor the BED policies were optimised.

Barreto et al. (2011a) performed the optimization of the heterogeneous BED of the chloroform-methanol azeotropic mixture by a GA coupled with a simplified model. The pollutant methanol was extracted with water. Barreto et al. (2011b) studied the same process, but by using a flow-sheet simulator and multiple objectives.

The aim of this paper is to optimize both the BD and BED separation of the mixture studied by Hegely et al. (2013). Optimization variables are the reflux ratios of all operation steps and the parameters of water feeding (feed plate, flow rate, duration). The optimization was performed by a GA with ChemCAD performing the dynamic simulation. The objective function to be maximized is the profit for one batch.

2. Vapour-liquid equilibrium conditions

The mixture contains A as main component, two organic pollutants in moderate concentration (B and D), and water (C). The boiling points of these components and their azeotropes, together with the azeotropic compositions are given in Table 1. For VLE calculations UNIQAUC model is applied. The charge contains 37.14 mass% A, 4.89 % B, 56.41 % C and 1.56 % D. The recovery of A is disturbed by the azeotropes A–B and A–D. The influence of water (C) as a potential entrainer on the relative volatilities of these azeotropic mixtures was investigated. The addition of a moderate amount of water moves both relative volatilities away from 1.0 considerably, that is, BED using water as entrainer is suitable for the removal of B and D in the fore-cuts more efficiently and with lower loss of A than BD (Hegely et al., 2013).

3. Separation methods

The BD process consists of the following separation steps (Hegely et al., 2013):

- Step 0: heating-up of the column under total reflux. At the end of heating-up, the distillate is rich in B and A, compositions and temperatures start to stabilize.
- Step 1: taking the first fore-cut, which contains a high amount of B and D in addition to A. The first fore-cut is incinerated.
- Step 2: taking the second fore-cut that already contains more A and less pollutant than the first fore-cut. The aim of both fore-cuts is the removal of organic pollutants. The second fore-cut is recycled to the next batch in order to decrease the loss of A.

Table 1. Boiling points and compositions of the azeotropes

Component	T_{bp} (°C)	Composition (mass%)			
		A	B	C	D
A – B	59.5	30.0	70.0	-	-
A – D	63.6	71.5	-	-	28.5
B – C	63.9	-	94.3	5.7	-
A	64.7	100	-	-	-
B	65.97	-	100	-	-
C – D	84.4	-	-	19.7	80.3
C	100.0	-	-	100	-
D	110.6	-	-	-	100

- Step 3: taking the main-cut that is the product A in high purity.
- Step 4: taking the after-cut, which contains aqueous A. The aim of this step is to remove A from the still residue, which is then sent to biological purification. As the after-cut contains a considerable amount of A, it is recycled to the next batch.

In the BED process Step 0 can be divided into two parts:
- Step 0a: heating-up without water feeding. The step ends as the vapour reaches the top of the column.
- Step 0b: heating-up with water feeding. Water is fed continuously to the column causing a decrease in $x_{D,A}$ and an increase in $x_{D,B}$.

Water feeding can be stopped at the end of Step 0b or it can be still continued during Steps 1 and 2, as well. If it is continued, the loss of A in the fore-cuts can be further reduced, but this dilutes the mixture from which A is to be recovered and can also increase the amount of the fore-cuts increasing the cost of incineration and energy.

4. Calculation method

The objective function (OF) to be maximized is defined as:

$$OF = m_{MC}p_A - m_{FC1}c_{inc} - c_{st}\frac{\dot{Q}_{st}}{r_{st}}t \tag{1}$$

where m_{MC} is the mass of the main-cut, m_{FC1} is that of the first-fore-cut, p_A is the price of methanol (0.46 \$/kg), c_{inc} is the cost of incineration (0.21 \$/kg), c_{st} is cost of heating steam of 3 bar (57.6 \$/t), r_{st} is its heat of condensation (2,263.5 MJ/t), $\dot{Q}_{st}$ is the heat duty (1800 MJ/h) and t is the duration of the whole process. The last term in Eq. (1) is the operation cost. The costs of water and biological purification are neglected. (These are not debited to the solvent recovery plant). The optimization is performed by a real-coded elitist GA written in VBA under Excel. GA was chosen as OF can only be evaluated by simulation. The parameters of the GA: mutation probability: 5 %, population size: 30, crossover probability: 70 %. OF is evaluated by dynamic simulation using different modules of the flowsheet simulator ChemCAD. If the purity of A does not reach the specified value (99.5 mass%), OF is changed to -10,000 \$.

The mass of charge is 22,678 kg. The number of theoretical plates: 25 (excluding the condenser and reboiler). The pressure of the column is 1.013 bar, its pressure drop: 0.25 bar. The hold-up of the condenser: 0.45 m^3, that of the column: 0.05 m^3/plate. The termination criteria for the steps (which are based on industrial experiences):
- Step 1: $x_{D,B}<20$ mass% (B content in the distillate)
- Step 2: $x_{D,B}<2$ mass%
- Step 3: $x_{product,A}<99.52$ mass%
- Step 4: $x_{D,C}>90$ mass%

4.1. Batch distillation

The optimization variables were the reflux ratios of the steps: R_1 (1st fore-cut), R_2 (2nd fore-cut), R_3 (main-cut), R_4 (after-cut). The lower and upper bounds for all reflux ratios were 0.6 and 15. Step 0 lasted 360 min. The results were compared with those of the policy applied in the plant, where R_1=R_2=R_4=6, R_3=2 (basic BD).

4.2. Batch extractive distillation

Step 0a lasted 160 min, after which water feeding (of 15 °C) was started. The duration of Step 0b was 200 min. There were seven optimization variables: the 4 reflux ratios and 3 new variables connected with water feeding whose ranges were:
feed plate (integer variable, counted from the top of the column with plate 1 being the condenser): $1 \le f \le 26$; flow rate: $0 \le F_{water} \le 3{,}000$ kg/h; duration (even integer): $0 \le t_F \le 1000$ min. (Water feeding was always stopped at the end of Step 2.)

5. Optimization results

The results for basic BD (Table 2) will serve as a basis for comparison. The optimum results (after 100 generations) for BD (Table 3) show a very significant increase in profit compared to BD basic, due to considerable changes in the reflux ratios. The income increased and the operation cost decreased by approximately 10 %.

The increase of reflux ratios increases the duration of the operation, thus the operational cost, but it may have also favourable effects (e.g. increase of recovery of A). R_1 was higher, which led to a decreased amount of first fore-cut with lower A content, therefore a lower loss of A. This is shown by the fact that the A content of the distillate (Figure 1) was always lower during Step 1. R_2 was significantly lower, which resulted in a much faster Step 2 with similar loss of A. R_3 was higher, which, even though made Step 3 longer, increased the recovery of A, that is, the income. With the reduction of R_4, the process duration became much shorter.

Comparing the results (after 170 generations) of BED (Table 4) and the optimised BD process, a further increase in profit can be observed. Though process duration and thus operation cost increased, this was offset by a strong increase in income. R_1 was only

Table 2. Reflux ratios and results for the basic BD process.

	First fore-cut	Second fore-cut	Main-cut	After-cut	Income ($)	2397
R	6	6	2	6	Incineration cost	472
Duration (min)	408	342	590	736		
Mass (kg)	2,245	1,489	5,210	1,805	Operation cost	1860
A (mass%)	47.2	81.2	99.5	51.4		
B	43.4	8.7	0.2	0.0	Profit	**66**
C	0.0	0.0	0.3	48.6		
D	9.4	10.1	0.1	0.0		

Table 3. Results for the optimised BD process.

	First fore-cut	Second fore-cut	Main-cut	After-cut	Income ($)	2652
R	9.17	1.39	3.29	1.22	Incineration cost	450
Duration (min)	550	108	924	252		
Mass (kg)	2,143	1,370	5,765	1,669	Operation cost	1675
A (mass%)	45.5	79.2	99.5	33.2		
B	46.4	7.4	0.3	0.0	Profit	**527**
C	0.0	0.0	0.1	66.8		
D	8.1	13.4	0.2	0.0		

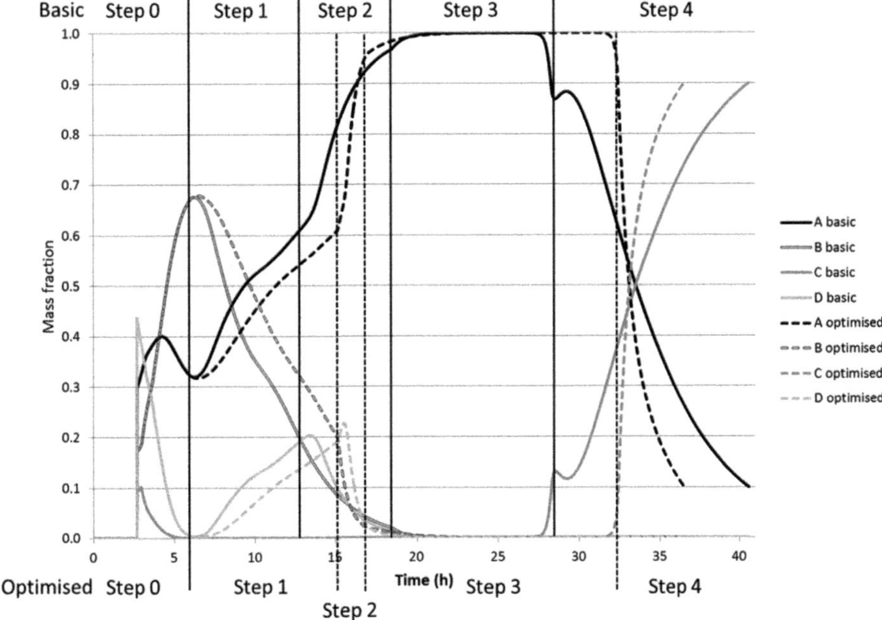

Figure 1. Evolution of condensate composition for the basic and optimized BD processes.

slightly lower, but water feeding had important favourable effects. The A content of the distillate (Figure 2) was much lower during Step 1. The mass of the first fore-cut (and the duration of Step 1) was also lower, which means a much lower loss of A, finally resulting in higher recovery (shown in Figure 3 by longer Step 3) and higher profit. R_2 and R_3 are slightly higher, while R_4 is practically unchanged. The optimal feeding location is the top plate of the column. The water feeding is still continued for 278 min during Step 1, as well. The increase of liquid volume in the still is moderate, the maximum volume surpasses by less than 1 m^3 that of the BD process. It must be still noted that both composition (the highest A/B and A/D ratios) and amount of the 2nd fore-cut to be recycled (minimal) are most favourable for the optimised BED process.

Table 4. Results for the optimized BED process.

	First fore-cut	Second fore-cut	Main-cut	After-cut	Income ($)	2930
R	9.02	2.33	3.90	1.24	Incineration cost	360
Duration (min)	424	150	1,170	266	Operation cost	1809
Mass (kg)	1,713	1,323	6,396	1,722	Profit	**761**
A (mass%)	22.4	84.0	99.5	28.9		
B	58.2	7.5	0.2	0.0	f	2
C	5.1	0.0	0.2	71.1	F_{water} (kg/h)	460
D	14.4	8.4	0.1	0.0	t_F (min)	478

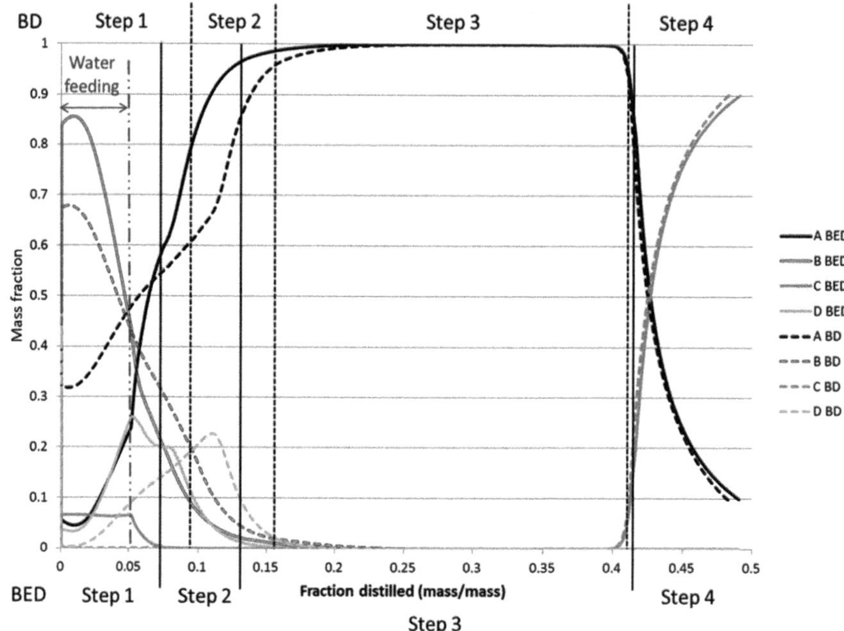

Figure 2. Evolution of distillate composition for the optimized BD and BED processes.

6. Conclusions

The recovery of methanol from a multicomponent azeotropic waste solvent mixture was studied by dynamic simulation and optimisation. The components of the mixture (methanol-THF-water-toluene) form several minimum azeotropes limiting the recovery of methanol by traditional batch distillation (BD). By batch extractive distillation (BED) using water as entrainer the separation process can be made more profitable. The optimization of both BD and BED processes was performed by a genetic algorithm coupled with the ChemCAD professional simulator performing the dynamic simulation. The optimization variables were the reflux ratios of all operation steps, location, flow rate and duration of entrainer feeding. The optimised processes provided much higher tprofit than the original industrial BD process. The highest profit was reached by the optimised BED process. Moreover this process gave the best results from the point of view off-cut recycling.

References

A. A. Barreto, I. Rodriguez-Donis, V. Gerbaud, X. Joulia, 2011a, Optimization of Heterogeneous Batch Extractive Distillation, Ind. Eng. Chem. Res, 50, 5204–5217.

A. A. Barreto, I. Rodriguez-Donis, V. Gerbaud, X. Joulia, 2011b, Multi-objective optimization of three-phase batch extractive distillation, Computer Aided Chemical Engineering, 29, 562–566.

L. Hegely, P. Lang, G. Kovacs, 2013, A New Batch Extractive Distillation Operational Policy for Methanol Recovery, Chemical Engineering Transactions, 35, 949-954.

P. Lang, L. Hegely, G. Kovacs , 2012, Method for the recovery of methanol from multicomponent solvent mixtures, P 1200245, Hungarian Patent.

P. Lang, G. Kovacs G., B. Kotai, J. Gaal-Szilagyi, G. Modla, 2006, Industrial application of a new batch extractive distillation operational policy, IChemE Symposium Series, 152, 830-839.

H. Yatim, P. Moszkowicz, M. Otterbein, P. Lang, 1993, Dynamic Simulation of a Batch Extractive Distillation Process, Comput. Chem. Eng., 17, S57-62.

Jiří Jaromír Klemeš, Petar Sabev Varbanov and Peng Yen Liew (Editors)
Proceedings of the 24th European Symposium on Computer Aided Process Engineering – ESCAPE 24
June 15-18, 2014, Budapest, Hungary.

An Optimisation-based Approach for Biopharmaceutical Manufacturing

Songsong Liu,[a] Ana S. Simaria,[b] Suzanne S. Farid,[b] Lazaros G. Papageorgiou[a,*]

[a]*Centre for Process Systems Engineering, Department of Chemical Engineering, University College London, Torrington Place, London WC1E 7JE, UK*

[b]*The Advanced Centre for Biochemical Engineering, Department of Biochemical Engineering, University College London, Torrington Place, London WC1E 7JE, UK*

l.papageorgiou@ucl.ac.uk

Abstract

This work addresses the integrated optimisation of upstream and downstream processing strategies in the manufacturing processes of monoclonal antibodies (mAbs). In the upstream processing (USP), the bioreactor sizing strategies are considered, while in the downstream processing (DSP), the chromatography sequencing and column sizing strategies are optimised, including the decisions on the resin selection, the number of columns, the column diameter and bed height, and number of cycles per batch. Also, the product's purity requirement is considered, in which the host cell protein level in the final product is examined. A mixed integer linear programming (MILP) model is developed with the objective function to minimise the annual total cost of goods (COG), involving both direct and indirect costs. Finally, an example with different USP and DSP ratios are studied.

Keywords: mAb, chromatography column sizing, chromatography sequencing, bioreactor sizing, MILP, COG

1. Introduction

Monoclonal antibodies (mAbs), as one of the fastest growing biopharmaceutical sectors, have been widely used as therapies to treat cancer and autoimmune diseases. Its global sales in 2011 are predicted to increase to 58 billion USD by 2016 (Butler, 2013). The optimisation of downstream purification processes of mAbs has drawn attention in the literature in recent years (Simaria et al., 2012). Liu et al. (2013a) developed a mixed integer linear programming (MILP) model for the optimisation of the chromatography column sizing decisions in the mAb manufacturing, considering an objective of the minimisation of cost of goods per gram (COG/g), for different facility configurations. Later, in Liu et al., (2013b), the above work was extended to a mixed integer nonlinear programming (MINLP) model to determine the optimal facility design for current cell culture titres and to assess the ability of fixed facilities to cope with higher titres, allowing for product loss due to the limitation of the equipment sizes.

In this work, we aim to develop an MILP model by extending our previous work (Liu et al., 2013a;b), to address the integrated optimisation of strategies in both upstream (USP) and downstream processing (DSP) for mAb manufacture. In addition to addressing the optimization of chromatography column sizes, chromatography sequences and bioreactor volumes are considered.

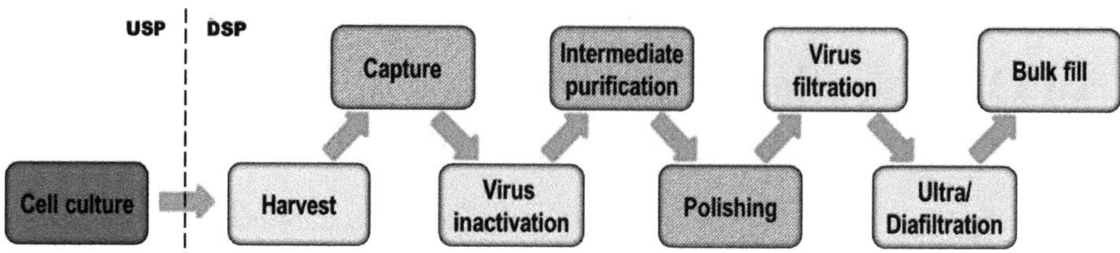

Figure 1. A typical mAb manufacturing process.

2. Problem Statement

This work aims to optimise mAb manufacturing strategies with particular focus on the bioreactor sizing strategies in the USP, and the column sequencing and sizing strategies in the DSP. Fig. 1 shows a typical mAb platform process studied in this work. After mammalian cells expressing the mAb are cultured in bioreactors in the USP, the mAb is recovered, purified and cleared from viruses by a number of operations in the DSP, including three packed-bed chromatography steps, i.e. capture step, intermediate purification step and polishing step, marked with diagonal pattern in Fig. 1.

The problem addressed in this work can be described as follows:
Given are:
process sequence of a mAb product; number of USP trains; product titre; candidate chromatography resins at each step, and their key characteristics; key characteristics of non-chromatography operations; cost data; candidate column diameters and heights, numbers of cycles and columns; initial and target host cell protein (HCP) levels.
to determine:
bioreactor sizing strategies; chromatography step sequencing strategies (i.e., resin for each step); chromatography column sizing strategies (i.e. column diameter and height, the number of cycles per batch, number of columns per step) of the resin used at each chromatography step; product mass and volume, and buffer usage volume; number of total completed batches; annual total processing time; annual total cost;
so as to:
minimise annual total cost of goods (COG), including both direct and indirect costs.

3. Mathematical Formulation

In this section, an MILP model is developed for the problem described above. Due to the limited space, only key equations are presented here.

3.1. Resin Selection

For each packed-bed chromatography step, only one resin can be used.

$$\sum_{r \in R_s} U_{sr} = 1, \ \forall s \in CS \tag{1}$$

It is assumed that in the selected chromatography sequence, each type and each resin should be used only once:

$$\sum_{s \in CS} \sum_{r \in R_s \cap R_t} U_{sr} \leq 1, \ \forall t \tag{2}$$

3.2. Protein Mass

In each batch, the protein mass from the upstream processes depends on the titre of the product and the working volume of bioreactor:

$$M_0 = titre \cdot \alpha \cdot BRV \tag{3}$$

The protein mass after each step is the product mass from the previous step multiplied by its yield. For non-chromatography and chromatography steps, we have

$$M_s = ncy_s \cdot M_{s-1}, \ \forall s \notin CS \tag{4}$$

$$M_s = \sum_{r \in R_s} (cy_{sr} \cdot U_{sr}) \cdot M_{s-1}, \ \forall s \in CS \tag{5}$$

The annual production should meet the annual demand, *d*:

$$AP = d \tag{6}$$

3.3. Resin Volume

The total column volume at each chromatography step is equal to the number of columns of the selected sizes multiplied by its corresponding column volume.

$$TCV_s = \sum_i cv_{si} \cdot CN_{si}, \ \forall s \in CS \tag{7}$$

where cv_{si} is the volume of the candidate column size *i* of chromatography step *s*, which is equal to $\pi/4 \cdot (dm_{si})^2 \cdot h_{si}$. Thus, the total amount of resin at each chromatography step must be sufficient to process all protein entering this step.

$$CYN_s \cdot TCV_s \geq RV_s, \ \forall s \in CS \tag{8}$$

The amount of resin required per batch for chromatography step *s*, depends on the mass of product to be purified, the dynamic binding capacity of the resin selected, and the resin utilisation factor:

$$RV_s = \frac{M_{s-1}}{\mu \cdot \sum_{r \in R_s} (dbc_r \cdot U_{sr})}, \ \forall s \in CS \tag{9}$$

3.4. Purity

Here, we consider HCPs as the critical impurities. In the USP, an initial level of HCPs (in ng HCP per mg of product) is known, and in the DSP, the measurement of the ability to remove HCPs for each resin is given using log reduction values (LRV). The selected purification sequence should be able to reduce the HCP level under a target level.

$$\frac{c^0}{10^{\sum_s \sum_{r \in R_s} lrv_{sr} \cdot U_{sr}}} \leq c^t \tag{10}$$

3.5. Costs

The cost of the manufacturing performance includes direct and indirect costs. The direct costs are based on the resource utilisation, including labour cost, chemical reagents cost, consumables cost, miscellaneous material cost, utilities cost, while the indirect costs are dependent on the facilities, including both capital cost and other indirect costs. The objective is to minimise the annual total COG. Meanwhile, the exact linearisation (Sherali and Adams, 1999) and piecewise linearisation techniques are used to linearise the nonlinear constraints. Overall, the problem is formulated as an MILP model.

4. Case Study

We applied the optimisation model to an industrially-relevant example with a single mAb product with a 500 kg annual demand. There are 11 candidate commercial chromatography resins (R1 to R11) of 5 types, including affinity chromatography(AFF), cation-exchange chromatography (CEX), anion-exchange chromatography (AEX), mixed-mode chromatography (MM) and hydrophobic interaction chromatography (HIC). As to the chromatography column sizing decisions, there are 11 discrete potential bed heights (15-25 cm) and 10discrete potential diameters (50-200 cm), and therefore a single column has 110 potential volumes. The number of cycles per batch can be up to 10, while at most 4 parallel columns are permitted at each chromatography step. The initial HCP level is 1,500,000 ng/mg, and the target HCP level is set to 100 ng/mg. Here, several cases of multiple USP trains feeding a single DSP train are investigated, considering four cases: 1 USP: 1 DSP, 2 USP: 1 DSP, 4 USP: 1 DSP and6USP:1DSP.

The proposed MILP model is implemented in GAMS 24.0 (Brooke et al., 2012) using CPLEX MILP solver with 4 threads. The optimality gap is 0 %, and CPU time limit is 10,000 s. The optimal computational results are reported in Table 1. The optimal annual COG increases with the increasing number of bioreactors. As to the CPU time, apart from the case 2USP:1DSP that takes 3,800 s, all other cases terminate within 2,000 s.

As to the optimal chromatography sequence, the same resin sequence is selected for all cases, i.e., AFF (R3) for capture, CEX (R6) for intermediate purification, and AEX (R7) for polishing, as given in Fig. 2. The total HCP LRV of the optimal sequence is 4.3. The obtained final HCP level is 75.2 ng/mg (<100 ng/mg), reduced from 1,500,000 ng/mg.

The optimal single bioreactor volumes and numbers of batches are shown in Fig. 3. In the last case 6USP:1DSP, to avoid the situation that the DSP window is too tight to complete, the single bioreactor volume is 4,551 L, and 103 batches are produced.

Table 1. Computational performance of the proposed model.

	1USP:1DSP	2USP:1DSP	4USP:1DSP	6USP:1DSP
Optimal annual COG (k£)	36,296	41,494	48,367	55,818
CPU (s)	1,817	3,800	1,542	1,428

Figure 2. Optimal chromatography sequencing strategies with all USP:DSP ratios.

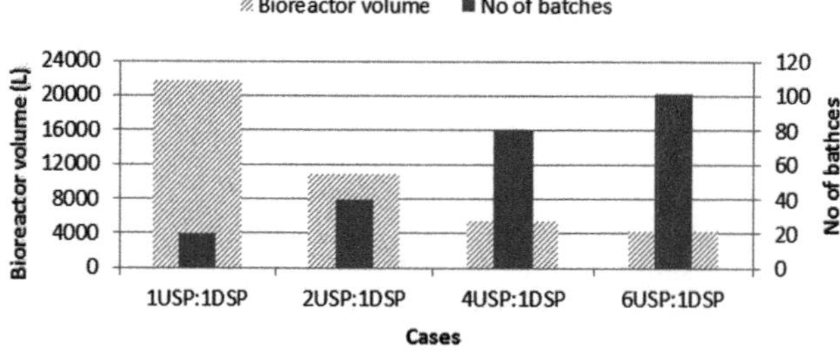

Figure 3. Optimal single bioreactor volumes (diagonal) and numbers of batches (solid).

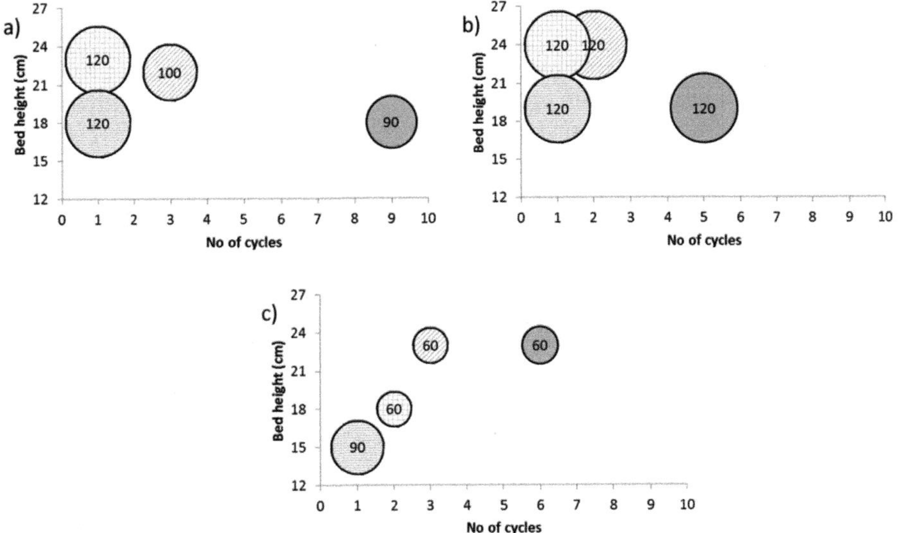

Figure 4. Optimal column sizing strategies of case study at a) capture step; b) intermediate purification step; c) polishing step, for cases 1USP:1DSP (solid), 2USP:1DSP (diagonal pattern), 4USP:1DSP (grid pattern), 6USP:1DSP (horizontal pattern).

The detailed optimal chromatography column sizing strategies at each step, including the number of cycles per batch (x-axis), the column bed height (y-axis), the column diameter (proportional to the bubble size, number in cm at the circle centre), are presented in Fig. 4. It should be noted that for all cases, only a single column is used at each chromatography step.

5. Concluding Remarks

In this paper, we have addressed the optimisation of the manufacturing processes of mAb products, considering bioreactor sizing, chromatography sequencing and column sizing strategies, simultaneously. An MILP model has been developed to minimise the annual total COG, using exact linearisation and piecewise linearisation techniques. An industrially-relevant example has been investigated considering different USP and DSP ratios. In the future, stochastic programming models can be developed to tackle uncertainty issues.

Acknowledgements

Funding from the UK Engineering & Physical Sciences Research Council (EPSRC) for the EPSRC Centre for Innovative Manufacturing in Emergent Macromolecular Therapies hosted by University College London is gratefully acknowledged. Financial support from the consortium of industrial and governmental users is also acknowledged.

Notation

Indices

i	column size
r	resin
t	resin type
s	process step

Sets

CS	set of chromatography steps, = capture, intermediate purification, polishing
R_s	set of resins suitable to operation$s$
R_t	set of resins of the resin type t

Parameters

c^0	initial HCP level, ng/mg
c^t	target HCP level, ng/mg
cv_{si}	volume of column size i at chromatography step s, L
cy_{sr}	product yield of resin r at chromatography step s
dbc_r	dynamic binding capacity of resin r, g/L
d	annual demand, kg
dm_{si}	diameter of column size i at step s, L
h_{si}	height of column size i at step s, cm
lrv_{sr}	HCP log reduction value
ncy_s	product yield of non-chromatography step s
$titre$	fermentation titre, g/L
α	bioreactor working volume factor
μ	chromatography resin utilisation factor

Continuous Variables

AP	annual production, kg
BRV	single bioreactor volume, L
M_0	initial product mass entering downstream processes per batch, g
M_s	product mass per batch after step s, g
RV_s	resin volume required at chromatography step s, L
TCV_s	total column volume at chromatography step s, L

Discrete Variables

U_{sr}	binary, 1 if resin r is selected for chromatography step s, 0 otherwise
CN_{si}	number of columns of size i at chromatography step s
CYN_s	number of cycles at chromatography step s

References

M. Butler, 2013, From the mold in Dr Florey's coat to blockbuster drugs, Pharmaceutical Bioprocessing, 1, 3-5.

A. Brooke, D. Kendrick, A. Meeraus, R. Raman, 2012, GAMS – A User's Guide, GAMS Development Corporation, Washington, D.C., USA.

S. Liu, A.S. Simaria, S.S. Farid, L.G. Papageorgiou, 2013a, Mixed integer optimisation of antibody purification processes, Computer Aided Chemical Engineering, 32, 157-162.

S. Liu, A.S. Simaria, S.S. Farid, L.G. Papageorgiou, 2013b, Designing cost-effective biopharmaceutical facilities using mixed-integer optimization, Biotechnology Progress, 29, 1472-1483

H.D. Sherali, W.P. Adams, 1999, A Reformulation-Linearization Technique for Solving Discrete and Continuous Nonconvex Problems, Kluwer Academic Publishers, Dordrecht, Netherlands.

A.S. Simaria, R. Turner, S.S. Farid, 2012, A multi-level meta-heuristic algorithm for the optimisation of antibody purification processes, Biochemical Engineering Journal, 69, 144-154.

Jiří Jaromír Klemeš, Petar Sabev Varbanov and Peng Yen Liew (Editors)
Proceedings of the 24th European Symposium on Computer Aided Process Engineering – ESCAPE 24
June 15-18, 2014, Budapest, Hungary.

Optimal Experiment Design for Model Discrimination using the Sigma Point Method

Dries Telen, Ioanna Stamati, Marcelo da Silva, Filip Logist, Jan Van Impe*

KU Leuven, Chemical engineering department, BioTeC & OPTEC,
Willem de Croylaan 46, Leuven3001, Belgium
jan.vanimpe@cit.kuleuven.be

Abstract

Bioprocesses can be controlled and optimised by dynamic process models. However, often different models are available for describing the dynamics in a similar way. In order to discriminate efficiently among rival models, optimal experiment design for model discrimination (OED-MD) has been developed. In this work the OED-MD method proposed by Schwaab et al. (2008) will be used for discriminating among dynamic models of microbial growth rate as a function of temperature. In this model discrimination procedurethe variance-covariance matrix of the parameters is needed, which is traditionally approximated by the inverse of the Fisher information matrix using the Cramer-Rao lower bound. For models nonlinear in the parameters, this can be a severe underestimation of the actual parameter uncertainty. A more accurate estimation of the variance-covariance matrix of the parameters can be obtained by using the so-called sigma point method (Schenkendorf et al., 2009). The main contribution of this paper is that the sigma point method is used for accurately computing the variance-covariance matrix of the parameters. This matrix is subsequently employed in the procedure for discriminating between two possible models of microbial growth rate as a function of temperature. In addition, the sigma point method is compared with the classic Fisher information matrix approach on the level of discriminating potential.

Keywords: optimal experiment design, model discrimination, sigma point method.

1. Introduction

Many industrial relevant bioprocesses, e.g., brewing and enzyme production, can be described by dynamic process models. The problem, however, is that sometimes different models are available to describe the dynamics in a similar way. To determine which model is the most appropriate, additional experiments have to be performed. To limit the experimental burden, optimal experiment design methods for model discrimination (OED/MD) are useful tools.

To this end, Buzzi-Ferraris et al. (1984) proposed a criterion that incorporates both the uncertainty of the measurements and the model predictions. This approach yields a variance-covariance matrix which is used to weigh the model outputs. In Schwaab et al. (2008) this criterion is extended with an anticipatory approach which takes the expected uncertainty of the parameters in the experiment into account. The question, however, remains how to compute the expected variance-covariance matrix of the experiment under design. The Fisher information matrix, which is widely used in optimal experiment design (Walter and Pronzato, 1997), can give an underestimation of the actual parameter variance-covariance. Consequently, Schenkendorf et al. (2009) try to address this issue at the expense of a higher computational burden.

The contribution of this paper is to illustrate with an in silico study that it is possible to design experiments which allow to discriminate between two different proposed models using the sigma point method.

2. Mathematical formulation

Many biochemical processes can be described in a time interval [0, t_f] by a set of differential equations:

$$\dot{y(t)} = g(y(t), p, u(t)) \text{ with } y(0) = y_0 \quad (1)$$

Here, $y(t)$ are the states variables, p the parameters and $u(t)$ are the controls, which are the degrees of freedom in the optimal experiment design procedure. The output of the system is denoted by $z(t) = h(y(t))$. The measurement error $\varepsilon \sim N(0, V)$ is assumed to be Gaussian distributed with zero mean and variance-covariance matrix$V$.

In model discrimination, the objective function of the optimisation procedure is typically a function that maximises the difference between the model outputs given the present uncertainty. The total number of past experiments isn_e. The criterion employed in this work to discriminate between models m and n for the experiment $\xi_{n_e+1} = [y_{m,n_e+1}(t), y_{n,n_e+1}(t), u_{n_e+1}(t), p_m, p_n]$ under design is (Schwaab et al., 2008):

$$D_{m,n}(\xi_{n_e+1}) = d_{m,n}^T(\xi_{n_e+1}) V_{m,n}^{-1} d_{m,n}(\xi_{n_e+1}) \quad (2)$$

in which $d_{m,n}(\xi_{n_e+1}) = z_m(\xi_{n_e+1}) - z_n(\xi_{n_e+1})$ and $V_{m,n}(\xi_{n_e+1}) = 2V + V_m(\xi_{n_e+1}) + V_n(\xi_{n_e+1})$. The posterior variance-covariance matrix of the difference between the models $V_{m,n}(\xi_{n_e+1})$ is determined by the uncertainty in the model outputs $V_m(\xi_{n_e+1})$ and $V_n(\xi_{n_e+1})$ and the uncertainty in the measurements. How $V_m(\xi_{n_e+1})$ and $V_n(\xi_{n_e+1})$ are computed is explained in the next section.

3. Computing the variance-covariance matrix

3.1. The Fisher information matrix approach

The first approach discussed in this work is based on the class is Fisher information matrix (FIM) approach (Walter and Pronzato, 1997). For model m, $V_m(\xi_{n_e+1})$ is computed as $V_m(\xi_{n_e+1}) = S_m(\xi_{n_e+1}) V_{p,m}(\xi_{n_e+1}) S_m^T(\xi_{n_e+1})$ in which $V_{p,m}(\xi_{n_e+1})$ is the posterior variance-covariance matrix of the model parameters and $S_m(\xi_{n_e+1})$ are the model output sensitivities with respect to the parameters resulting from experimental condition ξ_{n_e+1}. The matrix $V_{p,m}(\xi_{n_e+1})$ is computed by the Fisher information matrix by using the Cramer-Rao lower bound $V_{p,m}^{-1}(\xi_{n_e+1}) = F_{p,m}(\xi_{n_e+1})$ (Walter and Pronzato, 1997):

$$F_{p,m}(\xi_{n_e+1}) = V_{p,m}^{-1}(\xi_{n_e}) + \int_0^{t_f} S_m^T \frac{\partial h_m(y_m(t))^T}{\partial y_m} V^{-1} \frac{\partial h_m(y_m(t))}{\partial y_m} S_m \, dt \quad (3)$$

3.2. The sigma point method approach

The second approach is based on the sigma point (SP) method (Schenkendorf et al., 2008). This is a computational tractable method that allows a more accurate computation of the parameters' variance-covariance matrix. Given an expected experimental condition ξ_{n_e+1} with an expected model output z_{m,n_e+1} for a model m. Assume K samples scheduled in the experiment, in addition $2K$+1 error vectors are made based on the measurement error variance-covariance matrix V and added to the output trajectory:$\varepsilon_0 = 0$, $\varepsilon_j = -\sqrt{K+\lambda}\sqrt{V}_j$ with $j = 1 \dots K$ and $\varepsilon_j = \sqrt{K+\lambda}\sqrt{V}_{j-K}$ with $j = K+1 \dots 2K$. Note that $\sqrt{V}_j$ denotes the *j*-th column of the matrix square root. This 2*K*+1 error vectors are individually added to the nominal trajectory leading to 2*K*+1 data vectors. For each of these data vectors a parameter estimation procedure is performed, resulting in 2*K*+1 parameter estimates $\hat{p}_{m,n_e+1,j}$. The mean estimate $\bar{p}_{m,n_e+1}$ and the parameter variance-covariance matrix $V_{p,m,SP}$ are computed as follows:

$$\bar{p}_{m,n_e+1} = \sum_{j=0}^{2K} w_j^a \hat{p}_{m,n_e+1,j} \tag{4}$$

$$V_{p,m,SP} = \sum_{j=0}^{2K} w_j^c (\hat{p}_{m,n_e+1,j} - \bar{p}_{m,n_e+1})(\hat{p}_{m,n_e+1,j} - \bar{p}_{m,n_e+1})^T \tag{5}$$

The definition of the weights can be found in Schenkendorf et al. (2008). The sigma point method results in a more accurate computation of the parameter variance-covariance matrix, the price to pay, however, is a significant increase in computational cost as 2*K*+1 parameters are additionally performed.

4. Case study

4.1. Model description

The growth of microbial cells (cell density) as a function of time can be described by the primary model of Baranyi and Roberts (1994):

$$\frac{dn(t)}{dt} = \frac{Q(t)}{Q(t)+1}\mu_{max}(T(t))(1 - \exp(n(t) - n_{max})) \tag{6}$$

$$\frac{dQ(t)}{dt} = \mu_{max}(T(t))Q(t) \tag{7}$$

in which $n(t)$ [ln (CFU/ml)] denotes the cell density, $n_{max}(t)$ [ln (CFU/ml)] the maximum value for the cell density and $\mu_{max}(T(t))$ is the maximum specific growth rate. The state $Q(t)$ indicates the physiological state of the cells. Only $n(t)$ can be measured with a measurement variance of $\sigma_n^2 = 0.0327$. The effect of temperature on the maximum specific growth rate is incorporated by the secondary model called Cardinal Temperature Model with Inflection (Rosso et al., 1993). Although, CTMI is assumed to be valid for all strains. However, a divergence from this model has been observed for Listeria (Le Marc et al., 2002) and E. coli K12 (Van Derlinden and Van Impe, 2012). A slightly adapted model has been formulated, called the adapted CTMI or aCTMI (Le Marc et al., 2002). The difference between the two models is illustrated in Figure 1. The exact mathematical formulations can be found in the papers referenced above. Also it has to be emphasised that the deviation between the models is mainly in the temperature region in which food products are stored. Hence, the selection of an adequate model is highly important for the food and life sciences industry.

4.2. Experimental design procedure

To design a discrimination experiment, a dynamic temperature profile$T(t)$has to be determined. This profile is typically parameterised by four degrees of freedom (Van Derlinden et al., 2010). The first is the constant temperature at the start of the experiment T_{init}, the second is the duration time of the first constant phase, t_s the third is the rate of the temperature change, $\Delta T/\Delta t$ and the fourth is Δt, the duration of the temperature change. The degrees of freedom can be grouped in a vector

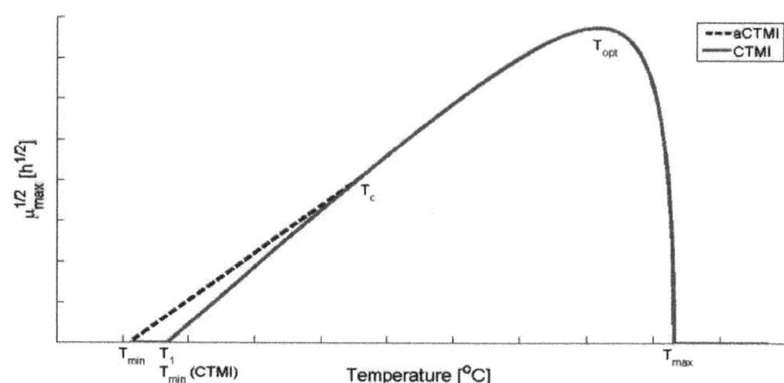

Figure 1. Illustration of the two secondary models.

$[T_{init}, t_s, \Delta T/\Delta t, \Delta t]$. For model validity reasons the dynamic temperature profile is constrained to:

$$0 \quad \leq t_s + \Delta t \leq 38 \text{ h} \tag{8}$$

$$0\,^{o}\mathrm{C} \quad \leq \quad T(t) \leq 45\,^{o}\mathrm{C} \tag{9}$$

$$-5\,^{o}\mathrm{C/h} \leq \Delta T/_{\Delta t} \leq 5\,^{o}\mathrm{C/h} \tag{10}$$

In addition, the experimental time is fixed to 38 hand samples are assumed to be taken every hour (Van Derlinden et al., 2010).The goal of this work is to illustrate that the described methods are able to discriminate the different models. The aCTMI can, by appropriate choices for $T_c$and T_1, coincide with the CTMI model. So, in this in silico study, it is assumed that the aCTMI is the correct model structure and is used to generate pseudo measurements instead of taking real samples. The procedure starts with a preliminary experiment, after which a parameter estimation is performed. This preliminary experiment yields an initialisation for the parameters of both models. The parameters for the correct aCTMI are assumed to be $\mu_{opt} = 2.411$/h, $T_{min} = 5.67\,^{o}$C, $T_c = 23\,^{o}$C, $T_1 = 12.3\,^{o}$C, $T_{opt} = 40.85\,^{o}$C and $T_{max} = 46.54\,^{o}$C (Van Derlinden and Van Impe, 2012). The difference between the two models is only evident in the lower temperature region, so $T_{opt}$and T_{max} are assumed to be the same for both. This leads to two remaining unknown parameters in the parameter estimation procedure for CTMI and four unknown parameters for aCTMI.

5. Results

5.1. The preliminary experiment

The experimental conditions for the first initial experiments are [13 ^{o}C, 10 h, 0.5 ^{o}C/h 25h]. These conditions are used to yield pseudo measurements based on the expected evolution of the aCTMI. Based on this data a parameter estimation is performed for both models using a weighted sum of squares errors (WSSE) objective function. The obtained parameter values can be found in Table 1. Note the relative difference between the obtained parameters of the aCTMI and the actual parameters. This may indicate low experimental information content for parameter estimation. A model adequacy test, i.e., the χ^2 test is performed and the result represented in Table 2. The χ^2 test with 95 % significance level indicates that both models are able to describe the data, i.e., both models have a WSSE score lower than expected by the χ^2 test. Note that *n* and *np* denote the number of samples and the number of free parameters, respectively.

Table 1. Parameter values and model adequacy test result after the preliminary experiment.

Model	μ_{opt}[1/h]	T_{min}[°C]	T_c[°C]	T_1[°C]	WSSE	$\chi^2_{n\text{-}np}$
	Exact parameter values					
aCTMI	2.41	5.67	23	12.3		
	Estimated values after preliminary experiment				*Adequacy test*	
CTMI	1.59	6.13			36.9	52.2
aCTMI	2.34	4.97	22.13	11.88	25.7	49.8

5.2. The discriminatory experiments

After the preliminary experiment is performed, a discrimination experiment is designed based on computations of the variance-covariance matrix using the Fisher information matrix and the sigma point methods. The obtained temperature profile using the FIM approach is described by the vector [40.9 °C, 3.9h, −5.0 °C/h, 6.7h], the sigma point method leads to [40.6 °C, 2.7h, −3.45 °C/h, 9.7h]. Both profiles and the preliminary experiment are depicted in Figure 1. Note the similarity in the obtained experimental conditions of the two methods. Furthermore, the majority of the experiment is spent in the temperature range [5°C - 25°C] which is the range in which the difference between the two models is the most evident. With this new temperature profile, a new set of pseudo-measurements is generated. The parameters of both models are estimated and a model adequacy test is performed. The resulting state evolution for both approaches is depicted in Figure 2. For both cases the evolution during the preliminary experiment is not adequately described by the CTMI. The resulting values for the model adequacy tests can be found in Table 2.

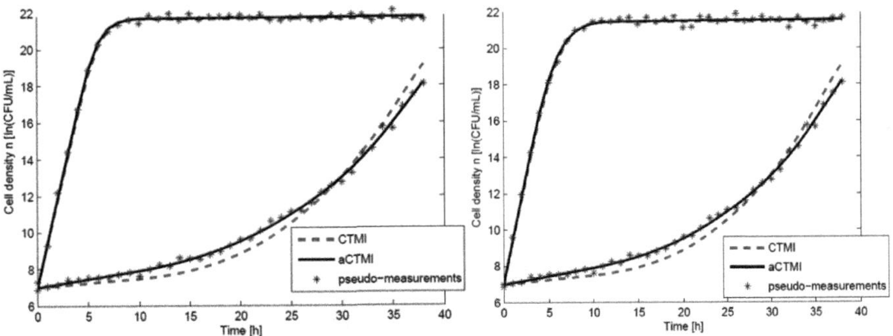

Figure 2. Calibrated cell density evolution after the discriminatory experiment for both approaches (Fisher information matrix approach, left and sigma point method approach, right).

Table 2. Parameter values &model adequacy test result after the discriminatory experiment.

Model	μ_{opt}[1/h]	T_{min}[°C]	T_c[°C]	T_1[°C]	WSSE	$\chi^2_{n\text{-}np}$
	Exact parameter values					
aCTMI	2.41	5.67	23	12.3		
	Estimated values after discriminatory experiment based on FIM approach					
CTMI	2.36	9.26			**382.2**	97.3
aCTMI	2.41	5.14	22.60	12.38	57.4	95.0
	Estimated values after discriminatory experiment based on SP approach					
CTMI	2.32	9.16			**368.5**	97.3
aCTMI	2.40	5.12	22.4	12.21	70.9	95.0

For both approaches, the χ^2 test indicates that the aCTMI is the most appropriate model to describe the initial experiment and the new data after the first discriminatory experiment as the WSSE score of the CTMI is significantly (95 % significance level) larger than the value expected by the χ^2 distribution. In case no significant difference is present, additional discrimination experiments have to be designed. Between the two approaches, there is also a computational difference. The objective function (2) is evaluated in 0.05 s in the FIM approach. The sigma point method requires 157 parameter estimation procedures for the evaluation of the objective function. This illustrates that the sigma point method can be become computationally expensive. In addition, for this specific case study there is no noticeable effect on the accuracy of the variance-covariance matrix compared with the Fisher information matrix approach.

6. Conclusions

In this paper optimal experiment design for model discrimination is considered. Two computational procedures for the parameter variance-covariance matrix are evaluated, i.e., the classic Fisher information matrix approach and a more accurate sigma point approach. The case study relates to the influence of temperature on microbial growth. To describe this effect two models, i.e., the CTMI and aCTMI are available. Both computation methods have been shown in silico to yield experiments that are able to discriminate between the two models after one experiment. Furthermore, both methods lead to similar designs, which indicate that both reached the same (global) optimum.

Acknowledgements

D. Telen has an IWT-PhD grant. J. Van Impe holds the chair Safety Engineering sponsored by the Belgian Chemistry and Life Sciences Federation essenscia. The research was supported by: PFV/10/002 (OPTEC), OT/10/035, FWO KAN2013 1.5.189.13, FWO-G.0930.13N and IAP VII/19 (DYSCO).

References

J. Baranyi, T.A. Roberts, 1994, A dynamic approach to predicting bacterial growth in food, Int. J. Food Microbiol., 23, 277-294.

G. Buzzi-Ferraris, P. Forzatti, G. Emig, H. Hofmann, 1984, Sequential experimental design for model discrimination in the case of multiple responses, Chem. Eng. Sci., 39, 81-85, 1984.

Y. Le Marc, V. Huchet, C. Bourgeois, J. Guyonnet, P. Mafart, D. Thuault, 2002, Modelling the growth kinetics of Listeria as a function of temperature, pH and organic acid concentration, Int. J. Food Microbiol., 73:219-237.

L. Rosso, J.R. Lobry, J.P. Flandrois, 1993, An unexpected correlation between cardinal temperatures of microbial growth highlighted by a new model, J. Theor. Biol., 162, 447-463.

R. Schenkendorf, A. Kremling, M. Mangold, 2009, Optimal experimental design with the sigma point method, IET Syst. Biol., 3, 10-23.

M. Schwaab, J.L. Monteiro, J.C. Pinto, 2008, Sequential experimental design for model discrimination. Taking into account the posterior covariance matrix of parameter uncertainties, Chem. Eng. Sci., 63, 2408-2419.

E. Van Derlinden, K. Bernaerts, J. Van Impe, 2010, Simultaneous versus sequential optimal experiment design for the identification of multi-parameter microbial growth kinetics as a function of temperature, J. Theor. Biol., 264, 347-355.

E. Van Derlinden, J. Van Impe, 2012, Modeling growth rates as a function of temperature: Model performance evaluation with focus on the suboptimal temperature range, Int.J. Food Microbiol., 158, 73-78.

E. Walter, L. Pronzato, 1997, Identification of Parametric Models from Experimental Data, Springer, Paris.

Jiří Jaromír Klemeš, Petar Sabev Varbanov and Peng Yen Liew (Editors)
Proceedings of the 24th European Symposium on Computer Aided Process Engineering – ESCAPE 24
June 15-18, 2014, Budapest, Hungary.

Batch Distillation with Vapour Compression Applying Different Working Fluids

Gabor Modla*, Peter Lang

Budapest University of Technology and Economics, Department of Building Services and Process Engineering, Muegyetem rkp. 3-5, Budapest, H-1521, Hungary
mgabor-bp@freemail.hu

Abstract

Application of a heat pump system (HP) is a possibility for decreasing the energy demand of distillation. The separation of a low relative volatility mixture (n-heptane - toluene) by batch distillation with vapour compression (BD-VC) is investigated. The working fluids (WFs) studied are n-pentane, n-hexane and methanol, ethanol, iso-propanol. The column equipped with standard reactor-reboiler is simulated in a rigorous way (including the conditions of heat transfer). The influence of the main operational parameters and of the selection of the WF on the effectiveness (cost saving, COP, payback time) of the process is investigated.

Keywords: batch distillation, heat-pump, vapour compression, energy saving.

1. Introduction

The energy demand of the distillation is usually very high. The heat duty to be furnished in the reboiler (at higher temperature) nearly equals to that to be withdrawn (at lower temperature) in the condenser therefore great saving of energy can be reached by the thermal coupling of the condenser and reboiler which requires the increase of the temperature and pressure (compression) of the working fluid (WF). The WF can be the top vapour itself (vapour recompression, VRC) or a material (pure substance or mixture) which is independent of the mixture to be separated (vapour compression, VC). The application possibilities of different heat pump (HP) systems for distillation were first studied for the continuous process. Bruinsma and Spoelstra (2010) gave a comprehensive review of the different methods.

About the application of VRC for batch distillation (BD) Jana and his team published several papers (e.g. Jana and Maiti, 2013) recently. Modla and Lang (2013) studied the BD separation of a close boiling hydrocarbon mixture (n-heptane – toluene) by dynamic simulation and cost calculations. The following HP methods were investigated: vapour recompression (BD-VRC), vapour recompression with the application of an external heat exchanger (BD-VRC-E) and vapour compression (BD-VC, WF: n-pentane). The most favourable results (shortest payback time of the additional investment) were obtained for the BD-VRC-E and BD-VC systems. In this paper the vapour compression system (Figure 1) will be studied by applying different WF-s. The goals of this paper:
-to study the process of BD with vapour compression by dynamic simulation,
-to study its economic feasibility by cost calculations,
-to compare the effectiveness of different working fluids.

For the simulation of the BD-VC system the different modules of the ChemCad professional flow-sheet simulator are used. Standard reactor-reboiler is applied and simulated in a rigorous way (including the conditions of heat transfer). The influence of the main operational parameters (e.g. compression ratio) on the effectiveness (cost saving, COP, payback time) of the process is investigated. The mixture to be separated is n-heptane – toluene. The working fluids applied are n-pentane, n-hexane and methanol, ethanol, iso-propanol.

2. Batch distillation with vapour compression

In batch distillation with vapour compression (VC, Figure 1) the working fluid (WF) is independent of the mixture to be separated. The basic parts of a VC cycle are as follows (Figure 2). The WF is evaporated at the condenser (between 1 and 2), compressed to a higher pressure with higher saturation temperature (3→4), condensed in the reboiler (5→6), and cooled down by expansion over a throttle valve (7→1) to a (saturation) temperature below the condenser temperature. The optional parts of the cycle depending among others on the thermodynamic properties of the WF are: superheating of the WF (2→3, if necessary in order to prevent the (partial) condensation of WF in the compressor) and in the reboiler cooling down of WF to its dewpoint (4→5, if it leaves the compressor as superheated vapour), subcooling of the condensed WF before expansion (6→7). The compressor (the heat pump system) can be already operated during the heating-up of the column.

3. Working fluids

The application of several WF-s was studied. The criteria for the selection were the following ones:

1. The bubble point of the working fluid at 1.01 bar must be less at least by 15 °C than the lowest temperature of the top vapour
(in our case the bubble point of the light component at 1.01 bar, 98.4-15=83.4 °C).

2. The critical temperature of the WF must be higher than the maximal temperature at the utility side of the reboiler (in our case the bubble point of the heavy component at

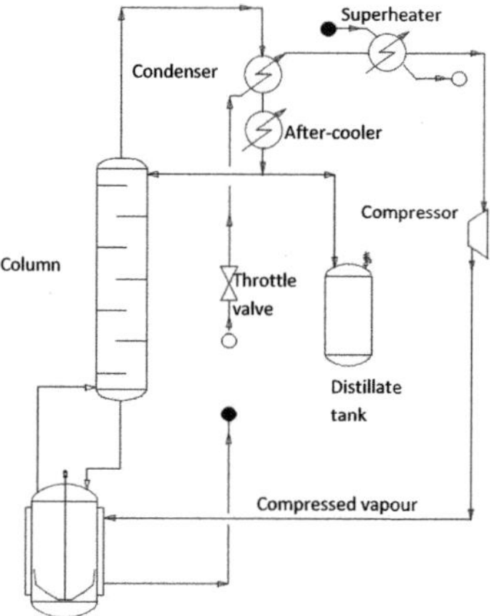

Figure 1. Scheme of batch distillation with vapour compression

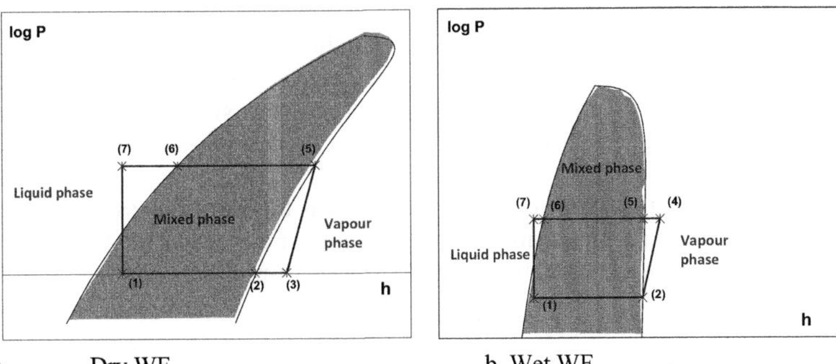

a. Dry WF b. Wet WF

Figure 2. Thermodynamic cycles of VC for different types of WFs

1.11 bar plus the temperature difference for the heat transfer: 111+15 = 126 °C or the saturation temperature of the heating steam of 4 bar: 143.7 °C). (If this criterion is satisfied the maximal pressure at the utility side of the reboiler remains under the critical pressure of the WF, as well.) Vapour pressure- temperature and pressure- enthalpy curves of the components to be separated and of some potential WFs are shown in Figure 3. The relevant thermodynamic data of these substances are given in Table 1.

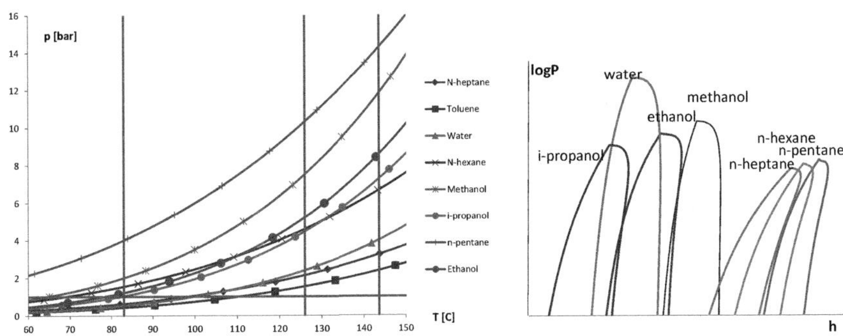

Figure 3. Vapour pressure-temperature and pressure-enthalpy curves

Table 1. Thermodynamic data of the substances studied

	NBP [° C]	p° [bar] 83.4	p° [bar] 126 ° C	p° [bar] 143.7	λ [kJ/mol 83.4	λ [kJ/mol 126 ° C	λ [kJ/mol 143.7	T_{cr} [° C]
n-pentane	36.07	3.99	10.24	14.23	22.65	18.74	16.70	196.5
n-hexane	68.73	1.53	4.46	6.47	28.07	24.54	22.84	234.2
methanol	64.70	2.01	7.54	11.98	33.85	30.07	28.25	239.5
ethanol	78.29	1.21	5.09	8.3	38.27	34.39	32.51	240.8
i-propanol	82.26	1.03	4.45	7.28	39.79	34.66	32.2	235.2
water	100.0	0.53	2.39	4.00	41.58	39.48	38.56	374.2
n-heptane	98.43	0.62	2.11	3.21	32.82	29.61	28.11	267.0
toluene	110.5	0.43	1.54	2.38	34.95	32.41	31.26	320.6

From the point of view of compression costs it is favourable if
-The increase of the vapour pressure to the given increase of the boiling point (ΔT) is the lowest possible ($\Delta p^0_{rel}/\Delta T$=min.). In this case the compression ratio is minimal resulting in lower operating cost (best WF: n-pentane, worst WF-s: i-propanol and ethanol),
-The latent heat of vaporisation at the operating pressures is the highest possible. In this case the flow rate of WF is minimal, smaller size compressor is needed resulting in the decrease of both investment and operating costs (best WFs: i-propanol, ethanol, worst: n-pentane).

The WFs can be divided into two different types from the point of view of compression. The saturated vapour side of the pressure-enthalpy curve of the two paraffins strongly inclines to the right (Figure 2a) and the saturated vapour (2) would partially condense in the compressor without superheating (to point 3) before compression. This type of WF-s is called dry fluid by Chen et al. (2010) who studied different Rankine cycles. The right branch of the logP-h curve is almost vertical (Figure 2b) for the alcohols (and water, "wet" fluids). Compressing the saturated vapour we get superheated vapour, which cools down to its dew point in the reboiler (5) before condensing. These WFs do not need superheating before compression. In our case n-pentane, n-hexane are dry and methanol, ethanol, isopropanol are wet fluids, respectively.

4. Calculation results

To compare the different working fluids the separation of a mixture of n-heptane (50 mol %)- toluene is considered. This is a mixture of low relative volatility where the heat pump system can be economical. The specified product purity ($x_{D,av}$) is 0.98. The number of theoretical stages is 50 (excluding the total condenser and the reboiler). The pressure drop of the column is 0.1 bar. The reboiler is of commercial type (DIN AE-1000).

At the beginning of the process the binary feed (charge) is filled in the reboiler and the column is empty. During the start-up total reflux is applied. The start-up ends when the x_D reaches 0.9975. During the next process step (production) the reflux ratio is 12.

First the flow rate of the heating steam is determined for the BD without VC which determines the duration of the heating up and that of the production. The highest heat duty must be provided during the start-up otherwise the length of this step (without product withdrawal) would be too high. The flow rates of the WFs are determined so that the duration of heating up is equal to that of the BD. Hence the duration of the production step is practically the same if the dew point of the different heating media (water steam and WFs) equals. The size of the compressor is determined for the heating up (highest heat duty). Polytropic compression with efficiency of 90 % is assumed.

4.1. Case 1

The dew point is minimal (126 °C). The duration of the heating up, from which the molar flow rates of the WFs (V_{WF}) are determined: 305 min. Before compression the WFs are superheated to minimal extent (if necessary at all). The batch operation time (BOT) is 1,402 min in all cases. The cost of compressor is proportional to the power of its motor (MP). The calculation results are shown in Table 2.

Table 2.Comparison of the different WFs (condensation at 126 °C).

Working fluid	P_{in} [bar]	DT [°C]	P_{out} [bar]	T_{out} [°C]	V_{WF} [kmol/h]	MP [kW]	Q_{ce} [MJ]	SMP [MJ]	COP	PBP [Y]
steam (2.39 bar)	-	-	-		5.55	-	-			
n-pentane	4	15	10.24	127.4	10	8.53	-501	717	2.6	36.9
n-hexane	1.53	32	4.46	126.1	7.6	7.69	-456	646	2.9	24.0
methanol	2.01	0	7.54	203.6	6.3	8.58	-109	720	2.6	37.7
ethanol	1.21	0	5.09	153.4	6.0	8.53	-163	717	2.6	36.8
i-propanol	1.03	0	4.45	131.6	5.7	8.03	-211	675	2.8	28.2

By the results we can conclude that
-The lowest MP is required for the n-hexane, it is nearly the same for all other WFs.
-The flow rate of WF is highest for the n-pentane.
-Since the compressor is operating with the same power during the heating up and the production, therefore during this latter when the heat duty of the distillation is lower, the compressor provides too much heat and extra cooling must be applied (the heat to be withdrawn is Q_{ce}).
-The average value of COP is low, because the compressor is still operated with high power in the production step whilst the heat duty is already low. Hence the payback time (PBT) is very high.

4.2. Case 2

The dew point of WFs is equal to that of heating steam of 4 bar (143.7 °C). The duration of the heating up is 211 min. The WFs are superheated to a minimal extent. BOT is 802 min in all cases. The calculation results are shown in Table 3. By the results we can conclude that:
-Because of the higher compression ratio a compressor of higher power is needed.
-The lowest MP is required for the isopropanol and ethanol.

Table 3. Comparison of the different WFs (condensation at 143.7 °C, without control)

Working fluid	P_{in} [bar]	DT [°C]	P_{out} [bar]	T_{out} [°C]	V_{WF} [kmol/h]	MP [kW]	Q_{ce} [MJ]	SMP [MJ]	COP	PBP [Y]
steam (4.0 bar)	-	-	-			-	-			
n-pentane	4	19	14.23	143.7	11	13.04	-311	627	3.1	15.5
n-hexane	1.53	24.5	6.47	143.8	8.2	11.57	-278	556	3.5	11.6
methanol	2.01	0	11.9	250.1	6.1	11.79	-60	567	3.4	12.0
ethanol	1.21	0	8.3	178.3	5.7	11.26	-87	542	3.6	10.9
i-propanol	1.03	0	7.28	149.6	5.8	11.22	-121	539	3.6	10.9

Table 4. Comparison of the different WFs (condensation at 143.7 °C, with control)

Working fluid	Pin [bar]	DT [°C]	Pout [bar]	Tout [°C]	$V_{WF, max}$ [kmol/h]	MP [kW]	Q_{ce} [MJ]	SMP [MJ]	COP	PBP [Y]
n-pentane	4	19	14.23	143.7	11	13.04	-244	496	3.9	12.9
n-hexane	1.53	24.5	6.47	143.8	8.2	11.7	-216	437	4.4	10.1
methanol	2.01	0	11.9	250.09	6.1	11.82	-42	405	4.8	10.0
ethanol	1.21	0	8.3	178.29	5.7	11.25	-63	402	4.8	9.3
i-propanol	1.03	0	7.28	149.63	5.8	11.4	-93	420	4.6	9.6

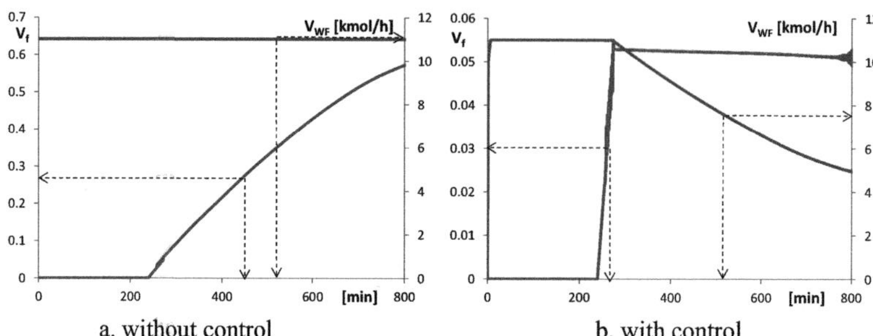

a. without control b. with control

Figure 4. The evolution of the vapour fraction in the WF leaving the reboiler and flow rate of WF

-The WF flow rates only slightly varied but in different ways (both increase and decrease occur).
-The average COP increased, therefore PBT decreased but it is still too high.

4.3. Case 3

Case 2 is so modified that during the production the increase of the vapour fraction (above 0.05) in the WF leaving the reboiler (Figure 4a) is prevented with a controller modifying the flow rate of the WF (Figure 4b). The results are shown in Table 4. Due to the increase of COP the PBP decreased further for each WF.

5. Conclusion

The effectiveness of different working fluids (n-pentane, n-hexane and methanol, ethanol, iso-propanol) for vapour compression HP system integrated to real batch distillation columns was compared. The separation of a mixture of low relative volatility (n-heptane - toluene) was simulated in a rigorous way with the dynamic modules of the ChemCad. Cost calculations were also performed. For the minimal condensation temperature of heating media (minimal compression ratio) the payback time was very high for all WFs. By increasing this temperature and by decreasing the flow rate of the WF during the production by the aid of a controller the payback times considerably decreased. The lowest payback time (somewhat less than 10 y) was obtained for ethanol and isopropanol.

Acknowledgement

This work was supported by the Hungarian Research Funds (OTKA, No.: K-106268).

References

D. Bruinsma, S. Spoelstra, 2010, Heat pumps in distillation, Distillation and Absorption Conference 2010, Eindhoven, 21–28.

H. Chen, D. Yogi Goswami, E. K. Stefanakos, 2010, A review of thermodynamic cycles and working fluids, Renewable and Sustainable Energy Reviews, 14, 3059–3067.

A. K. Jana, D. Maiti, 2013, Assessment of the implementation of vapour recompression technique in batch distillation, Separation and Purification Technology, 107, 1-10.

G. Modla, P. Lang, 2013, HP systems with mechanical compression for batch distillation, Energy, 62, 403-417.

Jiří Jaromír Klemeš, Petar Sabev Varbanov and Peng Yen Liew (Editors)
Proceedings of the 24th European Symposium on Computer Aided Process Engineering – ESCAPE 24
June 15-18, 2014, Budapest, Hungary.

Optimization of Alternative Distillation Sequences for Natural Gas Sweetening

C.E. Torres-Ortega[a], J. G. Segovia-Hernández[a]*, F.I. Gómez-Castro[a], S. Hernández[a], A. Bonilla-Petriciolet[b], B. G. Rong[c], M. Errico[d]

[a]*Universidad de Guanajuato, Campus Guanajuato, División de Ciencias Naturales y Exactas, Departamento de Ingeniería Química, Noria Alta S/N, Guanajuato, Gto., 36050, México*

[b]*Instituto Técnologico de Aguascalientes, Departamento de Ingeniería Química, Av. Adolfo López Mateos #1801 Ote., Fracc. Bona Gens, C.P. 20256, Aguascalientes, Ags., México*

[c]*Institute of Chemical Engineering, Biotechnology and Environmental Technology, University of Southern Denmark, Niels Bohrs Allé 1, DK-5230 Odense M, Denmark*

[d]*Universitá degli Studi di Cagliari, Dipartimento di Ingegneria Meccanica, Chimica e dei Materiali, Via Marengo 2, 09123 Cagliari, Italy*

g_segovia@hotmail.com

Abstract

The separation of CO_2 and/or H_2S from the natural gas processing is focused on preventing some undesired effects, as decreasing the heat capacity in the natural gas, and so on. Moreover, the carbon dioxide removal has an extensive interest in other application fields, like mitigating CO_2 emissions, being an entrainer in EOR (Enhanced Oil Recovery), among others. One novelty alternative to deal with CO_2 separation consists in the use of cryogenic extractive distillation by utilizing as entrainer the liquid hydrocarbon fraction obtained in the process. This process has some advantages, such as that the entrainer is CO_2 selective, noncorrosive, and waterless by-product, effective for high CO_2 concentration feedstock. In this work, the Aspen Plus One 7.0 process simulator was used to model the CO_2 - ethane azeotrope for different extractive distillation sequences and distinct entrainers, considering a rate based model. The study included the formal design and optimization (minimizing the Total Annual Cost (TAC) and maximizing the acid gas removal) to finally compare the alternative configurations with the conventional chemical absorption system used in the industrial field. Complementary studies regarding the controllability, thermodynamic efficiency and greenhouse gases generation were conducted. The proposed cryogenic extractive distillation sequences showed, in terms of costs and CO_2 emissions, better performance than the conventional chemical absorption configuration. Even more, the extractive thermally coupled distillation structures reached the best energy savings with appropriate dynamic behavior, making these alternatives competitive and environmentally friendly.

Keywords: Design, multi-objective-optimization, extractive distillation

1. Introduction

According to the BP (2012) due to the great abundance of the natural gas reservoirs, this fossil fuel will represent the 25 percent of the energy sources in 2030. It is clear that the optimization of the natural gas treatment process will be fundamental to use efficiently this energy source. The gas sweetening is a separation process aimed to remove acid gases, like carbon dioxide and hydrogen sulfide, from the natural gas. Not only the intensification of the CO_2 separation process for the sweetening section has been studied but also the carbon dioxide removal has an extensive interest in other application fields like in power plants, EOR, among others (Biliyok et al., 2013). The carbon dioxide removal, from natural gas or other sources, is a long studied topic and among all the alternatives proposed, the absorption using aqueous solution of alcohol-amines is for sure the most widely used process. This configuration is reported in Figure 2a. A promising alternative utilizing a cryogenic extractive distillation column where some of the natural gas liquid (NGL) is recycled as an entrainer has been recently studied (Lastari et al., 2010). Compared to the previous process, this alternative has some advantages like that the entrainer can be obtained from the same facility (as a by-product), it is effective for high carbon dioxide concentration feedstock, and the entrainer can work as a selective sweetener for CO_2, among others. On the distillation field, this separation process is characterized for its low thermodynamic efficiency, and consequently the huge energy requirements. Thus, inside the process design area, the thermally coupling concept has emerged as an efficient alternative to reduce the energy consumption, even in those cases where process integration is not possible. It was proved that for the separation of three component mixtures, thermally coupled sequences were able to reach important reduction of the energy consumption compared to the conventional distillation sequences (Errico et al., 2013). Moreover, as reported by different authors, the dynamic properties of these sequences are equal or even better than the corresponding conventional schemes (Segovia-Hernández et al., 2005).

Regarding the process optimization, it is necessary to define a set of fundamental equations and correlations in order to correctly predict the studied phenomena. For the nature of the process analyzed in this study, this is formulated as a multi-objective mixed integer non-linear programming problem (MMINLP). The non-equilibrium thermodynamic model has been used in different studies showing a good agreement with experimental data. The non-equilibrium thermodynamic model, based on MERSHQ equations, besides the MESH equations it includes the rate of mass and heat transfer and the hydrodynamic equations of pressure drop, and is characterized by high levels of non-linearity, and difficulties in the convergence are common problems for the optimization task. On the other hand, stochastic optimizers deal, in a robustly and efficiently way, with multi-modal and non-convex problems. Several heuristic techniques for global optimization mimicking biological evolution have been reported in the literature highlighting a new class of evolutionary methods called differential evolution (DE) algorithms, with just three relevant parameters: Np (size of population), F (mutation factor) and Cr (crossover probability). For different theoretical and practical problems, comparative studies have shown that the performance of DE-type algorithms are clearly better than those obtained for other stochastic algorithms (Xu and Li, 2007). Therefore, a multi-objective differential evolution method has been used for solving the MMINLP of our case of study.

2. Methodology

Due to the fact that the optimizer requires some initial guesses and suitable ranges of variation for the decision variables along the optimization, a preliminary sensitivity analysis was performed for all the cases studied by using Aspen Plus 7.0. Moreover, different solvents were considered. In the case of the thermally coupled distillation sequence, the starting procedure was supplemented by the methodology proposed by Hernández and Jiménez (1996). The thermodynamic property frameworks used were Peng-Robinson and Kent-Eisenberg for the extractive distillation sequences and the chemical-absorption system, respectively. After this stage, the best two sequences per each case were selected for the multi-objective optimization by using the multi-objective differential evolution method developed by Sharma and Rangaiah (2012). The transference of data from Microsoft Excel to Aspen Plus was by using DDE (dynamic data exchange) by COM (Component Object Model) technology, (Petzold 1999).

The objective functions were the minimization of the Total Annual Cost (TAC), Equation 1, and the maximization of the carbon dioxide removal.

$$TAC = \sum \left[\left(\frac{Capital\ Cost}{Time\ of\ Investment} \right)_i + (Cost\ of\ Utilities)_i \right] \tag{1}$$

Regarding the TAC calculation (i refers to every process equipment), the correlations and data for all the equipments and energy costs considered in the processes were taken from Turton et al. (2009). For this objective function, 10 years of investment and 8500 operating hours per year were fixed. The whole methodology is depicted in Figure 1. This multi-objective optimization procedure was followed by a complementary analysis on representative spots from each Pareto front in order to obtain general trends on controllability, thermodynamic efficiency and CO_2 emissions for each sequence.

(a) Controllability analysis by singular value decomposition (SVD): for this study, it was used the concept of dominant time constant with a supposed linear first-order response for the columns, defined by Skogestad and Morari (1987), to generate the transfer matrix of the process. Next, by means of the frequency response, it was accomplished the SVD (Klema and Laub, 1980) with a constant disturbance (+0.3%) on the control variable directly related to the product stream's purities.

(b) Thermodynamic efficiency: this study is based on the methodology described by Seader and Henley (2006). The analysis included the refrigeration cycles. All the thermodynamic properties were evaluated through the simulator Aspen Plus V7.0.

(c) CO_2 emissions: this analysis was performed based on the work of Gadalla et al. (2005). The CO_2 emissions were considered as generated by the steam used in the reboiler of the columns when methane is used as a fuel.

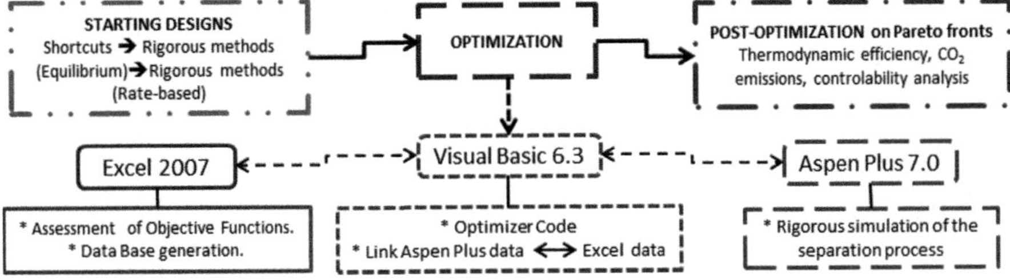

Figure 1. General methodology and the hybrid platform used in the optimization step

3. Case Studies

The sour feed composition was defined only considering the CO_2 and the ethane in the proportion inside the boundaries proposed by the Natural Gas Supply Association (2010) because of the main target of this study. Regarding the rate based model, the default correlations on sieve trays were used. The feed composition on molar basis, the temperature and the pressure analyzed are: 67.78 % ethane and 32.22 % CO_2 at 67 °C and 75.84 bar, respectively. The conventional cryogenic extractive distillation, CCED, Figure 2.(b), and the thermally coupled systems: the cryogenic extractive distillation sequence with side rectifier, CEDSR, Figure 2.(c), and the alternative Petlyuk sequence, PCED, Figure 2.(d), were simulated considering four different pure solvents: propane, n-butane, n-pentane and n-hexane. As benchmark process, the configuration with chemical absorption by an aqueous solution of methanol-amine or MEA (6.86 % MEA and 93.14 % water on molar basis), CCAS, Figure 2.(a), at 55°C was analyzed, as well. As regards the optimization, the purity restrictions are CO_2 and ethane streams ≥ 0.9, and the entrainer stream ≥ 0.93. Moreover, the algorithm parameter values for DE were established based on preliminary calculations: Np = 10 * No. of decision variables, F = 0.8 and Cr = 0.9, and the stopping criterion, number of generations, was 160.

The decision variables per each case are:

CCED ➔ S (1 & 2), RR (1 & 2), FS (1 & 2), D (1 & 2), DF (1 & 2), ES and EF, where S = number of stages, RR = reflux ratio, FS = feed stage, D = diameter, DF = distillate flow, ES = entrainer stage, EF = entrainer flow and the numbers refers to the column.

CEDSR ➔ S (1 & 2), RR1, FS1, D (1 & 2), DF (1 & 2), ES, EF, VF and LFS, where VF and LFS = vapour flow and liquid flow stage of interconnection.

PCED ➔ S1, RR1, FS1, D (1 & 2), DF1, ES, EF, SSF, SSS, LFa, LFSa, VFb and VFSb, where SSF and SSS = side stream flow and stage, LFa and LFSa = liquid flow and stage of intercon., VFb and VFSb = vapour flow and stage of interconnection.

CCAS ➔ S (1 & 2), RR2, FS2, D (1 & 2), DF2 and SF; where SF = solvent flow.

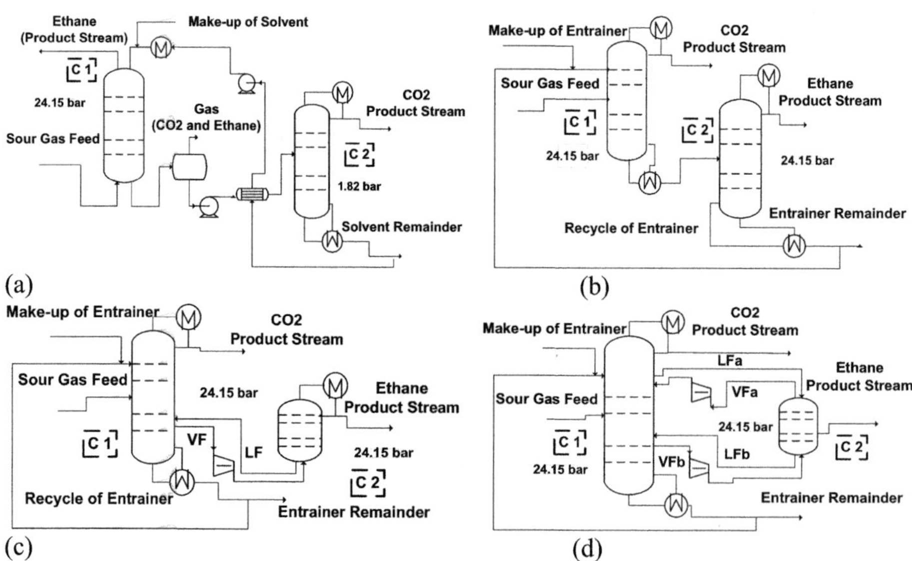

Figure 2. (a) CCAS, (b) CCED, (c) CEDSR, and (d) PCED arrangements

4. Analysis of Results

The data here presented satisfied all the constraints defined above, except for the case of the PCED sequence where the purity constraints were not satisfied in all the cases.
As reported in Figure 3, the CEDSR configuration with n-butane as entrainer reached the lowest TAC. All the alternative arrangements reached out a very high removal of the acid gas (up to 100 %). Because of higher amount of entrainer and reflux ratios, the case of the CCAS obtained less carbon dioxide removals and higher total annual costs. CEDSR needs fewer amounts of solvent than CCED and PCED. In general terms, we noted that the cost utilities were the dominant factor on the TAC, representing around the 90 to 95 % of the total value. As for the complementary analysis, the comparisons of the results are based on the best sequence found (CEDSR) during the optimization step.

As reported in Figure 4.(a), the thermodynamic efficiency (η) has a nonlinear decreasing trend due partly to the fact that at high gas acid removal, the efficiency is lower because of the increment in the system energy demand. The CEDSR sequence presented lower efficiency that the CCAS system because of the use of refrigerants in the extractive distillation process and for the higher CO_2 removals obtained. Concerning the CO_2 emissions (i.e., CO_2 generated), the CEDSR sequence generates less CO_2 in its reboiler than the total CO_2 removed by the scheme, see Figure 4.(b). Finally, the control properties were examined via condition numbers and minimum singular values. In this dynamic study, the condition number quantifies the sensitivity of the system with respect to errors on modeling, non-linearity and disturbances; thus, smaller condition numbers are preferred. High values of the reciprocal of the minimum singular value makes evident potential problems of the system under feedback control, then higher minimum singular values are sought. Inside the extractive sequences, CEDSR presented the most proper condition numbers and minimum singular values, even at operating conditions with high CO_2 removals and reasonable TAC.

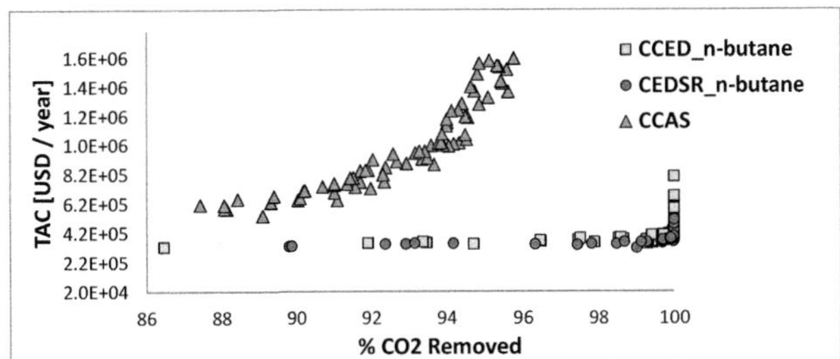

Figure 3. The best sequences after optimization. % of removal on molar basis.

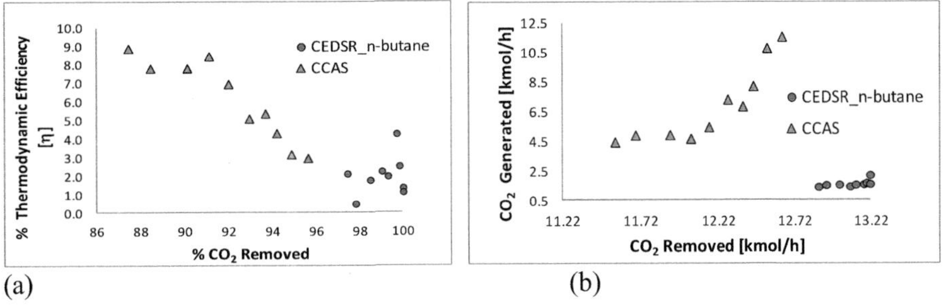

(a) (b)

Figure 4. (a) Thermodynamic efficiency and (b) CO2 emissions for CEDSR n-butane and CCAS

5. Conclusions

According to the analyzed data, it can be concluded that the alternative thermally coupled sequence (CEDSR) has better generalized performances than the conventional chemical absorption, scheme used in industrial field, for the carbon dioxide-ethane mixture considered at different CO_2 removals, being around four times cheaper than the conventional at 96 % of CO_2 removal. The type of the mixture (composition and nature) was not entirely suitable for all the thermally coupled systems here considered (TAC: PCED>CCED>CEDSR); moreover, several of the PCED simulation did not satisfy the purity restrictions. Thus, more alterative systems using the cryogenic principle could represent interesting options to improve the performance here obtained. Regarding the dynamic behavior for the cryogenic extractive distillation sequences, the CEDSR presented the best reasonable values. Only the CEDSR configuration was able to reduce significantly the greenhouse gases emissions, reaching high carbon dioxide removals, but also a low thermodynamic efficiency was observed, as well. Finally, the methodology used here resulted an effective technique (a pre-selection by using sensitivity analysis and a complementary-study on the Pareto fronts) but at the same time robust (multi-objective optimization of the designs).

References

C. Biliyok, R. Canepa, M. Wang, H. Yeunga, 2013, Techno-Economic Analysis of a Natural Gas Combined Cycle Power Plant with CO_2 Capture, Comput. Aided Chem. Eng., 32, 187–192.

BP, 2012, BP Energy Outlook 2030, London, UK

M. Errico, B.G. Rong, G. Tola, M, Spano, 2013, Optimal design of distillation systems for bioethanol separations: Part II. Extractive distillation with complex columns, Industrial and Engineering Chemestry Research, 52, 1620-1626.

M.A. Gadalla, Z. Olujic, P.J Jansens, M. Jobson, R. Smith, 2005, Reducing CO_2 Emissions and Energy Consumption of Heat-Integrated Distillation Systems, Environ. Sci. Technol., 39, 6860 - 6870.

S. Hernández, A. Jiménez, 1996, Design of optimal thermally-coupled distillation systems using a dynamic model, Transactions IChemE, 74, 357-362.

V.C. Klema, A.J. Laub, 1980, The Singular Value Decomposition: Its Computation and Some Applications, IEEE Transactions on Automatic Control, 25, 2, 164-176.

F. Lastari, V. Pareek, M. Trebble, M.O. Tade, D. Chinn, N.C. Tsa, K.I. Chan, 2010, Extractive Distillation for CO2-Ethane Azeotrope Separation, Chemical Engineering and Processing, 52, 155-161.

Natural Gas Supply Association, 2010, Background, <www.naturalgas.org>, accessed on 02/05/2013.

C. Petzold, 1999, Programming Windows, Fifth edition, Microsoft Press, Washington, USA.

J.D. Seader, E.J. Henley, 2006, Separation Process principles, 2a Ed., John Wiley & Sons Inc., New Jersey, USA, 27-29.

J.G. Segovia - Hernández, S. Hernández, A, Jiménez, 2005, Analysis of Dynamic Properties of Alternative Sequences to the Petlyuk Column, Comput. Chem. Eng., 29, 1389.

S. Sharma, G.P. Rangaiah, 2012, Modeling and optimization of a fermentation process integrated with cell recycling and pervaporation for multiple objectives, Ind. Eng. Chem. Res, 51, 5542-5551.

S. Skogestad, M. Morari, 1987, The Dominant Time Constant for Distillation Columns, Comput. Chem. Engng., 11, 6, 607-617.

R. Turton, R.C. Bailie, W.B. Whiting, J.A. Shaeiwitz, 2009, Analysis, Synthesis and Design of Chemical Process, Third edition, Prentice Hall, Upper Saddle River, New Jersey, USA.

X. Xu, Y. Li, 2007, Comparison between particle swarm optimization, differential evolution and multi-parents crossover, Proceedings of the IEEE International Conference on Computational Intelligence and Security, 124–127.

Jiří Jaromír Klemeš, Petar Sabev Varbanov and Peng Yen Liew (Editors)
Proceedings of the 24th European Symposium on Computer Aided Process Engineering – ESCAPE 24
June 15-18, 2014, Budapest, Hungary.

Decision Support for CO_2 Capture Process Options under Uncertain Market Conditions using Multi-objective Optimisation

Laurence Tock*, François Maréchal

Industrial Process and Energy Systems Engineering, Ecole Polytechnique Fédérale de Lausanne, Station 9, CH-1015 Lausanne, Switzerland.
laurence.tock@epfl.ch

Abstract

To meet the CO_2 reduction targets and ensure a reliable energy supply, the development of cost-competitive innovative low-carbon energy technologies is essential. Switching to renewable resources and CO_2 capture and storage in power plants, are regarded as promising alternatives. Post-, oxy- and pre-combustion CO_2 capture concepts are applicable for power plants using natural gas, coal or biomass as a feedstock. A systematic thermo-environomic optimisation strategy including thermodynamic, economic and environmental considerations is applied for the consistent modelling and optimisation of CO_2 capture options. The environmental benefit and the energetic and economic costs of CO_2 capture are assessed and optimised. The economic competitiveness appears to be strongly determined by the economic conditions such as the resource price and the carbon tax which are highly uncertain. A method that takes into account the economic parameter sensitivity to support decision-making based on the Pareto-optimal solutions is proposed here. The selection method aims at identifying the most economically competitive process configuration in terms of the polygeneration of electricity, heat and captured CO_2 in a wide range of market conditions.

Keywords: CO_2 capture, Decision-making, Economic conditions, Multi-objective optimisation, Power plant

1. Introduction

To meet the CO_2 reduction targets and to ensure a reliable energy supply, the development and wide scale deployment of cost-competitive innovative low-carbon energy technologies is necessary. Carbon capture and storage (CCS) in power plants is considered as such a promising measure. The performance of these CO_2 capture options depends on the power plant layout, the resources, the capture technology and the economic conditions. The economic competitiveness is highly influenced by the resource price and the introduction of a carbon tax. The penalty of CO_2 capture in terms of efficiency and costs has been evaluated by the European Technology Platform (ZEP, 2011), the International Panel on Climate Change (Metz et al., 2005) and the International Energy Agency (Finkenrath, 2011).

The analysis of the gas and carbon market over the last years reveals diverse patterns over time and with regard to the geographic location as reported by IEA (2011). According to the European Commission (EU, 2011) European gas prices are about twice as high as US gas prices and are projected to be 10 \$/GJ in 2020, 12 \$/GJ in 2030 and 16 \$/GJ in 2050 for the *EU 'Reference'* energy scenario. According to these predictions, the carbon tax prices which drop from around 25 €/t_{CO2} in 2008 to below 10 €/t_{CO2} in the second half of 2011, will for the current policy initiatives scenario rise moderately until 2030 (32 €/t_{CO2}) and then significantly to provide support to low carbon technologies and energy efficiency (51 €/t_{CO2} in 2050). Comparing the costs projections for different energy and policy scenarios a large variation of the predictions is found. This highlights the large uncertainty of costs projections and the need to account for different economic scenarios when evaluating the competitiveness of CO_2 capture options to support investment decisions in the power sector.

Rohlfs and Madlener (2013) showed that subsidies for renewable energies strongly influence investment decisions and reduce the value of CCS power plants. A method based on the cumulative probability is proposed by Zhang et al. (2014) to evaluate the optimal retrofit timing for CCS in supercritical power plants taking into account uncertainties among others in carbon prices. While Anantharaman et al. (2013) evaluate the optimum CO_2 capture unit capacity taking into consideration the trade-off between the CO_2 capture cost and the emissions cost for fluctuating operating conditions (i.e exhaust gas profiles). A fixed CO_2 tax was considered, however they concluded that further work should involve, the CO_2 tax variation to include the decision on when to install (or not) the CO_2 capture plant in addition to its optimal capacity.

The influence of the economic conditions is frequently investigated based on extreme scenarios or sensitivity analysis, and to evaluate retrofit options. However, no systematic approach taking into account the economic conditions fluctuation for the decision-making based on the optimisation results is applied and process integration aspects and life cycle assessment are not systematically assessed. Based on the systematic optimisation approach presented in Tock and Maréchal (2013) for assessing the performance of CO_2 capture options, a method, taking into account the economic parameter sensitivity, to support decision-making based on the Pareto-optimal solutions is proposed here. The influence of the economic scenario on the decision-making is studied by taking into account the sensitivity of the economic performance to the carbon tax, the resource price, the operating time, the investment and the interest rate.

2. Methodology

The applied thermo-environomic modelling and optimisation approach illustrated in Figure 1 combines flowsheeting and energy integration techniques with economic evaluation and life cycle assessment (LCA) in a multi-objective optimisation framework previously presented in Gassner and Maréchal (2009) and extended in Tock and Maréchal (2012) for combining flowsheets developed with different software. With regard to the competing objectives, it is a priori not obvious which configuration has to be chosen from the generated Pareto-optimal solutions. Therefore the aim is here to propose a decision support (Figure 1) which allows to identify the optimal process design from the Pareto-optimal solutions taking into account the economic conditions sensitivity.

In this approach, the economic conditions fluctuation is first described by probability distribution functions, such as the normal, uniform and beta distributions. The key parameters for the economic conditions are reported in Table 1. The lower and upper boundary values are defined from literature projections of international (IEA, 2012) and European institutions (ZEP, 2011). The variation of the carbon tax is defined by the projections of the European Commission (EU, 2011). The appropriate distribution function is selected and the characteristic parameters are identified based on the three scenarios values. For the carbon tax the beta distribution is chosen, because it is assumed that the tax price will most probably increase in the future. By applying the distribution functions a series of thousand economic scenarios is randomly generated.

For every single economic scenario and for each configuration of the Pareto frontiers the decision criteria is then recomputed. The selected decision criteria is the economic performance that is expressed by the electricity production costs (COE) including a carbon tax. From the Pareto-optimal solutions the five best configurations that yield the best performance with regard to the decision criteria (i.e. lowest COE incl.CO_2 tax) are then identified for each economic scenario. After having identified the five most economically competitive configurations in the wide range of economic scenarios, it can be found out if some configurations are dominating or if some are never part of the best performing ones. To evaluate this quantitatively, the probability to be part of the five best performing configurations is assessed for each point of the Pareto front. The different process configurations are ranked based on this probability. This allows identifying the most economically competitive process configurations in a wide range of economic scenarios.

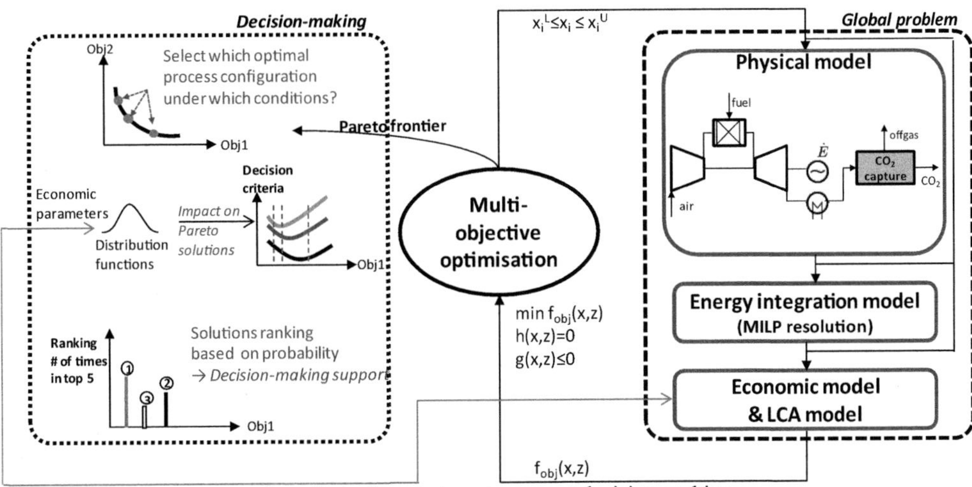

Figure 1. Thermo-environomic optimisation strategy to support decision-making.

Table 1. Definition of the economic scenarios and parameters of the distribution functions.

	Scenario			Distribution functions parameters			
	Base	Low	High	Distribution	Param. A	Param. B	Param. C
Resource price [$/$GJ_{res}$]	9.7	5.5	14.2	Normal	μ=9.7	σ=2.5	-
Carbon tax [$/$t_{CO2}$]	35	20	55	Beta	a=2	b=1.5	c=100
Yearly operation [h/y]	7,500	4,500	8,200	Beta	a=3.9	b=1.2	c=8,600
Economic lifetime [y]	25	15	30	Beta	a=5.8	b=4	c=40
Interest rate [%]	6	4	8	Normal	μ=0.06	σ=0.01	-
Investment cost [%]	-30 %	-	+30 %	Uniform	a=-0.3	b=0.3	-

3. Process description

The approach is illustrated for three representative CO_2 capture options:

1. Post-combustion CO_2 capture by chemical absorption with monoethanolamine (MEA) applied to a natural gas combined cycle (NGCC) plant (582 $MW_{th,NG}$)
2. Pre-combustion CO_2 capture by physical absorption with Selexol in a natural gas fuelled power plant based on autothermal reforming (ATR) (725 $MW_{th,NG}$)
3. Pre-combustion CO_2 capture by physical absorption with Selexol in a biomass fired power plant based on fast internally circulating fluidised bed gasification (380 $MW_{th,NG}$)

The biomass plant's scale is limited by the biomass availability and the logistics of wood transport as explained by Gerber et al. (2011). The different process options have been modelled and analysed previously for biomass (Tock and Maréchal, 2012a) and natural gas resources (Tock and Maréchal, 2012b). A multi-objective optimisation is performed with the objective of maximising the energy efficiency ε_{tot} and the CO_2 capture rate η_{CO2} with regard to the process operating parameters. The energy efficiency ε_{tot} is defined by the ratio between the net electricity output and the resources energy input, expressed on the basis of the lower heating value. The economic performance is evaluated by the electricity production costs (COE), including the annual capital investment and the operation and maintenance costs. The competitiveness is compared with a conventional NGCC plant (559 $MW_{th,NG}$) without CO_2 capture characterised by an efficiency of 58.7 %, specific CO_2 emissions of 105 kg_{CO2}/GJ_e, COE of 18.3 $/$GJ_e$ without carbon tax and 22 $/$GJ_e$ with a carbon tax for the base case economic conditions reported in Table 1.

4. Multi-objective optimisation and decision-making

The multi-objective optimisation results (Figure 3) reveal the trade-off between energy efficiency and CO_2 capture rate. An increase of the CO_2 capture rate leads to a decrease of the energy efficiency due to the energy consumption for CO_2 capture and compression to 110 bar. Considering

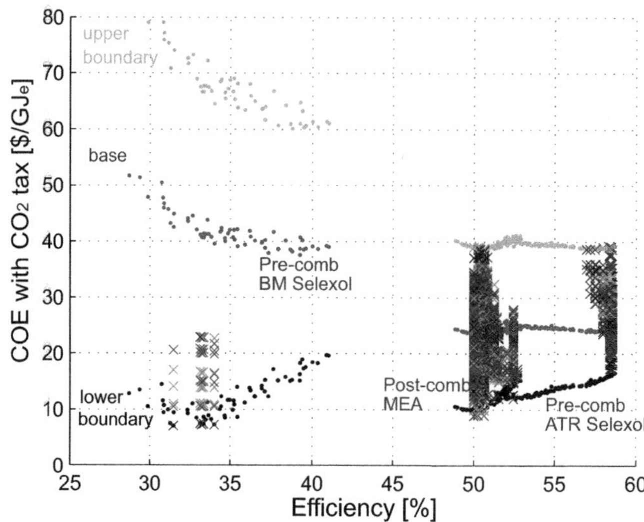

Figure 2. Power plants performance with CO_2 capture: Influence of the economic scenario on the decision-making based on the top 5 configurations yielding the best economic performance. The crosses (x) represent for each economic scenario the 5 selected configurations.

only these two performance indicators no evident decision in favour of one specific process configuration can be made; the economic dimension has to be added. CO_2 capture leads to an increase of the COE due to the reduced electricity production and the increased investment costs for the capture equipment. When a carbon tax is introduced the cost penalty is reduced by the benefit from the tax due to the lower emissions. Consequently, there are break even economic conditions for which CO_2 capture becomes beneficial. The economic performance of the Pareto-optimal solutions is illustrated in Figure 2 for the economic scenarios reported in Table 1. Depending on the economic scenario the most economically competitive configuration is different, therefore the proposed approach is applied for decision-making.

The configurations yielding the best economic performance are identified in Figures 2&3. Figure 3 illustrates by the black dots how the decision-making along the Pareto-optimal frontier changes. Figure 2 reports the variation of the COE of the most economically competitive configurations identified from the Pareto-optimal solutions between the upper and lower borderline. The crosses represent for each economic scenario the five selected configurations yielding the best economic performance. For the base case economic scenario biomass fed processes are not competitive and post-combustion CO_2 capture performs best for capture rates around 70-85 %. When gas prices increase, the natural gas based processes become uncompetitive compared to the base case biomass configurations. These results point out the competition between the processes and the influence of the economic scenario on the decision-making. This competition is highlighted in Figure 4 evaluating the overall competitiveness of each Pareto-optimal solution compared to the most-economically competitive solution. The post-combustion process configuration capturing 83 % of the CO_2 emissions yields a relative competitiveness of 1 since this solution is the most economically competitive one in the large range of economic conditions. These results clearly show the close competition between post- and pre-combustion and underline that the CO_2 capture rate is a key factor defining the economic performance. Pre-combustion CO_2 capture configurations, being slightly more expensive for similar capture rates, yield however slightly better efficiencies. Depending on the production scope, this could affect decision-making for the more expensive solution. For some marginal economic scenarios CO_2 capture in biomass fed power plants becomes a competitive alternative. In fact, the benefit from the carbon tax overweights the efficiency penalty for capture rates around 70 %. The performance results of the most economically competitive process configurations are compared with the conventional NGCC plant without CO_2 capture and summarised in Table 2.

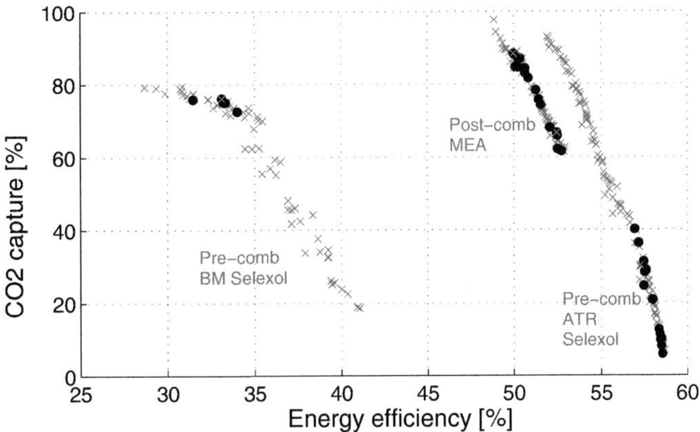

Figure 3. Multi-objective optimisation results.

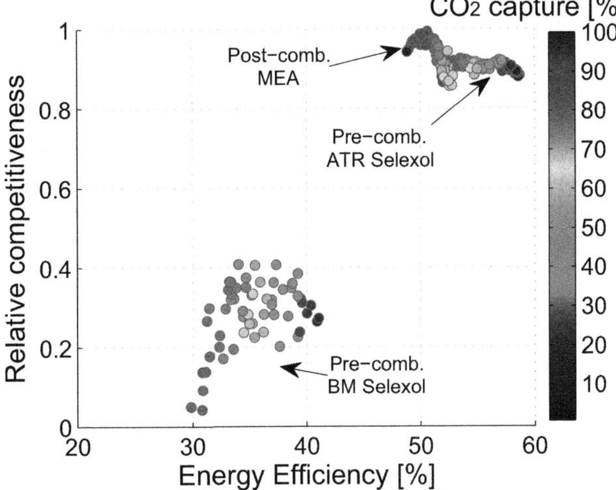

Figure 4. Relative competitiveness.

This shows how the most economically competitive process configurations can be identified from the Pareto-optimal solutions by applying the selection approach taking into account the economic conditions fluctuation.

5. Conclusion

This paper presents a selection approach taking into account the economic conditions fluctuation to identify economically competitive process designs from multi-objective optimisation results. The approach is applied to systematically assess CO_2 capture options in power plants. The results reveal that the choice of the optimal plant design is highly influenced by the resource price and the introduction of a carbon tax. By including the economic conditions sensitivity in the decision-making step, it appears that apart of the economic market conditions, the CO_2 capture rate is a key factor defining the economic competitiveness. Post-combustion CO_2 capture reveals to be economically competitive for capture rates between 70 and 80 % when a carbon tax is introduced. While pre-combustion CO_2 capture in natural gas fired power plants is advantageous in terms of energy efficiency and CO_2 capture in biomass based power plants is beneficial from an environmental point of view due to the advantage of capturing biogenic CO_2. The various natural gas fed power plants designs with CO_2 capture lead to an average efficiency decrease of 6.5 %-points (5-8 %). It is shown that for specific economic conditions CCS can become an energy, cost and environmental efficient alternative on the future energy market compared to a conventional NGCC.

Table 2. Process performance comparision of different CO_2 capture options.

System	NGCC (no CC)	Post-comb (MEA)	ATR (Selexol)	BM (Selexol)
Feed [$MW_{th,NG/BM}$]	559	582	725	380
CO_2 capture rate [%]	0	82.98	78.63	69.93
ε_{tot} [%]	58.75	50.65	53.59	35.45
		Base case economic scenario (Table 1)		
COE no CO_2 tax [$/GJ$_e$]	18.31	22.7	23.7	46.1
COE incl. CO_2 tax [$/GJ$_e$]	22	23.2	24.5	21.1
		Economic scenario variation (Table 1)		
COE incl. CO_2 tax [$/GJ$_e$]	18.3-28.8	9-40	12.8-42	15-69
		Environmental Performance (FU=1GJ$_e$)		
CO_2 emitted [kg_{CO2}/GJ_e]	105	13.9	22.2	-198.1
GWP (IPCC) [$kg_{CO2,eq}/GJ_e$]	120	35.4	42.2	-167

References

R. Anantharaman, S. Roussanaly, S. Westman, J. Husebye, 2013, Selection of optimal CO2 capture plant capacity for better investment decisions, Energy Procedia, 37, 7039 - 7045.

EU, 2011, Energy Roadmap 2050, Communication from the Commission to the Council, the European Parliament, the European Economic and Social Committee and the Committee of Regions, SEC(2011) 1565/2, European Commission, Luxembourg.

M. Finkenrath, 2011, Cost and performance of carbon dioxide capture from power generation, Report, International Energy Agency, Paris, France.

M. Gassner, F. Maréchal, 2009, Methodology for the optimal thermo-economic, multi-objective design of thermochemical fuel production from biomass, Computers & Chemical Engineering, 33, 769-781.

L. Gerber, M. Gassner, F. Maréchal, 2011, Systematic integration of LCA in process systems design: Application to combined fuel and electricity production from lignocellulosic biomass, Computers & Chemical Engineering, 35, 1265 - 1280.

IEA, 2011, Medium-term Oil & Gas Markets, Report, International Energy Agency, Paris, France.

IEA, 2012, Key World Energy Statistics, Report, International Energy Agency, Paris, France.

B. Metz, O. Davidson, H. de Coninck, M. Loos, L. Meyer, 2005, IPCC special report on carbon dioxide capture and storage, Report, Cambridge University Press, Cambridge, England.

W. Rohlfs, R. Madlener, 2013, Investment decisions under uncertainty: CCS competing with green energy technologies, Energy Procedia, 37, 7029 - 7038.

L. Tock, F. Maréchal, 2012a, Co-production of hydrogen and electricity from lignocellulosic biomass: Process design and thermo-economic optimization, Energy, 45, 339-349.

L. Tock, F. Maréchal, 2012b, H2 processes with CO2 mitigation: Thermo-economic modeling and process integration, International Journal of Hydrogen Energy, 37, 11785-11795.

L. Tock, F. Maréchal, 2012, Platform development for studying integrated energy conversion processes: Application to a power plant process with CO2 capture, Computer-aided Chemical Engineering, 31, 1015-1019.

L. Tock, F. Maréchal, 2013, Process engineering method for systematically comparing CO2 capture options, Computer-aided Chemical Engineering, 32, 367 - 372.

ZEP, 2011, The costs of CO2 capture, transport and storage - Post-demonstration CCS in the EU, Report, European Technology Platform, Brussels, Belgium.

X. Zhang, X. Wang, J. Chen, X. Xie, K. Wang, Y. Wei, 2014, A novel modeling based real option approach for CCS investment evaluation under multiple uncertainties, Applied Energy, 113, 1059 - 1067.

Jiří Jaromír Klemeš, Petar Sabev Varbanov and Peng Yen Liew (Editors)
Proceedings of the 24th European Symposium on Computer Aided Process Engineering – ESCAPE 24
June 15-18, 2014, Budapest, Hungary.

Operational Optimization of Compressors in Parallel Considering Condition-Based Maintenance

Dionysios P. Xenos[a,*], Georgios M. Kopanos[a], Matteo Cicciotti[b,c], Efstratios N. Pistikopoulos[a], Nina F. Thornhill[a]

[a]*Imperial College London, Department of Chemical Engineering, Centre for Process Systems Engineering, London, UK.*
[b]*BASF SE, Automation Technology, Ludwigshafen, Germany.*
[c]*Imperial College London, Department of Mechanical Engineering, London, UK.*
d.xenos@imperial.ac.uk

Abstract

This paper suggests an optimization framework for the process and maintenance operations of a network of compressors. The health condition of a compressor varies during its operation due to mechanically degrading effects (e.g. fouling and corrosion) which results in decreasing performance and increasing power consumption. Currently, the industrial maintenance strategy considers preventive maintenance cycles, i.e. maximum running time of the compressors. Typically, the maintenance schedule of a compressor is examined separately without considering the interactions between the compressor and the overall process. In this work, the increase in the power consumption of each compressor is linearly correlated to the periods of continuous operation, and the results demonstrate that the simultaneous optimization of condition-based maintenance and operation reduces the overall costs.

Keywords: scheduling, compressors, optimization, condition-based, maintenance, mathematical programming.

1. Introduction

The effective management of compressors is a priority in chemical and petrochemical industries. Industrial compressors are typically tailored to a particular application in a plant, have high capital costs and are integrated with other plant components. For these reasons, compressors are rarely replaced over the entire life cycle of the plant. The current industrial practice for the maintenance of compressors relies on preventive maintenance cycles which consider minimum and maximum running times (Forsthoffer, 2011). Although the literature about the optimization of the operation of compressors is broad, few researchers have studied the scheduling of compressors. Camponogara et al. (2012) presented a work on lift-gas compressors in oil fields neglecting start-up and shut down decisions. Paparella et al. (2013) examined the optimal distribution of the load and the selection of compressors operating in parallel without considering predictions in future time horizon.

The condition of a compressor varies over time and the gradual degradation of its performance is a consequence of effects such as fouling, erosion and corrosion of its rotating and stationary mechanical parts. One relevant effect of mechanical degradation is the drop of efficiency. Linear correlations between drop of efficiency and operating time have been used by researchers and industrial practitioners for conducing economic analysis of maintenance and washing cycles for single units (Aretakis et al., 2012). However, to the best of the authors' knowledge, this information has not yet been used for optimizing the operation and maintenance costs of a network of compressors.

This paper presents a general Mixed Integer NonLinear Programming (MINLP) formulation for the simultaneous optimization of the operation and maintenance of a compressors network connected in parallel considering the information of the condition of each compressor. The case of condition-based maintenance and operational optimization is compared with the case of a typical preventive maintenance strategy.

2. Mathematical formulation

The objective of the optimization is to reduce operational and maintenance costs for the network of air compressors which is part of an air separation plant. Figure 1 shows a schematic representation of the industrial plant which involves a network of air compressors $i \in I$, with different characteristics, that operate in a parallel configuration. The compressed air is supplied to different collecting headers $j \in J$. Two of the collecting headers, $j2$ and $j3$, are connected to air separation columns, whereas another, $j1$, is connected to a pipeline providing compressed air for utilities to nearby process plants. The optimization considers the following decisions: the operating status of each compressor (switch-on and switch-off), the assignment of the operating compressors to grids, the distribution of the load for each grid and the allocation of the compressors maintenance tasks.

The formulation of the optimization problem considers minimum start-up and shut-down times similar to those of Kopanos et al. (2013), plant constraints (e.g. a compressor provides flow to one grid at each time), feasible operating ranges of the compressors, mass balances in the oxygen and nitrogen tanks (the production of the columns must satisfy the demand requested and store product in the tanks), and the capacity limits of air separation columns and storage tanks. The mathematical model

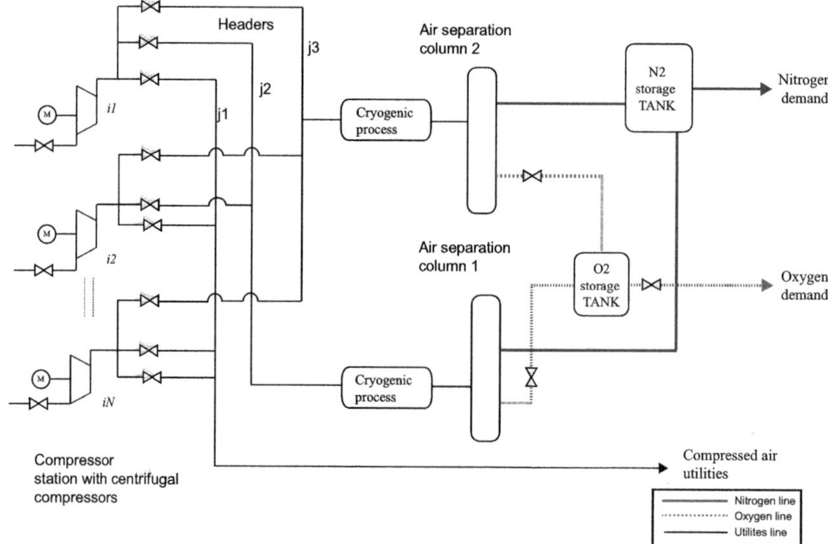

Figure 1. Air compressors network in an air separation plant.

considers a fixed scheduling horizon that is divided into a set of uniform time periods $t \in T$.

The optimization goal, Eq. (1), is to minimize the costs of electrical energy, switch-on and -off of a compressor, and the maintenance cost. The costs of start-up C_{st_i}, switch-off C_{f_i}, maintenance C_{ws_i} and the electricity price μ_t (€/kWh) are given as deterministic parameters. The objective function also includes other costs for example the cost when a compressor changes grid. This cost represents the energy associated with the compressed air which is vented to atmosphere during this change.
The power consumption $W_{el_{(i,j,t)}}$ of the motor of a compressor is estimated from two terms. The first term, $W^c{}_{el_{(i,j,t)}}\left(M_{a_{(i,j,t)}}, P_{r_{(i,j,t)}}, M_{w_i}\right)$, represents the power consumed when the compressor is clean and after maintenance. This power consumption is a function of mass flow rate ($M_{a_{(i,j,t)}}$), pressure ratio ($P_{r_{(i,j,t)}}$) and cooling water (M_{w_i}). The $W_{el}{}^c{}_{(i,j,t)}$ is generated from historical data using regression methods to fit polynomial models. The second term, $\Delta W_{(i,t)}$, represents the excess power consumed because of the deterioration of the compressor. Therefore, the product of the power consumption $W_{el_{(i,j,t)}} (= W^c{}_{el_{(i,j,t)}} + \Delta W_{(i,t)})$ and factor $d_c = 24$ h/d gives the energy consumed in a time interval. Eq.(10) demonstrates that this excess power is linearly related to $\Delta S_{(i,t)}$with a coefficient e_i. The variable $\Delta S_{(i,t)}$ is the continuous period a compressor has been operated since the time of the last maintenance. The constraints for the condition-based maintenance involve continuous and binary variables. The continuous variables are the excess power $\Delta W_{(i,t)}$ and the time period $\Delta S_{(i,t)}$. The binary variables describe the start ($F_{(i,t)}$), the end ($K_{(i,t)}$) of a maintenance action and if a compressor is under this maintenance action ($U_{(i,t)}$). It is assumed that when a compressor switches off, a maintenance episode must start, i.e. $F_{(i,t)}$ is equal to one. Moreover the status of a compressor (on or off) is given by $X_{(i,t)}$. The objective function and the major constraints of the proposed MINLP problem are given below:

$$\min \quad \sum_{t\in T}\sum_{i\in I}\left(S_{(i,t)}C_{st_i} + F_{(i,t)}C_{f_i} + F_{(i,t)}C_{ws_i}\right) + \sum_{t\in T}\mu_t\sum_{i\in I}\sum_{j\in J} d_c \cdot W_{el_{(i,j,t)}} + other\ costs \qquad (1)$$

subject to:

$$F_{(i,t)} - K_{(i,t)} = U_{(i,t)} - U_{(i,t-1)}\ , \forall i \in I, t \in T \qquad (2)$$

$$F_{(i,t)} + K_{(i,t)} \leq 1\ , \forall i \in I, t \in T \qquad (3)$$

$$\sum_{t\in T} F_{(i,t)} \leq O_{max}\ , \forall i \in I \qquad (4)$$

$$\sum_{t\in T} F_{(i,t)} \geq O_{min}\ , \forall i \in I \qquad (5)$$

$$\sum_{t'=max(1,t-\gamma+1)}^{t} K_{(i,t')} \leq 1 - U_{(i,t)}\ , \forall i \in I, t \in T \qquad (6)$$

$$1 - U_{(i,t)} + \sum_{t'=max(1,t-v_i+1)}^{t} F_{(i,t')} = 1\ , \forall i \in I, t \in T \qquad (7)$$

$$\sum_{i\in I} U_{(i,t)} \leq 1\ , \forall\ t \in T \qquad (8)$$

$$\Delta S_{(i,t)} = \Delta S_{(i,t-1)} \cdot \left(1 - U_{(i,t)}\right) + 1 \cdot X_{(i,t)}\ , \ \forall i \in I, t \in T \qquad (9)$$

$$\Delta W_{(i,t)} = e_i \cdot \Delta S_{(i,t)}\ , \forall i \in I, t \in T \qquad (10)$$

$$\Delta W_{(i,t)} \leq \omega\ , \ \forall i \in I, t \in T \qquad (11)$$

Eqs. (2) and (3) describe the logical relation between binary variables $F_{(i,t)}$, $K_{(i,t)}$ and $U_{(i,t)}$. Eqs. (4) and (5) represent the minimum (O_{min}) and maximum (O_{max}) number of maintenance events that could occur during the scheduling horizon considered. Eq. (6) describes the constraint for a minimum time (γ) between two consequent maintenance events for the same compressor *i*. Eq. (7) ensures that a compressor remains off-line for a v_i time period after it switches off and Eq. (8) describes that only one maintenance task could take place per time interval. Finally, Eq. (9) - (10) describe the constraints for the deterioration model, and Eq. (11) models the maximum permitted deterioration (ω).

3. Case study

The proposed mathematical formulation has been applied to an industrial air separation plant with eight compressors. The scheduling horizon is 30 d and a time interval with duration of one day has been used. The demand forecast is given for the considered scheduling horizon. Table 1 (at the end of the paper) shows the initial state of the connections between compressors and grids, and the history of the past operation of the compressors, i.e. how many days a compressor was on-line or off-line before that time. The minimum (O_{min}= 0) and the maximum (O_{max}= 2) number of maintenance tasks per compressors are given. Moreover, the duration of a maintenance task is three days (v_i= 3). There is also a minimum time of three days (γ=3) between two consecutive maintenance episodes. The resulting MINLP model was implemented in GAMS. The model involves 9,797 equations, 2,250 continuous and 2,820 binary variables.

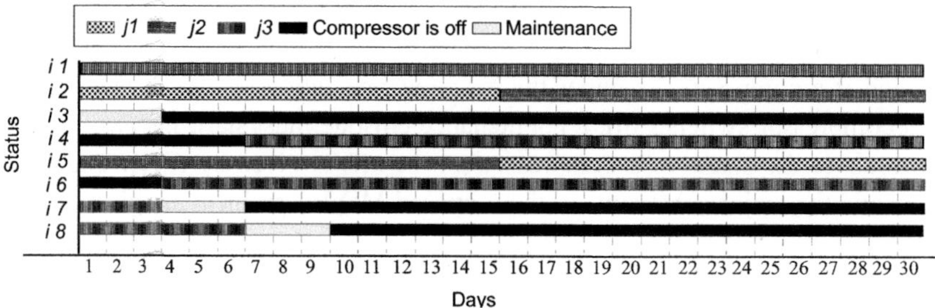

Figure 2. Schedule of the operation of the compressors and their maintenance both derived from the optimization when the condition of compressors is predicted.

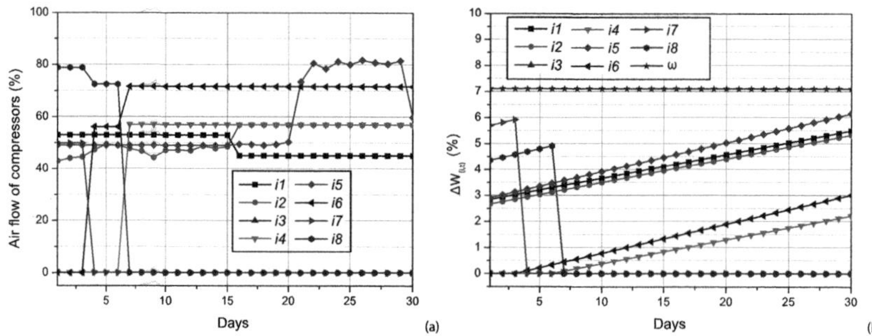

Figure 3. Distribution of the load of each compressor per time interval (a) and excess of power consumption due to fouling over time (b).

Figure 2 displays the optimal schedule resulting from the optimization. According to Figure 2, five compressors operate at every time interval to meet the demand. Therefore, compressor $i3$ shuts down on day 1 because the other five compressors, $i1$, $i2$, $i5$, $i7$ and $i8$ can satisfy the demand. Figure 2 shows that when an off-line compressor switches on, another compressor switches off in the same day to avoid operation of six compressors. This is because when a compressor is on-line, it has to operate at a minimum mass flow rate which results in unnecessary energy consumption.

Figure 3(a) shows the distribution of air mass flows on each day. Some of the compressors have constant flow rates while some others cover the demand fluctuations. This is due to the fact that compressors have different efficiencies, thus compressors with higher efficiency than others adjust their flow to meet the demand requirements. Figure 2 and 3(b) show that compressors $i3$, $i7$ and $i8$ have to be switched off for maintenance in days 1, 4 and 7. According to Figure 3(b), the degradation of these compressors is high in the beginning of the optimization due to many days of operation in the past (see Table 1). Therefore, the optimization suggests switching them off in the first days of the scheduling horizon to avoid costs of the extra power they consume. Moreover, one compressor is switched off after the shut down of the other due to constraint of Eq. (8).

In order to compare the condition-based optimization with the case of operation assuming a preventive maintenance scheme, the proposed mathematical model was modified. The second optimization model introduces a constraint for maximum running times and it is assumed that the information of the degradation of the performance of the machine is not available. Hence, the objective function does not consider costs of maintenance and extra power of the deterioration. The new Mixed Integer Linear Programming (MILP) model was implemented and solved in GAMS. This model involves 8,507 equations, 2,340 continuous and 1,770 binary variables. The resulting schedule is shown in Figure 4. The second schedule differs from the previous one (Figure 2) considering the condition of the compressors. According to Figure 4 there are more shut downs and maintenance events than in the previous case.

Figure 5 illustrates the difference in cost units for the condition-based and the preventive maintenance optimal schedule. The overall cost is reduced in the case of the condition-based maintenance by 11 %. This difference comes mostly due to the costs associated with the compressor switch ons and offs, which are reduced by 63 % in the case of condition-based maintenance. Although the electricity consumed in these 30 d is slightly lower by 1 % for the preventive maintenance optimization case, the overall cost is lower for the case of the condition-based maintenance.

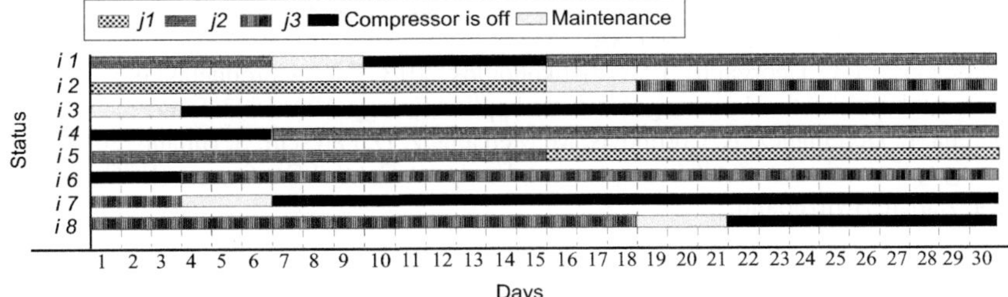

Figure 4. Schedule of the operation of the compressors and maintenance schedule both derived from the optimization when the condition of compressors is not considered.

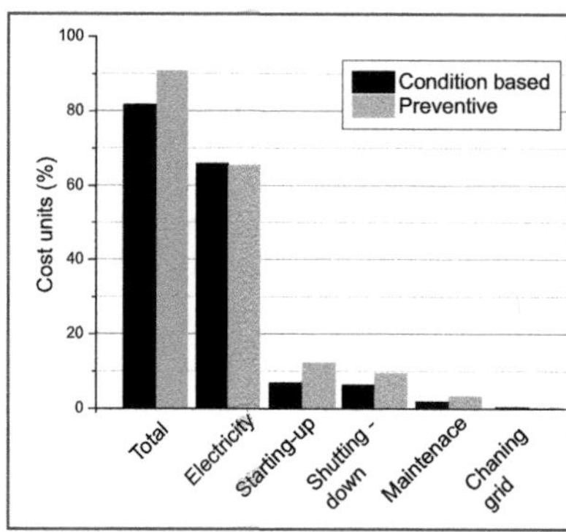

Table 1. Initial state of the system.

Comp	*i1*	*i2*	*i3*	*i4*	*i5*	*i6*	*i7*	*i8*
Grid	*j2*	*j1*	*j2*	-	*j1*	-	*j3*	*j3*
Days on	30	28	48	0	25	0	50	38
Days off	0	0	0	2	0	29	0	0

Figure 5. Comparison of total cost and its distribution in electricity, start-up, shut-down, maintenance and change grid cost between condition-based and preventive maintenance cases.

4. Conclusions

The state-of-the art of the optimization of compressors networks examines the optimal operation and maintenance of compressors without considering their gradual degradation over time. The current work studied the optimization of compressor networks taking into account the deterioration of the performance of a compressor over time. A case study of air compressors operating in parallel in an industrial air separation plant examines the optimal operation and maintenance considering the deterioration of the compressors. An illustrative example compared the condition-based maintenance approach with a typical preventive maintenance case. The condition-based approach achieved reduction in the overall cost by 11 %, especially in the start-up, shut-down and maintenance costs compared to the benchmark preventive maintenance strategy.

Acknowledgement

Financial support from the Marie Curie FP7-ITN project "Energy savings from smart operation of electrical, process and mechanical equipment– ENERGY-SMARTOPS", Contract No: PITN-GA-2010-264940 is gratefully acknowledged. The authors also acknowledge the financial support from the Engineering and Physical Sciences Research Council (EPSRC) under the Research Project EP/G059071/1.

References

N. Aretakis, I. Roumeliotis, G. Doumouras, K. Mathioudakis, 2012, Compressor washing economic analysis and optimization for power generation, Applied Energy, 95, 77-86.

E. Camponogara, L.F. Nazari, C.N. Meneses, 2012, A revised model for compressor design and scheduling in gas-lifted oil fields, IIE Transactions, 44, 5, 342-351.

W.E. Forsthoffer, 2011, Forsthoffer's Best Practice Handbook for Rotating Machinery, Butterworth-Heinemann, Boston, USA.

G. M. Kopanos, M. C. Georgiadis, E. N. Pistikopoulos, 2013, Energy production of a network of micro combined heat and power generators, Applied Energy, 102, 1522-1534.

F. Paparella, L. Domìnguez, A. Cortinovis, M. Mercangüz, D. Pareschi, S. Bittanti, 2013, Load sharing optimization of parallel compressors, European Control Conference (ECC), 4059-4064, Zürich, Switzerland.

Jiří Jaromír Klemeš, Petar Sabev Varbanov and Peng Yen Liew (Editors)
Proceedings of the 24th European Symposium on Computer Aided Process Engineering – ESCAPE 24
June 15-18, 2014, Budapest, Hungary.

Network Design and Planning of Resilient Supply Chains

Sónia R. Cardoso[a], Ana Paula F. D. Barbosa-Póvoa[a*], Susana Relvas[a], Augusto Q. Novais[b]

[a]*CEG-IST, Instituto Superior Técnico, Universidade de Lisboa, Av. Rovisco Pais, 1049-001 Lisboa, Portugal*

[b]*Unidade de Modelação e Optimização de Sistemas Energéticos, Laboratório Nacional de Energia e Geologia, Lisboa, Portugal*

apovoa@tecnico.ulisboa.pt

Abstract

The design and planning of resilient supply chains is a major challenge due to the difficulty of measuring resilience. In the present work we aim to address this challenge and a design and planning model that integrates demand uncertainty is applied to five supply chains with different structures that are submitted to three types of disruption. Their response towards the disruptions is evaluated considering two situations: 1) the disruption occurs with certainty and 2) the disruption is associated to a probability of occurrence. This last case incorporates both sources of uncertainty, i.e. demand and disruption occurrence. With a common objective of maximizing the expected net present value indicator (ENPV), six additional ones are considered to assess the supply chains' resilience: node and flow complexity, density and node criticality, customer service level and the investment made. A discussion on the results obtained is presented to provide a manager with insights on how to design and plan a resilient supply chain.

Keywords: Supply chain management, Resilience, Design, Planning, Uncertainty.

1. Introduction

Managing supply chains (SCs) is a difficult task due to increasing market competition and customers expectations in acquiring the right product, at the right time, in the right place with specified quality standards. SCs are also evolving into complex systems and are becoming more often exposed to disruptions as they operate in a global market, making use of outsourcing, centralization strategies and lean processes, under constant technological innovations. In order to deal with this context, while maintaining a profitable operation, it is necessary to ensure resilience in the design and planning of these systems (Colicchia et al., 2010). Resilience in SCs can be defined as the ability of a SC to return to its original state or move to a new one, more desirable state after being disturbed (Christopher and Peck, 2004). The need of investing on resilience has been recognized by academics, but has been also identified as a difficult problem to address. Maybe due to this, there is still a lack of quantitative models, since the majority of the literature is based on qualitative approaches and few quantitative measures have been developed (Spiegler et al., 2012). Kima et al. (2011) presented metrics derived from social network analysis related to network complexity, centrality and density and discussed how these factors can affect the reliability of SCs. Adenso-Diaz et al. (2012) applied thirteen metrics to forward, a.k.a. open-loop, SCs and concluded that node complexity, density and node criticality affect negatively the SC reliability, while flow complexity affects it positively. Zeballos et al. (2012) studied the resilience of the network design of a closed-loop supply chain (CLSC) toward a disruption caused by a cut on the raw materials supply, and used a combination of graph metrics derived from social network analysis and performance indices, to conclude on SCs resilience. Recently, Garcia-Herreros et al. (2013) addressed the planning and design of a small, forward and single product SC under the risk of disruptions in some facilities, namely distribution centres. After analyzing the works published on SC resilience, we can conclude that few authors attempted to quantify this concept, and that the ones who accomplished it only studied one type of disruption affecting only one echelon on a forward SC, rather than on those more complicated of the closed-loop type. Thus, there is still a large gap to explore on the resilience concept within SCs.

2. Problem definition

A Mixed Integer Linear Programming (MILP) formulation is developed, based on a previous work of the authors (Cardoso et al., 2013), for the design and planning of SCs. A generic structure is considered involving five echelons, namely raw materials' suppliers, plants, warehouses, final products suppliers and markets. The design decisions include the number, location and capacity of the various entities of the network, as well as of the processes that have to be installed, whether they are of production, assembling or dismantling. The planning decisions relate to production rates, inventory levels, flows and transportation links. As different SCs can exhibit different levels of resilience towards a disruption, the proposed model is applied to five different network topologies: Case A – a forward supply chain; Case B – similar to A, but with reverse flows; Case C – similar to B, but plants and markets can directly exchange products;Case D – similar to B, but with the possibility of transshipment at plants, disassembling centers and warehouses;Case E –encompasses all the previous ones. It is a CLSC where plants send products directly to markets and can also receive directly from markets the end-of-life products. Transshipment is allowed at plants, warehouses and disassembling centers. The performance of each one of these networks is measured and compared when three disruptions are applied: i) 100 % decrease in the production capacity of the most important plant, caused, for example, by a major natural catastrophe; ii) the most important raw material suppliers have their supply suspended, due to an assumed industrial action; and iii) the 3PL hired to operate those transportation links, with the highest loads of products, between plants and warehouses, goes out of business. This comparison is made considering two situations: 1) disruptions occur with certainty and 2) each disruption occurrence is associated to a given probability. Simultaneously to the above disruptions, the demand uncertainty is also modeled using a scenario tree approach. Three possible scenarios for each time period are considered, i.e. an optimistic, a realistic and a pessimistic. When the uncertainty in the occurrence of the disruption is also analyzed, there are two more scenarios corresponding to whether or not the disruption will occur. A scenario tree approach is used that combines both sources of uncertainty. In this way, the total number of scenarios is doubled, since both uncertainty sources are independent.Six indicators previously identified as important by works in this area (Adenso-Diaz et al., 2012), are also considered to assess the supply chains' resilience: node and flow complexity, density and node criticality that are classified as network design indicators, and the operational indicators which comprise the expected net present value (ENPV), customer service level and investment. Node complexity is defined as the total number of nodes in the network, flow complexity is the total number of flows, density is determined as the ratio between the number of total ties in the network and the number of potential ties and the node criticality is calculated in the present work as the number of inbound plus outbound flows at each node. A node is assumed critical when its node criticality is higher than 10. The objective function to be maximized is expressed by the economic indicator ENPV in Eq.(1). Eqs.(2) and (3) determine the other two economic indicators.

$$ENPV = \sum_{s} pb_s \times NPV_s \tag{1}$$

$$SC = \frac{\sum_{t}\left(1-\sum_{s} pb_s\left(1-\frac{\sum_{w:(w,v)\in F} Q_{wvpst}}{\sum_{v\in V_m}\sum_{p} D_{pvst}}\right)\right)}{NT} \tag{2}$$

$$INV = \sum_{i}\sum_{v} im_{iv} \times in_{iv}^{P} + \sum_{i}\sum_{v\in V_h}\sum_{t}\left(v_{ivt}^{P} \times CE_{ivt}^{P}\right) + \sum_{v} is_v \times in_v^{s} + \sum_{v\in V_z}\sum_{t}\left(v_{vt}^{s} \times CE_{vt}^{S}\right) \tag{3}$$

In Eq.(1) ENPV is calculated as the sum of the NPV obtained for each scenario multiplied by the probability of occurrence. Eq.(2) calculates the customer service level for all time periods. This is determined through the summation of the service level per time period. The service level is in turn obtained as the difference to unity of the sum, over all scenarios, of the product of the probability of each scenario (pb_s) by the differece between one and the ratio between the total flow of products sent to the market (Q_{wvpst}) and the whole demand for each scenario (D_{pvst}). The investment is determined in Eq.(3) and it includes the initial investment in the existing processes and storage entities by multiplying the existing capacities (im_{iv}/is_v) by the unitary investment (in^P_{iv}/in^S_v), as well as the investment in any subsequent expansions through the multiplication of the unitary investment (v^P_{ivt} / v^S_{vt}) by the continuous variable that holds the value of the capacity expansions of the processes (CE^P_{ivt}) and the storage entities in each time period (CE^S_{vt}).

3. Case study

The model was applied to a European SC formed by one plant in Hamburg with twelve production technologies and six disassembling technologies, one warehouse in Munich with six assembly lines and a storage capacity for 500 units. There are four raw materials suppliers in Frankfurt, Prague, Birmingham and Copenhagen and three final products suppliers located in Riga, Minsk and Warsaw, meaning that the SC can outsource only a part or all of the production. The SC supplies eighteen markets located in different European countries. Since the company aims to expand its business and simultaneously increase its resilience to disruptions, a reconfiguration of the existent SC is under evaluation with different possibilities being investigated. These involve the possibility of installing new plants in Bilbao and Milan, where each plant has its own set of four suppliers. New warehouses can also be installed in Portsmouth, Lyon, Bologna and Salamanca. Such options are coupled with the planned expansion of the existing facilities with the objective of maximizing the ENPV. A set of three 5-year periods is considered, adding up to a time horizon of 15 years. Before analyzing the results with disruptions, the five SCs were compared when no disruption affects their normal operation and results shown in Figures 1 and 2. Incorporating reverse flows in a SC does not always represent an economic benefit, as can be seen in Figure 1, by comparing case A with cases B and D. However, if this integration is done in a holistic way, it is possible to achieve better results, as found in cases C and E.

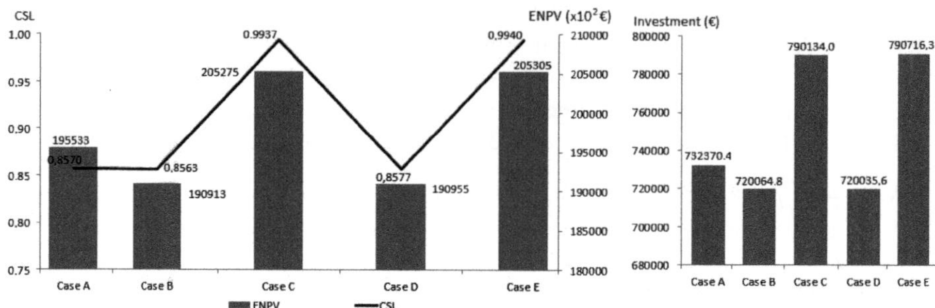

Figure 1. ENPV and customer service level in cases A to E. Figure 2. Investment made.

The most general network, case E, is the one with both the highest ENPV (205305×10^2€) and the highest customer service level (0.994). Cases C and E, although having the best results in terms of ENPV and customer service level, are the networks that made higher investments (see Figure 2), because in order to satisfy most demand, capacities of both processes and storage need to be raised. However such greater investments are compensated by the SC results and a higher structure generality that contributed to a more profitable SC operation. In addition, all networks installed two plants and four warehouses in time period 1, and maintained the same configuration during the entire planning horizon. In an attempt to find indicators that can help decision makers comparing different networks in terms of resilience, these five cases were evaluated regarding their network design indicators, with results shown in Table 1. In terms of node complexity, all cases that integrate reverse flows have an identical characterization. The same is found for node criticality, with similar networks having the same results. Case A is an exception, with the lowest number of critical nodes, but it is also the less complex network. In terms of flow complexity, according to Adenso-Diaz et al. (2012) it is expected that networks that are highly interconnected and have greater flexibility in terms of alternative transportation links, will have greater resilience than those less interconnected. Conversely, networks that are more geographically concentrated and therefore have a higher density can be expected to be more exposed to disruptions (Craighead et al., 2007).Case E is the supply chain that presents the highest flow complexity and the lowest density, so it can be expected for this network to present the highest resilience of all. In order to test these assumptions all networks are submitted to three different disruptions, as described in the problem definition section. Such disruptions are considered to occur at time 2. When probabilities are associated to their occurrence, the values assumed are 5 %, 30 % and 60 % respectively for disruptions 1, 2 and 3. Figure 3 shows the relative deviation between the ENPV obtained in each type of disruption and the ENPV obtained when no disruption affected the SCs. Note that when the disruptions have a probability associated, they are named disruption-ST.

Table 1. Network design indicators

	Node complexity			Flow Complexity			Density			Node criticality		
	t=1	t=2	t=3	t=1	t=2	t=3	t=1	t=2	t=3	t=1	t=2	t=3
Case A	36	37	37	45	46	47	0.288	0.295	0.301	1	1	1
Case B	38	41	41	67	99	100	0.184	0.272	0.275	2	6	6
Case C	38	41	41	83	113	113	0.175	0.238	0.238	7	8	8
Case D	38	41	41	67	101	103	0.169	0.255	0.260	2	7	7
Case E	38	41	41	82	116	118	0.162	0.229	0.233	7	8	8

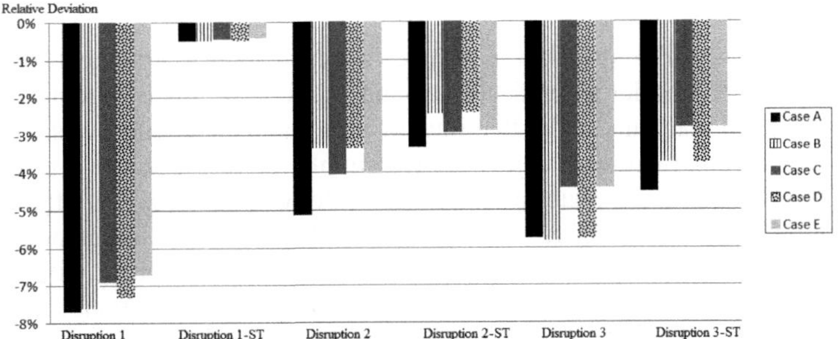

Figure 3. Influence of the disruptions on the ENPV.

Disruption 1 is the one that has the highest impact on the ENPV forall SCs. However, when it is considered with uncertainty its impact is the lowest, because only a small probability of 5 % is assumed and the SC design is optimized so as to respond adequately to this occurrence. It is interesting to notice that case A, the only forward SC, is the most sensitive toward the disruptions, presenting the highest relative deviations, except for disruption 3, but even in this case its ENPV relative deviation is fairly close to the highest value. Cases B and D present similar results between themselves, but always worse than cases C and E, except for disruption 2. Cases C and E have also similar results, while being the least sensitive to disruptions 1 and 3. Disruption 2, however, has a higher impact in their ENPV, because the suspended suppliers are responsible for transporting very high quantities of raw materials to the plants. As shown in Table 2, cases C and E present the highest values of CSL, as well as of ENPV, under all disruptions. In an attempt to meet demand without having to outsource, cases C and E present also the highest investment (see Table 2). Disruption 1 affects a plant and as a consequence implies an increase in supplementary investment, since all networks invest in a new plant at time period 3. In disruption 2 they all invest in more capacity, since they account from the onset to a decrease in suppliers' production capacity. Disruption 3 implies less investment for all non-stochastic cases. However, since this disruption affects the transportation link between plant P3 and warehouses W1, W2 and W4, all three SCs invest in more production capacity in the other plants. For this disruption, since case E presents a greater flexibility in terms of alternative transportation links, it is also the one with less supplementary investment in relation to the equivalent case without disruption. When the stochastic cases are considered (see table 3 where the relative deviations on the investment between the cases without disruption and with the disruptions are presented), a decrease in investment is found, with exception of disruption 3, since the occurrence are no longer certain events. The optimum stochastic solution is therefore the balance between two events, i.e. one where a probability of occurrence of a disruption is assumed and another where this probability is nil.

Table 2. Operational indicators

		A	B	C	D	E
ENPV (10^3€)	D1	18052.7	17637.9	19114.6	17700.4	19156.0
	D2	18551.9	18450.8	19694.9	18453.9	19701.1
	D3	18429.1	17981.9	19617.6	17991.1	19623.2
CSL	D1	0.769	0.778	0.950	0.798	0.951
	D2	0.831	0.832	0.959	0.831	0.959
	D3	0.823	0.822	0.990	0.822	0.990
Inv. (10^3€)	D1	855.2	829.3	964.6	828.9	951.9
	D2	862.0	854.6	925.1	855.7	926.7
	D3	782.3	764.1	832.6	760.9	831.3

Table 3. Relative deviation (%) on investment

Case	D1	D1-ST	D2	D2-ST	D3	D3-ST
A	16.8	2.6	17.8	14.8	6.8	9.9
B	15.1	2.5	18.7	12.9	6.1	9.2
C	22.1	2.1	17.1	13.6	5.4	6.0
D	15.1	2.5	18.8	9.3	5.7	9.3
E	20.4	2.0	17.2	13.5	5.1	5.7

4. Conclusions

The main objective of this work was to investigate the main characteristics of a SC that a manager should consider when designing and planning it to be resilient. In order to do that, a design and planning model that integrates demand uncertainty was applied to five SCs with different structures, ranging from a simple forward chain to a highly complex CLSC. These five SCs were submitted to three types of disruption that affected different network echelons and their performance compared using seven indicators. In addition, two different situations were also considered: 1) the disruptions occur with certainty and 2) a probability is associated to the occurrence of each disruption. Case E that incorporates all possible transportation links among all entities presents the highest ENPV and customer service level, whether under no-disruption or under any of the tested disruptions. This network also has the highest flow complexity and the lowest density. This suggests that these two metrics can be good indicators of resilience when decision makers have to compare and decide on different types of network. When designing and planning resilient supply chains, it was also shown that other strategies, such as flexibility in terms of transportation links and redundancy in terms of investment in extra capacity, are also important. On-going work is being undertaken to explore other disruptions and identify additional indicators, which can be employed to extend the work here presented on the measurement of SCs' resilience.

Acknowledgment

The financial support from Fundação para a Ciência e Tecnologia (FCT), grant SFRH/BD/64125/2009 is acknowledged.

References

B. Adenso-Diaz, C. Mena, S. Garcia-Carbajal, M. Lietchy, 2012, The impact of supply-network characteristics on reliability, SC management–An International Journal, 17, 3, 263-276.

C. Colicchia, F. Dallari, M. Melacini,2010, Increasing supply chain resilience in a global sourcing context, Production Planning and Control: The Management of Operations, 21, 7, 680-694.

C. Craighead, J. Blackhurst, M, Rungtusanatham, R. Handfield, 2007, The Severity of Supply Chain Disruptions: Design Characteristics and Mitigation Capabilities, Decision Sciences, 38, 1, 131-156.

L. Zeballos, M. Gomes, A. Barbosa-Póvoa, A. Novais, 2012, Optimum Design and Planning of Resilient and Uncertain Closed-Loop Supply Chains, Computer Aided Chemical Engineering, 30, 407-411.

M. Christopher, H. Peck, 2004, Building the resilient supply chain, International Journal of Logistics Management, 15, 2, 1-13.

P. Garcia-Herreros, I. Grossmann, J. Wassick, 2013, Design of Supply Chains under the Risk of Facility Disruptions, Computer Aided Chemical Engineering, 32, 577-582.

S. Cardoso, A. Barbosa-Póvoa, S. Relvas, 2013, Design and Planning of Supply Chains with Integration of Reverse Logistics Activities under Demand Uncertainty, European Journal of Operational Research, 226, 436-451.

V. Spiegler, M. Naim, J. Wikner, 2012, A control engineering approach to the assessment of supply chain resilience, International Journal of Production Research, 50, 21, 6162-6187.

Y. Kima, T. Choi, T. Yan, K. Dooley, 2011, Structural investigation of supply networks: A social network analysis approach, Journal of Operational Management, 29, 194-211.

Jiří Jaromír Klemeš, Petar Sabev Varbanov and Peng Yen Liew (Editors)
Proceedings of the 24th European Symposium on Computer Aided Process Engineering – ESCAPE 24
June 15-18, 2014, Budapest, Hungary.

Solubility Parameter Prediction for Kacip Fatimah Herb using Group Contribution-Based Models

Siti Nuurul Huda Mohammad Azmin[a], Azizul Azri Mustaffa[a], Sharifah Rafidah Wan Alwi[a*], Zainuddin Abdul Manan[a], Lee Suan Chua[b]

[a]*Process Systems Engineering Centre (PROSPECT), Faculty of Chemical Engineering, Universiti Teknologi Malaysia, 81310 UTM, Johor Bahru, Malaysia.*
[b]*Institute of Bioproduct Development (IBD), Universiti Teknologi Malaysia, 81310 UTM, Johor Bahru, Malaysia.*
shasha@cheme.utm.my

Abstract

This study is focusing on determining the most suitable solubility parameter prediction model for Kacip Fatimah herb based on Group Contribution (GC) approach. Stefanis,Van Krevelen, and Marrero and Gani GC models are used to predict Hansen Solubility Parameters (HSP) property of selected Kacip Fatimah active ingredients extracted using methanol solvent. From the results, solubility parameters predicted using Stefanis and Van Krevelen GC methods show high deviations with the experimental data. On the other hand, the HSP predictions using Marrero and Gani GC method is the best from the three GC Methods because it uses the data from organic compound and take into account the contribution of the third order groups. The variation in solubility parameter concludes that Van Krevelen and Stefanis GC parameter is not suitable for computing the parameter for herbs.

Keywords: Herbal extraction, Kacip Fatimah, phytochemical, Hansen Solubility Parameter , Group Contribution Method.

1. Introduction

Natural products are now being extensively marketed in the form of dietary supplements, nutraceuticals, health products, traditional medicines, or as prescriptions written from national pharmacopeias such as Chinese and Indian (Khan and Smillie, 2012). One of the premier Malaysian traditional medicinal plants, *Labisia pumila* (*L. pumila*) is being investigated scientifically for their medicinal properties. *L.pumila*, or locally known in Malaysia as Kacip Fatimah has their own unique characteristic such as anti-oxidant (Shahidi et al., 1992), anti-carcinogenic (Yamamoto and Gaynor, 2001), anti-stress (Choi et al., 2010), high in vitamin C (Tsao and Deng, 2004) and induced cancer cell death (Wei et al., 1990). These characteristics are due to the presence of active ingredients in *L.pumila* such as flavonoids, phenolic and gallic acid compound. There are many methods that have been applied to obtain these active ingredients, where solvent are used. Every solvent will attract different active ingredients as the "like dissolve like" theory is implemented (Barton, 1990). This is the reason why different solvent will give different result in the extraction process. As an example, Figure 1 shows the main phytochemicals in flavonoids group that have been extracted from *L.pumila* using methanol as a solvent.

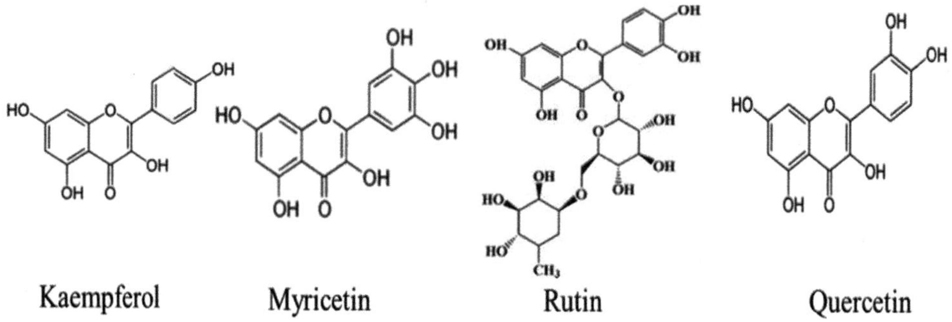

Kaempferol Myricetin Rutin Quercetin

Figure 1. Main phytochemicas in *L.pumila*, extracted using methanol

There are many approaches that are available to assess the solute-solvent interaction of a system, but it is a common practice to use Hildebrand and/or Hansen Solubility Parameter (HSP) in selecting the best solvent (Hansen, 2007).Hildebrand (1949) introduced the term solubility parameter with the symbol, δ and defines it as the square root of the cohesive energy density:

$$\delta = \left(\frac{E}{v}\right)^{1/2} \tag{1}$$

where v(cm^3/mol) is the molar volume of the pure solvent, and E (J^{2}cm^{3}mol) is its (measurable) energy of vaporization. This theory has been developed for mixing of nonpolar substances. However, many of solvent and solute in common use are polar and have dipole moment and/or have capabilities for hydrogen bonding (the factor that must be included in the theory). Hansen (1969) modified the theory by taking into account the hydrogen bonding (Van Krevelen, 2009)with:

$$\delta_t = \sqrt{{\delta_d}^2 + {\delta_p}^2 + {\delta_h}^2} \tag{2}$$

whereδ_d(MPa$^{1/2}$)is partial solubility due to dispersion forces,δ_p(MPa$^{1/2}$) ispartial solubility due to dipole forces and δ_h (MPa$^{1/2}$) is partial solubility due to hydrogen forces. For computing the partial solubilitiesof HSP, GC method can be used. To date, there are many GC which have been developed to predict the partial solubilities such as the Stefanis(Stefanis and Panayiotou, 2012), Van Krevelen (Van Krevelen, 2009)and Marerro and Gani(Marrero and Gani, 2001)GC methods. In this study, the three different methods will be evaluated to determine which method is the most suitable to predict the extraction of major phytochemicals from *L.pumila*.

2. Solubility Parameter Group Contribution Prediction Methods

2.1. Stefanis Group Contribution Method

The method describe two types of functional group which is first and second order groups to improve the accuracy of predictions(Stefanis and Panayiotou, 2008). In this method, each compound is represented as a hybrid of many conjugate forms, where each conjugate form is considered as a structure with integer-order localized bonds and integer charges on atoms. The following equation is used for determining partial solubility parameter:

$$\delta_d = (\sum_i NiCi + W \sum_i MjDj + 17.3231) MPa^{1/2} \quad (3)$$

$$\delta_p = (\sum_i NiCi + W \sum_i MjDj + 7.3548) MPa^{1/2} \quad (4)$$

$$\delta_h = (\sum_i NiCi + W \sum_i MjDj + 7.9793) MPa^{1/2} \quad (5)$$

where Ci is the contribution of the first order group of type i that appears Ni times while Mj is the contribution of the second ordet of the type j that appears Dj times. The contributions of the first and second order groups for Eqs. (3) to (5) are obtained from Stefanis and Panayiotou (2012).

2.2. Hoftyzer and Van Krevelen Group Contribution Method

The method is used for estimating the partial solubility of polymers and pure organic compounds from group contributions. In this method, the following equationsare used:

$$\delta_d = \frac{\sum Fdi}{v} \quad (6) \qquad \delta_p = \frac{\sqrt{\sum Fpi^2}}{v} \quad (7) \qquad \delta_h = \sqrt{\frac{\sum Ehi}{v}} \quad (8)$$

where Fdi $(MJ/m^3)^{1/2}/mol$ is dispersion forces, Fpi $(MJ/m^3)^{1/2}/mol$ is dipole forces, Ehi (J/mol) is hydrogen bonding energy and v is molar volume of the molecules. The contribution of Fdi, Fpi^2 and Ehi are obtained from Van Krevelen (2009).

2.3. Marrero and Gani Group Contribution Method

The Marrero and Gani (2001) prediction method can be used to estimate the properties of pure components. Eq. (9) shows the equation.

$$f(X) = \sum_i NiCi + w \sum_j MjDj + z \sum_k EkOk \quad (9)$$

where $f(X)$ is a function of property X (solubility parameter in this study) and may contain the additional adjustable model parameters (constant) depending on the property involved. Ci is the contribution of first order group that occurs Ni times, Mj is the contribution of second order group that occurs Di times and Ek is the contribution of third order group that occurs Ok times. Marrero and Gani (2001) introduced a higher level of approximation by defining third-order groups to provide more structural information about systems of fused aromatic and nonaromatic rings.In this study, the value of partial solubility of dispersion, δ_d, polar δ_p, and hydrogen bond δ_h was obtained from ICAS 12.0 software (Denmark).

2.4. Total solubility of phytochemical in solvent

The total solubility of phytochemical in solvent is very important in order to know the efficiency of the solvent used. The model for total solubility in solvent is shown by Eq. (10) as follows:

$$\Delta\delta = \left[(\delta_{d,P} - \delta_{d,S})^2 + (\delta_{p,P} - \delta_{p,S})^2 + (\delta_{h,P} - \delta_{h,S})^2 \right] \quad (10)$$

where $\delta_{d,P}$ ($MPa^{1/2}$) is partial dispersion solubility of phytochemical, $\delta_{d,S}$ ($MPa^{1/2}$) is partial dispersion solubility of solvent, $\delta_{p,P}$ ($MPa^{1/2}$) is partial polar solubility of phytochemical, $\delta_{p,S}$ ($MPa^{1/2}$) is partial polar solubility of solvent, $\delta_{h,P}$ ($MPa^{1/2}$) is partial hydrogen bond solubility of phytochemical and $\delta_{h,S}$ ($MPa^{1/2}$) is partial hydrogen bond solubility of solvent. Small value of $\Delta\delta$ indicates that the solvent is good for that compound (Van Krevelen, 2009).

Table 1. Comparison of predictions of total solubility of phytochemical, δt and total solubility of phytochemical in methanol solvent, Δa

Compound Name			Methanol	Kaempferol	Myricetin	Quercetin	Rutin
Group Contribution Methods	Stefanis	δd	16.0	22.1	22.9	22.5	21.5
		δp	6.9	16.7	20.0	18.3	24.4
		δh	14.4	4.4	19.2	11.8	35.1
		δh	22.6	28.1	36.0	31.3	47.9
		Δδ		15.3	15.6	13.5	27.7
	Van Krevelen	δd	27.5	14.7	16.9	15.7	3.9
		δp	9.4	20.3	32.2	25.8	17.8
		δh	19.4	115.2	182.4	146.4	321.9
		δh	117.9	117.9	185.9	149.5	322.4
		Δδ		97.3	164.9	128.7	303.6
	Marrero & Gani	δd	15.5	21.9	21.6	22.0	36.3
		δp	7.8	7.3	7.7	8.6	29.4
		δh	13.7	19.6	31.8	26.1	75.8
		δh	30.3	30.3	39.2	35.2	89.0
		Δδ		11.1	18.7	13.8	64.6

3. Results and Discussion

Table 1 shows the results for both total solubility of phytochemical, δt and total solubility of phytochemical in methanol solvent, Δδ. In theory, Δδ value can determine the degree of solubility of the phytochemical in the selected solvent. From the result obtained in Table 1, the phytochemical are ranked according to its solubility in the methanol (solvent) for all the three GC methods and are shown in Figure 2. This ranking is then compared with the experimental data as shown in Figure3.Figure 3 shows the total flavonoids content in *L.pumila* extraction using Soxhlet and microwave assisted extraction, (MAE) methods. The results for Soxhlet extraction is obtained from (Karimi et al., 2011) while the results for MAEisfrom (Karimi and Jaafar, 2011).

For the comparison in Figure 2, the Marrero and Gani, and Van Krevelen GC methods provide the same ranking from the lowest to the highest total solubility, Δδ in methanol. The results are then compared with Figure 3 which shows the concentration of phytochemicals in methanol after extraction. As in the theory, the highest concentration of phytochemicals in the solvent is obtained when the value of Δδ between the phytochemicals and the solvent is the lowest. Therefore, both GC methods are appropriate for the *L.pumila*extraction. However, the lowest value of Δδ is more accurate in predicting the Δδ. Thus, Van Krevelen GC cannot be used for predicting Δδ for phytochemical of *L.pumila* in methanol because the value is too high (ranges from 97-303 $MPa^{1/2}$) compared with Marrero and Gani GC (11-64 $MPa^{1/2}$). Besides that, Van Krevelen GC method is developed based on polymer data. From these three methods, Stefanis GC method cannot be used for predicting Δδ for phytochemicals of *L.pumila* in methanol even though this method is designed for organic compounds. It is because the solubility prediction method is not aligned with the experimental result. From the result obtained, Marrero and Gani GC method is the best in predicting Δδ of *L.pumila* phytochemicals in methanol because of two reasons. The first reason is that value of $\Delta\delta$ is smaller compared to the other methods and the second reason is based on the rankings (according to both $\Delta\delta$ value and concentration of phytochemicals) between the predictions and the experimental data which are similar. Furthermore, Marrero and Gani GC method is based on three order of estimation that makes the GC prediction method more accurate.

4. Conclusion

With the group contribution method which was introduced in this study, the direct prediction of Hansen solubility parameters of phytochemical in *L.pumila* is possible. Only the molecular structures of the phytochemical are required for the predictions, and no experimental data are needed. Marrero and Gani GC has been identifies as the best model to predict the solubility parameter for phytochemicals in *L.pumila.* It is envisioned that the same model can be used to predict the solubility property for the other herb.

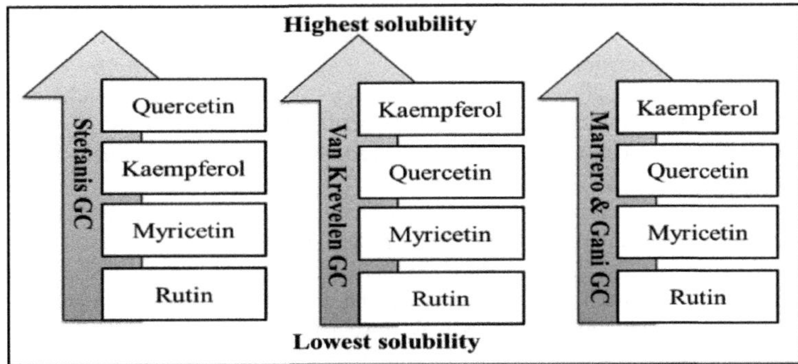

Figure 2. Ranking of phytochemical in term of total solubility of phytochemicals in methanol solvent, Δa for different GC methods.

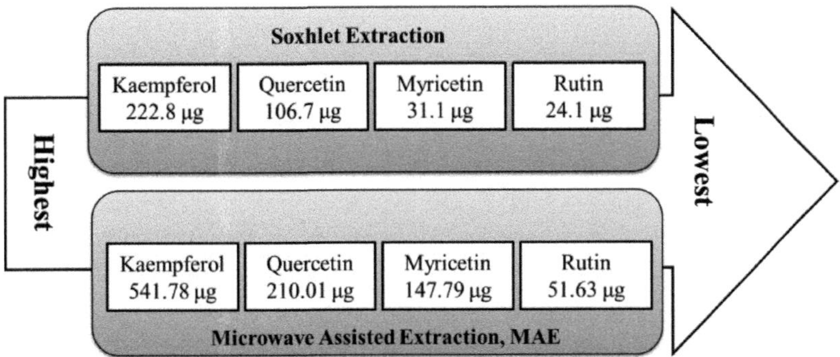

Figure 3. Ranking of phytochemical from different extraction method using methanol as a solvent.

References

A.F. Barton, 1990, polymer-liquid interaction parameters and solubility parameters, Boca Raton Florida, USA, CRC press.

H.-K. Choi, D.-H. Kim, J.W. Kim, S. Ngadiran, M.R. Sarmidi, C.S. Park, 2010, Labisia pumila extract protects skin cells from photoaging caused by UVB irradiation, Journal of Bioscience and Bioengineering, 109, 291-296.

T.U.I. Denmark, Copenhagen Denmark, <www.capec.kt.dtu.dk/Software/ICAS-and-its-Tools/103-Icas-71-Is-Ready> Accessed on 14/11/2013.

C.M. Hansen, 2007, Hansen solubility parameters: a user's handbook, Boca Raton Florida, USA, CRC press.

E. Karimi, H.Z. Jaafar, 2011, HPLC and GC-MS Determination of Bioactive Compounds in Microwave Obtained Extracts of Three Varieties of Labisia pumila Benth, Molecules, 16, 6791-6805.

E. Karimi, H.Z. Jaafar, S. Ahmad, 2011, Phytochemical analysis and antimicrobial activities of methanolic extracts of leaf, stem and root from different varieties of Labisa pumila Benth, Molecules, 16, 4438-4450.

I.A. Khan, T. Smillie, 2012, Implementing a “Quality by Design” Approach to Assure the Safety and Integrity of Botanical Dietary Supplements, Journal of Natural Products, 75, 1665-1673.

J. Marrero, R. Gani, 2001, Group-contribution based estimation of pure component properties, Fluid Phase Equilibria, 183, 183-208.

F. Shahidi, P.K. Janitha, P.D. Wanasundara, 1992, Phenolic antioxidants, Critical Reviews in Food Science and Nutrition, 32, 67-103.

E. Stefanis, C. Panayiotou, 2008, Prediction of Hansen solubility parameters with a new group-contribution method, International Journal of Thermophysics, 29, 568-585.

E. Stefanis, C. Panayiotou, 2012, A new expanded solubility parameter approach, International Journal of Pharmaceutics, 426, 29-43.

R. Tsao, Z. Deng, 2004, Separation procedures for naturally occurring antioxidant phytochemicals, Journal of Chromatography B, 812, 85-99.

D.W. Van Krevelen, K. Te Nijenhuis, 2009, Properties of polymers: their correlation with chemical structure; their numerical estimation and prediction from additive group contributions, Amsterdam, The Netherlands, Elsevier.

H. Wei, L. Tye, E. Bresnick, D.F. Birt, 1990, Inhibitory effect of apigenin, a plant flavonoid, on epidermal ornithine decarboxylase and skin tumor promotion in mice, Cancer research, 50, 499-502.

Y. Yamamoto, R.B. Gaynor, 2001, Therapeutic potential of inhibition of the NF-κB pathway in the treatment of inflammation and cancer, The Journal of Clinical Investigation, 107, 135-142.

Jiří Jaromír Klemeš, Petar Sabev Varbanov and Peng Yen Liew (Editors)
Proceedings of the 24th European Symposium on Computer Aided Process Engineering – ESCAPE 24
June 15-18, 2014, Budapest, Hungary.

On the Role of Mechanical Work Transfer in Optimization Procedures

Thassio Gomes[a,b,*], Heleno Bispo[b], João Manzi[b]

[a]*Federal Institute of Education, Science and Technology of Paraíba, Av.Tranquilino C. Lemos, 671 – Dinamérica, Campina Grande-PB, Brazil.*
[b]*Department of Chemical Engineering, Federal University of Campina Grande, Av. AprígioVeloso, 882 - Bodocongó, Campina Grande-PB, Brazil.*
thassiong@gmail.com

Abstract

This paper is concerned with the analysis of the role of the mechanical work transferred by the stirrer, applied to reactive and non-reactive systems. Classical methods for analysis and optimization take into account mass and enthalpy balances, emphasizing that the term referring to the energy in the form of work added to the system by stirring has usually been neglected. Since the entropy balance has also been considered in the optimization strategy, then the inclusion of work from stirring in such balances has permitted the degree of freedom for such a strategy to be increased. The analysis shows that the use of work in balance equations can play a pivotal role for a more realistic approach, besides providing a better understanding of the optimization mechanism, and when compared with the classical analysis, the results are much more consistent.

Keywords: Modeling; Entropy; Stirrer; Work.

1. Introduction

The classical approach of analysis and optimization applied to chemical processes has been systematically conducted, taking into account the mass and enthalpy balances (Fogler, 1999). Despite such a methodology being widely used, the sole use of the first law of thermodynamics in the analytical strategy has led the system to obtaining sub-optimal results (Andressen, 2011). In order to move towards better results, a methodology deemed entropy generation minimization (EGM) has been applied to non-reactive and reactive systems with a view to establishing optimal operating conditions (Manzi et al., 2008). The results obtained showed that for specific operating conditions, the minimum entropy generation rate can be reached, resulting in the global optimal solution for the performance of the process (Manzi et al., 2009).

However, due to the substantial changes in the key variables such as the residence time, particularly for the systems with restrictions, the practical implementation of the results obtained from the EGM methodology can require some physical modifications in the reactive system. In the most of cases, this seems unreasonable from the technical and economic standpoint. Thus, additional informations in the structure of the model need to be introduced so as to achieve results that outperform the ones achieved to date. It is well known that in a well-mixed system the work added by the stirring system is usually neglected. Such a consideration can interfere directly in the analytical procedures for non-reactive and reactive systems. Therefore, the leitmotif of this paper is focused on analysing the mechanical work transfer by the impeller when applied to the systems under consideration, while bearing the EGM methodology in mind.

2. The systems

The analysis of the mechanical work transferred by the stirrer to the bulk mass has been evaluated as per the two cases detailed below. The reactive and non-reactive systems are operated in stirred-tanks, as shown in Figure 1.

2.1. Non-reactive system

The first analysis deals with the crystallization of the monochloroacetic acid (MCAA). For simplicity, a solution of MCAA comprising 68 % (w/w) of MCAA and 32 % (w/w) of acetic acid (AA) is fed to a crystallizer at 310 K. The outlet from the crystallizer consists of two phases, namely: one with the residual mother liquor, i.e. a solution of MCAA, and the other with MCAA crystals in solution. Some data of the physical and chemical properties used in this system were taken from Koenig (1991).

2.2. Reactive system

The second case study, the production of propylene glycol by hydrolyses of propylene oxide, considers a well-mixed Continuous Stirred-Tank Rector (CSTR) with a volume of 1,135.36 L. The reactor has an inlet stream, which consists of a mixture in equal volumes of propylene oxide and methanol corresponding to 1,320.3 L/h for each stream plus water with a volumetric flow rate of 6,601.4 L/h. The inlet temperature for the whole stream is 297 K. Some of the data used in this system are taken from the literature (Fogler, 1999) while the basic physical and chemical properties have been taken from the handbook of chemistry and physics. Some results obtained by Manzi (2009) related to the EGM methodology are also listed in Table 2. It should be emphasized that it is not possible for the operating temperature to exceed 324.6 K.

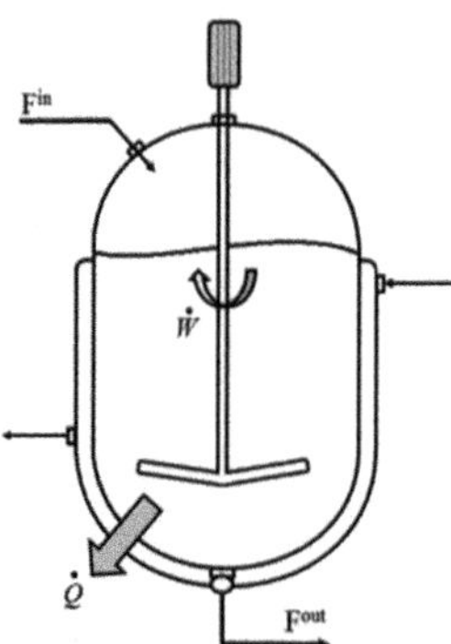

Figure 1. Configuration of a stirred-tank

Table 1. Operating conditions for the crystallization of MCAA.

Variable or Parameter	Value		Variable or Parameter	Value	
F^e	10	L/s	c_p	1.52	J/g.K
T^e	306.15	K	$\dot{Q}$	610	J/s
X^e_{MCAA}	0.68		ΔH_c	-11.58	J/g
ρ^e	1.58	g/L	PM_{MCAA}	94.5	g/mol
ρ	1.37	g/L	N_e	3.5	
V	100	L	D	2.44	m

Table 2. Operating conditions for the CSTR applied to propylene glycol production.

Variable or Parameter	Value		Variable or Parameter	Value	
F^e	2.567	L/s	$c_{p_{on}}$	146.54	J/mol.K
τ	442.44	s	$c_{p_{w}}$	75.36	J/mol.K
τ_{EGM}	5842.44	s	$c_{p_{na}}$	192.59	J/mol.K
C_{po}	2.12	mol/L	$c_{p_{m}}$	81.64	J/mol.K
V	1,135.36	L	k_0	47.11x10^8	s^{-1}
T^e	296.9	K	E	75,320	J/mol
T^e_{out}	324.6	K	R	8.314	J/mol.K
T_r	298	K	U	567.83	J/s.m^2.K
T^c	302.8	K	A	3.716	m^2
θ_w	18.65	-	$A_{\tau_{EGM}}$	35.7	m^2
θ_m	1.67	-	$\Delta H_{R_r}(298K)$	-84,589.11	J/mol
ρ	958	Kg/m^3	$\Delta G_{R_r}(298K)$	-68,274.08	J/mol
N_e	1.75	-	n		rev/s
			D	0.563	m

3. Theoretical Formulation

Both processes under analysis have been described by the equations of mass and enthalpy balances, in which the work transfer by the impeller to the system has been considered for a given power consumption.

3.1. Mass and enthalpy balance for the non-reactive system

Since no reaction occurs in the crystallizer, and knowing that the feed stream consists solely of MCAA and AA, the mass and enthalpy balances were established by the following Equations (Gomes, 2012);

$$PM_{MCAA}\left(\frac{dn_{MCAA}}{dt}\right) = F^e\rho^e X^e_{MCAA} - F\rho X_{MCAA} - F^e\rho^e\left[\frac{(X^e_{MCAA} - X_{MCAA})}{(1 - X_{MCAA})}\right] \tag{1}$$

$$PM_{AA}\left(\frac{dn_{AA}}{dt}\right) = F^e\rho^e X^e_{AA} - F\rho X_{AA} \tag{2}$$

$$\rho V C_p \frac{dT}{dt} = F^e\rho^e\left\{\left[\frac{X^e_{MCAA} - X_{MCAA}}{(1 - X_{MCAA})}\right]\Delta Hc + C_{pi}(T^e - T)\right\} - \dot{Q} + P \tag{3}$$

where $\dot{Q}$ is the rate of heat transferred from the system while P denotes the work carried out by the impeller.

3.2. Mass and enthalpy balance for the reactive system

The reactive system can be mathematically described by means of the following Equations which represent the mass and enthalpy balances respectively, besides kinetic considerations;

$$\frac{dn_i}{dt} = \mathrm{F}^e C^e_i - \mathrm{F}C_i \pm rV \tag{4}$$

$$\rho V c_p \frac{dT}{dt} = -F^e \left(\sum C_i^e c_{p_i}\right)(T - T^e) + \left(-\Delta H_{R_{ref}}\right) rV - \dot{Q} + P \tag{5}$$

$$\frac{dX}{dt} = -\frac{1}{\tau}X + \left[\frac{\dot{Q} - P}{C_{po} F^e (-\Delta H_c)}\right] \tag{6}$$

where r, $\dot{Q}$, X and P are respectively the rate of the reaction, the rate of the heat removal from the system, the reaction conversion and the work transferred by the impeller.

3.3. Entropic Modelling

The entropy balance for non-reactive and reactive systems was developed by Gomes (2013) and Manzi et al. (2009), respectively. Thus, taking the work transferred by the impeller to the system into account, the relationships for the entropy production rate ($\dot{\sigma}$) derived from the balance equation can be written as:

$$\dot{\sigma} = F^e \rho^e \left\{ \left[\frac{X_{MCAA}^e - X_{MCAA}}{(1 - X_{MCAA})}\right] \left(\frac{\Delta Gc}{T}\right) + C_{pi} \left(\left(\frac{T - T^e}{T}\right) + ln\left(\frac{T^e}{T}\right) \right) \right\} + \frac{P}{T} \tag{7}$$

(non-reactive system)

$$\dot{\sigma} = -\tilde{F}^e \left(\sum \theta_i c_{p_i}\right) \left[\frac{(T - T^e)}{T} + ln\left(\frac{T^e}{T}\right)\right] + \tilde{F}^e \left(\frac{\tau k_0 e^{\left(-\frac{E}{RT}\right)}}{1 + \tau k_0 e^{\left(-\frac{E}{RT}\right)}}\right) \left(-\frac{\Delta G_{R_{ref}}}{T_{ref}} + \Delta H_{R_{ref}} \left(\frac{T - T_{ref}}{T T_{ref}}\right)\right) + \frac{P}{T} \tag{8}$$

(reactive system)

3.4. Power Consumption

Classical expressions for the work of stirring were developed from dimensional analysis based on Rayleigh and Buckingham's methods, taking into consideration all the dimensional variables applied to the reactor and the stirring system (Zlokarnik, 1991). The power consumption in a stirred tank depends on various geometrical parameters, such as the rotational speed and fluid properties, as per Eq. (9).

$$P = \Psi(D, \rho, \mu, n) \tag{9}$$

where D, ρ and μ denote the diameter of the impeller, the density of the viscosity of the liquid and n is the speed of the impeller. By means of dimensional analysis, it is easy to show that the relationship for the Newton number can be given by Eq. (10)

$$Ne = \frac{P}{\rho . n^3 . D^5} \tag{10}$$

Hence, the work transfer or the power consumption, in a stirred tank results in:

$$P = \rho n^3 D^5 Ne \tag{11}$$

4. Results

4.1. Non-reactive system

Significant results have been obtained for crystallization processes when the mechanical work done by the stirrer is transferred to the system. Figure 2 enables the influence of the impeller to be observed in the crystallization of the monochloroacetic acid, in which increasing the rotation speed, results in an increase in the entropy production rate, in spite of the temperature of the system. An additional analysis can be made by comparing Figures 3 (A) and (B). This shows an increase in the entropy production rate when the mechanical work is transferred to the system, expressed by Figure 3 (B), in agreement with the theoretical prediction of thermodynamic behavior. Such a behavior can yield a significant impact on the design of the cooler system.

4.2. Reactive system

The analysis of the reactive system has made it possible to verify the influence of the work transferred by the impeller, as well as the increase in conversion as compared to the system proposed originally by the literature (Fogler, 1999). In Figure 4-I, case (A) represents the conversion of the system originally proposed, in which the work performed by the impeller is not considered. Case (B) represents the optimized system by the EGM method, resulting in a maximum conversion for a particular residence time in the reactor, which is much larger than that in the case (A). However, the results obtained by EGM can be reproduced when the work of the stirrer is taken into account, while keeping the residence time originally proposed, in addition to which this also yields the maximal conversion for the reactive system, as can be observed in case (C).

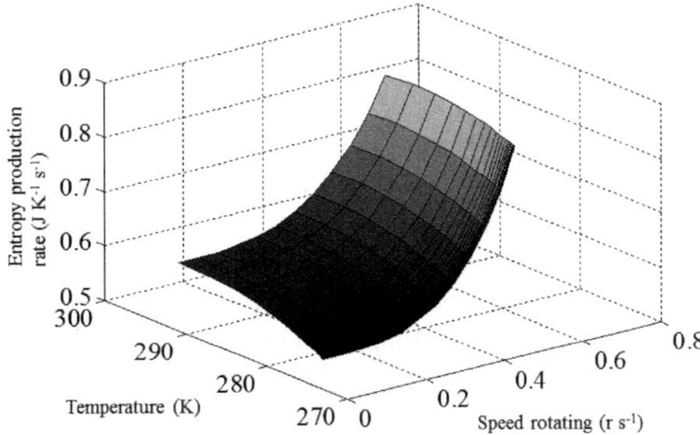

Figure 2. Behavior of the entropy production rate for a crystallization process

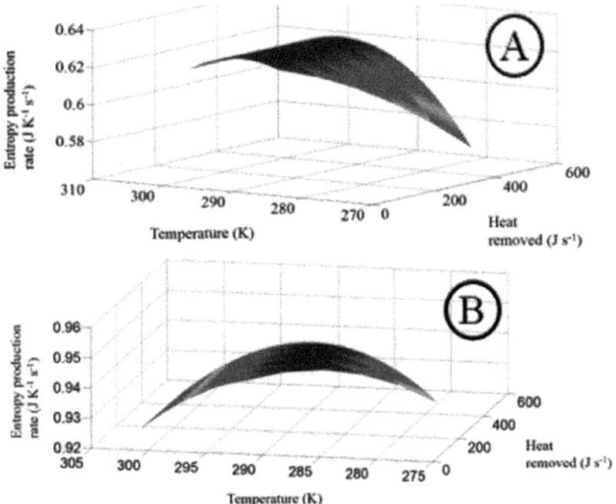

Figure 3. Behavior of the entropy production rate for a crystallization process without stirring (A) and with stirring (B)

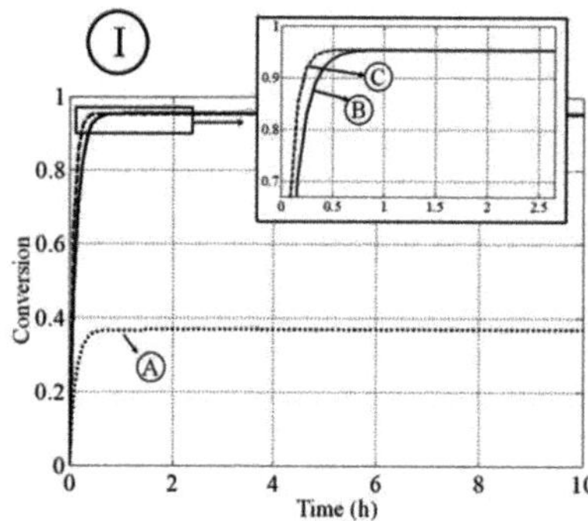

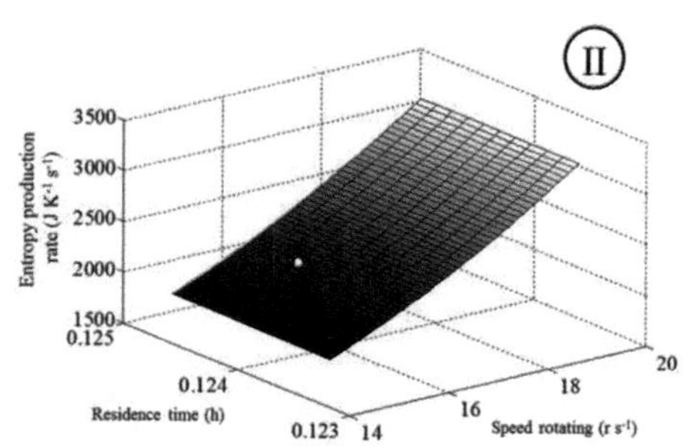

Figure 4. (I) The conversion for the reactive system; (II) Behavior of the entropy production rate for the reactive system

Figure 4-II shows that the increase in the entropy production rate of the system is directly proportional to the rotation speed. The white point in Figure 4-II represents the minimal entropy production rate required for that the process operates, when a specified impeller rotation speed is used, joint with the originally residence time. Thus, a maximal conversion of nearly 95 % has been obtained.

5. Conclusions

The effects of the mechanical work transfer by the impeller were presented and analyzed, for the proposed case studies. The work transferred by the impeller to the bulk was obtained by means of dimensional analysis and its introduction in the balance equations enabled the degree of freedom of the system to be increased. In accordance with the results obtained, the introduction of energy into the system in the form of work done by the stirrer should be considered whenever possible. Such a fact is important, at least, for optimization procedures, or otherwise, such procedures can lead the system to producing suboptimal solutions. Finally, it is important to mention the low computational effort, and the lower costs of implementing and operating such a methodology, which emphasizes that its potential for use in industrial applications is promising.

References

B. Andresen, 2011, Current trends in finite-time thermodynamics, Angew Chem Int, 50, 2690–704.

H. S. Fogler, 1999, Elements of Chemical Reaction Engineering, Prentice Hall, New Jersey, US.

H. Bispo, N. Silva, R. Brito, J. Manzi, 2013, On the equivalence between the minimum entropy generation rateand the maximum conversion rate for a reactive system, Energy conversion and management, 76, 26-31.

J. Manzi, E. Carrazzoni, 2008, Analysis and Optimization of a CSTR by Direct Entropy Minimization, J. Chem. Eng. Japan, 41, 3, 194-199.

J. Manzi, R. Vianna, H. Bispo, 2009, Direct entropy minimization applied to the production of propylene glycol, Chem. Eng. Proc., 48, 1, 470-475.

G. Koening, E. Lohmar, N. Rupprich, 1991, Choroacetic acids, Ullmann´s Encyclopedia of Industrial Chemistry, 6, Weinheim.

T.N. Gomes, 2012, Entropic minimization applied to the monochloroacetic acid crystallization, Master´s Dissertation, Federal University of Campina Grande, Brazil.

M. Zlokarnik, 1991, Dimensional Analysis and Scale-up in Chemical Engineering, Springer-Verlag Berlin, Heidelberg, Germany.

Jiří Jaromír Klemeš, Petar Sabev Varbanov and Peng Yen Liew (Editors)
Proceedings of the 24th European Symposium on Computer Aided Process Engineering – ESCAPE 24
June 15-18, 2014, Budapest, Hungary.

Scenario-based Analysis of Potential and Constraints of Alkaline Electrochemical Cells

Ulrike Krewer[a], Daniel Schröder[a], Christine Weinzierl[a]

[a]*Institute of Energy and Process Systems Engineering, TU Braunschweig, Germany,*

u.krewer@tu-braunschweig.de

Abstract

Alkaline electrochemical cells such as alkaline direct methanol fuel cells and secondary zinc air batteries are attractive low cost and high energy density alternatives to the presently favoured polymer electrolyte membrane fuel cell and Li ion battery. They are presently under development, and materials, geometry and operating conditions which allow high performance have not yet been determined. To assist the development of these exploratory cells, a model-based analysis methodology has been developed and applied. Scenario-based modeling with a reference model of minimum size and more complex variants is presented, and it is shown how feasible transport mechanisms, operating ranges and material properties are identified for these cells. In conclusion, the presented approach is flexibly applicable to various electrochemical and other systems and aids already in the first steps of process development.

Keywords: modeling, zinc air battery, alkaline fuel cell, feasibility range, water transport

1. Introduction

Electrochemical energy systems such as batteries and fuel cells allow for direct conversion of chemical into electrical energy with high efficiency and without a complex chain of processes. Major issues of the presently favoured electrochemical cells such as polymer electrolyte membrane fuel cell and Li ion battery are high cost of materials and, for batteries, low energy density and flammability.

In the fuel cell field, Platinum is used as catalyst in all polymer electrolyte fuel cells, as this is the only catalyst which is sufficiently stable and active in acidic environment. Since several years only, there is increasing interest in alkaline low temperature fuel cells based on hydroxide ions conducting polymer electrolytes. These fuel cells allow similarly easy handling of the electrolyte as the standard proton conducting polymer electrolyte membrane but - in contrast to these - they should permit also to use Pt free catalysts. Present performances of hydrogen or methanol fuelled alkaline cells are significantly lower than those using proton conducting membranes and the bottle-necks of these cells have not yet been identified (Yu et al. (2012)). Model-based analysis will help in understanding the governing processes inside the cells and elucidate limitations and constraints on material properties, design and operation of these cells (Verma and Basu (2007)). Recently, the first papers on alkaline fuel cell modeling appeared: the transient behaviour (Huo et al. (2012)) as well as water transport (Deng et al. (2013)) has been analysed on the anode; the investigations are limited to one electrode and as such omit to study the strong interaction and requirements of processes on cell level.

The battery field is dominated by Li ion batteries, as they presently show the best available practical energy densities, high power and high cycling stability. Alkaline Zn air batteries have a 3.5 x higher theoretical energy density than Li ion batteries, use non-flammable electrolyte in contrast to the organic electrolyte of Li ion batteries, and Zn is significantly cheaper and better available than active Li ion battery materials such as Co-oxides. Such cells have been already commercialised as primary battery for applications in the micro-Watt range, and recent research focusses to allow for recharging of Zn air batteries also, i.e. to establish reversible electrochemical and chemical reactions, so that they would be attractive also for larger applications, such as in the automotive or stationary energy field (Takeshita et al. (2013)). The studies are still in the fundamental research stage. Also here, except for one study (Deiss et al. (2002)), research is nearly exclusively experimental and conducted by material specialists and chemists (Li et al. (2013)), and there is a lack of understanding the processes and bottle-necks and physical limitations in such cells.

In summary, alkaline electrochemical cells are still at the fundamental research stage, and model-based analysis would significantly help in identifying bottle necks at an early stage to focus our limited resources on these.

Alkaline cells have in common that oxygen is reduced with water at the positive electrode to hydroxide ions which are then transported through the electrolyte to the negative electrode. Little to nothing is known about the transport and distribution of water in these cells and water availability at the air electrode. However, water at the air electrode is essential to maintain a stable electroactive area and, even more important, to allow for any reaction to occur:

$$O_2 + 2H_2O + 4e^- \longrightarrow 4OH^- \qquad (1)$$

Previous studies have elucidated that the feasibility for stabilisation of the water level in electrochemical systems open to the environment may significantly depend on environmental conditions (Zenith et al. (2010)). This contribution presents a model-based methodology for a principle analysis of water availability in alkaline cells and possible effects of external conditions. The methodology is applied on alkaline direct methanol fuel cell and on Zn air battery. Whereas details of the models including model equations and their results are presented elsewhere, e.g. by Schröder and Krewer (2014) for the Zn air battery, this contribution focuses on the underlying modeling methodology and its application.

2. Methodology

Roffel and Betlem (2006) present a general methodology on how to approach modeling and simulation to solve problems in physical reality. After the first step of system analysis, which contains problem definition and context and function analysis, a behavioral model is designed in the second step. Finally, the model is specified and analysed. We adopt this methodology to deduce and analyse our models.

2.1. System analysis

Scope of the modeling activity is to identify those processes which have an essential impact on water availability at the air electrode and to elucidate the limitations and requirements on environmental conditions and material or geometry properties to allow for an acceptable operating range.

The alkaline systems to study are still at such a fundamental research stage that no optimal system parameters such as geometry, materials and operating conditions have been fixed yet. As such, the model should contain as few details on them as possible and should be as general as possible. This also leads to the decision for a 0-dimensional, isotherm and lumped model approach. Only the basic processes essential for operation and containing a link to water availability are implemented: accumulation of species or charge, net (electro-)chemical reactions, basic species transport mechanisms, and selected algebraic equations such as gas/liquid equilibria. Dynamic state variables are reduced to an absolute necessary minimum and limited to those relevant for impact of water. As such, for each electrode only dynamic total and species mass balances and - if necessary - charge balances are taken into consideration.

Finally, extreme values for possible external variables which may impact water availability are determined. These can be either considered as disturbances or inputs and are

- composition of environmental air
- current and (where applicable) minimum required battery cycle number

2.2. Model design

The model consists of state equations and additional algebraic equations. These are formulated based on key variables and selected physico-chemical phenomena:

- Total and species mass balances for chemical components α at each electrode. This corresponds to a CSTR approach and results in first order ordinary differential equations:
$$V_{electrode}\frac{dc_\alpha}{dt} = \dot{n}_{\alpha,in} - \dot{n}_{\alpha,out} + \sigma_{\alpha,reaction} \quad (2)$$
- Mass transport mechanisms considered for $\dot{n}$:
  - convection, e.g. $\dot{n} = c_{\alpha,i}F_i$ (3)
  - diffusion, using diffusion coefficient D, e.g. $\dot{n} = A\frac{D}{\delta}(c_{\alpha,1} - c_{\alpha,2})$ (4)
  - migration, using the transference number t_α, e.g. $\dot{n} = \frac{I}{z_\alpha \mathrm{F}}t_\alpha$ (5)
  - electroosmotic drag of water, using the drag coefficient k, e.g. $\dot{n} = k\frac{I}{\mathrm{F}}$ (6)
- Net (electro-)chemical equations acting as sinks or sources, $\sigma_{\alpha,reaction}$, in the balances. For given constant cell current I, they are determined by Faradays law
$$\sigma_{\alpha,reaction} = \frac{I}{z_\alpha \mathrm{F}} \quad (7)$$
- Gas liquid and liquid solid phase equilibria based on solubility and Raoults or Henrys law to account for phase changes of species
- Electroneutrality and, if impact of water on voltage is wanted, current voltage curve and overpotential-dependent reaction and transport kinetics.

Known material parameters, such as density and Henry constants, are fixed. For the yet not optimised or unknown parameters, e.g. geometry or transport parameters through new material such as alkaline membranes, typical values for such electrochemical cells are selected based on literature or own experimental experience, and may be varied later during model analysis.

2.3. Model analysis

In this step, the general model resulting from model design is split up into several scenario-specific submodels as follows:

Minimal reference model: A minimal core or reference model is developed which contains only this source of water, where water is usually expected to come from. For the ADMFC, all reactants, i.e. also water, are expected to be convectively fed from outside. For an aqueous electrolyte based battery, water is part of the electrolyte and expected to come from there. Simulation is done by implementing and solving the set of equations in Matlab; as the set consists of only few equations, run time was usually in the millisecond to second range.

Analysis of this scenario yields the limitations and effect of this kind of water supply on availability of water at the air electrode. At this point also the question is answered, whether this kind of water supply method is sufficient or problematic.

Variants of reference model: Subsequently, various submodels representing more complex and realistic scenarios are formulated by selectively adding additional transport mechanisms or external disturbances. For the ADMFC, the additional transport mechanisms diffusion and electroosmotic drag, as well as water evaporation and water production on the air electrode by oxidation of diffused methanol are added. For the Zn air battery, water transport to or from the environmental air and effect of air composition, including the effect of reaction of environmental carbon dioxide with the electrolyte, are added.

The resulting scenarios for each cell are simulated with Matlab, and analysed and compared with respect to effect on water level in the air electrode and limitations of water level stabilisation. This allows to elucidate the dominating processes for water level stabilisation. At this point also minimum requirements on environmental conditions and material parameters are identified which guarantee reliable operation for a minimum required current or cycle number. Finally, considering all scenarios, a conclusion is drawn on the quality and quantity of conditions and processes needed to guarantee stable, acceptable performance of these cells. The information can then be used by experimental groups to adjust materials, geometry or operating conditions.

3. Results

3.1. Alkaline Direct Methanol Fuel Cell

Minimal reference model: This minimal reference model assumes that the water required for the reaction at cathode needs to be supplied solely by cathodic inlet. Therefore, either water content or the flow rate of inlet gas needs to be adjusted. The latter is defined via the air excess ratio λ^{C} while the water content is a function of temperature and relative humidity, RH. Simulation results for this minimal model of an ADMFC are displayed in Figure 1(a). Even in ideal conditions that assume water saturated inlet gas, $RH^{C,in} = 100$ %, as well as the possibility of total water consumption at cathode, $RH^{C} = 0$ %, either high inlet temperatures or high air excess ratios are required to feed sufficient water to the cathode. If conditions are not ideal, e.g. if the gas cannot be totally dehumidified and $RH^{C} = 10$ %, even higher excess ratios are required. Thus, cathodic inlet gas needs to be humidified at high temperatures or other processes need to be used for water supply.

Variants of reference model: The reference model is modified by including additional processes that consume or produce water. In the here presented scenario, water diffusion to the cathode is supposed to be equal to cathodic water consumption. This allows to determine the minimum required water diffusion coefficient through the membrane separating anode and cathode, which is displayed in Figure 1(b). The model is analysed for four variants: reference conditions that only consider water diffusion, and three other variants that additionally consider either water drag, methanol cross-over or water evaporation. Diffusion coefficients larger than the simulated ones enable sufficient water supply to the cathode. The effect of water drag is considerable while the influence of cross-over is insignificant and that of evaporation small but noticeable. In all variants, diffusion coefficient increases with current density. Assuming that future ADMFC need to reach typical current densities of other fuel cells of around 500 mA/cm^2, this yields the requirement for membranes to have a diffusion coefficient of above $1.5 \cdot 10^{-6}$ cm^2/s.

3.2. Secondary Zinc Air Battery

Minimal reference model: An illustrative simulation result for the minimal reference model of a secondary zinc air battery is shown with Figure 2. It can be observed that the water level changes periodically at each electrode during secondary zinc air battery cycling. This is explained by the volume change of metal particles at the zinc electrode during cycling, which causes a convective flow from or to the air electrode. Since this is an ideal model description with no water gain or loss accounted for, identical values after each cycle are reached. The observed 5 % change in water level at the air electrode might have a slight influence on battery

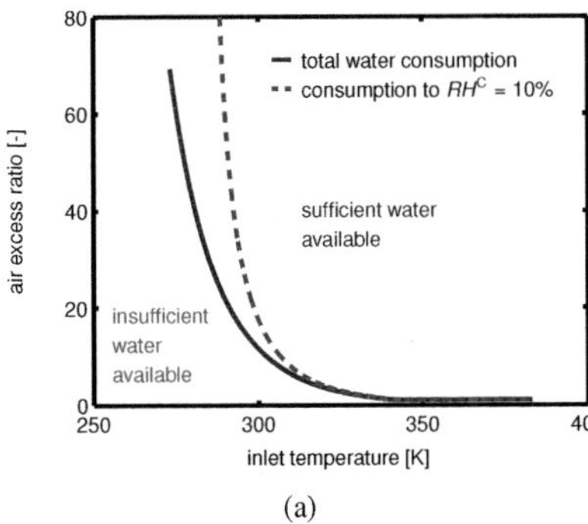

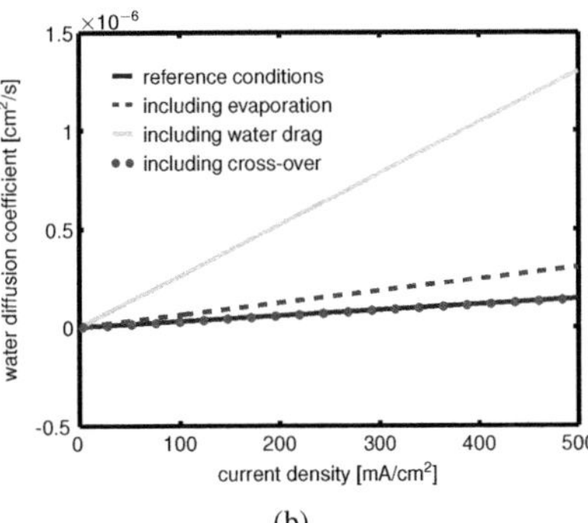

Figure 1: (a) Results of the minimal reference model showing the required air excess ratio as a function of cathodic inlet temperature to provide sufficient water by cathodic inlet for operation of an ADMFC. (b) Results of variants of the reference model showing the required diffusion coefficient to provide sufficient water by diffusion through the membrane of an ADMFC for different variants that consider or neglect water drag, methanol cross-over and evaporation.

performance; however, the change in water level strongly depends on geometry parameters, such as electrode thicknesses and porosity, and on operating conditions, such as current or depth of discharge.

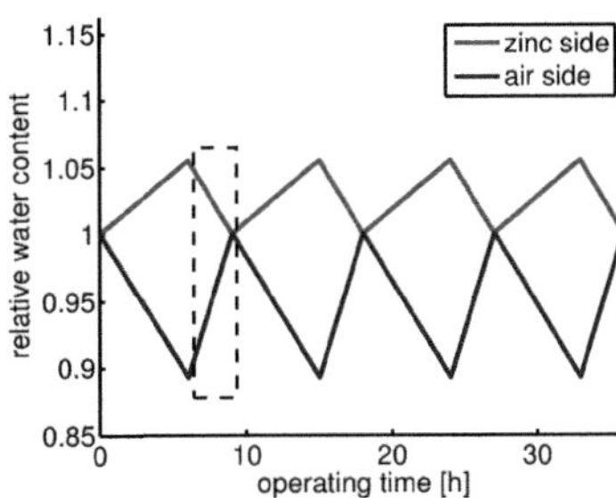

Figure 2: Simulation result for minimal reference model showing the relative water content in a secondary zinc air battery; 6 h charge and 3 h discharge at $T_{\mathrm{bat}} = 298$ K, initials: 0.05 g Zn, 0.5 g ZnO, 6 M KOH liquid electrolyte.

Variants of reference model: Two variations of the reference model are discussed in the following: the relative humidity scenario, accounting for water loss or gain due to a gradient in RH between cell and environment, and the combined relative humidity and carbonation scenario with includes in addition carbonation of the alkaline electrolyte via environmental CO_2. Selected results for the relative humidity scenario are shown with Figure 3 (a). For these, simulations of constant current cycles were conducted until the water content in the air electrode was lower than 0.5 or higher than 1.5. The presented plot can be interpreted as operation envelope, where a maximally achievable cycle number is determined by the environmental RH value. RH operation regions for electrode drying out and electrode flooding are denoted. For extreme RH values, only low cycle numbers are achievable, suggesting that operation at such conditions may need air conditioning. Figure 3 (b) depicts the evaluation of the combined relative humidity and carbonation scenario. There, carbonation of the alkaline electrolyte is caused by environmental CO_2 with concentrations of 150, 350 and 1,000 ppm. It can be observed that carbonation decreases the feasible operation range significantly. Finally, it is concluded that effects of environmental conditions may need to be mitigated to allow for reliable battery operation.

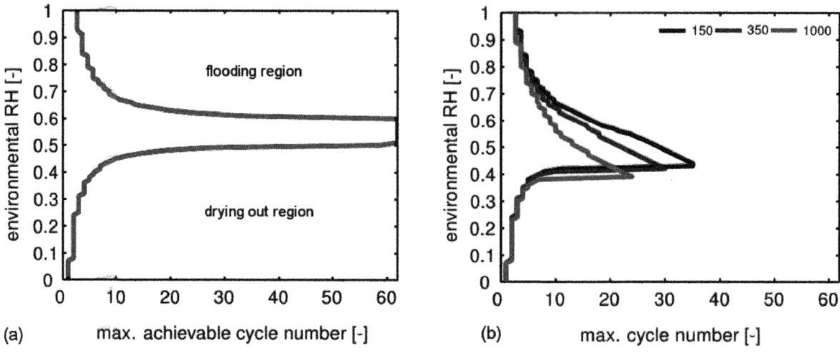

Figure 3: (a) Operation envelope for relative humidity (RH) influence for a secondary zinc air battery. (b) Operation envelope for relative humidity influence and carbon dioxide ppm concentration.

4. Conclusions

This contribution presented a model-based analysis approach to elucidate electrochemical cells that are still in the fundamental research state and for which little is known yet on optimal conditions, materials and geometry. The methodology contains the development of minimal reference models and selected variants. It has been applied to the alkaline direct methanol fuel cell and the secondary zinc air battery to elucidate the requirements for sufficient water supply to the cathode. For alkaline direct methanol fuel cell, the need to supply water by water diffusion through the membrane was elucidated and a minimum diffusion coefficient determined. For secondary zinc air battery, a fluctuating water level in the electrodes was identified. The water level may be destabilised by external influences such as RH and CO_2, which suggests that technical measures may be necessary to mitigate external disturbances. In conclusion, the presented approach is flexibly applicable to various electrochemical and other systems and aids already in the first steps of process development.

References

A. Verma, S. Basu, 2007. Experimental evaluation and mathematical modeling of a direct alkaline fuel cell. J. Power Sources 168, 200–210.

B. Roffel, B. Betlem, 2006. Process Dynamics and Control: Modeling for Control and Prediction. John Wiley and Sons, Chichester, England.

D. Schröder, U. Krewer, 2014. Model-based quantification of air composition impact on secondary zinc air batteries. Electrochimica Acta 117, 541–553.

E. Deiss, F. Holzer, O. Haas, 2002. Modeling of an electrically rechargeable alkaline zn-air battery. Electrochimica Acta 47, 3995–4010.

E. H. Yu, X. Wang, U. Krewer, L. Li, K. Scott, 2012. Direct oxidation alkaline fuel cells: from materials to systems. Energy Environ. Sci. 5, 5668.

F. Zenith, C. Weinzierl, U. Krewer, Aug. 2010. Model-based analysis of the feasibility envelope for autonomous operation of a portable direct methanol fuel-cell system. Chemical Engineering Science 65 (15), 4411–4419.

H. Deng, S. Huo, Y. Chang, Y. Zhou, K. Jiao, 2013. Transient analysis of alkaline anion exchange membrane fuel cell anode. International Journal of Hydrogen Energy 38 (15), 6509 – 6525.

S. Huo, H. Deng, Y. Chang, K. Jiao, 2012. Water management in alkaline anion exchange membrane fuel cell anode. International Journal of Hydrogen Energy 37 (23), 18389 – 18402.

Y. Li, M. Gong, Y. Liang, J. Feng, J.-E. Kim, H. Wang, H. Dai, 2013. Advanced zinc-air batteries based on high-performance hybrid electrocatalysts. Nature communications 4, 1805.

Y. Takeshita, S. Fujimoto, M. Sudoh, 2013. Design of Rechargeable Air Diffusion Cathode for Metal-Air Battery Using Alkaline Solution. ECS Transactions 50 (19), 3–12.

Jiří Jaromír Klemeš, Petar Sabev Varbanov and Peng Yen Liew (Editors)
Proceedings of the 24th European Symposium on Computer Aided Process Engineering – ESCAPE 24
June 15-18, 2014, Budapest, Hungary.

Complementary Modelling of CO_2 Capture by Reactive Absorption

Murat Yazgi[a], Alexander Olenberg[a], Eugeny Y. Kenig[a,b]*

[a]*University of Paderborn, Faculty of Mechanical Engineering, Chair of Fluid Process Engineering, Pohlweg 55, D-33098 Paderborn, Germany*
[b]*Gubkin Russian State University of Oil and Gas, Moscow, Russian Federation*
eugeny.kenig@upb.de

Abstract

Modelling of gas-liquid separation processes usually requires knowledge on fluid dynamic and mass transfer parameters, such as effective interfacial area and mass transfer coefficients. As a rule, these parameters cannot be determined without extensive experimental work. An alternative modelling approach for separation columns filled with structured packings is based on hydrodynamic analogies (HA) between real complex and simplified model flow. This way leads to a significant reduction of required experimentally determined parameters. Above all, the data on mass transfer coefficients are not necessary. Model parameters which cannot be directly determined within the HA approach can be estimated using a complementary modelling method. In this work, the complementary modelling approach is applied to the reactive absorption of carbon dioxide into aqueous solutions of sodium hydroxide and monoethanolamine. Two different types of structured packings are investigated. For the model validation, both our own experimental results and data from the literature are used.

Keywords: CFD, complementary modelling, fluid dynamics, reactive absorption, structured packing

1. Introduction

Carbon dioxide (CO_2) is a major greenhouse gas responsible for global warming, and hence, significant effort is being put into the development of technologies for its capture from flue gas streams. In many cases, the removal of CO_2 from gas mixtures is realised by absorption into a liquid solvent. The separation is usually performed in absorption columns filled with structured packings and operated countercurrently.

Adequate description of reactive absorption usually requires rigorous modelling methods. The widely used rate-based approach (RBA) depends on mass transfer coefficients that have to be determined in extensive experimental studies. An alternative modelling approach for separation columns filled with structured packings is based on hydrodynamic analogies (HA) between complex process hydrodynamics and combinations of geometrically simpler flow patterns. Once the observed complex flow is represented by a combination of simplified flow patterns, the partial differential equations governing momentum, energy and mass conservation are applied to describe flow and transport phenomena in an entire separation unit. Contrary to the RBA, separation columns can be described without using mass transfer coefficients. The HA approach has been validated for different distillation processes (Shilkin et al., 2006) as well as for a catalytic distillation process (Zhang et al., 2013). Furthermore, this method has also been applied toa sulphur dioxide absorption system (Brinkmann et al., 2009) and to reactive stripping (Brinkmann et al., 2010).

It is well known that reaction rates in different reactive absorption systems may variate significantly. Therefore, any general modelling of the process kinetics appears difficult. Rather, an individual adjustment is required. For this reason, the present work is aimed at extending the HA approach to the CO_2 reactive absorption. As representative case studies, absorption by sodium hydroxide (NaOH) and by monoethanolamine (MEA) solutions was selected. Depending on the operating conditions, the HA approach requires an additional parameter, namely the gas-phase turbulent viscosity. Since this parameter cannot be determined within the HA approach, complementary modelling is used, while the gas-phase turbulent viscosity is determined by computational fluid dynamics (CFD) and delivered to the HA model.

2. Modelling

The main features of the HA model applied in this work were suggested by Shilkin and Kenig (2005). The HA approach is based on a physical model of the structured packing, in which the latter is represented as a bundle of parallel inclined channels (see Figure 1). The specific characteristics of the physical model, e.g. channel diameter, are determined from the corrugation geometry and the effective interfacial area of the packing. Using a combination of simplified flow patterns (e.g. films) in these channels, partial differential equations for conservation of momentum and mass can be applied to govern the transport phenomena in an entire separation unit.

The gas flow behaviour depends on the operating conditions and varies from laminar to fully developed turbulent flow. The liquid flows counter-currently to the gas flow in form of laminar films over the inner surface of the channels. Turbulence can occur in the gas phase depending on the structured packing type and the gas and liquid loads. This phenomenon is largely accounted for by the gas-phase turbulent viscosity entering the equations for conservation of momentum and mass. Since the turbulent viscosity cannot be determined within the HA approach, a complementary modelling method has to be applied.

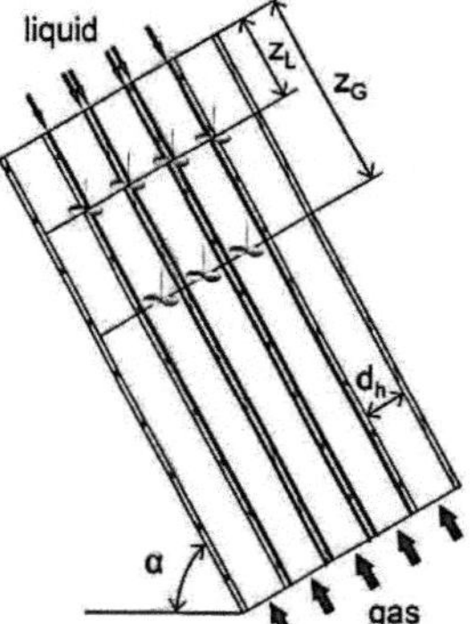

Figure 1. Physical model of structured packing (Shilkin et al., 2006).

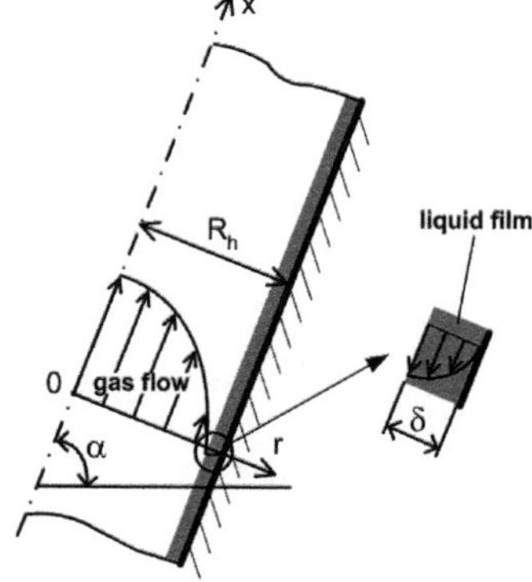

Figure 2. Schematic of the two-phase countercurrent flow in a channel (Shilkin et al., 2006).

CFD simulations of a representative small periodic packing element are carried out using the commercial software STAR CCM+ and, based on the simulation results, the required parameter is estimated. Since turbulence in structured packings cannot be measured directly, the CFD model is validated with experimental pressure drop data of the system air/water.

2.1. Mathematical model

The liquid flow is described by the system of Navier-Stokes equations in the film-flow approximation (Shilkin et al., 2006):

$$\frac{1}{r}\frac{\partial}{\partial r}\left(r\mu_{\mathrm{L}}\frac{\partial u_{\mathrm{L}}(r)}{\partial r}\right) - \frac{\partial P_{\mathrm{L}}}{\partial x} + \rho_L g \sin\alpha = 0, \quad \frac{\partial P_{\mathrm{L}}}{\partial r} = 0. \tag{1}$$

For the description of the gas phase, the Boussinesq approximation is adopted:

$$\frac{1}{r}\frac{\partial}{\partial r}\left(r\tilde{\mu}_G\frac{\partial u_{\mathrm{G}}(r)}{\partial r}\right) - \frac{\partial P_{\mathrm{G}}}{\partial x} + \rho_G g \sin\alpha = 0, \quad \tilde{\mu}_G = \mu_{G,\mathrm{lam}} + \mu_{G,\mathrm{turb}}, \quad \frac{\partial P_{\mathrm{G}}}{\partial r} = 0. \tag{2}$$

Boundary conditions exist at the solid surface (no-slip condition), channel symmetry axis (symmetry condition) and gas-liquid interface (coupled velocity and normal shear stresses). Eqs.(1)-(2) and the boundary conditions are supplemented by the following integral flow definitions:

$$q_{\mathrm{L}} = -2\pi\int_{R_{\mathrm{H}}-\delta}^{R_{\mathrm{H}}} u_{\mathrm{L}}(r) r dr, \qquad q_{\mathrm{G}} = 2\pi\int_{0}^{R_{\mathrm{H}}-\delta} u_{\mathrm{G}}(r) r dr. \tag{3}$$

The solution yields velocity profiles in both phases $u(r)$ together with the values of liquid film thickness $\delta(x)$ along the channel height which are used for the description of mass transfer.

2.2. Gas-phase turbulence

At higher gas loads, intensive turbulence occurs in the gas phase. This effect is considered in the HAmodel by the gas-phase turbulent viscosity $\mu_{G,turb}$, which cannot be determined within the HA-model,so that additional modelling is necessary (Shilkin et al., 2006). Therefore, an empirical correlation (zero-order equation) according to Gersten and Herwig (1992) is used, which is extended by a geometry parameter B to account for different corrugation geometries:

$$\mu_{G,\mathrm{turb}}(r) = B\left(\frac{\kappa}{6}\rho_G u_T (R_h - \delta)\left[1 - \left(\frac{r}{R_h - \delta}\right)^2\right]\left[1 + 2\cdot\left(\frac{r}{R_h - \delta}\right)^2\right]\right). \tag{4}$$

The geometry parameter B is estimated by keeping equal integral mean viscosities $\bar{\mu}_{G,\mathrm{turb}}$ in the zero-order equation and in the periodical packing element:

$$\bar{\mu}_{G,\mathrm{turb}} = \frac{1}{V_{\mathrm{pac}}}\iiint_{V_{\mathrm{pac}}} \hat{\mu}_{G,turb}(x,y,z) dxdydz = \frac{1}{\pi(R_h-\delta)^2}\int_0^{R_h-\delta} \mu_{G,\mathrm{turb}}(r) 2\pi r dr. \tag{5}$$

Here $\hat{\mu}_{G,\mathrm{turb}}(x,y,z)$ represents actual eddy viscosity in the packing.

2.3. CFD simulations

The required parameter for the proper description of the gas-phase turbulence in the HA model was estimated using CFD analysis of single-phase gas flow through a structured packing. Depending on the cutting plane of two packing layers, two different kinds of periodical element are possible (Said et al., 2011). The periodical element shown in Figure 3b has the advantagethat the choice of the boundary conditions can be done with less effort. Therefore, it is used as the geometry to be simulated.

The single-phase gas flow was considered as steady-state, incompressible and isotherm. For the description of the turbulence, the realisable k-ε turbulence model was used, whereby a validation with published experimental data for dry pressure drop by Olujić (1999) could be achieved. The geometry was discretised with the trimmer model of STAR CCM+. For an accurate resolution, especially in regions of high flow gradients (e.g. close to walls), prismatic mesh elements were chosen. To obtain grid independent results, approximately 500 thousand trimmer and prismatic elements were used. As a boundary condition for the wall, the standard no-slip condition was imposed. The inlet and outlet domains are interconnected via periodic boundary conditions. Pressure drop was determined by specifying the F-factor (gas capacity factor). The side faces of the simulated geometry were also linked via periodic boundary conditions. Finally, the evaluation of the geometry parameter B with Eq.(4) using least squares method gave $B = 4.72$ for the packing Mellapak 250.Y (corrugation angle of 45 degrees) and $B = 3.11$ for the packing Mellapak 250.X (corrugation angle of 60 degrees). Figure 4 shows the influence of geometry parameter B on the gas-phase velocity. With increasing B,the gas-phase velocity profile becomes flatter and the film thickness increases marginally. The velocity profiles directly affect the concentration profiles along the column height.

2.4. Mass transfer

Mass transfer in each phase in a system comprising n components is described by the following transport equations:

$$u(r)\frac{\partial C_i}{\partial x}=\frac{1}{r}\frac{\partial}{\partial r}\left(r\tilde{D}_i\frac{\partial C_i}{\partial r}\right)+R_i(\vec{C}),\ \tilde{D}_i=D_{i,\mathrm{lam}}+D_{i,\mathrm{turb}},D_{i,\mathrm{turb}}=\frac{\mu_{\mathrm{turb}}}{\rho \mathrm{Sc}_{i,\mathrm{turb}}},i=1...n \tag{6}$$

Boundary conditions are defined at the entrance, channel wall, symmetry axis and at the phase interface (thermodynamic equilibrium and mass flux continuity). Numerical solution of the system of equations using the Tri-Diagonal Matrix Algorithm (Patankar,

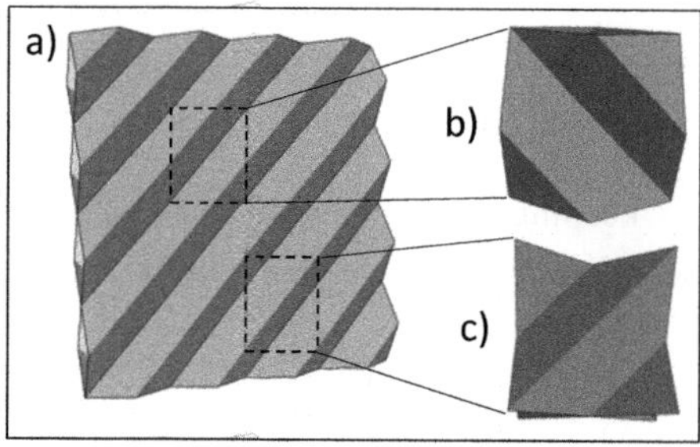

Figure 3. Two packing layers of Mellapak 250.Y (a); different kinds of periodical packing element (Said et al., 2011) (b-c).

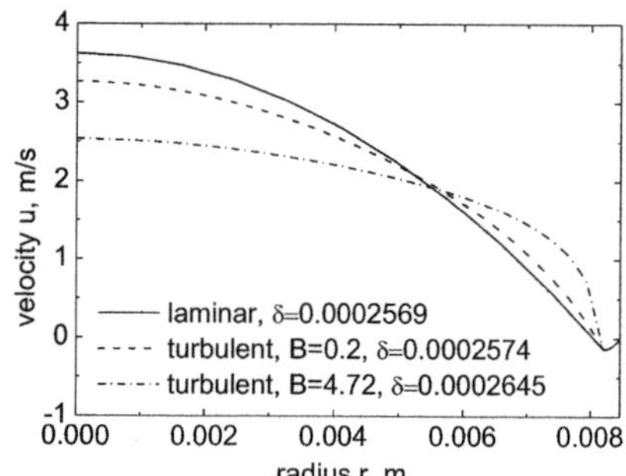

Figure 4. Influence of geometry parameter B on gas-phase velocity.

1980) yields concentration fields in both phases. These values are further used to obtain the average concentration profiles along the packing.

3. Simulation results

The validation of the HA model for the system CO_2/MEA is based on the reference experiment 1 of Notz et al. (2012). They performed experiments in a pilot plant with an inner diameter of 0.125 m filled with 4.2 m height Mellapak 250.Y. For the reference experiment 1, the F-factor was 1.58 $Pa^{0.5}$ and the liquid load was 15.54 $m^3/(m^2h)$ at the column bottom. The CO_2 loading in the liquid phase at the column top was 0.306 mol CO_2 / mol MEA. Full concentration profiles were measured for the liquid phase only.

Our own CO_2/NaOH absorption experiments were performed with a 0.3 meter inner diameter column, equipped with 2.3 m height Mellapak 250.X. The F-factor was 1 $Pa^{0.5}$ and the liquid load was 20 $m^3/(m^2h)$. The CO_2 in the air was at a concentration of 1000 ppm while the NaOH concentration in the solution was 1 $kmol/m^3$.In this case, gas-phase concentration profiles were determined experimentally.

The simulated CO_2massresp.mol concentration profiles and corresponding experimental valuesalong the column height, starting at the bottom, are shown for the CO_2/MEA system in Figure 5 and for the CO_2/NaOH system in Figure 6. The simulated concentration profiles are in good agreement with experimental data.

4. Conclusions

Accurate description of reactive absorption processes in columns filled with structured packings requires the use of rigorous modelling methods.The traditional models based on the film theory require experimentally determined parameters.An alternative modelling approach based on the application of hydrodynamic analogies does not need mass transfer coefficients. At higher gas loads, the additionally required parameter for the HA model, namely gas-phase turbulence viscosity, is determined by using CFD.

The described complementary modelling concept is applied to the reactive absorption of CO_2. Two different aqueous solutions, namely NaOH and MEA, and two different types

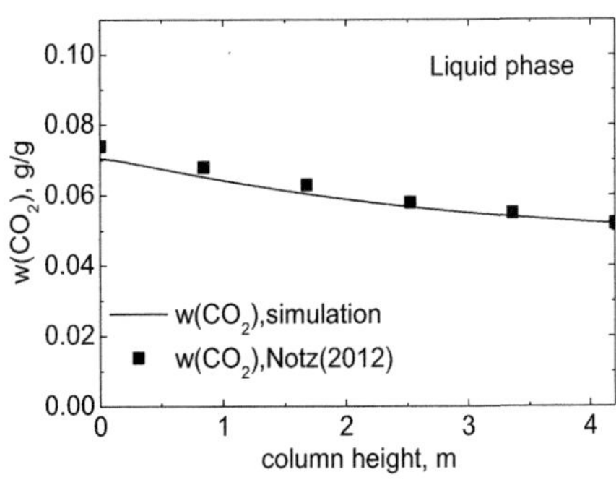

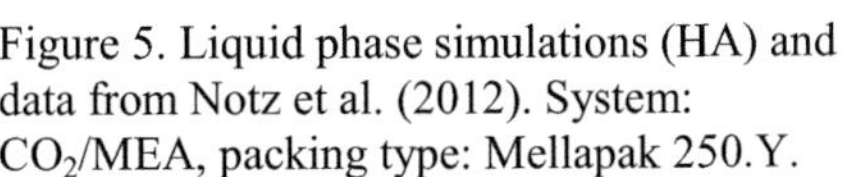

Figure 5. Liquid phase simulations (HA) and data from Notz et al. (2012). System: CO_2/MEA, packing type: Mellapak 250.Y.

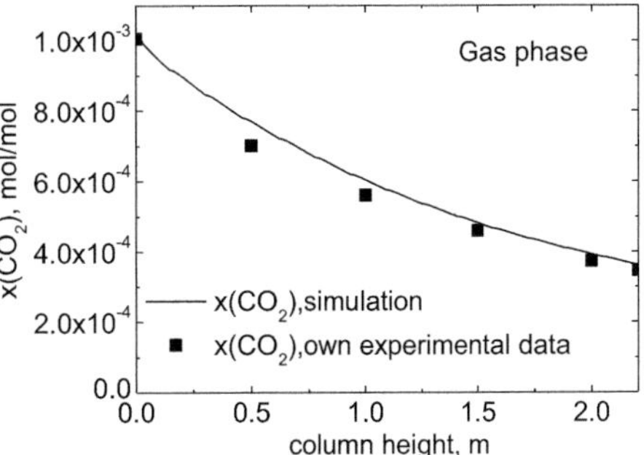

Figure 6. Gas phase simulations (HA) and our own experimental data. System: CO_2/NaOH, packing type: Mellapak 250.X.

of structured packings, namely Mellapak 250.X and Mellapak 250.Y, are investigated. The model validation is performed both with our own experimental results and with experimental data from the literature, anda good agreement is found. For the validation, qualitatively more exact column (concentration) profiles are used. Thus, for the first time,the complementary modelling approach is successfully applied to the description of CO_2 absorption systems.

Acknowledgements

The financial support of the European Commission in the context of the 7th Framework Programme of the European Union (Project CAPSOL, FP7-ENERGY-2011-282789) is greatly acknowledged.

Nomenclature

C	molar concentration of a component, mol m^{-3}
D	diffusivity, $m^2\ s^{-1}$
d_h	channel hydraulic diameter, m
g	gravity, m s^{-2}
P	pressure, Pa
q	volumetric flow rate, m^3 s
R_h	channel hydraulic radius, m
r	radial coordinate, m
Sc	Schmidt number
u	local velocity, m s^{-1}
u_T	shear velocity, m s^{-1}
x	axial coordinate, m
z	length of an undisturbed fluid flow, m

Greek letters

α	gravity flow angle
δ	film thickness, m
κ	von Karman constant
μ	dynamic viscosity, Pa s
ρ	density, kg m^{-3}

Subscripts

G	gas phase
i	component i
L	liquid phase
lam	laminar
turb	turbulent

References

U. Brinkmann, E.Y. Kenig, R. Thiele, M. Haas, 2009, Modelling and simulation of a packed sulphur dioxide absorption unit using the hydrodynamic analogy approach, Chem. Eng. Trans., 18, 195-200.

U. Brinkmann, T.J. Schildhauer, E.Y. Kenig, 2010, Hydrodynamic analogy approach for modelling of reactive stripping with structured catalyst supports, Chem. Eng. Sci., 65, 298-303.

K. Gersten, H. Herwig, 1992, Fluid Mechanics, Vieweg, Wiesbaden, Germany(in German).

Ž. Olujić, 1999, Effect of column diameter on pressure drop of a corrugtaed sheet structured packing, Trans. Inst. Chem. Eng., 77, 505-510.

R. Notz, H.P. Mangalapally, H. Hasse, 2012, Post combustion CO_2 capture by reactive absorption: Pilot plant describtion and results of systematic studies with MEA, Int. J. Greenhouse Gas Control, 6, 84-112.

S.V. Patankar, 1980, Numerical Heat Transfer and Fluid Flow, Hemisphere Publ. Corp., McGraw-Hill, New-York, USA.

W. Said, M. Nemer, D. Clodic, 2011, Modeling of dry pressure drop for fully developed gas flow in structured packing using CFD simulations, Chem. Eng. Sci., 66, 2107-2117.

A. Shilkin, E.Y. Kenig, 2005, A new approach to fluid separation modelling in the columns equipped with structured packings, Chem. Eng. J., 110, 87-100.

A. Shilkin, E.Y. Kenig, Ž. Olujić, 2006, A hydrodynamic-analogy-based model for efficiency of structured packing distillation columns, AIChE Journal, 52, 3055-3066.

H. Zhang, X. Li, X. Gao, H. Li, 2013, A method for modeling a catalytic distillation process based on seepage catalytic packing internal, Chem. Eng. Sci., 101, 699-711.

Jiří Jaromír Klemeš, Petar Sabev Varbanov and Peng Yen Liew (Editors)
Proceedings of the 24th European Symposium on Computer Aided Process Engineering – ESCAPE 24
June 15-18, 2014, Budapest, Hungary.

Multi-objective Optimization of a Rectisol® Process

Manuele Gatti [a,*], Emanuele Martelli [a], François Maréchal [b], Stefano Consonni [a]

[a] *Politecnico di Milano, Dipartimento di Energia, Via Lambruschini 4, Milano, Italy*
[b] *Industrial Process Energy Systems Engineering (IPESE), Ecole Polytechnique Fédérale de Lausanne, 1015, Lausanne, Switzerland*
manuele.gatti@polimi.it

Abstract

This work focuses on the design, simulation and optimization of a Rectisol®-based process tailored for the selective removal of H_2S and CO_2 from gasification derived synthesis gas. Such task is quite challenging due to the need of addressing simultaneously the process design, energy integration and utility design. The paper, starting from a Rectisol® configuration recently proposed by the authors, describes the models and the solution strategy used to carry out the multi-objective optimization with respect to exergy consumption, CO_2 capture level and capital cost.

Keywords: Rectisol, CO_2 Capture, Numerical Optimization, PGS-COM, Pareto frontier

1. Introduction

Coal to Liquids (CTL) as well as Integrated Gasification Combined Cycle (IGCC) plants take advantage from the conversion of a cheap, fossil fuel like coal into a clean synthetic gas, mainly composed of hydrogen, carbon monoxide, carbon dioxide and other minor species, either to produce Liquid Fuels or Electricity as output. In such plants, sulfur-containing compounds are among the most critical contaminants, and they should be separated from the raw syngas not only to cope with emissions regulations but, in the specific case of CTL, also to avoid any potential detrimental impact on the catalyst of the downstream chemical synthesis process. Moreover, in a near-future characterized by restrictions on CO_2 emissions, Carbon Capture and Storage (CCS) becomes a standard feature of acid gas removal processes.

As reported by Koss (2006), the Rectisol® process (Weiss, 1988), licensed by Linde and Lurgi-Air Liquide companies, represents the Acid Gas Removal (AGR) benchmark for syngas purification with more than 85 units currently operating worldwide. Even though there is a significant industrial know-how about the Rectisol® process, very few data and documents are available in literature. Indeed, to the best of our knowledge, just Sun and Smith (2012; 2013) published a detailed simulation model of the process. In any case, all the available studies are based on a given set of operating conditions rather than on an optimized design. Moreover, there are no studies dealing with the optimal design of the Rectisol® process targeted for CCS application.

The goals of this study are: (i) develop and efficiently solve a detailed model of a Rectisol®-like absorption process suitable to be used as AGR in a CTL and IGCC plant; (ii) identify and include a strategy to simultaneously perform the process heat integration and the selection and design of the utilities; (iii) formulate and solve the multi-objective optimization problem with respect to the three conflicting objectives, maximum CO_2 capture level, minimum exergy consumption, and minimum capital cost.

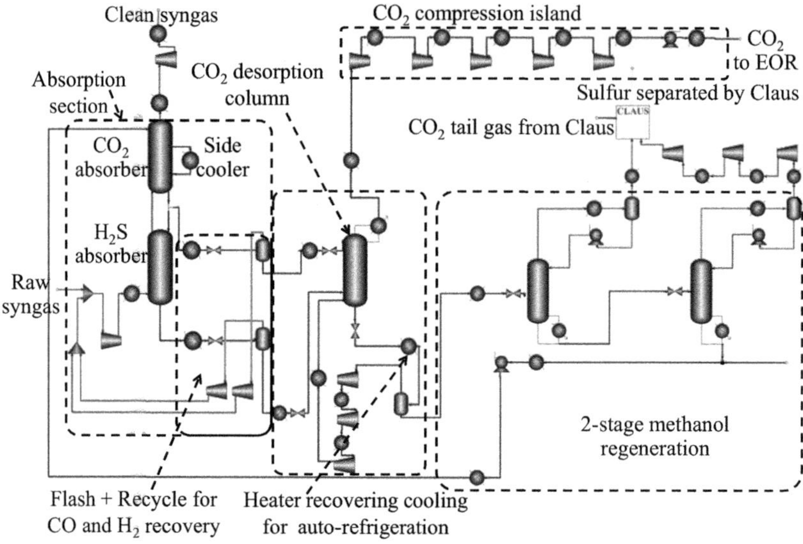

Figure 1. Process Flow Diagram of the Rectisol®-based AGR process to be optimized.

2. Rectisol® process configuration

Rectisol® is a quite flexible process which can be tailored to clean the raw syngas in order to meet the requirements of various type of downstream processes. Depending on the syngas route envisaged, and on the end-use of the side-product streams, namely CO_2 and H_2S concentrated flows, the process layout and the operating conditions may differ significantly (Weiss, 1988). In this paper we focus on the Rectisol® scheme recently proposed by Gatti et al. (2013), configured for the deep purification of a CTL syngas. The process, whose flowsheet is reported in Figure 1, is designed for producing the following outputs, whose specifications are reported in Table 1, together with the feedstock and input stream properties: a purified syngas stream suitable for Co-based Fischer-Tropsch synthesis; a CO_2-rich dense phase stream suitable for Enhanced Oil Recovery (EOR); an H_2S-rich stream suitable for a Claus process.

This novel Rectisol®-based version differs from Linde's patented Rectisol® (Weiss, 1988) for the following features: (i) the CO_2 desorption section instead of including a flash regeneration plus a rectifying column consists of a single desorption column exploiting CO_2 flashing, H_2S reabsorption and auto-refrigeration (in the sense that a significant fraction of the cooling duty is recovered within the process by flashing the bottom liquid stream of the CO_2desorber); (ii) the methanol regeneration section is split in two stages in order to minimize the exergy consumption of the reboiler.

3. Optimization framework

It's worth emphasizing that Gatti et al. (2013) developed the above-mentioned novel process configuration by applying pinch analysis rules and heuristic design criteria (based on simple rules of thumbs). In this paper the authors present a further improvement of such novel process achieved by the application of systematic heat integration tools and numerical optimization algorithms.

Table 1. Boundary conditions, assumptions and specifications of the process.

Inlet Stream Properties		Outlet H_2S rich stream to Claus Conditions	
Raw dried partly shifted syngas produced by GE gasifier fed with Illinois #6 coal		H_2S/CO_2 molar ratio	$\geq 1/2$
Composition	Mole %	Destination of CO_2 in tail gas	Recycled back as pure CO_2 stream
CO_2	28.02 %	Process assumptions	
H_2S (including COS)	1.27 %	Pressure loss $\Delta P/P_{in}$	2 %
CO	23.44 %	Polytropic efficiency of syngas and CO_2 compressors	84 %
N_2 (including other inerts)	0.40 %	Isentropic efficiency of expanders	88 %
H_2	46.87 %	Polytropic efficiency of refrigerator compressors	82 %
Total Molar Flow Rate	5.404 kmol/s	Mechanical/electric efficiency of the driver	92 %
Total Mass Flow Rate	110.2 kg/s	Utility assumptions	
Temperature	30 °C	Refrigeration cycle	Cascade Ethane/Ammonia
Pressure	35 bar	Cooling water	Closed loop between 15 and 25 °C
Outlet CO_2 Conditions		Steam for reboiling	Saturated steam at 0.5/1.5/3/10 bar
Destination: Enhanced Oil Recovery		$\Delta T_{min}/2$ for reboiler utility	10 °C
State: Supercritical dense at 150 bar		Outlet Syngas Conditions	
Temperature	25 °C	Temperature	25 °C
CO_2 molar concentration	> 97 %	Pressure	30 bar
H_2S molar concentration	< 150 ppmv	H_2S molar content	< 50 ppbv

3.1. Problem formulation and optimization approach

The optimization problem can be formulated as follows: for given inlet raw syngas thermodynamic conditions, determine the process design, heat integration and utility system design which minimizes the overall exergy penalty while satisfying a set of technological and environmental constraints reported in Table 1.

To tackle this problem, a robust black-box approach was adopted in which:

A. a derivative-free black-box algorithm optimizes the main process and utility design variables, namely seven stream temperatures (four of the process and three of the refrigeration cycle), five pressures, the mass flow rate of the solvent, the heat duty of the reboiler of the atmospheric regenerator, the split fraction of methanol sent to the H_2S absorber, the minimum approach temperature ΔT_{min}, and the number of trays of the absorber and desorber columns (19 optimization variables);
B. for given design variables listed in step A, the process is solved by a sequential flowsheeting software (Aspen Plus® V7.3);
C. for given utility design variables listed in step A, the process heat integration and the design of the utilities are simultaneously optimized;
D. the capital cost of the overall system is computed.

Within such approach, every black-box function evaluation includes steps B, C and D, and its outputs are the overall (process + utilities) exergy consumption (EXCON), CO_2Capture Level (CO_2CL) and capital cost (CAPEX). Compared to an equation oriented approach, this approach allows the use of different (specifically developed) algorithms for each step, and reduces the number of variables to be handled at each step, and thus increases the procedure robustness. The major drawback of this approach is the significant computational time required to compute the black-box function (steps B, C and D), between 5 and 15 s per evaluation, which poses a limit on the maximum number of objective function evaluations. In addition, the black-box output functions (exergy consumption, CO_2CL, and capital cost) have the following features:

- nonlinearity and multimodality, due to the nonlinearities of the process model,
- non-smoothness and discontinuity, due to the heat integration technique (i.e., integer variables associated to the selection of the best utilities, and non-differentiable points associated to the activation of pinch points),
- numerical noise, due to the numerical issues originated by the solution of the multiple recycle loops and absorption columns,
- the objective function value may not be defined in some points, due to the possible convergence failure of the process flowsheet,
- the feasible region turns out to be very small compared to the box defined by the bounds on the variables and a not-connected set.

Thus, the problem must be tackled with a robust derivative-free multi-objective algorithm. Among the several multi-objective evolutionary algorithms, we selected the Non-dominated Sorting Genetic Algorithm II (NSGA-II) by Deb et al. (2002) because it is quite effective on black-box problems (see Custodio et al., 2011), well-proven, and readily available within the MATLAB Global Optimization Toolbox (MathWorks, 2013). The major disadvantage of such algorithm, clearly shown by our computational experiments, is the lack of an intensification method capable of further refining the search around the non-dominated solutions. For this reason, a "push-Pareto" step is added to further improve the non-dominated solutions by applying the PGS-COM (Particle Generating Set – Complex algorithm) presented by Martelli and Amaldi (2014), a single objective direct-search algorithm specifically developed for constrained non-smooth problems.

3.2. Thermodynamic model and simulation assumptions

Due to the non-ideality of the physical transformations occurring within the process and because of the presence of many material recycle loops, particular attention was given to the definition of the flowsheet and its convergence features. We implemented and simulated a 0-D steady-state model of the process in Aspen Plus®, adopting the PC-SAFT equation of state, that, as described in Gatti et al. (2013), reproduces properly the Vapor Liquid Equilibria as well as the volumetric and thermal properties of the mixtures involved in the Rectisol®. Further details about the model are in Gatti et al. (2013).

3.3. Heat integration and utility design strategy

Once the process flowsheet is solved, the heat integration and the utilities are optimized with the algorithm proposed by Maréchal and Kalitventzeff (1998).The most significant exergy penalties of the process are: (i) the electric energy required to drive the process compressors and pumps, (ii) the electric energy required by the refrigeration cycle to supply the cooling duty needed by the process, (iii) the mechanical equivalent of the steam hypothetically extracted from the steam turbine for the reboiler, (iv) the chemical exergy associated to the co-captured fuel species (sent together with CO_2 to EOR). Among the utilities, a key impact is originated by the refrigeration cycle, whose design is customized to the T-Q profile of the process. The selected scheme is a state-of-the-art ammonia/ethane cascade cycle, featuring an evaporation level for each fluid. According to the method of Maréchal and Kalitventzeff (1998), given the set of utility systems and fixed the design variables optimized in step A, the "Problem Table Algorithm" is generalized into a Mixed Integer Linear Program (MILP) whose variables involve the selection of the utility systems and the mass flow rates of fluid at each utility temperature level. The objective function is the overall exergy consumption of the utilities. The MILP is implemented and solved with GLPK (GNU v4.47).

3.4. Multi-objective optimization

Instead of tackling a complex three-objective optimization problem with the conflicting objectives CO_2CL vs. EXCON vs. CAPEX, we noted the possibility of simplifying the problem into a set of bi-objective ones with respect to CO_2CL and EXCON. We noted that only the ΔT_{min} variable creates conflict between EXCON and CAPEX. Indeed, for fixed values of ΔT_{min} and CO_2CL, since the costs of the main equipment units depend on the power consumption (e.g., compressors), the higher is EXCON and the higher is CAPEX. As a result, for fixed values of ΔT_{min} and CO_2CL, EXCON and CAPEX are not-conflicting objectives. For this reason we converted the original three-objective problem into a set of bi-objective ones (CO_2CL vs EXCON) with fixed values of ΔT_{min}. In order to span the CAPEX space, we repeated the bi-objective optimization for three different values of ΔT_{min} (3, 5 and 10 K).

4. Optimization results

Given the significant computational time required by each function evaluation, we had to limit the number of function evaluations to approximately 6,000. Even though we used a 12-core computer featuring 2.8 GHz/core and executed both optimization algorithms (NSGA-II and PGS-COM) in parallel computing, the total computational time is close to 55 h. We decided to spend half of the available evaluations (3,000) to cover as much as possible the search space with the multi-objective algorithm, and the remaining ones to improve the most interesting non-dominated solutions with the single-objective optimizer. Figure 2 reports the Pareto frontiers generated by the multi-objective genetic solver on the left and after the subsequent application of the "Push-Pareto" algorithm on the right. The graph on the right highlights the improvement made by the PGS-COM algorithm. The relative improvement between the non-dominated points of the bi-objective and the corresponding "pushed" points varies in a range between 3 % and 10 % and is larger for the cases with ΔT_{min} = 10 K, meaning that this frontier was farther from Pareto-optimality than the others.

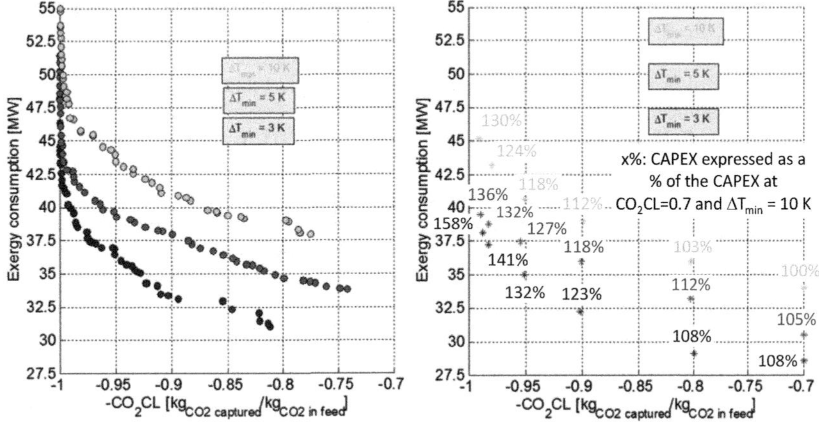

Figure 2. Left) Pareto frontiers for each ΔT_{min} considered after 30 generations of the bi-objective solver for a population of 100 individuals. Right) Trajectory of the Pareto frontiers after the application of PSG-COM and related CAPEX expressed as a percentage of a reference solution.

All of the frontiers share the same shape: the trend is almost linear between 70 % and 90 % CO_2 capture (with the exception of the curve related to the smallest ΔT_{min} which does not show a constant steep in the range); between 90 and 98% the linearity disappears and the slope tends to increase monotonically, whereas in the very high CO_2CL range above 98 % the exergy required tends to increase dramatically due to the finite solubility of CO_2 in methanol. So, it may not be economically justified to go beyond a CO_2 capture limit of 98 % - 99 %.

In order to assess the effectiveness of the multi-objective optimization, it is interesting to compare its best solution at ΔT_{min} = 10 K with the reference scheme proposed by Gatti et al. (2013), whose ΔT_{min} assumption where somehow in between the case with ΔT_{min} = 5 K and the one with ΔT_{min} = 10 K. The herein optimized configuration gives a specific exergy consumption of 662 kJ/kg of CO_2 captured whereas the reference one requires 755 kJ/kg of CO_2 captured, resulting into a 12% saving of exergy consumption.

5. Conclusions

This paper proposes a methodology for the multi-objective optimization of a novel Rectisol®-based process designed for CCS. The process and the utility systems are optimized with a black-box approach including a detailed process model as well as a heat integration & utility selection technique. The solution quality is improved by applying PGS-COM, a recently proposed direct-search method. Despite the large number of variables and the relatively small number of function evaluations allowed by the black-box solution time, the resulting Pareto frontier covers a wide range of CO_2 capture levels and shows a significant improvement with respect to the solution previously found by the authors on the basis of well-known design criteria.

Further research will focus on the application of such procedure to other pre-combustion CO_2 capture processes.

References

A. L. Custodio, J. F. A. Madeira, A. I. F. Vaz, L. N. Vicente, 2011, Direct multisearch for multiobjective optimization, SIAM Journal on Optimization, 21, 3, 1109-1140.

K. Deb, A. Pratap, S. Agarwal, T. Meyarivan, 2002, Fast and elitist multiobjective genetic algorithm: NSGA-II, IEEETransactions on Evolutionary Computation, 6, 182-197.

M. Gatti ,F. Marechal, E. Martelli, S. Consonni, 2013, Thermodynamic analysis, energy integration and flowsheet improvement of a methanol absorption acid gas removal process, Chemical Engineering Transactions, 35, 211-216.

U. Koss (Lurgi), 2006, Rectisol expands its scope in China, GTC Conference, Washington, USA.

F. Maréchal, B. Kalitventzeff, 1998, Process Integration - Selection of the Optimal Utility System, Computers and Chemical Engineering, 22, S149-S156.

E., Martelli, E., Amaldi, 2014, PGS-COM: A Hybrid Method for Constrained Non-Smooth Black-Box Optimization Problems-Brief review, Novel Algorithm and Comparative Evaluation. Computers & Chemical Engineering. DOI:10.1016/j.compchemeng.2013.12.014

MathWorks, 2013, Global Optimization Toolbox.

L. Sun, R. Smith, 2012, The Simulation and Analysis of Coal to Liquids Processes, Computer Aided Chemical Engineering, 31, 1221-1225.

L. Sun, R. Smith, 2013, Rectisol wash process simulation and analysis, Journal of Cleaner Production, 39, 1, 321–328.

H. Weiss (Linde), 1988, Rectisol wash for purification of partial oxidation gases, Gas Separation and Purification, 2, 4, 171-176.

Jiří Jaromír Klemeš, Petar Sabev Varbanov and Peng Yen Liew (Editors)
Proceedings of the 24th European Symposium on Computer Aided Process Engineering – ESCAPE 24
June 15-18, 2014, Budapest, Hungary.

Hybrid CFD-Compartment Approach for Modelling and Optimisation of a Leaching Reactor

Szabolcs Fogarasi[a]*, Attila Egedy[b], Florica Imre-Lucaci[c], Tamás Varga[b], Tibor Chován[b]

[a]*Babes-Bolyai University, Faculty of Chemistry and Chemical Engineering, Cluj Napoca, Romania*
[b]*University of Pannonia, Department of Process Engineering, 10 Egyetem Str., H-8200 Veszprém, Hungary*
[c]*Babeş-Bolyai, University, Interdisciplinary Research Institute on Bio-Nano-Sciences, Cluj Napoca, Romania*
szfogarasi@chem.ubbcluj.ro

Abstract

The study presents an alternative way to dissolve copper from waste printed circuit boards (WPCBs) using a specially designed leaching reactor and efficient leaching agents. Considering that the leaching reactor is equipped with a perforated rotating drum the fluid flow as well the other related processes (e.g. reactions) can be very complex. Therefore two different model approaches were applied regarding the leaching of copper with $FeCl_3$ and $Na_2S_2O_8$ as oxidants. The detailed models were validated against multiple measurements performed with the leaching reactor. Then the validated model was used to conduct sensitivity analysis of the operational parameters (reagent concentration, drum revolution speed), and optimal parameter intervals were obtained for the operation of the leaching reactor. COMSOL Multiphysics was used for hydrodynamic modeling and MATLAB for compartment model implementation and sensitivity studies.

Keywords: waste printed circuit board, computational fluid dynamics, leaching reactor

1. Introduction

In the recent years, the lifespan of consumer electronic devices has become relatively short, due to the rapid changes in equipment features and capabilities (Sepúlveda et al., 2010). Printed circuit boards (PCBs) are a key component in electronic equipment, representing about 3 % of the total amount of WEEE (van Beers et al., 2007) Thanks to the high metal content, WPCBs are considered an attractive secondary source of metals which can help to preserve the natural resources (Rubin et al., 2014).The high economical value makes precious metals, especially gold, the main targets in WPCBs recycling, followed by Cu, Ni and other base metals (Fogarasi et al., 2013). However, in order to obtain high purity precious metals it is necessary to separate the electronic components with high gold content, from the other parts of WPCBs (Fogarasi et al., 2012). It is also necessary to remove selectively Cu which has the most significant influence on gold recovery (Imre-Lucaci et al., 2012). The traditional methods like open burning, incineration and smelting (Huang et al., 2009) have low efficiency and selectivity in the separation of gold or gold rich electronic components. Moreover, pyrometallurgical methods involve hazardous operating conditions and generate toxic gases (dioxin, brominated flame retardants) and fumes metals (Hg, Pb and Cd) (Kim et al., 2011a). Thus in the last decades researchers focused on the development of hydrometallurgical processes which allow the enrichment of gold or the selective extraction of gold form WPCBs under mild operating conditions (Tuncuk et al., 2012). The hydrometallurgical routes also offer the possibility to recover base metals simultaneously with the preconcentration of gold (Fogarasi et al., 2012). Considering the high economical value of copper and its impact on gold recovery, many hydrometallurgical processes have been developed for copper dissolution (Kim, 2011b). However there still are issues that need to be solved, like increasing the leaching rate of copper while reducing the reagent and energy consumption and the volume of residual solutions. These requirements can be satisfied by using efficient oxidants, adequate leaching reactors and optimal operating conditions (Imre-Lucaci et al., 2012). With this purpose we tested several leaching agents of which $FeCl_3$ and $Na_2S_2O_8$ proved to be the most efficient and ecofriendly as well. Furthermore, our research group designed a special leaching reactor which can be used efficiently for the dissolution of copper with the parallel enrichment of gold from WPCBs (Fogarasi et al., 2013). In our recent study the basics of the leaching reactor model were developed, facilitating a hybrid CFD-compartment model (Egedy et al, 2013a). Beside the heuristic approach a deterministic compartment structure was also defined using a compartment model structure identification algorithm (Egedy et al., 2013b). The present study compares the two compartment models in the context of copper leaching with $FeCl_3$ and $Na_2S_2O_8$ using the designed leaching reactor. The goal of this investigation is to find out which compartment model approach is suitable for further evaluation and integration to the hybrid CFD-compartment model. The validated model allowed the identification of the optimal values of operating parameters for both leaching agents.

2. Experimental

The leaching reactor (Figure 1), with a volume of 343 mL, was equipped with a rotating perforated drum, immersed in the leaching solution, which contained the copper samples. All experiments were performed over a period of 2 h at room temperature using waste copper wires of approximately 4 g. The leaching solutions were prepared by using analytic grade chemicals ($FeCl_3$, HCl and $Na_2S_2O_8$) and double distillated water. Measurements were carried out by varying the concentration of the leaching agents (0.1-0.5 M) and the revolution speed (10-29 min^{-1}) at constant flow rate of 10 mL/min. After each experiment, the cell was disassembled and washed thoroughly with distilled water.

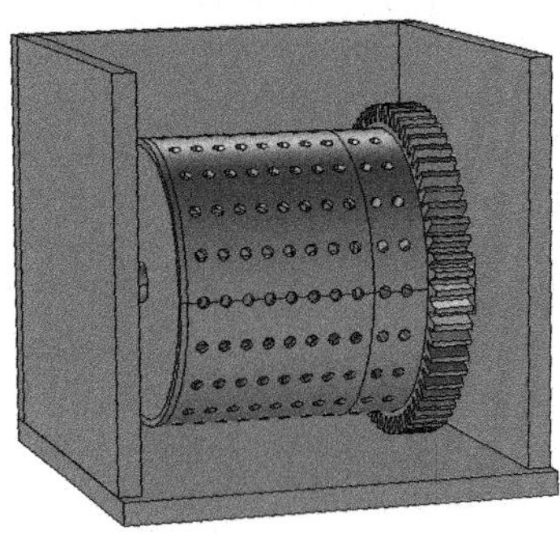

Figure 1. The leaching reactor

During the experiments, samples of 1 mL were taken in order to determine the amount of dissolved copper using an atomic absorption spectrophotometer (Avanta PM - GBC).

3. Modelling and validation

Two compartment models, differing by structure and parameters, were used to model the leaching reactor. One of the models was a heuristic compartment model (model 1) discussed in details in a previous work (Egedy et al., 2013a). The heuristic compartment model is basically a hybrid CFD-compartment model capable of handling revolution speed changes too. There is a different approach to define a compartment model (model 2) using a deterministic structure and parameter identification algorithm (Egedy et al. 2013b). We used residence time distribution measurement as input data to identify a compartment model, which uses a saturated KCl injection experiment. Figure 2 shows the identified deterministic compartment model and the model parameters (volumes (V_1-V_5), distribution ratio (α)). The drawback of this model is that it is not revolution speed dependent. Two different oxidants ($FeCl_3$ and $Na_2S_2O_8$) were applied and the models were validated against multiple measurements with different operating parameters (revolution speeds, initial oxidant concentrations). Figure 3 shows the results of the model validation with the two compartment models, and reagents.

The copper leaching kinetics was the same in both models, and identified using multiple measurements. There are major differences in the case of $FeCl_3$ between the two models. In case of model 1 the differences between the measured and the simulated results are almost the same in every experiments and the error between the curves is the same regardless to the revolution speed. In model 2 the error between the measured and the simulated curves increases at higher revolution speeds, due to the revolution speed independence of the model. For $Na_2S_2O_8$, the behavior of the model is almost the same in both cases. However the curves with this reagent are not getting near the stationary concentration, so a longer measurement will be needed in the future for better validation. In the case of $Na_2S_2O_8$ only two tests were conducted because the 0.1 M case was omitted due to the relatively small yields.

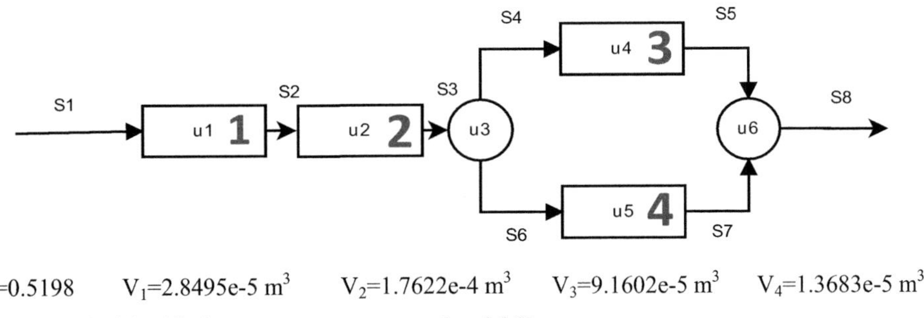

α=0.5198 V_1=2.8495e-5 m^3 V_2=1.7622e-4 m^3 V_3=9.1602e-5 m^3 V_4=1.3683e-5 m^3

Figure 2. The identified compartment structure (model 2)

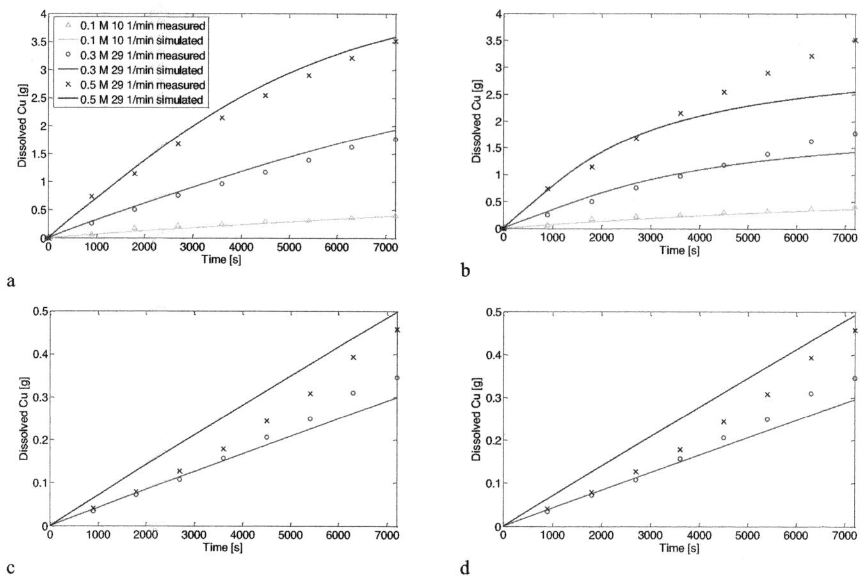

Figure 3. The results of the model validation step a) model 1 with $FeCl_3$, b) model 2 with $FeCl_3$ c) model 1 with $Na_2S_2O_8$ d) model 2 with $Na_2S_2O_8$

4. Optimisation

After the model validation step was completed we performed sensitivity analysis of the model parameters (revolution speed, reagent concentration), to define an optimal parameter interval for the operation of the leaching reactor. For the sensitivity analysis model 1 was used because it is capable of calculating the distribution ratios changes based on the revolution speed.

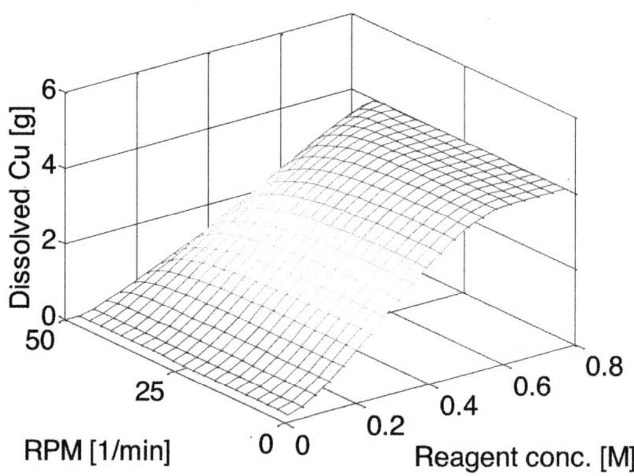

Figure 4. Sensitivity analysis for $FeCl_3$

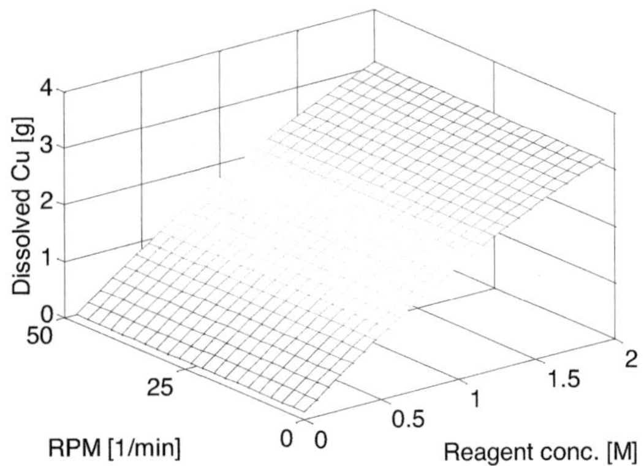

Figure 5. Sensitivity analysis for $Na_2S_2O_8$

Figure 4 and 5 shows the results of the sensitivity analysis performed for both of the reagents. The optimal parameter interval in case of the $FeCl_3$ revolution speed 20-30 min^{-1} and reagent concentration around 0.6 M. In case of $Na_2S_2O_8$ the optimal parameters are its maximum, and the effectiveness of the $FeCl_3$ reagent cannot be reached within the solubility limits (~2.33 M $Na_2S_2O_8$). However the application of the $Na_2S_2O_8$ reagent should be used as a more environment friendly alternative in comparison to acidic leaching agents such as $FeCl_3$.

5. Conclusion

A hybrid CFD-compartment model was developed to optimize the leaching reactor used for electrical waste recycling. Two different reagents were applied to examine the leaching process of a copper wire, which is the most frequent metal in WPBC. Two different compartment models were used to obtain compartment model structure and the models were compared to each other. Based on validation, model 1 which uses a heuristic approach, proved to be more adequate, allowing the detailed examination of the model parameters and the definition of the optimal operational regimes for the leaching reactor.

The comparison of the reagents indicates that $FeCl_3$ ensures a more rapid leaching and higher yields. On the other hand $Na_2S_2O_8$ as a more environment friendly reagent is better regardless its smaller leaching performance.

Acknowledgement

This work was supported by the Romanian-Hungarian Bilateral Program under project no. 673/2013, TET_12-RO-1-2013-0017 and by the European Union and the State of Hungary, co-financed by the European Social Fund in the framework of TÁMOP-4.2.2/A-11/1/KONV-2012-0071 project. Tamás Varga's research activity in this work was supported by the European Union and the State of Hungary, co-financed by the European Social Fund in the framework of TÁMOP-4.2.4.A/2-11/1-2012-0001 'National Excellence Program'.

References

D. van Beers, A. Kapur, T.E. Graedel, 2007, Copper and zinc recycling in Australia: potential quantities and policy options, Journal of Cleaner Production 15, 862-877.

A. Egedy, T. Varga, T. Chován, 2013a, Compartment model structure identification with qualitative methods for a stirred vessel, Mathematical and Computer Modelling of Dynamical Systems, 19, 2, 115-132.

A. Egedy, Sz. Fogarasi, T. Varga, Á. Imre-Lucaci, T. Chován, 2013b, CFD simulators in the development of electrical waste recycling technologies, Chemical Engineering Transactions, 35, 1327-1332.

S. Fogarasi, F. Imre-Lucaci, P. Ilea, Á. Imre-Lucaci, 2013, The environmental assessment of two new copper recovery processes from Waste Printed Circuit Boards, Journal of Cleaner Production, 54, 264-269.

S. Fogarasi, F. Imre-Lucaci, T. Varga, P. Ilea, 2012, Eco-friendly leaching of base metals from waste printed circuit boards: Experimental study and mathematical modeling, STUDIA UBB CHEMIA, LVII, 3, 91-100.

K. Huang, J. Guo, Z. Xu, 2009, Recycling of waste printed circuit boards: a review of current technologies and treatment status in China, Journal of hazardous materials, 164, 399-408.

F. Imre-Lucaci, S. Fogarasi, P. Ilea, M. Tămăşan, 2012, Copper recovery from real samples of WPCBs by anodic dissolution, Environmental Engineering and Management Journal, 11, 8, 1439-1444.

E.Y. Kim, M.S. Kim, J.C. Lee, B.D. Pandey, 2011a, Selective recovery of gold from waste mobile phone PCBs by hydrometallurgical process, Journal of hazardous materials, 198, 206-215.

E.Y. Kim, M.S. Kim, J.C. Lee, J. Jeong, B.D. Pandey, 2011b, Leaching kinetics of copper from waste printed circuit boards by electro-generated chlorine in HCl solution, Hydrometallurgy, 107, 124–132.

R.S. Rubin, M.A.S.d. Castro, D. Brandão, V. Schalch, A.R. Ometto, 2014, Utilization of Life Cycle Assessment methodology to compare two strategies for recovery of copper from printed circuit board scrap, Journal of Cleaner Production, 64, 297-305

A. Sepúlveda, M. Schluep, F.G. Renaud, M. Streicher, R. Kuehr, C. Hagelüken, A.C. Gerecke, 2010, A review of the environmental fate and effects of hazardous substances released from electrical and electronic equipments during recycling: Examples from China and India, Environmental Impact Assessment Review, 30, 28-41.

A. Tuncuk, V. Stazi, A. Akcil, E.Y. Yazici, H. Deveci, 2012, Aqueous metal recovery techniques from e-scrap: Hydrometallurgy in recycling, Miner. Eng., 25, 28–37.

Jiří Jaromír Klemeš, Petar Sabev Varbanov and Peng Yen Liew (Editors)
Proceedings of the 24th European Symposium on Computer Aided Process Engineering – ESCAPE 24
June 15-18, 2014, Budapest, Hungary.

Energy Saving in Conventional and Unconventional Batch Reactive Distillation: Application to Hydrolysis of Methyl Lactate System

Elmahboub A. Edreder[a,] *, Mansour Emtir[b], Iqbal M. Mujtaba[c]

[a]*National Oil Corporation, P.O. Box. 2655, Tripoli, Libya*
[b]*Libyan Petroleum Institute, P.O. Box. 3641, Tripoil, Libya*
[c]*School of Engineering, University of Bradford, Bradford BD7 1DP, UK*
eelmahboub@yahoo.com

Abstract

In this work, energy consumption in a middle vessel batch reactive distillation (MVBRD) column is considered for the production of lactic acid via hydrolysis of methyl lactate. A dynamic optimization problem incorporating a process model is formulated to minimize the batch time which consequently minimizes the total energy consumption. The problem is subject to constraints on the amount and purity of lactic acid. The optimisation variables are reflux ratio and/or reboil ratio which are treated as piecewise constant. The earlier work of the authors on energy consumption in conventional batch reactive distillation column (CBRD) for the same reaction system is used for comparative analysis with the energy consumption in MVBRD. As an example, for a given separation task, the optimization results show that MVBRD is capable of saving over 23 % energy compared to energy consumption in CBRD column for the same task.

Keywords: energy saving, lactic acid, middle vessel batch reactive distillation.

1. Introduction

The industrial manufacture of lactic acid (LA) is carried out by chemical synthesis or fermentation using sugar cane, whey, biomass, etc. Among the various methods for recovery and purification, the esterification of lactic acid with a suitable alcohol and subsequent hydrolysis of the purified ester is widely accepted as highly efficient. Hydrolysis of methyl lactate (ML) in a distillation column is one of the purification steps to enhance purity of lactic acid produced. Experimentally, purification of LA was considered by several authors. Kim et al. (2000) considered both esterification and hydrolysis reactions for the recovery of lactic acid in a batch reactive distillation and presented experimental and model based techniques to obtain optimum design and operation. Kim et al. (2002) analyzed the dynamic behaviour of batch reactive distillation for lactic acid production in terms of instantaneous rate of esterification reaction. Kumar et al. (2006) highlighted a novel reactive distillation strategy involving experimental esterification and hydrolysis reactions for the recovery of pure lactic acid. Edreder et al. (2011) investigated optimal operations of CBRD and Inverted batch reactive columns to produce lactic acid by hydrolysis of methyl lactate. Edreder et al. (2012) considered simulation of MVBRD column using rigorous dynamic model for the same reaction system but without explicit focus on the energy consumption. Mujtaba et al. (2012) showed that for a given vapour load, minimum batch time leads to minimum energy consumption for CBRD column. They highlighted that a significant reduction in thermal energy consumption (over 50 %) can be achieved for lactic acid production process in CBRD column by carefully controlling the reflux ratio but without compromising the product specification. Krishna et al. (2013) proposed a hybrid reactive stripper-membrane (RSM) process for the hydrolysis of methyl lactate and compared with reactive distillation process to produce LA. Martinez et al. (2013) reviewed the fermentative and biotechnical processes to produce lactic acid.

In this work, both CBRD and MVBRD columns are investigated. A dynamic optimization problem incorporating a process model is formulated considering total energy consumption as the objective function to minimise, subjected to constraints on the amount and purity of lactic acid (0.7 to 0.8 mole fraction). Reflux ratio and/or reboil ratio are considered as control variables of the system and are treated as a piecewise constant which are discretised using Control Vector Parameterization technique (CVP). This results in a Non Linear Programming (NLP) problem, which is solved using an SQP-based optimization technique available within gPROMS.

2. Batch column operation strategies and energy consumption

A batch distillation can be operated by one of the following specific strategies (Mujtaba, 2004): (a) Constant reboiler heat duty (b) Constant vapor boilup rate (V) by changing heat input to the reboiler and (c) Constant condenser vapor load (V_c) by changing heat input to the reboiler.

Mujtaba et al. (2012) showed that for a given mode of heat supply (Q_r) to the distillation column, minimizing the production time (i.e. batch time) without compromising the product specifications offers potential reduction in thermal energy consumption (Q_t) and in carbon footprint. The total energy requirement over the production batch time for this case can be given by:

$$Q_{Total} = \int_0^{t_f} Q_r dt \tag{1}$$

3. Model equations

A schematic representation of the two columns is given in Figure 1. For MVBRD process, the column is divided into rectifying and stripping sections by the feed vessel. Both columns are represented by detailed dynamic models in the form of Differential and Algebraic Equations system. The model assumes negligible vapour holdup, adiabatic plates, constant molar holdup on plates and in the condenser, perfect mixing on trays, fast energy dynamics, constant operating pressure and total condensation with no sub-cooling and assuming no azeotrope formation. The model includes mass and energy balances with constant molar holdup and rigorous thermodynamic properties. Dynamic model for feed tank and feed plate for MVBRD are shown in Figure 2. The kinetic model (Sanz et al., 2004) can be written as:

$$-r = k_1 \, exp(\frac{E_1}{RT}) a_1 a_2 - k_2 \, exp(\frac{E_2}{RT}) a_3 a_4 \tag{2}$$

Where $k_1 = 1.65 \times 10^5$ mol. gm^{-1}. min^{-1}, $k_2 = 1.16 \times 10^6$, E_1 and E_2 = - 50.91 and - 48.52 J. mol^{-1} respectively and a_i represent the activity of the component i ($a_i = \gamma_i \, x_i$).

The vapor-liquid equilibrium are computed as:

$$K = \gamma_i P_i^{sat} \,/\, P \qquad (3)$$

where γ_i is computed from UNIQUAC equation, the vapor pressure (P_i^{sat})of pure components estimated by using Antoine's equation.

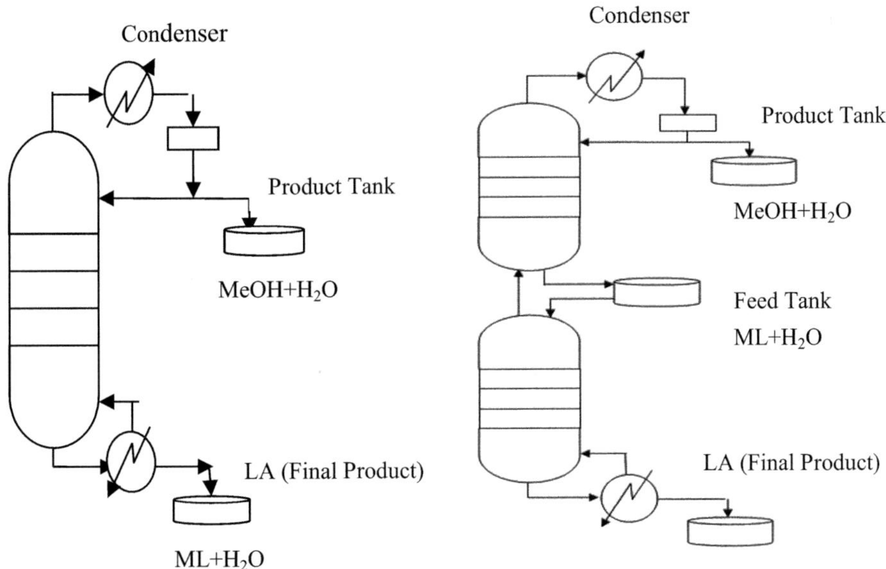

Figure 1. Column configurations (Left: CBRD Column; Right: MVBRD Column)

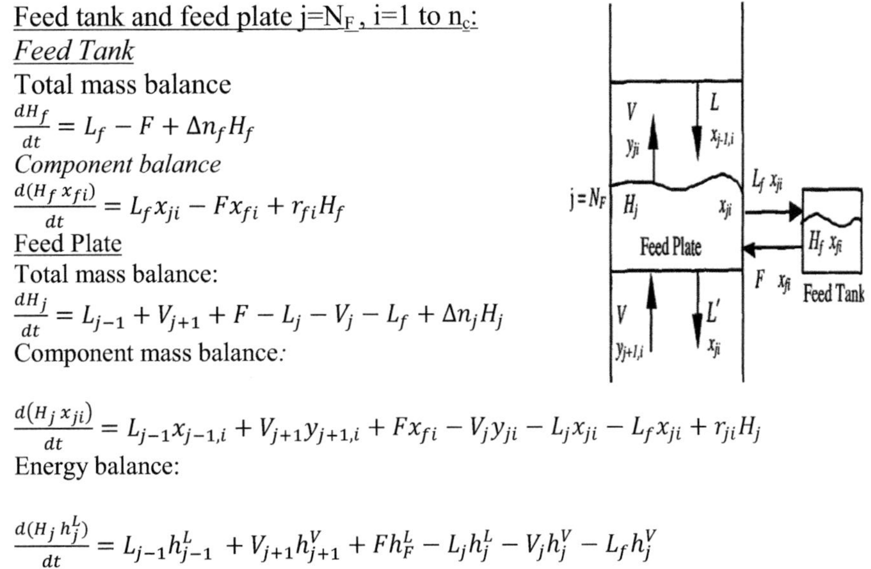

Feed tank and feed plate j=NF , i=1 to nc:
Feed Tank
Total mass balance
$\frac{dH_f}{dt} = L_f - F + \Delta n_f H_f$
Component balance
$\frac{d(H_f x_{fi})}{dt} = L_f x_{ji} - F x_{fi} + r_{fi} H_f$
Feed Plate
Total mass balance:
$\frac{dH_j}{dt} = L_{j-1} + V_{j+1} + F - L_j - V_j - L_f + \Delta n_j H_j$
Component mass balance:
$\frac{d(H_j x_{ji})}{dt} = L_{j-1} x_{j-1,i} + V_{j+1} y_{j+1,i} + F x_{fi} - V_j y_{ji} - L_j x_{ji} - L_f x_{ji} + r_{ji} H_j$
Energy balance:
$\frac{d(H_j h_j^L)}{dt} = L_{j-1} h_{j-1}^L + V_{j+1} h_{j+1}^V + F h_F^L - L_j h_j^L - V_j h_j^V - L_f h_j^V$
V
yji
L
xj-1,i
Lf xji
j=NF
Hj
xji
Feed Plate
Hf xfi
F xfi
Feed Tank
V
yj+1,i
L'
xji

Figure 2. Model for feed tank and feed plate for MVBRD

4. Minimum time problem

The optimal operation of for both CBRD and MVBRD processes can be described mathematically by:

$$\begin{array}{lll} OP & \min\limits_{R(t)\text{and or }Rb(t)} & t_f \end{array} \quad (4)$$

subject to:

$B = B^*$	(Inequality constraint)
$x_3 = x_3^* \pm \varepsilon$	(Inequality constraint)
$and \;\; f(t,x',x,u,\upsilon) = 0$	(Model Equation, equality constraint)
$with \; f(t_0,x'_0,x_0,u_0,\upsilon) = 0$	(Initial condition, equality constraint)
Linear bound on $R(t)$ *and* $Rb(t)$	(Equality constraint)

Where B, x_3 are the amount of bottom product (2.5 kmol) and composition of lactic acid at the final time t_f, (B^* and x_3^* are specified). *R(t)* and *Rb(t)* are the reflux ratio and reboil ratio profiles which are optimized and ε is small positive numbering in the order of 10^{-3}.

5. Problem description

Hydrolysis of methyl lactate (ML) is considered in both CBRD and MVDRD columns (Figure 1). In MVBRD column, a 5 kmol mixture consisting of 50 % by mole ML and 50 % of water (H_2O) is fed into the feed tank (stage 5) in order to produce Lactic acid (LA) and methanol (MeOH). The column has 10 stages (including condenser and reboiler) with condenser vapour load (V_c) of 2.5 kmol/h. The total column holdup is 4 % of the initial feed (of which 50 % is taken as the condenser hold up and the rest is equally divided in the plates to make plate holdup).

6. Results and discussions

Table 1 summarises the optimum results (optimal reflux ratio, optimal reboil ratio, minimum batch time and the total energy consumption) for MVBRD for a range of product purity. Moreover, the optimization results for CBRD are shown in the brackets in Table 1. As a comparison between the two columns, it can be observed that lower reflux ratio, operation time and energy consumption can be achieved when the MVBRD column is used. Figure 3 shows the total energy consumption profile for different product purity for both processes and it indicates a significant reduction in batch time and total energy consumption are possible for the same product purity in case of MVBRD. Table 2 gives the percent of energy saving when the MVBRD column is used as opposed to CBRD.

Table 1. Optimization results for MVBRD and CRBD columns

LA purity (%)	t_f(hr)	R	R_b	Qt (mKJ)
0.70	6.68 (7.340)	0.8530 (0.8638)	0.8362	0.731 (0.859)
0.75	8.28 (10.20)	0.8796 (0.9020)	0.8586	0.904 (1.182)
0.80	11.98(14.88)	0.9204 (0.9330)	0.8926	1.321(1.722)

Note: The optimization results of CRBD columns are in brackets (0.8 purity results are taken from Mujtaba et al., 2012)

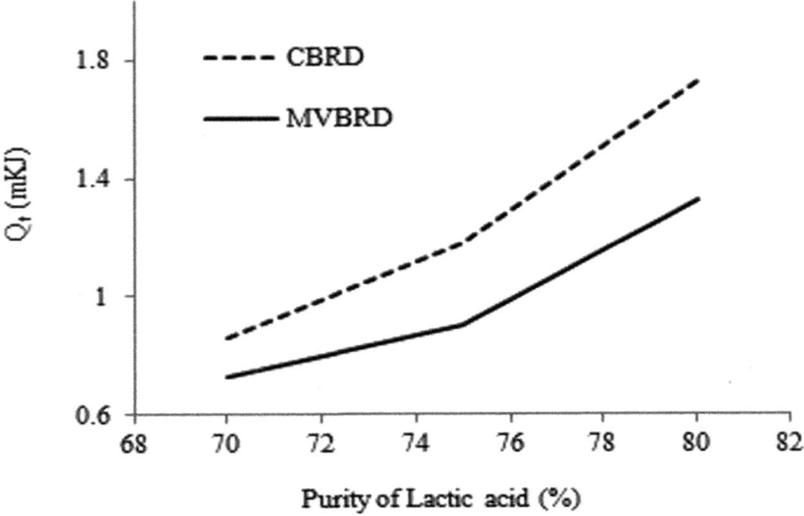

Figure 3. Total energy consumption profile

Table 2. Energy saving by MVBRD with different product purity

LA purity (%)	70	75	80
Energy saving (%)	14.9	23.5	23.3

It can be seen that, the maximum energy savings achieved are 23.5 % and 23.3 % at LA purity of 75 % and 80 % respectively compared to that obtained by using CBRD column.

7. Conclusions

Among many different types of batch reactive distillation column configurations, conventional (CBRD) and middle vessel batch (MVBRD) columns are considered here for the production of lactic acid via hydrolysis of methyl lactate. In this work, a dynamic optimization problem incorporating a process model is formulated to minimize the batch time subject to constraints on the amount and purity of lactic acid (0.7 to 0.8 mole fraction). Control variables (reflux ratio or/and a reboil ratio) are treated as a piecewise constant which is discretised using Control Vector Parameterization technique (CVP). For a given vapor load for both configurations, minimum batch time led to minimum energy consumption for both columns (CBRD & MVBRD).

For a given separation task, the optimization results show that MVBRD has more potential compared to CBRD in terms of energy savings. For example, for product purity of 0.80 mole fraction, an energy reduction of 23.3 % is achieved with MVBRD column compared to that obtained by using CBRD column.

References

E. A. Edreder, I. M. Mujtaba, M. M. Emtir, 2011, Optimal operation of different types of batch reactive distillation columns used for hydrolysis of methyl lactate to lactic acid, Chemical Engineering Journal, 172, 467-475.

E. A. Edreder, I. M. Mujtaba, M. M. Emtir, 2012, Simulation of Middle vessel batch reactive distillation column: application to hydrolysis of methyl lactate, Chemical Engineering Transactions, 29, 595-600.

M. T. Sanz, R. Murga, S. Beltran, J. L. Cabezas, J. Coca, 2004, Kinetic study for the reactive system of Lactic Acid esterification with methanol: Methyl lactate hydrolysis, Industrial Engineering Chemistry Research, 43, 3, 2049-2053.

J. Y. Kim, Y. J. Kim, W. H. Hong, G. Wozny, 2000, Recovery process of lactic acid using two distillation columns, Biotechnol Bioprocess Engineering, 5, 196-201.

Y. J. Kim, W. H. Hong, G. Wozny, 2002, Effect of recycle and feeding method on batch reactive recovery system of lactic acid, Korean Journal of Chemical Engineering, 19, 5, 808–814.

R. Kumar, S. M. Mahajani, H. Nanavati, S. B. Noronha, 2006, Recovery of lactic acid by batch reactive distillation. Journal Chemistry Technical Biotechnology, 81, 1141-1150.

I. M. Mujtaba, 2004, Batch Distillation: Design and Operation, Series on Chemical Engineering, Imperial Collage Press, UK.

I. M. Mujtaba, E. A. Edreder, M. M. Emtir, 2012, Significant thermal energy reduction in lactic acid production process, Applied Energy,89, 74–80.

F. A. C. Martinez, E. M. Balciunas, J. M. Salgado, J. M. D. Gonzalez, A. Converti, R. P. de Souza Oliveira, 2013, Lactic acid properties, applications and production: A review, Trends in Food Scinece and Technology, 30, 70-83.

G. Krishna, G. P. Rangaiah, S. Lakshminarayanan, 2013, Modeling and Analysis of Hybrid Reactive Stripper-Membrane Process for Lactic Acid Recovery, Industrial Engineering Chemistry Research, 52, 2907−2916.

Jiří Jaromír Klemeš, Petar Sabev Varbanov and Peng Yen Liew (Editors)
Proceedings of the 24th European Symposium on Computer Aided Process Engineering – ESCAPE 24
June 15-18, 2014, Budapest, Hungary.

Multiobjective Optimization of Biomass to Energy Supply Chains in an Uncertain Environment

Şebnem Yılmaz Balaman*, Hasan Selim

Department of Industrial Engineering, Dokuz Eylul University, Tınaztepe Campus, Buca, 35160 Izmir, Turkey
s.yilmaz@deu.edu.tr

Abstract

The aim of this study is to design supply chain network for biomass to energy conversion systems for the regions having high potential of animal wastes and energy crops production and to reveal economical and environmental benefits from these systems. To this aim, a fuzzy multiobjective mixed integer linear programming (MILP) model is constructed. The model includes environmental and monetary objectives and it is structured as a multiperiod model in order to consider variation in the parameters. The model is solved by using different fuzzy goal programming (FGP) approaches.

Keywords: Biomass, Supply chain design, FGP, MILP

1. Introduction

Design and planning an efficient biomass to energy supply chain based on designing a transportation network, selection of locations and capacities of conversion plants and storages, arrangement of feedstock supply, energy distribution, process residue handling and distribution, and tactical operation schedules in a cost effectively manner. As biomass to energy supply chains include various activities, it is hard to analyze, design and manage the whole supply chain. The planners have to consider economical, environmental and social concerns related with establishing biomass to energy conversion systems and specific difficulties related with uncertain decision environment. Facing such a complex and hard task, a systematic analysis and evaluation procedure is necessary. Čuček et al. (2013) presented a multi-period MILP model for synthesis and optimization of a regional biorefinery's supply networks, for the selection of technologies, raw materials, products, and the planning of harvesting, biofuels production, storage, and logistics. Ekşioğlu et al (2009) proposed a study to design the supply chain and manage the logistics of a biorefinery using MILP that and scenario generation. Dal Mas et al. (2010) developed a MILP model for the design and planning of multi-echelon biofuels supply chain under uncertainty. The majority of the literature focuses on optimization of biomass to energy supply chains that uses energy crops as biomass feedstock. However, design of biomass to energy supply chains which utilizes waste type biomass is only rarely mentioned. In addition, anaerobic digestion systems, which convert organic feedstock to biogas through a fermentation process, have not received the same level of attention as the other types of biomass to biofuel conversion systems. Also, fuzzy decision making methods have not been used to deal with uncertain decision environment in the current state of the art about biomass to energy supply chain design. Considering these gaps, a fuzzy multiobjective MILP model is developed for the optimal design of anaerobic digestion based biomass to energy supply chains in this study. Besides making strategic decisions such as determining the numbers, locations and capacities of biogas production plants and biomass storages, energy crop cultivation area can be determined and biomass supply and fertilizer distribution plans can be made by the model.

2. Problem Statement

The proposed model considers two types of biomass feedstock to be transformed into energy; 1) waste biomass in the form of animal manure which can be taken from available farms and 2) energy crops that can be collected from out-of-use arable lands. Energy crops are used as feedstock to increase the productivity of the system. The collected biomass is shipped to the biomass storages and then to biomass to energy conversion plants. The biomass is fed into a fermenter in the anaerobic digestion facilities, and transformed into biogas. Combined Heat and Power station is used to convert the treated biogas into electrical and thermal energy. The generated electricity can be fed into the national electricity grid. In wet digestion process, some water has to be added to the digester to adjust the total solid content of the feedstock mixture. Process residues are sold to local farmers to be used as organic fertilizer in agricultural activities. The storages include three parts; the first one is for liquid/semi-solid waste biomass with low total solid content, the second one is for solid waste biomass with relatively high solid content and the third one is for energy crops. Inventory turnover is only allowed for energy crops due to natural decay of animal wastes. The biomass to energy supply chain distribution network considered in this study includes the sets of biomass supply regions, candidate sites for the location of storages and biomass to energy conversion plants with capacity options.

3. The Proposed Model

Sets: *p*: Plant location sites, *d*: Storage location sites, *r*: Supply regions, *t*: Time periods, *Wf*: Waste feedstock types, *ECf*: Energy crop types, *c*: Plant capacity levels.

Parameters: *PCAP*: Biomass availability (t), *PEC*: Electricity production capacity (kW), *MaxDC*: Maximum waste biomass storage capacity (t), *g*:Biomass to fertilizer conversion rate (%), *e*:Biomass to biogas conversion rate (m^3/t), *v*: Biogas to electricity conversion rate (kW/m^3), *c*:Biogas to electricity conversion efficiency of cogeneration unit (%), *TS*: Total solid content of biomass (%), *AA*:Available animal stock , *k*:Monthly waste amount per animal (t), *V*: Cultivated energy crop (t/da), *EA*: Arable empty area (da), *Wr*: Weight for the urgency level of waste disposal, *MinTS*: Minimum total solid content of biomass slurry (%), *MaxTS*: Maximum total solid content of biomass slurry (%), *IC*: Discounted investment cost per kilowatt of installed power (€/kW), *OC*: Discounted operational cost per kilowatt of installed power (€/kW), *TC*: Unit transportation cost of biomass from storage to plant (€/t), *CO*: Unit transportation cost of biomass from supply region to storage (€/t), *TCF*: Unit transportation cost of process residue (organic fertilizer) (€/t), *ULC*: Unit land cost of location sites (€/ t), *UCL*: Unit construction cost of liquid biomass storage (€/t), *UCS*: Unit construction cost of solid biomass storage (€/ t), *TCA*: Total cultivated area (da), *EP*: Price of electricity (€/kW), *FP*: Price of fertilizer (€/ m^3), *WP*: Price of water (€/ m^3), *PCW*: Purchasing cost of waste biomass (€/t), *PCEC*: Purchasing cost of energy crop (€/t), *PP*: Prespecified upper limit for energy crop cultivation (as proportion of the arable empty area

Decision Variables: *Y*: Integer variable that indicates the number of biogas plants to be constructed, *XW*: Integer variable that indicates the number of waste biomass storages to be constructed, *BW*: Amount of biomass transported from supply regions to storages (t), *BEC*: Amount of energy crop transported from the supply region to the storages (t), *W*: Amount of biomass transported from storages to plants (t), *AEC*: Amount of energy crop transported from storages to plants (t), *FER*: Amount of fertilizer transported from plants to supply regions (t), *W*: Water usage amount of plants (t), *SLWC*: Liquid biomass capacity of storages (t), *SSWC*: Solid biomass capacity of storages (t), *SSECC*: Energy crop capacity of storages (t), *DSECC*: Amount of energy crop stored in storages (t), *ECAP*: Proportion of energy crop cultivation area to total arable empty area (%), *Outbio*: Biogas output of plants (m3), *Outelc*: Electricity output of plants (kW)

3.1. Objective function

3.1.1. First objective: Maximization of the overall profit

The first objective function (O1) includes two terms; total revenue and total cost.

Total Profit = Total Revenue- (Discounted Investment Costs + Operational Costs + Total Transportation Cost + Biomass Purchasing Cost)

Total Revenue = Revenue from electricity sales + Revenue from fertilizer sales

Total revenue is calculated with Eq. (1) as in the following.

$$Total\ Revenue = \left(EP * \sum_{p}\sum_{t} Outelc_{pt} \right) + \left(FP * \sum_{p}\sum_{r}\sum_{t} FER_{ptr} \right) \tag{1}$$

Eqs. (2) and (3) shows the investment cost of plants and storages, respectively.

$$Investment\ Cost_{p} = \left(\sum_{c} IC_{pc} * PEC_{pc} * Y_{pc} \right) \quad \forall p \tag{2}$$

$$Investment\ Cost_{d} = \begin{pmatrix} \left(UCL * SLWC_{d} \right) + \left(UCS * (SSWC_{d} + SSECC_{d}) \right) \\ + ULC_{d} * \left(SLWC_{d} + SSWC_{d} + SSECC_{d} \right) \end{pmatrix} \quad \forall d \tag{3}$$

Eqs. (4 to 8) show operational costs of plants and storages, water cost of plants, total transportation cost and biomass purchasing cost, respectively.

$$Operational\ Cost_{pt} = \left(\sum_{c} OC_{ptc} * PEC_{pc} * Y_{pc} \right) \quad \forall p, \forall t \tag{4}$$

$$Operational\ Cost_{dt} = Investment\ Cost_{d} * 0.05 \quad \forall d, \forall t \tag{5}$$

$$Water\ Cost_{pt} = W_{pt} * WP \quad \forall p, \forall t \tag{6}$$

$$\begin{aligned} Transportation\ Cost = & \left(\sum_{r}\sum_{t}\sum_{d}\sum_{Wf} CO_{rtdWf} * BW_{rtdWf} \right) + \left(\sum_{r}\sum_{t}\sum_{d}\sum_{ECf} CO_{rtdECf} * BEC_{rtdECf} \right) \\ & + \left(\sum_{d}\sum_{t}\sum_{p}\sum_{Wf} TC_{dtpWf} * AW_{dtpWf} \right) + \left(\sum_{d}\sum_{t}\sum_{p}\sum_{ECf} TC_{dtpECf} * AEC_{dtpECf} \right) + \left(\sum_{p}\sum_{t}\sum_{r} TCF_{ptr} * FER_{ptr} \right) \end{aligned} \tag{7}$$

$$Biomass\ Purchasing\ Cost = \left(\sum_{r}\sum_{t}\sum_{d}\sum_{Wf} PCW_{Wf} * BW_{rtdWf} \right) + \left(\sum_{r}\sum_{t}\sum_{d}\sum_{ECf} PCEC_{ECf} * BEC_{rtdECf} \right) \tag{8}$$

3.1.2. Second objective: Minimization of the weighted unprocessed waste biomass amount

Since environmental protection is a significant dimension of this study, amount of unprocessed biomass that are not collected from the supply regions is used as a key measure besides monetary considerations. Different from the previous research in this area, different weights are assigned to supply regions to reflect the urgency level of waste disposal from the regions. Eq. (9) represent the second objective function (O2).

$$\text{Weighted Unused Waste Biomass Amount} = \sum_r \sum_t \sum_{Wf} W_r * \left[\left(AA_{rtWf} * k_{Wf} \right) - \sum_d BW_{rtdWf} \right] \quad (9)$$

3.2. The constraints

• Biomass availability and energy crop cultivation area constraints

$$\begin{aligned} &\sum_d BW_{rtdWf} \leq AA_{rtWf} * k_{Wf} \quad \forall r, \forall Wf, \forall t \\ &\sum_d BEC_{rtdECf} \leq ECAP_{rt} * V_{tECf} * EA_{rt} \quad \forall r, \forall ECf, \forall t \\ &ECAP_{rt} \leq PP \quad \forall r, \forall t \end{aligned} \quad (10)$$

• Flow conservation constraints

$$\begin{aligned} &\sum_r BW_{rtdWf} = \sum_p AW_{dtpWf} \quad \forall d, \forall Wf \\ &\sum_r BEC_{rtdECf} + DSECC_{d(t-1)} = \sum_p AEC_{dtpECf} + DSECC_{dt} \quad \forall d, \forall ECf, \forall t \end{aligned} \quad (11)$$

• Capacity constraints

$$\begin{aligned} &\sum_r \sum_{Wf} BW_{rtdWf} \leq SLWC_d \quad \forall d, \forall Liquid / Semisolid\ Wf, \forall t \\ &\sum_r \sum_{Wf} BW_{rtdWf} \leq SSWC_d \quad \forall d, \forall Solid\ Wf, \forall t \\ &DSECCAP_{dt} \leq SSECC_d \quad \forall d, \forall t \\ &SLWC_d + SSWC_d \leq MaxDC * XW_d \quad \forall d, \forall t \\ &\sum_d \sum_{Wf} AW_{dtpWf} + \sum_d \sum_{ECf} AEC_{dtpECf} \leq \sum_c PCAP_{pc} * Y_{pc} \quad \forall p, \forall t \end{aligned} \quad (12)$$

• Total solid content of biomass slurry constraint

$$MinTS \leq \frac{\left(\sum_d \sum_{Wf} TSW_{Wf} * AW_{dtpWf} \right) + \left(\sum_d \sum_{ECf} TSEC_{ECf} * AEC_{dtpECf} \right)}{\sum_d \sum_{Wf} AW_{dtpWf} + \sum_d \sum_{ECf} AEC_{dtpECf} + W_{pt}} \leq MaxTS \quad \forall p \quad (13)$$

• Fertilizer distribution constraints

$$\begin{aligned} &\left(\sum_d \sum_{Wf} AW_{dtpWf} * gW_{Wf} \right) + \left(\sum_d \sum_{ECf} AEC_{dtpECf} * gEC_{ECf} \right) = \sum_r FER_{ptr} \quad \forall p, \forall t \\ &\sum_p \sum_r FER_{ptr} \leq \sum_r TCA_{rt} * 1.45 \quad \forall t \end{aligned} \quad (14)$$

• Biogas and electricity production constraints

$$\left(\sum_{d}\sum_{Wf} AW_{dtWpf} * eW_{Wf}\right)+\left(\sum_{d}\sum_{ECf} AEC_{dtECpf} * eEC_{ECf}\right)= Outbio_{pt} \quad \forall p,\forall t$$

$$Outbio_{pt} * v * c = Outelc_{pt} \quad \forall p,\forall t \tag{15}$$

$$Outelc_{pt} \leq \sum_{c} PEC_{pc} * Y_{pc} \quad \forall p,\forall t \tag{16}$$

4. Case Study

To explore the viability of the proposed model, computational experiments are performed on a real-world problem. In this regard, we design a biomass to energy supply chain network in İzmir/Turkey considering all 20 counties of İzmir as potential biomass supply zones and potential sites for the biogas plants and biomass storages. A diagrammatic representation of the supply chain network considered in this study is presented in Figure 1. The length of the time period used in our computational analyses is one month and the planning horizon is three years. We assume that corn silage is cultivated in a part of arable empty area. The urgency levels of the waste disposal for the supply regions are determined by considering the region specific properties that are distance to the seacoast, ground and surface waters and the residential areas. We treat uncertainty about the objectives and energy crop cultivation area. To provide the decision makers for a more confident solution set for policy decision making, the model is solved by using different FGP approaches. In this regard, five different fuzzy solution approaches are employed, namely Bellman and Zadeh's min operator (1) (Bellman and Zadeh, 1970) , Li's two-phase approach (2) (Li, 1990), Tiwari et al.'s weighted additive approach (3) (Tiwari et al., 1987), Lai and Hwang's approach (4) (Lai and Hwang, 1992) and Lin's weighted max-min approach (5) (Lin, 2004). The proposed model is solved by using ILOG CPLEX Optimization Studio (Version 12.2). Besides the overall profit and unused biomass amount, payback period (PBP) is considered. The results are presented in Tables 1 and 2. To provide the decision makers a broader perspective, solutions with two different weight structures are obtained as reported in Table 2.

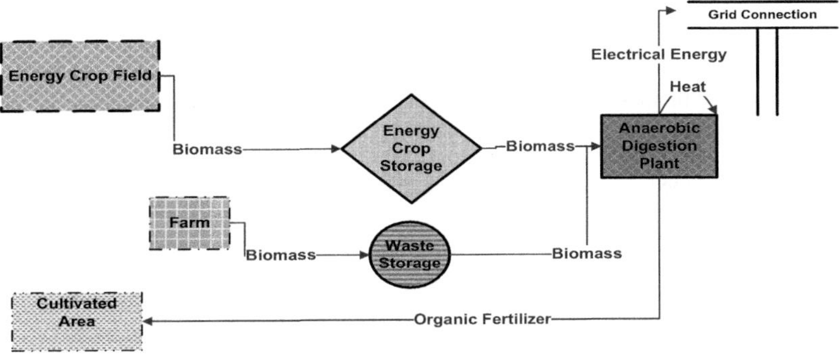

Figure 1. Representation of the supply chain network

Table 1. Solutions with (1) and (2)

Solution with (1)			Solution with (2)		
O1(€)	O2(t)	PBP(y)	O1(€)	O2(t)	PBP(y)
461,074,569	51	7.62	462,378,173	0	7.32

Table 2. Solutions with (3), (4) and (5)

Weights			Solution with (3)			Solution with (4)			Solution with (5)		
O1	O2	ECAP	O1(€)	O2(t)	PBP(y)	O1(€)	O2(t)	PBP(y)	O1(€)	O2(t)	PBP(y)
0.5	0.4	0.1	535,477,767	0	5.46	533,805,320	0	5.39	469,562,910	3816	6.78
0.85	0.1	0.05	535,372,168	0	5.64	535,283,710	0	5.40	470,596,893	4203	6.69

The tables show that the best value of profit is obtained with Tiwari et al.'s weighted additive approach (535,477,767 €) with a reasonable PBP (5.46 y) and zero unused waste biomass amount. However, the shortest PBP is reached with Lai and Hwang's approach (5.39 y) with a decrease of 1,672,447 € in profit. The investment decision can be made according to the decision maker's priorities of different objectives. Pay back periods of the biomass to energy conversion system design options obtained in this study change between 5 and 8 y, which are reasonable considering the fact that payback period of anaerobic digestion systems generally change within a range of 3 to 15 y in real world implementations (Menind and Olt, 2009).

5. Conclusions

Different from the previous researches in the field of biomass to energy supply chain design, in this study a MILP model is developed to design and analyze anaerobic digestion based biomass to energy supply chains which uses mainly waste biomass as feedstock considering uncertain system parameters with fuzzy modeling approach. The results reveal that the proposed model can effectively be used in practice, and that the economic and environmental benefits of biogas to energy systems are significant for Turkey. It is believed that this study will raise awareness on the potential of energy production from biomass and will provide a perspective for the investments in this field that will be realized by public or private sector. Although the problem under concern is modeled with problem specific constraints, the proposed model is generic in its structure and can be tailored to handle a region-specific problem with different types of feedstock.

References

L. Čuček, M. Martín, I. E. Grossmann, Z. Kravanja, 2013, Multi-period Synthesis of a Biorefinery's Supply Networks, Computer Aided Chemical Engineering, 32, 73-78.

S. D. Ekşioğlu, A. Acharya, L. E. Leightley, S. Arora, 2009, Analyzing the design and management of biomass-to-biorefinery supply chain, Computers and Industrial Engineering, 57, 4, 1342-1352.

M. Dal Mas, S. Giarola, A. Zamboni, F. Bezzo, 2010, Capacity planning and financial optimization of the bioethanol supply chain under price uncertainty, Computer Aided Chemical Engineering, 28, 97-102.

R. E. Bellman, L. A. Zadeh, 1970, Decision-making in a fuzzy environment, Management Science, 17, 141-164.

R. J. Li, 1990, Multiple objective decision making in a fuzzy environment, PhD Thesis, Department of Industrial Engineering, Kansas State University, Manhattan, US.

R. N. Tiwari, S. Dharmar, J. R. Rao, 1987, Fuzzy goal programming: An additive method, Fuzzy Sets and Systems, 24, 27-34.

Y. J. Lai, C. L. Hwang, 1992, Possibilistic linear programming for managing interest rate risk, Fuzzy Sets and Systems, 49, 121-133.

C. C. Lin, 2004, A weighted max–min model for fuzzy goal programming, Fuzzy Sets and Systems, 142, 407-420.

A. Menind, J. Olt, 2009, Biogas plant investment analysis, cost benefit and main, Engineering for Rural Development, 339-343.

Jiří Jaromír Klemeš, Petar Sabev Varbanov and Peng Yen Liew (Editors)
Proceedings of the 24th European Symposium on Computer Aided Process Engineering – ESCAPE 24
June 15-18, 2014, Budapest, Hungary.

Using Thermodynamic Insight in the Optimization of LNG Processes

Bjørn Austbø,* Truls Gundersen

Department of Energy and Process Engineering, Norwegian University of Science and Technology (NTNU), Kolbjoern Hejes vei 1B, NO-7491 Trondheim, Norway
bjorn.austbo@ntnu.no

Abstract

In pure-refrigerant cascade processes for natural gas liquefaction, several stages must be combined in order to obtain energy efficient designs. This introduces a large number of degrees of freedom in the optimization problem. In this work, the power consumption of a simple and a complex cascade process has been minimized. Thermodynamic insight has been used to facilitate the choice of decision variables and their respective bounds. For the studied cases, the results indicate that refrigerant superheating improves the energy efficiency, while the effect of refrigerant sub-cooling is the opposite.

Keywords: LNG, pure refrigerant, cascade, optimization.

1. Introduction

Liquefied natural gas (LNG) is a profitable alternative to pipe-line transport for long transport distances and moderate volumes. The natural gas is liquefied at near atmospheric pressure to reduce its volume, enabling transport of large quantities in tanks. Condensation of natural gas takes place at gliding temperature, requiring energy intensive low-temperature refrigeration. Hence the energy efficiency of the liquefaction process is an important factor in the LNG value chain.

Heat transfer across a finite temperature difference leads to irreversibilities, which directly translates to increasing power consumption in the refrigeration process. The influence of the heat-transfer temperature driving force increases with decreasing temperature level at which the heat transfer takes place. Thus, in processes for natural gas liquefaction, the temperature difference in the heat exchangers should be small to achieve an energy efficient design. This is also the reason why rigorous thermodynamic models should be applied in the design procedure to ensure practical feasibility of the final design solution.

In a conventional pure-refrigerant refrigeration process, cooling is provided by evaporation at constant temperature. As the natural gas condenses at gliding temperature, this is not suitable for LNG processes. The power consumption may be reduced by using a refrigerant providing cooling at gliding temperature, or alternatively by combining refrigeration cycles with refrigerants operating at different temperature levels. The latter process concept is the subject of this study.

In a pure-refrigerant cascade process, several different refrigerant operating at different temperature levels are combined. Each of these refrigeration cycles may be divided in stages to further improve the energy efficiency. This introduces a high number of degrees of freedom in the design. However, as the different stages in a cascade refrigeration process hold similar thermodynamic properties, the optimization problem formulation may be simplified through thermodynamic insight and analysis.

Barnés and King (1974) proposed a synthesis method for the design of pure-refrigerant cascade processes, formulated as a network problem and solved using dynamic programming to minimize the annual cost. In the proposed method, heuristic rules for appropriate use of economizers, side loads, after-coolers, intercoolers, pre-saturators and internal heat exchangers are applied in order to reduce the number of design alternatives prior to the optimization. According to Cheng and Mah (1980), potentially favourable design may be omitted in the method proposed by Barnés and King (1974). They presented heuristics for the synthesis of cascade refrigeration, supported by the guidelines proposed by Barnés and King (1974). Heat capacities and heat transfer properties were assumed constant (Cheng and Mah, 1980).

Quite recently, Zhang and Xu (2011) presented a superstructure for optimal synthesis of a pure-refrigerant cascade process, originally developed for the retrofit design of the refrigeration system in an olefin plant. In the proposed superstructure, vapour formed during expansion is fed directly to the compressor, and cooling is provided solely through evaporation, hence there is no opportunity for refrigerant superheating. Exergy analyses of a cascade LNG process with propane, ethane and methane as the refrigerants have been performed by Kanoğlu (2002) and Cipolato et al. (2012).

2. Research method

In this study, a multistart local deterministic optimization approach has been used. The sequential quadratic programming method NLPQLP (Schittkowski, 2006) has been connected with the commercial process simulation tool Aspen HYSYS® (Aspen Technology, Inc., V7.3) which is used for the process simulation with the Soave-Redlich-Kwong equation of state.

3. Case study

The objective of the process design is to minimize the total power consumption required to liquefy a natural gas stream as given in Table 1. The natural gas is cooled at elevated pressure and LNG is produced by expanding the product stream to near atmospheric pressure. A small amount of flash gas will be produced in the expansion process.

Table 1. Natural gas process specifications.

Variable	Unit	Value
Flow rate	kg/s	1.0
Feed pressure	bar	55
Feed temperature	K	293.15
Product temperature	K	115
Molar composition:		
Methane	-	0.897
Ethane	-	0.055
Propane	-	0.018
N-butane	-	0.002
Nitrogen	-	0.028

All heat-exchanger pressure drops have been neglected in this study. The process design is constrained by a minimum temperature difference required in the heat exchangers equal to 2 K, to accommodate the trade-off between operating costs and investment costs of the process. In addition, a minimum superheating of 10 K is required for the compressor suction streams in order to avoid liquid inlet. For the compressors, a constant isentropic efficiency of 80 % has been assumed.

The temperature of all the hot streams exiting a refrigeration stage is assumed to be equal. However, the refrigerant hot streams are only cooled if their entrance temperature is higher than the given heat-exchanger outlet temperature. Likewise, the coolers are only used if the temperature of the inlet stream exceeds the cooler outlet temperature of 293.15 K. The lower bound on the pressure is set to 1 bar for all the refrigerants.

3.1. Simple cascade process

First, a simple cascade process consisting of three refrigeration cycles is studied. As illustrated in Figure 1, a simple refrigeration cycle contains only one level of refrigerant evaporation. In this study, the refrigerants used in order of descending cooling temperature are propane, ethene (ethylene) and methane. In total, 11 degrees of freedom are available for the process design. These could be the two pressure levels and the refrigerant flow rate in each cycle, in addition to the two intermediate temperature levels of the natural gas stream.

One alternative choice of decision variables for the simple cascade process is given in Table 2. Exergy considerations suggest that the temperature difference in heat transfer should be as small as possible to reduce the power consumption, especially at low temperature levels. Hence the heat-exchanger cold-end temperature difference should be equal to the minimum required. When the cold-end temperature difference is used as a decision variable, the lower bound is the minimum temperature difference $\Delta T_{\mathrm{min,HX}}$.

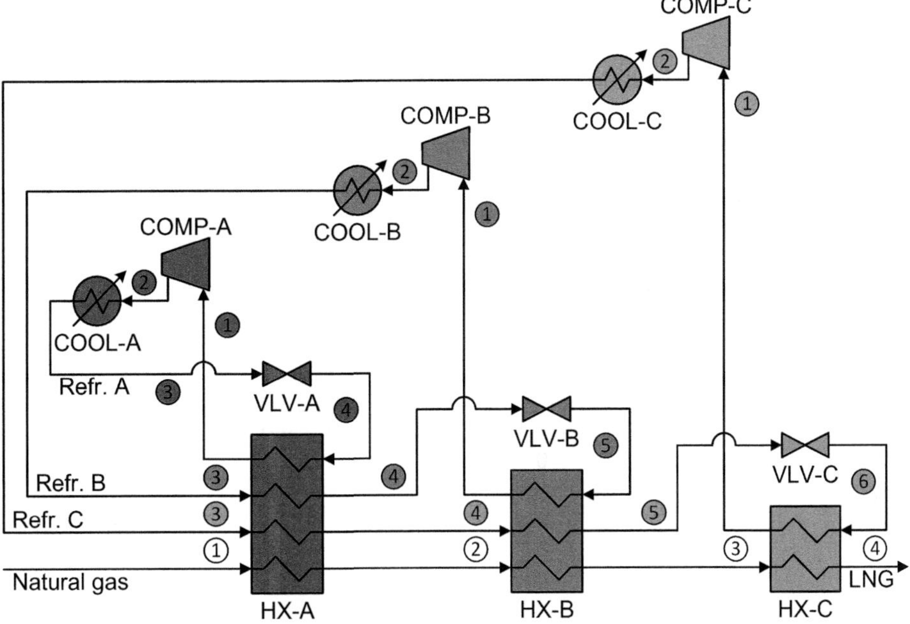

Figure 1. Simple cascade process with three refrigeration cycles for natural gas liquefaction.

The refrigerant low pressure levels determine the evaporation temperature in the different refrigeration cycles, and thus the cooling load distribution. Increasing the low pressure level in a given cycle will lead to reduced power consumption in the same cycle but increased power consumption in the subsequent cycle. In this study, the upper bound has been set to assure that the high pressure level in the subsequent refrigeration cycle will not exceed the critical pressure. The variables Δp_{sub} describe the pressure elevation above the minimum high pressure level required for the different refrigerants to be fully condensed before expansion. If the value is zero, the refrigerant entering the expansion valve will be saturated liquid, while for values above zero it will be in the state of sub-cooled liquid.

The refrigerant superheating is expressed through the parameters x_{sup} which determines the refrigerant temperature in the warm end of the heat exchangers. For minimum superheating, the value is zero, and the refrigerant temperature in the warm end of the heat exchanger is equal to the evaporation temperature plus the minimum superheating required. Maximum superheating is denoted as unity, and the warm-end temperature difference is equal to the minimum required. For limited nonlinearity of the natural gas cooling curve, the smallest temperature difference in the heat exchangers will be observed in the endpoints. In this case, by using this choice of decision variables, the design will fulfil the constraints for all combinations.

As expected, the results in Table 2 indicate that the cold-end temperature difference should be equal to the minimum required. The optimal value of the low pressure level is found to be at the lower bound for both the propane cycle and the ethene cycle. In the methane cycle, the low pressure level is at the upper bound, so that the cold-end temperature difference also in this cycle is equal to the minimum required.

Refrigerant superheating will lead to increasing compressor suction temperature, and thereby increasing specific compression power. However, it also results in a smaller refrigerant flow rate as the specific cooling capacity also increases. In this case, the results indicate that the effect of reduced refrigerant flow rate more than compensates the effect of increasing specific compression power, hence the total power consumption is reduced with increasing refrigerant superheating.

Table 2. Alternative choice of decision variables for the simple cascade process.

Variable	Lower bound	Upper bound	Best
$\Delta T_{cold,A}$	$\Delta T_{min,HX}$	-	$\Delta T_{min,HX}$
$\Delta T_{cold,B}$	$\Delta T_{min,HX}$	-	$\Delta T_{min,HX}$
$p_{L,A}$	p_{min}	$p_{sat,A}(T_{crit,B} - \Delta T_{min,HX})$	p_{min}
$p_{L,B}$	p_{min}	$p_{sat,B}(T_{crit,C} - \Delta T_{min,HX})$	p_{min}
$p_{L,C}$	p_{min}	$p_{sat,C}(T_{NG,out} - \Delta T_{min,HX})$	$p_{sat,C}(T_{NG,out} - \Delta T_{min,HX})$
$\Delta p_{sub,A}$	0	-	0
$\Delta p_{sub,B}$	0	-	0
$\Delta p_{sub,C}$	0	-	0
$x_{sup,A}$	0	1	1
$x_{sup,B}$	0	1	1
$x_{sup,C}$	0	1	1

Increasing the refrigerant high pressure level will result in both increasing specific compression power as the pressure ratio increases, and increasing specific cooling capacity as the vapour formation in the expansion process is reduced. The former effect has a stronger influence for all the refrigerants, hence refrigerant sub-cooling leads to increasing power consumption in all the refrigeration cycles.

3.2. Complex cascade process

In a complex refrigeration cycle, evaporation takes place at two or more temperature levels. By introducing intermediate pressure levels, the temperature driving forces in the heat transfer process is reduced and the energy efficiency of the process improved. In the process studied, each of the three refrigeration cycles are divided in three stages as illustrated in Figure 2.

In total, there are 29 degrees of freedom in the design of the complex cascade process. By assuming the findings for the simple refrigeration cycle also hold for the complex cascade process, the number of decision variables may be reduced to six. In this study, it is assumed that the cold end temperature difference in all heat exchangers is equal to the minimum required, and that the low pressure level of the propane and ethene refrigerants should be at the lower bound. In addition, the refrigerant superheating is at the maximum in all heat exchangers and no refrigerant sub-cooling is applied.

The intermediate stage temperatures of the natural gas stream are restricted by the temperature given at the inlet and outlet of each cycle. In addition, the cooling in each refrigeration stage must be large enough to enable the required refrigerant superheating without violating the minimum temperature difference constraint.

With the variable bounds given in Table 3, it is possible for the temperatures to cross, indicating that the natural gas will be heated in a refrigeration stage. In order to avoid this, the temperature variables T_b have been reformulated to use the temperatures T_a in the calculation of the upper bound. An alternative choice of decision variables is to use the intermediate pressure levels of the different refrigerants. The total power consumption in the best solution found for the complex cascade process is 785.6 kW.

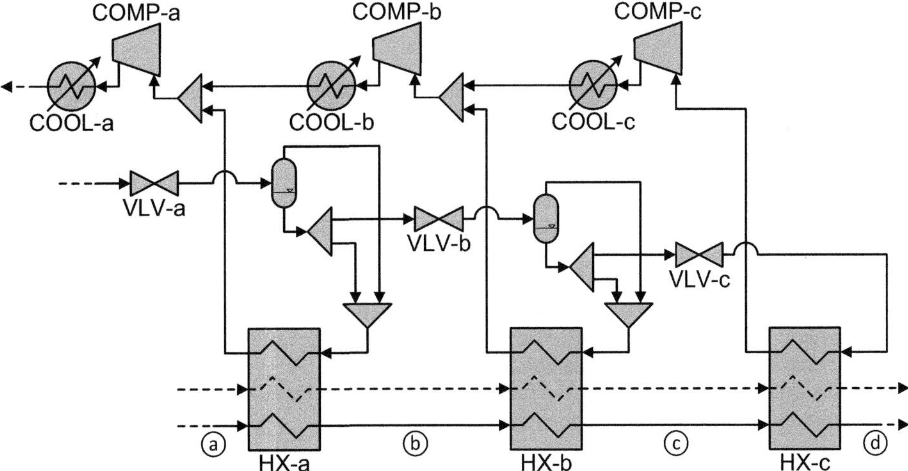

Figure 2. Vertical stage in cascade process with three horizontal stages.

Table 3. Decision variables used for the complex cascade process.

Variable	Lower bound	Upper bound	Best
$T_{a,A}$	$T_{sat,A}(p_{min}) + 2{\cdot}\Delta T_{min,sup} + \Delta T_{min,HX}$	$T_{NG,in} - \Delta T_{min,sup}$	278.5 K
$T_{b,A}$	$T_{sat,A}(p_{min}) + \Delta T_{min,sup} + \Delta T_{min,HX}$	$T_{NG,in} - 2{\cdot}\Delta T_{min,sup}$	261.3 K
$T_{a,B}$	$T_{sat,B}(p_{min}) + 2{\cdot}\Delta T_{min,sup} + \Delta T_{min,HX}$	$T_{sat,A}(p_{min}) - \Delta T_{min,sup} + \Delta T_{min,HX}$	209.2 K
$T_{b,B}$	$T_{sat,B}(p_{min}) + \Delta T_{min,sup} + \Delta T_{min,HX}$	$T_{sat,A}(p_{min}) - 2{\cdot}\Delta T_{min,sup} + \Delta T_{min,HX}$	192.3 K
$T_{a,C}$	$T_{NG,out} + 2{\cdot}\Delta T_{min,sup}$	$T_{sat,B}(p_{min}) - \Delta T_{min,sup} + \Delta T_{min,HX}$	148.8 K
$T_{b,C}$	$T_{NG,out} + \Delta T_{min,sup}$	$T_{sat,B}(p_{min}) - 2{\cdot}\Delta T_{min,sup} + \Delta T_{min,HX}$	129.9 K

For the simple cycle, the best solution found has a power consumption equal to 1,205.9 kW. The minimum exergy input required to cool the natural gas is 403.8 kW.

4. Conclusions

For the two cases studied, the results indicate that the refrigerant should not be sub-cooled prior to expansion. The heat-exchanger cold-end temperature difference should be equal to the minimum temperature difference required, as motivated by exergy considerations. As opposed to most process designs presented in the literature, this study indicates that refrigerant superheating is beneficial.

The results obtained in this study indicate that use of thermodynamic insight may improve the performance of LNG process design optimization, by choosing decision variables that are easily bounded. An objective for future work on this subject is to generalize the use of thermodynamic analysis in pure-refrigerant cascade process optimization, and further translate the ideas to also handle mixed-refrigerant processes.

5. Acknowledgements

This publication is based on results from the research project "Enabling low-emission LNG systems", performed under the Petromaks program. The authors acknowledge the project partners; Statoil and GDF SUEZ, and the Research Council of Norway (193062/S60) for financial support, and Per Eilif Wahl, SINTEF Energy Research, for providing the interface software required for this study.

References

F.J. Barnés, C.J. King, 1974, Synthesis of Cascade Refrigeration and Liquefaction Systems, Industrial and Engineering Chemistry Process Design and Development, 13, 4, 421-433.

W.B. Cheng, R.S.H. Mah, 1980, Interactive Synthesis of Cascade Refrigeration Systems, Industrial and Engineering Chemistry Process Design and Development, 19, 3, 410-420.

L. Cipolato, M.C.A. Lirani, T.V. Costa, F.M. Fábrega, J.V.H. d'Angelo, 2012, Exergetic optimization of a refrigeration cycle for natural gas liquefaction, Computer Aided Chemical Engineering, 31, 440-444.

M. Kanoğlu, 2002, Exergy analysis of multistage cascade refrigeration cycle used for natural gas liquefaction, In ternational Journal of Energy Research, 26, 8, 763-774.

K. Schittkowski, 2006, NLPQLP (Version 2.2), Computer program, <www.ai7.uni-bayreuth.de/nlpqlp.htm> accessed on 31/01/2014.

J. Zhang, Q. Xu, 2011, Cascade refrigeration system synthesis based on exergy analysis, Computers and Chemical Engineering, 35, 9, 1901-1914.

Jiří Jaromír Klemeš, Petar Sabev Varbanov and Peng Yen Liew (Editors)
Proceedings of the 24th European Symposium on Computer Aided Process Engineering – ESCAPE 24
June 15-18, 2014, Budapest, Hungary.

An Adaptive Normal Constraint Method for Bi-Objective Optimal Synthesis of Energy Systems

Maike Hennen, Philip Voll, André Bardow*

RWTH Aachen University, Institute of Technical Thermodynamics, Schinkelstraße 8, 52062 Aachen, Germany

andre.bardow@ltt.rwth-aachen.de

Abstract

A novel approach is proposed for the efficient generation of the Pareto front for bi-objective optimal synthesis of energy systems. To avoid computationally expensive calculations of solutions not relevant to the decision maker, the proposed method adapts the computation of the Pareto front to the part relevant for practical energy systems. The algorithm produces an evenly distributed set of Pareto optimal solutions employing a modified normal constraint method. In contrast to the classical normal constraint method, the algorithm is no more initialized at the – usually computationally most expensive – single-objective optima but uses an aggregated objective function as starting point for an adaptive exploration of the Pareto front. The presented approach is applied to a real-world synthesis problem of a distributed energy supply system. It is shown that the adaptive normal constraint algorithm automatically generates the most relevant part of the Pareto front for the bi-objective optimal synthesis of an energy system computationally more efficient than the weighted sum method or the ε-constraint method.

Keywords: Pareto front Generation, Distributed Energy Supply Systems, Bi-Objective Optimization, MILP, Synthesis and Optimization.

1. Introduction

For optimal synthesis of distributed energy supply systems, optimization algorithms are used to determine the kind and number of energy conversion technologies, their design, and operational strategies. Generally, multiple, contradicting objectives have to be considered leading to multi-objective optimization problems. In practice, multi-objective optimization approaches for energy systems synthesis usually focus on two objectives, often balancing cost versus environmental impact (see e.g. Buoro et al., 2013). In this work, we address rigorous bi-objective optimization of energy systems. For illustration, we regard investment cost as economic and primary energy consumption as environmental criterion.

The result of this optimization is a so-called Pareto front that incorporates a set of Pareto-optimal solutions. A solution is Pareto-optimal if the value of one objective function can only be improved by worsening at least one other criterion. Common algorithms to obtain the Pareto front are the weighted sum method (Zadeh, 1963) and the ε-constraint method (Haimes et al., 1971). Established methods aim at exploring the whole Pareto front. The bi-objective Pareto front of energy systems problems regarding one economic and one environmental criterion has a typical shape (see Figure 1a): The part of the Pareto front with good performance of the economic criterion is very steep. Contrary, the other end of the Pareto front has a very flat gradient (Salcedoet al., 2012).

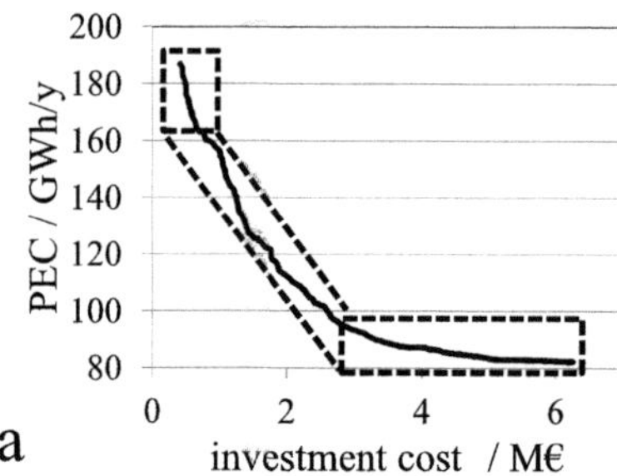

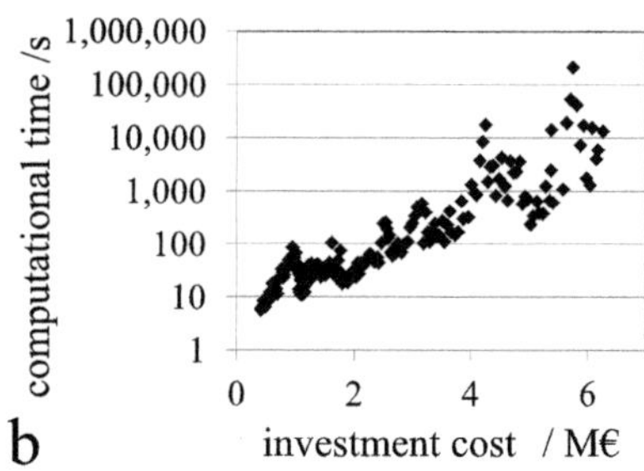

Figure 1.(a) Typical shape of a Pareto front for optimization problems of the synthesis of energy systems; (b) Computational effort as function of the investment cost; on the example of the real-world case (section 3.1) regarding investment cost and primary energy consumption (PEC)

Between the steep and the flat part of the Pareto front is a transition region containing good compromise solutions. Moreover, very energy-efficient solutions mostly use many units for operational flexibility, and thus require high investments. Due to high complexity of the underlying unit commitment problems, the identification of these solutions requires most of the computational effort (Figure 1b; note that the computation times are listed on a logarithmic scale). However, for practical cases, these solutions are usually not taken into consideration for the final decision because of excessively large investments and low environmental benefits. Previous methods for computations of the Pareto front still require the computation of these solutions. In this paper, a method is proposed that avoids the calculation of points with excessively high investment cost. Instead, the optimum regarding an aggregated objective function is computed as initial solution of the Pareto front, which is then further explored by the normal constraint method. During the Pareto front generation, gradients are computed and employed to terminate the algorithm. By focusing on the most relevant part of the Pareto front, computational effort is significantly reduced which we regard as mandatory to establish multi objective optimization in daily industrial practice.

This paper is structured as follows: In section 2, the novel adaptive normal constraint method is proposed. In section 3,this method is applied to a real-world example from energy systems engineering and compared to the weighted sum method and the ε-constraint method regarding the resulting Pareto front and the required computational effort. In section 4, the results are summarized.

2. Adaptive normal constraint method

In this section, the proposed adaptive normal constraint algorithm is described for bi-objective optimal synthesis of energy systems. The purpose of this method is to support decision makers by providing the most interesting part of the Pareto front at low computational cost. The novel algorithm is based upon the normal constraint method by Ismail-Yahaya and Messac (2002). For bi-objective optimization, the normal constraint method starts by calculating the anchor points of the Pareto fronts, i.e. the Pareto-optimal solutions which are optimal for one objective function. Following, the two points are connected by a line. The normal on this line is used as a constraint to one objective and is shifted stepwise between the anchor points to obtain the desired number of Pareto-optimal solutions.

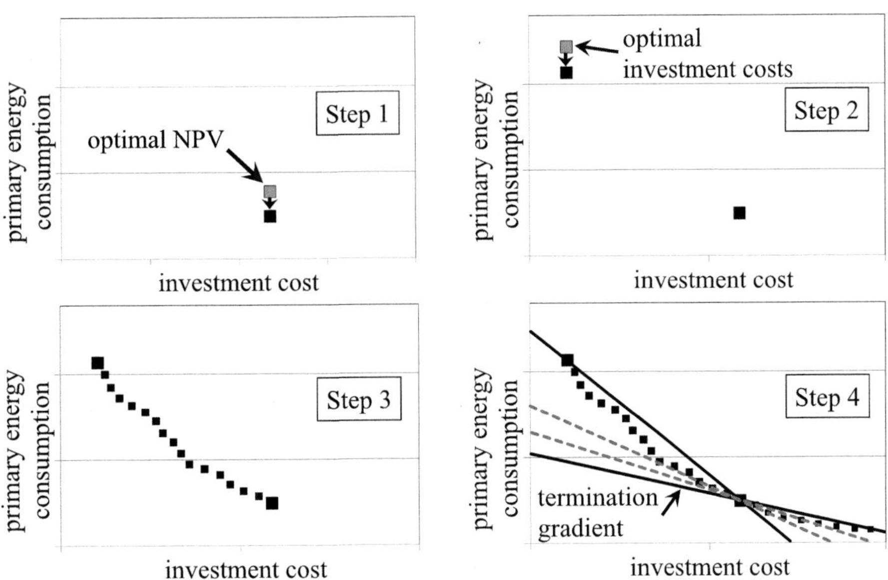

Figure 2. Stepwise graphical representation of the adaptive normal constraint method

For optimization of distributed energy supply systems, most computational effort arises from computations of very energy-efficient solutions with low environmental impact but high investment cost. These solutions usually contain many energy conversion units leading to high complexity of the underlying unit commitment problems. The proposed method avoids the calculation of the anchor point with high investment cost and instead uses the solution of an aggregated objective function as initialization point. For energy systems, a suitable aggregated objective function is the net present value (NPV) (Kasaš et al., 2011). In the following, the steps of the adaptive normal constraint method are described in detail (Figure 2).

2.1. Step 1: Optimum of aggregated objective function

First, the synthesis problem is solved optimizing an aggregated objective function. Afterwards, the economic objective function is fixed and the other objective function is optimized. This step is necessary, since the optimal solution regarding the aggregated objective function is in general not part of the Pareto front.

2.2. Step 2: Optimum of economic objective

In the second step, this procedure is repeated for the economic objective. In our case, investments are minimized. Then, the objective function value representing the investment cost is fixed and optimization is repeated minimizing the environmental criterion (primary energy consumption).

2.3. Step 3:Pareto front between the solutions of step 1 and step 2

The two solutions from step 1 and 2are taken as anchor points for the normal constraint method by Ismail-Yahaya and Messac (2002), which is applied to explore the Pareto optimal points between the optimum of the aggregated objective function and the optimum of the economic criterion. The line between these two solutions can be graphically interpreted as a secant to the Pareto front. The number of Pareto-optimal solutions to be generated has to be specified by the user before the optimization. The step size to shift the normal constraint is based on this number.

2.4. Step 4:Further exploration of the Pareto front and termination criterion

In step 4, the Pareto front is extended from the optimum of the aggregated objective function towards solutions with better performance regarding the environmental criterion. For the calculation of these points, the same step size as for the already known solutions is chosen. The exploration of the Pareto front is terminated when a predefined minimum gradient of the Pareto front is reached (see also Figure 1). For this purpose, the slope of the Pareto front section already explored in step 3 is used: First, the gradient Δ between the optimum of the aggregated objective function(AOF) and the optimum of the economic objective function(minimal cost) is determined by

$$\Delta = \frac{Z_{2,\,AOF} - Z_{2,\,minimal\ cost}}{Z_{1,\,AOF} - Z_{1,\,minimal\ cost}}, \tag{1}$$

where Z_1 represents the economic objective function and Z_2 the environmental objective function. In the same way, the gradient between the current point and the optimum of the aggregated objective function is computed. If this gradient falls below a predefined fraction of the gradient Δ, the algorithm stops. The ratio between the current and the secant gradient Δ can be chosen freely. In preliminary studies, a ratio of 0.5 was found to be suitable as termination criterion for energy systems synthesis problems.

3. Case study

In this section, the adaptive normal constraint method is applied to a real world synthesis problem and compared to the weighted sum algorithm and the ε-constraint method. The algorithms and the model of the energy system are implemented using GAMS (McCarl et al., 2011) and solved using CPLEX (IBM ILOG, 2013).

3.1. Real-world example

The real-world application originates from the pharmaceutical industry and deals with time-varying supply of heating, cooling and electricity to six distributed buildings. The demands can be satisfied by combinations of different energy conversion technologies. The employed equipment models of boilers, CHP engines, compression chillers and absorption chillers include linearized part-load performance and investment curves to allow an optimization as MILP. The model also incorporates already existing equipment. The industrial site and the used equipment models are described in detail by Voll et al. (2013).

3.2. Comparison of the results of different algorithms

To show the benefit of the novel adaptive normal constraint method, the weighted sum method (Zadeh, 1963) and the ε-constraint method (Haimes et al., 1971) are applied to the real-world case study as well. In the weighted sum method, the objective functions are summed up with varying weights and this sum is optimized. In the ε-constraint method, one objective function is optimized while the other objective function is limited to a varying value. The resulting Pareto fronts are compared regarding the computational effort and the quality of the front. The quality can be measured by three criteria (Alarcon-Rodriguez et al., 2010): Accuracy, diversity of the solutions and spread of the solutions over the whole solution space. The criterion spread is neglected in this comparison because it is the central idea of the adaptive normal constraint method to avoid computationally expensive but practically irrelevant solutions.

The results of the optimization regarding the two objective functions investment cost and primary energy consumption (PEC) are shown in Figure 3. For each algorithm, a Pareto front consisting of 10 Pareto-optimal solutions is calculated. The Pareto front

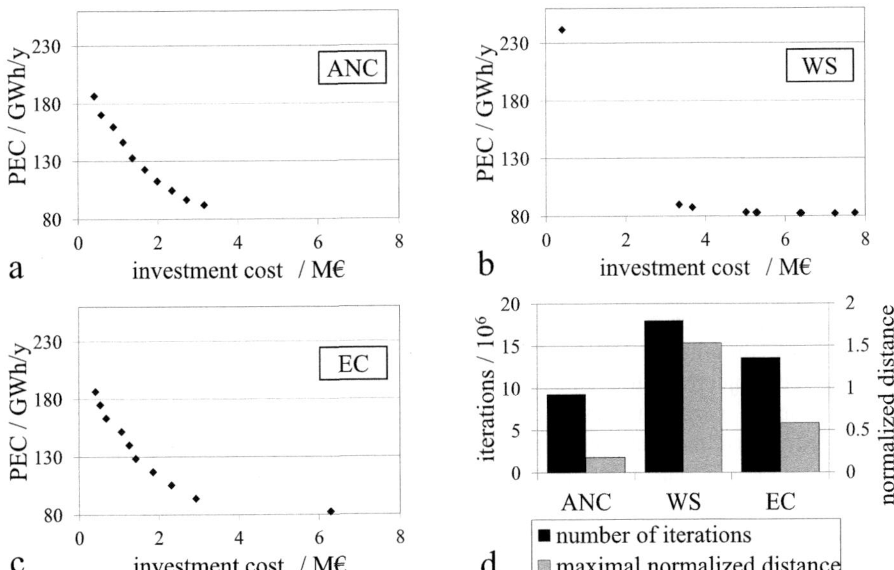

Figure 3.(a) – (c): Comparison of the Pareto fronts of adaptive normal constraint method (ANC, a), weighted sum method (WS, b), and ε-constraint method (EC, c) for the real-world example; (d): Comparison of computational effort for generating the Pareto front and maximal normalized distance of two Pareto-optimal solutions for adaptive normal constraint method (ANC), weighted sum method (WS), and ε-constraint method (EC)

computed by the adaptive normal constraint method represents an evenly distributed set of Pareto-optimal solutions regarding both criteria. Solutions with high investment cost and therefore high computational effort are not considered in this method. As we neglect the criterion spread, the adaptive normal constraint method fulfills both quality criteria diversity and accuracy. Using the weighted sum method, the solutions are not evenly distributed over the solution space. The anchor points of this front are not even Pareto-optimal, because only one objective is taken into account to identify these points. Thus, the two considered quality criteria of a Pareto front, namely accuracy and diversity, are not met. In contrast, the ε-constraint method calculates Pareto-optimal solutions that are only evenly distributed regarding one objective function (in our case: PEC).Therefore, only the quality criterion diversity is not met.

The maximal normalized Euclidean distance between two Pareto-optimal solutions is considered to evaluate the distribution of the generated Pareto fronts (Kim and de Weck, 2006). The normalization was carried out regarding the minimal and maximal values of the objective functions obtained with the ε-constraint method. The solutions on the Pareto front obtained with the weighted sum method are poorly distributed due to a lack of normalization (Figure 3d). The solutions on the Pareto front of the adaptive normal constraint method are evenly distributed while the ε-constraint method produces only evenly distributed solutions regarding one criterion and therefore has a larger maximal normalized distance. The required computational effort to generate the Pareto fronts shown in Figure 3 a-c is highest in case of the weighted sum method (Figure 3d),since it identifies many solutions with a large number of conversion units. The adaptive normal constraint method requires only 52 % of the iterations needed in the weighted sum method and 68 % of the iterations for the ε-constraint method.

In summary, the adaptive normal constraint method successfully generates a good, i.e. evenly distributed, representation of the most interesting part of the Pareto front containing good compromise solutions(see section 1) while reducing computational effort to generate this front compared to popular algorithms.

4. Conclusions

In this paper, an adaptive normal constraint method is proposed for bi-objective optimization of distributed energy supply systems. Taking one economic and one environmental criterion as objective functions, the decision maker usually is not interested in solutions with only marginal environmental improvements but high additional cost. Thus, these solutions are excluded from consideration in the proposed method by initializing the normal constraint method at a solution optimizing an aggregated objective function. An adaptive termination criterion then avoids the calculation of computationally expensive and practically irrelevant solutions. The proposed algorithm is applied to a real-world example. The novel method reduces the required computational effort compared to the popular weighted sum and ε-constraint method while generating an evenly distributed set of Pareto-optimal solutions. The number of iterations to generate 10 Pareto-optimal solutions is only 52 % of the iterations required for the weighted sum method and 68 % of the iterations for the ε-constraint method while improving the distribution of the Pareto-optimal solutions. The adaptive normal constraint algorithm successfully and efficiently explores the relevant part of the Pareto front.

Acknowledgements

Funding by the European Institute of Innovation & Technology, Climate Knowledge and Innovation Community (EIT Climate-KIC) is gratefully acknowledged.

References

A. Alarcon-Rodriguez, G. Ault, S. Galloway, 2010, Multi-objective planning of distributed energy resources: A review of thestate-of-the-art, Renew Sust Energ Rev, 14, 1353-1366.

D. Buoro, M. Casisi, A. De Nardi, P. Pinamonti, M. Reini, 2013, Multicriteria optimization of a distributed energy supply system for an industrial area, Energy, 58, 128-137.

Y. Haimes, L. Lasdon, D. Wismer, 1971, On a Bicriterion Formulation of the Problems of Integrated System Identification and System Optimization, IEEE T Syst Man Cyb, 1, 296-297.

IBM ILOG, 2013, IBM ILOG CPLEX Optimization studio (V 12.5), User's manual, Armonk, USA.

A. Ismail-Yahaya, A. Messac, 2002, Effective Generation of the Pareto Frontier using the Normal Constraint Method, AIAA-2002-0178.

M. Kasaš, Z. Kravanja, Z. N. Pintaric, 2011, Suitable modeling for process flow sheet optimization using the correct economic criterion, Ind Eng Chem Res, 50, 3356-3370.

I. Y. Kim, O. L. de Weck, 2006, Adaptive weighted sum method for multi-objective optimization: a new method for Pareto front generation, Struct Multidiscip O, 31, 105-116.

B. A. McCarl, A. Meeraus, P. V. D. Eijk, M. Bussieck, S. Dirkse, P. Steacy, F. Nelissen, 2011, McCarl GAMS User Guide, GAMS Development Corporation, Washington, USA.

R. Salcedo, E. Antipova, D. Boer, L. Jiménez, G. Guillén-Gosálbez, 2012, Multi-objective optimization of solar Rankine cycles coupled with reverse osmosis desalination considering economic and life cycle environmental concerns, Desalination, 286, 358-371.

P. Voll, C. Klaffke, M. Hennen, A. Bardow, 2013, Automated superstructure-based synthesis and optimization of distributed energy supply systems, Energy, 50, 374-388.

L. Zadeh, 1963, Optimality and non-scalar-valued performance criteria, IEEE T Automat Contr, 8, 59-60.

Jiří Jaromír Klemeš, Petar Sabev Varbanov and Peng Yen Liew (Editors)
Proceedings of the 24th European Symposium on Computer Aided Process Engineering – ESCAPE 24
June 15-18, 2014, Budapest, Hungary.

A Quick Knapsack Heuristic Solution for Pharmaceutical R&D Pipeline Management Problems

Brianna Christian, Selen Cremaschi*

Department of Chemical Engineering,The University of Tulsa, 800 S Tucker Drive, Tulsa,OK, USA
selen-cremaschi@utulsa.edu

Abstract

The paper presents a novel knapsack decomposition algorithm for solving multistage stochastic programs (MSSPs) with endogenous uncertainty, specifically focusing on pharmaceutical R&D pipeline management problem. The algorithm decomposes the MSSP into a series of knapsack problems, which are created and solved at key decision points on a rolling horizon fashion. Based on the results of the five case studies, the algorithm generates implementable solutions with several orders of magnitude decrease in the CPU times required to solve the rigorous MSSP.

Keywords: Multistage Stochastic Program, Endogenous Uncertainty, R&D Pipeline Management, Knapsack.

1. Introduction

Pharmaceutical manufacturers pursue approaches to develop optimal investment strategies for new product developments, i.e., to manage their pharmaceutical R&D pipeline. The characteristics of the R&D pipeline management problem are several new-product-development projects, different levels of resources necessary to complete each project, limited amounts of available resources, and returns once the products reach the market. The development of new products involves a stage-gate process: if a product fails to successfully complete a stage, the product does not continue through the subsequent stages, and the return of that product is not realized. The decisions are to select which projects to pursue, and the best way to assign the resources to the chosen projects to maximize the returns (Subramanian et al., 2001). The necessary resources, the returns, and which products will make it to the market are not known with certainty at the time the decisions are made, and the uncertainties are resolved slowly as the decisions are executed (Colvin and Maravelias, 2010). This type of uncertainty, whose resolution depends on the decisions, is referred to as endogenous uncertainty (Goel and Grossmann, 2006). The approaches developed to solve the R&D pipeline management problem can be grouped into two main categories: conventional optimization and simulation optimization. When conventional optimization approaches, the focus of this paper, are used, the R&D pipeline management problems yield MSSPs with endogenous and exogenous uncertainty (Colvin and Maravelias, 2008).

Stochastic programs represent each of the possible outcomes as a scenario. In order to prevent anticipative decisions, a set of logic constraints, called non-anticipativity (NA) constraints, are added. These constraints are used to relate scenarios whose outcomes are indistinguishable. Colvin and Maravelias (2008) showed that as the number of products increases the problem become intractable due to exponential growth in the number of NA constraints. Recent studies focused on developing techniques to reduce the number of NA constraints and the solution time. Colvin and Maravelias (2010) presented a branch and cut algorithm, which exploits the inactivity of the majority of NA constraints to bound and solve the problem to optimality. The algorithm significantly reduces the number of NA constraints. Gupta and Grossman (2011) presented several strategies to reduce the solution time: (1) a k-stage approximation approach, (2) a NA relaxation algorithm, (3) a Lagrangian decomposition method (Gupta and Grossman 2011). The k-stage approximation approach enforces only the first k-stages of NA constraints. The NA relaxation algorithm improved the implementability of NA reduction techniques presented by Colvin and Maravelias (2010) in commercial solvers. The Lagrangian decomposition method utilizes the duals of the NA constraints to solve the problem scenario-wise. In a more recent study, Gupta and Grossman (2013) used a scenario grouping strategy to reduce the number of conditional NAs needed to specify the full problem space. It was found that if uncertainty was revealed early in the planning horizon the k-stage approach yielded the global optimum quickly. For problems where the uncertainty was revealed later in the planning horizon, it was found that the NA relaxation algorithm performed better. The MSSPs become computationally intractable with the size of the portfolio because the scenario and decision trees grow exponentially. To date, the largest R&D pipeline management problem solved included seven products (Colvin and Maravelias, 2010).

In this paper, we present a novel heuristic decomposition approach that yields implementable solutions for the pharmaceutical R&D pipeline management problem. The approach decomposes the MSSP into a series of knapsack problems, which are solved very quickly on a rolling horizon fashion throughout the planning period. The next section gives a brief description of the pharmaceutical R&D pipeline management problem. Section 3 explains the heuristic algorithm. In Section 4, the computational results for several case studies are given. The last section summarizes our conclusions.

2. Problem Description

The objective of the pharmaceutical R&D pipeline management problem is to maximize the value of investment decisions given a set of potential outcomes (scenarios). The problem assumes that there is a known set of products ($d \in \mathbf{D}$) with known maximum revenues (Rev_d^{max}). Each of these products is required to complete a set of stages ($j \in \mathbf{J}$) with fixed durations ($\omega_{d,j}$). Given a continuous planning period of n months, a discrete planning horizon ($t \in \mathbf{T}$) with length $|\mathbf{T}|$ is created with $\Delta t = n/|\mathbf{T}|$. Each decision has a monetary cost ($C_{d,j}$), and a resource(s) ($r \in \mathbf{R}$) based cost(s) ($\rho_{d,j,r}$). The resource(s) available to use for investments are constrained by ($\rho_r^{\max}$).

The value of the decision tree is estimated with its expected net present value (ENPV). The NPV of each scenario is calculated by deducting the cost(s) of the decisions and the penalties from the total revenue realized. The revenue realized is given by the depreciated revenue for all product(s) reaching the market within the planning horizon and the potential revenue of product(s) that are waiting to be started. There are two penalties associated with the products sitting idle in the pipeline: (1) loss in active patent life, and (2) loss of market share to competitors. They are estimated using a linear-time model with parameters γ_d^L (loss of patent life) and γ_d^D (loss of market share).

3. The Knapsack Decomposition Approach (KDA)

The algorithm for the KDA (Figure 1) solves a series of knapsack problems at allowable time periods, which are determined based on the uncertainty outcomes and availability of the decisions. The algorithm starts by generating the set of items, **I**, by enumerating all possible decisions, i.e., the product ($d\in\mathbf{D}$) – stage ($j\in\mathbf{J}$) pairs. The value of each item i at each time period t ($V_{i,t}$ $i\in\mathbf{I}$) is calculated based on the likelihood that the product successfully passes the remaining stages and its potential revenue, *viz.* Eq. (1).

$$V_{i,t} = \left[Rev_d{}^{max} - \gamma_d{}^{L}(t + \omega_{d,j^{max}} + 1)\right] \prod_{j \geq I(j)} P\left(P_{d,j} = Pass\right) \quad (1)$$

In Eq. (1), Rev_d^{max} represents the potential revenue for the product associated with the item i. The revenue is penalized using a linear time model with parameter γ_d^L for loss in active patent life. The value of the depreciated revenue is then weighted using the probability that the product will pass the remaining stages.

The objective of each knapsack problem is to maximize the value of the knapsack without violating the maximum weight constraint(s). The resource requirement(s) of each item give(s) its weight(s), and the total available resource(s) are the maximum weight(s) of the knapsack. Which items can be packed in the knapsack at any given time is restricted by uncertainty outcomes and decision availability (i.e., items defined for the first stage of a product must be packed before the items defined for the second stage). For each knapsack problem, the algorithm generates an eligible items subset ($\mathbf{E}_{t,k}$). Eq. (2) is added as a constraint to each knapsack formulation to avoid bottlenecking down the pipeline due to unavailability of resources. Eq. (2) ensures that each product pushed through the pipeline at the current time can complete the remaining stages sequentially.

$$\sum_{i}\left[\sum_{j\geq j(i)} \rho_{d(i),j,r}\,\omega_{d(i),j}\right] X_i \leq |T|\rho_r{}^{max} \qquad \forall r\in\mathbf{R} \quad (2)$$

In Eq. (2), $\rho_{d(i),j,r}$ represents the resource requirement of each stage (j) for each product (d) associated with knapsack item i and resource type (r), and $\omega_{d(i),j}$ represents the duration of each stage for each product associated with knapsack item i and stage (j). The total resource of type r required to complete the remaining stages for all products is calculated by summing over all products and their remaining stages.

Given W_i, τ_i, and W_{max}:

- *Generate I*
- *Set $t = 0$*
- *Calculate $V_{i,0}$ for all $i \in I$*
- *Generate $E_{i,0,0}$ for all $i \in I$*
- *Solve knapsack using W_{max}, W_i, $V_{i,0}$, $E_{i,0,0}$*
- *Set α = knapsack solution*
- *Calculate $\varphi = \text{argmax}\{\tau_i \text{ for } i \in \alpha\}$*
- *Generate $S_{\varphi,0}$*
- *$P_{max} = 1$*
- *Set $t = t + 1$*

While $t < t_{max}$:

For p=1 to P_{max}:

For k=0 to $|S_{t,p-1}|$:

- *Calculate $V_{i,t}$ for all $i \in I$*
- *Generate $E_{i,t,k}$*
- *Solve knapsack using W_{max}, W_i, $V_{i,t}$, $E_{i,t,k}$*
- *Set α = knapsack solution*
- *Calculate $\varphi = \text{argmax}\{\tau_i \text{ for } i \in \alpha\}$*
- *Generate $S_{t+\varphi,p}$*

Next k

Next p

Figure 1. The knapsack decomposition algorithm.

Once, the first knapsack problem is solved at the root node, i.e., at $t = 0$, sets of smaller knapsack problems ($\mathbf{S}_{\tau,p}$) are generated for each outcome of uncertainty. In order to reduce the number of knapsack problems that should be solved, the current implementation of the algorithm only generates subproblems once all the uncertainty is realized for all the items in the current knapsack, *viz.*at ϕ = Argmax$\{\tau_i\ \forall i \in$current knapsack$\}$.The algorithm terminates either when there are no more available items or at the end of the planning horizon.

3.1. An Example Application of the Knapsack Decomposition Approach

A two-product, two-stage example will be used to demonstrate how the decomposition approach generates the initial and the subsequent knapsack sets, and the resulting decision tree. The planning horizon for the example problem is 15 months divided into five equal 3-month time-periods. Table 1 gives the durations, probabilities of success, resources requirements, and costs of stages along with the revenue and the penalty for late completion of the last stage for each product.

The first step of the algorithm is to create the items set: $\mathbf{I}$ = {(D_1P_1), (D_1P_2), (D_2P_1), (D_2P_2)}. Each items value at the initial time, t = 0, is calculated using Eq. (1). For example, for the first item (D1P1), $V_{1,t}$= [3100 – 19.2(t + 4 + 1)](0.3)(0.5) = 450.6. The next step is to identify the items that can be placed in the knapsack. At t = 0, none of the products have completed the first-stage, therefore any items corresponding to the second-stage decisions are removed, which yields the eligible items subset: $\mathbf{E}_{0,0}$= {(D_1P_1), (D_2P_1)}. Using the information in Table 1 with the eligible items subset, the knapsack formulation solved at t = 0 is given in Eq. (3). The solution of this knapsack problem is item (D_2P_1). The decision for t = 0 for the original problem is pushing product one at stage one, shown in the decision-outcome tree of the solution in Figure 2.

$$\begin{aligned}
&\max NV\\
&NV = (1)(450.6)(D_1,P_1) + (1)(756.5)(D_2,P_1)\\
&2 \geq 1(D_1,P_1) + 1(D_2,P_1)\\
&3 \geq 1(D_1,P_1) + 1(D_2,P_1)\\
&10 \geq 6(D_1,P_1) + 8(D_2,P_1)\\
&15 \geq 10(D_1,P_1) + 5(D_2,P_1)
\end{aligned} \tag{3}$$

The next step in the algorithm is to calculate the time period when outcomes of all the uncertainties associated with the first-stage decisions are realized, i.e., to calculate ϕ. For the example problem, ϕ= 2. At $t = t + 2$= 2, two outcomes are possible: product two (D2) either passes or fails stage one (P1).Then, we generate the first set of knapsack subproblems ($S_{2,0}$) for each outcome. One knapsack subproblem considers items $E_{2,1}$= {(D_1P_1), (D_2P_2)}, which is obtained for the outcome where D2 passes P1. The other knapsack subproblem considered item(s) $E_{2,2}$= {(D_1P_1)}, which is obtained for the outcome where D2 fails P1 and cannot be pushed through the second stage. A similar formulation to Eq. (3) is generated and solved for each subproblem at t = 2. The solution to the first knapsack subproblem recommends pushing item (D_1P_1) for the case where D2 fails P1 and pushing (D_2P_2) for the case where D2 passes P1 (Figure 2). For the outcome where D2 fails P1 at t = 2, the two generated subproblems at t = 4 corresponding to the two possible outcomes of (D_1P_1). Values of the items are calculated, and the subset of eligible items is determined based on the outcome at t = 4. For the outcome where D2 passes P1 at t = 2, the stage duration of (D2P2) is longer than the remaining planning horizon, and hence, the problem is solved.

Table 1. Data for the two-product example

	Trial Duration		Prob.		Cost ($M)		rev^{max}	γ^L	Res. 1 (ρ^{max}=2)		Res. 2 (ρ^{max}=3)	
	P1	P2	P1	P2	P1	P2			P1	P2	P1	P2
Drug 1	2	4	0.3	0.5	10	90	3100	19.2	1	1	1	2
Drug 2	2	3	0.4	0.6	10	80	3250	19.6	1	2	1	1

4. Case Studies

The KDA is used to solve four different pharmaceutical R&D pipeline management problems in addition to the two-product, two-stage problem: three-, five-, seven-, and ten-product cases each with three stages. Parameters for the three-product, three-stage case are taken from Colvin and Maravelias (2008). Parameters of the remaining case studies are available upon request from the authors. In order to assess the quality of the solutions generated by the KDA, the rigorous MSSP presented in Colvin and Maravelias (2008) is solved for the two-, three-, and five-product cases. The objective function values of the solutions (i.e., the decision trees generated by both approaches) are calculated using the expected net present value (ENPV) defined in Colvin and Maravelias (2008). The knapsack decomposition algorithm is scripted in Python 2.7 using Coopr Pyomo 3.3 (Sandia Corporation) on 64-bit Ubuntu 12.04. All problems (including MSSPs) were solved to optimality with a relative gap of 0.00001 using CPLEX 12.51 on Intel Xeon CPU E5606 @2.13 GHz x 8.

4.1. Results and Discussion

The number of products that can be in the pipeline at any given time are limited by the availability of two resources. The planning horizons are 36 months divided into twelve 3-month periods, 36 months divided into six 6-month periods, 48 months divided into eight 6-month periods, and 60 months divided into ten 6-month periods for the three-, five-, seven-, and ten-product problems, respectively. Except the two-product case study (where there are only two stages), each product must complete three stages to reach the market. The number of product-stage-planning horizon combinations yield a total of nine, 64, 1042, 16,384, and 1,048,576 scenarios for the two-, three-, five-, seven-, and ten-product case studies, respectively. The decision trees are available upon request.

The ENPVs of solutions obtained using the KDA and the rigorous MSSP, the corresponding CPU seconds to solve the problems, and the number of knapsack problems solved for each case study are given in Table 2. A solid line in Table 2 for the ENPVs under Stochastic Programming heading indicates that a solution could not be obtained for these problems using the rigorous MSSP using Intel Xeon CPU E5606 @2.13 GHz x 8due to the memory requirements for generating the NA constraints.

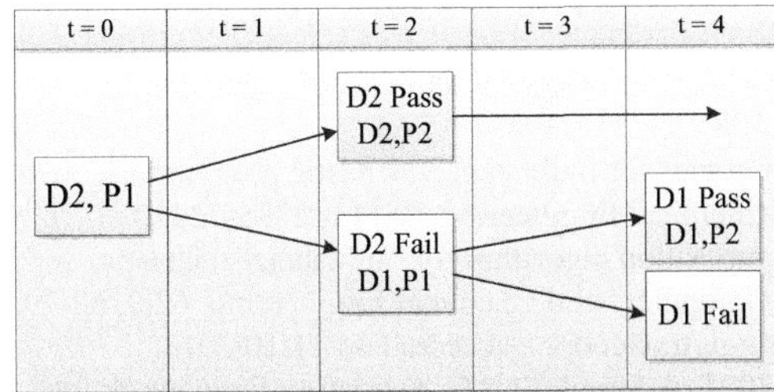

Figure 2. The two-product knapsack solution

Table 2. Computation results for case studies

	Knapsack Decomposition Algorithm			Stochastic Programming	
	Knapsacks Solved	Solver Time (CPU Sec)	Objective ($M)	Solver Time (CPU Sec)	Objective ($M)
2-Product	5	0.09	1104	0.41	1104
3-Product	35	0.52	1180	29.98	1189
5-Product	27	0.51	2009	6620.35	2082.76
7-Product	496	12.04	2870	---	---
10-Product	3392	586.3	4004	---	---

Comparing ENPVs obtained by the KDA and the rigorous MSSP reveals that the KDA solution is within 4 % of the rigorous MSSP solution for the cases where rigorous MSSP can be solved. The quality of the KDA solution deteriorates as the number of products and the length of the planning horizon increases. However, the CPU times necessary to obtain the solutions using the KDA are significantly shorter (12,000 times in the best case, and 4 times in the worst case) than the ones using the rigorous MSSP.

The solution times of the KDA approach in CPU seconds increase almost linearly with the number knapsack problems solved, which increases with the number of products, stages, and the planning horizon. The linear increase in solution times with the number of knapsack problems suggest that the size of the knapsack problems at each time point does not change significantly, and up to ten-product case, they are solved fairly quickly.

5. Conclusions and Future Directions

This paper presents a novel heuristic approach, knapsack decomposition approach (KDA), that yields implementable solutions for MSSPs with endogenous uncertainty. The approach was tested using several case studies of the pharmaceutical R&D pipeline management problem, and displayed several orders of magnitude improvement in the solution times compared to the rigorous MSSP. Future work will investigate how the solution times change with growing problem sizes, the possibility of developing theoretical bounds on the solution times of the KDA, and the usage of KDA solution as a tight lower bound for solving the rigorous MSSP.

References

G. Blau, B. Mehta, S. Bose, J. Pekny, G. Sinclair, K. Keunker, P. Bunch, 2000, Risk management in the development of new products in highly regulated industries, Computers and Chemical Engineering, 24, 2-7, 659-664.

M. Colvin, C.T. Maravelias, 2008, A stochastic programming approach for clinical trial planning in new drug development, Computers and Chemical Engineering, 32, 11, 2626-2642.

M. Colvin, C. T. Maravelias, 2010, Modeling methods and a branch and cut algorithm for pharmaceutical clinical trial planning using stochastic programming, European Journal of Operational Research, 203, 1, 205-215.

V. Goel, I.E. Grossmann, 2006, A Class of stochastic programs with decision dependent uncertainty, Mathematical Programming, 108, 2/3, 355-394.

V. Gupta, I. E. Grossmann, 2011, Solution strategies for multistage stochastic programming with endogenous uncertainties,Computers and Chemical Engineering, 35, 11, 2235-2247.

V. Gupta, I.E. Grossmann, 2014, A new decomposition algorithm for multistage stochastic programs with endogenous uncertainties, Computers and Chemical Engineering, 62,0, 62-79.

Sandia Corporation, Pyomo <software.sandia.gov/trac/coopr> accessed on 11/10/2013.

D. Subramanian, J.F. Pekny, G.V. Reklaitis, 2001, A Simulation-Optimization Framework for Research and Development Pipeline Management, AIChE Journal, 47, 10, 2226-2242.

Jiří Jaromír Klemeš, Petar Sabev Varbanov and Peng Yen Liew (Editors)
Proceedings of the 24th European Symposium on Computer Aided Process Engineering – ESCAPE 24
June 15-18, 2014, Budapest, Hungary.

Clustering Urban Areas for Optimizing the Design and the Operation of District Energy Systems

Samira Fazlollahi[a], Luc Girardin[b], François Maréchal[b*]

[a]*Veolia Environnement Recherche et Innovation (VERI), 291 avenue Dreyfous Ducas, 78520 Limay, France*

[b]*Industrial Process and Energy Systems Engineering Laboratory, Ecole Polytechnique Fédérale de Lausanne,CH-1015 Lausanne, Switzerland*

Francois.marechal@epfl.ch

Abstract

Solving the MILP model for optimizing the design and operating strategy of district energy systems (DES) is a computationally demanding task due to the large number of subsystems (i.e. resources, conversion technologies, buildings and networks) and corresponding decision variables. In order to reduce the number of decision variables and therefore the computational load of the problem, this paper presents a systematic procedure to represent an urban area with a macroscopic view as a set of "integrated zones". The integrated zone is an area where consumers, resources and energy conversion technologies are integrated. This is obtained by developing aggregated district integration models based on GIS data and applying k-means clustering techniques. By using the proposed method, the regional DES is partitioned into limited number of integrated zones. The selected zones allow us to achieve accurate representation of the whole district while significantly reducing the number of decision variables for which more detailed optimization methods can be applied.

Keywords: District energy systems (DES), Geographical information systems (GIS), CO_2 mitigation, Mixed Integer Linear Programming (MILP), *k-means* clustering.

1. Introduction

Higher efficiency, CO_2 mitigation and renewable energy usage in the urban area are achieved by proper system integration. Optimization techniques using mixed integer linear programming (MILP) method have been developed (Fazlollahi and Maréchal, 2013a) to optimize the energy system integration in the urban systems. These methods are however limited by the size of the problem and the number of decision variables (i.e. number of conversion technologies, buildings and networks) that prevents to solve regional scale problems.

Several researches concerned with developing reduction techniques for large-scale optimisation models. For example Holló et al. (2009) reviewed the reduction techniques for the process network synthesis (PNS). Lam et al. (2011) proposed an analytical method for merging several zones to analyse the biomass supply networks. Ng et al. (2013) introduce a functional clustering approach for integrating the industrial facilities of material supply networks.

This paper presents a systematic procedure and an optimization model to represent an urban area with a set of optimal integrated zones. The integrated zone is an area where resources, energy conversion technologies, and energy requirements of consumers are aggregated. The developed model allows to geo-localise the zones in which a distribution network has a good potential to be implemented, and for which the energy system design using multi-objective, multi-period optimizations approach can be applied. The method is demonstrated and discussed by its application to a test case.

2. Methodology

In order to represent the district area using a limited set of "integrated zones", a method based on GIS data and the k-means clustering technique is developed. The aim of the developed model is to optimize the number of integrated zones (N_k^*). k-means is a greedy optimization algorithm, which goal is to minimize the squared error over clusters (Eq.(1)), for a given value of N_k.

$$k - means\text{: } min[\sum_{k=1}^{N_k}\sum_{i=1}^{N_s}(\sum_{a=1}^{N_a}(\hat{\mu}_{k,a}^{v} - \hat{s}_{i,a})^2 \times z_{i,k}^{v})],\ \forall v\ , \forall N_k \quad (1)$$

S={$s_{i,a}$} is a set of N_S subsystems such as buildings to be grouped into a set of N_k integrated zone. The main attributes (a∈{1,...,N_a}) of subsystems ($s_{i,a}$ ∀i∈{1,...,N_S}) are their locations with geographical coordinates, and the temperatures of requirement (i.e. heating and hot water demands). The normalized set of attributes ($\hat{s}_{i,a}$) is calculated by Eq.(2). $\mu_{k,a}^{v}$ refers to the center of each zone, $\hat{\mu}_{k,a}^{v}$ denotes the normalized center, v is an index for starting point, and $z_{i,k}^{v}$ is a binary variable equal to 1 if a subsystem s_i is assigned to the zone k.

$$\hat{s}_{i,a} = \frac{s_{i,a}}{max\{s_{i,a}\ \forall i \in \{1,\ldots,N_S\}} \quad \forall a, i \quad (2)$$

The k-means algorithm requires two user-specified parameters, firstly the initial partitioning or starting point (v) and secondly the number of clusters (N_k). The result of the k-means greedy optimization algorithm depends on the starting. In order to overcome this issue, the k-means algorithm is applied with several random starting points ($\forall v \in \{1, \ldots, v_{max}\}$, i.e. $v_{max} = 1{,}000$). For selecting the best initial partitioning option (v_{Nk}^*) of N_k zones, the total costs of distribution networks ($\sum_{k=1}^{N_k} TAC_{v,k}$ in Eq.(3)) is proposed as an additional indicator. $TAC_{v,k}$ \$/MWh/y (Eq.(3)) is the specific cost of the heating and the gas distribution networks in zone k of evaluation v. It is estimated based on the following two scenarios.

$$TAC_{v,k} = min\{TAC1_{v,k}\ , TAC2_{v,k}^{d}\ \forall d\}, \qquad \forall v \in \{1, \ldots, V_{max}\}, \forall k \in \{1, \ldots, N_k\} \quad (3)$$

$TAC1_{v,k}$: All buildings inside the integrated zone k are connected to the heating distribution network (centralized option). The specific distribution cost ($TAC1_{v,k}$ \$/MWh/y) is equal to the annual investment cost of the heating pipelines (Girardin 2012) divided by the total heat and hot water energy consumptions in zone k.

$TAC2_{v,k}^{d}$: Buildings which are located inside d % (0 < d < 90) of distance from the center of the integrated zone k are connected to the heat distribution network as a centralized option, while the rest (last (100-d)%) are connected to the gas distribution network for supplying gas to decentralized boilers (combination of decentralized and centralized solutions). The specific distribution cost ($TAC2_{v,k}^{d}$ \$/MWh/y) is equal to the total annual investment cost of the heating pipelines and the gas pipelines divided by the total heat and hot water energy consumptions in zone k. As an assumption $TAC2_{v,k}^{d}$ is estimated for $\forall d$ ($d \in \{0{,}10\ \%, \ldots, 90\ \%\}$) with step of 10 %.

Three statistical indicators are defined to optimize the number of "integrated zones" (N_k^*) for selected starting point ($v_{N_k}^*$); the average intra-clusters distance, which evaluates the compact character of the clusters $(C(v_{N_k}^*) = \frac{1}{N_k}\sum_{k=1}^{N_k}\sum_{i=1}^{N_S}(z_{i,k}^{v^*} \times \sum_{a=1}^{N_a}(\hat{\mu}_{k,a}^{v^*} - \hat{s}_{i,a})^2), \forall N_k)$, the average inter-clusters distance, which evaluates the separation between the clusters $(D(v_{N_k}^*) = \frac{1}{N_k^2}\sum_{k=1}^{N_k}\sum_{j=1}^{N_k}(\sum_{a=1}^{N_a}(\hat{\mu}_{k,a}^{v^*} - \hat{\mu}_{j,a}^{v^*})^2), \forall N_k)$, and the statistical measure $ESE(v_{N_k}^*)$ (Pham et al. 2004), which evaluates the ratio of observed to expected squared errors for N_k clusters (Eq.(4) and Eq.(5))

$$ESE(v_{N_k}^*) = \begin{cases} 1 & if\ N_k = 1, \forall v \\ \frac{N_k \times C(v_{N_k}^*)}{\alpha_{N_k} \times (N_k - 1) \times C(v_{N_k-1}^*)} & if\ C(v_{N_k-1}^*) \neq 0, \forall N_k > 1, \forall v \\ 1 & if\ C(v_{N_k-1}^*) = 0, \forall N_k > 1, \forall v \end{cases} \quad (4)$$

$$\alpha_{N_k} = \begin{cases} 1 - \frac{3}{4 \times N_a} & if\ N_k = 2,\ N_a > 1 \\ \alpha_{N_k-1} + \frac{1 - \alpha_{N_k-1}}{6} & if\ N_k > 2,\ N_a > 1 \end{cases} \quad (5)$$

N_a is the number of data set attributes and α_{N_k} is the weight factor.

An optimal value for N_k^* should yield; a low value for the average intra-clusters distance $(C(v_{N_k}^*))$, a high value for the average inter-clusters distance $(D(v_{N_k}^*))$, and a low value for the $ESE(v_{N_k}^*)$ measure. It can be expressed as Eq.(9).

To sum up, Eq.(6) can express the developed method.

$$N_k^*: \quad [min\{C(v_{N_k}^*)\ \forall N_k\},\ max\{D(v_{N_k}^*)\ \forall N_k\},\ min\{ESE(v_{N_k}^*)\ \forall N_k\}] \quad (6)$$

Subject to:

$$v_{N_k}^*: \quad min\{(\sum_{k=1}^{N_k} TAC_{v,k})\},\ \forall v \in \{1, \ldots, V_{max}\}, \forall N_k \in \{1, \ldots, N_{max}\} \quad (7)$$

$$k - means: min[\sum_{k=1}^{N_k}\sum_{i=1}^{N_s}(\sum_{a=1}^{N_a}(\hat{\mu}_{k,a}^{v} - \hat{s}_{i,a})^2 \times z_{i,k}^{v})],\ \forall v, \forall N_k \quad (8)$$

The solving strategy of the proposed model (Eq.(6)) proceeds as following:

Step 1: Run *k-means* for values of $N_k \in \{1, \ldots, N_{max}\}$, with $\forall v \in \{1, \ldots, V_{max}\}$ random starting points (e.g V_{max}=1,000, N_{max}=25).
Step 2: Estimate the total costs of distribution networks $(\sum_{k=1}^{N_k} TAC_{v,k})$ for $N_k \in \{1, \ldots, N_{max}\}$, and $\forall v \in \{1, \ldots, V_{max}\}$ (Eq.(3)).
Step 3: Select the best starting point ($v_{N_k}^*$) for $\forall N_k$ (Eq.(7)).
Step 4: Once $v_{N_k}^*$ have been selected, calculate values of average intra-clusters distance $(C(v_{N_k}^*))$, average inter-clusters distance $(D(v_{N_k}^*))$ and $ESE(v_{N_k}^*)$ for $\forall N_k$.
Step 5: Define the ascending order set of $C(v_{N_k}^*)\ \forall N_k$, the descending order set of $D(v_{N_k}^*)\ \forall N_k$, and the ascending order set of $ESE(v_{N_k}^*)\ \forall N_k$.
Step 6: Chose the best integrated zones (N_k^* Eq.(6)) in which;

$$N_k^*: R(N_k^*) = min[max\{R_C(v_{N_k}^*), R_D(v_{N_k}^*), R_{ESE}(v_{N_k}^*)\}\ \forall N_k \in \{1, \ldots, N_{max}\}] \quad (9)$$

Where $R_C(v^*_{N_k})$ refers to the rank of N_k clusters (zones) in ascending order set of $C(v^*_{N_k})$, $R_D(v^*_{N_k})$ is the rank of N_k clusters in descending order set of $D(v^*_{N_k})$ and $R_{ESE}(v^*_{N_k})$ denotes the rank of N_k clusters in ascending order set of $ESE(v^*_{N_k})$.

3. Illustrative example

The case study presented by Fazlollahi et al. (2013b) is used to illustrate the advantage of the proposed method. The aim is to supply the heating requirements of a city with 475 small zones (Figure 1) with a central plant via heating distribution networks or individually with decentralized equipment. The k-means clustering is applied to split up the area into limited number of integrated zones. For $N_k \in \{1,\ldots,25\}$, and V_{max}=1,000 random starting points, $N_k^* = 13$ has the lowest value for the average intra-clusters distance, the highest value for the average inter-clusters distance and the lowest value for *ESE* measure (Figure 3, Eq.(6)). In addition, the total annual costs of distribution networks for $\forall N_k$, are presented by Figure 3, where the optimal costs observed by $N_k^* = 13$. Therefore, the city can be split up into 13 integrated zones (Figure 2). There are four candidate locations (S1, S2, S3 and S4 in Figure 5) for placing new central plants in the urban area. The design and operation optimizations of the district system are performed with respect to three objectives (Fazlollahi et al., 2013b); maximizing the system efficiency (*EFF*), minimizing the total investment and operating costs (*TAC*), and minimizing the environmental impacts (M_{CO2}). Alternative conversion technologies for supplying power and heat services are; solar thermal, natural gas and biomass boilers, natural gas and biomass engines and turbines. These technologies can be placed in locations S1 to S4. There is also a possibility of investing on heat pumps in locations S1 and S2 to recover the waste heat from the wastewater plant. The hourly heating demands, the solar irradiation and electricity price are given by Fazlollahi et al. (2013b).

Among all multi objective optimization results inform of the first Pareto frontier (Figure 4), configuration "A" is selected for more details evaluation. In this solution two central plants, in locations S2 and S4, are chosen (Figure 5). Centralized plant S2 supplies heat via DHN to locations C3, C5, C6 and C8. This center features; 6 MW gas engine, 4 MW gas turbine, 29.5 MW gas boiler and 28 MW backup boiler. Centralized plant S4 features 28 MW biomass boiler and 10 MW backup natural gas boiler for supplying heat via DHN to locations C7, C9 and C10. Due to the transportation cost of biomass fuel the biomass boiler is only placed in S4. It is economically viable that individual gas boilers supply heat directly to locations C1 (with total capacity of 1.1 MW), C2 (2.4 MW), C4 (1 MW), C11 (4 MW), C12 (3.8 MW) and C13 (0.2 MW) as decentralized solutions and without local networks. The extension of pipelines between locations in solution "A" is illustrated in Figure 5.

4. Conclusions

In order to reduce the size of the district energy system design optimization model, a systematic procedure is proposed. The goal is to aggregate the urban area into a limited number of integrated zones for which the distribution cost and the aggregated energy demand can be calculated. The integrated zones are obtained using GIS data and applying k-means clustering techniques. The selected zones allow us to achieve accurate representations of the whole district while significantly reducing the number of decision variables. Table 1 presents the size of the optimization model of illustrative example for different number of integrated zones. It demonstrates the optimization size is decreased significantly by applying the proposed clustering model.

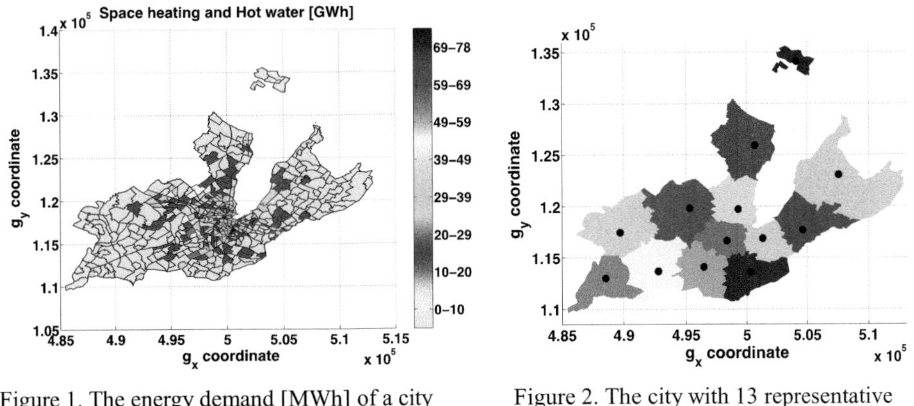

Figure 1. The energy demand [MWh] of a city with 100,000 populations

Figure 2. The city with 13 representative "Integrated zones"

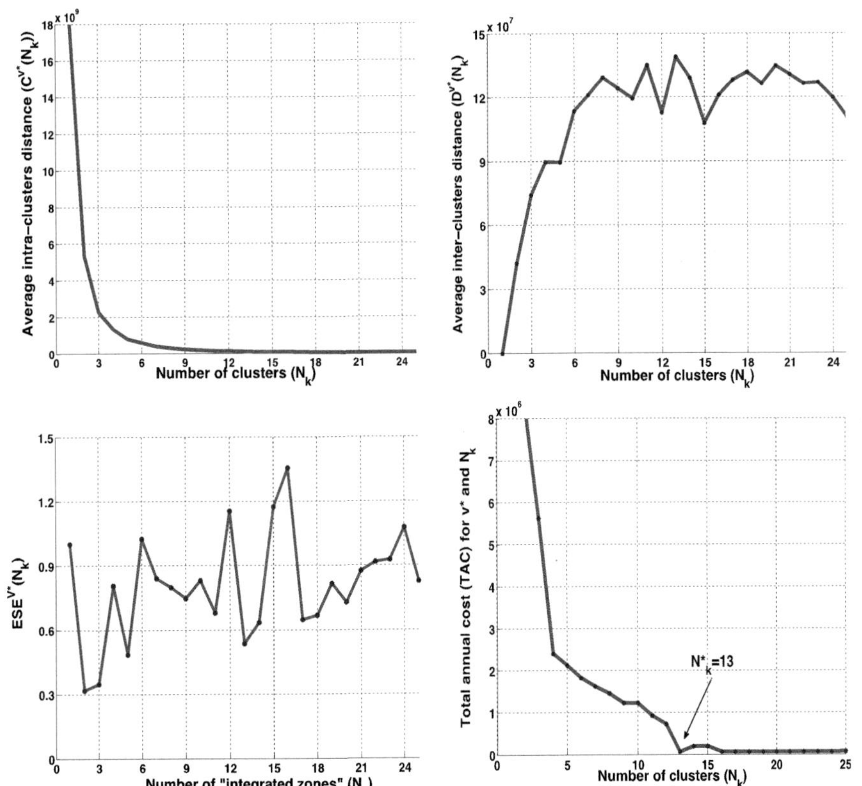

Figure 3. Intra and inter-clusters distances, $ESE(v^*_{N_k})$, and the total annual costs of DHN

Table 1. Comparison between the sizes of the optimization for various number of integrated zones

Number of "integrated zones"	5	7	13	475
Constraints	63,225	88,225	209,499	$\approx 9*10^6$
Variables	191,029	226,500	576,337	$\approx 27*10^6$

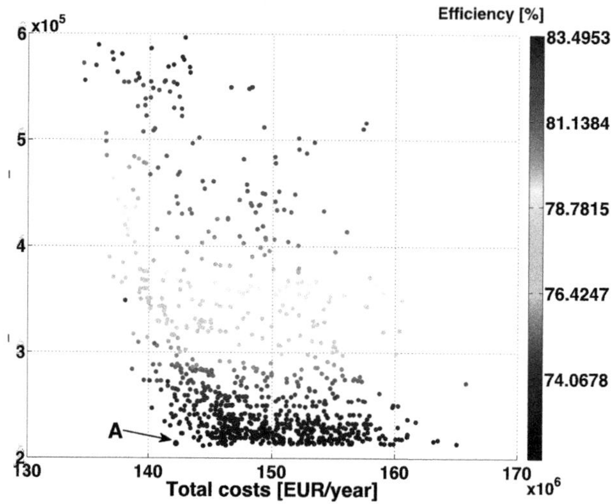

Figure 4. Multi-objective optimization results- first Pareto frontier

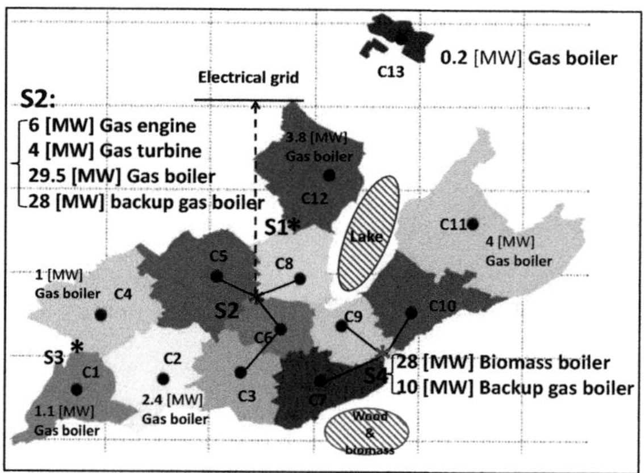

Figure 5. Illustrative example: Solution "A"

References

C. Holló, B. Imreh, C. Imreh, 2009, Reduction techniques for the PNS problems: a novel technique and a review, Optimisation Engineering, 10, 351–361.

D.T. Pham, S.S. Dimov, C.D. Nguyen, 2004, Selection of k in k-means clustering, Mechanical Engineering Science, 219, 103–119.

H.L. Lam, J.J. Klemeš, Z. Kravanja, 2011, Model-size reduction techniques for large-scale biomass production and supply networks, Energy, 36, 8, 4599-4608.

L.Girardin, 2012, A GIS-based Methodology for the Evaluation of Integrated Energy Systems in Urban Area, PhD thesis, Ecole Polytechnique Federale de Lausanne, Switzerland.

S. Fazlollahi, F. Maréchal, 2013a, Multi-objective, multi-period optimization of biomass conversion technologies using evolutionary algorithms and mixed integer linear programming (MILP), Applied Thermal Engineering, 50, 2, 1504–1513.

S. Fazlollahi, G. Becker, F. Maréchal, 2013b, Multi-objectives, multi-period optimization of district energy systems: II-Daily thermal storage, Computers and Chemical Engineering, DOI: 10.1016/j.compchemeng.2013.10.016.

W.P.Q. Ng, H.L. Lam, 2013, A supply network optimisation with functional clustering of industrial resources, Journal of Cleaner Production, DOI: 10.1016/j.jclepro.2013.11.052.

Jiří Jaromír Klemeš, Petar Sabev Varbanov and Peng Yen Liew (Editors)
Proceedings of the 24th European Symposium on Computer Aided Process Engineering – ESCAPE 24
June 15-18, 2014, Budapest, Hungary.

Integrating Queuing Theory and Finite Automata in a Systems Framework for Financial Risk Modelling of Engineering Process Systems

Indranil Pan*, Anna Korre, Sevket Durucan

Department of Earth Science and Engineering, Royal School of Mines, Imperial College London, SW7 2BP, United Kingdom
i.pan11@imperial.ac.uk

Abstract

This is the second of a series of two papers presenting a reliability based methodology to quantify the financial risks involved in an engineering process systems operation which can be represented as a flow of discrete entities. Each component in the process chain is abstracted as a risk item and a logic based on finite automata is incorporated in the model to transition between the states of no-failure, maintenance, failure and lead time. The process operation is abstracted into a model composed of several servers and queues and employs discrete event simulation techniques. To illustrate the proposed method, the model is applied to the case of a copper ore production system and the risk profile is characterised. Multi-objective evolutionary algorithms are used to optimise these models and obtain a Pareto optimal set of solutions with different risk profiles. This kind of queuing theory based modelling can be used to represent many types of systems like those in production engineering, supply chain management, manufacturing engineering, logistics etc. Hence this risk model can easily be adapted to different disciplines with minor modifications.

Keywords: financial risk modelling; reliability based risk modelling; quantitative risk assessment; process systems optimisation; systems thinking;

1. Introduction

A quantitative assessment of the risks involved in a process system operation is of prime importance as it dictates the long term profitability of a company. To this end, various modelling approaches have been proposed in literature and probable risk mitigation alternatives have been suggested. Financial risks for process system operations have been studied in relation to scheduling of batch plants (Bonfill et al., 2003). Many studies look at specific mechanisms of failure and try to model these using different techniques. In Wu et al. (2012), corrosion based failure mechanisms for petrochemical plants are identified and a knowledge based reasoning model is developed for predicting the same. Structural safety assessments of building collapse in the context of reliability have been documented in Raphael et al. (2011). However this does not look at the reliability and the risks involved in the overall process operation. Most other risk modelling techniques use process dynamics equations of mass and energy balance to analyse the effects of uncertainty or failures in certain components and arrive at a risk profile (Podofillini and Dang, 2012). These methods are effective in a data rich environment but would fail, or give highly inaccurate results, if accurate and sufficiently representative data is not available. The systems modelling philosophy introduced in this paper aims to handle the vagueness of information and use dynamic models as a leverage for accuracy in circumstances where these are available. Financial risk in the present context refers to the loss of expected production targets due to equipment breakdown and other associated risks.

The underlying process system is modelled with various interconnections of servers and queues. This is especially useful where discrete events are involved and the temporal information for the occurrence of a specific event needs to be preserved. The systems based risk models control the propagation of the entities to the subsequent queues and servers in the process chain. They also keep track of the cumulative costs incurred due to the failures of each sub-system. This approach towards risk modelling is superior than the traditionally adopted technique of calculating probability distributions of failure costs from prior historical data. This is because it might be a new type of process system which has no prior historical data, but has reliability data of each component from the manufacturers. Also the probability distribution based data fitting approach neglects the underlying root causes which give rise to the failures and therefore might over or under estimate the risks involved. This kind of reliability based risk modelling can be used by the insurance industry to assess the risks involved in a specific process system and formulate their policies and insurance premiums. Such modelling is also helpful to the management of the process system, as they can gauge quantitatively the main bottlenecks in their process operation and take appropriate measures in the form of maintenance policies, backup equipment, or transfer the risk to a third party like an insurance company for effective amelioration and mitigation of the financial risks.

Lastly, a multi-objective optimisation approach is adopted using Non-dominated Sorting Genetic Algorithm II (NSGA II) to optimise the developed risk model. This can help in decision making to implement better policies for improving the risk profile of the system. Similar work has been carried out for managing financial risk in supply chains in Ruiz-Femenia et al. (2013) and La'inez et al. (2009) using a stochastic mixed integer linear programming formulation. However, the complexity of the present risk model with the presence of multiple stochastically interacting finite automatons and different queues and servers makes the problem harder to solve using traditional optimisation methods and therefore an evolutionary approach is adopted.

2. Risk modelling methodology developed

2.1. Overview of the systems modelling framework with queuing theory

Each component of the engineering process system is modelled with servers and queues as shown in Figure 1. The discrete entities might represent physical quantities like trucks, excavators etc. or might represent abstract quantities like decision to drill, blast etc. Each server has a specified service time which represents the time it takes to complete the operation. The server can output the entities only if the gate in front of it is open. The gate receives the signal from a systems based risk model and remains open or closed depending on whether a failure has occurred in the system or not. The risk model can be nested in structure or might affect multiple gates (which represents failures which affect multiple components).

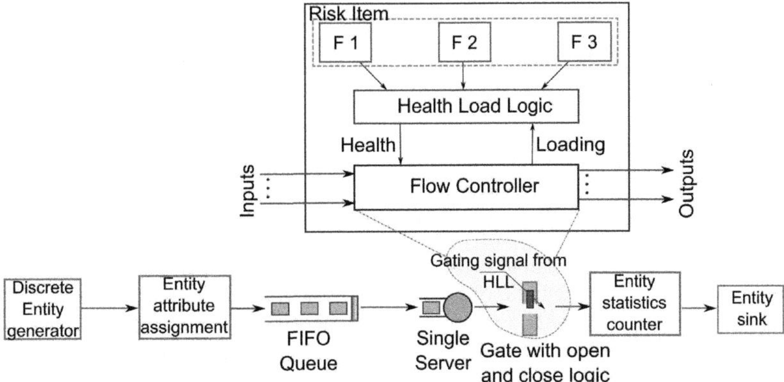

Figure 1. Systems approach integrated with queuing theory for risk modeling.

The risk model is composed of various failure modes which represent the different causes which might result in the component failure. It also has a health-load logic which reflects the system health and a flow controller which regulates the flow of the output from the input. In this case the input is a constant open signal to the gate and the output is the gating signal modified by the different failure modes and the health load logic.

2.2. A finite automata model for a systems based risk item

Figure 2 (a), (b) and (c) present the finite automata model of the failure mode, health-load-logic and flow controller respectively. For the failure mode model in (a) the system transits between the NoFailure and Failure states depending on the sampling generated by the probability distribution curves of Time Between Failures (TBF) and Outage Duration (OD) with the associated costs being calculated through the state dependent

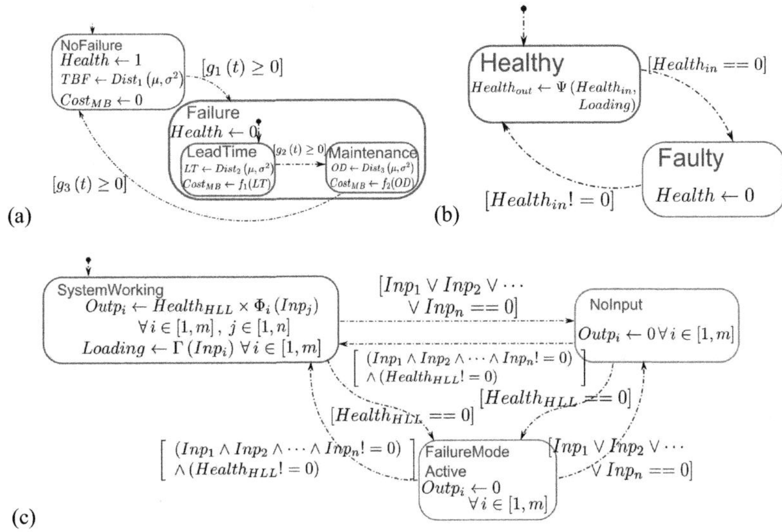

Figure 2. Finite automata model of (a) failure mode, (b) health-load-logic and (c) flow controller logic for each risk item.

functions f_1 and f_2. In Figure 2 (c), the transitions from the different states are governed by the conditions of the system. The outputs ($Outp_i$) are functions (Φ_i) of the inputs (Inp_i) multiplied by the Health of the system. The loading is calculated in the SystemWorking state using a user defined function (Γ) which depends upon the inputs to the risk item.

3. Model application to the case of a mining operation

3.1. Process system layout and queuing theory based risk model development

Figure 3 illustrates the schematic of the process flow of an entire copper ore production operation which is used in the present work. The corresponding queuing theory based implementation is shown in Figure 4. Each subsystem as shown in Figure 3 has a TBF and OD probability distribution associated with it and remains in the states of failure or no-failure depending on a random number drawn from the probability distribution when entering each state. The costs are dependent on the OD and are calculated when the system transits to the failure mode.

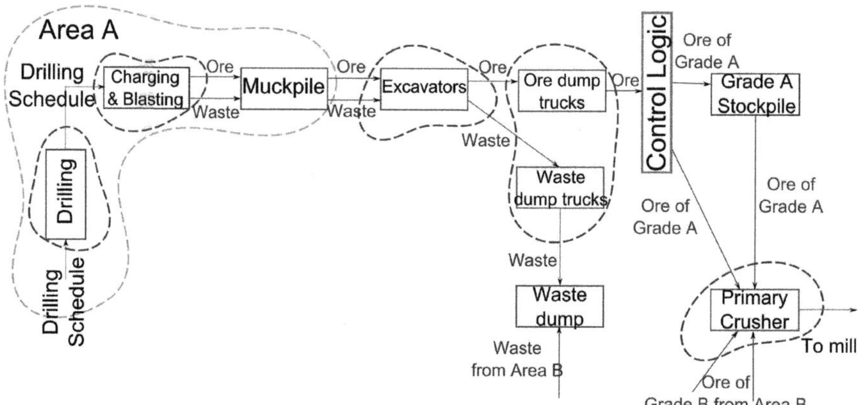

Figure 3. Systems representation of the copper ore production process system operation.

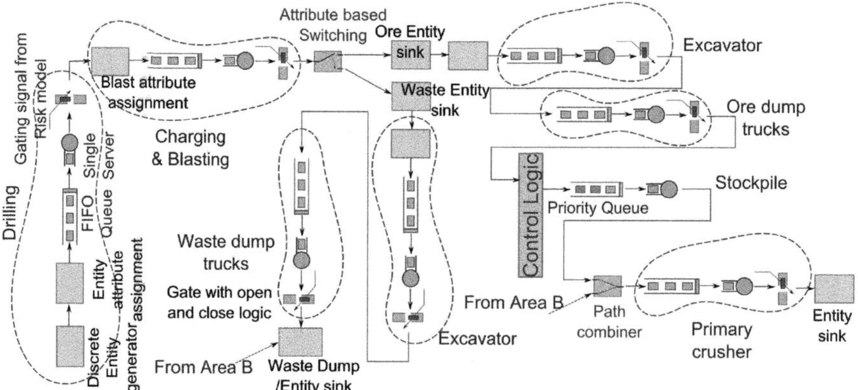

Figure 4. Queuing theory based representation of the process operation coupled with the finite automata based risk models.

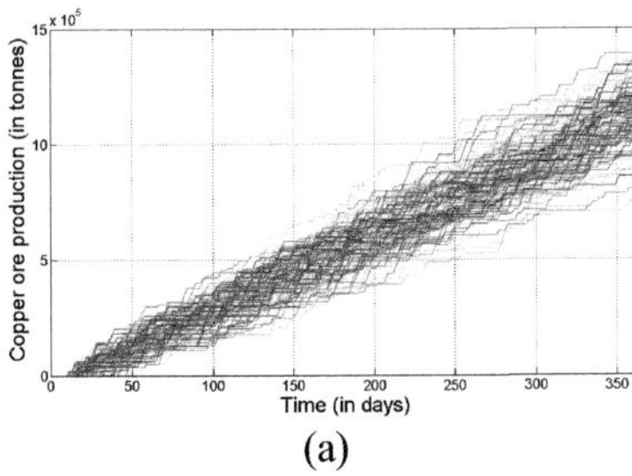

(a)

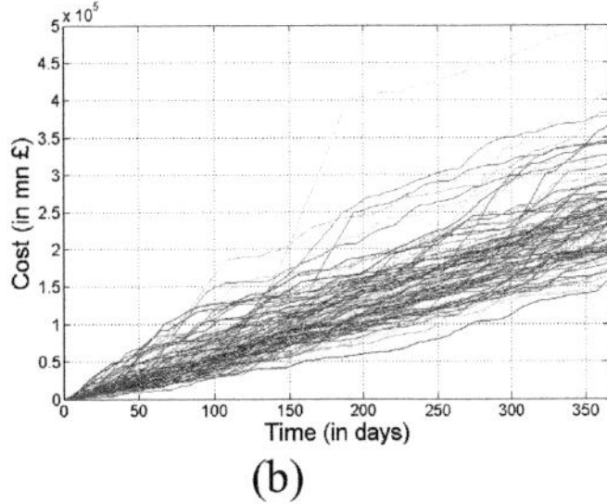

(b)

Figure 5. One hundred Monte Carlo runs of the evolution of (a) copper ore production and (b) cost over time for the base case.

3.2. System characterisation and simulation results

The copper ore production process operation as defined in Section 3.1 is simulated for a period of one year with various failure modes. The time evolution of the cumulative cost curves and copper output for 100 Monte Carlo (MC) simulations are shown in Figure 5 for easier visualisation. More MC simulations can be done while characterising the system. Different failure modes occur at different instants of time which result in different trajectories of evolution in both the curves. As can be seen from Figure 5, there is considerable variability in final values at the end of one year.

3.3. Multi-objective evolutionary optimisation results

Next, an optimisation algorithm is employed to find out the capacities of the stockpiles of both areas. For system optimisation, the following two cost functions are considered and a multi-objective genetic algorithm is employed for the same.

$$J_1 = E\left(\int_{t=0}^{365} (P_a)\,dt\right) \tag{1}$$

$$J_2 = E\left(\int_{t=0}^{365} (MB_{tot})\,dt + \sum_{i=1}^{N} H_{\text{tank}_i}\right) \tag{2}$$

where, P_a is the actual production per day, MB_{tot} is the total maintenance and breakdown cost associated with the whole operation per day, $E(.)$ represents the expectation operator and N represents the maximum number of stockpiles, $H_{\text{tank1}} = 5 + 0.1 * Cap_{\text{tank1}}$, $H_{\text{tank2}} = 7 + 0.15 * Cap_{\text{tank2}}$ with Cap_{tank1} and Cap_{tank2} being the capacities of stockpiles 1 and 2 in tonnes respectively and $H_{\text{tank1}}, H_{\text{tank2}}$ are in million pounds . The system is optimised through the NSGA II algorithm and the algorithm tries to maximise J_1 while simultaneously trying to minimize J_2. The number of individuals is taken as 10 and the NSGA II algorithm is run for 25 generations. The Pareto front obtained from the multi-objective optimisation is shown in Figure 6. The results are in accordance with intuitive understanding that lower stockpile capacities require lower cost, but cannot make up for the lost production sufficiently and therefore result in lower copper ore output from the mine. The system designer needs to choose one of the trade-off points for the final design. It is possible to combine J_1 - J_2 using different weights and then

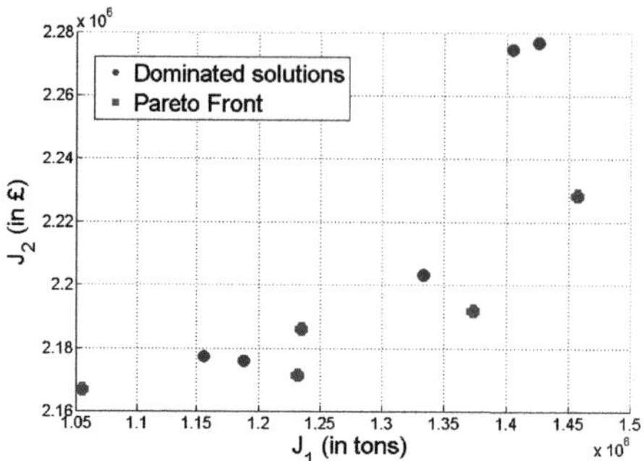

Figure 6. Multi-objective optimisation results with non-dominated Pareto solutions and dominated solutions.

use single objective optimisation to maximize the composite objective function. However such a method would result in a single solution and the weights for scaling J_1 and J_2 are not always known a-priori. To overcome this problem a multi objective formalism is used and the system designer is presented with a range of Pareto optimal solutions to judge the trade-offs and choose one solution for implementation.

4. Conclusions

In this paper a systems model using finite automata is presented for financial risk modelling and is coupled with a queuing theory based model of a process system. The modelling methodology is applied to the case of a mining operation and the risk profile is characterised. It is also shown that the developed risk models can be coupled within a multi-objective optimisation framework and a set of Pareto optimal solutions can be obtained for the same.

Acknowledgements

The authors gratefully acknowledge SCIEMUS Ltd. for sponsoring this research.

References

A. Bonfill, J. Cantón, M. Bagajewicz, A. Espuña, L. Puigjaner, 2003, Managing financial risk in scheduling of batch plants, Computer Aided Chemical Engineering, 14, 41–46.

J. Miguel La'inez, G. V. Reklaitis, L. Puigjaner, 2009, Managing financial risk in the coordination of supply chain and product development decisions, Computer Aided Chemical Engineering, 26, 1027–1032.

L. Podofillini, V. Dang, 2012, Conventional and Dynamic Safety Analysis: Comparison on a Chemical Batch Reactor. Reliability Engineering and System Safety, 106, 146-159.

W. Raphael, R. Faddoul, R. Feghaly, A. Chateauneuf, 2011, Analysis of Roissy Airport Terminal 2E collapse using deterministic and reliability assessments, Engineering Failure Analysis, 20, 1-8.

R. Ruiz-Femenia, G. Guillén-Gosálbez, L. Jiménez, J.A. Caballero, 2013, Multi-objective optimization of environmentally conscious chemical supply chains under demand uncertainty, Chemical Engineering Science, 95, 1-11.

W. Wu, G. Cheng, H. Hu, Y. Zhang, 2012, A knowledge-based reasoning model using causal table for identifying corrosion failure mechanisms in refining and petrochemical plants, Engineering Failure Analysis, 25, 97-105.

Jiří Jaromír Klemeš, Petar Sabev Varbanov and Peng Yen Liew (Editors)
Proceedings of the 24th European Symposium on Computer Aided Process Engineering – ESCAPE 24
June 15-18, 2014, Budapest, Hungary.

An Integrated Design Method for Rotating Packed Beds for Distillation

Daniel Sudhoff*, Kolja Neumann, Philip Lutze

TU Dortmund University, Laboratory of Fluid Separations, Emil-Figge-Str. 70, 44225 Dortmund, Germany
daniel.sudhoff@bci.tu-dortmund.de

Abstract

In this work a design method is presented that is capable of calculating design and operating parameters of a rotating packed bed (RPB) for distillation for a given separation task. As part of this design method an approach to model the mass transfer inside RPBs is presented. Therefore, a new, equiareal discretization is introduced and the mass transfer is modeled using a flexible, but simple correlation based on the newly introduced integrated centrifugal acceleration, which is capable of describing the additionally applied energy to each discrete element. The design procedure is addressed and successfully applied to a floating methanol process. The results prove the applicability of the design method to industrial separation tasks for distillation and the feasibility of the implementation of RPBs to the floating methanol process.

Keywords: centrifugally enhanced distillation, rotating packed bed, equiareal discretization, floating methanol process

1. Rotating Packed Beds for Distillation

Besides the world- and large-scale chemical production plants that produce a single product, apply well established apparatuses and use an available infrastructure a new, flexible and sustainable processing for specialized products arises. These require highly flexible, continuously operating and mobile processes as well as compact and modular designed apparatuses to process products with flexible specifications, flexible capacities and special properties such as very high viscosities. To meet these requirements new and intensified apparatuses are needed. A potential alternative to conventional columns applied for distillation and absorption are rotating packed beds (RPBs) as sketched in Figure 1.

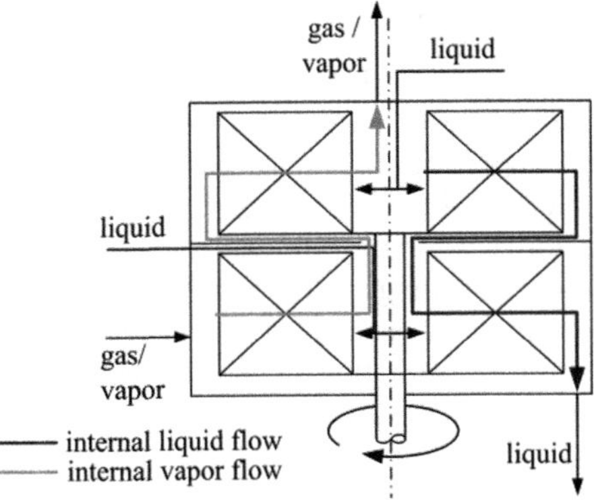

Figure 1. Sketch of a two stage rotating packed bed.

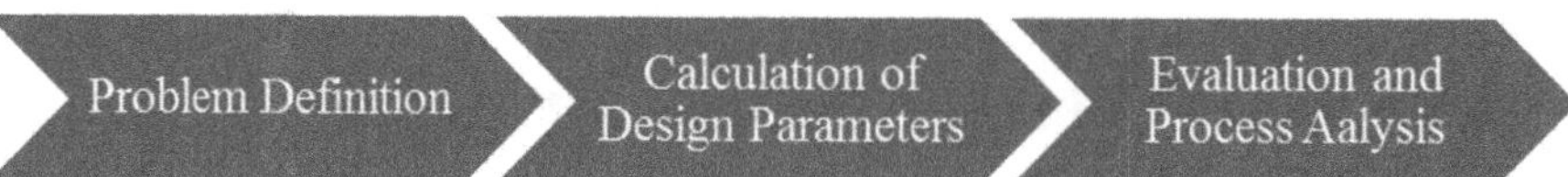

Figure 2. Stepwise design method.

These machines enable the intense contact between liquid and vapor by introducing a centrifugal field. Different flow patterns are possible, however the counter-current flow, in which the liquid is driven radially outwards by the centrifugal force and the vapor is pushed radially inwards, is the most common and most promising design alternative. The centrifugal field is generated by a rotor consisting of different types of packing. Different types of RPBs including their benefits and drawbacks have comprehensively been reviewed by Wang et al. (2011). The advantages of these RPBs, among others, are the intense mixing and quick mass transfer, the flexibility of the rotational speed and therefore of the separation efficiency as well as the high capacity at a very compact design. The exploitation of these benefits for unit operations such as reaction, absorption and stripping, have extensively been summarized in a review by Zhao et al. (2010).

However, the understanding of RPBs for distillation is very limited. Besides some experimental studies (Chu et al., 2013) only few approaches for prediction of the mass transfer in distillation in RPBs have been reported. Prada et al. (2012) used mass transfer correlations for conventional distillation columns and transferred them to RPBs by replacing the gravitational by the centrifugal acceleration. Agarwal et al. (2010) applied a similar approach to design individual case studies.

Nevertheless, the lack of tools with a low complexity for the universal estimation of separation efficiencies of RPBs for distillation leads to an exclusion of RPBs during the conceptual process design. Therefore, the advantages cannot be utilized. Consequentially, the major goal of this work is to overcome this drawback and to provide a specific design method for the conceptual process design phase which provides an estimation of the separation efficiency of RPBs for distillation. For this, a new model for RPBs is developed including a new approach for discretization and for consideration of the centrifugal acceleration. The design procedure is addressed and applied to the floating methanol process.

2. Design Method for RPBs for Distillation

The design method for distillation in RPBs developed in this work consists of three main steps (see Figure 2): Step 1: Problem definition; Step 2: Calculation of design parameters; and Step 3: Process analysis. In step 1, based on the defined problem, internal and external streams are calculated due to mass and energy balances. Additionally, the problem definition is translated into constraints for operation and design such as maximum sizes or flexibilities of the apparatus. In step 2 the model is applied to calculate the operating and design parameters for the separation task considering flooding behavior, mass and heat transfer. Finally, in step 3 the pressure drop, the electrical power consumption of the motor, both based on publications by Singh et al. (1992), and the space requirement of the RPB are calculated to evaluate the design results. The detailed workflow behind each step is not shown here, however, the model for the RPB is explained in detail in sub-chapter 2.1.

2.1. Model for RPBs for Distillation

The model has been developed using a systematic model development procedure (Heitzig et al., 2011). In the resulting model one or multiple rotors of an RPB are divided into discrete rings that comprise the calculation of heat and mass transfer based on correlations, packing and property data. Besides the usual parameters for distillation, the model considers operating parameters such as rotational speed and design parameters such as diameters, heights and number of the rotors or number of RPBs.

To be able to calculate the mass transfer inside the rotating packing for different radii and rotational speeds, it has to be assured that its particular geometry and the additional energy input due to the rotation are properly addressed. For this reason a new approach to discretization and to calculation of the centrifugal force are discussed in the following. The applied mass transfer correlation and its validation are presented subsequently.

2.1.1. Discretization of the Rotor

The model presented has to be capable of describing the mass transfer inside the rotating packing for varying design parameters. In literature, the mass transfer approaches are usually applied to the entire RPB and only mean values for the rotational speed or the loads are used because they are changing over the radius.

However, in order to describe more rigorously the influence of the centrifugal forces depending on the position of the rotor, two discretization approaches may be applied. First, in analogy to conventional distillation, an equidistant discretization (see Figure 3 (left)) and, second, a new equiareal discretization (see Figure 3 (right)) can be applied to create discrete rings of the packing.

$$A_{disc} = \pi \cdot \left(r_{o,disc}{}^2 - r_{i,disc}{}^2\right) = const. \tag{1}$$

In the first one, the mass transfer between the liquid and the vapor, which also is discretized in these rings, is volume specific. In the equidistant discretization the volume of a discrete element increases by the power of two with increasing radius, is therefore not appropriate and the equiareal discretization is used. Within the equiareal discretization the discrete rings have the same ground area and therefore the same volume. By Eq.(1) the inner $r_{i,disc}$ and outer radii $r_{o,disc}$ of the discrete elements are defined to ensure a constant ground area A_{disc}. Hereby, it is assured that the same interfacial area in each discrete element is applied.

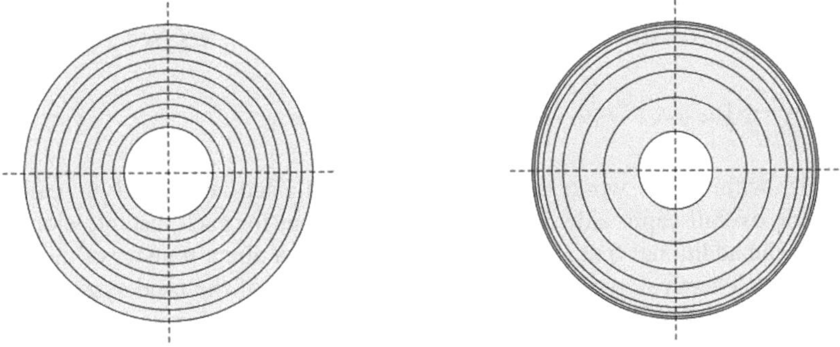

Figure 3: Discrete rings of an equidistant (left) and equiareal discretization (right).

2.1.2. Integrated Centrifugal Acceleration

The centrifugal force, generated by the rotating packing, is strongly dependent on the rotational speed and radial distance to the center. The latter, the radial position inside the packing, leads to a linear increase of the centrifugal acceleration with the radius. It should be noted that the centrifugal acceleration can be up to three magnitudes higher than the gravitational acceleration.

Describing the mass transfer inside an RPB not only the centrifugal acceleration, but also its dependency on the radius have to be taken into account. Additionally, the volume element, to which the centrifugal force is applied, has to be considered, since the cross sectional area also is dependent on the radius. To satisfy these particular circumstances a new characteristic parameter, the integrated centrifugal acceleration $a_{c,int}$ is introduced. This parameter is a measure for the totally applied force by rotation to a certain ground area of the packing. This mathematical parameter is a very useful reference value for the mass transfer in one discrete packing element. The integrated centrifugal acceleration can be calculated according to Eq.(2) by integrating the angular velocity a_c over the ground area element dA. As a result in this work it was found that the integrated centrifugal acceleration has the greatest potential to create comparability of the mass transfer compared to the mean rotational acceleration.

$$a_{c,\,int} = \int a_c \, dA \tag{2}$$

2.1.3. Mass Transfer Correlation

Because the fundamentals of the hydrodynamics and the mass transfer inside the rotating packing are not sufficiently understood, yet, a mass transfer correlation with a low complexity but a wide flexibility is used.

The rotational speed in form of the centrifugal force and the loads are the main influencing factors for the mass transfer. Therefore, as a first approach, a correlation describing the mass transfer performance in dependency of these factors is derived. As the mass transfer of the systems considered in this work is mainly limited on the vapor side, the overall vapor side mass transfer coefficient is applied. The surface area of the packing is combined with the mass transfer coefficient to the volumetric overall vapor side mass transfer coefficient $K_G a$ (see Eq.(3)). This coefficient is described using an extension of the correlation of Mondal et al. (2011) developed originally to describe the overall performance within an RPB. In the new form u_G, ρ_G and $a_{c,int}$ represent the vapor velocity, the density of the vapor and the integrated centrifugal acceleration, respectively. The coefficients c_1, c_2 and c_3 are fitting parameters (see Eq.(3)).

$$K_G a = c_1 \frac{\alpha}{\alpha_{ref}} \cdot \left(u_G \sqrt{\rho_G}\right)^{c_2} \cdot \left(a_{c,\,int}\right)^{c_3} \tag{3}$$

However, within this work the correlation is adjusted and used to calculate the volumetric overall vapor side mass transfer coefficient for each discrete element of the packing. The additional first term in Eq.(3) allows for a direct transfer of the correlation to a different chemical system. The separation factor α of the used system at a certain composition is related to the separation factor α_{ref} of the chemical mixture used for parameter fitting. This assumption is valid for chemical systems with comparable properties to the reference system.

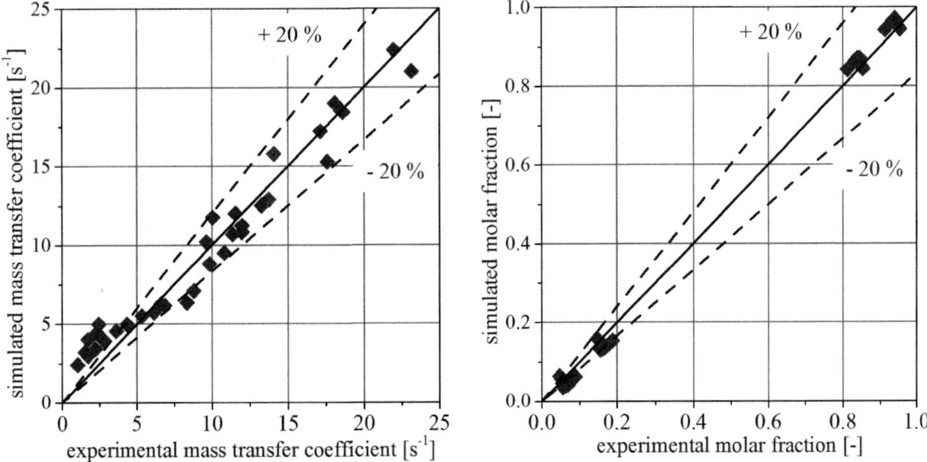

Figure 4. Parity plots of the mass transfer coefficients and of the molar fractions of distillate and bottoms product of simulated and experimental data.

Table 1. Design results for the distillation task in the floating methanol process.

Parameter	Unit	Value	Parameter	Unit	Value
operating pressure	*bar*	1	axial height	*m*	0.33
reflux ratio	-	1.30	number of rotors	-	2
distillate to feed ratio	-	0.94	number of RPBs	-	8
rotational speed	*Hz*	25	pressure drop	*bar*	0.50
inner radius	*m*	0.15	power consumption	*kW*	133.2
outer radius	*m*	0.35	space requirement	m^3	18.2

The parameters c_1, c_2 and c_3 have been fitted using the discretized form of Eq.(3) against experimental data of Mondal et al. (2011) and Lin et al. (2002). In both publications the binary mixture of ethanol and methanol was investigated at ambient pressure. The parity plot of the mean volumetric overall vapor side mass transfer coefficients of the simulated and experimental data are shown in Figure 4 (left) and are in good agreement.

2.1.4. Model Validation

To prove the concept of transferability, experimental data of Chu et al. (2013) has been used for validation. The system methanol-water was investigated in their work and has been simulated in this study. The molar compositions of the distillate and bottoms product are within an error of 20 % as shown in the parity plot in Figure 4 (right).

3. Case Study

The presented model and design method are applied to a floating methanol process. This process is built onto a floating vessel that can be moved between small or remote offshore natural gas fields. The natural gas is converted to reformed gas and synthesized to methanol and water. The subsequent step is the distillation of the water-methanol mixture to remove the water and to ship only the desired product methanol (Tonkovich et al., 2007). Such a process requires compact and stable apparatuses that are insensitive to movement, that is true for RPBs due to its high centrifugal forces.

In this case study the distillation within the process is investigated. Tonkovich et al. (2007) published a theoretical study of a floating methanol process utilizing micro channel unit operations. Their specifications for the distillation have been used. A feed stream of 44.2 t h^{-1} of a mixture containing 90 mol-% methanol is separated into a product streams containing 95 mol-% and 1 mol-% methanol at the top and the bottom of the distillation unit, respectively.

The results to this study are presented in Table 1 and show that the separation task can be solved using eight two stage rotating packed beds demanding 18.2 m^3 of space. Since 28 m^3 of the vessel (Tonkovich et al., 2007) are provided for the distillation section, the application of rotating packed beds for the floating methanol process seems to be feasible. To further reduce the demanding space, more than two rotors may be arranged onto a single shaft into a single casing. Subsequent experimental investigations have to be carried out to prove this conceptual study.

4. Conclusion

In this work a model for distillation in RPBs is developed that employs the new concept of equiareal discretization as well as the integrated centrifugal acceleration. This model is set in the context of a design method that also incorporates evaluation parameters such as pressure drop, space requirements and power consumption. The method can be used to evaluate the feasibility of distillation processes in RPBs for special applications. The method is successfully applied to an industrial separation task, the floating methanol process. The results show that RPBs can be applied to a floating plant such as the floating methanol plant.

5. References

L. Agarwal, V. Pavani, D. P. Rao, N. Kaistha, 2010, Process intensification in HiGee absorption and distillation: Design procedure and applications, Ind. Eng. Chem. Res., 49, 20, 10046-58.

G. W. Chu, X. Gao, Y. Luo, H. K. Zou, L. Shao, J. Chen, 2013, Distillation studies in a two-stage counter-current rotating packed bed, Sep. Purif. Technol., 102, 62-66.

C. C. Lin, T. J. Ho, W. T. Liu, 2002, Distillation in a rotating packed bed, J. Chem. Eng. Jpn, 35, 12, 1298-1304.

M. Heitzig, G. Sin, M. Sales-Cruz, P. Glarborg, R. Gani, 2011, Computer-Aided Modeling Framework for Efficient Model Development, Analysis and Identification: Combustion and Reactor Modeling, Ind. Eng. Chem. Res., 50, 9, 5253-5265.

A. Mondal, A. Pramanik, A. Bhowal, S. Datta, 2011, Distillation studies in rotating packed bed with split packing, Chem. Eng. Res. Des., 90, 4, 453-457.

R. J. Prada, E. L. Martínez, M. R. W. Marciel, 2012, Computational Study of a Rotating Packed Bed Distillation Column, Comput. Aided Chem. Eng., 30, 1113-1117.

S. P. Singh, J. H. Wilson, R. M. Counce, J. F. Villiersfisher, H. L. Jennings, A. J. Lucero, G. D. Reed, R. A. Ashworth, M. G. Elliott, 1992, Removal of Volatile Organic-Compounds from Groundwater Using a Rotary Air Stripper, Ind. Eng. Chem. Res., 31, 2, 574-580.

A. L. Tonkovich, K. Jarosch, R. Arora, L. Silva, S. Perry, J. McDaniel, F. Daly, B. Litt, 2007, Methanol production FPSO plant concept using multiple microchannel unit operations, Chem. Eng. J., 135, 1, S2-S8.

G. Q. Wang, Z. C. Xu, J. B. Ji, 2011, Progress on Higee distillation - Introduction to a new device and its industrial applications, Chem. Eng. Res., 89, 1434-1442

H. Zhao, L. Shao, J. Chen, 2010, High-gravity process intensification technology and application, Chem. Eng. J., 156, 3, 588-593.

Jiří Jaromír Klemeš, Petar Sabev Varbanov and Peng Yen Liew (Editors)
Proceedings of the 24th European Symposium on Computer Aided Process Engineering – ESCAPE 24
June 15-18, 2014, Budapest, Hungary.

Water Network Design with Treating Units by Four-Step Calculation Procedure

Sarut Thongpreecha*, Kitipat Siemanond

Petroleum and Petrochemical College,Chulalongkorn University, 254 Pathumwan, Bangkok 10330, Thailand

Abstract

This contribution describes a new four-step calculation strategy for the synthesis of optimal water network with treatment units. The proposed strategy involves the solution of four models consist of linear programming (LP) and mixed-integer nonlinear programming (MINLP) followed by mixed-integer linear programming (MILP) and the last is MINLP where the main objective is to minimize total annual cost (TAC) of water network with treating unit. The most economical network is slightly found from first through the last step. This work use data from published work of Sotelo-Pichardo et al. (2011) as case study which is fixed flowrate problem with several treatment units. Similar water network result is found by this work strategy compared with published work. The water network is represented in grid diagram. All mathematical models of this work are solved by DICOPT as solver of General Algebraic Modelling System (GAMS).

Keywords: Water network, Treatment unit, Mathematical programming, MINLP.

1. Introduction

Water is an essential natural resource for process industries such as extraction, absorption or distillation with steam. Wastewater generated at the end of process contains substance from each unit that is contaminant. Because of wastewater discharge regulation, treatment unit is used for wastewater treatment to lower the contaminant before discharge to environment. For fixed flowrate problem, all the inlet streams and outlet streams are regarded as sinks and sources. Compared to heat exchanger network (HEN), sink and source are analogous to cold and hot streams. There are many techniques to target minimum freshwater required and minimum wastewater discharged in process. The graphical technique was proposed as Water Composite Curve (El-Halwagi et al., 2003) which is similar to composite curves from HEN synthesis is a tool to target minimum amount of freshwater usage and wastewater. Water Cascade Analysis (Foo, 2008) is a table algorithm procedure which can identify minimum amount of freshwater and wastewater more accurately than graphical methods. In the recent year, Tan et al. (2007) developed a retrofit of water networks by adding more constraints that make more complex in calculation. WCA can be used to consider minimum freshwater flowrate with optimal treatment unit but the optimal network is difficult to generate by hand calculation. Mathematical programming is another technique to solve complex problem. Linear programming (LP) is used to solve water network with simple direct reuse proposed by Dunn et al. (2001). For single contaminant objective is to minimize amount of waste discharge. Bragalli et al. (2012) do a water distribution network to adjust water flow framework in city. Ahmetović et al. (2013) proposed optimal simultaneous water and heat exchanger networks of fixed load problem by two-step approaches. First, they solve for the optimal water network where objective is to minimize freshwater used as initial value for second solving step for overall water and heat exchanger network. Sotelo-Pichardo et al. (2011) design the optimal water network by Mixed-integer nonlinear programming (MINLP) where objective is to minimize total annual cost. They illustrated a lot of examples by considering several treatment units, several freshwater source, waste contaminant discharge regulation, etc. Because of difficulty and non-convexity of MINLP model, good initialization and proper bounding are required. This work proposed a new strategy of "four-step calculation" to solve the MINLP model for the optimal solution by comparing to the result from Sotelo-Pichardo et al. (2011).

2. Problem Statement

The problem in this paper is stated as the water network design model as shown in Figure 1. Index i is an index for the process source, r is an index for the freshwater source, j is an index for the sink, u is an index for stream before treated and type of treatment unit, w is an index for stream after treated by treatment unit, and n is an index for stages of treatment unit. A set of process sources i with composition (CS_i) and flowrate (FS_i) is addressed. A set of process sinks j for the process units that require specific flowrate (FK_j) and specific composition (CK_j) is also given. Freshwater flowrate ($FW_{r,j}$) is determined by a set of composition (CFW_r) and its cost. The main propose of this paper is to generate optimal water network with treatment unit by the water network design model.

3. Model Formulation

Since model is MINLP problem, it needs initialization technique that the water network model must be calculated for four steps sequentially with four objectives shown in Figure 2. First, LP is introduced to calculate initial network with direct reuse from source (i) to sink (j). And flowrate of this reuse ($xF_{i,j}$) is solved where objective is to minimize overall freshwater annual cost (FAC). Second, result from first calculation is used as initial point for MINLP solving where objective is to minimize FAC, annual treatment capital cost (TTC) and annual treatment operation cost (TOC). From this step, optimal treatment flowrate from source ($yF_{i,u}$) at proper treatment unit and stage (u,n) is founded. Likewise, re-treat flowrate ($tF_{u,w}$), regenerated flowrate to sink ($zF_{w,j}$) and wastewater flowrate ($WW1_i$, $WW2_w$) are calculated. For the third step, all calculated variables from the second step are fixed. Mixed-integer linear programming (MILP) is used to solve for piping annual cost (PAC) where objective is to minimize total annual cost (TAC) consisting of FAC, TTC, TOC and PAC. After all variables are solved at third step, all values are used as initial and bound to finally design minimum TAC water network using MINLP. Variables are slightly improved for the better solution in each step. This cascading calculation will reduce non-convexity and give the optimal result.

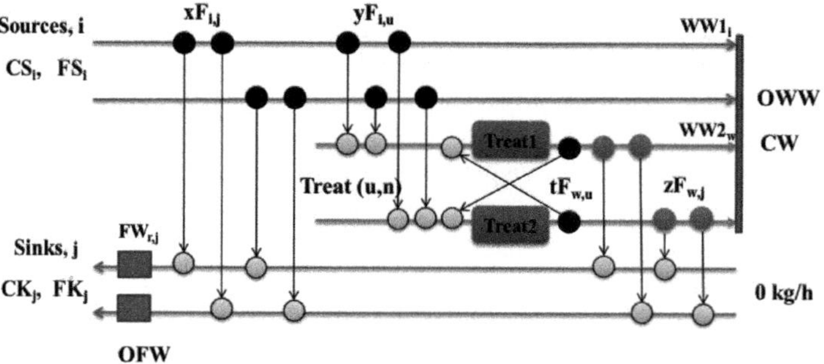

Figure 1. Water network model in grid diagram.

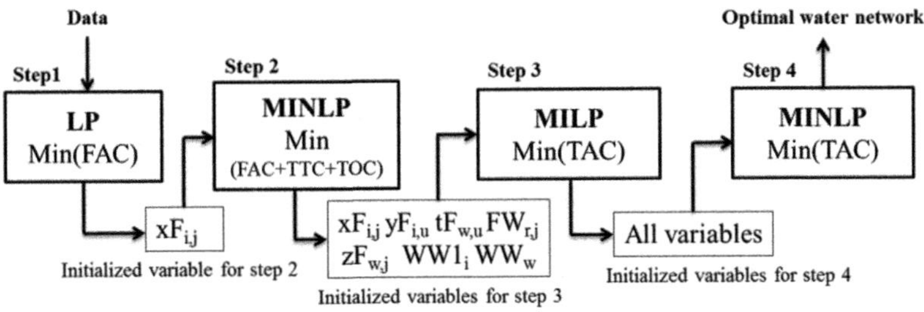

Figure 2. Four-step calculation procedure flowchart.

4. Example

This example is taken from Sotelo-Pichardo et al. (2011) consisting of two process sources and two process sinks with known flowrate and single composition shown in Table 1. Waste composition limit (CWL) is 0.015. Data from treatment unit are shown in Table 2 having two units with different efficiency and cost. And piping cost data are shown in Table 3 containing fixed cost (FC) and variable cost (VC) of each stream. There are two sources of freshwater; one with composition of zero where cost is 0.0019 \$/kg and the other of 0.005 where cost is 0.0014 \$/kg. The minimum flowrate of each stream is 300 kg/h. Operation time per year and annualization factor of investment are fixed to 8,000 hour per year and 0.333 year^{-1}. The optimal solution is carried out by cascading four-step calculation procedure. First LP solver is run for initialization to the second solver. Second solver is run by initializing some variables in order to make all flowrates over 300 kg/h. And the proper treatment unit and stage is chosen from this step. For lowering the load of fourth solver, all variables from previous step are fixed in order to calculate PAC at the third calculation. Then, all variables are re-calculated to find the most optimal solution. At the fourth calculation, some variables are changed its value to reach the most economical network, such as flowrate from source 2 to sink 1 ($xF_{2,1}$) changed from 1,457.074 to 1,518.324 kg/h and flowrate from source 2 to sink 2 ($xF_{2,2}$) changed from 1,037.509 to 976.259 kg/h. The results from each step calculation are shown in Table 4 where the minimal TAC is 39,331.12 \$/y. The optimal water network is shown in Figure 3 and the result comparison is shown in Table 5.

Table 1. Sources and sinks data.

Source i	Flowrate, FS_i (kg/h)	Composition, CS_i	Sink j	Flowrate, FK_j (kg/h)	Composition, CKL_j
1	2,500	0.035	1	2,800	0.014
2	2,870	0.024	2	2,300	0.012
Fresh r	**Flowrate, $FW_{r,j}$**	**Composition, CFW_r**	**Waste**	**Flowrate, OWW**	**Composition, CWL**
1	-	0	1	-	0.015
2	-	0.005			

Table 2. Treatment unit data.

Treatment unit	Unit 1	Unit 2
Efficiency factor	0.91	0.72
0≤ Flowrate ≤1,790		
Installation fixed cost ($)	9,875.43	7,822.52
Installation variable cost ($/kg)	8.58269	7.14466
1,791≤ Flowrate ≤3,580		
Installation fixed cost ($)	13,852.9	11,133.56
Installation variable cost ($/kg)	6.36064	5.29491
3,580≤ Flowrate ≤5,370		
Installation fixed cost ($)	16,125.94	13,025.75
Installation variable cost ($/kg)	5.72571	4.76637
Unitary operation cost ($/kg)	$0.79x10^{-3}$	$0.63x10^{-3}$
Capacity increasing - fixed cost ($)	800	900
Capacity increasing - variable cost ($/kg)	1.1367	0.9548

Table 3. Piping cost data.

Source i to sink j			Source i to treat u		
i,j	FC ($/y)	VC x 10^{-4} ($/kg)	i,u	FC ($/y)	VC x 10^{-4} ($/kg)
1,1	1.1	1.1	1,1	1.2	1.2
1,2	1.3	1.2	1,2	1.4	1.1
2,1	0.8	0.8	2,1	1.1	0.9
2,2	1.4	1.3	2,2	1.5	1
Fresh r to sink j			Treat w to sink j		
r,j	FC ($/y)	VC x 10^{-4} ($/kg)	w,j	FC ($/y)	VC x 10^{-4} ($/kg)
1,1	1.4	1.6	1,1	1.4	1.3
1,2	1.7	1.7	1,2	1.3	1.1
1,3	1.3	1.4	2,1	1.2	1.1
1,4	1.9	1.5	2,2	1	0.8
Treat w to treat u			Source to waste		
w,u	FC ($/y)	VC x 10^{-4} ($/kg)	i	FC ($/y)	VC x 10^{-4} ($/kg)
1,2	0.4	0.5	1	0.6	0.7
2,1	0.6	0.4	2	1.3	1.4
Treat to waste					
w	FC ($/y)	VC x 10^{-4} ($/kg)			
1	1.1	0.2			
2	0.9	0.2			

Table 4. Result by four-step calculation procedure.

Result	Calculation 1	Calculation 2	Calculation 3	Calculation 4
$FW_{r,j}$ (kg/h)	$FW_{2,1}$= 1,473.684 $FW_{2,2}$= 1,452.632	$FW_{1,2}$=405.417	$FW_{1,2}$=405.417	$FW_{1,1}$=405.417
$xF_{i,j}$ (kg/h)	$xF_{2,1}$= 1,326.316	$xF_{2,1}$=1,457.074	$xF_{2,1}$=1,457.074	$xF_{2,1}$=1,518.324
	$xF_{2,2}$=847.368	$xF_{2,2}$=1,037.509	$xF_{2,2}$=1,037.509	$xF_{2,2}$=976.259
$yF_{i,u}$ (kg/h)	-	$yF_{1,1}$=2,500	$yF_{1,1}$=2,500	$yF_{1,1}$=2,500
$tF_{w,u}$ (kg/h)	-	-	-	-
$zF_{w,j}$ (kg/h)	-	$zF_{1,1}$=1,342.926	$zF_{1,1}$=1,342.926	$zF_{1,1}$=876.259
		$zF_{1,2}$=857.074	$zF_{1,2}$=857.074	$zF_{1,2}$=1,323.741
$WW1_i$ (kg/h)	-	$WW1_2$=375.417	$WW1_2$=375.417	$WW1_2$=375.417
$WW2_w$ (kg/h)	-	$WW2_1$=300	$WW2_1$=300	$WW2_1$=300
CW	-	0.0147	0.0147	0.0147
FAC ($/y)	32,774.74	6,162.33	6,162.33	6,162.33
TTC ($/y)	-	9,908.25	9,908.25	9,908.25
TOC ($/y)	-	15,800	15,800	15,800
PAC ($/y)	-	-	7,592.44	7,460.54
TAC ($/y)	-	-	39,463.02	39,331.12

Table 5. Result comparison.

Result	Sotelo-Pichardo (2011)	Four-step calculation
Waste composition	0.015	0.0147
Freshwater flowrate (kg/h)	405.42	405.417
Waste flowrate (kg/h)	675.42	675.417
Freshwater cost ($/y)	6,162.384	6,162.333
Treatment capital cost ($/y)	9,908.248	9,908.248
Treatment operation cost ($/y)	15,800	15,800
Piping cost ($/y)	7460.544	7,460.54
Total annual cost ($/y)	39,331.176	39,331.12

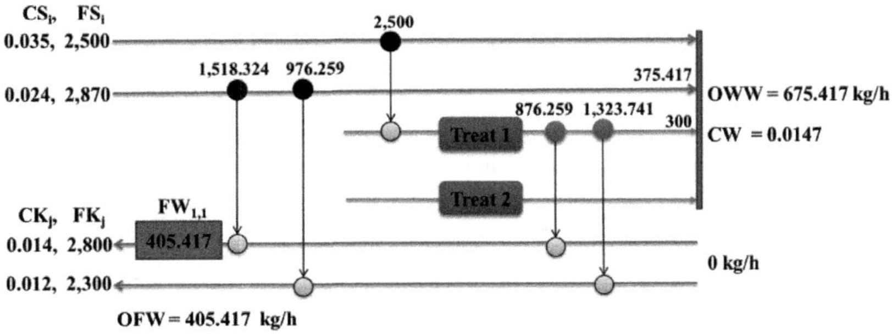

Figure 3. Optimal water network in grid diagram.

5. Conclusion

The presented calculation procedure is another method to solve MINLP problem of water network synthesis. The best solution are slightly improved by each step as seen in Table 4 because of previous calculated variables are used as initial value for next calculation. Second calculation is the key step where the proper treatment unit is chosen to treat wastewater to a desire composition. Third calculation is for piping calculation for the last calculation. In the last calculation, some flowrates are adjusted to lower piping annual cost, resulting in generating economical water network. This cascading calculation helps share the burden of solvers to reduce non-convexity of MINLP problem. The optimal water network result is close to one from literature (Sotelo-Pichardo et al., 2011) ensured that four-step calculation gives the optimal result. CPU time of this procedure is 1.00 sec while the literature is 1.45 sec.

Nomenclature

FS_i	Flowrate of sources (kg/h)	$FW_{r,j}$	Freshwater usage for each sink (kg/h)
CS_i	Contaminant composition of sources	CFW_r	Contaminant composition of freshwater
CK_j	Contaminant composition of sinks	CW	Contaminant composition of wast
CKL_j	Contaminant composition limit of sink	OFW	Overall freshwater (kg/h)
FK_j	Flowrate of sinks (kg/h)	OWW	Overall wastewater (kg/h)
$xF_{i,j}$	Flowrate from source i to sink j (kg/h)	FAC	Freshwater annual cost ($/y)
$yF_{i,u}$	Flowrate from source i to treatment u (kg/h)	TTC	Treatment annual capital cost ($/y)
$tF_{u,w}$	Flowrate from treatment u to other w (kg/h)	TOC	Treatment operation cost ($/y)
$zF_{w,j}$	Flowrate from treatment w to sink j (kg/h)	PAC	Piping annual capital cost ($/y)
$WW1_i$	Wastewater generated from source (kg/h)	TAC	Total annual cost ($/y)
$WW2_w$	Wastewater generated from source after treated (kg/h)		

Acknowledgements

Authors would like to express our gratitude to the Petroleum and Petrochemical College, Chulalongkorn University, National Center of Excellence for Petroleum, Petrochemicals and Advance Materials, and Government Budget Fund.

References

C. Bragalli, C. D'Ambrosio, J. Lee, A. Lodi, P. Toth, 2012, On the optimal design of water distribution networks: a practical MINLP approach, Optimization and Engineering, 13, 2, 219-246.

C. Sotelo-Pichardo, J.M. Ponce-Ortega, M.M. El-Halwagi, S. Frausto-Hernández, 2011, Optimal retrofit of water conservation networks, Journal of Cleaner Production, 19, 14, 1560-1581.

D.C.Y. Foo, 2008, Flowrate targeting for threshold problems and plant-wide integration for water network synthesis, Journal of Environmental Management, 88, 2, 253-274.

E. Ahmetović, Z. Kravanja, 2013, Simultaneous synthesis of process water and heat exchanger networks, Energy, DOI: 10.1016/j.energy.2013.02.061.

M.M. El-Halwagi, F. Gabriel, D. Harell, 2003, Rigorous Graphical Targeting for Resource Conservation via Material Recycle/Reuse Networks, Industrial & Engineering Chemistry Research, 42, 19, 4319-4328.

R. Dunn, H. Wenzel, M. Overcash, 2001, Process integration design methods for water conservation and wastewater reduction in industry, Clean Technologies and Environmental Policy, 3, 3, 319-329.

Y.L. Tan, Z.A. Manan, D.C.Y. Foo, 2007, Retrofit of Water Network with Regeneration Using Water Pinch Analysis, Process Safety and Environmental Protection, 85, 4, 305-317.

Jiří Jaromír Klemeš, Petar Sabev Varbanov and Peng Yen Liew (Editors)
Proceedings of the 24th European Symposium on Computer Aided Process Engineering – ESCAPE 24
June 15-18, 2014, Budapest, Hungary.

Extractive Distillation Process Optimisation of the 1.0-1a Class System, Acetone - methanol with Water

Xinqiang You [a,b], Ivonne Rodriguez-Donis [a,b], Vincent Gerbaud [a,b*]

[a] *Université de Toulouse, INP, UPS, LGC (Laboratoire de Génie Chimique), 4 allée Emile Monso, F-31432 Toulouse Cedex 04 – France.*

[b] *CNRS, LGC (Laboratoire de Génie Chimique), F-31432 Toulouse Cedex 04 – France*

vincent.gerbaud@ensiacet.fr

Abstract

The optimal design of an extractive distillation column and entrainer regeneration column sequence is studied with a MINLP method. The objective function minimizes the energy consumption per product flow rate under purity and recovery constraints. Total annual cost (TAC) for the process is calculated. A trade-off between the two columns variables is found and optimal parameters with lower energy consumption and TAC than literature results are found. A case study is provided with the extractive distillation separation of acetone-methanol with entrainer water (class 1.0-1a).

Keywords: extractive distillation, optimisation, energy saving, optimal design.

1. Introduction

Extractive distillation is considered as an alternative distillation process to azeotropic distillation for the separation of azeotropic or close-boiling mixtures. Hot topics of extractive distillation are focused on two main issues: entrainer selection and process optimisation. The entrainer selection issue for the separation of all non-ideal zeotropic or azeotropic mixtures with heavy, light or intermediate entrainer, and how it sets the attainable products and process configuration is now well understood, though the combined analysis of residue curve maps and univolatility curve location (Shen et al., 2012). Here we focus on the most frequent case, the separation of a minimum boiling azeotrope acetone – methanol with a heavy entrainer water, corresponding to the (1.0-1a) extractive class separation (Rodriguez-Donis et al., 2009).

Regarding the extractive process performance, Lynn et al. (1986) carried out the extractive dehydration process of ethanol with ethylene glycol as entrainer and found that it was competitive in terms of energy consumption compared with azeotropic distillation. A well-designed extractive distillation process should enable to get high product purity, low entrainer loss and low energy consumption both for the extractive column and the regeneration column (Knapp and Doherty, 1990). Thus, we optimise the homogeneous extractive distillation process with the regeneration column.

2. Optimal process design method

2.1. Method

For a detailed process design, an economic trade-off must be found between the investment and operating costs. For the extractive distillation process both the extractive column and the entrainer regeneration column should be included and connected with the solvent recycle stream. For finding optimal parameters for the acetone – methanol separation with water, some authors have run a sensitivity analysis over the process variables, namely the reflux ratio, the entrainer–feed flow rate ratio, the number of trays in each of the rectifying, extractive, stripping column sections and the distillate flow rate (Hilal et al., 2002, Langston et al., 2005, Lyuben, 2008, Gil et al., 2009). However, the procedure is tedious and may fail to find the best solution. Mixed integer nonlinear programming (MINLP) optimisation can solve this issue but may require some programming outside a process simulator as used for the same mixture (Kossack et al., 2008) or for ethanol dehydration (Garcia-Herreros et al., 2011).

In this work, we use UNIQUAC model with binary parameters built-in Aspen plus and De Figueiredo et al. (2011) optimising procedure: basing on an SQP scheme built in Aspen plus simulator for optimising the continuous variables and a sensitivity analysis over the stage numbers. Unlike de Figueiredo's work and following Kossack et al. (2008), we consider the two column sequence of extractive distillation process as in Figure 1. The two columns are strongly coupled: The entrainer-feed flow rate ratio F_E/F_F and composition x_{FE} are key optimisation variables, along with the reflux ratio R_1. But as F_E/F_F and x_{FE} impact the liquid residue which feeds the entrainer regeneration column, they also affect the reflux ratio of the entrainer regeneration column R_2. Besides, the entrainer recycle purity and flow rate from the regeneration column affect the extractive column separating effect, possibly preventing to achieve the distillate purity as specified. The optimisation flowsheet is an open loop (Figure 1b) and the optimal solution is ultimately simulated in the closed loop flowsheet (Figure 1a).

2.2. Objective function (OF)

De Figueiredo et al. (2011) used the ratio of the reboiler heat duty of extractive distillation column and the specified production flowrate (Q_R/D) as objective function. The condenser heat duty is then neglected despite its impact on the process cost; and the regeneration column is not taken into account. Arifin and Chien (2008) used the total annual cost (*TAC*) including capital cost and operating cost as objective function. They showed that it exhibits a minimal value vs the total number of trays for the extractive process sequence columns. Our objective function for the optimization of variables is:

$$\begin{aligned} \min OF &= \frac{Q_{r1} + m \cdot Q_{c1} + Q_{r2} + m \cdot Q_{c2}}{k \cdot D_1 + D_2} \\ \textit{subject to}: & \; x_{acetone,D1} \geq 0.995 \\ & \; x_{acetone,W1} \leq 0.001 \\ & \; x_{methanol,D2} \geq 0.995 \\ & \; x_{water,W2} \geq 0.9999 \end{aligned} \tag{1}$$

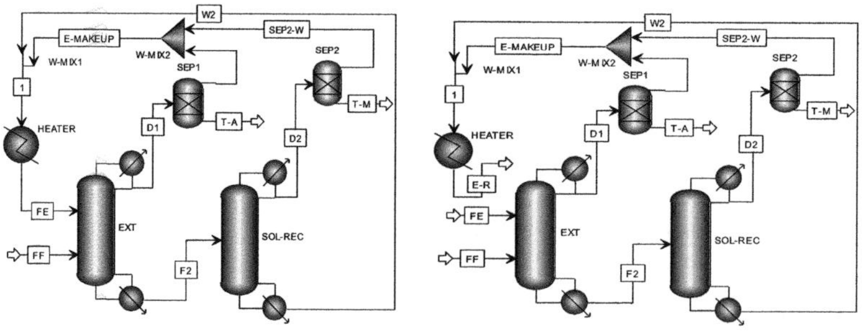

Figure 1. Extractive distillation process flow sheet (a) simulation (b) optimization.

Constraints 1 and 3 concern the products purity in D_1 and D_2. Constraint 2 in bottom W_1 aims at keeping high the main product recovery. Constraint 4 focuses on the recycling entrainer purity. Q_{r1} and Q_{c1}: extractive column reboiler and condenser duty, Q_{r2} and Q_{c2}: entrainer regeneration column reboiler and condenser duty, D_1 and D_2 extractive column and entrainer regeneration column distillate flow rate, k = 5.9: product price factor for acetone vs methanol, m = 0.036: energy price difference factor for condenser vs reboiler. Update of k and m is done by using chemicals prices and Douglas (1988) costs method with Marshall and Swift inflation index corrections.

The meaning of OF is the energy consumption used per product unit flow rate (kJ/kmol). It accounts for both columns and also reflects the weight coefficient of the two product prices and reboiler - condenser heat duty. OF is sensitive to the variables F_E/F_F, R_1, R_2, D_1, D_2 and the thee feed location as well.

Finally the TAC is calculated for each optimal solution for a given total number of trays. We use the TAC formula of Li and Bai (2012) with Douglas' costs correlations. The capital cost includes column shell, tray and heat exchanger costs; the operating cost group the reboiler and condenser energy cost. Pump, pipe, valves costs are neglected.

$$TAC = \frac{capital\ cost}{payback\ \ period} + operating\ costs \tag{2}$$

2.3. Optimisation procedure

- Step 1, minimizing OF by optimising continuous variable F_E, R_1 and R_2 under fixed stage numbers N_{Ext} and N_{Reg} and feed positions N_{FE}, N_{FF}, N_{FReg}.
- Step 2, minimizing OF by optimising D_1, D_2, F_E, R_1 and R_2 as variables.
- Step 3, minimizing OF, taking N_{FE}, N_{FF}, N_{FReg}, F_E, R_1 and R_2 as variable with to get optimal value while keeping values of D_1 and D_2.
- Step 4, corroborating the optimal values by simulation and calculating TAC.

3. Result

3.1. First step.

Table 1 displays the optimised F_E, R_1, R_2 while the other variables are kept constant. Results are compared to Luyben's (2008) results that were taken for initializing the procedure. N_{Ext}=57, N_{Reg}=26, N_{FE}=25, N_{FF}=40, N_{FReg}=14, equimolar F_F=540 kmol/h.
We observe (1) a OF significant decrease as more variables are taken into account. (2) a 4.9 % energy consumption saving if F_E, R_1 and R_2 are optimised at the same time. (3) that optimising the regeneration column together with the extractive column improves further the OF: when R2 is taken into account, R1 becomes bigger, FE decreases and R_2 gets smaller, If less entrainer is fed to the extractive column, a greater R_1 is needed to get the same separation effect. Meanwhile the concentration of entrainer fed to the rege-

Table 1. Step 1, optimal results of F_E, R_1 and R_2

variable	Optimised value			
	Luyben (2008)	F_E	F_E and R_1	F_E R_1 and R_2
F_E, kmol/h	1100	809.0	922.7	883.3
R_1	3.44	3.44	3.228	3.277
R_2	1.6	1.6	1.6	1.491
OF, kJ/kmol	36,194.4	35,564.1	34,864.7	34,421.7

neration column decreases due to mass balance, and less energy (R_2 decrease) is used to recycle the entrainer.

3.2. Second step.

As the effect of D_1 and D_2 on the product purity is strongly non-linear, the simulation cannot converged steadily, so D_1 and D_2 are varied with a discrete step of 0.1 kmol/h from 270 kmol/h (recovery = 99.5 %) to 271.3 kmol/h (recovery = 99.98 %) and the SQP optimisation is run for F_E, R_1 and R_2. The results are shown in Figure 2.

From Figure 2, we observe that D_1=270.7 kmol/h and D_2=271.1 kmol/h published in Lyuben's results are not optimal values for our *OF*. Also, *OF* decreases with the increase of D_2 (resp. D_1) when D_1 (resp. D_2) is fixed. As we will optimise other variables such as N_{FE}, N_{FF}, N_{FReg}, N_{Ext} and N_{Reg} in the subsequent steps, we select D_1=271 kmol/h and D_2=271.1 kmol/h; those values corresponding to a product recovery high enough but not too high so as to make the flow sheet convergence difficult. The corresponding *OF* value is 33911.2 kJ/kmol, with F_E=901.5 kmol/h, R_1=3.255 and R_2=1.406.

3.3. Third step.

The variables N_{FE}, N_{FF} and N_{FReg} are varied through sensitivity analysis and F_E, R_1, R_2 are optimised while D_1 and D_2 are fixed. N_{FE}, N_{FF}, N_{FReg} impact the *OF* not independently of each other. Thus, the sensitivity analysis over the thee feed positions with ranges [25;50] for N_{FE}, [>N_{FE} ;56] for N_{FF}, [5;25] for N_{FReg} was made by using experimental planning procedure so as to avoid local minimum. Results are in Table 2.

From Table 2, we observe that (1) F_E, R_1 and R_2 are changing as the thee feed stages change. The impact on *OF* is nonlinear, highlighting again the coupling of all variables and the necessity to consider the regeneration column as well. (2) The best *OF* value is 30741 kJ/kmol, a 9.3 % decrease compared to step 2 and 15.1 % decrease compared to the *OF* for Luyben's design. (3) The minimum value of *OF* is found for a greater number of trays in the extractive section than Luyben. Rodriguez Donis et al. (2009) have explained for the (1.0-1a) class separation that this is needed to keep the methanol content as low as possible in the extractive section stable node composition.

Table 2. Optimal results of F_E, R_1, R_2, N_{FE}, N_{FF}, N_{FReg} under fixed D_1 and D_2

N_{FE}	N_{FF}	N_{FReg}	F_E	R_1	R_2	*OF* kJ/kmol
25	40	14	901.5	3.255	1.406	33,911.2
25	40	15	911.8	3.246	1.340	33,541.9
29	44	16	847.3	2.934	1.264	31,618.6
29	46	17	776.3	2.910	1.216	31,104.6
30	44	16	904.0	2.871	1.289	31,589.9
31	44	17	927.7	2.866	1.344	31,917.1
31	48	15	846.0	2.760	1.321	31,145.3
31	48	16	810.8	2.791	1.254	30,851.4
31	48	17	806.3	2.797	1.230	30,741.4
31	49	18	802.3	2.816	1.258	30,962.9

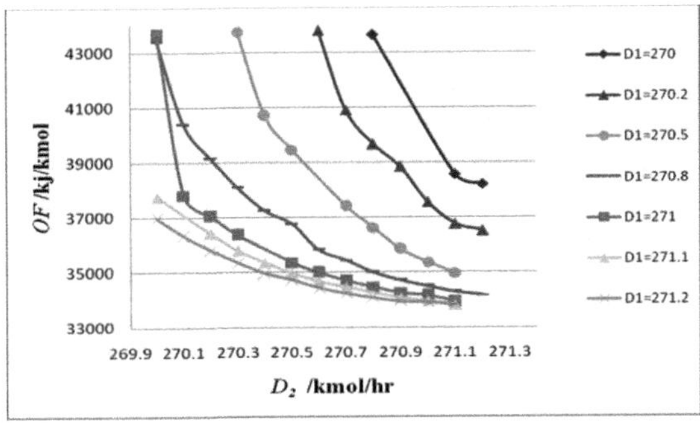

Figure 2. Effects of D1 and D2 on OF with D1, D2, FE, R1 and R2 as variables

3.4. Fourth step.

All the optimisation procedure was done with an open loop flowsheet (Figure 1b) where F_E is pure water. As the product purities are constrained in the objective function, they are satisfied. For example, we obtain $x_{acetone,D1}$ = 0.995002 with optimal values from step 3. However when simulating the extractive process flowsheet with a closed recycle loop as in practice, we obtain $x_{acetone,D1}$ = 0.99484 with the optimal values from step 3. This happens because the recycled entrainer purity is then 99.98 % and not pure water and show the importance of the purity of recycled entrainer. Increasing R_2 would seem at first relevant to improve the recycled entrainer purity, but it is not efficient here because that purity is already very high: a small increase of R_2 to 1.495 to get $x_{water,W2}$= 0.99999 affects the *OF* that increases from 30741 to 32142 kJ/kmol. Increasing R_1 from 2.797 to 2.823 keeps *OF* low and raises $x_{acetone,D1}$ from 0.99484 to 0.99500 in the closed loop simulation.

The final results are shown in Table 3 and 4. For practical implementation, we have ultimately rounded up the optimal values: F_E = 807 kmol/h, R_1 = 2.880, D_1 = 271 kmol/h, R_2= 1.231, D_2= 271.1 kmol/h, N_{FE}= 31, N_{FF}= 48, N_{FReg}= 17. We can see (1) a 14.5 % energy consumption reduction compared to Luyben's design based on the same stage number of columns (N_{Ext}=57, N_{Reg}=26). (2) a 12.0 % saving in TAC (3) a greater production (D_1) while maintaining the product purity and using less both energy and total annual cost. (4) the recovery of acetone is greater though the recovery of methanol is smaller as the weigh coefficient of acetone is higher than methanol.

Table 3. Comparison of our optimal results with Luyben's design

variable	F_E	R_1	R_2	D_1	D_2	N_{FE}	N_{FF}	N_{FReg}	*OF* kJ/kmol	TAC 10^6\$
This work	807	2.880	1.231	271	271.1	31	48	17	30916.6	3.069
Luyben	1100	3.44	1.61	270.7	271.1	25	40	14	36194.8	3.489

Table 4. Product purities from optimal results and Luyben's design

mole fraction	Mole Frac	D_1	D_2	W_2=*water*	W_1=F_2	*recovery*
This work	Acetone	0.99516	0.00115	1.88E-12	0.00029	99.88%
	Methanol	0.00066	0.99529	9.84E-05	0.25084	99.93%
	Water	0.00418	0.00356	0.999901	0.74887	
Luyben	Acetone	0.99573	0.00168	9.51E-15	0.00033	99.83%
	Methanol	0.00017	0.99578	5.64E-06	0.19715	99.98
	Water	0.00410	0.00254	0.999994	0.80252	

4. Conclusions

We have obtained optimal parameters for an extractive distillation process for separating the minimum boiling azeotropic mixture acetone-methanol with water (class 1.0-1a) as entrainer, taking into account the both extractive distillation and the entrainer regeneration columns and compared it with Luyben's design under the constraint of 0.995 mole fraction acetone and methanol products. In a MINLP scheme we have combined SQP optimization for the continuous variables F_E, R_1, R_2, and sensitivity analysis for D_1, D_2, N_{FE}, N_{FF}, N_{FReg}. We have proposed a new objective function accounting for all the energy consumption of per product flow rate value. Compared with Luyben's design in literature, the total annual cost and energy consumption are reduced by 12.0 % and 14.5 % respectively based on the same column stage numbers. It can be pridict that more energy and total annual cost will be saved if the column stage numbers are changed and optimised follow the optimization process mentioned in this work.

References

S. Arifin, I.L. Chien, 2008, Design and control of an isopropyl alcohol dehydration process via extractive distillation using dimethyl sulfoxide as an entrainer, Ind. Eng. Chem. Res., 47, 790-803.

G. Li, P. Bai, 2012, New Operation Strategy for Separation of Ethanol–Water by Extractive Distillation. Industrial & Engineering Chemistry Research, 51, 6, 2723-2729.

I. Rodriguez-Donis, V. Gerbaud, X. Joulia, 2009, Thermodynamic Insights on the Feasibility of Homogeneous Batch Extractive Distillation. 1. Azeotropic Mixtures with Heavy Entrainer, Ind. Eng. Chem. Res., 48, 7, 3544–3559.

I.D. Gil, D. C. Botia, P. Ortiz, O.S. Sanchez, 2009, Extractive distillation of acetone/methanol mixture using water as entrainer, Ind. Eng. Chem. Res., 48, 4858-4865.

J.P. Knapp, M. F. Doherty, 1990, Thermal integration of homogeneous azeotropic distillation sequences, AIChE Journal, 36, 7, 969-984.

J.M. Douglas, 1988, Conceptual design of chemical processes, McGrawHill, New York, US.

M.F. de Figueiredo, B. Pontual Guedes, J. Manzi Monteiro de Araújo, L. Gonzaga Sales Vasconcelos, R. Pereira Brito, 2011, Optimal design of extractive distillation columns—a systematic procedure using a process simulator, Chem. Eng. Res. Des., 89, 3, 341-346.

N. Hilal, G. Yousef, P. Langston, 2002, The reduction of extractive agent in extractive distillation and auto-extractive distillation, Chem. Eng. Proc. Process Intensification, 41, 8, 673-679.

P. García-Herreros, J. M. Gómez, I. D. Gil, G. Rodriguez, 2011, Optimization of the design and operation of an extractive distillation system for the production of fuel grade ethanol using glycerol as entrainer, Ind. Eng. Chem. Res., 50, 7, 3977-3985.

P. Langston, N. Hilal,, S. Shingfield, Webb S., 2005, Simulation and optimisation of extractive distillation with water as solvent, Chem. Eng. Proc. Process Intensification, 44, 3, 345-351.

S. Kossack, K. Kraemer, R. Gani, W. Marquardt, 2008, A systematic synthesis framework for extractive distillation processes, Chem. Eng. Res. Des., 86, 781-792.

S. Lynn, D. N. Hanson,1986, Multi-effect extractive distillation for separating aqueous azeotropes, Ind. Eng. Chem. Proc. Des. Dev., 25, 4, 936-941.

W.L. Luyben, 2008, Comparison of extractive distillation and pressure-swing distillation for acetone –methanol separation, Ind. Eng. Chem. Res., 47, 2696-2707.

W. Shen, H. Benyounes, V. Gerbaud, 2012, Extension of Thermodynamic Insights on Batch Extractive Distillation to Continuous Operation. 1. Azeotropic Mixtures with a Heavy Entrainer. Ind. Eng. Chem. Res, 52, 12, 4606–4622.

Z. Lei, C. Li, B. Chen, 2003, Extractive distillation: a review, Separation & Purification Reviews, 32, 2, 121-213.

Jiří Jaromír Klemeš, Petar Sabev Varbanov and Peng Yen Liew (Editors)
Proceedings of the 24th European Symposium on Computer Aided Process Engineering – ESCAPE 24
June 15-18, 2014, Budapest, Hungary.

Design and Implementation of a Real Time Optimization Prototype for a Propylene Distillation Unit

Elyser E. Martínez[a,*], Fabio D.S. Liporace[b], Rafael D.P. Soares[c], Galo A.C. Le Roux[a]

[a]*Dep. of Chem. Eng., University of São Paulo, Av. Luciano Gualberto, Trav. 3, São Paulo, Brazil*
[b]*CENPES/PETROBRAS S.A, Av. Horácio Macedo, 950, Rio de Janeiro, Brazil*
[c]*Dep. of Chemical Eng., Federal University of Rio Grande do Sul, Rua Sarmento Leite 288, Porto Alegre, Brazil*
elyser.estrada@gmail.com

Abstract
The design of a steady state RTO system prototype to be tested in an industrial unit is presented. A software architecture (SA) approach is carried out proposing an object-oriented software framework. SA patterns are used in the architecture design. The framework aims to allow the implementation of different RTO approaches. A RTO system prototype is being developed using the framework integrating EMSO (Soares and Secchi, 2003) as the modeling and optimization engine. The framework opens opportunities for academic uses and deeper researches on the field.

Keywords: real-time optimization, software framework, software architecture.

1. Introduction
Chemical process industry has a high demand for methods and tools to optimize processes in order to enhance their profitability. It is the consequence of the global market which leads to increasing competition, tightening product requirements, pricing pressures and environmental issues (Darby and White, 1988). Real-time optimization (RTO) is a CAPE method that frequently reevaluates the process operating conditions to maximize the economic productivity under operational constrains. It seeks to improve process performance iteratively by adjusting selected optimization variables using measurement data. A continuous adaptation is carried out to drive the operating point towards the actual plant optimum (Chachuat et al., 2009). RTO involves many concerns. The real-time collection of process data is its initial step. Measure instruments combined with distributed control systems (DCS) and data collection and analysis solutions, like Plant Information System from OSI Software (PI System) (www.osisoft.com), have proved its value in this context. Steady-state identification is also a vital step in RTO that includes gross error detection and data reconciliation. Several approaches have been proposed for RTO (Chachuat et al., 2009). Once an optimal state is calculated the information must be sent to the plant. Advanced control methods like model based predictive control (MPC) are responsible for bringing the process to the indicated state. Transforming multicomponent CAPE methods like RTO into useful tools requires appropriate software architectures (Braunschweig and Gani, 2002). In order to cope with that demand, a software framework aiming to cover several

RTO concerns is presented here. A system prototype is being developed with the framework to be tested in REPLAN refinery owned by PETROBRAS.

2. The RTO software application framework

A software application framework is an abstraction in which generic functionalities can be selectively overridden in order to develop specific domain applications. It provides an architecture and building blocks for a family of systems likewise places where adaptations should be made (Buschmann et al., 1996). The default framework's behavior guarantees to achieve its mission in a predefined way. In an object-oriented environment this behavior can be modified overriding abstract classes and interfaces.

Proven commercial software solutions exist for RTO. Two well-known are ROMeo, commercialized by Invensys (www.invensys.com), and Aspen RTO, from AspenTech (www.aspentech.com). Both solutions cover real-time nonlinear optimization of continuous processes. Although they can be broadly parameterized there is always a black box style related with the way they carry out operations. Usually, the inclusion of new RTO methods and algorithms is not a feasible option. That issue motivated the development of the framework as a technically open workbench tool that can be used for test, research and innovation purposes. The implementation of a RTO system prototype in a PETROBRAS unit can be accomplished developing over this framework.

2.1. The software architecture approach

Software architecture (SA) is a form of software design that occurs earliest in a system's creation at a very high abstraction level and its key issue is organization. The IEEE 1471 standard defines SA as "the fundamental organization of a system embodied in its components, their relationships to each other and to the environment, and the principles guiding its design and evolution". Bass et al. (2013) defines SA as the structure or structures of a computing system, comprising software elements, the externally visible properties of those elements, and the relationships among them. Systems can and do comprise more than one structure, each of them providing a different perspective and design handle. The term "software elements" encompasses all the architectural buildings blocks: components, connectors, configurations and constrains. A component is an abstract building element, a unit of computation or a data store which constitutes a part of a software product. Connectors are used to model and govern interactions among components. Configurations are connected graphs of components and connectors that describe architectural structures. SA issues include gross organization and global control structure; protocols for communication, synchronization, and data access; likewise assignment of functionality to design elements and physical distribution. Works like Muñoz et al. (2011) and Silvente et al. (2012) present software architecture approaches in chemical process engineering.

2.2. Framework architecture description

The description of the framework architecture is presented using just the conceptual architectural structure (Bass et al., 2013). The description follows the rules and visual elements defined by ACME (Garlan et al., 1997), an architecture description language, and a drill down or by levels approach. Starting from level zero each level contains a set of components linked in some configuration. The higher the level number the lower the design abstraction. Components exposed in a deeper level shed light on how prior level functionalities are reached. For space reasons not every component in each level will be depicted.

2.2.1. Level zero

Level zero follows the Client/Server architectural pattern (Buschmann et al., 1996). A notable design feature is the embedding of RTO operations inside a server shell component, named "RTO Process". This component carries out the RTO related operations and act as a server resolving client requests. As Figure 1 shows it interacts with the plant computer systems getting real process data and sending calculated RTO solutions.

The following elements complete the overall configuration:

- Process Control System: Architectural representation of plant control systems. Encapsulates the process data collection and control systems.
- Process Communication Protocol: Connector representing communication between the RTO Process server and the plant systems. A default implementation for this connector is provided.
- Server Communication Protocol: Connector encapsulating the server mechanism to implement communication with clients. Classifies also as a Stream type connector. A default implementation is provided.
- Client RTO Application: Represents a client application oriented to manage the RTO operations. In practice it can be one or several web or desktop applications.
- External Client Process: Represents a legacy or third part external process that uses information generated by the RTO Process.

2.2.2. Level one

Description of level one will be centered in the depiction of the internal structure of the RTO Process component, as shown in Figure 2. The elements that complete the configuration are:

- Performance comparison and parametric optimization of subcritical Organic Rankine Cycle (ORC)Process Agent: Acts as a proxy for the requests sent to the Process

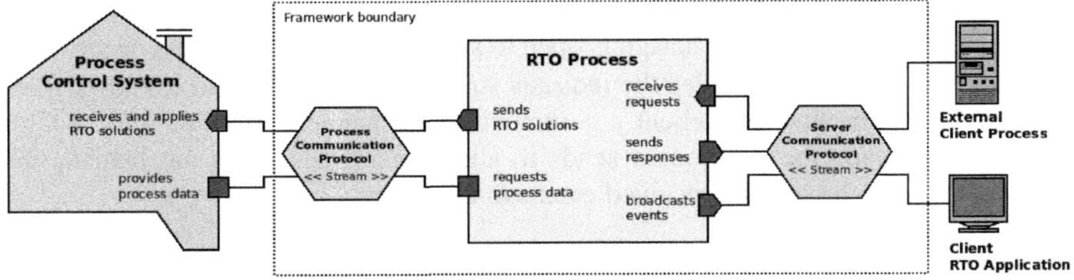

Figure 1. Level zero of the RTO framework architecture.

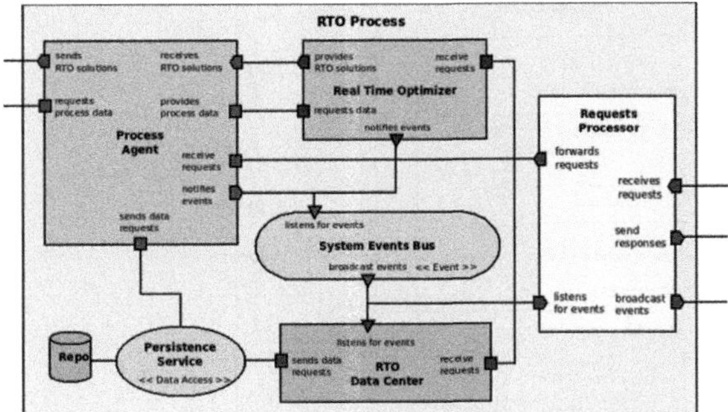

Figure 2. RTO Process component internal structure.

Control System. It also accomplishes RTO vital operations. At real time it says if the plant is in steady-state. When it is the case the component keeps recalculating a representative state and once the steady-state is off it is stored into the framework repository for further use. The component uses internal or repository information to handle requests. Every relevant process event is notified to the System Event Bus. The Process Agent is also responsible for sending the RTO solution to the Process Control System.

- Persistence Service: Represents the data access mechanism used to persist and get information from the framework repository. The default implementation of this component is based in the Java Persistence API (JPA) (www.oracle.com).
- Framework Repository: Its mission is to store internal information generated and used by the framework components. In practice it is implemented using a PostgreSQL database (www.postgresql.org).
- Real Time Optimizer: Central component of the architecture. It provides the core of the framework mission. Its role is to perform the optimization of the plant. It relies on an optimization engine to determine the optimal operational point. Its internal design follows the Bridge design pattern (Gamma et al., 1994), allowing several implementations. The component asks the Process Agent for data about actual and past plant states. According to the supplied objective function and constrains the optimization engine finds an RTO solution which is sent to the Process Agent.
- System Events Bus: Internal bus that distributes information based in the implicit invocation mechanism (Garlan and Shaw, 1994). It permits other components to subscribe to all or specific events. Once an event is received it is broadcasted to all the subscribed components, each of them taking their own actions.
- RTO Data Center: Its main role is the synthesis of notable RTO related information. It provides the framework with a place and mechanism to build that information based on events received. Frequently used information is kept active and the rest is persisted to the repository. A typical stored information is the most recent RTO solutions. The component's design is open to support future information needs.
- Requests Processor: It handles the requests submitted by clients and it knows where to forward them. For each client a communication channel is created and once the response is ready the component sends it, all in an asynchronous mechanism. The component also broadcasts received events to clients.

2.2.3. Level two

The configuration for the Process Agent functionalities is shown in Figure 3.

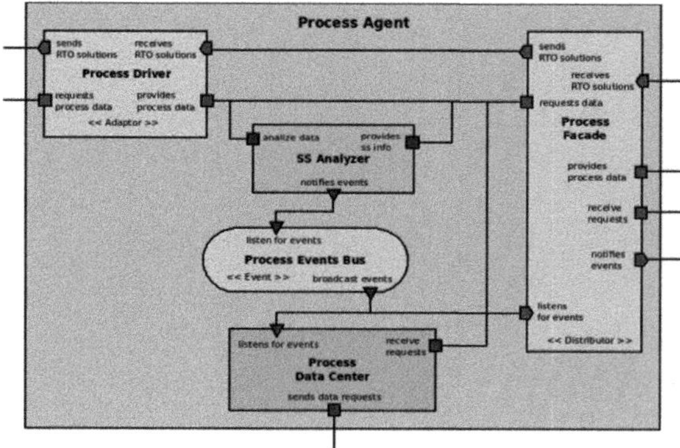

Figure 3. Process Agent component internal structure.

The elements of the structure are:

- Process Driver: Acts as a driver for communication with the plant. Following the Adaptor pattern (Gamma et al., 1994) it encapsulates the process data acquisition and RTO solutions delivery, allowing adapting the framework to the several information technologies that can be used in plants. A PI System driver is its default implementation.
- SS Analyzer: Determines at real time if the plant is in steady-state. It keeps reading and analyzing data through the Process Driver. For every plant state change it generates and dispatches an event to the Process Event Bus. Once the plant stabilization is detected the component keeps calculating a representative state and includes it in the event generated when the stabilization is off. The component's internal design allows using several steady-state detection methods.
- Process Event Bus: A connector with similar functionalities to those of the System Event Bus.
- Process Data Center: Synthesizes notable information, persisting some of them in the repository, about the actual and past plant states based on received events. This component provides a place and mechanism supporting future information needs.
- Process Facade: Remembers the Facade design pattern (Gamma et al., 1994), but used at an architectural level. It acts as a distributor of requests and forwards them to components with the capacity to generate the responses. The Process Agent notifies events to the external context through this component.

2.2.4. Level three

Here we describe the SS Analyzer and the Process Data Center. The SS Analyzer is built by three components. The Process Sampler asks periodically the Process Driver to sample the process. Filters can be applied here to perform gross error detection. Samples are sent to the Samples Buffer who creates a mobile data window. The windows size can be configured, as well the sampling frequency. The Steady State Detector analyzes periodically the Samples Buffer data running a method to detect plant stability. Every generated event is processed by the Process Data Center synthesizing rewarding information. Two internal elements are combined for that: the Info Synthesizer and the Requests Processor. Info Synthesizer's structure follows the Interceptor pattern (Buschmann et al., 1996). Independent interceptors with specific roles intercept the events and carry out the information synthesis. One of the interceptors stores representative steady-state data in the framework's repository. Gross error detection can also be implemented with interceptors. The Process Data Center tracks the plant route, so requests for past information are forwarded to it. The Request Processor distributes requests to the Info Synthesizer or directly to the framework's repository.

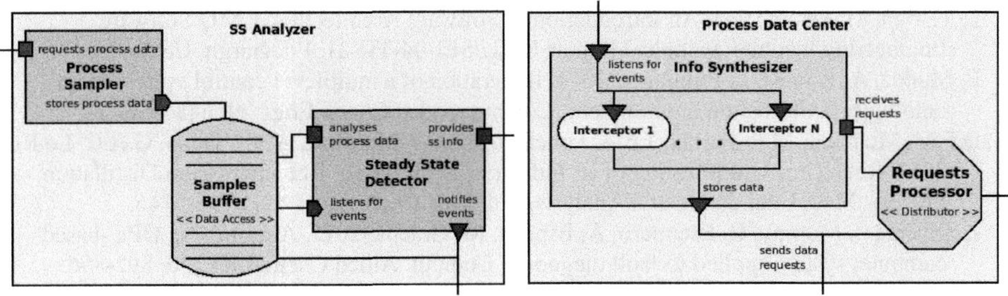

Figure 4. SS Analyzer and Process Data Center internal structures.

3. Application in a PETROBRAS unit

PETROBRAS's investments in evaluation of RTO technology motivate the building of a system prototype for the REPLAN's C3 Splitter distillation unit. The aim to use equation oriented models and to test several optimization algorithms justifies the use of EMSO (Soares and Secchi, 2003). EMSO proposes a language for dynamic or steady-state processes modeling and provides an open source models library. It is capable to solve high-index DAE systems and has a built-in symbolic and automatic differentiation system. Its functionalities can be extended and new nonlinear-algebraic solvers can be added. A model of the REPLAN's distillation unit has been developed in EMSO (Muñoz et al., 2013). Interfaces for DCS and PI System, gross error detection filters and steady-state identification algorithms are being implemented. Several RTO approaches are being tested and implemented. Software libraries containing established and recent parameter estimation methods and optimization solvers are been developed as well.

4. Conclusions

The software framework architecture presented attempts to cover several RTO concerns. It provides the opportunity to customize several functionalities to approach RTO issues. A prototype application for a propylene production unit is under development. A workbench for the RTO issues exploration and its application to a real production unit are the main contribution of this work. It can open new horizons for more sophisticated RTO applications, giving chances to study in practice unexplored combinations of techniques.

References

L. Bass, P. Clements, R. Kazman, 2013, Software Architecture in Practice, Third Edition, Addison-Wesley, Westford, USA.

B. Braunschweig, R. Gani, 2002, Software Architectures and Tools for Computer Aided Process Engineering, Comput. Aided Chem. Eng., 11.

F. Buschmann, R. Meunier, H. Rohnert, P. Sommerland, M. Stal, D. Schmidt, K. Henney, 1996, Pattern-Oriented Software Architecture, John Wiley & Sons, 1-5, Chichester, UK.

B. Chachuat, B. Srinivasan, D. Bonvin, 2009, Adaptation Strategies for Real-Time Optimization, Comput. Chem. Eng., 33, 1557-1567.

C.R. Cutler, R.T. Perry, 1983, Real-Time Optimization with Multivariable Control is Required to Maximize Profits, Comput. Chem. Eng., 7, 663-667.

M.L. Darby, D.C. White, 1988, On-Line Optimization of Complex Process Units, Chem. Eng. Prog., 67, 10, 51-59.

E. Gamma, R. Helm, R. Johnson, J. Vlissides, 1994, Design Patterns–Elements of Reusable Object-Oriented Software, Addison Wesley, New York, USA.

D. Garlan, R.T. Monroe, D. Wile, 1997, ACME: An Architecture Description Interchange Language, Tepper School of Business, paper 322, CMU, Pittsburgh, USA.

D. Garlan, M. Shaw, 1994, An Introduction to Software Architecture, CMU Software Engineering Institute Technical Report CMU/SEI-94-TR-21, Pittsburgh, USA.

E. Muñoz, A. Espuña, L. Puigjaner, 2011, Integration of a multilevel control system in an ontological information environment, Comput. Aided Chem. Eng., 29, 648-652.

D.F.M. Muñoz, L.M.P. Garcia, J.E.A. Graciano, C.A.R. Martinez, A.S. Vianna, G.A.C. Le Roux, 2013, Real-Time Optimization of an Industrial-Scale Vapor Recompression Distillation Process. Model Validation and Analysis, Ind. Eng. Chem. Res., 52, 5735-5746.

J. Silvente, I. Monroy, G. Escudero, A. Espuña, M. Graells, 2012, A promising OPC-based computer system applied to fault diagnosis, Comput. Aided Chem. Eng., 30, 892-896.

R.D.P. Soares, A.R. Secchi, 2003, EMSO: A new Environment for Modelling, Simulation and Optimization, Comput. Aided Chem. Eng., 14, 947-952.

Jiří Jaromír Klemeš, Petar Sabev Varbanov and Peng Yen Liew (Editors)
Proceedings of the 24th European Symposium on Computer Aided Process Engineering – ESCAPE 24
June 15-18, 2014, Budapest, Hungary.

Simple Equation for Suitability of Heat Pump Use in Distillation

Valentin Pleşu[a], Alexandra E. Bonet Ruiz[a,b], Jordi Bonet[b*], Joan Llorens[b]

[a]*UniversityPOLITEHNICA of Bucharest, Centre for Technology Transfer in Process Industries (CTTPI), 1, Gh. Polizu Street, Bldg A, Room A056, RO-011061 Bucharest, Romania*

[b]*University of Barcelona, Department of Chemical Engineering, 1,Martí i Franquès Street, 6th Floor, E-08028 Barcelona, Spain*

bonet@ub.edu

Abstract

A distillation column can be considered as a heat engine that produces separation instead of work. The heat is provided in the reboiler and collected degraded at a lower temperature at the condenser. The energy collected at low temperature at the top of the column can be upgraded back to higher temperatures by means of a heat pump and reused to heat a lower column stage.This can bring saving in terms of the overall amount of energy required. However, the energy required to increase the pressure is of higher quality and price than hot services. The aim of the present paper is to provide an easy way to check, in the early stages of design, when the use of a heat pump can provide a more sustainable distillation process decreasing its energy requirements. After several simplifications, it can be stated that it depends mainly on the efficiency of Carnot. When the efficiency of Carnot is evaluated for the industrial systems where the heat pumps are used, it is concluded that all have Carnot efficiency around 0.1 or lower. Therefore, in the early design of a new distillation column, this criterion is useful to decide when a heat pump is worth to be included in the more rigorous simulations.

Keywords: heat pump assisted distillation (HPDA), Carnot efficiency, energy savings

1. Introduction

Efficient use of the energy is as important as effective energy production from the sustainability point of view. Distillation is the most mature and widely used separation process in the chemical and allied industries, accounting for most of the separations in chemical process industries. Any small improvement of distillation column efficiencies will be translated into great energy savings.

A distillation column is a heat engine that instead of work produces a decrease of entropy, i.e. chemical separation (Plesu et al., 2013). The heat is provided to the reboiler and collected in the distillate degraded at a lower temperature. The heating energy consumption can decrease when condenser and reboiler are coupled and therefore the integration between a heat pump and a distillation column is an attractive option in some cases as show in the review of Ulyev et al. (2013). Although most of the pumping systems research is for continuous flow operations, there are also authors applying it to batch processes (Modla and Lang, 2013).

Some authors consider that the performance of the heat pumps is mostly case specific and the only guideline to apply it supposes that larger heat load and smaller column temperature difference provide shorter payback time for heat pumping (Jana, 2014). Nevertheless, some authors claim that the heat pumps can provide also important energy saving in wide boiling mixtures when intermediate reboilers and condensers are used. However, no industrial application of multistage heat pumps with intermediate heat exchanger(s) exists in the industry. The heat integration makes difficult the start up control (Eden et al., 2000). For instance, for the case of a C_4 splitter, the double stage scheme provides the lowest cost but the most difficult operation (Fonyo et al., 1995). More recently, Kiss et al. (2012) proposed a set of guidelines to select the most promising thermally integrated distillation column based on several qualitative criteria: type of separation tasks, product flow and specifications, operating pressure, difference in boiling points, reboiler duty and its temperature level. A reasonable performance estimate for conventional vapour compression and vapour recompression heat pumps was calculated dividing the Carnot efficiency by 2. But actual performance of heat pumps could easily vary to a large extent (Van de Bor and Infante Ferreira, 2013) and make a heat pump implementation profitable. Recently, the heat pumps have been proposed for other cryogenic processes such as air separation (Fu and Gundersen, 2013) or natural gas (Van Duc Long and Lee, 2013). The energy can become expensive due to the high cost of each unit of energy, e.g. cryogenic, or due to a high amount of energy consumption, e.g. trichlorosilane synthesis (Long et al., 2013). An expensive energy favorise the heat pump implementation in distillation.

A quantitative criterion to determine when the heat pump is a good option is missing in the literature. The present paper provides a simple and general quantitative criterion based on the literature cases. Once determined that heat pump is advantageous, the most suitable heat pump scheme can be selected: vapor compression, mechanical vapor recompression, thermal vapor recompression, compressor resorption heat pump, absorption heat pump, thermo-acoustic heat pump, a.s.o.

2. Mathematical expression to evaluate the energy savings

The input data required for the present study are the distillate enthalpy of vaporization and the characteristics of input and output streams, i.e. composition, flow rate and temperature for the feed, distillate and bottoms. To simplify the model, the temperature of the feed is not taken into account because usually the energy required for collecting the distillate (vaporization) is higher that the heating energy. The assumptions of reversible process have also important implications such as, for coherence, the temperature of the condenser or reboiler and their corresponding cooling or heating services are at a differential increment of temperature. In this section, the deduction under the above simplifying assumptions of a simple expression to evaluate if a heat pump is advantageous is provided.

As indicated previously, a distillation column is equivalent to a heat engine working between hot and cold sources, but instead of producing work, produces separation. Besides the energy used for separation, energy is also used to vaporize and collect the distillate (Plesu et al., 2013). The heat required for a certain distillation separation can be calculated according to Eqs. 1 and 2.

$$Q = \frac{T_c \cdot \Delta S_{sep}}{\eta} = \frac{T_c \cdot (T_r - T_c) \cdot \Delta S_{sep}}{T_r} \tag{1}$$

where for ideal behavior

$$\Delta S_{sep} = R \cdot \left[(D+B)\cdot\left(\sum x_i^{feed} \cdot ln\, x_i^{feed}\right) - D\cdot\left(\sum x_i^{distil} \cdot ln\, x_i^{distil}\right) - B\cdot\left(\sum x_i^{residue} \cdot ln\, x_i^{residue}\right)\right] \quad (2)$$

Q is the reboiler duty, T_c is the condenser temperature, T_r is the reboiler temperature, η is the Carnot efficiency, ΔS_{sep} is the change of entropy associated to the separation, R is the ideal gas constant, D and B are the distillate and bottoms flow rates and x indicates the molar fractions of component i in the feed, distillate and residue stream.

From the heat pump equation, a higher quantity of heat is provided for each unit of work (W) provided. Assuming a Carnot cycle for the pump Eq. 3 is obtained.

$$Q = W \cdot \frac{T_c}{T_c - T_r} \quad (3)$$

The heat provided by the heat pump (Eq. 3) satisfies the overall heat distillation requirements in the reboiler (Eq. 1). In the condenser, a quantity of heat similar to W should be eliminated. Solving Eqs. 1 and 3 assuming that Q is equal in both, then Eq. 4 is obtained:

$$W = -T_r \cdot \Delta S_{sep} + \lambda \cdot D \cdot \frac{T_r - T_c}{T_c} \quad (4)$$

Dividing Eq. 4 by Eq. 1, substituting Eq. 3 and rearranging, Eq. 5 is obtained, where A, B and C are the concentration terms of Eq. 2 (A corresponds to the feed, B to the distillate and C to the residue).

$$\frac{Q}{W} = \frac{\frac{D}{F}\cdot\left(\frac{\lambda}{R}\cdot(T_c - T_r)^2 + (B-C)\cdot\left(T_c^2 \cdot T_r\right)\right) + (C-A)\cdot\left(T_c^2 \cdot T_r\right)}{\frac{D}{F}\cdot\left(\frac{\lambda}{R}\cdot(T_c - T_r)^2 + B\cdot\left(T_c^2 \cdot T_r - T_c \cdot T_r^2\right) + C\cdot\left(T_c \cdot T_r^2 - T_c^2 \cdot T_r\right)\right) + (A-C)\left(T_c \cdot T_r^2 - T_c^2 \cdot T_r\right)} \quad (5)$$

The ratio between the thermal and electrical energy alternatives is quite independent of the energy cost. Nowadays, the electrical energy is produced mostly in thermal plants and the cost of electrical energy becomes related to the cost of thermal energy by the efficiency of thermal plants and distribution losses. For instance, assuming that the cost of electrical energy is more than 5 times higher than thermal energy, then the use of a heat pump is advantageous only when the ratio Q/W is at least higher than 5. Dividing the Carnot efficiency by 2 as a reasonable estimate of the real efficiency and therefore, the first processes where it was successfully applied had a Q/W ratio of 10 or higher. Assuming that the energy required by the distillation corresponds to the entropy requirements, e.g. no enthalpy of mixing or vaporization, then Eq. 5 becomes simplified as shown in Eq. 6. The Q/W ratio becomes equal to the inverse of the efficiency of the heat pump. The advantage of Eq. 6 is that depends only on output temperatures.

$$\frac{Q}{W} = \frac{1}{\eta}(heat\ pump) = \frac{T_c}{T_r - T_c} \quad (6)$$

The generally accepted assumption that the heat pump use is favoured when the difference between boiling points is small, is valid according to Eq. 6. But this difference alone does not provide a valid criterion to decide when to use a heat pump because the temperature level on the condenser is also an important parameter. Flow rates, compositions and enthalpy of vaporization of the distillate also play their role but the equation is not any more so simple (Eq. 5).

Table 1. Q/W ratio for mixtures where a heat pump is advantageous for its distillation

	Tb (°C)	Tc (°C)	Q/W
Water / Methanol	100	64.7	9.6
Water / Ethanol	100	78	16
Water / Acetone	100	55.9	7.5
Acetic acid / Water	117.9	99.4	20.1
Toluene / Benzene	110.6	80.1	11.6
Xylene / Ethylbenzene	140	136.2	107.7
Stirene/ Ethylbenzene	145	136.2	46.5
Propane / Propylene	-42	-47.7	40.5
Butane / Isobutane	-0.5	-11.7	-24.3

The generally accepted assumption that the heat pump use is favoured when the difference between boiling points is small, is valid according to Eq. 6. But this difference alone does not provide a valid criterion to decide when to use a heat pump because the temperature level on the condenser is also an important parameter. Flow rates, compositions and enthalpy of vaporization of the distillate also play their role but the equation is not any more so simple (Eq. 5).

3. Validation based on literature data

Several mixtures, for which the use of heat pump is advantageous according to a literature search, are evaluated in this section (Table 1). The ratio Q/W is calculated using Eq. 6 to identify if the mixtures are suitable for a distillation using a heat pump. The mixtures and results are shown in Figure 1. Some of the mixtures, for which the heat pumps are successfully used, present a rather big difference of temperature between the boiling points, for instance the toluene / benzene mixture has a difference of 30.5 °C which cannot be considered small but the Q/W ratio of 11.6 is favorable. This means that for each unit of energy provided at the heat pump, then 11.6 units of heating energy are saved. All the examples studied provide a high ratio of Q/W, except the mixture water / acetone that it is between 5 and 10. Use of heat pump in a distillation column section

An example of a mixture for which would not be favourable to use a heat pump is the Methanol / Chlorobenzene (Gao et al., 2013). Methanol and chlorobenzene have boiling points of 64.7 °C and 131 °C respectively. This means that the ratio Q/W according to Eq. 6 is 5.1 which is rather unfavorable. The big differences between boiling points are the main reason. The separation is not easy because a pinch zone near pure methanol is detected (vapor and liquid compositions are very close Figure 1).

According to Plesu et al. (2013), the minimum energy to perform a certain separation by distillation does not depend on the driving force of the separation but on temperatures and stream characteristics of distillate and bottoms. The existence of a pinch zone influences the minimum number of transfer units required but not the minimum energy. However, the number of stages required for a certain separation depend on the reflux used, i.e. as the reflux becomes higher, the number of stages approaches its minimum

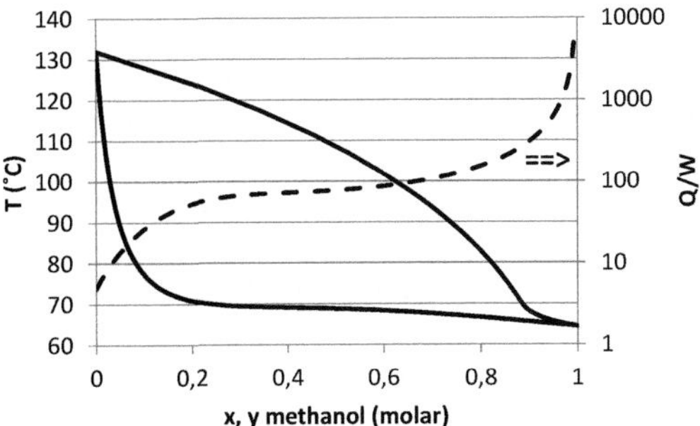

Figure 1. Vapor liquid equilibrium for the mixture methanol/chlorobenzene and Q/W ratio for a column from a certain composition to pure methanol.

value. Figure 2a shows the minimum reboiler duty as a horizontal line of reference. When the distillate is fixed to pure methanol, then the bottom composition change evaluated is called "upper". When the bottom is fixed to pure chlorobenzene, then the distillate composition evaluated is called "lower". Notice that when the variable evaluated approaches the pure component, then the required energy becomes equal to the minimum required energy for the overall column. For the "upper", when the bottom composition becomes closer to the distillate, the difference of temperature becomes very small and the efficiency of distillation decreases drastically requiring huge amounts of energy. The same happens for the bottom, when the distillate and bottoms composition of the lower column get close, in this case is not so accentuated as the temperature changes faster with the composition. It is important to notice that when the column is divided, the overall energy requirements of the parts are always higher than the minimum energy requirements of the entire column. Nevertheless, the lower segment runs under the minimum energy requirements and it is due to the "upper" that the "overall" is higher. An option is to use a heat pump just in the upper column. Assuming Q/W of 5, the division in two columns is clearly advantageous (Figure 2b).

Assuming Q/W of 10, a decrease in the minimum energy requirements is not so clear but it has the advantage to use a different reflux for each column and the upper column reflux ratio can be manipulated in order to obtain a desired column number of transfer units. Therefore, a possible solution for the illustrative example is the use of a first distillation column until a molar fraction of 0.5 methanol without heat pump and a second distillation column from a molar fraction of 0.5 until pure methanol using a heat pump. A study of this system by rigorous simulation is available (Gao et al., 2013).

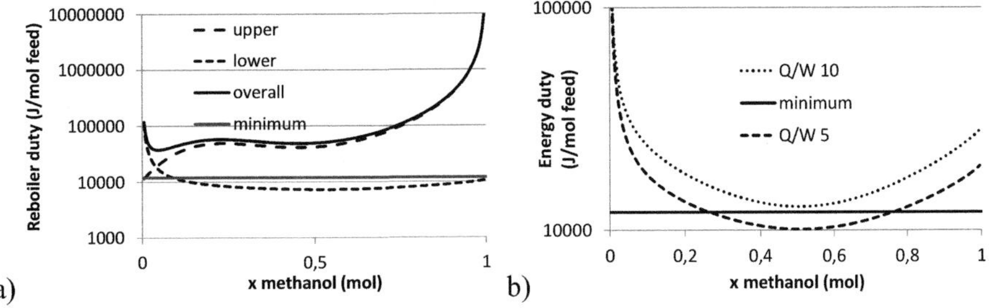

Figure 2. Minimum energy requirements when dividing the column.

4. Conclusions

The suitability of using a heat pump combined with a distillation column depends on the enthalpy of vaporization of the distillate, flow rates and compositions, difference in temperature at condenser and reboiler and temperature level on the condenser. However, assuming that the distillation energy requirements are derived from the entropy change, then it is demonstrated that the suitability of a heat pump depends only on the Carnot efficiency. The Carnot efficiency limits the efficiency of the heat pump but also the efficiency of the distillation column that can be considered as a heat engine that instead of work provides a decrease of entropy, i.e. separation. Therefore, a new simple parameter, to evaluate the suitability of using heat pumps, is provided according to an evaluation of literature results. When the inverse of the Carnot efficiency is higher than 10, the heat pump is clearly recommended. Between 5 and 10 it should be evaluated in more detail. The use of heat pumps in a column section is also presented in an illustrative example.

References

M.R. Eden, A. Koggersbøl, L. Hallager, S.B. Jørgensen, 2000, Dynamics and control during startup of heat integrated distillation column, Computers and Chemical Engineering, 24, 2-7, 1091-1097 .

Z. Fonyo, N. Benko, 1996, Enhancement of process integration by heat pumping, Computers and Chemical Engineering, 20, SUPPL.1, S85-S90.

C. Fu, T.Gundersen, 2013, Recuperative vapor recompression heat pumps in cryogenic air separation processes, Energy, 59, 708-718.

X. Gao, Z. Ma, L. Yang, J. Ma, 2013, Simulation and optimization of distillation processes for separating the methanol-chlorobenzene mixture with separate heat-pump distillation, Industrial and Engineering Chemistry Research 52, 33, 11695-11701.

A.K. Jana, 2014, Advances in heat pump assisted distillation column: A review, Energy Conversion and Management, 77, 287-297.

A.A. Kiss, S.J.F. Landaeta, C.A.I. Ferreira, 2012, Mastering heat pumps selection for energy efficient distillation, Chemical Engineering Transactions, 29, 397-402.

N.V.D. Long, Y. Kwon, M. Lee, 2013, Design and optimization of thermally coupled distillation schemes for the trichlorosilane purification process, Applied Thermal Engineering, 59, 1-2, 200-210.

G. Modla, P. Lang, 2013, Energy saving for batch distillation with mechanical heat pumps, Chemical Engineering Transactions, 35 , 301-306.

V. Plesu, A.E. Bonet Ruiz, J. Bonet, J. Llorens, P. Iancu, 2013, Minimum number of transfer units and reboiler duty for multicomponent distillation columns, Applied Thermal Engineering, 61, 1, 67–79.

L.M. Ulyev, P.A. Kapustenko, M.A. Vasilyev, S.A. Boldyryev, 2013, Total site integration for coke oven plant, Chemical Engineering Transactions, 35 , 235-240.

D.M. Van de Bor, C.A. Infante Ferreira, 2013, Quick selection of industrial heat pump types including the impact ofthermodynamic losses, Energy, 53, 312-322.

N. Van Duc Long, M. Lee, 2013, A novel NGL (natural gas liquid) recovery process based on self-heat recuperation, Energy, 57, 663-670.

Jiří Jaromír Klemeš, Petar Sabev Varbanov and Peng Yen Liew (Editors)
Proceedings of the 24th European Symposium on Computer Aided Process Engineering – ESCAPE 24
June 15-18, 2014, Budapest, Hungary.

Optimal Extractive Distillation Process for Bioethanol Dehydration

Anton A. Kiss,[a,*] Radu M. Ignat,[b] Costin S. Bildea[b]

[a] *AkzoNobel Research, Development & Innovation, Process Technology ECG, Zutphenseweg 10, 7418 AJ Deventer, The Netherlands.*
[b] *University Politehnica of Bucharest, Department of Chemical Engineering, Str. Gh. Polizu 1-7, 011061 Bucharest, Romania*
tony.kiss@akzonobel.com

Abstract

The large-scale production of bioethanol fuel requires energy demanding distillation steps to concentrate the diluted streams from the fermentation step and to overcome the presence of the ethanol-water azeotrope. The conventional separation sequence consists of three distillation columns performing several tasks with high energy penalties: pre-concentration distillation (PDC), extractive distillation (EDC) and solvent recovery (SRC) columns. Remarkable, almost all papers on this topic focus on the azeotropic separation only, while neglecting the pre-concentration step. Usually, the ethanol concentration in the first distillate stream is arbitrarily considered close to the azeotropic composition. While the energy usage in the PDC increases as the distillate composition gets closer to the azeotrope, the energy requirements in the EDC-SRC units decreases as the feed to EDC becomes richer in ethanol – and the other way around. This paper addresses this key trade-off of the distillate composition – a fundamental issue that was not studied before. Aspen Plus simulations were used to investigate how this parameter affects the energy usage and investment costs of the complete system. This issue applies in any other methods using a pre-concentration column (e.g. extractive and azeotropic distillation). The optimal economics is reached at a distillate concentration of 91.0 %wt ethanol, where the specific energy use is only 2.11 kWh (7,596 kJ) per kg ethanol.

Keywords: extractive distillation, economic optimum, process optimization

1. Introduction

Bioethanol is one of the most promising alternative and sustainable biofuel. The bioethanol production at industrial scale relies on several processes, such as: corn-to-ethanol, sugarcane-to-ethanol, basic and integrated lignocellulosic biomass-to-ethanol. After the initial pre-treatment steps, the raw materials enter the fermentation stage where ethanol is produced (Vane, 2008). A common feature of all these technologies is the production of diluted bioethanol – about 5-12 %wt ethanol – that needs to be further concentrated to a maximum allowed water content of 0.2 %vol (EU), 0.4 %vol (Brazil) or 1.0 %vol (US) according to various bioethanol standards.

Several energy demanding separation steps are required to reach high purities, mainly due to the presence of the binary azeotrope ethanol-water (95.63 %wt ethanol). The first step is carried out in a pre-concentration distillation column (PDC) that concentrates ethanol from 5-12 % up to near azeotropic compositions (Frolkova, 2012). The second step is the ethanol dehydration up to higher concentrations above the azeotropic composition, hence it is more complex and of greater research interest.

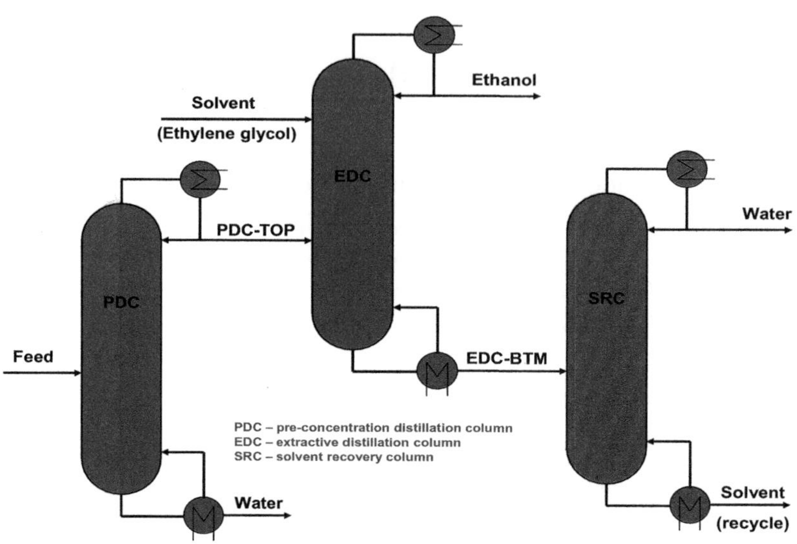

Figure 1. Flowsheet for bioethanol pre-concentration and dehydration by extractive distillation

Several alternatives are also available and well described in the literature (Frolkova, 2012): pervaporation, adsorption, pressure-swing distillation, extractive distillation (ED), azeotropic distillation (AD), as well as hybrid methods (Vane, 2008). Extractive distillation (ED) remains the option of choice in case of large scale production of bioethanol fuel, and it involves an extractive distillation column (EDC) and a solvent recovery column (SRC) for the ethanol dehydration – see Figure 1. Almost all reports focus only on the separation of ethanol-water azeotrope, neglecting the pre-concentration step. Typically, the ethanol concentration in the first distillate stream is arbitrarily considered close to the azeotropic composition. Though the energy usage in the PDC increases as the distillate composition approaches the azeotrope, the energy requirements in the EDC and SRC units decrease correspondingly as the feed to EDC becomes richer in ethanol. This paper addresses this key trade-off of the distillate composition – a fundamental issue that was not studied before. A mixture of 10 %wt (4.2 %mol) ethanol is concentrated and dehydrated using ethylene glycol as solvent. Rigorous Aspen Plus simulations were used to investigate how this parameter affects the energy usage and investment costs of the complete system. Note that this important issue applies in any other dehydration methods using a pre-concentration column.

2. Problem statement

The composition of the distillate from the PDC unit is a key design optimization variable that was so far neglected in the optimal design of extractive distillation systems for ethanol dehydration. For example, Ryan and Doherty (1989) assumed a composition of 94.9 %wt (88 %mol) ethanol which is rather close to the azeotropic composition, while other authors (Kiss and Suszwalak, 2012; Li and Bai, 2012) selected more practical compositions of about 93.5 %wt (85 %mol). The problem is how to select this key design parameter such that the energy requirements and the capital cost of the two sections of the process (pre-concentration and dehydration of ethanol) are economically balanced to minimize the overall costs. To solve this problem, we investigate here the effect of the PDC distillate composition and prove that the optimal value is lower than what was considered so far in the literature.

3. Results and discussion

Extractive distillation performs the separation of close boiling components or azeotropes in the presence of a miscible, high boiling, relatively non-volatile component that forms no azeotrope with the other components in the mixture. For the ethanol-water mixture, ethylene glycol remains the most common entrainer used in extractive distillation processes. However, the use of ethylene glycol could become restricted in the future due to its toxicity. For this reason novel solvents are currently explored, as for example: glycerol, hyperbranched polymers and ionic liquids. In this work, Aspen Plus simulations were performed using the rigorous RADFRAC unit for distillation. NRTL (non-random two-liquid) was used as the most adequate property method, due to the presence of a non-ideal mixture containing polar components. The ternary mixture ethanol-water-glycol presents a single binary azeotrope and no liquid phase splitting – as shown in previous work (Kiss and Suszwalak, 2012). The feed used here is the diluted bioethanol stream (10 %wt or 4.2 %mol ethanol) obtained by fermentation. This is distilled to a composition below the azeotropic one, and then dehydrated to a purity of over 99.8 %wt ethanol, to comply with all the bioethanol standards. The production rate considered in this work is 100 ktpy bioethanol.

The conventional sequence presented in Figure 1 consists of three distillation units: pre-concentration distillation column (PDC), extractive distillation column (EDC) and solvent recovery column (SRC). The first column (PDC) in the sequence has the function to separate water as bottom stream and a near-azeotropic composition mixture as distillate – sent afterward to the second column (EDC). In the EDC unit, ethylene glycol is added on a stage higher than the feed stage of the ethanol-water mixture. Due to the presence of the solvent the relative volatility of ethanol-water is changed such that the separation becomes possible. High purity ethanol is collected as top distillate product of the EDC, while the bottom product contains only solvent and water. The solvent is then completely recovered in the bottom of the third column (SRC), cooled in a heat recovery system, and then recycled back to the extractive distillation column. An additional water stream is obtained as distillate of the SRC unit. The bottom product of the SRC unit constitutes the solvent recycle stream. The SQP optimization method and the effective sensitivity analysis tool from Aspen Plus® were used in the optimization procedure of all processes. The SQP (sequential quadratic programming) method has become one of the most successful methods for solving nonlinearly constrained optimization problems (Bartholomew-Biggs, 2008). In this particular study, the objective of the optimization is to find the optimal trade-off between the energy requirements and the equipment cost, both translated into the total annual cost (TAC). The objective function that is used approximates very well the minimum of total annualized cost of a conventional distillation column. The procedure was described in detail in our recently published work (Kiss and Ignat, 2012).

$$\min N_T(RR+1) = f(N_{T,i}, N_{F,i}, SFR, RR_i, V_i) \tag{1}$$

Subject to $\vec{y}_m \geq \vec{x}_m$

where i is the distillation column (PDC, EDC, SRC), N_T is the total number of stages, N_F is the feed stage, SFR is the solvent-to-feed ratio, RR is the reflux ratio, V is the boilup rate for each of the three columns, while y_m and x_m are vectors of the obtained and required purities for the m products.

Table 1. Results of the sensitivity analysis: key performance indicators (KPI) as function of the composition of the pre-concentrated ethanol stream

Pre-concentrated EtOH (%wt)	Total investment cost (TIC)	Total operating cost (TOC)	Total annual cost (TAC)	Reboiler duties: PDC, EDC, SRC (kW)	Specific energy use (kW/kg EtOH)
75.0	$4,299,460	$6,003,454	$6,433,400	18135 / 6658 / 4025	2.31
80.0	$4,197,003	$5,842,719	$6,262,419	18427 / 6347 / 3292	2.25
85.0	$4,138,478	$5,684,488	$6,098,336	18487 / 6259 / 2578	2.19
87.0	$4,054,603	$5,590,383	$5,995,843	18547 / 6021 / 2315	2.15
89.0	$3,983,370	$5,506,929	$5,905,266	18608 / 5833 / 2051	2.12
90.0	$3,951,436	$5,493,809	$5,888,952	18680 / 5823 / 1927	2.12
91.0	$3,915,109	$5,475,770	$5,867,281	18847 / 5673 / 1829	2.11
91.5	$3,969,593	$5,542,080	$5,939,039	19208 / 5658 / 1793	2.13
92.0	$3,994,262	$5,624,435	$6,023,861	19777 / 5589 / 1679	2.16
93.0	$4,199,949	$6,042,605	$6,462,600	21885 / 5577 / 1542	2.32
93.5	$4,409,534	$6,445,864	$6,886,817	23865 / 5574 / 1453	2.47

In order to perform a fair comparison between all process alternatives, the total investment costs (TIC), total operating costs (TOC) and total annual costs (TAC) were calculated, as described in our previous studies (Kiss and Suszwalak, 2012). The equipment costs are estimated using correlations from the Douglas textbook, updated to the level of 2010. The Marshall and Swift equipment cost index (M&S) considered in this work has a value of 1468.6. Moreover, a price of 600 US \$/m^2 was used for calculating the cost of the sieve trays, and the following utility costs were considered: US \$ 0.03 per ton cooling water and US \$ 13.0 per ton steam. For the TAC calculations, a total plant lifetime of 10 years was considered (Kiss and Ignat, 2012).

The composition of the pre-concentrated ethanol stream was varied in the range 75-93.5 %wt (54-85 %mol) ethanol and for each value considered the process flowsheet was optimized. Table 1 shows the main results of the sensitivity analysis, including the total investment costs (TIC), total operating costs (TOC) and the total annual cost (TAC) as well as the total reboiler duty and the specific energy use per kg product. In addition, Figure 2 shows the optimal composition value of the pre-concentrated ethanol stream for minimal specific energy use and lowest total annual cost (TAC). It is worth noting that when the pre-concentrated ethanol stream has a composition below the optimal value, the duty of the PDC decreases with the ethanol concentration in the distillate, while the duties of the EDC and SRC units increases since more effort is needed to remove the higher amount of remaining water.

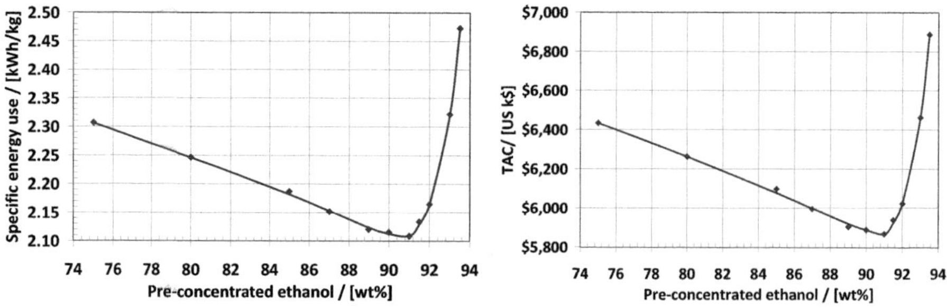

Figure 2. Specific energy use per kg of ethanol product (left) and total annual cost (right), as function of the composition of the pre-concentrated ethanol stream

Similarly, for pre-concentrated compositions higher than the optimal value, the duties of the EDC and SRC units is lower since less effort is needed to remove the smaller amount of remaining water. However, the duty of the PDC unit has a very steep increase due to approaching the azeotropic composition. Balancing these two effects lead to the optimal value of 91.0 %wt ethanol in the pre-concentrated stream. Remarkable, just by changing this key parameter, over 15 % energy savings are possible in existing plants that still use a pre-concentrated stream of near azeotropic composition. It is also worth mentioning that a similar value for the trade-off concentration (80 %mol ethanol in beer-still distillate) was reported for a heterogeneous azeotropic distillation process for ethanol dehydration, using a slightly more concentrated ethanol feed (5 % mol) and benzene or cyclohexane as light entrainers (Luyben, 2012). Table 2 lists the key design and process parameters of the optimized flowsheet. Note that in case of the non-optimal configurations, the number of stages varies within ± 20 % more or less stages depending on the separation difficulty. The effect of the pre-concentrated ethanol composition on the equipment design can be summarized as follows: the number of stages and the diameter of the PDC column increases with the ethanol concentration in the pre-concentrated stream, due to the more difficult separation and higher reflux required. However, for the EDC and SRC columns the variation of the required number of stages is rather minor due to the insignificant change in the separation difficulty, while the column diameters are increasing at lower pre-concentrated composition since more water is present in the feed.

In order to assess the controllability of the optimal design, a dynamic simulation model was built using Aspen Dynamics. For all columns, the pressure is controlled by condenser duty, while the distillate and bottoms flow rates are used to control the levels in the reflux drums and column sumps, respectively. The pre-concentration column is operated at constant reflux ratio, while the temperature in the stripping section (stage 25) is controlled by the reboiler duty. Similarly, the EDC unit is operated at constant reflux, constant solvent to feed ratio, the temperature in the lower part (stage 15) being controlled by the reboiler duty. Dual temperature control (stages 4 and 13), by means of reflux rate and reboiler duty, is employed for the solvent recovery column. Figure 3 presents results of dynamic simulation which prove the controllability of the optimal design. Starting from the steady state, the feed flow rate is increased by 10 %, from 125 to 137 ton/h (Figure 3, left). The transitory regime lasts for about 2 h, new values for the product flows being established. The water and ethanol purity remain very close to the initial value. In a second simulation (Figure 3, right), the concentration of the raw material is reduced from 10 - 8 %wt ethanol. The new values of the product flow rates are achieved in about 2 h, with minor deviations of the product purities.

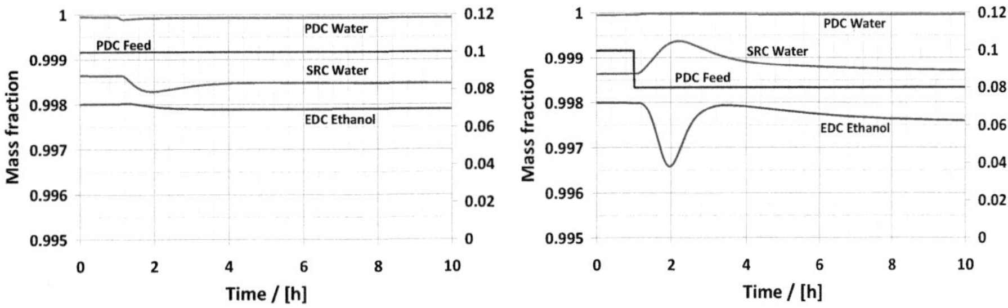

Figure 3. Dynamic simulation results for +10 % feed flowrate disturbance (left) and a reduction from 10 to 8 %wt of ethanol concentration in the feed (right)

Table 2. Design parameters of an optimal conventional ED sequence for bioethanol dehydration

Design parameters	PDC	EDC	SRC	Unit
Total number of stages	30	17	16	–
Feed stage number	19	11	8	–
Feed stage of extractive solvent	–	4	–	–
Column diameter	2.9	1.5	1	m
Operating pressure	1	1	1	bar
Ethanol : water (feed mass fraction)	0.1 : 0.9	0.91 : 0.09	–	kg/kg
Water : solvent (feed mass fraction)	–	–	0.055 : 0.945	kg/kg
Ethanol (amount in feed stream)	12500	12494	0.625	kg/hr
Water (amount in feed stream)	112500	1236	1215	kg/hr
Solvent (amount in feed stream)	0	20793	20788	kg/hr
Reflux ratio	1.31	0.24	0.45	kg/kg
Reboiler duty	18847	5673	1829	kW
Condenser duty	-8600	-3652	-1112	kW
Ethanol recovery	–	99.96	–	%
Water recovery	99.98	–	99.98	%
Solvent (EG) recovery	–	–	99.91	%
Purity of bioethanol product	–	99.80	–	%wt
Purity of water by-product	99.99	–	99.99	%wt
Purity of ethylene glycol recycle	–	–	99.99	%wt

4. Conclusions

A key contribution of this study is creating awareness that the composition of the pre-concentrated ethanol stream is an important design optimization variable for bioethanol dehydration, as well as calculating the optimal value of this parameter in order to obtain minimum total annual costs. Aspen Plus simulations were used to investigate how the trade-off of the distillate composition affects the energy usage and the investment costs of the complete system for ethanol dehydration by ED. Aspen Dynamics was employed as well to prove the controllability of the optimized process. The economical optimum was found at a distillate concentration of 91.0 %wt (or ~80 %mol) ethanol, where the specific energy use is 2.11 kWh (7596 kJ) per kg ethanol (Kiss and Ignat, 2013).

References

M. Bartholomew-Biggs, 2008, Nonlinear optimization with engineering applications, Springer, New York, US.

K. Frolkova, V. M. Raeva, 2012, Bioethanol dehydration: State of the art, Theoretical Foundations of Chemical Engineering, 44, 545-566.

A. Kiss, R. M. Ignat, 2012, Innovative single step bioethanol dehydration in an extractive dividing-wall column, Separation & Purification Technology, 98, 290-297.

A. Kiss, D. J-P. C. Suszwalak, 2012, Enhanced bioethanol dehydration by extractive and azeotropic distillation in dividing-wall columns, Separation & Purification Technology, 86, 70-78.

A. Kiss, R. M. Ignat, 2013, Optimal economic design of a bioethanol dehydration process by extractive distillation, Energy Technology, 1, 166-170.

G. Li, P. Bai, 2012, New operation strategy for separation of ethanol-water by extractive distillation, Industrial and Engineering Chemistry Research, 51, 2723-2729.

W. L. Luyben, 2012, Economic optimum design of the heterogeneous azeotropic dehydration of ethanol, Industrial and Engineering Chemistry Research, 51, 16427-16432.

P. J. Ryan, M. F. Doherty, 1989, Design/optimization of ternary heterogeneous azeotropic distillation sequences, AIChE Journal, 35, 1592-1601.

L. M. Vane, 2008, Separation technologies for the recovery and dehydration of alcohols from fermentation broths, Biofuels, Bioproducts and Biorefining, 2, 553-588.

Jiří Jaromír Klemeš, Petar Sabev Varbanov and Peng Yen Liew (Editors)
Proceedings of the 24th European Symposium on Computer Aided Process Engineering – ESCAPE 24
June 15-18, 2014, Budapest, Hungary.

Synthesizing Flexible Process Networks by Two Stage P-graphs

Eva Konig, Karoly Kalauz, Botond Bertok*

Department of Computer Science and Systems Technology, University of Pannonia, Egyetem u. 10, Veszprem, H-8200 Hungary
bertok@dcs.uni-pannon.hu

Abstract

Daily competitiveness of a process system highly depends on its flexibility, i.e., how the operation can follow the actual market. However, those processes are seldom flexible, which were not designed and constructed to be. The present paper review different approaches for synthesizing robust process networks, e.g., stochastic optimization (Birge and Louveaux, 2011), stochastic LP optimization (Kall and Mayer, 2005), two stage stochastic MIP optimization (Qin et al., 2013) and the forced incorporation of redundancies in process systems (Bertok et al., 2013). Two stages of the models are distinguished according to the two levels of decisions, i.e., level one for figuring out the investments and level two for controlling the operation. At level one operating units are selected to be involved in the investments and capacities of them are determined according to the estimated future circumstances. At level two start ups, shut downs, and optimal loads of the operating units are defined in agreements with real situations. In the current examination both stages, as well as their relations, are represented by process graphs or P-graphs originally introduced by Friedler et al. (1992) for chemical process design. Optimal decisions are computed according to two stage stochastic optimization, where expected alternative scenarios at level two helps evaluating the consequences of the decisions at level one. As an alternative approach robust systems are to be synthesized by forced installation of redundant capacities. Effectiveness of the methods is illustrated by applying them to supply chain design.

Keywords: P-graph, Process network synthesis, PNS, redundant structures, stochastic optimization.

1. Introduction

In a synthesis problem one has to build a system from building blocks capable to perform some task. The main difficulty of the synthesis problem is that there are plethora of possibilities. It has to be decided which blocks should be used in the system, how they should be ordered, how they should work towards the given task, etc.

Synthesis problem appears in many area of the industry. In chemical industry, for example, some kind of material is to be produced; in vehicle routing problem, the optimal routes of freighters are to be determined; in reaction network synthesis the objective is to identify candidate mechanisms of chemical reactions from a set of elementary reactions. In the present specific supply chain synthesis problem, decisions have to be made about biodiesel transportation depended on the availability of the resources of the different plants.

In the last decades, several robust and reliable process network optimization algorithms and software have been developed and implemented on the basis of the P-graph framework, e.g., Algorithm SSG (Friedler et al., 1995), Algorithm ABB (Friedler et al., 1996), Software PNS-Studio (Bertok et al., 2013b). The approach based on the P-graph framework appears to be the only one being capable of generating mathematical model automatically, and providing the N-best networks for process synthesis. Moreover, all steps involved are mathematically proven, comprising superstructure generation, construction of the mathematical model, optimization, and the solution interpretation.

In the P-graph framework, algorithm MSG produces the maximal structure, i.e., the superstructure, for the PNS problem (Friedler et al., 1993). This maximal structure serves as the input to the generation and solution of the mathematical model by algorithm ABB (Friedler et al., 1996).

The goals of a decision maker can be altered, like which solution would cause the best profit, which is the most reliable, or which one would cause the least environmental damage, etc. The P-graph based algorithms are inordinately effective for enumerating feasible structural alternatives as well as determining the optimal or near optimal n-best solutions, and thus, providing options for decision makers. The forthcoming sections illustrate the process synthesis based decision preparing process by a Case study.

2. Case Study

A supply network synthesis problem illustrates the proposed methodology (Bertok et al., 2013a). An oil company operates plants at three locations which are the towns of Pécs, Dombóvár, and Kaposvár. The task to be performed is to satisfy biodiesel demands of the plant in Kaposvár from the other two locations with a minimal overall risk. A limited amount of biodiesel and its components are available in Dombóvár and Pécs. In Pécs, a limited capacity for blending biodiesel from available components can be taken into consideration as well as consuming the four main components of biodiesel: HDS gasoline, kerosene, K7 component (gasoline without sulphur), and FAME bio-component. The biodiesel can be uploaded at any of the plants, transported to a target location by trucks, and finally downloaded.

There are three uncertain operating units in this system and our goal is to provide solutions to reduce this uncertainty in two different ways using two different methodologies. Both the methods are recent enhancements of the above mentioned P-graph framework. The first method is able to generate redundancy into the system that increases the reliability (Bertok et al., 2013a); see Figure 1. Optimization often removes redundancies, thus it has to be forced by artificial activities requiring redundancies at certain steps of the supply chain.

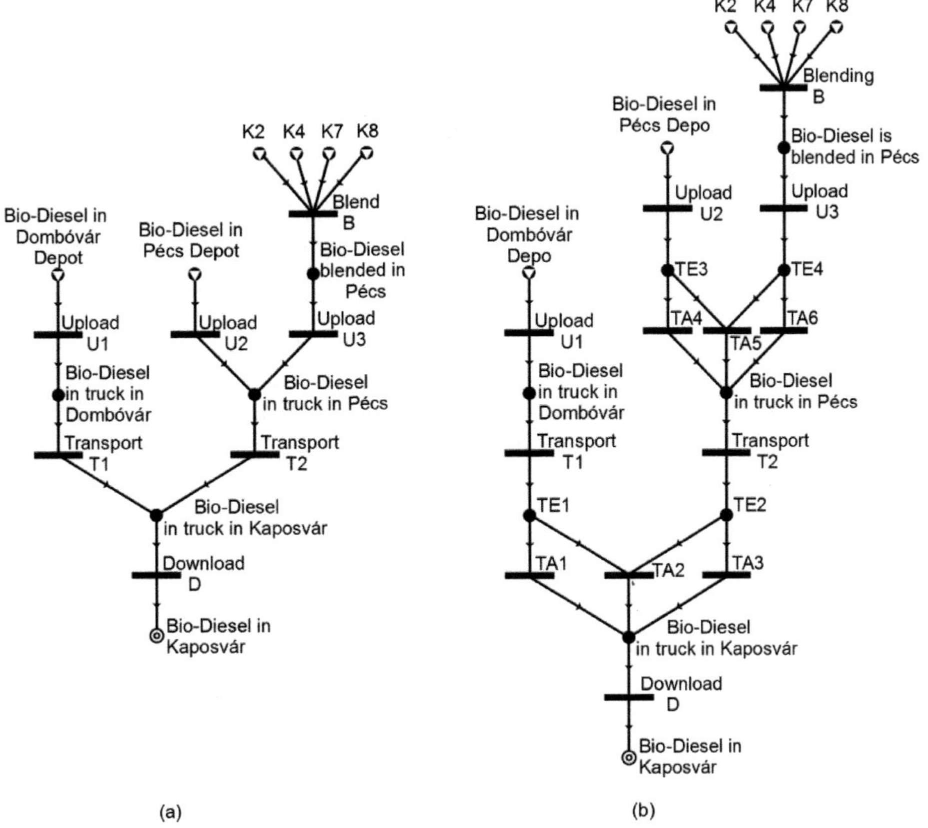

Figure 1. (a) Maximal structure of the basic model (b) and maximal structure of the redundant model.

Another possible approach is creating a dual-stage structure with different scenarios at the second stage. In order to be able to get solutions for different scenarios, all the cost parameters of the operating units were sorted out from the basic structure. In the first stage, all the major decisions are made, e.g., start ups or shut downs. In the second stage volumes of the activities are determined according to the actual situations, i.e., scenarios. Consequently, the first stage has effect on fix costs while the second stage on the variable (e.g., proportional) costs. The scenarios are weighted according to their probabilities, see Table 1.

Table 1. Probabilities of the scenarios

	Probabilities			
Activities	U1T1	T2	Blending	
Available	96,04 %	98 %	98 %	
Not available	3.96 %	2 %	2 %	
Scenario 1	Available	Available	Available	92.23 %
Scenario 2	Available	Available	Not available	1.882 %
Scenario 3	Available	Not available	Not available	0.03842 %
Scenario 4	Available	Not available	Available	1.882 %
Scenario 5	Not available	Available	Available	3.80318 %
Scenario 6	Not available	Available	Not available	0.07762 %
Scenario 7	Not available	Not available	Not available	0.00158 %
Scenario 8	Not available	Not available	Available	0.07762 %

Table 2. Optimal structures of the basic systems.

Methodology	Structure	Operating units	Cost (€/y)
Structures resulted by redundancy generation	Str R1	u1,u3,t2,d,b,t1	749 652
	Str R2	u3,u2,t2,d,b	762 872
	Str R3	u1,d,t1	770 056
	Str R4	u2,t2,d	950 876
	Str R5 (redundant)	u1,u3,u2,u2,d,b,t1	1 532 810
	Str R6 (redundant)	u1,u2,t2,d,t1	1 720 810
Basic structures resulted by the dual-stage model for a single scenario	Str DS1	u1t1,t2,d,bu3	749 652
	Str DS2	u2,t2,d,bu3	762 872
	Str DS3	u1t1,d	770 056
	Str DS4	u2,t2,d	950 876

In order to minimize the size of the dual stage model, i.e., the number of decision variables, we have enumerated the feasible scenarios by software PNS Studio (Bertok et al., 2013b) as a pre-processing step. Algorithm ABB provided 6 feasible scenarios and 4 structures (DS1, DS2, ..., DS4) optimal for the 6 scenario; see Table 2. Note that, in Table 3 the first four solutions provided by the two approaches (i.e., structure R1, R2, ..., R4 and DS1, DS2, ..., DS4) are identical, but redundant structures only appear for a single scenario if they are forced to (R5 and R6). Determining the optimal structure for the 6 different scenarios not necessarily provides the globally optimal solution. That is why all the scenarios are incorporated into a single maximal structure; see Figure 2.

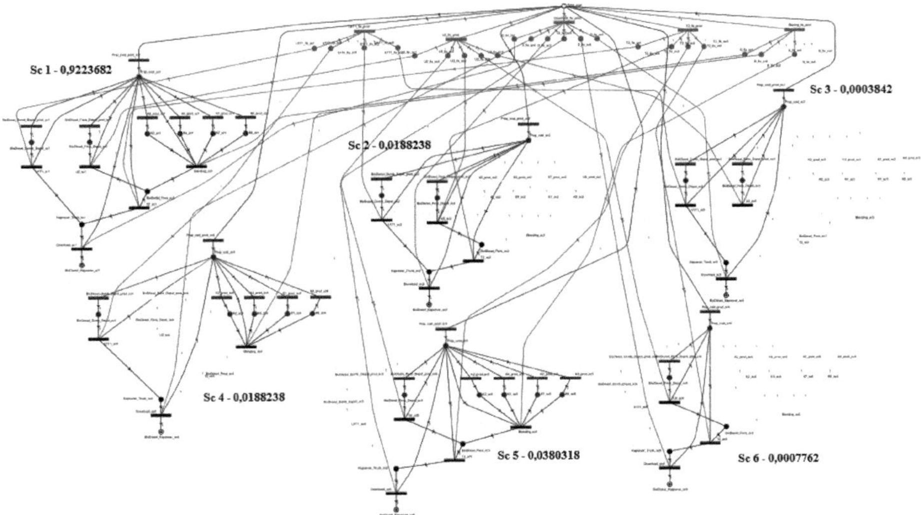

Figure 2. Maximal structure for the dual-stage stochastic model with 6 scenarios

Table 3. Cost and Expected Profit results from the two methodology.

Structure (Redundancy generation)	Operating units involved	Expected Profit (€/y)	Structure (Dual-stage stochastic model)	Operating units involved	Expected Profit (€/y)
Str R5	u1,u3,u2, u2,d,b,t1	339 137	Str D1	u1t1,u2, bu3,t2,d	346 445
Str R6	u1,u2,t2, d,t1	321 671	Str D34	u1t1, bu3,t2,d	333 633
Str R2	u3,u2,t2, d,b	314 748	Str D103	u2,bu3, t2,d	323 060
Str R3	u1,d,t1	312 998	Str D119	u1t1,u2, t2,d	320 932
Str R1	u1,u3,t2, d,b,t1	312 711	Str D175	u1t1,d	315 422
Str R4	u2,t2,d	141 715	Str D369	u2,t2,d	142 555

Entering the price of the product into the model not only by the minimal costs but by the maximal expected profit can be calculated. The two-stage stochastic model results optimal and alternative suboptimal decisions by taking into account each scenario in parallel and their costs and results summed up weighted by their probabilities. The redundancy generator always gives a lower estimation to the profit because it simulates less flexibility, i.e., each structure is optimized only once and cannot be adapted to every scenario. Contrarily, the stochastic model can provide the expected values precisely but since it is a huge model we get hundreds of solutions (584 suboptimal structures for the example of concern) and we have to sort out those represent different decisions at the first stage not at the second stage (D1, D34, D103, D119, D175, and D369); see Table 3.

3. Conclusion

Two methods have been applied to estimate the profit can be expected from the operation of a supply chain including activities with uncertain availability. Both methods have their advantages: the dual-stage stochastic optimization results precise values on the expected value of profit. Meanwhile the process synthesis with redundancy generation solves much smaller optimization problems, and thus, it is expected to be able to handle more complex problems. Integrating the two approaches, where redundancy generation can rapidly estimate the feasible scenarios and promising decision alternatives but they are evaluated in a dual-stage stochastic model, can be a promising future field of research.

4. Acknowledgement

Research of E. Konig and B. Bertok has been supported by the European Union and Hungary and co-financed by the European Social Fund through the project TÁMOP-4.2.2.C-11/1/KONV-2012-0004 - National Research Center for Development and Market Introduction of Advanced Information and Communication Technologies. Research of K. Kalauz was realized in the frames of TÁMOP 4.2.4. A/2-11-1-2012-0001 „National Excellence Program – Elaborating and operating an inland student and researcher personal support system convergence program" The project was subsidized by the European Union and co-financed by the European Social Fund.

References

B. Bertok, K. Kalauz, Z. Sule, F. Friedler, 2013a, Combinatorial Algorithm for Synthesizing Redundant Structures to Increase Reliability of Supply Chains: Application to Biodiesel Supply, Ind. Eng. Chem. Res., 52, 181-186.

B. Bertok, M. Barany, F. Friedler, 2013b, Generating and Analyzing Mathematical Programming Models of Conceptual Process Design by P-graph Software, Ind. Eng. Chem. Res., 52, 166-171.

J.R. Birge, F.V. Louveaux, 2011, Introduction to Stochastic Programming, Springer Verlag, New York, United States.

F. Friedler, K. Tarjan, Y.W. Huang, L.T. Fan, 1992, Graph-Theoretic Approach to Process Synthesis: Axioms and Theorems, Chem. Eng. Sci., 47, 1973-1988.

F. Friedler, K. Tarjan, Y.W. Huang, L.T. Fan, 1993, Graph-Theoretic Approach to Process Synthesis: Polynomial Algorithm for Maximal Structure Generation, Comput. Chem. Eng., 17, 929-942.

F. Friedler, J.B. Varga, L.T. Fan, 1995, Decision-mapping: A Tool for Consistent and Complete Decision in Process Synthesis, Chem. Eng. Sci., 50, 1755-1768.

F. Friedler, J. B. Varga, E. Feher, L. T. Fan, 1996, Combinatorially Accelerated Branch-and-Bound Method for Solving the MIP Model of Process Network Synthesis, Nonconvex Optimization and Its Applications, State of the Art in Global Optimization, Computational Methods and Applications, Kluwer Academic Publishers, Norwell, MA, USA, 609-626.

X. Qin, X. Liu, L. Tang, 2013, A two-stage stochastic mixed-integer program for the capacitated logistics fortification planning under accidental disruptions, Comput. Ind. Eng., 65, 614–623.

P. Kall, J. Mayer, 2005, Stochastic Linear Programming: Models, Theory and Computation, International Series in Operations Research & Management Science, 80, Springer, New York, USA.

Jiří Jaromír Klemeš, Petar Sabev Varbanov and Peng Yen Liew (Editors)
Proceedings of the 24th European Symposium on Computer Aided Process Engineering – ESCAPE 24
June 15-18, 2014, Budapest, Hungary.

Process Scheduling by Synthesizing Time Constrained Process-Networks

Marton Frits,* Botond Bertok

Department of Computer Science and Systems Technology, University of Pannonia, Egyetem u. 10, Veszprem, H-8200 Hungary

frits@dcs.uni-pannon.hu

Abstract

Process-network synthesis was originally introduced for conceptual process design. However, recent developments extend the capabilities of the P-graph framework to consider such time constraints in process-network synthesis that mainly arise in process operation. The current paper shows how to formulate and solve process scheduling as time constraint process synthesis, i.e., how to synthesize the optimal process schedule. Multiple classes of classical scheduling problems are revisited and reformulated. Algorithm is proposed for generating superstructure involving each candidate schedule in a way that the operating units are regarded as resources and changeovers as potential steps of the process. Various storage policies are incorporated. The differences of the storage policies are graphically highlighted both in the superstructures and in the solutions. The mathematical model constructed and analyzed, integrates the variables and constraints related to process synthesis, as well as, a precedence based formulation of the time constraints.

Keywords: scheduling, process-network synthesis, P-graph,

1. Introduction

Significant effort has been investigated in batch process scheduling in the past two decades and various approaches have been published to solve multiple classes of scheduling problems. Generally, the aim of the scheduling problems is to assign available equipment units to the tasks of a process in the most favorable way. Batch production plants provide a variety of scheduling problems that can be classified on the basis of their parameters. A batch process is usually defined by a recipe that gives an arrangement of tasks to produce the required products. In general, the relations of tasks are described as a network. In contrast, the tasks of the process have sequential ordering in most case studies and literature examples. Even for sequential processes, two subclasses of recipes have to be differentiated, i.e., multiproduct and multipurpose recipes. In multiproduct processes every product has the same sequential recipe, while in the multipurpose case each product is produced by different sequences of the same production steps.

The most commonly used objectives are the minimization of the overall processing time, called makespan; and the maximization of throughput or the profit for a given time horizon. In practice, often arise other aspects as constraints or objectives, such as wastewater generation (Majozi, 2009) or heat recovery (Adonyi et al., 2003). The intermediate storage policy is an essential parameter for batch scheduling problems that can affect the problem's complexity as well as the optimal solution. Unlimited Intermediate Storage (UIS) policy expresses that the materials can be stored practically any amount without constraints. Contrarily, if the storage has limited capacity, it is known as Finite Intermediate Storage (FIS). In FIS case the intermediate materials have dedicated storage units, while Common Intermediate Storage (CIS) policy allows sharing storages among the equipment. According to Non-intermediate Storage (NIS) policy, storage equipment is absent, and the intermediates can be stored only in the processing units until they are transferred to another unit for further production. The most strict storage policy is called Zero Wait (ZW), when an intermediate material has to be further processed exactly at the moment when it is available. Mixed Intermediate Storage (MIS) policy represents the combinations of the abovementioned policies. Typically, the available solution methods for batch process scheduling consider a single storage policy. Only a limited number of methods can provide the optimal solution for mixed storage policy. Susurla et al. (2009) utilize unit-slots to formulate a continuous-time mixed integer linear programming (MILP) model for the short-term scheduling of multipurpose batch processes. Kopanos et al. (2009) introduced a new precedence-based MILP scheduling framework, based on a continuous-time representation for the scheduling in multi-stage batch plants.

As an extension of the classical scheduling problem, Malleable Parallel Task Scheduling problem (MPTS), aims at minimizing the makespan in such a way, that each task can be processed simultaneously by more than one processor. Such flexibility could dramatically reduce the makespan, but greatly increases the difficulty for solving the problem. Numerousalgorithms exist for MPTS, which are suitable for some specific cases only, but not effective for others. Recently, a set of improving techniques yielded to a 2-approximation algorithm for solving MPTS problems (Fan et al., 2012).

In the forthcoming sections a novel approach will be introduced, which formulates the scheduling problems as a process-network synthesis (PNS) problem, furthermore it allows the automatic model generation, handles the mixed intermediate storage policy cases, and gives general solution for the MPTS problems while guarantees the optimal solution.

2. Time Constrained Process-Network Synthesis

It has been shown that the P-graph approach to PNS, which originally conceived for conceptual design of chemical processes (Friedler et al., 1992; 1996) provides adequate tools for generating and analyzing structural alternatives for supply scenarios (Barany et al.;2010). The Time Constrained Process-Network Synthesis (TCPNS) is an extension of the original framework to handle constraints specific to supply scenarios and improve the practical applicability of this methodology (Kalauz et al. 2012). TCPNS handles time constraints on the availability of the resources, duration of activities, and deadlines for the final target are incorporated into the mathematical model as well as into PNS algorithms. The duration of an activity is defined by a fixed and a proportional constant of the function, which estimate the duration of each activity based on its volume.

3. Formulating scheduling problem as TCPNS problem

The combinatorial components of a PNS problem is given by a triplet (P, R, O) where there exists a set of M for which $P \subseteq M$ is the set of final target to be achieved, $R \subseteq M$ is the set of resources, and $O \subseteq \wp(M) \times \wp(M)$ is the set of candidate activities to form a network, and reach each of the final targets by deploying any of the available resources.

Each activity is defined by its preconditions and outcomes. A precondition can be the availability of the resource or an outcome of another activity. It is assumed that $P \cap R = \emptyset$. A parametric problem definition with fixed charged linear cost function serves the optimal volumes of the activities besides the optimal process structure (Barany et al. 2011).

The PNS framework depicts the structures of the processes by a directed bipartite graph as mathematical model that is called P-graph. In graphical representation the circles denote the available resources, the required products, and the intermediate materials. The other class of the nodes is the horizontal bars indicating activities. The superstructure of the problem can be generated algorithmically, which involves all the possible solution structures.

By the method presented herein scheduling problems are solved as time constrained process-network synthesis problems. Several benefits of the P-graph framework are utilized, e.g., the mathematical model for solving the scheduling problems can be generated automatically, the solution method guaranties the optimality, and N-best solution can be provided. Furthermore, any mixture of UIS, NIS, and ZW storage policies can be handled. Moreover, there is no need to define time intervals.

First, the superstructure is to be generated in order to formulate the TCPNS problem based on the recipe-graph of the scheduling problem. In this formulation the equipment units are resources to the process. The goal is to determine the process-network which ensures to reach each final target while taking into account the connection of tasks in In this paper the model transformation will be introduced for UIS, NIS, and ZW storage policies by examples.

Superstructure generation contains three main steps. At first, the structure has to map the basic activities of tasks, which are the following: allocating equipment to task, loading input to the equipment and performing the task. These activities with their intermediate states will create a branch in the P-graph for all the possible tasks and its related equipment units. In the next step, recipe edges are added to the graph to ensure the order of the tasks according to the recipe of the given product. As a result arcs arise in the network leading from an outcome of each preceding activity to each forthcoming activity. Thus, the forthcoming task can only start if each of the preceding tasks has been completed. The third step depends on the storage policy. In case of unlimited intermediate storage the transfer operation can always be performed, therefore the structure ensures the transition of any equipment unit into empty state after performing a task. In the respect of the previously mentioned steps Figure 1. shows the generated superstructure. In case of non-intermediate storage policy the transfer operation can be performed only if the equipment unit of the next task is available. Meanwhile the material is assumed to be stored in the equipment unit. Consequently, the structure ensures that the equipment unit cannot start further task till the transfer is not finished. The third step of the structure generation is modified as follows. New states are added to the structure indicating that a certain task has been finished by one of the possible equipment units. These states become preconditions to each of the activities, which can potentially upload an equipment unit performing the forthcoming task. With these additional states the structure allows the next task to start only when the output of the previous task is transferred into other equipment unit. The last step has to ensure that the equipment unit can reset to its initial state after the execution of a task. The superstructure of the NIS type scheduling problem is shown on Figure 2.

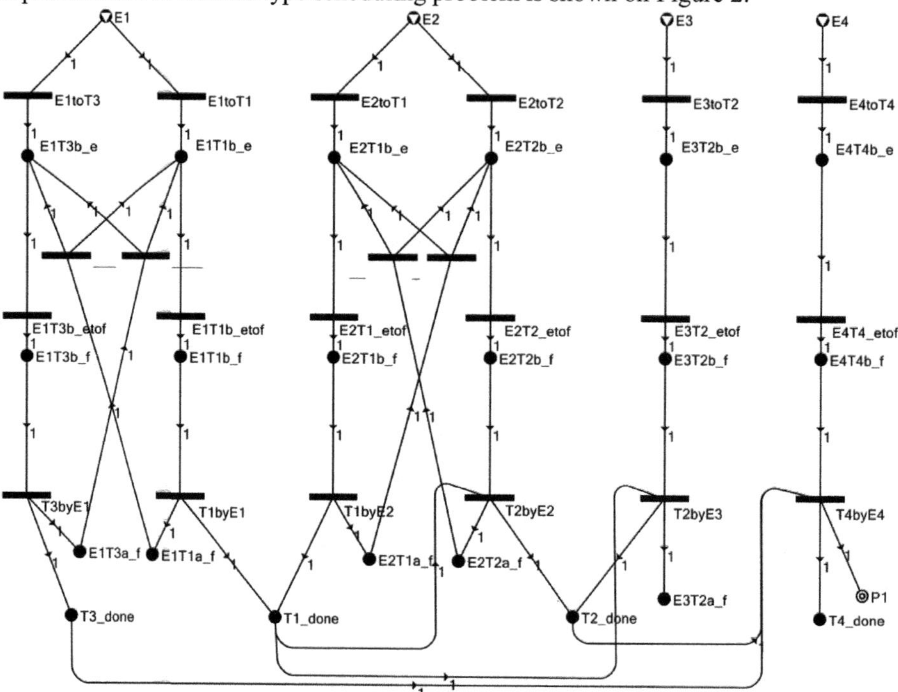

Figure 1. Superstructure generated for scheduling problem with UIS policy

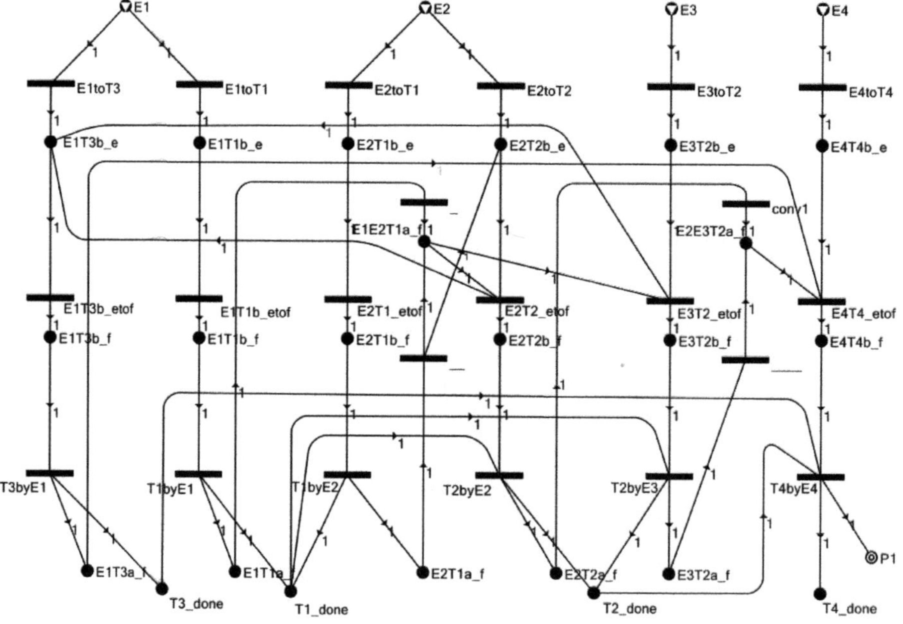

Figure 2. Superstructure generated for scheduling problem with NIS policy

For ZW storage policy, new constraints have to be added to the MILP model of TCPNS. The problem defines a Z set of ZW materials with such a restriction that transfer operation has to be started immediately after performing a task. Starting time of the equipment unit has to be extended to ZW materials. Starting time of any equipment units consuming a material zi ∈ Z has to be equal to the earliest available time of material zi. Furthermore, an upper bound has to be added into the earliest available time, which eliminates the gap between the availability time and the starting time of the activity. Applying this extended MILP model, scheduling problem with ZW materials can be solved without modification of the structure generator algorithms.

Malleable Parallel Task Scheduling problems can also be solved, because in TCPNS the volume of an activity may vary, and duration of the activity can be defined as proportional to its volume. Consequently, if the scheduling problem defines proportional part in the time function of an activity, the solution algorithm automatically investigates the possibility of performing the task in parallel.

The Figures 3 describes the main parameters of a scheduling problem and Figure 4 shows its solution for the UIS, NIS, ZW and MPTS cases.

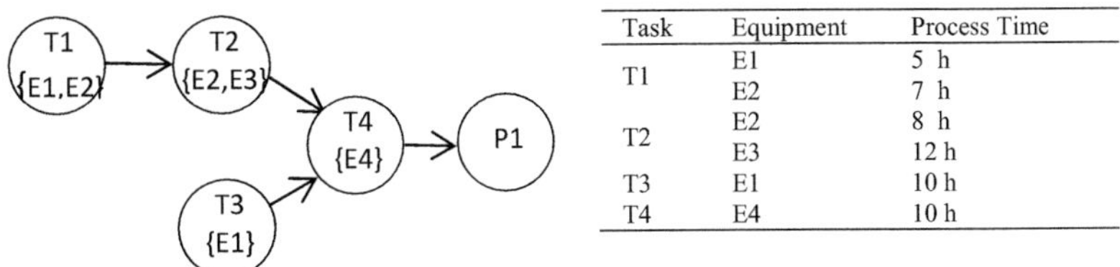

Task	Equipment	Process Time
T1	E1	5 h
	E2	7 h
T2	E2	8 h
	E3	12 h
T3	E1	10 h
T4	E4	10 h

Figure 3. The definition of a scheduling problem where it is assumed that the equipment E2 is available from t=6 time unit.

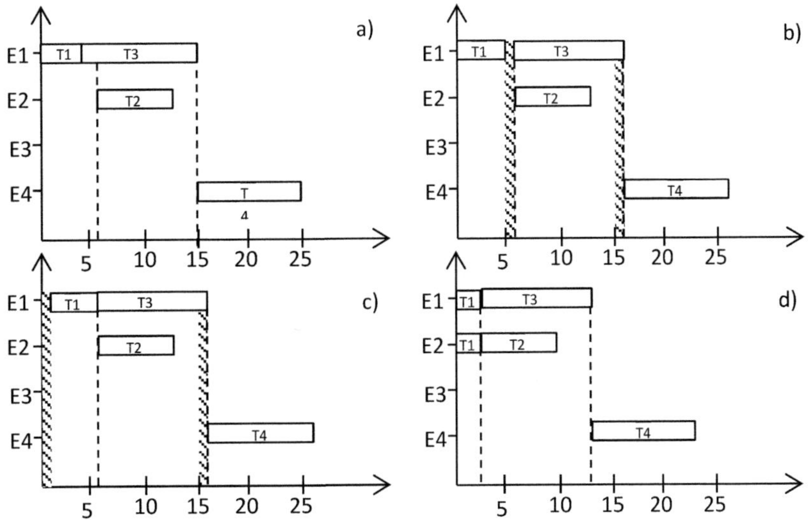

Figure 4. Gantt charts representing solutions for the scheduling problem given in Figure 3 for different storage polices: a) UIS; b) NIS; c)NIS with ZW material after the task T1;and d) MPTS problem, where duration of task T1 is proportional to the loads of the performing equipment.

4. Conclusions

It has been illustrated that solving scheduling problems as time constrained process-network synthesis problem inherits several benefits of the P-graph framework. The mathematical model for solving the scheduling problems can be generated automatically, even with mixed intermediate storage policies, and there is no needto define time intervals. The solver for TCPNS guarantees the optimal solution.

Acknowledgement

The research has been supported by the European Union and Hungary and co-financed by the European Social Fund through the project TÁMOP-4.2.2.C-11/1/KONV-2012-0004 - National Research Center for Development and Market Introduction of Advanced Information and Communication Technologies.

References

F. Friedler, K. Tarjan, Y.W. Huang, L.T. Fan, 1992, Combinatorial Algorithms for Process Synthesis, Computers Chem. Engng., 16, S313-320.

F. Friedler, J.B. Varga, E. Feher, L.T. Fan, 1996,Combinatorially Accelerated Branch-and-Bound Method for Solving the MIP Model of Process Network Synthesis, Nonconvex Optimization and Its Applications, State of the Art in Global Optimization, Nonconvex Optimization and Its Applications, 7, 609-626.

B. Bertok, R. Adonyi, F. Friedler, L.T. Fan, 2011, Superstructure Approach to Batch Process Scheduling by S-graph Representation, Computer Aided Chem.Engng., 29, 1105-1109.

B. Bertok, M. Barany, F. Friedler, 2013, Generating and Analyzing Mathematical Programming Models of Conceptual Process Design by P-graph Software, Ind. Engng. Chem. Res., 52, 1, 166-171.

K. Kalauz, Z. Sule, B. Bertok, F. Friedler, L.T. Fan, 2012, Extending process-network synthesisalgorithms with time bounds for supply network design, Chem. Engng. Trans., 29, 259-264.

J. Gouws, T. Majozi, 2009, Usage of inherent storage for minimization of wastewater in multipurpose batch plants, Chemical Engineering Science, 64, 3545-3554.

R. Adonyi, J. Romero, L. Puigjaner, F. Friedler, 2003, Incorporating heat integration in batch process scheduling, Applied Thermal Engineering, 23, 1743-1762.

L. Fan, F. Zhang, G. Wang, Z. Liu, 2012, An effective approximation algorithm for the Malleable Parallel Task Scheduling problem, J. of Parallel and Distributed Comp., 72, 693-704.

M. Barany, B. Bertok, Z. Kovacs, F. Friedler, L.T. Fan, 2010, Optimization software for solving vehicle assignment problems to minimize costs and environmental impacts of transportation, Chemical Engineering Transactions, 21, 499–504.

M. Barany, B. Bertok, Z. Kovacs, F. Friedler, L.T. Fan, 2011, Solving vehicle assignment problems by process-network synthesis to minimize cost and environmental impact of transportation, Clean Technologies and Environmental Policy, 13, 4, 637-642.

N. Susarla, J. Li, I.A. Karimi, 2009, Unit Slots Based Short-Term Scheduling for Multipurpose Batch Plants, Computer Aided Chem. Eng., 27, 1989-1994.

M. Pan, Y. Qian, X. Li, 2008, A novel precedence-based and heuristic approach for short-term scheduling of multipurpose batch plants, Chem. Engineering Science, 4313-4332.

G.M. Kopanos, L. Puigjaner, 2009, A MILP Scheduling Model for Multi-stage Batch Plants, Computer Aided Chem. Eng., 369-374.

Jiří Jaromír Klemeš, Petar Sabev Varbanov and Peng Yen Liew (Editors)
Proceedings of the 24th European Symposium on Computer Aided Process Engineering – ESCAPE 24
June 15-18, 2014, Budapest, Hungary.

Equation-Oriented Models of Multistream Heat Exchangers for Flowsheet Optimization

Richard C. Pattison, Michael Baldea*

University of Texas at Austin McKetta Dept. of Chemical Engineering, 200 East Dean Keeton Street, Austin, TX, 78712, United States.
mbaldea@che.utexas.edu

Abstract

Cryogenic processes, including air separation and natural gas liquefaction, require tight heat integration. Multistream heat exchangers (MHEXs), typically of the plate-fin type, are a key enabler to this end. Developing MHEX models that lend themselves to flowsheet optimization calculations is challenging, especially when streams with phase change are present. In this paper, we present a methodology for equation-oriented, optimization-friendly MHEX modeling, using a pseudo-transient approach. We illustrate our developments with a natural gas liquefaction process case study.

Keywords: Multistream Heat Exchangers, Equation-Oriented Modeling, Flowsheet Optimization, Cryogenic Processes, Liquefied Natural Gas.

1. Introduction

Heat integration – the recovery and recycling of energy – is a ubiquitous and desirable feature in modern chemical processes. Initially implemented ex post facto by carrying out a pinch analysis after completing the plant design, the design of heat integrated processes has evolved towards the simultaneous design of the heat exchanger network and the plant (Biegler et al., 1997). Multistream heat exchangers (MHEXs) are a key enabler of heat integration, facilitating the thermal contact and heat exchange between multiple hot and cold streams. They are particularly important in applications such as air separation and gas liquefaction, where their low driving-force requirements (i.e., low temperature differences) afford advanced energy (refrigeration) recovery.

The design of energy-integrated processes featuring such multi-stream units requires that accurate MHEX models be available, which are able to robustly account for complex nonlinear phenomena such as phase transitions and the associated (and significant) changes in the fluid properties. The steady-state simulation of a MHEX is limited to identifying the outlet temperature of one of the streams (with the others being specified) based on an overall energy balance. Openly-available literature references on a robust methodology for solving the MHEX energy balance equations, including phase change behavior, in an equation-oriented environment that is suitable for performing process optimization calculations, remain scarce. Several contributions have focused on optimizing heat exchanger networks with phase change (Ponce-Ortega et al., 2008), however, these developments have achieved limited success in simultaneous flowsheet optimization because they assume that the inlet and outlet temperatures and pressures, flowrates and compositions are fixed at the design stage and cannot be optimized. More recently, a disjunctive-programming based framework has been proposed (Kamath et al., 2012), which relies on modelling all possible phases of all streams simultaneously in order to capture phase change behaviour. Dowling and Biegler (2014) recently proposed an extension of the simultaneous heat integration approach of Duran and Grossman (1986), by modeling MHEXs as several zones in series, which however requires multiple iterative calculations to obtain an optimal solution.

Here, we introduce a novel pseudo-transient approach to derive transparent, computationally robust equation-oriented models of MHEXs. Within this framework, (a subset of) the nonlinear algebraic equations of the process are converted to statically-equivalent (i.e., having the same steady-state solution) ordinary differential equations (ODEs) through dynamic filtering (Coffey et al., 2003). The model is solved via computationally efficient time integration, starting from a set of initial conditions that can be "far away" from the solution. We begin with the conventional division of the heat exchanger into enthalpy intervals that correspond to the heat exchange segments between points where streams either enter or exit the MHEX. We then introduce a novel means for computing stream temperatures in each interval by obtaining explicit statically-equivalent dynamic expressions of temperature, which are robust to phase transitions. Finally, we illustrate these ideas with a flowsheet optimization case study.

2. Pseudo-Transient Modeling of MHEXs

MHEX models consist of energy balances across the entire unit, and constraints which are imposed to ensure that temperature crossover does not occur along the length of the unit. The generic model equations for a MHEX unit are given by Eq.(1-2):

$$\sum_i (H_i^{out} - H_i^{in}) = \sum_j (H_j^{in} - H_j^{out}) \tag{1}$$

$$T_h(z) - T_c(z) \geq \Delta T_{min} \quad \forall z \tag{2}$$

where the set $i \in I$ denotes the set of cold streams, and the set $j \in J$ corresponds to the hot streams. T_h and T_c correspond to the temperatures of the hot and cold composite curves, respectively. MHEX models typically have only one degree of freedom: inlet and outlet temperatures and flow rates are specified for all but one stream, and Eq.(1) is used to calculate the enthalpy of the remaining stream. However, to satisfy the temperature crossover constraints (Eq.(2)), stream temperatures must be calculated from enthalpy for the entire exchanger. If stream phase is not known a priori, this calculation involves solving a system of equations that include piecewise-continuous functions which are non-differentiable at the phase boundaries. Computing the solution with a conventional Newton-based nonlinear solver often fails if the initial guess is not close to the solution. To mitigate this, we propose the following general framework for equation-based, optimization-oriented modelling of MHEXs.

2.1. Construct Enthalpy Intervals

We make use of enthalpy intervals that segregate the heat exchanger into segments between the locations where streams enter and exit, and discretize the heat duty within each interval. The use of intervals for equation-oriented MHEX modelling and for optimization of process flowsheets with MHEXs has been avoided in the literature due to the inherent requirement of making discrete decisions when constructing the intervals (Duran and Grossmann, 1986). Our main assumption in this work is that the order of the segments and associated intervals (based on the inlet and outlet temperatures of every stream) does not change, even if the temperatures and pressures in the process are free to vary. In the case of the cryogenic applications of interest (e.g., air separation, natural gas liquefaction), this assumption is in typically true.

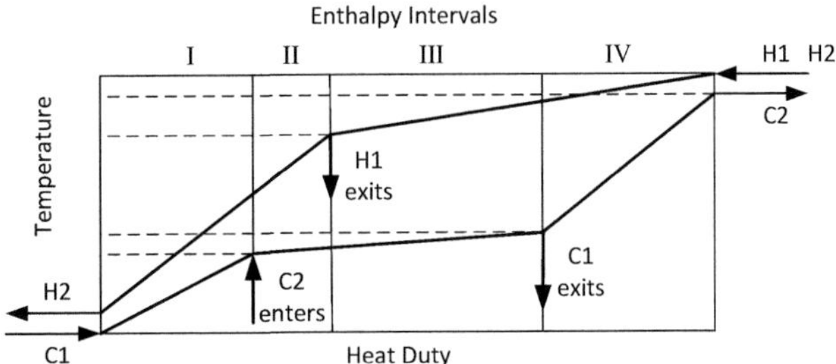

Figure 1. Temperature-enthalpy plot of the composite streams within a MHEX.

We begin by establishing the order of the enthalpy intervals. Consider for example, a heat exchanger with two hot streams and two cold streams, and assume that the exit temperature of cold stream 2 (C2 in Figure 1) must be calculated from the model. Figure 1 shows the temperature-enthalpy plot for this heat exchanger. Without specifying any of the inlet or outlet temperatures (the dashed lines are free to move vertically as long as they don't "jump over" one another), the order of the inlet and outlet streams can be established. For this example, the order is (from left to right): i) C1 enters and H2 exits, ii) C2 enters, iii) H1 exits, iv) C1 exits, and v) H1 and H2 enter and C2 exits. Thus, four enthalpy intervals, which we will denote by $\delta \in \{\delta_1, \ldots, \delta_4\}$, can be constructed.

2.2. Establish Heat Balance on Enthalpy Intervals

In process optimization calculations, the enthalpy of the inlet and outlet of each stream can typically be computed explicitly from the process optimization decision variables (temperature, pressure, and composition). This information can be used to establish the heat balance between the composite curves in each interval:

$$\Delta H_h(\delta) = \sum_j (H_j^{in}(\delta) - H_j^{out}(\delta)) = \Delta H_c(\delta) = \sum_i (H_i^{out}(\delta) - H_i^{in}(\delta)) \quad \forall i, j \in S_\delta \tag{3}$$

$$H_i^{out}(\delta) = H_i^{in}(\delta+1) \quad \forall i \in S_\delta \bigcap S_{\delta+1} \tag{4}$$

$$H_j^{in}(\delta) = H_j^{out}(\delta+1) \quad \forall j \in S_\delta \bigcap S_{\delta+1} \tag{5}$$

where S_δ is the set of streams present in the exchanger in the interval δ, and $S_\delta \cap S_{\delta+1}$ indicates the set of streams that are in both intervals δ and $\delta+1$. The total energy balance is computed by solving the linear system of equations (Eq. (3-5)) where the unknowns are the enthalpies of the composite hot or cold curves at the interval boundaries (assuming that temperatures, pressures, and compositions necessary for calculating the enthalpies are decision variables in the optimization, and can be treated as parameters during the simulation step).

2.3. Discretize the Enthalpy Intervals

For cryogenic applications, the approach temperature is typically very small, and nonlinearities in the heat capacities (as well as phase change) can have a significant impact on the crossover constraints. Therefore, we discretize duty in each interval δ further into $\mathrm{N}(\delta)$ heat duty sub-intervals.

$$H_c(z) = \frac{\Delta H_c(\delta)}{N(\delta)} \left(z - \sum_{k=1}^{ord(\delta)-1} N(\delta_k) \right) + \sum_{i \in S} H_i^{in}(\delta) \tag{6}$$

$$H_h(z) = \frac{\Delta H_h(\delta)}{N(\delta)}\left(z - \sum_{k=1}^{ord(\delta)-1} N(\delta_k)\right) + \sum_{i\in S} H_j^{out}(\delta) \tag{7}$$

where $z = 0$ corresponds to the inlet of the coldest stream, and $z = \sum_k N(\delta_k)$ corresponds to the inlet of the hottest stream. The operator $\mathrm{ord}(\delta)$ refers to the corresponding enthalpy interval number.

2.4. Compute Stream Temperatures

The minimum temperature approach constraint must be satisfied at each of the $\sum_k N(\delta_k)$ discretized enthalpy points. Calculating temperature with a Newton or Newton-like solver is difficult because it is an implicit, highly nonlinear, and piecewise-continuous function of enthalpy, pressure, and composition. To solve this problem, we translate this implicit function into an explicit ordinary differential equation in time. We propose converting temperature into a dynamic variable, whose time derivative is proportional to the difference between stream enthalpy determined from, i) the energy balance (Eq. 6-7) and, ii) as an explicit function of each stream's state variables. Here, we assume that a physical properties package is available to compute the enthalpy as a function of temperature, composition and pressure, $H^{calc}(T, P, Fx)$. The function is computed differently in every regime (superheated vapor, subcooled liquid, and two-phase).

$$\tau\frac{dT_c(z)}{dt} = \frac{H_c(z) - \sum_{i\in S_\delta} H_i^{calc}(T_c(z), P_i(z), F_i x_i)}{\sum_i F_i Cp_i^{ref}} \tag{8}$$

$$\tau\frac{dT_h(z)}{dt} = \frac{H_h(z) - \sum_{j\in S_\delta} H_j^{calc}(T_h(z), P_j(z), F_j x_j)}{\sum_j F_j Cp_j^{ref}} \tag{9}$$

where F is the stream flow rate and Cp^{ref} is the heat capacity at the reference temperature. The transient filter effectively relaxes the equality initially, but enforces it at steady state, where the enthalpy of each composite curve must be equivalent to the sum of the enthalpies of the respective streams. Regardless of the time constants selected, τ, for the temperature ODEs, the dynamics will be stable because enthalpy is a globally increasing function of temperature (e.g., if the temperature is higher than the steady state solution, the calculated enthalpy will be larger than the specified enthalpy, and the time derivative for temperature will be negative). Solving the nonlinear equations (Eq. 8-9) consists of providing initial conditions for the pseudo-dynamic variables (temperature), and simulating through pseudo-time (i.e., integrating) the DAE system corresponding to the model until steady state is reached. The initial condition for the temperature in every interval can simply be set to the inlet temperature of each stream. The steady state values of the differential variables are equivalent to the solution of the original algebraic equations. We note that the pressure drops for each stream are typically assumed by the designer (often considered to vary linearly with heat duty), a feature that can be easily accounted for in this framework.

3. Case Study: PRICO Liquefaction Process

The PRICO process for natural gas liquefaction makes use of a MHEX (Price and Mortko, 1996). The process, shown in Figure 2 uses a (variable) mixed refrigerant of nitrogen, methane, ethane, propane, and butane in a single stage refrigeration cycle to liquefy natural gas with a flowrate of 1 kmol/s. The natural gas enters the heat exchanger at 25 °C and 55 bar and is cooled to -155 °C. The inlet composition is 89.7 % methane, 5.5 % ethane, 1.8 % propane, 0.1 % n-butane, and 2.8 % nitrogen. There is a 5 bar pressure drop for the natural gas stream across the heat exchanger, and a 4 bar and 1 bar pressure drop for the hot and cold refrigerants, respectively, and a 0.1 bar pressure drop across the salt water (SW) cooler. The compressor has a fixed isentropic efficiency of 80 %. The SRK cubic equation of state is used to model the thermodynamics. Optimization of the process poses several challenges: the phase of the refrigerant at different points is not known (i.e. the streams S5, S6, and S7 might be superheated, subcooled, or two-phase), the composition of the refrigerant can be varied, and the pressures and temperatures throughout the process are also free to be optimized.

We apply the proposed method to model the MHEX and optimize the process design. The heat exchanger has just two enthalpy intervals ($size(\delta) = 2$), separated by the point where the natural gas exits (see Figure 2). Since far less cooling is required for the hot refrigerant in the second segment, only $N(\delta_2) = 5$ heat duty sub-intervals are used. $N(\delta_1) = 45$ heat duty intervals are used in the first segment for the optimization. Optimization of the PRICO process consists of minimizing the work done by the compressor, and has been studied previously by Del Nogal et al. (2008) and Kamath et al. (2012). The decision variables are the composition and flow rate of the refrigerant, the high and low pressures in the refrigeration cycle, and the exit temperature of the hot refrigerant. The exit temperature of the cold refrigerant is the single degree of freedom for the heat exchanger, and this temperature is constrained above 10 °C to ensure that the feed to the compressor is superheated. A minimum temperature approach of 1.2 °C is imposed. A time relaxation-based optimization algorithm (for which the proposed pseudo-transient MHEX model is ideally suited) was used to solve the design optimization problem (Zanfir et al., 2011). Several distant initial guesses were used for the optimization in an attempt to find the global optimum. The results of the optimization are presented in Table 1 and Figure 2, and are compared with the solutions found in previous publications. The optimum point suggests a potential 5.7 % reduction in energy consumption compared to the results in Kamath et al. (2012) and a 17.3 % reduction compared to the design of Del Nogal et al. (2008). This is due to a smaller flow rate of refrigerant, but higher operating pressure than the solution presented by Kamath et al. (2012). The optimal refrigerant compositions are comparable in each case. The composite curves are shown in Figure 2.

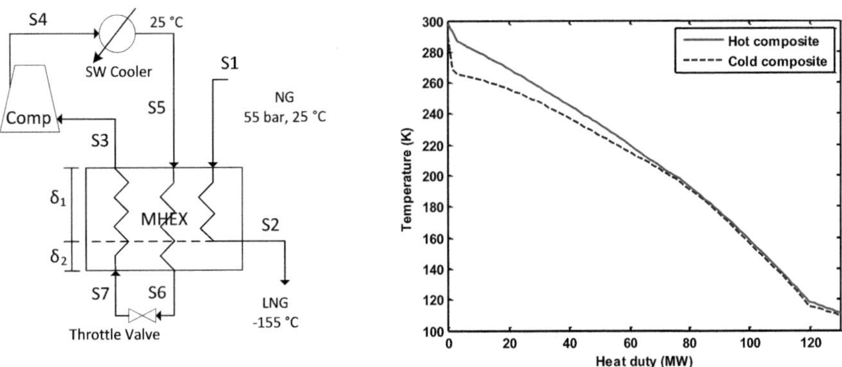

Figure 2. (left) PRICO process for natural gas liquefaction (Price and Mortko, 1996). (right) Composite temperature-enthalpy curves in the MHEX at the optimum.

Table 1. Optimization results

	Del Nogal et al. (2008)	Kamath et al. (2012)	This Work
Power (MW)	24.53	21.51	20.288
Pressure S3 (bar)	4.84	2.02	3.26
Pressure S4 (bar)	43.87	17.129	27.424
Flow (kmol/s)	3.53	2.928	2.899
N_2 (mol %)	10.08	5.82	8.63
CH_4 (mol %)	27.12	20.62	32.68
C_2H_6 (mol %)	37.21	39.37	31.41
C_3H_8 (mol %)	0.27	0.0	0.67
n-C_4H_6 (mol %)	25.31	34.19	26.62

4. Conclusions

Developing MHEX models that accurately capture phase change behaviour, and are amenable to equation-oriented process modeling and flowsheet optimization is a challenging task. The complications lie in determining stream temperatures in the presence of phase transformations, and dealing with the associated nonlinearities. Our contribution consists of using an intuitive pseudo-transient reformulation of the energy balance equations for the enthalpy intervals of the MHEX, to obtain a numerically robust and computationally efficient MHEX model. This model lends itself naturally to process flowsheet optimization calculations using a previously developed time-relaxation algorithm. The efficacy of this modeling approach is demonstrated successfully by performing flowsheet optimization on the PRICO natural gas liquefaction process.

References

L.T. Biegler, I.E. Grossmann, A.W. Westerberg, 1997, Systematic methods of chemical process design, Prentice Hall, Englewood Cliffs, NJ, USA.

T.S. Coffey, C.T. Kelley, D.E. Keyes, 2003, Pseudotransient continuation and differential-algebraic equations. SIAM J. Scientific Comp. 25, 2, 553-569.

A.W. Dowling, L.T. Biegler, 2014, A framework for efficient large scale equation-oriented flowsheet optimization, Comp. Chem. Eng., http://dx.doi.org/10.1016/j.compchemeng.2014.05.013.

M.A. Duran, I.E. Grossmann, 1986, Simultaneous optimization and heat integration of chemical processes, AIChE J., 32, 1, 123-138.

R.S. Kamath, L.T. Biegler, I.E. Grossmann, 2012, Modeling multistream heat exchangers with and without phase changes for simultaneous optimization and heat integration, AIChE J., 58, 1, 190-204.

F.D. Nogal, J.K. Kim, S. Perry, R. Smith, 2008, Optimal design of mixed refrigerant cycles, Ind. Eng. Chem. Res., 47, 22, 8724-8740.

J.M. Ponce-Ortega, A. Jiménez-Gutiérrez, I.E. Grossmann, 2008, Optimal synthesis of heat exchanger networks involving isothermal process streams, Comp. Chem. Eng., 32, 8, 1918-1942.

B.C. Price, R.A. Mortko, 1996, PRICO - A simple, flexible proven approach to natural gas liquefaction, Proceedings of the 17th International LNG/LPG conference, Gastech '96, Vienna, Austria.

M. Zanfir, M. Baldea, P. Daoutidis, 2011, Optimizing the catalyst distribution for countercurrent methane steam reforming in plate reactors, AIChE J., 57, 9, 2518-2528.

Jiří Jaromír Klemeš, Petar Sabev Varbanov and Peng Yen Liew (Editors)
Proceedings of the 24th European Symposium on Computer Aided Process Engineering – ESCAPE 24
June 15-18, 2014, Budapest, Hungary.

Framework to Batch Process Retrofit - A Continuous Improvement Approach

Tânia Pinto-Varela, Ana Carvalho*, Ana Barbosa-Póvoa

CEG-IST, Instituto Superior Técnico, Universidade de Lisboa, Av. Rovisco Pais, 1049-001, Lisboa, Portugal
anacarvalho@tecnico.ulisboa.pt

Abstract

To be competitive in the global market, companies need to ensure that they run more efficient than ever. This fact forces companies to apply continuous improvement actions in their plants which often involve a series of retrofitting activities that have to be conducted during the whole Life Cycle of their industrial process. Within this context, the present work proposes a framework, *BatchRetroLC*, which aims to guide decision-makers in continuous improvement actions, leading to a sequence of iterative improvement steps. *BatchRetroLC* integrates an indicator based methodology, *SustainPro*, with optimization models developed for the batch retrofit problem. The applicability of the proposed framework is shown through a multipurpose batch plant case study.

Keywords: Retrofit; Batch; Life Cycle

1. Introduction

An increasing importance of plants retrofit and utilities rationalization is constantly observed caused by the need of costs rationalization and minimization of environmental impacts. This ought to be considered while maintaining plants efficiency and efficacy. Guinand (2001) defined retrofit as: "The redesign of an operating chemical process to find new configuration and operating parameters that will adapt the plant to changing conditions to maintain its optimal performance." Based on this concept several authors have been developing heuristics, meta-heuristics and optimization models attempting to systematize procedures that will help practitioners in their retrofit activities. However as identified by Barbosa-Póvoa (2007) new methodologies are still required, which should integrate in a single framework heuristics and optimization methods in order to solve complex problems in batch retrofit actions in a real time context. Dedieu et al (2003) developed a heuristic procedure, based on a genetic algorithm, to solve batch plant design or retrofit problems. A discrete event systems embedded in the optimization loop is used both to determine the feasibility of each solution proposed by the optimizer and to compute the various objective functions. Halim and Srinivasan (2006) explored heuristics approaches and presented an intelligent system for waste minimization assessment of batch processes – BATCHENVOP Expert. Recently, Chibeles et al. (2010) presented a meta-heuristic approach to improve computation results of design and scheduling of multipurpose batch plants using Simulated Annealing and compared the results with exact methods. Fumero (2013) proposed a multiperiod MILP model for design and planning of multistage multiproduct batch plants integrating, simultaneously, scheduling decisions. Although some work has been appearing on the combination of methods to address the retrofit design problem in batch processes further work is still required. Some authors have applied heuristic models, these models only indicate possible improvements at the strategic level, and however the operational planning is not taken into consideration. Moreover there are complex optimization models that try to optimize the whole structure from the strategic to the operational level, however to obtain solutions from these models it takes a long period or the authors cannot even reach a solution. Therefore new frameworks that can efficiently deal with the complexity of such problems are required. The present work aims to contribute to the fulfilment of this gap and presents a generic and systematic approach to identify in existing plants possible retrofit actions that will improve the performance of their processes accounting for mass and energy alternatives. The *BatchRetroLC* framework involves an iterative process that allows the continuous improvement of existing plants, based on a combination of heuristics and optimization steps.

2. Methodology

The *BatchRetroLC* framework is presented in Figure 1. This framework integrates an indicator heuristic based methodology (Carvalho et al., 2009), which is incorporated in a software tool called *SustainPro* (Carvalho et al., 2013), with an exact formulation developed for design and detailed scheduling of multipurpose batch plants (Pinto et, al.,, 2003). *BatchRetroLC* as a decision support tool identifies the process/plants bottlenecks and proposes possible retrofit actions that will improve the plant/process under analysis. This will allow the elimination and reduction of the identified bottleneck impacts and simultaneously optimize new design alternatives at the operational level leading to more efficient solutions that can easily be implemented in the original processes' topology.

In the following points, each step of the proposed framework is described in more detailed.

Step 1: Batch Plant Analysis

The framework starts by considering the analysis of an existent plant where the decision maker (DM) has identified the need for improvements. A first step towards the collection of plant/process relevant data is performed involving mass and energy consumptions, operation times, costs, recipes, among others, so that a further analysis within the framework developed can be undertaken.

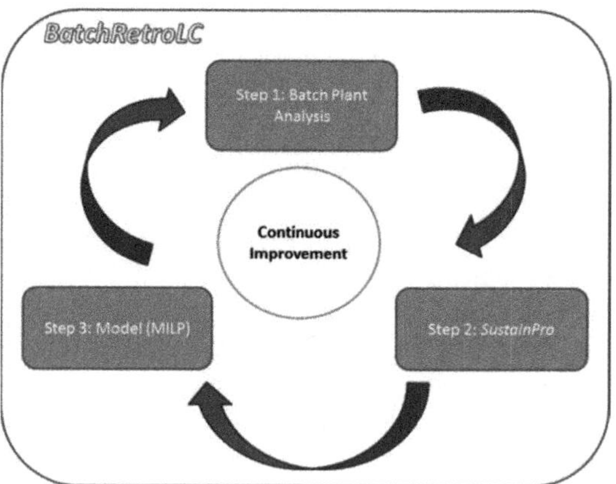

Figure 1. *BatchRetroLC* framework

Step 2: SustainPro

After the identification of a need for improvements, *SustainPro* is applied to, screen, generate and prioritize sustainable design alternatives. This tool is characterized by a six task procedure: 1) data collection; 2) plant/process decomposition in close or open and accumulation paths; 3) indicators calculation; 4) 5) indicators and operational sensitivity analysis, 6) new design alternatives proposal.

After importing the data from step 1, *SustainPro* performs the process decomposition into closed-, open- and accumulation paths for energy and mass (second *SustainPro's* task). *SustainPro* requires as input the mass and energy balances, the time of each operation, the equipment volume and the purchase and sale prices for each chemical. Closed-paths are defined as process recycles or flow-paths which start and end in the same unit of the process. While the open-path consists of an entrance and an exit of a specific compound in the process, accumulation-paths are related to the build-up of mass and energy in the batch operations. A set of indicators are then quantified at each path, in order to define the process bottlenecks and possible retrofit actions (*SustainPro* third task). These indicators assess several aspects such as material, energy, costs, material accumulation and time problems (e.g. MVA-Material Value Added; EWC-Energy Waste Cost; AF-Accumulation Factor; TF-Time Factor). A sensitivity analyses is then conducted in order to identify the most critical plant units that should be improved through retrofit design. Finally new retrofit design alternative are proposed, through a guide map based on a set of heuristics. After *SustainPro* have ranked the process bottlenecks/critical points, based on its importance, which was determined through steps 4 and 5, a list of priorities will be followed to improve process efficiency. The output of this step is a list of solutions that will further be tested and optimized through the optimization model.

Step 3: Optimization Module – OptimRHI

The process bottlenecks ranking and the list of priorities from the *step 2* is used as input data into the *BatchRetroLC's* optimization model, stated as Optimization Retrofit Heat Integration-***OptimRHI***. These are considered simultaneously within a superstructure that models all considered retrofit alternatives proposed by *SustainPro* considering the priority list. The module involves a Mixed Integer Linear Problem (MILP), where binary variables characterize operational and topological choices, while continuous variables define the equipment capacities and the amounts of materials and energy within the overall process.

The ***OptimRHI*** provides, the plant design, considering operational aspects such as task processing, material transfers, operational constraints (e.g. task precedence and changeovers), as well as heat-integration requirements and utilities economic savings. The ***OptimRHI*** output provides, optimal plant structure that will include not only the main processing equipment and the associated connectivity but also all the auxiliary equipment design structures based on the plant utility requirements so as to achieve a pre-defined goal, translated in the objective function. Additional to the plant/process topology a final scheduling is obtained which translates the best operational policies, not only in terms of the main processing tasks but also in terms of material storage and transfers as well as heat-integration policies. For the latter, the optimal schedule may lead to alternatives that can range from the exclusive utilisation of external or of internal utilities to the combination of both, translating the best energy rationalization at the operational level.

It is important to mention that approaches, *SustainPro* and the *OptimRHI* are aligned, since *SustainPro* indicates solutions that minimize costs and environmental impacts and the optimization model finds the optimal planning solution that minimizes the costs.

3. Case Study

A multipurpose batch plant working cyclically on a basis of 40 hours, must be designed at a maximum plant profit to produce three final products C, D and E for commercial proposes and three intermediated products B', C' and D' to be sold in secondary market. The process recipe is shown in Figure 2 and Table 1, which characterize some operations conditions, such as: which equipment are able to process each tasks (reaction, sedimentation, purifications, among others), the energy requirement based on the processing batch and Task´s processing time. The production range allowed for each final and intermediated product are [150; 400], [100;150] and [100; 350] for the intermediates C', C'' and final product C, respectively. A production range of [100; 400] is assumed for the remaining materials.

Step 1: Plant Analysis

The existent process is analysed by the DM and improvement alternatives are identified, based on the knowledge of materials and energy requirements for the several Tasks. In order to prioritize the retrofit actions and to identify which bottlenecks should be considered first, *SustainPro* is applied. All data required in Step 2 by *BatchRetroLC's* is collected from the case study. Some of the required data is shown is Table 1.

Step 2: SustainPro Results

After the input of first´s step data by *SustainPro,* the plant topology is decomposed in closed-, open- and accumulation-paths and a set of indicators has been obtained. One of the most important indicators applied to paths' assessment is the Energy Waste Cost (EWC), which will be followed in this case. This indicator represents the maximum

Table 1. Energy requirements and equipment suitability, for each Task.

	T1	T2	T3	T4	T5	T6	T7	T8	T9
Heat	Endo	Exo	-	Exo	Endo	Endo	Exo	Exo	Endo
KJ	43,229	14,151	-	348	11,103	904	4,032	198	17,176
Unit	1 and 3	1	3	4	5	6	7	6	7

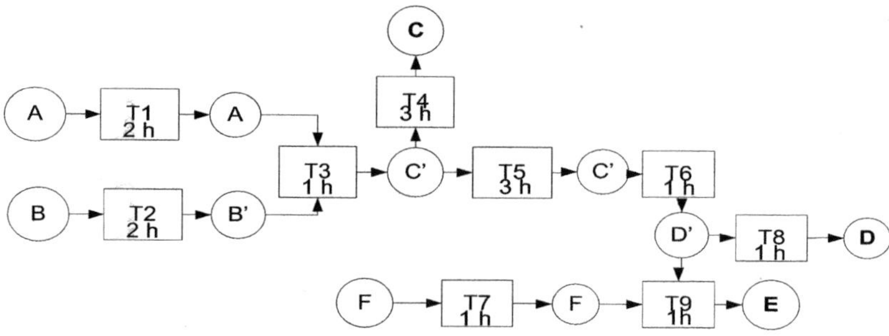

Figure 2. Process Flow sheet.

theoretical amount of energy that can be saved in each path within the process, in other words this indicator gives the energy cost related to each path. High values of EWC point out to the need for improvements in a specific path. From the *SustainPro* analysis 11 open-paths and 9 accumulation-paths were found. It turned out that the most critical indicators were the EWC for open-paths 10 (path starting in production of compound E and storage after production), 7 (path starting in production of compound C in task T3 and reaction of that compound in task T6 to produce compound D) and 2 (entry of compound B in task T2 for heating and storage of that compound) since these paths presented very high values of EWC. Through the sensitivity analysis steps, it was possible to verify that tasks T9, T6 and T2 were the most critical ones in terms of energy consumption. *SustainPro* through the use of set of heuristic rules suggested that energy integration between Tasks T9 with T8, T5 with T4, and T2 with T1 should be performed. Despite the time horizon consideration, the inflow material of task T9 is unstable, requiring a zero wait storage police, and some operational constraints in terms of time scheduling are impossible the reach, leading to the Task T9/Task T8 impossible integration. Since the others integration alternatives verify time and operations constrains are considered as feasible and are then to be analysed in the optimization module.

Step 3: OptimRHI Results

The optimization procedure is applied to the set of alternatives previously identified as feasible. The optimal scheduling is shown in Figure 3, where a multipurpose operation is followed by Units (U) 1, 3, 6 and 7, while the remaining units are allocated to a single Task.

In term of heat integration, an integration mixed policy is observed by Task 1 and Task 2. Those operate not only, in an integrated mode as HI_T1/HI_T2 requiring an additional heat exchange equipment and processing, as illusration example, a bach of 70 and 150 mass units, starting at t=7, respectively, but also operating as non-integrated mode as T1 and T2. On the other hand, a single heat-integration policy is used by Task T4 and T5, as HI_T4 and HI_T5 (requiring an additional heat exchange equipment). From the integration approach a utility reduction was achieved corresponding to a reduction of 24.6 % of fresh water (451 monetary units against 598 monetary units) and 36.8% of super-heat steam (991 monetary units against 1,569 monetary units).

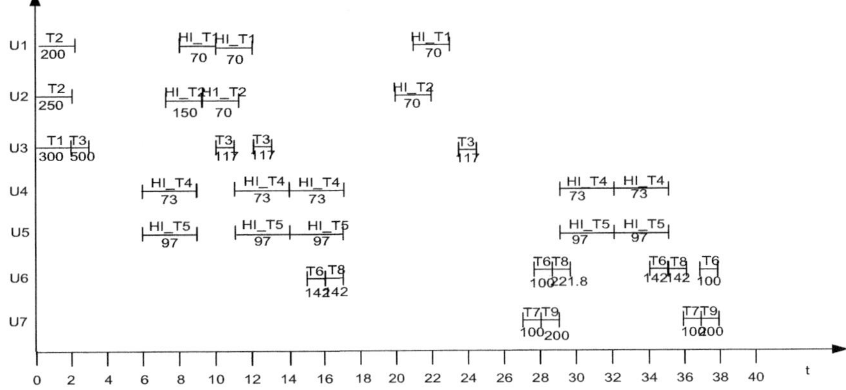

Figure 3. Optimal Scheduling

In this example it was conducted, only one iteration of the retrofit cycle presented in Figure 1. For the continuous improvement, *SustainPro* would be run again to find the most critical indicators. In the second run of *SustainPro* TF indicators were the most critical indicators. The investment on equipment to conduct parallel production might be a solution to reduce this problem. If this option would be considered then the optimization model would have to be run again in order to find the optimal planning solution.

4. Conclusions

A life cycle framework, *BatchRetroC,* for the retrofit of batch plants has been developed and its applicability tested through an example. This framework appears as a promising decision tool to help, guide and support decision-makers in a continuous improvement action in operational contexts. The framework integrates a *SustainPro* module with an optimization module, *OptimRHI,* where a set of propose retrofit alternatives based in indicators values are considered and optimized. The proposed framework allows for the identification of a set of promising alternatives through a heuristic procedure which permits the reduction of a set of alternatives to be considered at the optimization level leading to a decrease of computational burden that characterizes the type of problems under analysis. The work developed is still in its first stage of application and further cases are under analysis namely the solution of real process/plants in the pharmaceutical area are to be optimized.

References

A. P. F. D. Barbosa-Póvoa, 2007, A Critical Review on the Design and Retrofit of Batch Plants, Comp. Chem. Eng., 31, 833-855.

A. Carvalho, H. A. Matos, R. Gani, 2009, Design of batch operations: Systematic methodology for generation and analysis of sustainable alternatives, Comput. Chem. Eng., 33, 2075-2090.

A. Carvalho, H. A. Matos, R. Gani, 2013, SustainPro – A tool for systematic process analysis, generation and evaluation of sustainable design alternatives, Comput. Chem. Eng., 50, 8-27.

N. Chibeles-Martins, T. Pinto-Varela, A. P. Barbosa-Povoa, A. Q. Novais, 2010, A Meta-Heuristics Approach for the Design and Scheduling of Multipurpose Batch Plants, Comput. Aided Chem. Eng., 28, 1315-1320.

S. Dedieu, C. Azzaro-Pantel, L. Pibouleau, S. Domenech, 2003, Design and retrofit of multiobjective batch plants via a multicriteria genetic algorithm, Comput. Chem. Eng., 27, 12, 1723-1740.

E. A. Guinand, 2001, Optimization and Network Sensitivity Analysis for Process Retrofitting, PhD-thesis, Massachussetts Institute of Technology (MIT), Chemical Engineering Department, Boston, USA.

I. Halim, R. Srinivasan, 2006, Systematic waste minimization in chemical processes, Part III. Batch operations, Ind. Eng. Chem. Res., 45, 4693–4705.

T. Pinto, A. P. Barbosa-Póvoa, A.Q. Novais, 2003, Optimal Design of Heat-Integrated Multipurpose Batch Facilities with Economic Savings in Utilities: A Mixed Integer Mathematical Formulation, Annals of Operations Research, 120, 201-230.

Y. Fumero, M. S. Moreno, G. Corsano, J. M. Montagna, 2013, A multiproduct batch plant design model incorporating production planning and scheduling decisions under a multiperiod scenario, Computer Aided Chemical Engineering, 32, 505-510.

Jiří Jaromír Klemeš, Petar Sabev Varbanov and Peng Yen Liew (Editors)
Proceedings of the 24th European Symposium on Computer Aided Process Engineering – ESCAPE 24
June 15-18, 2014, Budapest, Hungary.

The Integration of the Synthesis Methodology in the Design of a Five-Component Distillation Sequence

Massimiliano Errico,[a*] Pietro Pirellas, [a] Ben-Guang Rong,[b] Carlo E. Torres-Ortega,[c] Juan Gabriel Segovia-Hernandez [c]

[a]*Universitá degli Studi di Cagliari, Dipartimento di Ingegneria Meccanica, Chimica e dei Materiali, Via Marengo 2, 09123 Cagliari, Italy*
[b]*University of Southern Denmark, Department of Chemical Engineering, Biotechnology and Environmental Technology, Niels Bohrs Allé 1, DK-5230 Odense M, Denmark*
[c]*Division de Ciencias Naturales y Exactas, Departamento de Ingenieria Quimica, Universidad de Guanajuato, Noria Alta S/N, 36050 Guanajuato, Mexico*
massimiliano.errico@dimcm.unica.it

Abstract

The separation of a multicomponent stream by distillation represents a common problem in the industrial field. The possibility to realize the same separation task by means of different sequences have opened an unique research topic focused on the definition of a complete searching space that includes all the possible alternatives. The searching space can be generated following different approaches based on a mathematical background, like superstructures, or based on the connection of the simple column sequences with the alternatives generated. The correspondence between simple column sequences and the alternatives predicted is the principle of the generation method followed in the present work. Using this type of approach the generation and the design method used to screen and evaluate the alternative's performance are deeply related. The correspondence between the functionality of the column's sections of the simple columns and the corresponding alternatives was used to get the initialization parameters, then these parameters were optimized by a sensitivity analysis. The proposed design method was called Sequential Design Method (SDM). The method was applied for a five component separation sequence considering a particular class of alternative configurations called Modified Simple Column (MSC) sequences. In order to test the proposed methodology, the same sequences were designed using an optimization procedure based on a hybrid multi-objective (HMO) algorithm. It was found that the SDM is a fast and reliable design procedure that allows the user to easily define the column sequences' parameters. Moreover the SDM can be used to correctly initialize the multi-objective algorithm. When the HMO algorithm is initialized with the design parameters obtained from the SDM, the computational time is reduced by 21 % compare to a random initialization.

Keywords: multicomponent distillation, optimal design, column sequence synthesis, Aspen Plus simulation.

1. Introduction

The identification of the optimal separation sequence can be summarized in a five step procedure that includes:

1. definition of the separation method

2. generation of the alternatives
3. design of the alternatives
4. screening of the alternatives by means of an objective function
5. selection of the best sequence.

Considering distillation as separation method, the second step still represents an open issue in the chemical engineering research community (Caballero and Grossmann, 2014). For many years the prediction of a complete searching space that includes all or most of the possible distillation sequences, has been considered independently from the design method used for the economic evaluation of each single sequence. It is a well-known procedure that, when a multicomponent mixture is separated by distillation, the first class of alternatives considered are the simple column sequences. These sequences are usually preferred because of the easiness of the design and control and their diffusion in the industrial practice. Simple column sequences represent the term of comparison with all the alternatives predicted and considered. This last point expresses very clearly that at the beginning of the alternatives screening phase, the designer has already designed and identified the best or the sub set of best simple column sequences.

In previous studies (Errico et al., 2009) the main research work was focused on developing a systematic method that, starting from the simple column sequences, allows the designer to predict a wide set of alternatives. The whole searching space of distillation sequences can be decomposed in different subspaces each with specific peculiarities (Errico et al., 2012). The subspace of simple column sequences includes only simple columns formed by a single feed, a distillate and a bottom product. The subspace of thermally coupled sequences contains one or more bidirectional vapor-liquid stream between two consecutive columns, the subspace of the thermodynamically equivalent sequences is obtained recombining the column sections associated to a thermal coupling, the subspace of the intensified sequences is generated by substitution of single column section (transport section) by means of a side stream, finally the divided wall columns are considered as the ultimate possibility to obtain more than two products from a single distillation column. Following this headway, it is very useful, from a design point of view, to define a procedure that connects each simple column sequence with the alternatives included in the searching space. Applying this concept to the identification of best distillation sequence, it is possible to define first a sub set of the best simple column sequences and then considering only the alternatives derived from them, limiting the design to a selected set of alternatives and making the screening phase faster. This modus operandi relates the alternatives generation method to the possibility of calculation reduction, but the design method used still remains an independent issue. Even if, many design methods are today available in the literature for the distillation design (Gani and Bek-Pedersen, 2000) or for the separation network synthesis, (Heckel et al., 2009), the Sequential Design Method (SDM) was introduced as a complementary tool to the systematic prediction of the distillation sequences alternatives. It is based on the correspondence among the column's sections function of the simple column sequences and the corresponding alternatives. Despite its simplicity, the SDM was proved to be a reliable design method even compared to methods based on strong mathematical background like the Hybrid Multi-objective Optimization (HMO) algorithm, able to minimize different objective functions screening huge amounts of alternatives. A five component mixture is considered as example to prove the potential of the proposed methodology.

2. Problem definition

The feed composition considered and the product purity specifications are reported in Table 1. It is required to design the distillation sequence reported in Figure 1.

For a five component separation the simple column sequences are composed by four columns, since the sequence considered employs only three columns, is expected to be more convenient. The sequence reported in Figure 1 was identified as a Modified Simple Column (MSC) configuration because each product is obtained as a distillate or as a residue. The CD side stream is considered in the vapor phase according to the heuristic rules defined by Kim and Wankat (2004) and confirmed by Errico et al. (2009). The software Aspen Plus was used to design all the sequences reported in the present work and also for the capital cost evaluation. The NRTL method was used to estimate the liquid phase activity coefficients and the vapor phase was considered as ideal. The rigorous stage-to-stage equilibrium model for distillation columns RadFrac was chosen together with total condensers and kettle reboilers. All the calculations were performed with an Intel Core i5, 2.67 GHz, 10GB ram in Windows 7 environment (Ultimate edition 64 bit).

Table 1. Feed composition and product purity

Component	Feed molar fraction	Product molar purity
A: C_5H_{12}	0.35	0.999
B: C_6H_6	0.1	0.989
C: C_7H_{16}	0.1	0.990
D: C_8H_{18}	0.4	0.988
E: $C_{10}H_{22}$	0.05	0.979
Feed Pressure [bar]	2	
Vapor fraction	0	

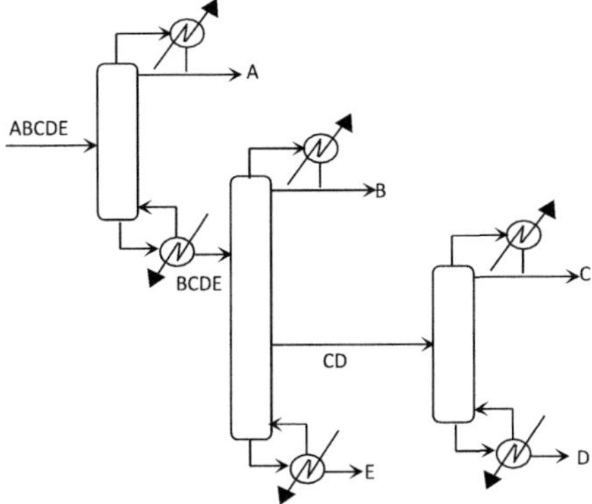

Figure 1. Sequence considered for the design.

3. The sequential design and the hybrid multi-objective approach

To apply the sequential design method it is necessary to identify the simple column sequence corresponding to the configuration considered. Focusing on the sequence reported in Figure 1, the complete derivation method is out of the scope of the present work and is reported elsewhere (Rong and Errico, 2012), anyway in Figure 2 the derivation steps necessary to move from the simple column sequence to the MSC sequence, are reported.

From the simple column sequence of Figure 2(a) it is possible to generate the thermally coupled (TC) sequence of Figure 2(b), then recombining the column section 6 associated to the thermal coupling, the thermodynamically equivalent sequences (TES) of Figure 2(c) is obtained. Finally substituting the transport section 5, the required sequences is reported in Figure 2(d). It is evident that the SC sequences of Figure 2(a) and the MSC in Figure 2(d) are deeply related and the SDM uses this correspondence to relate the design of the SC to the MSC. The results are summarized in Table 2.

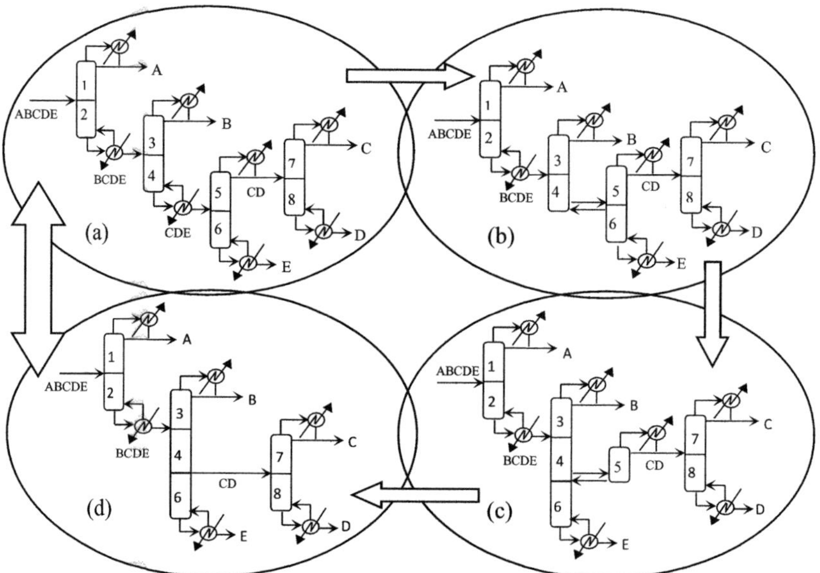

Figure 2. Systematic procedure for the MSC sequence generation: (a) SC sequence, (b) TC sequence, (c) corresponding TES, (d) MSC sequence

Table 2. Design parameters and energy consumption of the SC of Figure 2(a)

	C1	C2	C3	C4
Number of stages	22	47	29	36
Feed stage	13	29	17	21
Distillate flowrate [kmol/h]	35.00	10.10	50.20	9.90
Bottom flowrate [kmol/h]	65.00	54.90	4.70	40.30
Reflux ratio	1.80	11.85	0.21	7.1
Diameter [m]	0.85	1.07	0.81	0.90
Total condenser duty [kW]			-3,087.460	
Total reboiler duty [kW]			3,174.043	
Capital cost [$/y]			226,120	

Based on the correspondence between the column sections functionality, the design parameters of the simple column sequence were used to define those of the MSC configuration in Figure 2(d). The results obtained are reported in Table 3.

The rigorous method used to have a comparison with the SDM is based on the differential evolution algorithm with taboo list. The taboo list is randomly initialized using the initial population and continuously updated with the newly generated trial individuals. The optimal design was found by using the HMO algorithm as optimization method implemented in Microsoft Excel and coupled with Aspen Plus.

The objective function is composed by the total annual cost (TAC) calculated according to Turton et al. (2009) and by the thermodynamic efficiency as defined by Seider et al. (2009).

The results, obtained after 48 h and 15 min, are reported in Table 4. About 15,000 simulations were performed before the final design has been identified, 99 % of the simulations converged to the required purity specifications.

Now if the results obtained applying the SDM are used to initialize the HMO algorithm, the computational time is reduced to 38 h and the resulting design is reported in Table 5. About 10,000 alternatives were evaluated in order to get the final design. All the alternatives satisfied the product purity requirements.

Table 3. SDM design parameters and energy consumption of the MSC of Figure 2(d)

	C1	C2	C3
Number of stages	22	56	36
Feed stage	13	30	15
Side stream stage	--	47	--
Distillate flowrate [kmol/h]	35.00	10.10	9.90
Bottom flowrate [kmol/h]	65.00	4.70	40.30
Side stream flowrate [kmol/h]	--	50.20	--
Reflux ratio	1.80	12.27	10.65
Diameter [m]	0.85	1.34	1.05
Total condenser duty [kW]		-2,849.644	
Total reboiler duty [kW]		2,936.311	
Capital cost [$/y]		212,940	

Table 4. HMO design parameters and energy consumption of the MSC of Figure 2(d)

	C1	C2	C3
Number of stages	39	66	43
Feed stage	27	30	16
Side stream stage	--	54	--
Distillate flowrate [kmol/h]	35.00	10.10	9.90
Bottom flowrate [kmol/h]	65.00	4.70	40.30
Side stream flowrate [kmol/h]	--	50.20	--
Reflux ratio	0.93	12.10	10.65
Diameter [m]	0.74	1.33	1.05
Total condenser duty [kW]		-2622.522	
Total reboiler duty [kW]		2709.16	
Capital cost [$/y]		271000	

Table 5. HMO plus SDMdesign parameters and energy consumption of the MSC of Figure 2(d)

	C1	C2	C3
Number of stages	26	58	39
Feed stage	16	31	15
Side stream stage	--	47	--
Bottom flowrate [kmol/h]	65.00	4.70	40.30
Side stream flowrate [kmol/h]	--	50.20	--
Reflux ratio	1.53	12.10	10.65
Diameter [m]	0.81	1.33	1.05
Total condenser duty [kW]		-2769.026	
Total reboiler duty [kW]		2855.671	
Capital cost [$/y]		215330	

4. Conclusions

As can be noticed from the results reported in Tables 3-5, the designs obtained with the SDM and the HMO algorithm are in good agreement. When the HMO method is randomly initialized, the total condenser and reboiler duty are 7.8 % and 7.7 % less than the corresponding values obtained with the SDM. On the other side the capital cost is 27 % higher. When the HMO is initialized with the parameters obtained by the SDM the computational time is reduced of about 21 %. Compare to the SDM, in this case, the total condenser and reboiler duty are 2.8 % and 2.7 % less. The capital cost obtained is almost the same for both designs. Depending on the ability in using the simulation software, it is possible quantify in six hours the time requested to complete the simulations applying the SDM. This method is fast and reliable even if any possible error in the initial simple column design is directly transferred to the derived design without any possibility of control. Coupling the SDM with a robust optimization algorithm like the HMO allows to obtain the optimal distillation column design in a reasonable time.

References

J.A. Caballero, I.E. Grossmann, 2014, Optimal synthesis of thermally coupled distillation sequences using a novel MILP approach, Computers and Chemical Engineering, 61, 118-135.

M. Errico, B.-G. Rong, G. Tola, I. Turunen, 2009, A method for systematic synthesis of multicomponent distillation systems with less than N-1 columns, Chemical Engineering and processing: Process Intensification, 48, 907-920.

M. Errico, B.-G. Rong, 2012, Modified simple column configurations for quaternary distillations, Computers and Chemical Engineering, 36, 160-173.

R. Gani. E. Bek-Pedersen, 2000, Simple new algorithm for distillation column design, AIChE Journal, 46, 1271-1274.

I. Heckl, F. Friedler, L.T. Fan, 2009, Solution of separation network synthesis ploblems bu theP-graph methodology, Computer Aided Chemical Engineering, 26, 641-646

J.K. Kim, P.C. Wankat, 2004, Quaternary distillation systems with less than N-1 columns, Industrial and Engineering Chemistry Research, 43, 3838-3846.

B.-G. Rong, M. Errico, 2012, Synthesis of intensified simple column configurations for multicomponent distillations, Chemical Engineering and processing: Process Intensification, 62, 1-17.

W.D. Seider, J.D. Seader, D.R. Lewin, S. Widagdo, 2009, Product and process design principles. Synthesis, analysis and evaluation,Third ed., John Wiley and Sons, Inc, Asia.

R. Turton, R.C. Bailie, W.B. Whiting, J.A. Shaeiwitz, 2009, Synthesis and design of the chemical process, Second ed., Prentice Hall, USA.

Jiří Jaromír Klemeš, Petar Sabev Varbanov and Peng Yen Liew (Editors)
Proceedings of the 24th European Symposium on Computer Aided Process Engineering – ESCAPE 24
June 15-18, 2014, Budapest, Hungary.

Isobutane Alkylation Process Synthesis by means of Hybrid Simulation-Multiobjective Optimization

María J. Fernández-Torres*, Norberto García, José A. Caballero

Department of Chemical Engineering, University of Alicante, Apdo 99 E-03080, Alicante, Spain

fernandez@ua.es

Abstract

Multiobjective Generalized Disjunctive Programming (MO-GDP) optimization has been used for the synthesis of an important industrial process, isobutane alkylation. The two objective functions to be simultaneously optimized are the environmental impact, determined by means of LCA (Life Cycle Assessment), and the economic potential of the process. The main reason for including the minimization of the environmental impact in the optimization process is the widespread environmental concern by the general public. For the resolution of the problem we employed a hybrid simulation-optimization methodology, i.e., the superstructure of the process was developed directly in a chemical process simulator connected to a state of the art optimizer. The model was formulated as a GDP and solved using a logic algorithm that avoids the reformulation as MINLP -Mixed Integer Non Linear Programming-. Our research gave us Pareto curves compounded by three different configurations where the LCA has been assessed by two different parameters: global warming potential and ecoindicator-99.

Keywords: Generalized Disjunctive Programming (GDP), Multiobjective (MO) optimization, Isobutane alkylation, Life Cycle Assessment (LCA).

1. Introduction

Environmental considerations have only been recently included into process engineering optimization. Traditionally any process optimization was based on profitability. The best way to include the environmental criteria into the process design is by multiobjective (MO) optimization (Azapagic 1999). Life cycle assessment (LCA) provides a comprehensive means to account for environmental impact as indicated by the same author. Since then many examples of MO optimization can be found in literature, for instance, Ruiz-Femenia et al. (2013) made use of this methodology to optimize chemical supply chains. Wang et al. (2013) employed MO optimization to the configuration of a hydrocarbon biorefinery. Gebrelassie et al. (2013a) obtained the sustainable design of a hydrocarbon biorefinery via fast pyrolysis. Gebreslassie et al. (2013b) presented the synthesis of an algae-based biorefinery that includes carbon sequestration. Our aim in this work is to show how the inclusion of LCA into the MO optimization is a helpful procedure for industrial process design and optimization. This paper combines MO optimization together with hybrid simulation-optimization approach formulated as a GDP problem and solved with logic based algorithm without MINLP reformulation (Türkay et al. 1996; Caballero et al. 2007). Particularly, in this paper we present the MO optimization methodology applied to the isobutane alkylation process. As a result, we obtain a set of flowsheet configurations (together with its process variables) able to manufacture isooctane that simultaneously optimizes the production cost and minimizes the associated environmental damage.

2. Procedure for the synthesis of the optimized process

Three steps are necessary for the synthesis of the optimized isobutane alkylation process:

- First step is to propose a superstructure of alternatives. Ours (Figure 1) is based on the licensed processes by Stratford Engineering Corporation and Exxon Research and Engineering. To that base we added extra alternatives that include: an extension of the post reaction separation alternatives, the possibility of feed purification as pretreatment, existence of purge, etc. Two main reactions have been considered for the present study: C4 + i-C4 → C8 (main reaction) and C4 + C8 → C12 (unwanted reaction) where C4 stands for 1-butene, i-C4 for isobutane, C8 for isooctane and C12 for dodecane. Propane (C3) inevitably enters with 1-butene to the process but behaves like an inert substance. Presence of sulfuric acid is required in the reactor chamber to act as a catalyst. This acid is later separated by means of a settler and recirculated back to the reactor.
- Second step is to write the mathematical model as a hybrid simulation-optimization multi-objective generalized disjunctive programming (GDP) problem (see section 3).
- Third step is to solve the GDP problem using logic-based algorithms without reformulation to MINLP (Türkay et al. 1996) (see section 3).

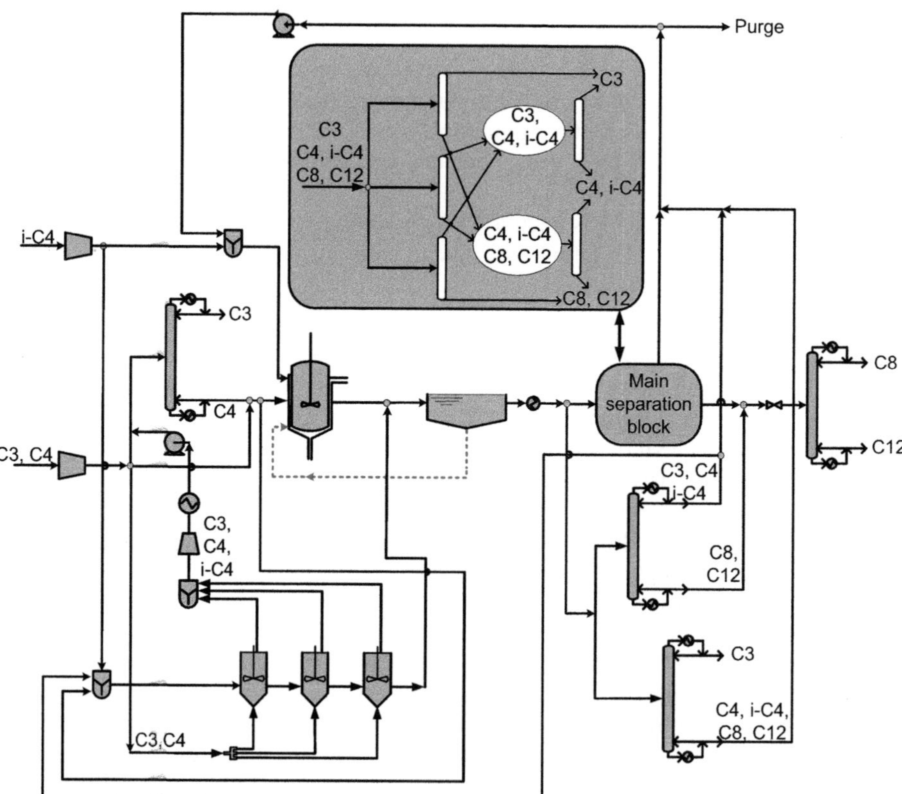

Figure 1. Superstructure considered in the present study.

3. Mathematical model

Conceptually the model can be written as follows:

$$
\begin{aligned}
& \min :\{f_{Ec}(\mathbf{x_D},\mathbf{x_I}), f_{En}(\mathbf{x_D},\mathbf{x_I})\} \\
& \quad s.t. \quad \mathbf{x_D} = \mathbf{r}_{im}(\mathbf{x_I}) \\
& \quad \mathbf{r}_{ex}(\mathbf{x_D},\mathbf{x_I}) = \mathbf{0} \\
& \quad \mathbf{s}_{ex}(\mathbf{x_D},\mathbf{x_I}) \le \mathbf{0} \\
& \quad \begin{bmatrix} Y_i \\ \mathbf{x_D} = \mathbf{h}_{im,i}(\mathbf{x}_{\mathbf{I},i}) \\ \mathbf{h}_{ex,i}(\mathbf{x_D},\mathbf{x}_{\mathbf{I},i}) = \mathbf{0} \\ \mathbf{g}_{ex,i}(\mathbf{x_D},\mathbf{x}_{\mathbf{I},i}) \le \mathbf{0} \end{bmatrix} \underline{\vee} \begin{bmatrix} \neg Y_i \\ \mathbf{x}_{\mathbf{I},i} = \mathbf{0} \end{bmatrix} \quad \forall i \in D \qquad (1) \\
& \quad \Omega(\mathbf{Y}) = True \\
& \quad \mathbf{x_I} \in X \subseteq \Re^n \\
& \quad \mathbf{Y} \in \{True, \ False\}^p
\end{aligned}
$$

Where f_{Ec} and f_{En} are the economic and the environmental objective functions respectively. $\mathbf{x_D}$ is a vector of dependent variables like those calculated by the process simulator used (Aspen-Hysys^{TM}). $\mathbf{x_I}$ is a vector of independent variables on which the programmer has full control. The index "*im*" stands for implicit equation calculated by third party model (process simulator, other matlab models, etc.). The index "*ex*" indicates explicit equation. The boolean variable Y_i takes only two values, true if equipment "*i*" is selected or false if not. Finally p denotes the number of Boolean variables.

The disjunction of the model (Eq. 1) explicitly indicates that if a given item of equipment is selected, then all the equations related to it must be used, if not, all the independent variables corresponding to that item of equipment are set to zero. This equation only allow for two term disjunction which is the procedure for process network and synthesis. The equations related to each equipment are the sizing, costing and environmental impact.

All the thermodynamic data required and all of the equipment simulation (excluding those corresponding to the distillation columns) are calculated by Aspen-Hysys^{TM}. The distillation columns simulations and sequence optimization were performed according to the procedure described in (Caballero et al. 2001), (Caballero et al. 2006) and (Caballero et al. 2013). The simulation of thermal couples is performed by the methodology described in (Navarro-Amorós et al. 2013).

Eq.(6) of the model represents all the logical relationships used with the intention to obtain feasible configurations. This collection of relationships includes:

- Select the isothermal or the three autorefrigerated reactors.
- The inert substance (C3) is either removed before entering the system with a prefractionator or at a later stage in the main separation block shown in Figure 1.

- At most only one of the initial separations in the main separation block can be selected after the reaction. Such a statement must be necessarily followed by a connectivity relation to indicate which separation or separations can follow.
- Finally, another set of logical relationships are necessary to indicate if reboilers and/or condensers are to be used in the different distillation columns. This is necessary since we are explicitly including thermally coupled distillation alternatives.

Once the mathematical model to describe the MO optimization problem is completed we proceed to its resolution. To achieve that we used the epsilon constraint method (Ehrgott 2005). The results are obtained as Pareto curves (environmental indicators vs economic potential), the steps are the following:

- First step, find the two extremes of the Pareto curves by optimizing each individual objective (single-objective optimization).
- Second step, reformulate the model (equations 1 to 8) by moving the environmental objective equation to the constraints.
- Third step, solve a sequence of problems with a single objective by changing the value of epsilon(Ehrgott 2005) between the two extremes of the Pareto curve found on the first step.

This type of problems is quite complex, therefore it is convenient to perform a sensitivity analysis beforehand to decide which variables are convenient to use as independent variables. Our study indicated that we should employ the following: the molar flowrate ratio of the two fresh input streams to the system, the volume of the reactor(s), the temperature of the isothermal reactor, the split fraction in the purge stream and the individual flows and temperature in the recycle stream.

Some parameter values that have been fixed are: the recovery of the key component in the distillation column (0.99) and the reflux ratio in the distillation column (1.3).

4. Results

As indicated in the previous section, the results have been obtained as Pareto curves (see Fig. 2) where the environmental impact is plotted against the economic potential. Each curve corresponds to the MO optimization process conducted with a different environmental indicators, global warming potential (GWP) and ecoindicator-99 (Ei-99). It can be seen in the figure that each curve is compounded by three distinctive sections which correspond to three different processes also shown and depicted by A, B and C.

5. Conclusions

An important industrial process (isobutene alkylation) is synthesized by means of hybrid simulation multiobjective optimization. New alternatives for the alkylation process have been considered. The present study shows that GDP is the ideal framework to solve hybrid problems of simulation-optimization with the final aim to perform successful process synthesis. Each of the Pareto curves we obtained refers to three different structures. The designer(s) can now decide at which point of the optimized solution they would like to work by choosing any point on these curves.

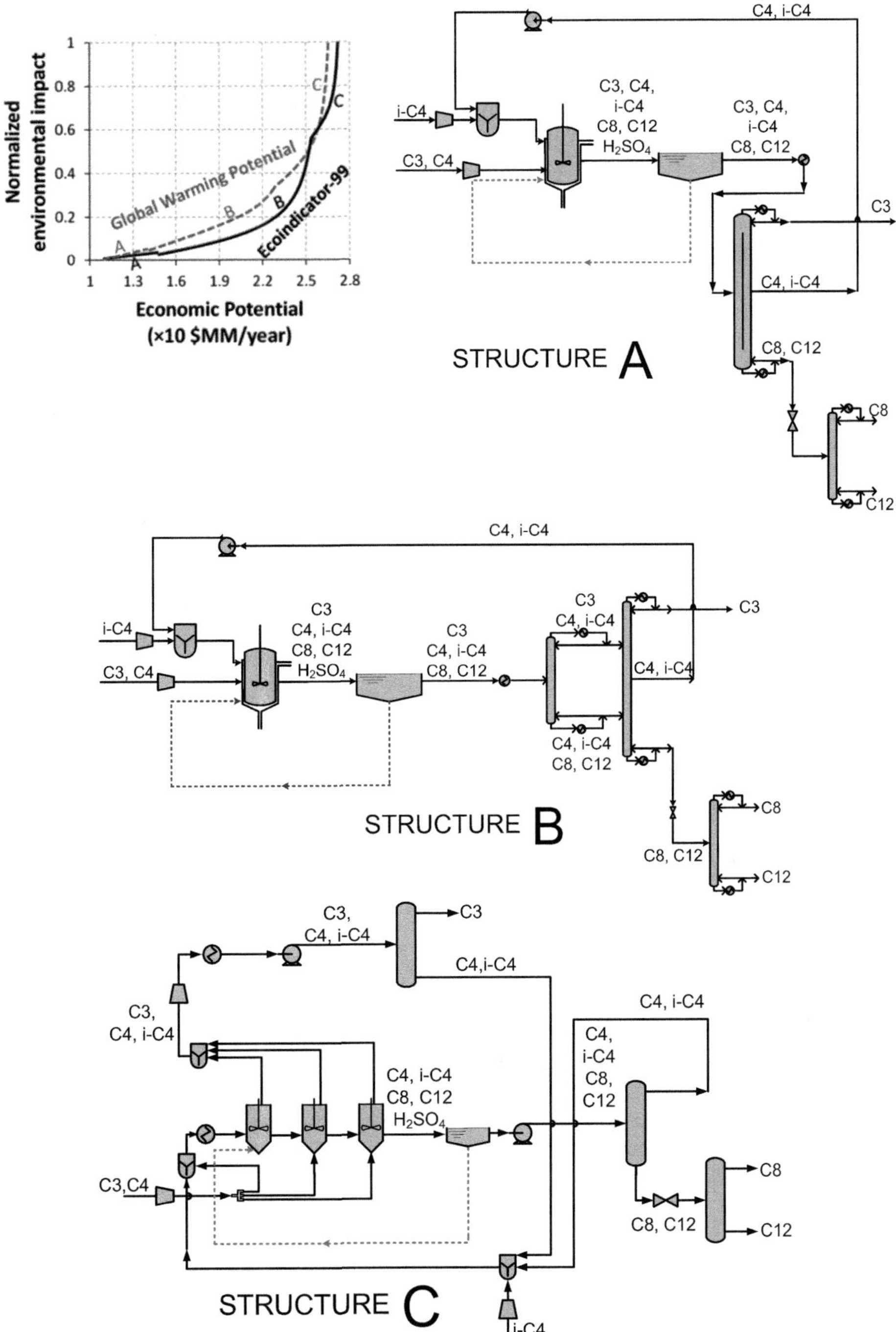

Figure 2. Comparison between the Pareto's curves obtained using both environmental indicators (GWP and Ei-99) together with the three structures that compound them (A, B and C). A is a configuration where the main separation is achieved with a divided wall column. B is a configuration where the separation uses a prefractionator without thermal couple. And C is a configuration where the reaction takes place in three auto-refrigerated reactors in series.

Our suggestion would be to choose a point on line segment C in Figure 2 because of its steep slope toward the right end of the curve (maximum economic potential). For example, if we were to operate under conditions at which the EP equals 26.0 \$MM/y instead of its maximum value (27.3 \$MM/y on the EI-99 curve, a slight drop of 4.7 %) the environmental indicators would decrease up to 26.1 %.

Acknowledgement

We acknowledge the support from the Spanish Ministry of Science and Innovation (CTQ2012-37039-C02-02)

References

A. Azapagic, 1999, Life cycle assessment and its application to process selection, design and optimisation, Chemical Engineering Journal, 73,1, 1-21.

J. A. Caballero, I. E. Grossmann, 2001, Generalized Disjunctive Programming Model for the Optimal Synthesis of Thermally Linked Distillation Columns, Industrial and Engineering Chemistry Research, 40, 10, 2260-2274.

J. A. Caballero, I. E. Grossmann, 2006, Structural Considerations and Modeling in the Synthesis of Heat-Integrated–Thermally Coupled Distillation Sequences, Industrial and Engineering Chemistry Research, 45, 25, 8454-8474.

J. A. Caballero, I. E. Grossmann, 2013, Synthesis of complex thermally coupled distillation systems including divided wall columns, AIChE Journal, 59, 4, 1139-1159.

J. A. Caballero, A. Odjo, I. E. Grossmann, 2007, Flowsheet optimization with complex cost and size functions using process simulators, AIChE Journal, 53, 9, 2351-2366.

M. Ehrgott, 2005. Multicriteria optimization, Berlin, New York, Springer.

B. H. Gebreslassie, M. Slivinsky, B. Wang, F. You, 2013a, Life cycle optimization for sustainable design and operations of hydrocarbon biorefinery via fast pyrolysis, hydrotreating and hydrocracking, Computers and Chemical Engineering, 50, 71-91.

B. H. Gebreslassie, R. Waymire, F. You, 2013b, Sustainable design and synthesis of algae-based biorefinery for simultaneous hydrocarbon biofuel production and carbon sequestration, AIChE Journal, 59, 5, 1599-1621.

M. A. Navarro-Amorós, J. A. Caballero, R. Ruiz-Femenia, I. E. Grossmann, 2013, An alternative disjunctive optimization model for heat integration with variable temperatures, Computers and Chemical Engineering, 56, 12-26.

R. Ruiz-Femenia, G. Guillén-Gosálbez, L. Jiménez, J. A. Caballero, 2013, Multi-objective optimization of environmentally conscious chemical supply chains under demand uncertainty. Chemical Engineering Science, 95, 1-11.

M. Türkay, I. E. Grossmann, 1996, Logic-based MINLP algorithms for the optimal synthesis of process networks, Computers and Chemical Engineering, 20, 8, 959-978.

B. Wang, B. H. Gebreslassie, F. You, 2013, Sustainable design and synthesis of hydrocarbon biorefinery via gasification pathway: Integrated life cycle assessment and technoeconomic analysis with multiobjective superstructure optimization, Computers and Chemical Engineering, 52, 55-76.

Jiří Jaromír Klemeš, Petar Sabev Varbanov and Peng Yen Liew (Editors)
Proceedings of the 24th European Symposium on Computer Aided Process Engineering – ESCAPE 24
June 15-18, 2014, Budapest, Hungary.

Mechanical Design and Hydraulic Analysis of Sieve Trays in Dividing Wall Columns

Mario A. Rodríguez-Ángeles[a], Fernando I. Gómez-Castro [a], Juan G. Segovia-Hernández[a], Claudia Gutiérrez-Antonio[b], Abel Briones-Ramírez[c]

[a]*Universidad de Guanajuato, Campus Guanajuato, Division de Ciencias Naturales y Exactas, Departamento de Ingeniería Química, Noria Alta S/N. Guanajuato, Guanajuato, 36050, Mexico*

[b]*Universidad Autónoma de Querétaro, Facultad de Química, Cerro de las Campanas S/N Las Campanas, Querétaro, Querétaro, 76000, Mexico*

[c]*Exxerpro Solutions, Av. del Sol 1B Interior 4B, Plaza Comercial El Sol, Queretaro, Queretaro, 76134, Mexico*

Abstract

Dividing wall column (DWC) is a relatively new technology generated by integrating fully thermodynamically coupled columns into a single shell, which represents both capital and operation savings. Since the conception of this technology, many researchers have made extensive studies about it, mainly focused to optimization and control; however some of the best advances have been developed by private industry. A topic which has received only little interest in optimization of DWC is the internal operation of the column, together with the mechanical design of the column. Nevertheless, there is not a methodology in open literature to perform this analysis. In this work a strategy for the mechanical design and simulation of a dividing wall column with sieve trays is presented. Hydraulic parameters have tested through CFD simulations and results were used for adjustment and optimization of physic parameters. Final tray geometry was tested for operation regime and flooding, and streamlines were analyzed for malfunctions in the tray to ensure the proper function of the distillation column within established limits. CFD analysis was carried out using ANSYS FLUENT software.

Keywords: DWC, sieve tray, mechanical design, CFD simulation

1. Introduction

Dividing wall column (DWC) is a technology whose concept first appeared in 1933 in a patent by Luster, which specifies that the column could be used in cracking process. Later, Wright (1949) proposed the same idea of the DWC, however he specified that it could be used for general purposes. Although the idea seemed promissory, both the design and the construction of such column were too complicated to perform with the tools available on those days. Years later and with the advancement of technology and discovery of new methods and models for the design of columns, the idea of building DWC returned, being the private sector the most advanced in these studies. In 1985 the private enterprise BASF built and installed the first known DWC, which had structured packing. For years, the BASF Company was recognized as the only company working with DWC, being Kaibel its main promoter; who in 1984 had already conceived DWC separations even for four-component mixtures. It was not until the publication of the work of Kaibel (1987) that the first DWC studies published out of BASF began. Most of the research about DWC has been developed in the field of design and optimization, but in terms of the determination of the dimensions of such columns there is still very few information in the open literature. Olujic et al. (2009) have proposed methods such as using the TU Delft model for dimensioning distillation columns; however, some authors report that DWC construction companies point out that a good method is to build on the columns with standard sizing methodology and modify it to the DWC (Dejanovic et al., 2010). In this paper we take this last idea as a starting point for the mechanical design of perforated trays for DWC. Obtained design is subsequently used to analyze, by a Computational Fluid Dynamics (CFD) approach, the internal behavior of the column. There are only few works dealing with the analysis of dividing wall columns trays using CFD (Wang et al., 2012). In the study presented by Wang et al. (2012), the analysis is performed over a single existing tray. In this work, the design of the trays is obtained from a theoretical perspective, looking for a methodology for the preliminar mechanical design and the prediction of potential malfunctions of sieve trays in dividing wall columns.

2. Mechanical design of sieve tray

The strategy for the mechanical design of trays presented in this paper is based on the method proposed by Kister (1992) for perforated trays in conventional distillation columns. Data required for column design was obtained from the work presented by Gomez-Castro et al. (2011) in which a dividing wall column was designed and optimized to separate a mixture of n-pentane, n-hexane and n-heptane with feed molar compositions of 0.4, 0.2 and 0.4 respectively. The tray design procedure started by dividing the column into six zones taking as division points those trays where an input, output, or flow division exists, as shown in Figure 1. For each of the marked zones, the trays with the highest and the lowest liquid flow were selected to be designed. For zones 1 and 2 we used the standard design methodology because they contain only conventional trays. Zones 3 and 4 (corresponding to the prefractionator) and the zones 5 and 6 (corresponding to the main column adjacent to the dividing wall) were designed together because they were complementary parts of the same tray, and the diameter of the column in this region affects the operation of the zones in both sides of the wall. Due to this the zones corresponding to the central column, the prefractionator and the region adjacent to the wall were designed through an iterative process by adjusting the area and diameter of the column through flooding and weeping point tests using semi-empirical equations. The trays were optimized to obtain the smallest possible diameter to cover the needs of the flow. The main parameters to obtain after the design is the length (W) and position (Wd) of the wall, along with the length (Lw) and position (WDC) of the weir, which can be seen in Figure 2. Other parameters obtained were the height of the clearance and exit weir, the spacing between trays, the hole diameter and the pitch.

3. CFD simulations

The obtained design data was used to develop a representative geometry of each tray, in order to perform simulations on the operational hydrodynamic behavior of the column. The geometry of the trays was created using CATIA V5R20 and later was exported to Desing Modeler to be "healed", because the first is a specialized software in mechanical design for application in industry while the latter is specialized in simulation. Dimensional geometries were created with two plates as shown in Figure 3.

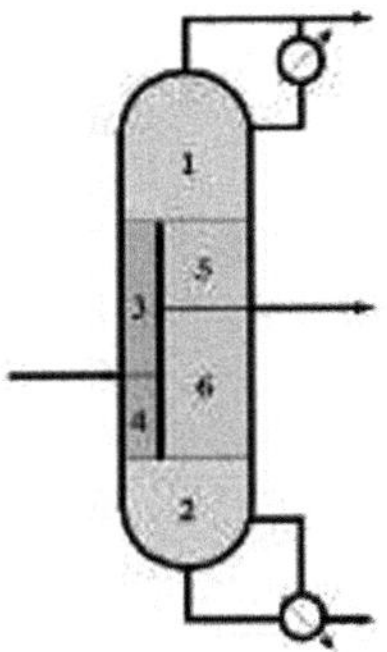

Figure 1. Definition of zones in the DWC

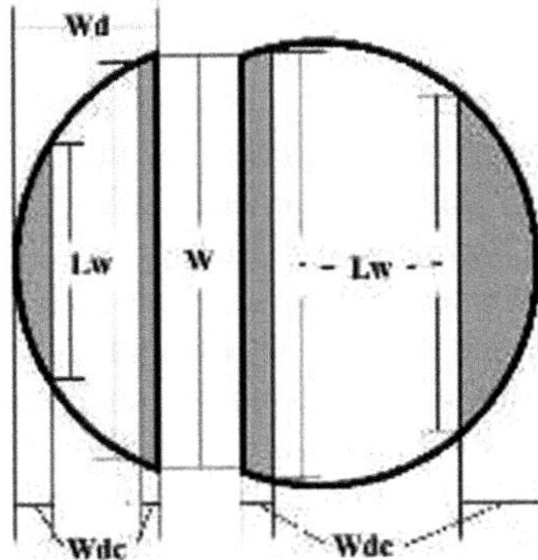

Figure 2. Physic design parameters for tray construction

Geometries were discretized using Meshing, refining the final mesh in perforated zones; meshes were bounded to obtain a distribution of cells with a more or less constant aspect ratio and acceptable skewness in cells, as shown in figure 4. Simulations were performed using the software Fluent, carried out in transient state, an Eulerian model was used for multiphase flow simulation and k-epsilon realizable model was used for turbulence. The trays were tested first using a water-air system to reduce the computational cost and subsequently with the hydrocarbon mixture to the operating conditions of each tray.

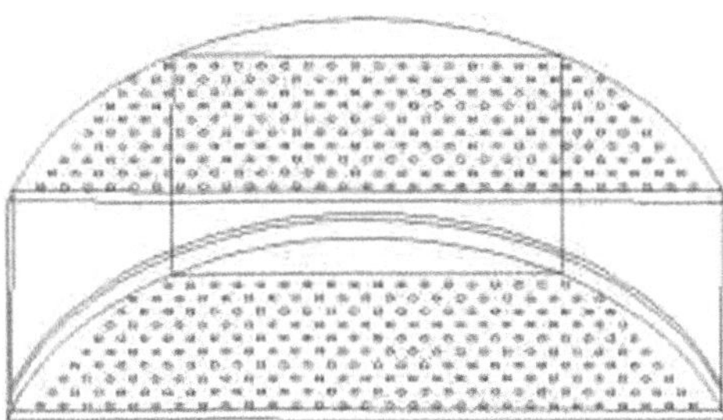

Figure 3. Example of geometry elaborated for tray simulation

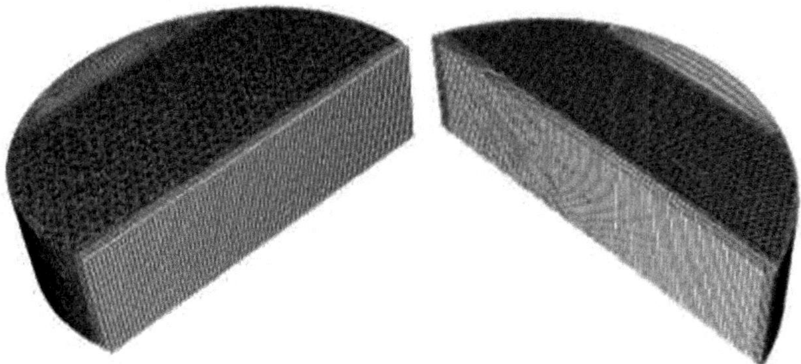

Figure 4. Mesh for tray simulation in main column (left) and prefractionator (right)

4. Results

The design of sieve trays for zones 1 and 2 resulted in a 4.5ft diameter column; thus, the design of the trays of other sections was performed taking this result as a basis, with the objective of homogenize the column diameter. After optimization of the transversal areas, it was obtained that a diameter of 4.5ft was suitable for operation of the column wall area. The trays were designed considering half-inch holes, a 2 in height of the exit weir, a 1.5 in inlet clearance and spacing between trays of 18 in. Preliminary tests made with water and air showed good hydrodynamic functioning in the trays, however the test with hydrocarbons mixture on operating conditions showed excess steam flow causing spray flooding on the column so the trays were redesigned using the new parameters. As consequence of the observation of the simulations the hole diameter was decreased to 0.375 in with a pitch of 1.13 in, both the inlet clearance and the exit weir height was increased in a half-inch and separation of trays was decreased to 12 in. With the new settings, the trays were redesigned and a column diameter of 5.5 in was obtained. Again trays were tested under the same methodology as the previous ones, showing a marked improvement in the operation of the column.

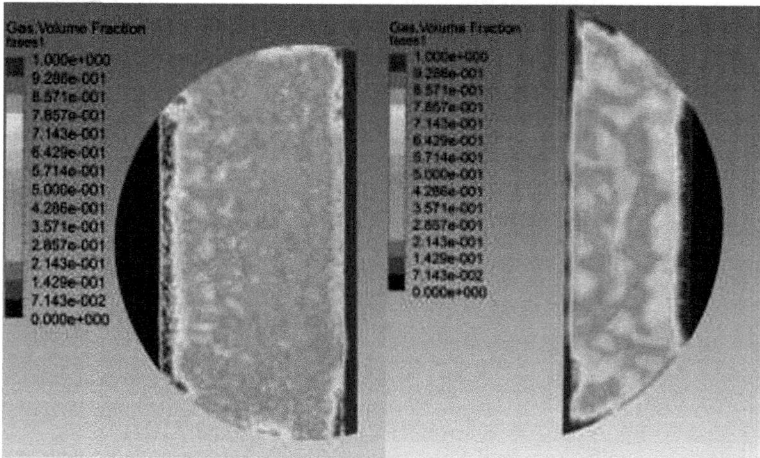

Figure 5. Volume fraction contours in simulated trays

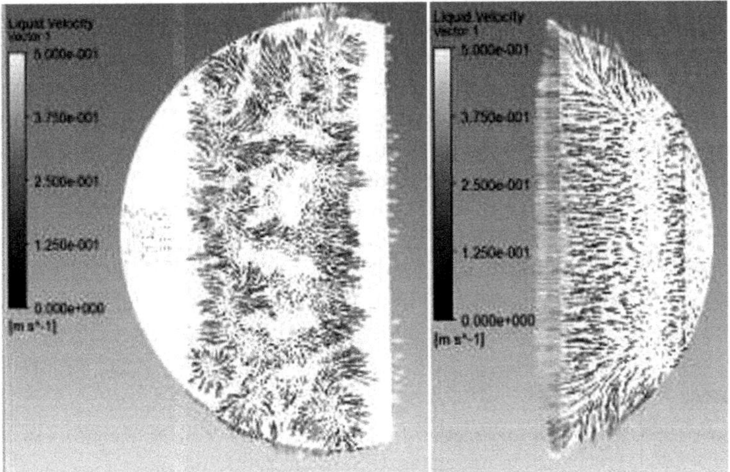

Figure 6. Vectors velocity in liquid surface during DWC operation

Figure 5 shows the profiles of the phases in the trays corresponding to the wall zone, it can be seen that the tray has a uniform distribution and a good mixing of the phases, with an average volume fraction of 0.43 in the central column and 0.58 in the prefractionator. Figure 6 shows the velocity vectors of the fluid on the trays. In this Figure it can also be seen that the velocity is kept uniform along the tray indicating that there are no stagnant areas in any region, this stimulates mixing phases on the plate and increases efficiency. Figure 7 shows the fluid flow lines, it can be seen that the mixed zone is greater near the entrance of the liquid to the plate, the cross flow causes a drop of liquid against the top wall while still advancing to the bottom creating a high turbulence in this area and increasing the height of the liquid seal.

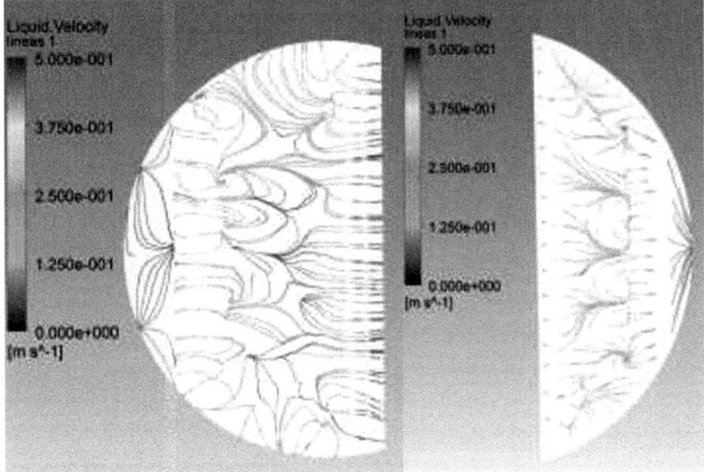

Figure 7. Stream lines of liquid in divided wall zone trays

5. Conclusions

Sieve trays for a dividing wall column were designed and simulated. The design methodology was obtained as a modification of the procedure proposed by Kister for conventional distillation columns. During designing, the trays were tested to avoid both flooding and weeping. Designed trays were tested using CFD simulations to observe its hydrodynamic performance during operation of the column. The trays that failed the test were redesigned taking into account the new hydrodynamic parameters obtained during the simulations. The final distillation column has a diameter of 5.5 ft with spacing trays of 12 in and hole diameter of 0.375 in. The final simulation results showed good hydrodynamic performance of the finished trays. Thus, the proposed method is an efficient tool for the preliminar design of the complex trays required for the dividing wall columns. By the other hand, CFD tests have been presented as an important tool for a more specialized analysis of the performance of the trays on a DWC.

References

E.W. Luster, 1933, Apparatus for Practionating Cracked Products, U.S. Patent 1,915,681.

R.O. Wright, 1949, Fractionation Apparatus, U.S. Patent 2,471,134.

G. Kaibel, 1987, Distillation Column with Vertical Partitions, Chemical Engineering Technology, 10, 1, 92-98.

Z. Olujic, M. Jödecke, A. Shilkin, G. Schuch, B. Kaibel, 2009, Equipment improvement trends in distillation, Chemical Engineering and Processing, 48, 6, 1089-1104.

I. Dejanovic, Lj. Matijasevic, Z. Olujic, 2010, Dividing wall column - A breakthrough towards sustainable distilling, Chemical Engineering and Processing, 49, 6, 559-580.

Y. Wang, S. Du, H. Zhu, H. Ma, S. Zuo, 2012, CFD simulation of hydraulics of dividing wall sieve trays, Advances Materials Research, 476-478, 1345-1350.

H.Z. Kister, 1992, Distillation Design, Mc Graw Hill, Boston, U.S.A., 259 – 372.

F.I. Gómez-Castro, M.A. Rodríguez-Ángeles, J.G. Segovia-Hernández, C. Gutiérrez-Antonio, A. Briones-Ramírez, 2011, Optimal Designs of Multiple Divided Wall Columns, Chemical Engineering and Technology, 34, 12, 2051-2058.

Jiří Jaromír Klemeš, Petar Sabev Varbanov and Peng Yen Liew (Editors)
Proceedings of the 24th European Symposium on Computer Aided Process Engineering – ESCAPE 24
June 15-18, 2014, Budapest, Hungary.

Economic Optimisation of Seawater Reverse Osmosis Desalination with Boron Rejection

Georgios Patroklou, Iqbal M. Mujtaba*

School of Engineering, University of Bradford, West Yorkshire BD7 1DP, UK
I.M.Mujtaba@bradford.ac.uk

Abstract

Reverse Osmosis (RO) process is widely used for seawater desalination. In this work, we considered a small scale SWRO (Spiral Wound Reverse Osmosis) desalination unit which is enough to cover the need of a medium size hotel complex at Limassol city in Cyprus. The pH of the seawater in the region is 7.95 and the temperature varies from 17 to 27 °C. The aim of this study is to identify the configuration of the RO process and the optimum operating parameters such as pH and pressure that can minimise the total annualised cost of the process subject to acceptable quality of freshwater in terms of boron concentrations throughout the year. For this purpose, the mathematical model for boron rejection developed earlier by the authors is used but incorporates cost functions. The model is based on solution-diffusion model which can describe solvent and solute transport mechanism through the membranes. With the variation of seasonal seawater temperature, the key finding of this study was that by choosing the right combination of pH and pressure, substantial economical savings up to 16 % could be achieved.

Keywords: Reverse osmosis; Boron rejection; Modelling; Economic optimisation.

1. Introduction

Nonlinear growth in population and improved standards of living are impacting the freshwater demand and are putting serious strain on the limited quantity of naturally available freshwater. With most of the accessible water around us being saline (94 percent of the world's water), desalination technology is vital for our sustainability. Among different processes, desalination via RO is a membrane separation process for making freshwater from seawater which has seen significant growth in recent years (Desalination Market, 2010).

Boron is an important element for growth of living being, although excessive exposure of it can cause detrimental effects to plants, animals and humans. It exists in water as boric acid and borate ions and the consumption of water with high boron concentrations leads to toxicological effects on human's health (Mane et al., 2009). For this reason, removal of boron from freshwater (produced by desalination techniques) by an acceptable level (Table 1) is very important. There are several alternative processes for boron removal from water including softening, coagulation, electrodialysis, activated carbon and RO membranes (Kabay et al., 2010). Boron rejection by RO process is highly depended on the temperature, pressure and the boric acid/borate ion ratio which is mainly function of seawater pH. With increasing pH and operating pressure of the feed water, the boron rejection increases and with increasing feed water temperature the boron rejection decreases (Patroklou et al., 2013).

Table 1. Regulations for boron in drinking water (Tu et al., 2010)

Region	Maximum boron concentration (mg//L)	Regulation issued year
European Union (EU)	1.0	1998
Australia	4.0	2004
Abu Dhabi	1.5	2001
U. S. A. (California)	1.5	2001
Japan	1.5	2000
WHO recommendation	0.3	1990
	2.4	2011

Here, we considered a design and operation of a small scale SWRO desalination unit with a capacity of 270 m^3/day of freshwater. The production target is based on the demand of a medium size hotel complex in Cyprus. The selection of this specific geographic region has to do with available data related to seawater temperature, salinity and pH levels. The average pH of Mediterranean Sea is 7.95 and the winter and summer temperature is 17 °C and 27 °C. Model based technique is used to obtain the optimum operating parameters such as pH and pressure which minimises the total annualised cost of the RO process subject to acceptable quality of freshwater in terms of boron concentrations. For this purpose, the mathematical model developed by the authors (Patroklou et al., 2013) is used.

2. RO Boron Rejection Model

For the purpose of completeness, Patroklou et al. (2013) model is presented here in brief. Refer to original reference for the explanation of each equations and nomenclatures.

$$P_W = A_0 e^{\left(-\frac{E_A}{R}\left(\frac{1}{T}-\frac{1}{298.15}\right)\right)}\left(\frac{10^{-3}}{24\times 60\times 60}\right) \tag{1}$$

$$P_S = B_{st0} e^{\left(-\frac{E_{Bst}}{R}\left(\frac{1}{T}-\frac{1}{298.15}\right)\right)}\left(\frac{10^{-3}}{24\times 60\times 60}\right) \tag{2}$$

$$\pi_F = \left(0.6955+0.0025(T-273.15)\right)\times 10^8 \times \frac{C_{SF}}{\rho} \tag{3}$$

$$\pi_P = \left(0.6955+0.0025(T-273.15)\right)\times 10^8 \times \frac{C_{SP}}{\rho} \tag{4}$$

$$\Delta\pi = \pi_F - \pi_P \tag{5}$$

$$J_W = P_W(\Delta P - \Delta\pi) \tag{6}$$

$$K_S = 1.63\times 10^{-3} Q_F^{0.4053} \tag{7}$$

$$J_S = P_S(C_{SM} - C_{SP}) \tag{8}$$

$$\frac{C_{SM}-C_{SP}}{C_{SF}-C_{SP}} = e^{\left(\frac{J_W}{K_S}\right)} \tag{9}$$

$$pH = pK_a + \log \frac{C_{Bborate}}{C_{Bboric}}; \qquad C_{BF} = C_{Bborate} + C_{Bboric} \tag{10}$$

$$pK_a = \frac{2291.9}{T} + 0.01756 - 3.385 - 3.904 \times C_{SM}^{\frac{1}{3}} \tag{11}$$

$$C_{Bboric} = \frac{C_{BF}}{1 + 10^{(pH - pK_a)}} \tag{12}$$

$$\alpha_0 = \frac{C_{Bboric}}{C_{BF}}; \qquad \alpha_1 = \frac{C_{Bborate}}{C_{BF}}; \qquad \alpha_0 + \alpha_1 = 1 \tag{13}$$

$$K_S = 0.97 K_B; \; K_{BT} = K_{B0} e^{(0.04(T - 298.15))} \tag{14}$$

$$P_B = \alpha_0 P_{Bboric} e^{(0.051(T - 298.15))} + \alpha_1 P_{Bborate} e^{(0.033(T - 298.15))} \tag{15}$$

$$BR = 1 - \frac{C_{BP}}{C_{BF}} \tag{16}$$

3. Economic Cost Function

The total annualized cost is the combination of the capital and operating costs for one year of operation and is presented as (Sassi, 2012):

$$TAC = (C_{WPT} + C_{pu} + C_{me})1.411 \times 0.08 + OC_{pu} + OC_{me} + OC_{ch} + OC_{sc} \tag{17}$$

Pump or turbine (energy recovery) capital cost:

$$C_{pu} = 52 Q_{HP} \, \Delta P_{HP} \tag{18}$$

where, Q_{HP} is the flow entering the pump or turbine (m^3/h), ΔP_{HP} pressure difference across the pump or turbine in (bar). Membrane and pressure vessels cost ($) is given by:

$$C_{me} = sN(C_{mele} n_e + C_{PV}) \tag{19}$$

where, s represents the number of stages, N represents the number of pressure vessels. C_{mele} represents the membrane module cost, n_e represents the number of elements in each pressure vessel, C_{pv} represents the pressure vessel capital cost. Feed pre-treatment cost ($) is given by:

$$C_{WPT} = 996(Q_{f,t} 24)^{0.8} \tag{20}$$

where, $Q_{f,t}$ is the feed flow to RO unit in (m^3/h). Net pumping cost ($/year) is:

$$OC_{pu} = E_{pu} E_c \tag{21}$$

where, E_{pu} represents the annual electricity consumption by pump (kWh). E_c represents the electricity price ($/kWh). Membrane replacement cost ($/year), Chemical treatment cost ($/year) and Annual Spares cost ($/year) are:

$$OC_{me} = 0.2 C_{me} \tag{22}$$

$$OC_{che} = Q_{f,t} l_f 24 \times 365 \times 0.018 \tag{23}$$

$$OC_{sc} = Q_{p,t} l_f \, 24 \times 365 \times 0.033 \tag{24}$$

where, $Q_{p,t}$ is the total permeate flow (m^3/h).

4. Case Study

4.1. Scenario 1 (base case)

The first scenario will be investigating the TAC breakdown of the unit, while operating at regional (Limassol Cyprus) annual highest temperature of 27 °C, and at pH of 7.95 and at 42 bar pressure. The remaining input data is given in Table 2. The seawater salinity is 42000 ppm and the boron concentration is 6.5 mg/L which is the regional boron concentration according to Jaehong et al. (2009). For the given input data it will be interesting to see the boron concentration in the desalinated water throughout the year. The number of pressure vessels (determining the configuration of RO) is found to be 68 which is the required minimum to produce the required amount of freshwater (11.25 m^3/d = 270 m^3/d). Table 3 shows that the boron concentration (as calculated by the model) limit is achieved in most months. However, in August with peak temperature (27 °C), the boron concentration level in the permeate stream was 1.19 mg/L (higher than the 1 mg/L limit of the EU Union, Table 1) although a boron rejection of 81.76 % is achieved.

Table 2. Input Data

Total System Feed Flow	$Q_{f,t}$	141.875
Pump efficiency	η_{pu}	0.8
Total System Permeate Flow	$Q_{p,t}$	11.25
Number of Stages	s	1
Membrane module cost	C_{mele}	$700.00
number of elements in each pressure vessel	n_e	1
Electricity price	E_c	$0.24/kWh
System Load Factor	l_f	0.607

Table 3. Boron concentration in the permeate (freshwater) throughout the year

Temp C	Jan 18	Feb 17	Apr 18	May 20	June 24	July 26	Aug 27	Oct 25	Nov 22	Dec 19
Boron mg/l	0.65	0.61	0.65	0.75	0.98	1.11	1.19	1.04	0.86	0.70

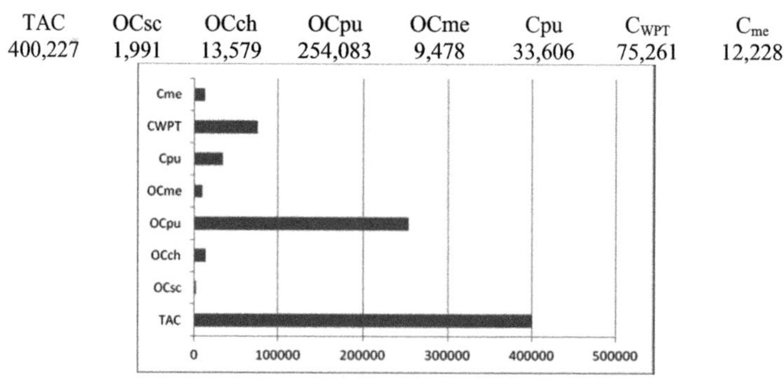

Figure 1. Total Annulaised Cost and Other Cost Elements (Scenario 1)

Figure 1 shows the annualised cost of the unit to be \$ 400,227 while its highest constituent seems to be the pumping cost (\$ 254,083), followed by the feed water pre-treatment cost (\$ 75,261). The third highest is the high pressure pump capital cost (\$ 33,606). As can be seen, the pumping cost is about 63.48 % of the TAC while the capital cost of High Pressure (HP) pump is only about 8.40 %.

The consequence of increasing the feed water pH to 9.5 on Boron rejection and TAC is also studied. Note, the model used in this work is not able to predict the increase in chemical treatment costs due to increase in pH. However, it is noted by Hyung and Kim (2006) that by artificially increasing the pH of the feed water beyond the 9.5 limit, scaling problems start to appear at the hardware of the system causing extra replacement and maintenance costs but the cost of increasing the pH up to 9.5 is negligible. With pH = 9.5 the boron rejection was improved to 88.65 % from 81.76 % and the resulting permeate boron concentration was reduced to 0.74 mg/L from 1.19 mg/L. This is within the 1mg/L limit of the EU, but is higher than the WHO guideline of 0.5 mg/L (Table 1).

4.2. Scenario 2

For the same RO configuration (as in scenario 1), here, 93.07 % boron rejection is set, in order to produce permeate (freshwater) with boron concentration of 0.45 mg/L (below WHO recommended limit). For given seawater temperature of 27 °C and at average pH level of 7.95, optimum pressure is selected and the effect of it on the TAC and other cost components is evaluated. The results are shown in Fig. 2. It can be seen that TAC, compared with the scenario 1, is increased significantly by 42 %. This increase is partially due to the increase of the pumping cost and the pump capital cost by over 57 % due to pressure increase by about 55 % (from 42 bar to 65 bar).

4.3. Scenario 3

Again, for the same RO configuration and for a given pH of 9.5 and boron rejection of 93.07 %, the aim of this simulation is to find the required pressure and to evaluate the process economy. The results are shown in Figure 3. It can be seen that TAC, compared with the scenario 1, is increased by just 19 %. This increase is again due to the increase in the pumping cost and the pump capital cost by over 26 % due to pressure increase by about 24 %. Clearly, the results obtained by scenario 3 are much better (in terms of costs) compared to scenario 2. For the same water quality (in terms of boron concentration), scenario 3 offers 16 % savings in TAC compared to that given by scenario 2.

Optimum P	TAC	OCsc	OCch	OCpu	OCme	Cpu	CWPT	Cme
65 bar	566362	1992	13579	400810	9478	53014	75261	12228

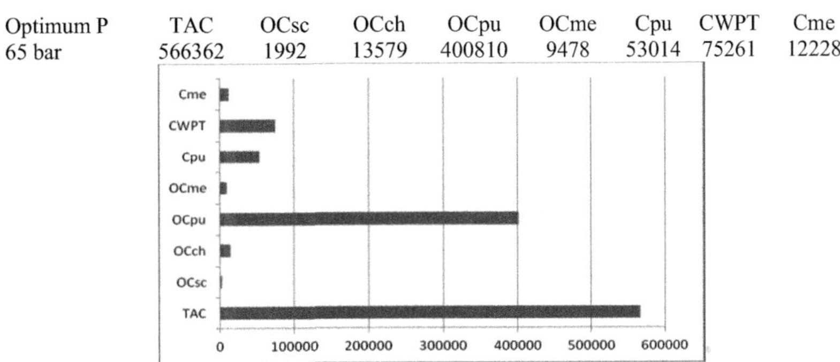

Figure 2. Total Annulaised Cost and Other Cost Elements (Scenario 2)

Optimum P	TAC	OCsc	OCch	OCpu	OCme	Cpu	CWPT	Cme
52 bar	476414	1992	13579	321369	9478	42506	75261	12228

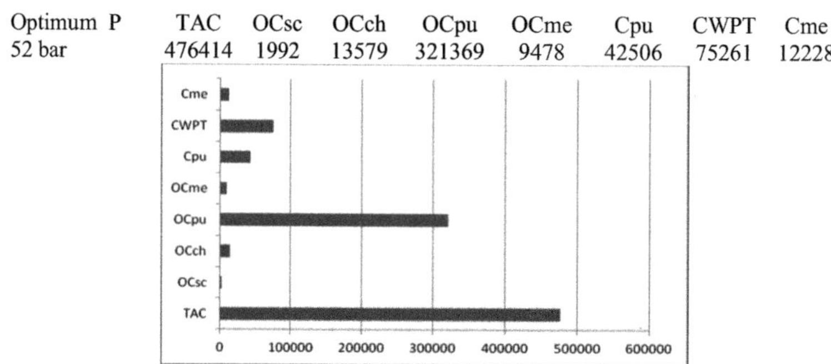

Figure 3. Total Annulaised Cost and Other Cost Elements (Scenario 3)

5. Conclusions

In this work, a reliable model for RO desalination process based on well known solution- diffusion model, incorporating a correlation for effective boron rejection (recently developed by the authors) and cost functions is used to carry out economic optimisation of a small scale RO desalination process producing sufficient amount of freshwater for a medium size hotel complex in Cyprus. Boron rejection evaluated at moderate pressure for the whole year shows that the European Union boron limit on drinking water could not be achieved for about 4 months (July to October) of the season without increasing the pH to the maximum recommended limit of 9.5. However, this would not achieve the WHO boron concentration limit. Through further simulations optimum pressures for two pH values are evaluated which would meet the WHO boron concentration limit and the economic analysis are carried out for all cases. It is found that the maximum pH case (9.5) leads to moderate operating pressure (52 bar as opposed to 65 bar) leading to 16 % saving in the total annualized cost (capital and operating).

References

Desalination Market, 2010, Global Forecast and Analysis, Global Water Intelligence, <www.globalwaterintel.com> accessed on 20/01/2013

H. Hyung, J.H. Kim, 2006, A mechanistic study on boron rejection by sea water reverse osmosis membranes, Journal of Membrane Science, 286, 269-278.

K. Jaehong, H. Hoon, W. Mark, 2009, Boron Rejection by Reverse Osmosis Membranes: National Reconnaissance and Mechanism Study, US Department of the Interior Bureau of Reclamation, US.

N. Kabay, E. Guler, M. Bryjak, 2010, Boron in seawater and methods for its separation - A review, Desalination, 261, 212-217

P. Mane, P. Park, H. Hyung, J.C. Brown, J. Kim, 2009, Modelling boron rejection in pilot- and full-scale reverse osmosis desalination processes, Journal of Membrane Science, 338,119-127.

G. Patroklou, K.M. Sassi, I.M. Mujtaba, 2013, Simulation of boron rejection by seawater reverse osmosis desalination, Chemical Engineering Transactions, 32, 1873-1878

K.M. Sassi, 2012, Optimal Scheduling, Design, Operation and Control of Reverse Osmosis based Desalination, PhD Thesis, University of Bradford, UK.

K.L Tu, L.D. Nghiem, A.R. Chivas, 2011, Coupling effects of feed solution pH and ionic strength on the rejection of boron by NF/RO membranes, Chemical Engineering Journal, 168, 700-706.

Jiří Jaromír Klemeš, Petar Sabev Varbanov and Peng Yen Liew (Editors)
Proceedings of the 24th European Symposium on Computer Aided Process Engineering – ESCAPE 24
June 15-18, 2014, Budapest, Hungary.

Suitable Process Modelling for Proper Multi-Objective Optimization of Process Flow Sheets

Zorka Novak Pintarič*, Zdravko Kravanja

University of Maribor, Faculty of Chemistry and Chemical Engineering, Smetanova 17, SI-2000 Maribor, Slovenia
zorka.novak@um.si

Abstract

This paper presents the use of different economic criteria during the generation of the Pareto optimal solutions within the multi-objective optimization of process flow sheets. It is shown that various economic criteria have a significant effect on the set of the Pareto solutions, which differ in the maximum values of the selected environmental criterion as well as in the ranges of their values. The reasons for variations are different stationary conditions of economic criteria. However, significant differences could be observed only if sufficiently accurate and precise process models were used, in which proper relations were established between the investment and the cash flow. In this case, the net present value would be the most appropriate economic measure for multi-objective optimization of process flow sheets.

Keywords: multi-objective optimization, net present value, different Pareto curves

1. Introduction

Multi-objective optimization recently became an important tool for decision-making through generating a set of non-dominant (Pareto) solutions from which a compromise process design could be selected. A lot of work has been done on solving practical industrial problems for multiple objectives; for example, Tokos et al. (2012) performed a bi-objective optimization of water network within the brewery. While the measures of the economic performance are well established, the selection of the environmental criteria is more or less optional, therefore several environmental measures were defined and applied recently, such as the Environmental Performance Index (Hsu et al., 2013), and various footprints (Čuček et al., 2012). As the number of the objectives can be very large, some authors developed the reduction techniques for eliminating the non-conflicting objectives and keeping only the conflicting ones (Kostin et al., 2012).

The rules for using the economic criteria within a single- and multi-objective optimization are stringent because only some of them are suitable and appropriate for process flow sheet optimization. In our previous work (Kasaš et al., 2012) it was established: 1) the type of the economic criterion used in the process model is of decisive importance for the economic, operational and environmental efficiencies of optimal process flow sheet, and 2) the accuracy and preciseness of process models are crucial for establishing the correct relationship between the investment and cash flow, and consequently, for generating proper compromises during a single-objective optimization. In this contribution, our research was extended to process flow sheet optimization regarding more than one objective. It is shown that different economic criteria generate different Pareto curves, and that the net present value should be used as the most appropriate economic objective during the multi-objective optimization of process flow sheets.

2. Generating Pareto curves with different economic criteria

Assume the two-criteria optimization where one criterion maximizes the economic performance (f_{econ}) while the other one minimizes the environmental impact (f_{env}). Both criteria can be optimized independently, yielding the two extreme points: $\left(f_{econ}^{UP}, f_{env}^{UP}\right)$ when maximizing the economic performance, Eq. (1a), and $\left(f_{econ}^{LO}, f_{env}^{LO}\right)$ when minimizing the environmental impact, Eq. (1b). These two points would be different only if both criteria are conflicting, otherwise a single optimal solution would be obtained with a maximum value of f_{econ} and minimum value of f_{env}.

$$
\begin{array}{llll}
\max f_{econ} & & \min f_{env} & \\
\text{s. t.} & & \text{s. t.} & \\
h(x)=0 & \text{(a)} & h(x)=0 & \text{(b)} \\
g(x)\leq 0 & & g(x)\leq 0 & \\
x\in \Re & & x\in \Re &
\end{array}
\qquad (1)
$$

Figure 1 represents the courses of both criteria with respect to the investment. A bold dashed line represents the environmental criterion which decreases (improves) with the investment because, for example, the emissions could be reduced by investing money. A continuous line represents the economic criterion which achieves its maximum value f_{econ}^{UP}, and decreases (worsen) at higher investment levels.

If the criteria are conflicting, several non-dominant solutions may be generated between the two extreme solutions, forming a Pareto curve of non-dominant solutions (shaded region in Figure 1). The most used method for generating a set of Pareto solutions is the epsilon-constraint method, where optimization problem is optimized for one objective while the other is added to the constraints and limited with a parameter ε (Eq.(0)):

$$
\begin{array}{l}
\max f_{econ} \\
\text{s. t.} \\
f_{env} \leq \varepsilon \\
h(x)=0,\ g(x)\leq 0 \\
x\in \Re
\end{array}
\qquad (2)
$$

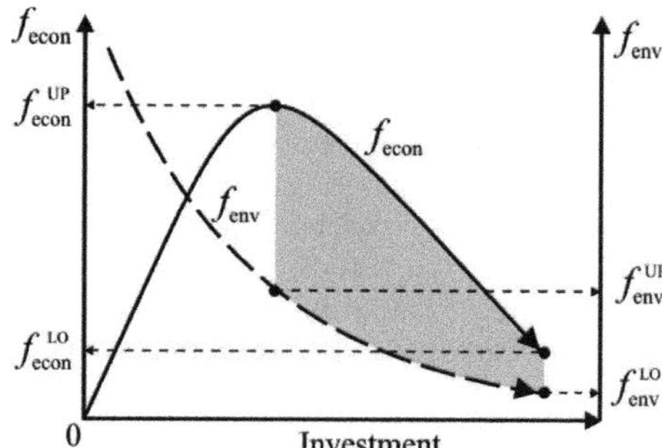

Figure 1. Conflicting criteria vs. investment

Parameter ε is varied between the upper and lower bounds, $f_{\text{env}}^{\text{LO}} \leq \varepsilon \leq f_{\text{env}}^{\text{UP}}$, in the specified increments.

Several economic criteria are normally used for process flow sheet optimization. They could be classified as qualitative, e.g. the internal rate of return (IRR) and the payback time, the quantitative, e.g. the profit before tax (PB) and the total annual cost (TAC), and the compromise criteria, such as the net present value (NPV). It was shown in our previous work (Kasaš et al., 2012), that various economic objectives generate different optimal solutions during a single-objective optimization due to different stationary conditions of the economic criteria. In addition, process flow sheet models should be precise and accurate enough to produce monotonically increasing cash flow function vs. investment, and flat derivative curve. Only in this case significant differences between optimal solutions would be observed. Too simplified and aggregated process models would generate steep derivative curve and negligible differences. Figure 2 presents a flat cash flow derivative curve together with the stationary conditions for three specific economic criteria: IRR, NPV and PB.

It follows from Figure 2 that the investment levels of optimal solutions obtained by maximizing IRR, NPV and PB (or TAC), obey the following rule:

$$I_{\text{IRR}} \leq I_{\text{NPV}} \leq I_{\text{PB (or TAC)}} \tag{3}$$

This means that the maximum peak of the economic objective curve in Figure 1 would occur at the lowest investment level when maximizing IRR, at intermediate level for NPV, and at the highest level when maximizing PB. Considering also a decreasing shape of the environmental curve in Figure 1, it could be concluded that the upper value of the environmental impact will be the highest when using the IRR as the economic objective, and the lowest when using the profit or TAC. The maximum NPV solution would have the intermediate upper value of the environmental impact.

$$\left(f_{\text{env}}^{\text{UP}}\right)_{\text{PB (or TAC)}} \leq \left(f_{\text{env}}^{\text{UP}}\right)_{\text{NPV}} \leq \left(f_{\text{env}}^{\text{UP}}\right)_{\text{IRR}} \tag{4}$$

The lowest value of the environmental impact ($f_{\text{env}}^{\text{LO}}$) is independent on the economic criteria used, and is usually obtained when any design variable reaches its lower or upper bound, e.g. the minimum approach temperature or the upper value of the reactor's volume. Therefore, the range of the environmental impact values would be the largest

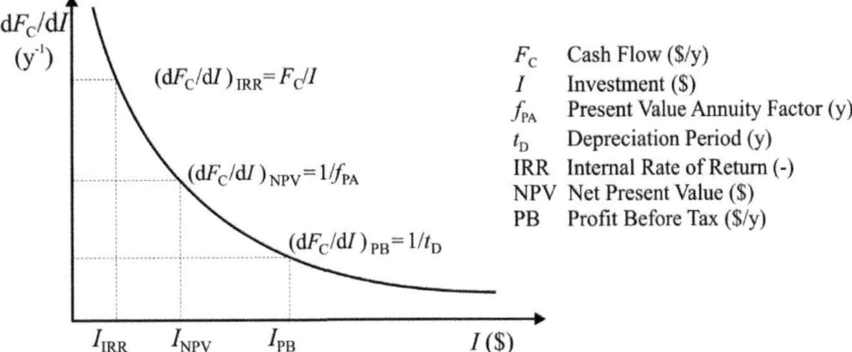

Figure 2. Cash flow derivative curve and stationary conditions for IRR, NPV and PB

when a set of Pareto solutions would be generated by the IRR criterion, and the smallest when using the profit or TAC criteria.

$$\left(f_{\text{env}}^{\text{UP}} - f_{\text{env}}^{\text{LO}}\right)_{\text{PB (or TAC)}} \leq \left(f_{\text{env}}^{\text{UP}} - f_{\text{env}}^{\text{LO}}\right)_{\text{NPV}} \leq \left(f_{\text{env}}^{\text{UP}} - f_{\text{env}}^{\text{LO}}\right)_{\text{IRR}} \tag{5}$$

Similarly as in the case of a single-objective optimization, it could be expected during the multi-objective optimization that the above differences would be significant only if process flow sheet model would involve sufficient trade-offs between the investment and cash flow generated, which could only be achieved if the precise and accurate process models were used.

3. Case study 1 – Process flow sheet design

In this case study, a process flow sheet design problem (Figure 3) was firstly solved by using a stoichiometric reactor model with fixed conversion.

Pareto curves were generated using the Global Warming Potential (GWP) as an environmental measure, and the PB, NPV or IRR as the economic objective. GWP was calculated as the annual equivalent CO_2 emission originating from the utility usage, and the emission of the inert component C in the purge stream. The minimization of GWP generated its lower value of 816,344 t/y, while the upper values obtained when maximizing PB, NPV or IRR were as follows: 834,045 t/y, 835,795 t/y and 846,101 t/y, respectively. The Pareto solutions generated between the extreme GWP points are shown in Figure 4, indicating that very similar shapes were obtained by using three economic criteria. Note that in the Pareto curves obtained by the TAC and IRR, the values in the y-axes were converted into the corresponding NPVs after optimization in order to show all three Pareto curves within the same graph.

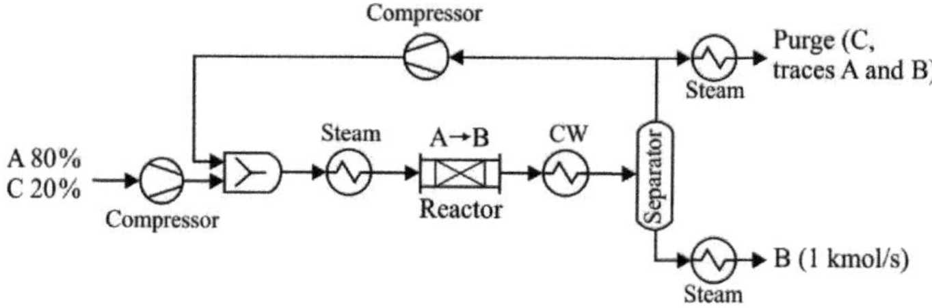

Figure 3. Process flow sheet of case study 1

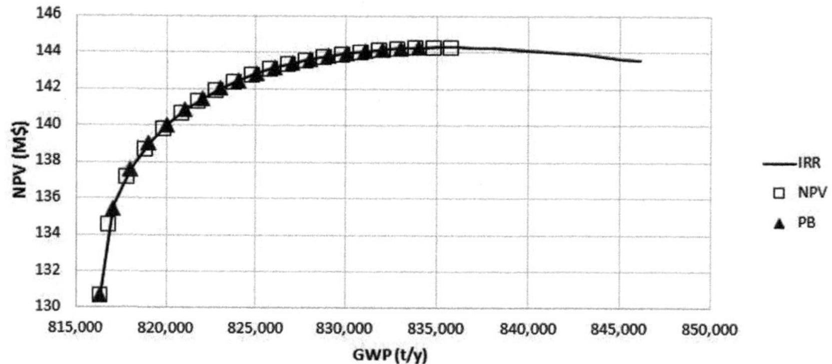

Figure 4. Pareto curves of simplified flow sheet model

Similar Pareto curves resulted from the simplified and aggregated process model with inadequate relationship between the reactor's investment, expressed as a function of the reactor's flow rate, and the benefits achieved. Namely, the increased investment could not improve the conversion in the stoichiometric reactor, but rather increased the recycle flow rate which resulted in very steep cash flow derivative curve.

In the next step, the stoichiometic reactor model was replaced by the kinetic one, and minimum utility consumption targeting was included. Both changes resulted in better trade-offs because larger/more expensive reactor resulted in the increased conversion, yielding monotonically increasing cash flow function, and flat derivative. Heat integration also positively contributed to these effects. As the result, the Pareto curves were significantly different regarding the ranges of the NPV values as well as the GWP values (Figure 5).

4. Case study 2 – Heat Exchanger Network design

In this case study, a heat exchanger network (HEN) was designed using the TAC, NPV or IRR as the economic objectives. The GWP was applied as an environmental measure, expressed as the annual equivalent CO_2 emission originating from the utility usage, and the HEN construction.

Minimization of GWP yielded its lowest possible value of 3592 t/y, while the maximum values obtained were 3603 t/y by TAC minimization, 3615 t/y by NPV maximization, and 4102 t/y when maximizing IRR. Figure 7 represents the Pareto curves obtained by the three economic criteria, of which the IRR curve was the most outstanding regarding the ranges of the GWP values.

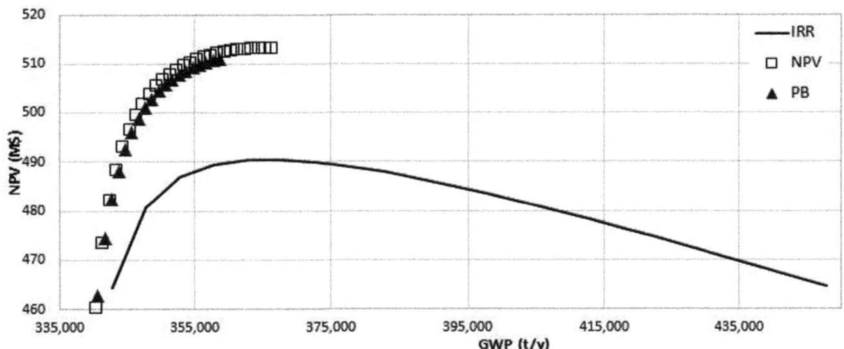

Figure 5. Pareto curves of heat integrated flow sheet with the kinetic reactor model

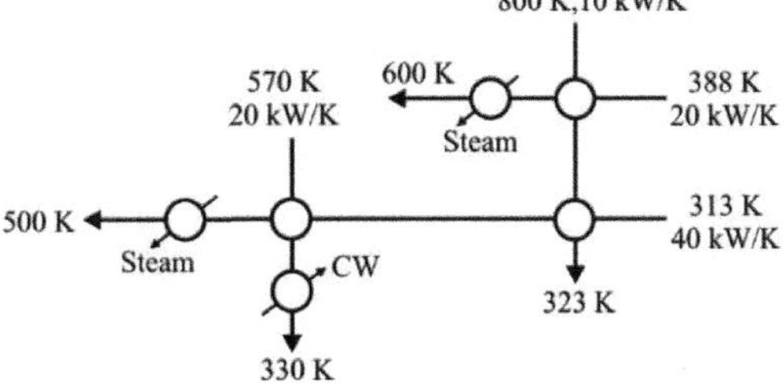

Figure 6. Heat exchanger network of case study 2

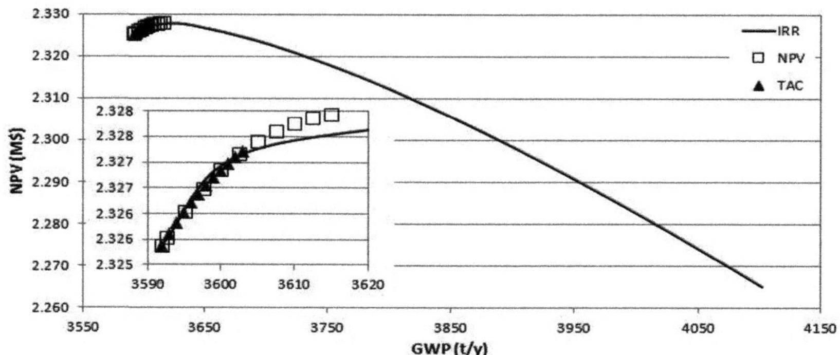

Figure 7. Pareto curves of HEN example

The HEN design model is known for its well-established trade-offs. The increasing investment, i.e. the heat exchanger area, resulted in the increased level of heat integration, decreased utility consumption, and consequently, lower GWP. The resulting cash flow curve increased monotonically with the investment which resulted in a flat derivative curve, and substantially different Pareto curves.

5. Conclusions

In this paper, the Pareto curves were generated by using different economic criteria for optimizing the economic performance. It was shown that the economic objective had a significant impact on the Pareto curves generated during the multi-objective optimization only if sufficiently accurate and precise process models were used. Qualitative criteria, such as the IRR, produced the Pareto curves with the widest range of the environmental objective values, while the quantitative criteria, such as the profit or cost, the smallest range. The NPV criterion produced the intermediate Pareto curves which are close to the environmentally most friendly solutions obtained by the profit. Considering also the fact that the NPV establishes the suitable compromises between the process profitability and the long-term sustainable cash flow generation, it could be concluded that the NPV would be the most appropriate economic criterion for multi-objective optimization. It establishes proper trade-offs between the environmental impacts, profitability, and sustainable financial growth of the non-dominant optimal process designs.

References

L. Čuček, J. J. Klemes, Z. Kravanja, 2012, A Review of Footprint Analysis Tools for Monitoring Impacts on Sustainability, Journal of Cleaner Production, 34, 9-20.

A. Hsu, A. LLoyd, J. W. Emerson, 2013, What progress have we made since Rio? Results from the 2012 Environmental Performance Index (EPI) and Pilot Trend EPI, Environmental Science and Policy, 33, 171-185.

M. Kasaš, Z. Kravanja, Z. Novak Pintarič, 2012, Achieving Profitably, Operationally, and Environmentally Compromise Flow-Sheet Designs by a Single-Criterion Optimization, AIChE Journal, 58, 7, 2131-2141.

A. Kostin, G. Guillen-Gozalbez, F. D. Mele, L. Jimenez, 2012, Objective Reduction in Multi-Criteria Optimization of Integrated Bioethanol-Sugar Supply Chains, Computer Aided Chemical Engineering, 30, 1-5.

H. Tokos, Z. N. Pintarič, Y. Yang, 2012, Bi-objective MINLP Optimization of an Industrial Water Network via Benchmarking,Computer Aided Chemical Engineering, 31, 475-479.

Jiří Jaromír Klemeš, Petar Sabev Varbanov and Peng Yen Liew (Editors)
Proceedings of the 24th European Symposium on Computer Aided Process Engineering – ESCAPE 24
June 15-18, 2014, Budapest, Hungary.

Computational Fluid Dynamics Modeling for Chromatographic Purification of Free Lutein

Weerapong Choopakdee[a], Phattanon Prasitchoke[b], Artiwan Shotipruk[a], Pimporn Ponpesh[a,*]

[a]*Chemical Engineering Research Unit for Value Adding of Bioresources, Department of Chemical Engineering, Faculty of Engineering, Chulalongkorn University, Phayathai Rd., Patumwan, Bangkok, 10330, Thailand*

[b]*PTT Global Chemical Public Company Limited, Muang Rayong, Rayong, 21150, Thailand*

pimporn.p@chula.ac.th

Abstract

Computational Fluid Dynamics (CFD) modeling has been applied to investigate the transport phenomena of free lutein purification in the preparative chromatography column. The mass transfer in the column was solved by the Ideal and Equilibrium Dispersive Models with user defined functions (UDF) of linear adsorption isotherm. In addition, the laminar flow model was applied to simulate the momentum transfer. It was found that the Equilibrium Dispersive Model (EDM) incorporating the linear adsorption isotherm and the laminar flow model could successfully predict the chromatographic and flow behaviors of free lutein. The models were applied in further analysis of the effects of flow rate, column porosity, and column height on the purification efficiency.

Keywords: column chromatography, computational fluid dynamics, free lutein

1. Introduction

Lutein, an antioxidant in carotenoid family, has been recognized for its health benefits such as lowering risk of cancers, enhancing immune function (Slattery et al., 2000), and preventing eye damage from UV blue light (Bhaskaran and Mohan, 2007). While lutein is present in certain fruits and vegetables, one of the most abundant and economical plant sources of lutein is marigold flowers (Tagetes erecta L.) (Khachik, 2007). Lutein is normally found in esterified form with fatty acids. It must be sponified to free lutein and purified to achieve more than 90 % purity to be suitable for human consumption (Khachik, 2007).

Over the past decade, several studies have focused on recrystallization as a purification method for free lutein from the sponified marigold oleoresin. Although this method can yield free lutein with high purity (Khachik, 2001), it requires multiple recrystallization steps and is very time consuming (Shibata et al., 2004). Moreover, the efficiency decreases as the purity of free lutein is increased (Shibata et al., 2004). As a result, the overall yield and purity of free lutein may be reduced (Boonnoun et al., 2012). An alternative method for free lutein purification is column chromatography. It has been frequently applied in the purification of organic compounds. Studies showed that column chromatography could provide free lutein with high purity (e.g., >96 %) (Hamburger et al., 2003). Shibata et al. (2004) could obtain the purity of more than 99 % using flash column chromatography on a silica gel. In addition, this technique is simple and feasible for repeated injections with little loss of performance (Hamburger et al., 2003). Column chromatography has been generally applied in both laboratory and industrial scales (Shibata et al., 2004). Consequently, it has become an attractive alternative to purify lutein from the sponified marigold extracts. However, there are limited numbers of reports on chromatographic purification of free lutein. In addition, no studies have been published on its industrial-scale application.

Computational Fluid Dynamics (CFD) modeling is an analysis and design tool for solving problems in transport phenomena based on numerical methods and algorithms. It provides insight into dynamic behaviors of the fluids which may be difficult and expensive to obtain by a physical process, especially in a large-scale. CFD modeling has been successfully applied to describe the transport phenomena in chromatographic separation. For example, an attempt was made by Pathak et al. (2008) at applying CFD modeling to investigate the effect of column's hardware and flow rate on flow distribution and cleaning effectiveness of a large-scale chromatography column. They found that CFD modeling combined with other empirical techniques could provide useful information about the chromatographic process and hardware selection. In addition, Ghosh et al. (2014) applied CFD modeling to investigate the scale-up of membrane chromatography capsules. They found that the CFD model could provide truly quantitative data and reduce the resources required in physical experiments. It has also been applied in several studies to determine the effect of reconstructing bed packing of chromatography columns (Schmidt et al., 2012).

In this study, CFD modeling was applied to simulate the purification of free lutein in a preparative chromatography column. The mathematical models for the transport phenomena of free lutein in the column were developed and simulated using a commercial CFD code (Fluent 14, ANSYS Inc., Lebanon, NH). The models were validated with the experimental data such as the concentration and band profiles of free lutein. The suitable models which could correctly describe the chromatographic and flow behavior of free lutein were applied to guide the design and operation of the chromatography column for a large scale production.

2. Materials and methods

2.1. Problem description and computational domain

The computational domain was constructed based on the experimental prototype of the chromatography column, i.e., a glass column 20 cm high and 3.5 cm in diameter. It was packed with the silica gel of 30 μm wet diameter. The packing porosity was approximately 0.3. The solutions of the free lutein mixture and eluent (i.e., hexane: ethyl acetate solution in a ratio of 70:30 v/v, based on the study by Boonnoun et al. (2012)) were introduced into the column through an inlet of 0.5 cm diameter, which was located at the bottom of the column. A two-dimensional axisymmetric geometry was created for the computational domain. Based on grid sensitivity analysis, the grid resolution of 7,500 cells was applied.

2.2. Mathematical models

The chromatographic purification in this study was operated at relatively constant temperature and, thus, isothermal system was assumed. Consequently, the fundamentals that dictated the transport phenomena occurred in the column were the momentum and mass transfers.

Momentum transfer: an appropriate mathematical model for momentum transfer in the chromatography column was determined based on the Reynolds number for flow through a packed bed. It was found that the Reynolds number was less than 1, which was well below the critical value for fully laminar flow through a packed column (i.e., Re<10) (Rhodes, 2008). As a result, Navier-Stokes equation for laminar flow was applied to solve for the flow profiles in this study.
Mass transfer: the most widely used mathematical model for chromatographic separation is the EDM. The model is based on homogeneous packed bed and spherical packing material assumptions. In addition, the model also assumes infinitely fast mass transfer across the column. However, axial dispersion is finite. This model is generally appropriate for columns with high efficiency (Guiochon, 2002). Schmidt et al. (2011) also showed that it could accurately predict the effect of packed-bed structure on column performance. The mass balance equation for the EDM is as follows.

$$\varepsilon_T \frac{\partial C_i}{\partial t} + (1-\varepsilon_T)\frac{\partial q_i}{\partial t} + u\frac{\partial C_i}{\partial z} = \varepsilon_e D_L \frac{\partial^2 C_i}{\partial z^2} \quad (1)$$

where C_i and q_i are the concentration of component 'i' in the mobile phase and in the adsorbed phase respectively, u is the mobile phase velocity, ε_T and ε_e are the total and external porosity respectively, and D_L is the coefficient of axial dispersion.

For the preliminary analysis in this study, the mass balance equation was further simplified by assuming negligible axial dispersion. Now it can be written as follows.

$$\frac{\partial C_i}{\partial t} + \frac{1-\varepsilon_T}{\varepsilon_T}\frac{\partial q_i}{\partial t} + u\frac{\partial C_i}{\partial z} = 0 \quad (2)$$

The model is known as the Ideal Model. It can be applied to analyze the qualitative behavior of chromatographic processes and to determine the influences of different process parameters during the initial investigation (Dunnebier and Klatt, 2000). Furthermore, the adsorption rate $(\partial q_i/\partial t)$ in the additional source term of both models must be incorporated into the general mass transport equation in the CFD program using the UDF, in order to make the program suitable for simulating the chromatographic separation in this study. In addition, the Linear Driving Force (LDF) Model was applied to describe the adsorption rate as follows (Cherrak et al., 2000).

$$\frac{\partial q_i}{\partial t} = k_{ext}(q_e - q_i) \quad (3)$$

where k_{ext} is the external mass transfer coefficient of free lutein in the eluent and q_e is the equilibrium concentration of free lutein adsorbed on the silica gel. An appropriate adsorption isotherm equation is required to determine the value of q_e. Based on the experimental results, the adsorption behavior of free lutein on the silica gel in this study could be described by linear adsorption isotherm as follows.

$$q_e = 6.0641C \quad (4)$$

, where C is the concentration of free lutein in the eluent.

The models were simulated based on the Finite Volume Method in Fluent (Fluent 14, ANSYS Inc., Lebanon, NH).

2.3. Initial and boundary conditions

The chromatography column was initially filled with the eluent which remained in equilibrium. In addition, there was no free lutein in either the mobile phase or the stationary phase.

$$C_i(0,z)=0 \tag{5}$$

$$q_i(0,z)=0 \tag{6}$$

The free lutein mixture was introduced into the column using pulse injection. Danckwert's conditions for efficient columns were applied for the boundary conditions (Guiochon et al., 2006).

$$C_i(t,0)=C_0 \quad (0<t\leq t_p) \tag{7}$$

$$C_i(t,0)=0 \quad (t\geq t_p)\text{, where } C_0=40\ \text{kg/m}^3 \text{ and } t_p=10\ \text{s} \tag{8}$$

$$\left.\frac{\partial C_i}{\partial z}\right|_{z=L}=0 \tag{9}$$

Furthermore, no-slip condition was applied for the column's wall. The separation process was operated at 303.5 K and atmospheric pressure was assumed at the outlet.

2.4. Validation experiment

Some experiments were conducted to obtain the data for comparison and validation of the mathematical models. For chromatographic separation, one of the most widely used experimental data for model validation is the outlet concentration of the solute. In this study, some samples of the eluate were collected at the outlet at every 1 min and for the total time of 120 min. They were then analyzed using a high performance liquid chromatography (HPLC). The results were used to plot the elution chromatogram for comparison with the models' prediction. The difference between the simulation and experimental results was evaluated based on the Absolute Average Deviation (AAD) value (Lucas et al., 2004). If AAD $\leq$ 0.1, the data are highly consistent; AAD < 0.15, the data are probably consistent; and AAD > 0.15, the data are probably inconsistent (assumed preparative/pilot column). In addition, the images of band profile from the experiment were also applied for model validation (data not shown).

3. Results and discussion

Figure (1) illustrates the chromatograms of free lutein from the experiments and the simulations. The EDM can predict the experimental results well and outperforms the Ideal Model. In addition, the shape of the chromatograms from the experiments and the EDM's prediction (i.e., broad peak) implies about the effect of axial diffusion on the mass transfer of free lutein. Moreover, from the AAD values of the Ideal Model (i.e., 0.36 and 0.41 when compared with experiment 1 and 2, respectively) and the EDM (i.e.,

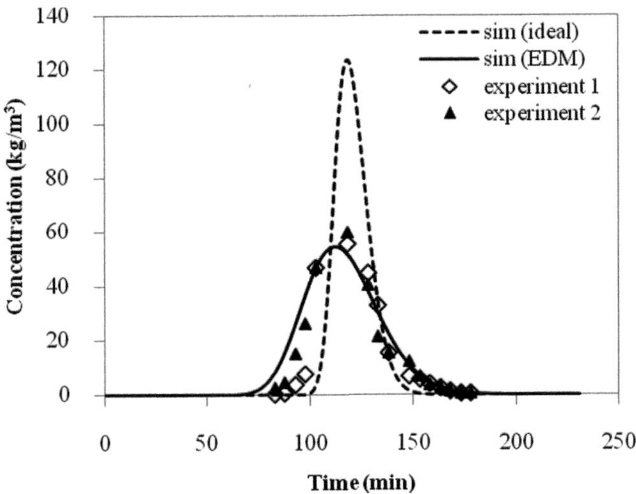

Figure 1. Comparison of the chromatograms of free lutein from the experiments and simulations.

0.15 and 0.09 when compared with experiment 1 and 2, respectively), it can be concluded that the prediction from the EDM is statistically consistent with the experimental results. However, the results from the Ideal Model are probably inconsistent with the experiment. Furthermore, it was found that the EDM was also able to predict the band profiles and capture the diffusion behavior of free lutein as it moved through the column (data not shown). Consequently, the EDM was applied in further analysis to determine the critical design and operational parameters of the chromatographic purification of free lutein.

4. Conclusion

It was shown that the EDM with the UDF of linear adsorption isotherm was able to predict the transport phenomena of free lutein in the preparative chromatography column. In addition, the effect of axial diffusion of free lutein in the mobile phase was important and should not be neglected. The model was applied in further study to determine critical design and operational parameter guidelines which should be adaptable for a large-scale operation.

Acknowledgements

This research was supported by PTT global chemical public company limited, Thailand Research Fund (MRG5680179), and Chemical Engineering Research Unit for Value Adding of Bioresources, Chulalongkorn University.

References

S. Bhaskaran, V. Mohan, 2007, A Process for Isolating, Purifying and Formulating a Stable, Commercial Grade Lutein Paste from Oleoresin, European Patent, 1,704,134 B1.

P. Boonnoun, T. Opaskonkun, P. Prasitchoke, M. Goto, A. Shotipruk, 2012, Purification of Free Lutein from Marigold Flowers by Liquid Chromatography, Engineering J., 16,5, 146-155.

D.E. Cherrak, S. Khattabi, G. Guiochon, 2000, Adsorption Behavior and Prediction of the Band Profiles of the Enantiomers of 3-Chloro-1-Phenyl-1-Propanol: Influence of the Mass Transfer Kinetics, J.Chromatogr. A., 877, 1–2, 109-122.

G. Dünnebier, K.-U. Klatt, 2000, Modeling and Simulation of Nonlinear Chromatographic Separation Processes: a Comparison of Different Modeling Approaches, Chem. Eng. Sci., 55, 373-380.

J.M. Fernández-Sevilla, F.G. Fernández, E.M. Grima, 2012, Obtaining Lutein-Rich Extract from Microalgal Biomass at Preparative Scale, Methods Mol. Biol., 892, 307-14.

P. Ghosh, K. Vahedipour, M. Leuthold, E. von Lieres, 2014, Model-Based Analysis and Quantitative Prediction of Membrane Chromatography: Extreme Scale-Up from 0.08 ml to 1200 ml, J. Chromatogr. A., 1332, 8-13.

G. Guiochon, 2002, Review: Preparative Liquid Chromatography, J. Chromatogr. A., 965, 129-161.

G. Guiochon, A. Felinger, D.G. Shirazi, A.M. Katti, 2006, The Mass Balance Equation of Chromatography and Its General Properties, Fundamentals of Preparative and Nonlinear Chromatography, 2nd ed, Amsterdam, The Netherlands, Elsevier Inc., 33-35.

M. Hamburger, S. Adler, D. Baumann, A. Forg, B. Weinreich, 2003, Preparative Purification of the Major Anti-inflammatory Triterpenoid Esters from Marigold (Calendula officinalis), Fitoterapia, 74, 328–338.

F. Khachik, 2001, Process for Extraction and Purification of Lutein, Zeaxanthin and Rare Carotenoids from Marigold Flowers and Plants, United States Patent, 6,262,284 B1.

F. Khachik, 2007, Process for Extraction and Purification of Lutein, Zeaxanthin and Rare Carotenoids from Marigold Flowers and Plants, United States Patent, 7,173,145 B2.

S. Lucas, M. P. Calvo, C. Palencia, M. J. Cocero, 2004, Mathematical Model of Supercritical CO2 Adsorption on Activated Carbon: Effect of Operating Conditions and Adsorption Scale-up, J. Supercrit. Fluids, 32, 1–3, 193-201.

N. Pathak, C. Norman, S. Kundu, S. Nulu, M. Durst, Z. Fang, 2008, Modeling Flow Distribution in Large-Scale Chromatographic Columns with Computational Fluid Dynamics, Bioproc. Intl., 6, 72-81.

M. Rhodes, 2008, Introduction to particle technology, 2nd ed, John Wiley & Sons Ltd., West Sussex, U.K.

S. Shibata, C. Ishihara, K. Matsumoto, 2004, Improved Separation Method for Highly Purified Lutein from Chlorella Powder Using Jet Mill and Flash Column Chromatography on Silica Gel, J. Agric. Food Chem., 52, 6283-6286.

I. Schmidt, F. Lottes, M. Minceva, W. Arlt, E.H. Stenby, 2011, Estimation of Chromatographic Columns Performances Using Computer Tomography and CFD simulations, Chem. Ing. Tech., 83, 1-2, 130-142.

I. Schmidt, M. Minceva, W. Arlt, 2012, Selection of Stationary Phase Particle Geometry Using X-ray Computed Tomography and Computational Fluid Dynamics Simulations, J. Chromatogr. A., 1225, 141-149.

M.L. Slattery, J. Benson, K. Curtin, K. Ma, D. Schaeffer, J.D. Potter, 2000, Carotenoids and Colon Cancer, Am. J. Clin. Nutr., 71, 575-582.

Jiří Jaromír Klemeš, Petar Sabev Varbanov and Peng Yen Liew (Editors)
Proceedings of the 24th European Symposium on Computer Aided Process Engineering – ESCAPE 24
June 15-18, 2014, Budapest, Hungary.

Optimal Design of a Hybrid Membrane System Combining Reverse and Forward Osmosis for Seawater Desalination

Raquel Salcedo-Diaz*, Ruben Ruiz-Femenia, Jose A. Caballero

Department of Chemical Engineering, University of Alicate. Ap. Correos 99, E-03080, Alicante, Spain.
raquel.salcedo@ua.es

Abstract

In this work we study Forward Osmosis (FO) as an emerging desalination technology, and its capability to replace totally or partially Reverse Osmosis (RO) in order to reduce the great amount of energy required in the current desalination plants. For this purpose, we propose a superstructure that includes both membrane based desalination technologies, allowing the selection of only one of the technologies or a combination of both of them seeking for the optimal configuration of the network. The optimization problem is solved for a seawater desalination plant with a given fresh water production. The results obtained show that the optimal solution combines both desalination technologies to reduce not only the energy consumption but also the total cost of the desalination process in comparison with the same plant but operating only with RO.

Keywords: optimal design, seawater desalination, emerging membrane technologies, forward osmosis.

1. Introduction

Clean water scarcity is affecting over one third of the world's population. As 97 % of all the water on the planet is saline, desalination has gained wider interest in the last decades. Reverse Osmosis (RO) is currently the most widely used desalination technology. However, RO is an energy-intensive process because of the high pressure required, especially for seawater desalination (60-70 bar). This main drawback of the RO not only makes this technology energy availability and cost dependent, but also produces a great amount of global warming emissions. The energy required for the seawater RO is 2.5-4 kWh/m^3, which translates into 3 kg of CO_2/m^3 of water treated (Nirmalakhandan et al., 2010). This high energy consumption joint with the growing environmental concerns is promoting the development of alternative environmentally friendly technologies. In the last few years, Forward Osmosis (FO) has emerged as an alternative membrane technology for water purification and desalination (Chung et al., 2012a). FO is a natural osmosis-driven process involving a semipermeable membrane and a draw solution. The draw solution has a higher osmotic pressure and is able to extract water from the feed solution. The main advantage of FO is that it operates at no hydraulic pressures which has resulted in rapidly growing interests in it from various disciplines, being one of them seawater desalination. FO based seawater desalination involves at least two steps: extraction of water from the seawater by a draw solution and separation of the product water from the diluted draw solution by means of other membrane separation processes (RO, Ultrafiltration (UF), Nanofiltration (NF)) or thermal methods (distillation). However, there are still some challenges that must be overcome to bring FO to commercialization. Currently, one of the major challenges of FO technologies is the lack of draw solutes that can be easily recycled (Chung et al., 2012b). Therefore, remarkable efforts have been devoted to discover suitable draw solutes. Qingchun et al. (2013), presented a comprehensive and critical review on the existing draw solutions and their applications in FO processes. Some of the many compounds proposed in the literature as draw solutes are: inorganic salts, ammonia and carbon dioxide and macromolecules (fructose, sucrose, fatty acid-polyethylene glycol). The most challenging task is to develop sustainable integrated systems for water production and draw solute recycle. Among the existing technologies for the draw solute recovery UF is one of the most promising because its low energy demand. Some authors have presented studies on FO desalination at pilot scale using thermal methods for the draw solute recovery (McGinnis et al., 2013). However, in the literature there is a lack of studies investigating the actual possibility of implementing an industrial scale system integrating the FO and UF technologies for a cost efficient desalination process. The aim of this work is to study the capabilities of an integrated FO/UF system, as a desalination technology alternative to RO.

2. Problem statement

The design problem is to address the optimal configuration of a superstructure-based hybrid membrane system for seawater desalination. The superstructure proposed comprises both, RO and FO, desalination units and a set of membrane filtration units in series (UF, NF). In a first stage, the exiting draw solution from the FO unit enters a UF unit. If necessary, the permeated stream would enter another UF or NF unit to recover the product water and concentrate the draw solution from the FO. The network includes also mixer and splitter units to distribute the streams allowing the alternative connections between the units that may enhance the performance of the system (Figure 1).

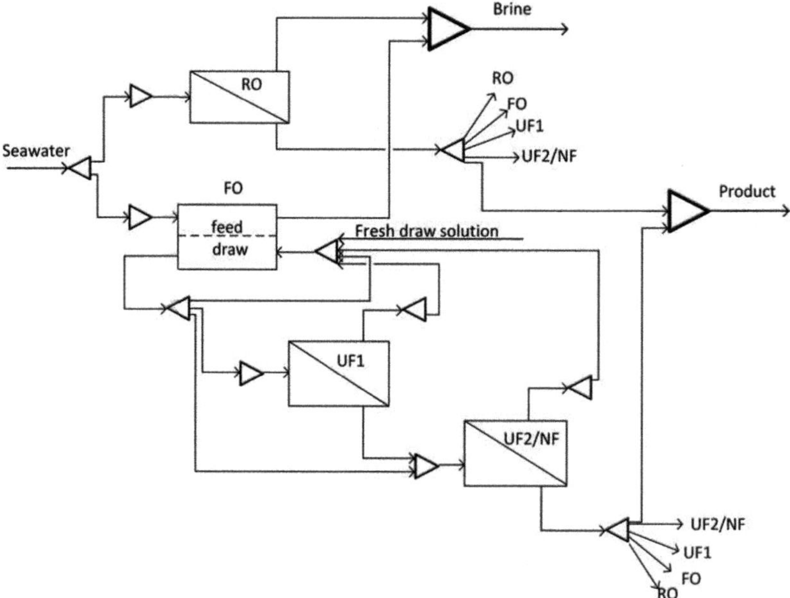

Figure 1. Superstructure for the hybrid membrane system proposed.

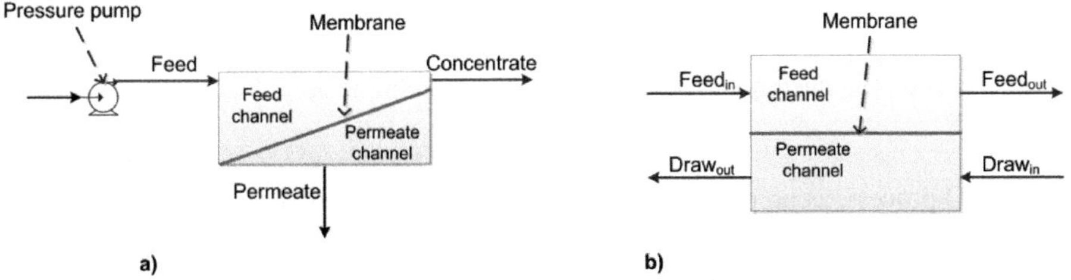

Figure 2. Schemes of the process units: a) Membrane separation processes (RO, UF, NF); b) Forward Osmosis.

The superstructure must take into account also the different input/output topology of the FO unit with respect to the other membrane processes units, due to their different driving forces. The need of a draw solution in FO forces this unit to have two inlet streams unlike the other membrane units whose unique inlet is the pressurized feed stream. The schemes of both types of units are depicted in Figure 2.

The goal is to determine the optimal design of a seawater desalination plant that may use either one of the desalination technologies or both of them (hybrid system), to optimize its economic performance.

3. Mathematical model

We use the mathematical programming approach to calculate the optimal network configuration of the plant. This method has been successfully used for the design of optimal RO networks (Saif et al., 2008) and wastewater treatment plants including different types of treatment units (Galan and Grossmman, 2011).

Mass balances in all units and short-cut models describing the performance of the membrane processes lead to a non-linear programming (NLP) problem of the form

$$\begin{aligned} &\min_{\mathbf{x}} \; \{ STC(\mathbf{x}) \} \\ &s.t. \;\; \mathbf{h}(\mathbf{x}) = \mathbf{0} \\ &\qquad \mathbf{g}(\mathbf{x}) \leq \mathbf{0} \end{aligned} \tag{1}$$

where the objective is to minimize the specific total cost (STC, \$/m^3 of fresh water produced).

The environmental performance of the plant has also been assessed using the global warming potential (GWP, kg CO_2/ m^3 of fresh water produced) indicator as described by the IPCC 2007 (Intergovernmental Panel on Climate Change) (Hischier et al., 2007).

3.1. Membrane processes models

The membrane processes have been modeled according to their transport mechanism across the membrane. The transport in the desalination units occurs through a solution-diffusion mechanism, while the other membrane processes are size exclusion filtrations.

In the following subsections, we detail the short-cut models used to describe the transport mechanism of each process.

3.1.1. Desalination units

The transport across the RO membrane is described through the osmotic pressure law

$$F_p^{RO} = K_m^{RO} A_{memb}^{RO} \left(\Delta P - \Delta \pi \right) \tag{2}$$

F_p is the permeate flow, A_{memb} is the total membrane area, K_m is the membrane permeability, ΔP is the pressure applied and$\Delta\pi$ is the osmotic pressure difference across the membrane. The design variables here are the membrane area A_{memb} and the pressure applied ΔP.

For the FO process, as no pressure is applied, Eq. (2) is modified as follows

$$F_p^{FO} = K_m^{FO} A_{memb}^{FO} \left(\pi_d - \pi_f \right) \tag{3}$$

where π_d and π_f are the osmotic pressures of the draw and feed solutions, respectively. In this case the design variables are A_{memb} and π_d, which depends on the concentration of the draw solution.

Note that in these models the concentration polarization phenomenon has been neglected.

3.1.2. Filtration units

The only difference among the membrane filtration processes, UF and NF in this particular case, is the size of the solute removed from the feed stream. In this processes the transport across the membrane can be modeled using a modified Darcy's law

$$F_p^M = \frac{\Delta P^M}{\mu R_m^M} A_{memb}^M \quad ; \qquad \forall M \in \{UF, NF\} \tag{4}$$

R_m is the resistance of the membrane to the pass of water and μ is the dynamic viscosity of water. The design variables are also A_{memb} and the ΔP.

3.2. Objective function

The objective function is the specific total cost (STC). The cost terms include the annualized investment cost (IC), which is mainly the cost of the membrane modules, the operation and maintenance of the membranes (O&M) and the cost of the electricity required for the entire system.

$$STC = \frac{\sum_{memb} IC + \sum_{memb} (O\&M) + Elect}{F_{product}} \tag{5}$$

4. Case study

The proposed model has been applied to the design of a medium-size seawater desalination plant with a given production of 50 kg/s of fresh water. It is assumed that the plant operates during 24 h/d. For the FO process a polyglycol polymer was selected as draw solute.

5. Results and discussion

The model has been implemented in GAMS and solved to global optimality using the solver BARON, version 9.0.6. The results show that the minimum specific cost is achieved when both desalination technologies (RO and FO) are used together (Figure 3). In the economically most efficient configuration of the network, the total seawater flow rate treated in the plant is split into two streams; almost the 60 % is treated in the RO unit and the rest in the FO unit.

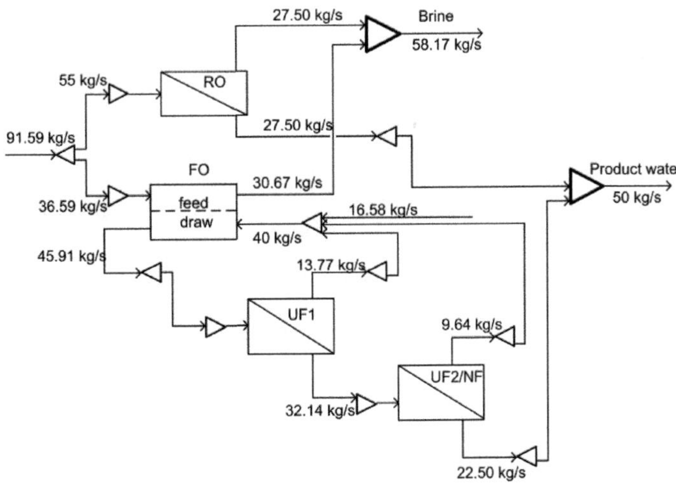

Figure 3. Optimal configuration of the network.

The system was also solved with some structural variables of the network fixed, in order to enforce the plant to operate either using only RO or only FO. In Figure 4 the economical and environmental performances of these three configurations are compared.When the plant operates using the hybrid membrane system, the cost is reduced 16 % with respect to the cost of the RO plant and 45 % with respect to the FO plant. Regarding the environmental indicator, the hybrid system shows a worse performance than the FO plant, but it is enhanced in more than 30 % with respect to the RO plant. In this latter case the greenhouse gas emissions are so significant due to the great amount of electricity required by the RO. On the contrary, when FO is the only desalination technology used, these emissions are highly reduced due to the reduction on the electricity consumption, while the total cost is increased due to the high investment and maintenance cost of the membranes. Note that these calculations consider only the desalination part of the plant. We assume that other processes involving pre and post treatments, are the same regardless the desalination technology used.

The cost breakdown of the compared configurations, which is depicted in Figure 5, shows the higher cost of the electricity when only RO is used and the higher investment cost when only FO is used.

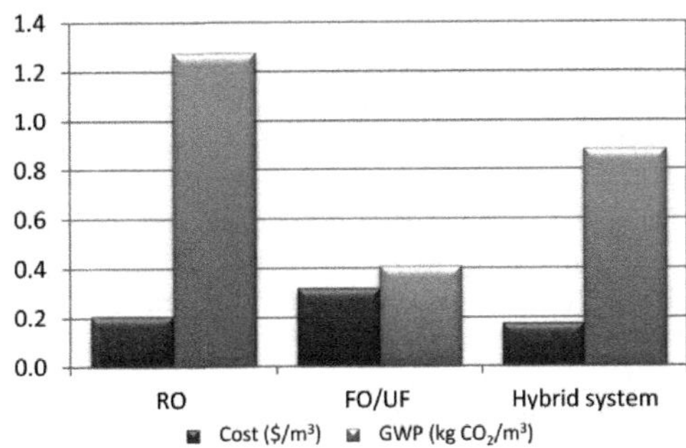

Figure 4. Comparison between the performances of the three desalination plant configurations.

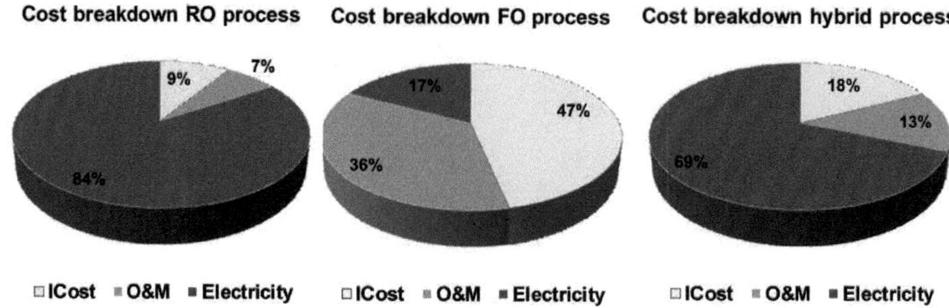

Figure 5. Cost breakdown of the three plant configurations.

6. Conclusions

A superstructure-based hybrid membrane desalination system using reverse and forward osmosis has been proposed for the synthesis of the economical most efficient plant. The membrane processes have been described using short-cut models. The design problem has been illustrated through a case study of a seawater desalination plant with a given production. The results highlight that, at the current state of development of the FO technology, it cannot totally replace the RO technology due to its high investment cost. A better solution to improve simultaneously the environmental and economic performance of seawater desalination plants, is to integrate both technologies in the desalination process.

Acknowledgements

The authors wish to acknowledge support from the Spanish Ministry of Education and Science (CTQ2012-37039-C02-02) and the University of Alicante (GRE11-19).

References

T.S. Chung, X. Li, R.C. Ong, Q. Ge, H.L. Wang, G. Han, 2012a, Emerging forward osmosis (FO) technologies and challenges ahead for clean water and clean energy applications, Curr. Opinion Chem. Eng., 1, 1246–257.

T.S. Chung, S. Zhang, K.Y. Wang, J.C. Su, M.M. Ling, 2012b, Forward osmosis processes: yesterday, today and tomorrow, Desalination, 287, 78-81.

B. Galan, I.E. Grossmann, 2011, Optimal design of real world industrial wastewatertreatment networks, Computer Aided Chemical Engineering, 29, 1251–1255.

R. Hischier, W. Beidema, H.-J. Althaus, C. Bauer, G. Doka, R. Dones, R. Frischknecht, S. Hellweg, S. Humbert, N. Jungbluth, T. Köllner, Y. Loerincik, M. Margni, T. Nemecek, 2010, Implementation of Life Cycle Impact Assessment Methods, Final report ecoinvent v2.2 in, Swiss Centre for Life, Dübendorf, Switzerland.

R.L. McGinnis, N.T. Hancock, M.S. Nowosielski-Slepowron, G.D. McGurgan, 2013, Pilot demonstration of the NH3/CO2 forward osmosis desalination process on high salinity brines, Desalination, 312, 67–74.

N. Nirmalakhandan, S. Deng, V.G. Gude, 2010, Renewable and sustainable approaches for desalination, Renew. Sustain. Energy Rev., 14, 9, 2641–2654.

Q. Ge, M. Ling, T.-S. Chung, 2013, Draw solutions for forward osmosis processes: Developments, challenges, and prospects for the future, Journal of Membrane Science, 442, 225–237.

Y. Saif, A.Elkamel, M. Pritzker, 2008, Optimal design of reverse-osmosis networks for wastewater treatment, Chemical Engineering and Processing: Process Intensification, 47, 2163–2174.

Jiří Jaromír Klemeš, Petar Sabev Varbanov and Peng Yen Liew (Editors)
Proceedings of the 24th European Symposium on Computer Aided Process Engineering – ESCAPE 24
June 15-18, 2014, Budapest, Hungary.

Comparison between Interval Methods to Solve Initial Value Problems in Chemical Process Design

Carlos Perez-Galvan, I. David L. Bogle*

Centre for Process Systems Engineering, Department of Chemical Engineering, University College London, Torrington Place, London WC1E 7JE, United Kingdom
d.bogle@ucl.ac.uk

Abstract

This paper presents results on the comparison of using two interval methods for the reduction of overestimation in the validated solution of Initial Value Problems (IVP) for Ordinary Differential Equations (ODE). The interval methods used are the Krawczyk contractor and the Newton contractor. The use of these interval contractors significantly enhances the tightness of the upper and lower bounds obtained when applied to an interval Taylor series method. The algorithms were applied to two reactor examples to demonstrate the effectiveness of the methods.

Keywords: Interval Contractors, Overestimation Reduction, Initial Value Problems.

1. Introduction

Validated methods of initial value problems (IVP) for ordinary differential equations (ODE) provide enclosures which are guaranteed to contain all the solutions of the problem (Enszer et al., 2011). These methods are desirable in applications where critical variables such as safety or environmental performance are an issue and these solutions are required in order to guarantee safe operation. In recent years several software packages for the validated solution of IVPs for ODEs have been developed, popular software packages include: VNODE-LP which implements the Interval Hermite-Obreschkoff with the High Order Enclosure method (Nedialko, 2011), VSPODE makes an implementation of Taylor Models and constraint propagation is used as a way to reduce overestimation (Lin and Stadtherr, 2007), ValEncIA-IVP finds the validated exponential enclosure of a nonvalidated solution and uses some interval methods to reduce overestimation (Rauh et al., 2009). Nonetheless tighter and more efficient bounds are required in applications such as global optimisation with embedded ODEs or guaranteed parameter estimation. Because of this a number of ways to deal with this problem have been developed e.g. convex and concave relaxations (McCormick relaxations) have been incorporated along with interval bounds (Sahlodin and Chachuat, 2011b). These relaxations have been used in the Taylor Model method in the remainder term in addition to the interval bounds (Sahlodin and Chachuat, 2011a), and for this purpose McCormick relaxations have been applied in a method to derive an auxiliary system of ODEs that uses interval bounds (Scott et al., 2013). Interval contractors have not been broadly applied in the overestimation reduction of validated solutions of IVPs for ODEs algorithms. This paper gives results on the comparison of two interval contractors implemented in an Interval Taylor Series method with parameter dependence. The remainder of the paper is organised as follows, in section 2 the formulation of the problem to solve and preliminaries are given, in section 3 the contractors used are described, in section 4 the application of the algorithms to case studies is presented and in section 5 conclusions and future research directions are given.

2. Preliminaries

The mathematical formulation of the problem we are aiming to solve is for systems of ODEs with parameter dependence of the form

$$\dot{x}(t) = f(x(t), p), \quad x(t_0) = x_0, \quad t \in [t_0, t_f] \tag{1}$$

Where *x(t)* is a vector of states and *p* is a vector of unknown parameters. In this paper an Interval Taylor Series method with High-Order Enclosure (HOE) has been used. This method consists of two main steps: validating existence and uniqueness, and computing a tighter enclosure. In the remainder of the paper intervals are represented by a lower endpoint and an upper endpoint between square brackets. Interval vector or matrices are represented by capital letters unless otherwise specified.

The first step involves the computation of an a priori enclosure and an appropriate step size, this step is performed through a HOE method. With this enclosure larger time step sizes can be obtained compared to a constant enclosure method. The high-order enclosure method satisfies

$$\widetilde{Y}_j = Y_j + \sum_{i=1}^{k-1} [0, h_j]^i f^{[i]}(Y_j, P) + [0, h_j]^k f^{[k]}(\widetilde{Y}_j^0, P) \subseteq \widetilde{Y}_j^0 \tag{2}$$

where k is the order of the Taylor series expansion, Y_j is a tight enclosure of the solution, h_j is the time step, $\widetilde{Y}_j$ is the a priori enclosure, $\widetilde{Y}_j^0$ are the ranges of the states, P are the parameters and $f^{[i]}$ are the ith order Taylor coefficients defined by $f^{[0]}(y, p) = y$; $f^{[i]}(y, p) = \frac{1}{i}\left(\frac{\partial f^{[i-1]}}{\partial y} f\right)(y, p)$, for $i \geq 1$.

The second step consists on using the a priori enclosure $\widetilde{Y}_j$ and the time step h_j obtained in the first step. The Interval Taylor Series Method uses a Taylor series expansion in the IVP combined with the mean value theorem evaluation in the form

$$Y_{j+1} = \hat{y}_j + \sum_{i=1}^{k-1} h_j^i f^{[i]}(\hat{y}_j, \hat{p}) + h_j^k f^{[k]}(\widetilde{Y}_j^0, P) + \left\{\sum_{i=0}^{k-1} h_j^i \frac{\partial f^{[i]}}{\partial y}(Y_j, P)\right\}(Y_j - \hat{y}_j) + \left\{\sum_{i=0}^{k-1} h_j^i \frac{\partial f^{[i]}}{\partial p}(Y_j, P)\right\}(P - \hat{p}) \tag{3}$$

where $\hat{y}_j$ and $\hat{p}$ were taken as the midpoints of Y_j and P, respectively.

In order to reduce the overestimation caused by the so called wrapping effect the QR-factorization technique devised by Lohner (1992) was used.

3. Interval contractors

Assume we have n_y variables linked by n_f relations of the form

$$f_j(y_1, y_2, \ldots, y_{n_x}) = 0, j \in \{1, 2, \ldots, n_f\}. \tag{4}$$

Each variable y_i belongs to a domain Y_j, an interval. Equation (4) can be written in vector form and a constraint satisfaction problem (CSP) can be formulated as

$$(f(y) = 0, y \in Y_j) \tag{5}$$

The solution set S of (5) is defined as

$$S = \{y \in Y_j \mid f(y) = 0\} \tag{6}$$

Contracting the CSP in (5) means replacing Y_j by a smaller domain Y_j' such that the solution set remains unchanged, i.e. $S \subset Y' \subset Y$. The contractors used in this paper are interval counterparts of classical point algorithms such as Gauss-Seidel and Newton algorithms. For more details see (Jaulin et al., 2001) and for application examples in global optimisation refer to (Balendra and Bogle, 2009).

3.1. Krawczyk contractor

The Krawczyk contractor considers a CSP as in (5) where the number of variables is the same as the number of relations and f is assumed to be differentiable. The function $\psi(y) = y - Mf(y)$ where M is any invertible matrix is a fixed-point subsolver for (5) and its centred inclusion function is

$$\Psi(Y_j) = \psi(\hat{y}_j) + \{J_\psi(Y_j)\}(Y_j - \hat{y}_j) \tag{7}$$

where J_ψ is an inclusion function for the Jacobian matrix of ψ and $\hat{y}_j$ is the midpoint of Y_j. With the intersection between the original domain and the domain obtained with (7) the following fixed–point contractor is obtained:

$$Y_j' = Y_j \cap (\psi(\hat{y}_j) + \{J_\psi(Y_j)\}(Y_j - \hat{y}_j)). \tag{8}$$

3.2. Newton contractor

We consider again a CSP as in (5) and apply the mean value theorem to obtain

$$(f(\hat{y}_j) + \{J_f(\xi)\}(y_j - \hat{y}_j), y_j \in Y_j, \xi \in Y_j). \tag{9}$$

The CSP in (9) can be arranged as

$$(Ap + f(\hat{y}_j) = 0, p = (y_j - \hat{y}_j), A = J_f(\xi), b = -f(\hat{y}_j), y_j \in Y_j, \xi \in Y_j). \tag{10}$$

In this way a linear contractor can be used such as the Gauss-Seidel contractor. The Gauss-Seidel contractor is able to contract domains of linear systems of interval equations of the form

$$Ap - b = 0 \tag{11}$$

If A is square it can be decomposed as the sum of a diagonal matrix and a matrix with zeros on its diagonal (extdiag):

$$diag(A)p + extdiag(A)p = b \tag{12}$$

Also if A is invertible (12) can be rewritten as

$$p = (diag(A))^{-1}(b - extdiag(A)p) \tag{13}$$

The solution of the Gauss-Seidel contractor is defined as the intersection of the original domain p and the new p calculated with (13)

$$p \leftarrow p \cap (diag(A))^{-1}(b - extdiag(A)p). \tag{14}$$

Finally, the Gauss-Seidel contractor solution in (14) is used to update Y_j and the intersection $Y_j \leftarrow Y_j \cap (p + \hat{y}_j)$ is obtained to finish with the Newton procedure.

4. Case Studies

Using the interval Taylor series method the interval contractors presented above were implemented at each iteration step for some chemical process examples and upper and lower bound for the solutions were obtained. The program used was written in C++ and the Profil/BIAS (Knuppel, 1994) and FADBAD++ (Stauning and Bendtsen, 2003) libraries were used for the implementations of interval arithmetic and automatic differentiation.

Case 1. The first example is an Exothermic Batch Reactor in which the reaction A→B takes place in a batch reactor. The model of this system describes the conversion of the species and the temperature profile of the reactor. The parameters of the model can be found in (Enszer et al., 2011). In this example some interval parameters and initial conditions were introduced in the model in order to verify the effectiveness of the interval contractors used. Both of the contractors were also used a different number of times in the algorithm at each iteration step. The results of the application of each of the interval contractors 5 and 20 times can be seen in Figure 2. The model for the Exothermic Batch Reactor is:

$$\dot{x}(t)=k_0\left(1-x(t)\right)e^{-\frac{E_a}{RT(t)}},\quad \dot{T}(t)=\frac{UA}{C_{A0}VC_p}\left(T_a-T(t)\right)-\frac{\Delta H_R k_0}{C_p}\left(1-x(t)\right)e^{-\frac{E_a}{RT(t)}} \tag{15}$$

The interval values used in this model were T_a=[294,306], x(0)=[0,0.1] and T(0)=[350,370]. In order to compare, the model without using contractors is shown in Figure 1a.

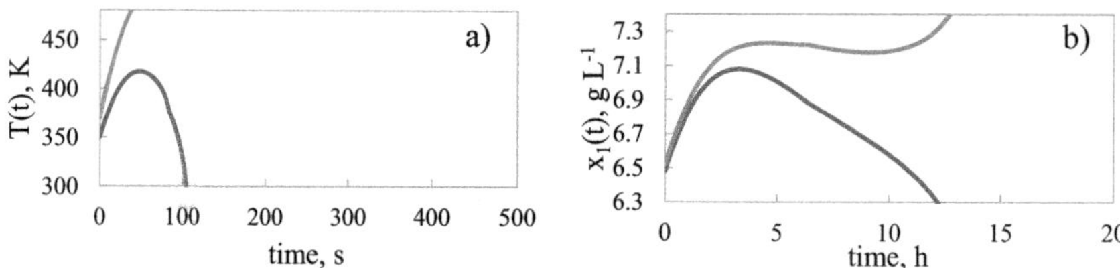

Figure 1. Exothermic batch reactor (a) and three-state bioreactor (b) without using contractors.

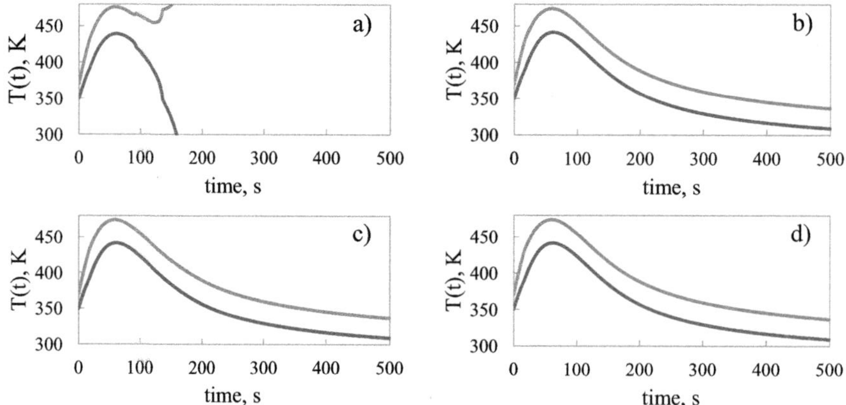

Figure 2. Interval bounds of (12) using Krawczyk contractor 5 times (a), using Krawczyk contractor 20 times (b), using Newton contractor 5 times (c) and using Newton contractor 20 times (d).

The results obtained show that the applied contractors are able to reduce the overestimation in the bounds. In this example a better contraction was achieved with the Newton contractor with Gauss-Seidel step in the case when the contractors were applied 5 times since tighter bounds can be observed in Figure 2c than in Figure 2a. However their performance was similar when they were applied 20 times (Figures 2b and 2d).

Case 2. The second example consists of a three-state bioreactor. Details for the model can be found in (Bequette, 1998). As in the previous example for this test problem some interval initial conditions and interval parameters were introduced in order to compare the performance of the contractors used. The results for this problem can be seen in Figure 3. The model for the three-state bioreactor is:

$$\dot{x}_1(t)=(\mu-D)x_1(t),\quad \dot{x}_2(t)=D(x_{2f}-x_2(t))-\frac{\mu x_1(t)}{Y}$$
$$\dot{x}_3(t)=-Dx_3(t)+(\alpha\mu+\beta)x_1(t)\ \text{with}\ \mu=\frac{\mu_{max}\left(1-\left(\frac{x_3(t)}{x_{3m}}\right)\right)x_2(t)}{k_s+x_2(t)} \tag{16}$$

The interval values used in this model were k_s=[1.074,1.076], α=[2.19,2.21], μ_m=[0.464,0.466], $x_1(0)$=[6.48,6.52], $x_2(0)$=[4.99,5.01] and $x_3(0)$=[14.99,15.01]. As in the previous case, in order to compare, the simulation without using contractors can be seen in Figure 1b, note how the overestimation make the bounds to rapidly blow up.
(b), using Newton contractor 5 times (c) and using Newton contractor 20 times (d).

For this example, the overestimation was reduced with the contractors used. The results indicate that the application of the Newton contractor with Gauss-Seidel step provided better bounds contraction compared to the use of the Krawczyk contractor since tighter bounds are obtained with the former when they were used 5 times. Tighter bounds can be seen in Figure 3a compared to Figure 3c but when they were applied 20 times a similar bound contraction was obtained which can be seen in Figures 3b and 3d.

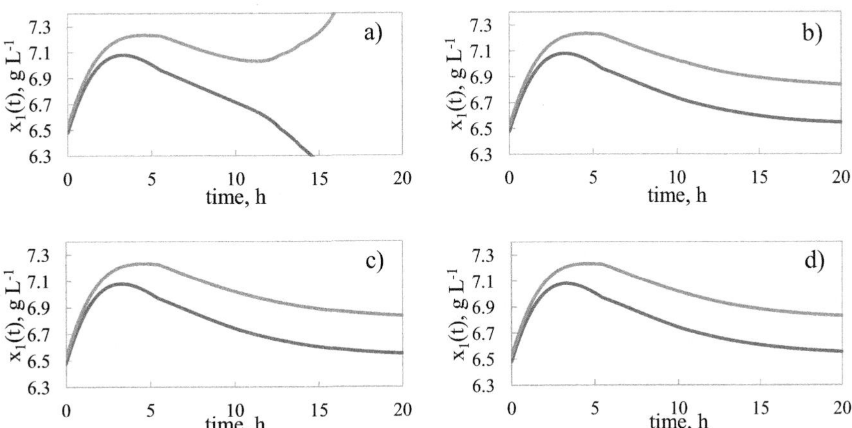

Figure 3. Interval bounds of (13) using Krawczyk contractor 5 times (a), using Krawczyk contractor 20 times

5. Conclusions

The Krawczyk and Newton with Gauss Seidel step interval contractors were used to reduce the overestimation in the validated solution of IVPs for ODEs. Improvement in the tightness of the bounds is obtained when the contractors are applied in these algorithms. The contractors were applied a maximum of 20 times as experience has shown that no further reduction was observed after this. The Newton contractor proved to perform better as it provided tighter bounds than the Krawczyk contractor when the contractors were applied 5 times, however, similar results were obtained when they were applied 20 times. A future aim for this investigation is to test combinations of these contractors and new ones as well as other interval methods to reduce overestimation. We are also interested in the application of these methods in Global Optimisation algorithms for dynamic systems since tight bounds are needed, for example in a branch and bound or branch and reduce framework.

6. Acknowledgements

Financial support from the Mexican National Council for Science and Technology (CONACyT) and University College London (UCL) is gratefully acknowledged.

References

S. Balendra, I. D. L. Bogle, 2009, Modular Global Optimisation in Chemical Engineering, Journal of Global Optimization, 45, 1, 169–185.

B. W. Bequette, 1998, Process Dynamics: Modeling, Analysis and Simulation, Prentice-Hall, Upper Saddle River, NJ, USA.

J. A. Enszer, Y. Lin, S. Ferson, G. F. Corliss, M. A. Stadtherr, 2011, Probability Bounds Analysis for Nonlinear Dynamic Process Models, AIChE Journal, 57, 2, 404–422.

L. Jaulin, M. Kieffer, O. Didrit, E. Walter, 2001, Applied Interval Analysis, Springer, London, UK.

O. Knuppel, 1994, PROFIL/BIAS-A Fast Interval Library, Computing, 53, 277–287.

Y. Lin, M. A. Stadtherr, 2007, Validated Solutions of Initial Value Problems for Parametric ODEs, Applied Numerical Mathematics, 57, 10, 1145–1162.

R. J. Lohner,1992, Computation of Guaranteed Enclosures for the Solutions of Ordinary Initial and Boundary Value Problems, In Computational Ordinary Differential Equations, edited by Jeffrey R. Cash and I. Gladwell, Clarendon Press, Oxford, UK, 425–435.

S. N. Nedialko, 2011, Implementing a Rigorous ODE Solver through Literate Programming, Mathematical Engineering, 3, 3–19.

A . Rauh, M. Brill, C. Günther, 2009, A Novel Interval Arithmetic Approach for Solving Differential-Algebraic Equations with ValEncIA-IVP, International Journal of Applied Mathematics and Computer Science - Verified Methods: Applications in Medicine and Engineering, 19, 3, 381–397.

A. M. Sahlodin, B. Chachuat, 2011a, Convex/concave Relaxations of Parametric ODEs Using Taylor Models, Computers and Chemical Engineering, 35, 844–857.

A. M. Sahlodin, B. Chachuat, 2011b, Discretize-Then-Relax Approach for Convex/concave Relaxations of the Solutions of Parametric ODEs, Applied Numerical Mathematics, 61, 7, 803–820.

J. K. Scott, , B. Chachuat, P. I. Barton, 2013, Nonlinear Convex and Concave Relaxations for the Solutions of Parametric ODEs, Optimal Control Applications and Methods, 34, 145–163.

O. Stauning, C. Bendtsen, 2003, FADBAD++ Web Page, <www.fadbad.com/fadbad.html> accessed on 16/01/2014.

Jiří Jaromír Klemeš, Petar Sabev Varbanov and Peng Yen Liew (Editors)
Proceedings of the 24th European Symposium on Computer Aided Process Engineering – ESCAPE 24
June 15-18, 2014, Budapest, Hungary.

Optimization of Extractive Distillation Process with a Single Column for Anhydrous Ethanol Production

Wagner B. Ramos*, Marcella F. Figueiredo, Romildo P. Brito

Chemical Engineering Department, Federal University of Campina Grande, Av. Aprigio Veloso, 882, Bodocongo, Campina Grande – PB – CEP 58429-140 , Brazil
wagnerbr_cg@yahoo.com.br

Abstract

Distillation is one of the oldest and most used separation processes that exist in chemical industries worldwide. In cases of azeotropic mixtures, simple distillation is unable to perform separation at a certain composition, so they are separated using azeotropic distillation. Traditionally, there are two different configurations used to produce anhydrous ethanol by azeotropic distillation. One of them is the heterogeneous azeotropic distillation and the other one is the homogeneous azeotropic distillation. In both configurations, it is necessary to add a third component (solvent) to promote separation and it is also necessary to use a second distillation column in order to recover the solvent. This paper deals with homogeneous azeotropic distillation (also called extractive distillation) and the process of obtaining anhydrous ethanol was chosen as a case study. For this case, the solvent used to break the azeotrope was ethylene glycol. The purpose of this work is to determine the optimal conditions of a new configuration of extractive distillation process for producing anhydrous ethanol using only one column with a sidestream withdrawal, using the process simulator Aspen Plus®. After optimization, it was possible to achieve a reduction of 18.53 % in the reboiler heat duty. A comparison, in terms of energy consumption of the reboilers, between the traditional extractive configuration and the new configuration, was also assessed.

Keywords: Distillation; optimization; extraction; ethanol.

1. Introduction

In all petrochemical industries worldwide, distillation is the most important and most used separation process. According to the U.S. Department of Energy, there are more than 40,000 distillation columns in North America, and they consume about 40 % of the total energy used to operate a plant. Regarding to this, the optimal operation of distillation columns is the objective of several studies all over the world. The fundamental principle of the distillation process is the difference in volatility of the components forming the mixture. However, there are cases in which occurs the presence of azeotrope points. When such case occurs, conventional distillation may not be able to promote a separation with the desired degree of purity. Azeotropic mixtures can be separated by azeotropic distillation, which can behomogeneous or heterogeneous. In both cases, a third component, called solvent, is added to promote separation. The general purpose of this work is to optimize, in terms of energy reduction, the process of dehydration of aqueous mixtures of ethanol using only one distillation column. The optimization procedure uses a process simulator (Aspen Plus®), in a systematic way, in order to obtain the optimal operational conditions of an extractive distillation column

(Figueiredo et al., 2010).The production of anhydrous ethanol was chosen as a case study due to its increasingly importance as a sustainable biofuel. According to Segovia-Hernández et al. (2012), Brazil and the United States are major users and producers of bioethanol and together, they were responsible for 88 % of the world´s ethanol fuel production in 2010. Several recent studies assessing optimization of anhydrous ethanol distillation can be found in literature. Kiss et al. (2011) showed that the use of an extractive dividing wall column configuration can lead to energy savings, however, in spite of the recovery column be eliminated, this type of configuration requires two condensers. Alcántara-Avila et al. (2012) proposed a multiobjective optimization procedure using MILP (Mix Integer Linear Programming) that evaluates various distillations structures, entrainers and energy conservation methods in order to optimize the total annual cost, but the authors do not consider the column with sidestream withdrawal in their studies and the optimization procedure used does not use a rigorous process simulator. Vázquez-Ojeda et al. (2013) used a stochastic global optimization algotithm to optimize the conventional and an alternative configuration, but both configurations use solvent recovery columns. Studies that assess optimization of extractive columns with sidestream withdrawal for production of anhydrous ethanol, which is what this paper proposes, was not found in literature. The main advantage of the configuration presented in this work is that the use of a solvent recovery column is not necessary, which implies in a reduction in investment costs and utilities (reboiler and condenser).

2. Problem Definition

Normally, in extractive distillation, the lighter component is removed at the top of the extractive column. At the base of the column, the solvent and the intermediate component are collected and pumped to the recovery column. As in the azeotropic distillation, a second column is required in order to recover the third component, as shown in Figure 1. However, considering the simplicity of the recovery column, attention is often focused only on the extractive column. Figure 2 shows the composition profiles (liquid and vapor) normally obtained by the extractive distillation column of the flowchart presented in Figure 1, where it is possible to observe that, below the feeding stage, the vapor phase contains virtually only water. This behavior suggests that a sidestream may be used, so that a single column can be used to obtain all three components with high purity. Figure 3 shows the extractive distillation column with a sidestream withdrawal.

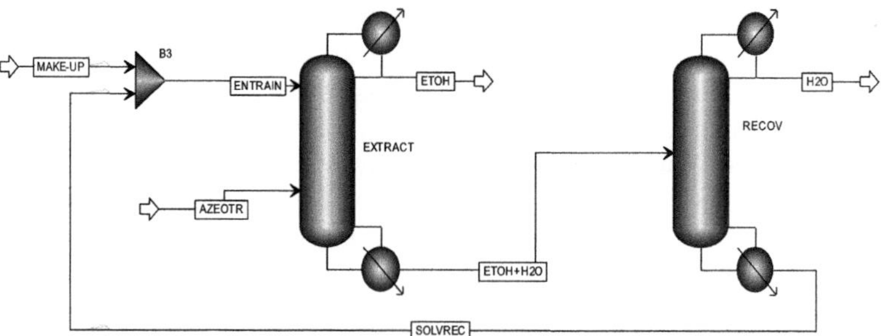

Figure 1. Simplified process diagram used for the dehydration of aqueous ethanol mixture using ethylene glycol as solvent.

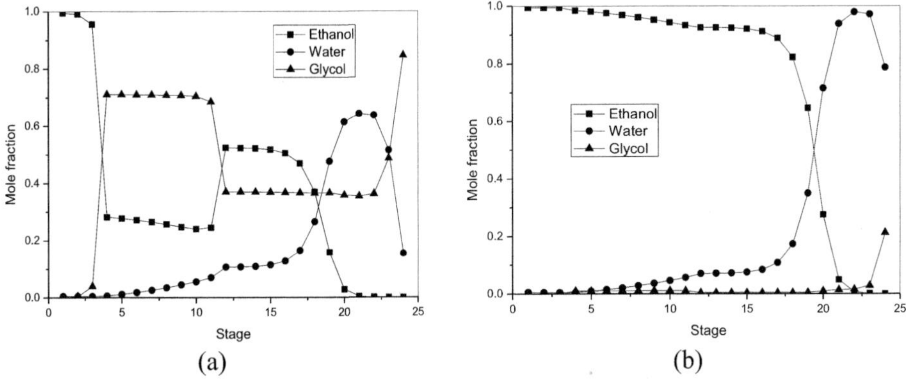

Figure 2. Composition profiles in liquid phase (a) and vapor phase (b) obtained by the extractive distillation column of the flowchart presented in Figure 1.

However, if there is a considerable difference between the boiling points of the components, it may be economically possible to obtain the intermediate component at the sidestream with high purity (Rooks et al., 1996). The objective of this work is to perform the optimization of the column shown in Figure 3 in order to find the operational conditions that provide the lowest energy consumption. A comparison of the energy consumption between the two configurations (the one presented in Figure 1 and the one presented in Figure 3) will also be presented.

3. Process Modeling

Steady state simulations were performed using the commercial software simulator Aspen Plus®, version 7.2, following the flowchart shown in Figure 3.The extractive distillation column (EXTRACT) aims to produce anhydrous ethanol, as top product, with a composition of 99.5 mass% of ethanol, as a function of the azeotropic mixture (ethanol-water) which has molar composition of 85.0 mol% of ethanol. The solvent used, ethylene glycol, was chosen based on studies that showed it to be the most favorable for this process (Dias, 2008).

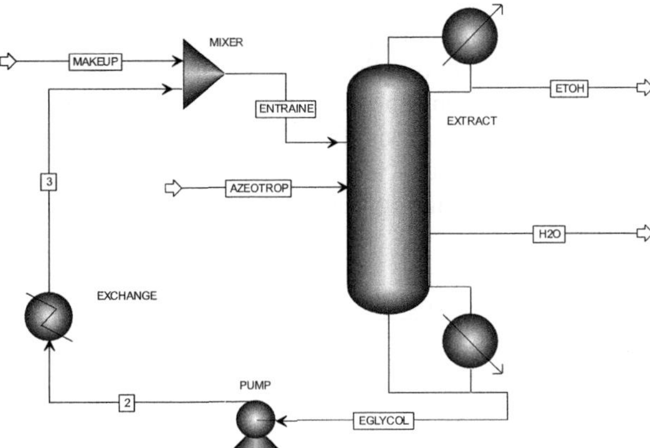

Figure 3. Extractive distillation column with a sidestream withdrawal.

The flowchart in Figure 3 was implemented in Aspen Plus® using RadFrac routine and the Fract1 model for defining the distillation column. The input data of the feed streams and sidestream withdrawal, as well as the extractive column specifications were taken from literature (Brito, 1997). The extractive column has 24 stages (including reboiler and condenser), the azeotropic mixture is fed on stage 13, the solvent is fed on stage 5 and the sidestream is connected at stage 19.The feed streams data are shown in Table 1:

4. Steady-State Results and Optimization

The optimization process analyzes all the variables simultaneously, searching for optimal values that provide the lowest energy consumption. Once the objective function and constraints are defined, the variables reflux ratio, solvent flow rate, distillate flow rate, sidestream flow rate, feed streams (AZEOTROP and ENTRAIN) and sidestream (H2O) positions will vary until the minimum value of the objective function is reached.The optimization procedure was performed using the Model Analysis Tools/Optimization in Aspen Plus®, which uses the Sequential Quadratic Programming (SQP) method to search for the optimal point. The objective function J was defined as the reboiler heat duty (Qr).Ethanol mass fraction of 0.995 at the top (x_D^{etoh}), ethylene glycol mass fraction of 0.999 at the bottom (x_B^{eg}) and watermass fraction of 0.956 at sidestream (y_S^{wt}) were defined as constraints. Mathematically we have:

Objective function to be minimized:

$$\text{Min} J = Q_r \tag{1}$$

Sunject to:

$$x_D^{etoh} \geq 0.995 \tag{2}$$

$$x_B^{eg} \geq 0.999 \tag{3}$$

$$y_S^{wt} \geq 0.956 \tag{4}$$

The manipulated variables used for optimization are represented here by SF (solvent feed flow), R (reflux ratio), D (distillate flow rate), SS (sidestream flow rate), SFS (solvent feed stage), AFS (azeotrope feed stage) and SWS (sidestream withdrawal stage).First, using the Model Analysis Tool/Optimization, the optimization procedure was performed using the continuous variables SF, D, SS and R. The results are shown in Table 2. The optimization involving variables SF, D, SS and R was able to reduce the

Table 1. Feed Streams Input Data

Stream	Variable	Value
Azeotropic (AZEOTROP)	Temperature (°C)	40.0
	Ethanol mole fraction	0.85
	Molar flow (kmol/hr)	100.00
Solvent (ENTRAIN)	Temperature (°C)	80.0
	Ethylene glycol molar fraction	1.00
	Molar flow (kmol/hr)	70.0

Table 2. Optimization Results

Variable	Initial Value	Final Value
SF (kmol/hr)	70.0	74.62
D (kmol/hr)	85.43	86.08
SS (kmol/hr)	14.7	13.84
R	0.85	0.346
Reboiler heat duty (GJ/hr)	8.72962	7.1119

reboiler heat duty by 18.53 %. Due to convergence problems using the Model Analysis Tools/Optimization tool to evaluate the influence of feed streams and sidestream positions (discrete variables), the sensitivity analysis tool Model Analysis Tools/Sensitivity of Aspen Plus® was used to find these optimal values.

The solvent feed position varied from stage 3 to 10, the position of the azeotropic feed varied from stage 11 to 19 and the sidestream position varied from stage 18 to 22. However, the results of this simulation showed that the influence of these variables on the reboiler duty was insignificant and they were not taken into account.

5. Comparison between the two configurations

To compare energy consumption between the two configurations, data were collected from the literature (Figueiredo et al., 2010). The flowchart used is similar to that shown in Figure 1 and the results are optimized. The specifications of the feed streams are the same as described in Table 1 of this paper. The number of stages of the extraction column is also the same, as well as the purity of the ethanol obtained as distillate product. The comparative results are shown in Table 3.

It was observed an increase in energy consumption by approximately 23% for the configuration with sidestream column with respect to the conventional configuration, but remember that only the extractive column was evaluated. So in order to have a more accurate comparison, another simulation was made in order to evaluate the energy consumption of the reboiler of the recovery column. The results of this simulation showed that the total energy consumption of the conventional configuration (two columns) was 0.08112 GJ/kmol of ethanol produced.

With this result, the difference in energy consumption of the two configuration drops to about 1.5%. It is important to mention that an optimization procedure to the recovery column was also carried out, where the distillate flowrate and reflux ratio were manipulated in order to obtain the lowest heat duty on the reboiler so that the required purity for the ethylene glycol recovered at the bottom of the column was equal to or higher than 99.9 mass%.

Table 3. Energy consumed per kmol of ethanol produced. Comparison between the two configurations.

Configuration	Qr/D (GJ/kmol)
Conventional extracitve column	0,06690
Sidestream column	0,08262

6. Conclusions

By using this configuration, the product compositions at the sidestream and bottom stream are as important as the composition at the top where ethanol, the product of interest, is recovered, since all three components should be separated with high purity. After performing the optimization procedure, the energy consumption of the reboiler was reduced by 18.5 %. The optimized values of the variables are close to the values of the initial condition, except for reflux ratio, which had a considerable reduction.

The comparison between the two configurations showed that the extractive distillation column with sidestream withdrawal can be competitive when compared to conventional configuration in terms of energy consumption of the reboiler.

Acknowledgement

The authors thank the National Council for Scientific and Technological Development (CNPq) for the financial support.

References

J. R. Alcántara-Avila, M. Kano, S. Hasebe, 2012, Environmental and economic optimization of distillation structures to produce anhydrous ethanol, Computer Aided Chemical Engineering, 30, 712-716.

R. P. Brito, 1997, Processo de destilação extrativa: modelagem dinâmica, simulação e avaliação de nova configuração, 202 f, Tese (Doutorado em Engenharia Química) – Faculdade de Engenharia Química, Universidade Estadual de Campinas, Campinas-SP.

M. O. S. Dias, 2008, Simulação do processo de produção de etanol a partir do açúcar e do bagaço, visando a integração do processo e a maximização da produção de energia e excedentes do bagaço, 253 f. Dissertação (Mestrado em Engenharia Química) – Faculdade de Engenharia Química, Universidade Estadual de Campinas, Campinas-SP.

M. F. Figueirêdo, B. P. Guedes, J. M. M. Araújo, L. G. S. Vasconcelos, R. P. Brito, 2010, Optimal design of extractive distillation columns – A systematic procedure using a process simulator, Chemical Engineering Research and Design, 89, 341-346.

A. A. Kiss, D. J-.P.C. Suszwalak, 2011, Enhanced bioethanol dehydration by extractive and azeotropic distillation in dividing-wall columns, Separation and Purification Technology, 86, 70-78.

R. E. Rooks, M. F. Malone, M. F. Doherty, 1996, Geometric Design Method for Side-Stream Distillation Columns, Ind. Eng. Chem. Res., 35, 3653-3664.

J. G. Segovia-Hernández, M. Vázquez-Ojeda, S. Hernández, A. Hernández-Aguirre, A. A. Kiss, 2012, Design and optimization of an ethanol dehydration process using stochastic methods, Separation and Purification Technology, 105, 90-97.

M. Vázquez-Ojeda, J. G. Segovia-Hernández, S. Hernández, A. Hernández-Aguirre, A. A. Kiss, 2013, Optimization of an Ethanol Dehydration Process Using Differential Evolution Algorithm, Computer Aided Chemical Engineering, 32, 217-222.

U.S. Dept. of Energy, Office of Energy Efficiency and Renewable Energy, Distillation Column Modeling Tools, DOE, Washington, DC, <http://www1.eere.energy.gov/manufacturing/industries_technologies/chemicals/pdfs/distillatidi.pdf> Accessed on 20/10/2013.

Jiří Jaromír Klemeš, Petar Sabev Varbanov and Peng Yen Liew (Editors)
Proceedings of the 24th European Symposium on Computer Aided Process Engineering – ESCAPE 24
June 15-18, 2014, Budapest, Hungary.

Modelling and Optimization of Methylene Blue Adsorption from Aqueous Solution Using Bentonite Clay

Ivana Savic,[a] Dragoljub Gajic,[b, c]* Stanisa Stojiljkovic,[a] Ivan Savic,[a] Stefano di Gennaro[b]

[a]*Department of Chemical Engineering, Faculty of Technology, University of Nis, Serbia,*

[b]*Department of Information Engineering, Computer Science and Mathematics, University of L'Aquila, Italy,*

[c]*Department of Signals and Systems, School of Electrical Engineering, University of Belgrade, Serbia.*

dragoljub.gajic@imperial.ac.uk

Abstract

Dyes are widely used in many process industries such as textiles, food, paper, cosmetics, plastics and rubbers. The adsorption process of dye from industrial wastewaters is an ideal alternative than other expensive treatment options. For the removal of methylene blue from aqueous solutions the different adsorbents were used such as wheat shells, kaolin, activated carbon, activated carbon from oil palm wood and bamboo, Indian Rosewood sawdust, natural zeolite and perlite. The aim of this paper was to model and optimize the adsorption process of methylene blue from aqueous solutions at room temperature using bentonite clay as the adsorbent. The central composite design was used as the suitable mathematical approach for investigation the interactions between process variables. The contact time (4.8 - 55.2 min), initial dye concentration (16.6 - 33.4 mgL^{-1}), and adsorbent concentration (1,113.7 - 12,886.3 mgL^{-1}) was consider as the independent variables, while the percentage of a dsorbed methylene blue was selected as the adequate response. The reduced second order polynomial model was successfully applied for fitting the experimental data. The optimal conditions were obtained using the numerical optimization. The predicted optimal value of adsorbed methylene blue was in agreement with the experimentally obtained value that clearly showed us both applicability and reliability of the numerical optimization applied in this particular case study.

Keywords: methylene blue, bentonite clay, adsorption, optimization, experimental design.

1. Introduction

Process industry is the largest global source of water pollution. For example, in the textile industry many colours and their degradation products are cancerogenic, mutagenic or toxic for organism (Mathur et al., 2005). Methylene blue is dark blue dye that can be found in wastewater. Having in mind the mentioned side effects, methylene blue has become the subject of strict legal regulations that require building plants within the industries which produce the high amount of this dye in water. The most efficient and cost effective procedure for maximal removal of methylene blue from aqueous medium is adsorption. The different adsorbents such as wheat shells (Bulut and Aydin,

2006), activated carbons (Hassan et al., 2014) and natural zeolite (Han et al., 2009) were used for adsorption of methylene blue from aqueous solutions. Bentonite clay is widely used in various industries as adsorbent due to its specific properties. Previous studies especially defined the level of porosity and adsorption properties of bentonite clay during adsorption process of methylene blue (Husein et al., 2007). Thus, the aim of this paper was to model and optimize the adsorption process of methylene blue from aqueous solutions at room temperature using bentonite clay as the adsorbent. The central composite design was used as the suitable mathematical approach for investigation the interactions between process variables. The advantages of this modeling in compared with "one variable at a time" approach are the reduced number of experiments, as well as the consumption of chemicals and time. In this paper, the contact time, initial dye concentration and adsorbent concentration was consider as the independent variables, while the percentage of adsorbed methylene blue was selected as the adequate response.

2. Experimental

2.1. Reagents.

The chemical used in experiments is methylene blue (Sigma Aldrich Chemie GmbH, Steinheim, Germany) and distilled water. A chemical composition of dried bentonite clay (from Prisjan, Serbia) at 110 °C is: 51.82% SiO_2, 0.34 % TiO_2, 26.86 % Al_2O_3, 2.30 % Fe_2O_3, 0.10 % MnO, 1.27 % MgO, 1.44 % CaO, 0.75 % Na_2O i 2.07 % K_2O.

2.2. Procedure of methylene blue adsorption.

The effect of contact time, methylene blue concentration and bentonite clay concentration on adsorption methylene blue was investigated at room temperature. Batch adsorption was performed in 250 mL flask. The total volume of investigated samples was 100 mL. The stock solution of methylene blue (1,000 mgL^{-1}) was prepared by dissolving methylene blue in the volumetric flask of 100 mL. The initial concentrations of methylene blue in all analyzed samples were obtained by dilution of the stock solution. After adsorption of methylene blue, the particles of bentonite clay were separated from liquid phase by vacuum filtration. Then, the filtrates were further analyzed by UV-VIS spectrophotometric method. The efficiency of adsorption was expressed in Eq. 1:

$$Y(\%) = \frac{(c_o - c_t)}{c_o} \cdot 100 \tag{1}$$

where is, c_o – the initial concentration of methylene blue, c_t – the concentration of methylene blue after adsorption, Y – the percentage of adsorbed methylene blue.

2.3. Determination of methylene blue.

The direct UV-VIS spectrophotometric method was used for determination of methylene blue in the samples. The absorption maxima of methylene blue is between 500 and 700 nm. The wavelength of 665 nm was selected as the most sensitive for monitoring methylene blue in the aqueous mediums. A linear regression curve y = 0.14307 x + 0.16903 was achieved in the concentration range of 1 – 20 mgL^{-1} with a correlation coefficient of 0.9976. The absorption spectra were recorded on UV-Vis spectrophotometer VARIAN Cary-100 Conc. at room temperature in the quartz cuvette 1×1 cm. Cary Win-UV software was used for processing spectra. Instrument has an automatic adjustment of wavelength with accuracy of 0.1 nm. The distilled water was used as the blank sample.

2.4. Central composite design.

The considered contact time was in the range of 4.77- 55.23 min, methylene blue concentration was from 16.59 to 33.41 mgL^{-1}, while the bentonite clay concentration was from 0.61 to 12.39 gL^{-1}. These important variables were selected based on the previously knowledge about analyzed process and estimation of parameters. In accordance with the central composite design matrix, the total number of experiments was 20. The interactions between these process variables were investigated using the experimental design, *i.e.*, the central composite design. The levels of rotatable central composite design are given in Table 1, where the values of α was 1.68.

3. Result and Discussion

The central composite design is more useful methodology for modelling various technological processes in the case of small number of preformed experiments compared with "one variable at a time" approach. Thus, in this paper it was applied for modelling adsorption process of methylene blue from aqueous medium using bentonite clay as adsorbent. A second order polynomial equation was successfully used for describing this process. The equation was reduced due to the presence of statistical insignificant term polynomial equation. The equation in terms of coded variables can be presented in the following way (Eq. 2):

$$Y = 99.62 + 4.70x_1 - 4.7x_1^2 - 1.53x_2 - 0.87x_2^2 + 0.59x_3 + 0.69x_1x_2 - 0.35x_1x_3 + 0.43x_2x_3 \quad (2)$$

The polynomial equation in terms of uncoded variables of factors was obtained by exchange of coded variables with actual values (Eq. 3).

$$Y = 66.012 + 1.377\tau - 0.0209\tau^2 + 0.986C_m - 0.035C_m^2 - 0.246C_b + 0.009\tau C_m - 0.007\tau C_b + 0.025C_mC_b \quad (3)$$

The results of analysis of variance (ANOVA) test is presented in Table 2. The statistical significance of equation terms was estimated based on p-values. The model terms are significant when this value is less than 0.0500, while the values greater than 0.1000 indicate that the model terms are not significant. The statistical insignificant terms is excluded from model in the aim its improvement. In this case, only x_3^2 is excluded from polynomial equation. The "Lack of Fit F-value" of 2.7 implies that the Lack of Fit is not significant relative to the pure error. There is a 14.76 % chance that a "Lack of Fit F-value" this large could occur due to noise. The important thing is that the non-significant lack of fit is good for purposed model. The values of root mean square error (RMSE), mean square error (RMSE) and mean absolute error (MAE), as well as the values of correlation coefficient (R^2) and cross-validated R^2 (Q^2) are also presented in Table 2. As it can be seen, a good agreement of R^2 and Q^2 and low values of errors indicate the adequacy of proposed model.

Table 1. Coded and actual levels of independent variables

Independent variable	Symbol		Actual values of coded levels				
	Coded	Uncoded	-1.68	-1	0	+1	+1.68
Contact time [min]	x_1	τ	4.77	15	30	45	55.23
Methylene blue concentration [mg L^{-1}]	x_2	C_m	16.59	20	25	30	33.41
Bentonite concentration [g L^{-1}]	x_3	C_b	0.61	3	6.5	10	12.39

Table 2. ANOVA for response surface reduced quadratic model

		SS	df	MS	F	p
(1)Var1	(L)	301.22	1	301.22	1,436.03	<0.0001
Var1	(Q)	320.95	1	320.95	1,530.08	<0.0001
(2)Var2	(L)	31.93	1	31.93	152.20	<0.0001
Var2	(Q)	10.90	1	10.90	51.95	<0.0001
(3)Var3	(L)	4.80	1	4.80	22.88	0.0006
1L by 2L		3.86	1	3.86	18.41	0.0013
1L by 3L		0.99	1	0.99	4.70	0.0530
2L by 3L		1.49	1	1.49	7.09	0.0221
Lack of Fit		1.76	6	0.30	2.70	0.1476
Pure Error		0.54	5	0.1088		
Error		2.31	11	0.21		
Total SS		670.38	19			
R^2=0.9966; Q^2=0.9966; RMSE=0.3386; MSE=0.1147; MAE=0.2723						

The experimental and predicted values of adsorbed amount of methylene blue with random order of experimental runs are given in Table 3. The combination of process parameters is in accordance with matrix of the central composite design.

In this study, the residues have a normal distribution, because they follow a straight line with minimal variation from its direction. In this way, the adequacy of proposed model for observed sets of data was confirmed.

The effect of contact time and methylene blue concentration at bentonite clay concentration of 6.5 mg L^{-1} is given in Figure 1a. The contact time has the significant impact than the initial concentration of dye. The maximum dye adsorption was achieved after 35 min. The impact of contact time and bentonite clay concentration on the amount of adsorbed methylene blue at methylene blue concentration of 25 mg L^{-1} is presented in Figure 1b. The parameter of adsorbent concentration has a negligible effect on the amount adsorbed compound. The effect of methylene blue concentration and bentonite clay concentration on the amount of adsorbed dye at the contact time of 30 min is shown in Figure 1c.

The following optimal conditions of adsorption, contact time of 31.85 min, methylene blue concentration of 24.78 mg L^{-1} and bentonite clay concentration of 5.25 g L^{-1} were obtained using numerical optimization. The predicted amount of adsorbed methylene blue (100 %) under these conditions is almost the same as the experimental value of 99.7 %.

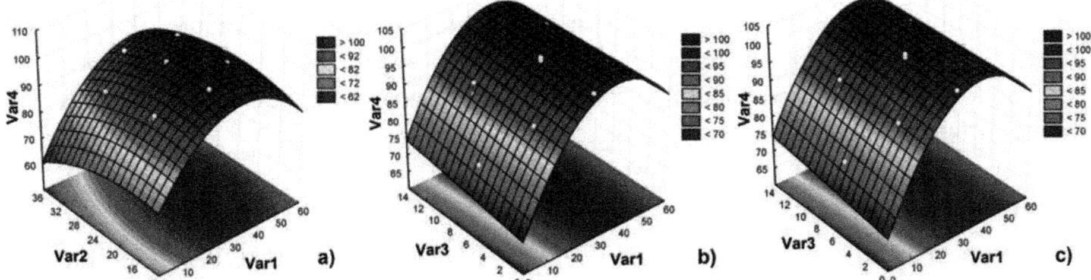

Figure 1. The effect of process parameters on the adsorption of methylene blue from aqueous solution using bentonite clay

Table 3. The experimental runs of central composite design for methylene blue adsorption from aqueous medium

Std	t, min	C_m, mg L^{-1}	C_b, mg L^{-1}	Percentage of adsorbed methylene blue	
				$Y_{observed}$	$Y_{predicted}$
14	30.00	25.00	12.39	100.00	100.62
3	15.00	30.00	3.00	85.70	85.77
20	30.00	25.00	6.50	99.79	99.62
10	55.23	25.00	6.50	94.70	94.24
4	45.00	30.00	3.00	97.10	97.25
9	4.77	25.00	6.50	78.03	78.44
15	30.00	25.00	6.50	99.95	99.62
16	30.00	25.00	6.50	99.92	99.62
2	45.00	20.00	3.00	99.16	99.78
7	15.00	30.00	10.00	89.11	88.52
11	30.00	16.59	6.50	100.00	99.75
6	45.00	20.00	10.00	99.44	99.40
8	45.00	30.00	10.00	98.54	98.60
17	30.00	25.00	6.50	99.59	99.62
18	30.00	25.00	6.50	99.07	99.62
5	15.00	20.00	10.00	92.22	92.10
19	30.00	25.00	6.50	99.80	99.62
13	30.00	25.00	0.61	98.90	98.63
1	15.00	20.00	3.00	91.10	91.08
12	30.00	33.41	6.50	94.40	94.60

4. Conclusions

In this study, the adsorption process of methylene blue from aqueous medium was successfully modeled and optimized by the central composite design. A second order polynomial equation with excluded quadratic term of dye concentration was presented as a suitable for describing this process. The highest effect on the dye adsorption has the contact time. The optimal conditions of adsorption were obtained using numerical optimization. The predicted and experimental values of adsorbed amount of methylene blue are almost the same. A high value of R^2 and good agreement between R^2 and Q^2, as well as low values of errors indicate the adequacy of proposed model in the investigated range of independent variables.

Acknowledgements:

The support from the Marie Curie FP7-ITN "ENERGY-SMARTOPS", Contract No: PITN-GA-2010-264940, the Erasmus Mundus Action II EUROWEB Project and the Ministry of Education, Science and Technological Development of the Republic of Serbia under the project TR-34012 is gratefully acknowledged.

References

A.F. Hassan, A.M. Abdel-Mohsen, M.M. Fouda, 2014, Comparative study of calcium alginate, activated carbon, and their composite beads on methylene blue adsorption, Carbohydrate Polymers, 102, 192-198.

H. Hussein, H. Khudhaier, N. Al-Khafaji, H. Hadi, H. Ali, 2007, Study of the Adsorption of Methylene Blue from Aqueous Solution: a Comparison between Iraqi & English bentonite Activity as Adsorbents, Jornal of Kerbala University, 5, 1.

N. Mathur, P. Bhatnagar, P. Bakre, 2005, Assessing mutagenicity of textile dyes from pali (Rajasthan) using Ames bioassay, Applied Ecology and Environmental Research, 4, 111-118.

R. Han, J. Zhang, P. Han, Y. Wang, Z. Zhao, M. Tang, 2009, Study of equilibrium, kinetic and thermodynamic parameters about methylene blue adsorption onto natural zeolite, Chemical Engineering Journal, 145, 3, 496-504.

R. Han, Y. Wang, W. Zou, Y. Wang, J. Shi, 2007, Comparison of linear and nonlinear analysis in estimating the Thomas model parameters for methylene blue adsorption onto natural zeolite in fixed-bed column, Journal of Hazardous Materials, 145, 1-2, 331-335.

Y. Bulut, H. Aydin, 2006, A kinetics and thermodynamics study of methylene blue adsorption on wheat shells, Desalination, 194, 1-3, 259-267.

Jiří Jaromír Klemeš, Petar Sabev Varbanov and Peng Yen Liew (Editors)
Proceedings of the 24th European Symposium on Computer Aided Process Engineering – ESCAPE 24
June 15-18, 2014, Budapest, Hungary.

Optimization of a Multiproduct Lignocellulosic Biorefinery using a MILP Approximation

Aristide Giuliano[a], Raffaele Cerulli[b], Massimo Poletto[a], Giancarlo Raiconi[b], Diego Barletta[a,]*

[a] *Department of Industrial Engineering, University of Salerno, Via Giovanni Paolo II, 132, 84084 Fisciano (SA), Italy*

[b] *Department of Mathematics and Computer Science, University of Salerno, Via Giovanni Paolo II, 132, 84084 Fisciano (SA), Italy*

dbarletta@unisa.it

Abstract

A methodology to reduce the complexity of the process optimization was applied to a multiproduct biorefinery fed by lignocellulosic biomass. A process superstructure was built to consider alternative process pathways to levulinic acid, succinic acid and ethanol. A Mixed Integer Non-Linear Problem was obtained and transformed in a Mixed Integer Linear Problem by means of a discretization procedure of the non-linear variables. Preliminary results for the base case problem yielded a biomass allocation of about 65 % to levulinic acid, 24 % to succinic acid and 11 % to ethanol. A sensitivity analysis highlighted the significant effect of the price of the high value chemicals, levulinic acid and succinic acid, and of the plant size on the optimal biomass allocation.

Keywords: biorefinery, optimization, ethanol, succinic acid, levulinic acid.

1. Introduction

The increasing ratio between the worldwide demand for fuels and chemicals and the amount of petroleum reserves and the planned reduction of greenhouse gas emissions are fostering the development of non-petroleum based processes. In this framework, second generation biorefineries are considered promising processes in order to convert lignocellulosic biomass not only into biofuels for transportation, but also to added-value chemicals (Werpy and Peterson, 2004). However, the commercialization of conversion technologies have been hindered by several factors including unavailability of reliable feedstock supply systems, and non optimized conversion systems. For the latter issue, the optimization of the process synthesis and integration can help to identify the most promising pathways and to increase the profitability of bio-based fuels and chemicals production.

Process synthesis methods have been widely used in the conceptual design and optimization of sustainable and cost-effective bioethanol production plants (Fumero et al., 2011). The process synthesis is based on mathematical programming. A systematic methodology of mathematical programming consists in discrete/continuous optimization problems referred to as Mixed Integer Non-Linear Programming (MINLP) problems. Several authors considered different methods of process optimization (Cheali et al., 2013) like disjunctive programming (Ponce-Ortega et al., 2012) and MINLP problem solution (Nawaz et al., 2011). In some cases optimization methods include iterative methods, interfacing the optimization software with technical computing software (e.g. Matlab) and process simulation software (e.g. Aspen Plus) (Geraili et al., 2014). In all these cases the authors identified the best process pathways among the available alternatives or the best end products to maximize a techno-economic objective function. However, only few works addressed the optimization of the biomass distribution among alternative pathways of a biorefinery co-producing alcohols (ethanol or butanol), high-value chemicals (succinic acid) and electricity (Nawaz et al., 2011). Significant improvements in the techno-economic feasibility can be also obtained by thermal conversion of the biomass components that cannot be easily converted by chemical or enzymatic processes (Cheali et al., 2013).

In this paper a simplified approach based on Mixed Integer Linear Programming is presented and applied to find an approximate solution of the non-linear problem of the economic optimization of a multiproduct lignocellulosic biomass refinery. In particular, the co-production of two of the top value added chemicals (Werpy & Peterson, 2004), levulinic acid and succinic acid, and of ethanol is studied. The aim of the work is twofold. The first one is the assessment of a linearization methodology for the process synthesis and optimization. The second one is the evaluation of the optimal mass flow rate of each product in order to maximize the net profit, considering the investment costs and the operating costs.

2. Superstructure of the biorefinery process

After an accurate literature survey of the available process pathways, a superstructure of a biorefinery for the co-production of succinic acid, levulinic acid and ethanol was built. The biorefinery superstructure consists of six sections (Figure 1). The biomass pretreatment section is not included and, thus, the process is directly fed by cellulose, hemicellulose and lignin. Lignin pathways are not considered.

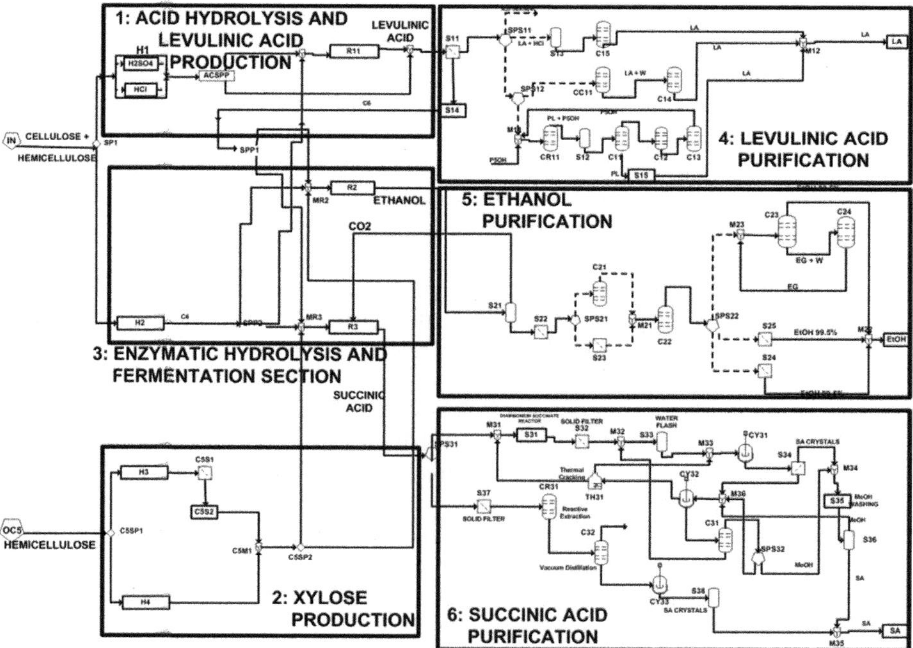

Figure 1. Superstructure of the multi-product biorefinery.

Solubilized hemicellulose and solid cellulose can be sent separately or mixed together to either acid or enzymatic hydrolysis separately. Section 1 includes the acid hydrolysis to produce glucose and xylose, and the production of levulinic acid and formic acid. Two different acid catalysts (H_2SO_4 and HCl), for which relevant reaction kinetics, were considered. In section 2 xylose is produced by acid hydrolysis reactor or enzymatic hydrolysis reactor. The third section includes the enzymatic hydrolysis to produce glucose and xylose, and subsequent fermentation to obtain succinic acid or ethanol using two appropriate microorganisms. The stream of dissolved sugars produced by enzymatic hydrolysis is mixed with the sugars stream produced by the acid hydrolysis and the hemicellulose hydrolysis. The resulting stream is sent to fermentation stages. Sections 4, 5 and 6 concern the purification of the desired products. In section 4 levulinic acid is recovered and purified to 99 %wt by means of three alternative processes: a) separation and recovery of acid catalyst HCl and subsequent distillation; b) recovery of H_2SO_4 by a chromatographic column and subsequent separation from water by distillation; c) solvent extraction of organic compounds with subsequent train of distillations and recovery of H_2SO_4. The purification section (section 5) of ethanol, up to 99.5 % purity, includes both commonly used techniques as distillation and extractive distillation, and alternative techniques as pervaporation membranes or molecular sieves. The purification of succinic acid (section 6) is carried out alternately by: a) reactive crystallization and purification with methanol; b) solvent extraction combined with a distillation column and a crystallizer. In this superstructure a potential mass integration between different pathways can be identified by using intermediate by-products as feedstock for other process units for the alternative main products. For example, CO_2 formed by the ethanol fermentation can be used as a feed for the succinic acid fermentation and sugars formed by acid hydrolysis on the levulinic acid pathway can be used as a feed for the fermentation units.

3. Model derivation and optimization methodology

The optimization problem consisted in finding the distribution of the products mass flows to optimize an objective function. An economic objective function, *Z*, was derived as a simplified profit of the biorefinery. It was calculated as the difference between the revenues of the sales of the three products and the sum of the annualized capital costs, CC_q, and the operating costs, OC_r:

$$Min\ Z = -\left(\sum_{p \in P} p_p F_p^{out} - \sum_{q \in Q} \frac{CC_q}{years} - \sum_{r \in R} OC_r\right) \quad (1)$$

where F_p^{out} are the mass flow rate of the products, p_p are the product prices. The optimization problem included the mass and energy balance equations on the units of the superstructure (reactors, fermenters, splits, mixers, separators) using the product yield of each unit. In these equations all mass flow rates appear linearly (Ahmetovic & Grossmann, 2011). Differently, the yields to product are nonlinear functions of the residence times and of the operating conditions. Non-linear relationships between the yield to product and the residence time of reactors were derived by separately solving the material balance ODEs by means of Matlab. Simplified design equations were used for the other units. In particular, the shortcut method proposed by Biegler et al. (1997) was used for the sizing of separation columns. The quantity of catalysts, nutrients and enzymes and the utilities flows (LP and HP steam, energy consumption) were estimated by linear relationships with the main stream flow rates or energy. Equipment costs were estimated by power law equations with scaling factors.

The process optimization problem was completed by two types of inequality constraints: 1) constraints limiting the mass or energy flows or the size of a piece of equipment; 2) constraints for selecting process alternatives by means of splits. The last constraints were coupled to mass balances corresponding to the splits. In particular, in the reaction sections of the superstructure (sections 1 to 3 in Figure 1) the splits can feed different process pathways at the same time. This allows the biomass allocation to different products. Thus, the relevant split ratios of different paths are real variables. Instead, in the separation sections of the superstructure (sections 4 to 6 in Figure 1) the split can feed only one pathway among the alternative ones. Therefore, the split ratios are binary variables {0, 1}.

Once the mathematical problem was formulated, a Mixed Integer Non Linear Problem (MINLP) was obtained. The search of the optimal solution of a MINLP problem might be very difficult. As a result, a variable discretization method was applied to linearize the problem (Scott et al., 2013). In particular, for each nonlinear variable (residence time, process yield) a vector of possible values of the variable was considered. The original variable was set equal to the sum of the product of each of these values and a binary variable. In the problem solution only one of these binary variables was allowed to be equal to 1. This transformation can be expressed in mathematical terms as follows for a yield variable η:

$$\eta \approx \sum_{i=1}^{n} \bar{\eta}_i y_i^d \quad ; \quad \sum_{i=1}^{n} y_i^d = 1 \; ; \; y_i^d \in \{0,1\} \tag{2}$$

where η is the yield non-linear function, $\bar{\eta}_i$ are the discretized values of the non-linear variable η, y^d are the binary variables of the discretization. The calculation of the discrete values of yields and residence times was performed by solving the material balance ordinary differential equations by using Matlab. This transformation allowed obtaining a mixed linear problem (MILP) as an approximation of the initial MINLP problem:

$$\begin{cases} Min\, Z = \alpha\, x^L + \beta\, y + \gamma\, y^d \\ A\, x^L + B\, y + \Gamma\, y^d = \delta \\ A' x^L + B' y + \Gamma' y^d \le \delta' \\ x^L \in R^+,\ y,\ y^d \in \{0,1\} \end{cases} \tag{3}$$

where α, β, γ, δ, δ' are parameter vectors, A, B, Γ, A', B', Γ' are parameter matrices. On the one hand, this simplification allowed using more efficient solution methods for MILP optimization problems. On the other hand, a significant increase of the number of binary variables and real variables was implied. Finally, the non linear equations for the equipment investment costs were approximated by means of a piecewise linearization in order to obtain also a linear economic objective function.

The resulting MILP problem consisted in one objective function, 2,161 equality constraints, 4,653 inequality constraints, 4,167 real variables and 1,371 binary variables.

Table 1. Parameter values used in the sensitivity analysis.

	Base case value	Low value	High value
Fed Biomass (t/h)	50	5	500
Levulinic Acid Price ($/kg)	5.0	2.5	7.5
Succinic Acid Price ($/kg)	7.5	3.75	11.25
Ethanol Price ($/kg)	0.75	0.375	1.125

The resolution of the MILP problem was performed by means of the optimization code CPLEX with the modeling system AMPL.

4. Results

The base case optimization problem was solved for a 50.0 t_{dry}/h biomass flowrate with a composition of 50 $\%_{wt}$ of cellulose, 25 $\%_{wt}$ of hemicellulose and 25 $\%_{wt}$ of lignin and ash. The base case values of the price of the three products are reported in Table 1. The computation time required for each optimization performed was around a few tens of minutes by using a workstation with a Intel Xeon 2 GHz CPU/8GB RAM. Considering the complexity of the process system, this computation time appears encouraging and the use of the approximation method seems promising to tackle the complexity of large superstructures.

The results of the optimization problem for the base case yielded a maximum net profit equal to 276.84 M$/y. Biomass allocation can be represented by the mass percentage of the fed biomass that is converted into levulinic acid, succinic acid and ethanol. For the base case, the problem solution indicated an optimal allocation of 65.2 % of the biomass to levulinic acid (87,408 t/y), 24.0 % to succinic acid (1,800 t/y) and 10.8 % to ethanol (648 t/y). The production of levulinic acid is limited by the availability of cellulose present in the biomass, while succinic acid production is limited by the production of CO_2 from ethanol fermentation.

A sensitivity analysis was performed on the effect of the products price by varying the base case values by ± 50 %. Corresponding values are reported in Table 1. The corresponding optimal values of the biomass allocation are reported as bars in the Tornado diagrams of Figure 2. The base case values are reported along the vertical line. Inspection of the diagrams reveals that the price of levulinic acid and succinic acid has a significant effect on the optimal allocation. In fact, either a 50 % increase of the levulinic acid price or a 50 % decrease of the succinic acid price makes the succinic acid production equal to zero. Conversely, either a 50 % decrease of the levulinic acid price or a 50 % increase of the succinic acid price makes the succinic acid production double. Differently, the ethanol price variation does not significantly affect the biomass allocation due to its much lower value.

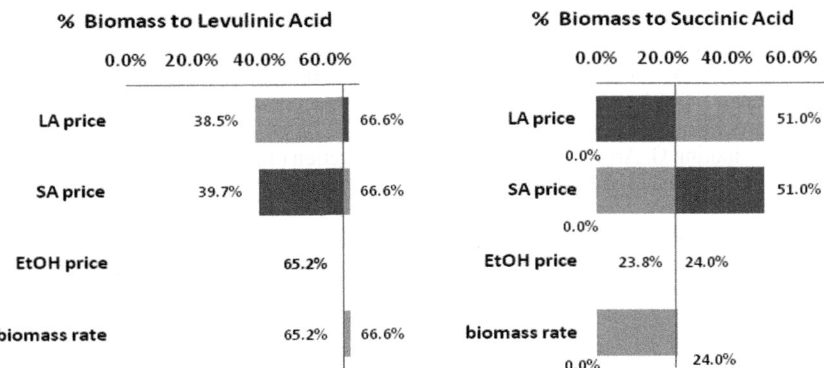

Figure 2. Tornado diagram of biomass allocation by mass: dark coloured bar, low value of the independent variable; light coloured bar, high value of the independent variable.

Finally, a sensitivity analysis was performed also on the plant size by increasing and decreasing the biomass flowrate by a factor of 10. The Tornado diagram of Figure 2 shows that the levulinic acid production remains unchanged, while a 10 times larger biomass rate implies an increase of the ethanol production at the expenses of the vanishing of the succinic acid. As expected, an increasing biomass rate plays a beneficial role on the return on investment. Approximated values of the ROI calculated only on the base of the bare module capital costs indicated an increase of about 4 percentage points for a biomass rate increasing from 5 t/h to 500 t/h.

5. Conclusions

This work demonstrated that the proposed linearization procedure was able to successfully reduce the complexity of a process optimization problem such as that of a multi-product biorefinery. Results showed the economic advantage of a multiple product biorefinery due to a better exploitation of all the biomass components. A sensitivity analysis highlighted the significant effect of the price of the high value chemicals, levulinic acid and succinic acid on the optimal biomass allocation. Future work will focus on completing the superstructure by including also the process section of the biomass pretreatment and the process section of the thermochemical valorization of lignin. The heat integration opportunities on the complete process plant will be also assessed.

References

E. Ahmetovic, I.E. Grossmann, 2011, Global superstructure optimization for the design of integrated process water networks, AIChE Journal, 67, 2, 434 – 457.

L.T. Biegler, I.E. Grossmann, A.W. Westerberg, 1997, Systematic Methods of Chemical Process Design, Prentice-Hall, USA.

P. Cheali, K.V. Gernaey, G. Sin, 2013, Synthesis and Design of optimal biorefinery using an expanded network with thermochemical and biochemical biomass conversion platforms, Computer Aided Chemical Engineering, 32, 985 – 990.

Y. Fumero, G. Corsano, J.M. Montagna, 2011, Simultaneous design and scheduling of a plant for production and derivates, Computer Aided Chemical Engineering, 29, 1416 – 1420.

A. Geraili, P. Sharma, J.A. Romagnoli, 2014, A modeling framework for design of nonlinear renewable energy systems through integrated simulation modeling and metaheuristic optimization: Applications to biorefineries, Computers and Chemical Engineering, 61, 102 – 117.

M. Nawaz, E. Zondervan, J. Woodley, R. Gani, 2011, Design of an Optimal biorefinery, Computer Aided Chemical Engineering, 29, 371 – 376.

J. M. Ponce-Ortega, V. Pham, M. M. El-Halwagi, A. A. El-Baz, 2012, A Disjunctive Programming Formulation for the Optimal Design of Biorefinery Configurations, Industrial & Engineering Chemistry Research, 51, 3381 – 3400.

F. Scott, F. Venturini, G. Aroca, R. Conejeros, 2013, Selection of process alternatives for lignocellulosic bioethanol production using a MILP approach, Bioresource Technology, 148, 525 – 534.

T. Werpy, G. Peterson, 2004, Top Value Added Chemicals From Biomass Volume I: Results of Screenin for Potential Candidates from Sugars and Synthesis Gas, U.S. Department of Energy, NREL/TP-510-35523, Golden, USA.

Jiří Jaromír Klemeš, Petar Sabev Varbanov and Peng Yen Liew (Editors)
Proceedings of the 24th European Symposium on Computer Aided Process Engineering – ESCAPE 24
June 15-18, 2014, Budapest, Hungary.

Sustainable Design and Synthesis of Algal Biorefinery for Biofuel Production

Jian Gong, Fengqi You*

Northwestern University, 2145 Sheridan Road, Evanston, IL 60208 , USA
you@northwestern.edu

Abstract

We develop a new process superstructure of algal biorefinery for biological carbon sequestration and hydrocarbon biofuel production that encompasses off-gas purification, algae cultivation, harvesting and dewatering, lipid extraction, remnant treatment, biogas utilization and algal oil upgrading stages. Multiple technology alternatives are considered in the process superstructure, including direct off-gas and purified carbon dioxide by monoethanolamine process; open pond and three types of photobioreactors for algae culture; flotation thickening, filtration and centrifugation to dehydrate algal slurry; hexane and n-butane as lipid extractant; anaerobic digestion and catalytic gasification to exploit algal remnant; two catalysts, Co-Mo and Ni-Mo in the hydroprocessing reactor. This process reuses all the produced CO2 from the processing units that leads to zero direct greenhouse gas emission of the entire process. Based on the superstructure, we propose a mixed-integer nonlinear programming model to minimize the unit carbon sequestration and utilization cost. We further apply a tailored branch-and-refine algorithm based on successive piecewise linear approximation to globally optimize problem efficiently. The optimization results indicate clear economic and environmental advantage when the feed gas is limited only during the day.

Keywords: Superstructure optimization, algal biorefinery, biological carbon sequestration, zero GHG emission.

1. Introduction

Climate change, a well-recognized fact currently, is critical enough to jeopardize our society and environment. As a result, researchers are seeking every possible method to mitigate side effects of global warming. One of the most appealing methods involves biological carbon sequestration and utilization by algal biorefinery. "Algae" refers to a diverse category of organisms which consume carbon dioxide during photosynthesis and have excellent potential of accumulating lipid materials that can be upgraded to hydrocarbon liquid fuels through transesterification or hydroprocessing. Martin and Grossmann (Martin and Grossmann, 2013) studied the optimal algal composition for the simultaneous production of bioethanol and biodiesel. Gebreslassie et al. (Gebreslassie et al., 2013b) proposed a superstructure-based optimization framework of algal biorefinery for hydrocarbon biofuel production and carbon sequestration. However, none of these works considers the latest technologies such as thermal chemical conversion of wet algae remnant, and none addresses the computational issues by apply tailored strategies and algorithms to the mixed-integer nonlinear programming (MINLP) problem.

In this work, we first develop a new process superstructure of the algal biorefinery for biological carbon sequestration and utilization that comprises seven major sections: off-gas purification, algae cultivation, harvesting and dewatering, lipid extraction, remnant treatment, biogas utilization and algal oil upgrading. Each section includes multiple technology/process alternatives. Based on the process superstructure, we propose a mixed-integer nonlinear programming model to determine the most economical process design and the corresponding operation subject to mass balance constraints, energy balance constraints, techno-economic constraints and life cycle assessment (LCA) constraints (You et al., 2012). To improve the computational efficiency, we apply a tailored branch-and-refine algorithm based on successive piecewise linear approximation to globally optimize the resulting non-convex MINLP problem. The major novelties of this work are:

- a new superstructure of algal biorefinery for biological carbon sequestration and utilization and the corresponding MINLP model for process design and synthesis
- a tailored branch-and-refine algorithm to efficiently and globally solve the non-convex MINLP problems for superstructure optimization
- the minimum unit carbon sequestration and utilization cost is \$1.48 /t of CO_2 when the flue gas from a 600 MW coal-fired power plant is delivered to the biorefinery only during daytime. The optimal process design of this case employs open pond, flotation thickening, n-butanol solvent extraction, anaerobic digestion, biogas utilized to produce hydrogen and Ni-Mo as the catalyst in algal oil upgrading reactor.

2. Process Description

As shown in Figure 1, the algal biorefinery for biological carbon sequestration integrated with hydrocarbon production encompasses seven major sections: off-gas purification, algae cultivation, harvesting and dewatering, lipid extraction, remnant treatment, biogas utilization and algal oil upgrading. Each section contains multiple alternative technologies. If biogas combustion is selected in biogas utilization section, the resulting off-gas will be a mix of nitrogen, carbon dioxide, oxygen and water. One easy option is to send the off-gas directly to bioreactors; the other employs monoethanolamine adsorption (MEA) to separate carbon dioxide from the off-gas. In this work, we choose microalga Phaeodactylum tricornutum to cultivate in one of the four alternatives: open pond, flat plate photobioreactor, bubble column photobioreactor and tubular photobioreactor. Open pond is less expensive in terms of construction and operation, while closed photobioreactors tend to show high productivity. Free sunlight radiation is available only during the day, therefore it becomes a critical decision whether to provide artificial light source after sunset or to store all the feed gas and recycled gas at night for algae production in the next day. The mature algae slurry is considerably dilute, so firstly a sedimentation basin is employed to concentrate algae slurry to 1%. Then one advanced dehydration technology among flotation thickening, filtration or centrifugation, is required to further reduce the moisture. The existence of some algal biological features, such as cell wall, physically prevents the contact of solvent with lipid materials. As a result, microwave for cell disruption is an essential step prior to lipid extraction process. We consider hexane or n-butanol as the solvent for lipid extraction. Following lipid extraction, the remaining algae body or remnant can be handled by anaerobic digestion or catalytic gasification. Both pathways produce biogas, liquid effluent rich in soluble nutrition and solid waste regarded as a farming fertilizer. Besides, catalytic gasification produces an extra oil stream which is counted as renewable diesel in the process. Biogas can be utilized directly on site by combustion or steam reforming. If biogas is burned with adequate pressurized air in the combustor, the energy of the hot flue gas is converted to electricity in both gas turbine and HRSG.

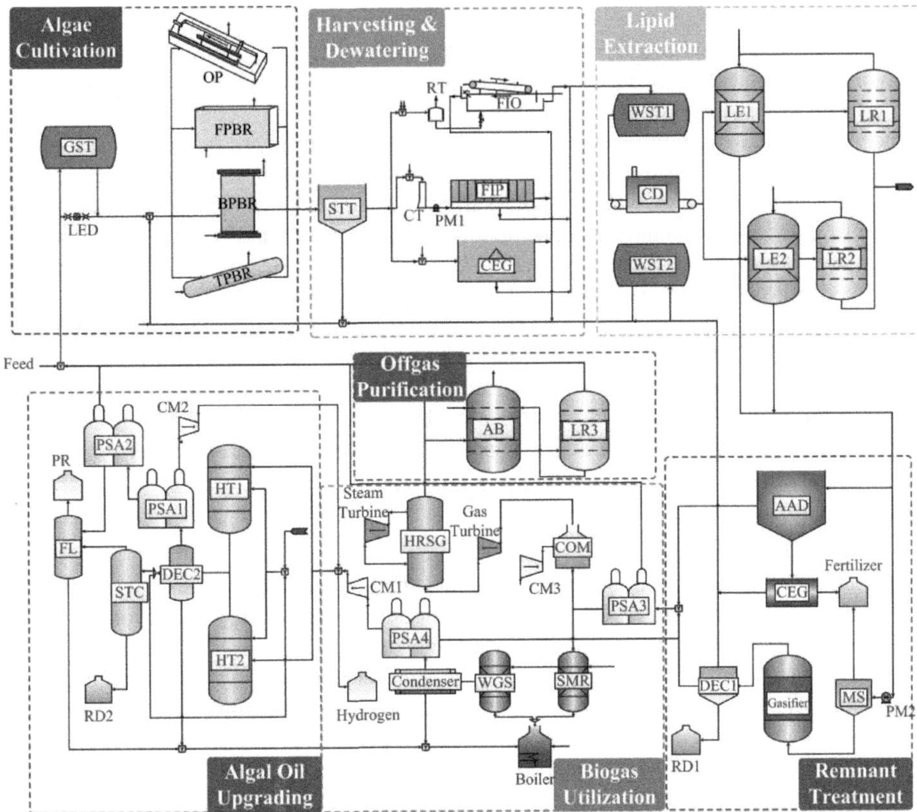

Figure 1. Superstructure of the algal biorefinery for feed gas delivered 24 h a day. GST, gas storage tank; LED, light-emitting diode; OP, open pond; FPBR, flat-plate photobioreactor; BPBR, bubble photobioreactor; TPBR, tubular photobioreactor; STT, sedimentation basin; RT, retention tank; CT, conditioning tank; PM, pump; FIO, flotation thickening; FIP, filtration; CEG, centrifugation; WST, liquid storage tank; CD, cell disruption; LE, lipid extractor; LR, extractant recovery; AAD, anaerobic digestion; MS, mineral separator; DEC, decanter; PSA, pressure swing adsorption; COM, combustor; CM, compressor; HRSG, heat recovery steam generation; AB, monoethanolamine adsorption; SMR, steam reforming; WGS, water gas shift; HT, hydrotreating; STC, distillation column; FL, flash drum; RD, renewable diesel; PR, propane.

On the other hand, if biogas from upstream was sequentially sent to steam reforming and water gas shift reactors to assist hydrogen production, the natural gas purchase cost would be largely reduced. For algal oil upgrading, there are two major hydroprocessing mechanisms: hydrodeoxygenation (Ni-Mo) and decarboxylation (Co-Mo). There is no clear boundary in practical experiments, but a dominant mechanism is recognized for different catalysts.

3. Model formulation

(P1)	min	Unit sequestration and utilization cost
	s.t.	Mass balance constraints
		Energy balance constraints
		Economic evaluation constraints
		Environmental impact constraints

We propose an MINLP problem as the above. In mass balance constraints, the physical separation operations are model by mass balance of each species. The process units involving chemical reactions are modeled by atomic balance if the reaction details are available; otherwise, product distribution is applied. The energy constraints include heat and power generation and consumption. Most of them are given by the product of unit energy production or usage times the target flow rate. The economic constraints identify the total annualized cost which is the sum of annualized investment cost and annual operating cost. The annualized investment cost is derived based on the capital cost of each unit which is evaluated by sizing equations. At last, environmental impact is assessed following the principles of LCA (You and Wang, 2011). We choose global warming potential (GWP) (Gebreslassie et al., 2013a) with a time horizon of 100 years as the metric of LCA (Wang et al., 2013). The objective function is formulated as the actual unit annual sequestration and utilization cost. The actual annual sequestration and utilization cost is defined by total annualized cost minus the revenue from selling all products, including renewable diesel, propane, extra hydrogen and fertilizer.

4. Solution approaches

4.1. Model reformulation and relaxation

The nonlinear terms in the optimization model include one bilinear term to quantify the volume of the bioreactor and some power functions in the capital cost evaluation. The bilinear term, which is the product of a non-negative continuous variable and a binary variable, can be linearized by introducing an auxiliary variable, a big-M parameter and auxiliary constraints. We approximate the concave power functions by piecewise secant functions (Yue and You, 2013). For convex power functions, we apply multiple tangent functions (Quesada and Grossmann, 1995). As shown in Figure 2, the piecewise linear approximations in both concave and convex cases are under estimators of the corresponding power functions. After reformulation and relaxation, the original problem is converted to a mixed-integer linear programming (MILP) problem (P2).

4.2. Branch-and-refine algorithm

The algorithm (You and Grossmann, 2011) starts by initializing (P2), the upper bound and the lower bound. (P2) can be solved efficiently by linear solvers. The new upper bound is determined as the smaller one between the feasible objective function value of (P1) and the previous upper bound; the lower bound is selected as the larger one of optimal objective function value of (P2) and the existing lower bound.

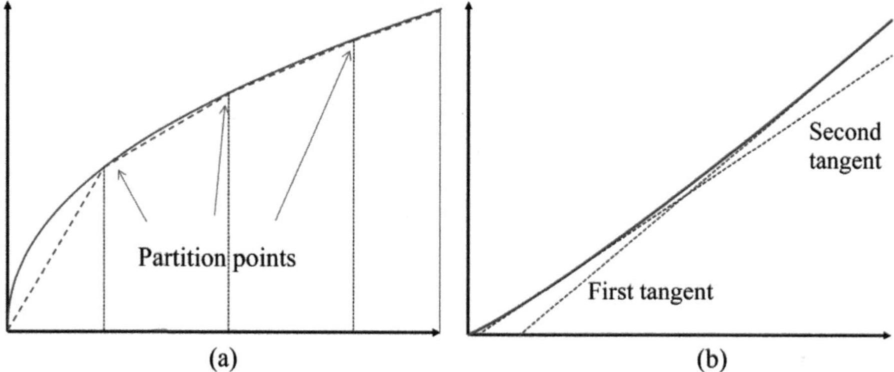

Figure 2. Illustration of piecewise linear approximation of power functions. (a) Concave function lower bounded by secants. (b) Convex function lower bounded by tangents.

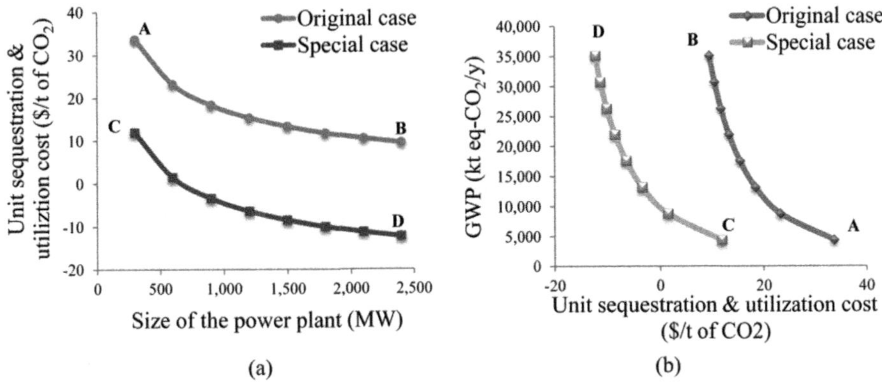

Figure 3. Optimal results of both cases. (a) Economic behavior. (b) Environmental impact.

If the gap between the upper bound and the lower bound is larger than the optimality tolerance, the algorithm will proceed to the next iteration. Following the optimal solution of (P2), a new partition point can be added to the current interval and piecewise linear approximation is refined. After the new (P2) is solved, we apply similar updating procedure to examine the new solutions.

5. Result and discussion

For the sake of establishing a more cost effective algal biorefinery, the possibility of feed gas delivery restricted only during the day is examined as a special case of the original superstructure. Correspondingly, we eliminate the selection of night production method and add a permanent gas storage device becomes necessary to temporarily hold recycled gas produced within the process at night.

The relationships between the optimal unit carbon sequestration and utilization cost and the size of the upstream coal-fired power plant in both original and special cases are illustrated in Figure 3(a). The horizontal axis is measured by comparing the annual sequestrated carbon dioxide amount to the annual carbon dioxide emissions of a 600 MW coal-fired power plant.We assume that the carbon dioxide emissions rate increase linearly with the size of the power plant. Each point stands for an optimal process design when the relating carbon dioxide flow rate is considered. The optimal unit sequestration cost decreases when the size of the upstream coal-fired power plant increases. The trend is due to the economy of scale, which is mathematically defined by power functions in capital cost evaluation. The optimal design of point B in the original case includes gas storage during the night, open pond for algae cultivation, flotation thickening in advanced dehydration, n-butanol as the solvent in lipid extractor, anaerobic digestion to break down algae remnant, hydrogen production for biogas utilization and finally Ni-Mo catalyst in algal oil upgrading reactor. The optimal design for point D is rather similar to the design of point B except for the selection for night production which is unnecessary in the special case. Figure 3(b) presents the environmental performance of our algal. GWP increases biorefinery in both cases when the unit sequestration and utilization cost of the corresponding biorefinery decreases. For points with the same sequestration amount, their GWPs are identical. Consequently, special case demonstrates clear environmental advantage over the original case when the unit cost is fixed. Judged from both economic and environmental behavior, optimal design from special case is superior to that in the original case.

However, one may point out that the benefits of the special case are based on the prerequisite that feed gas is delivered to the algal biorefinery only during the day, while most power plants operate continuously in practice. This deficiency can be handled by integrating multiple sequestration approaches: algal biorefinery takes care of the carbon emission during the day and geological sequestration stores the carbon dioxide produced at night. The geological sequestration method benefits from larger sequestration capacity, while algal biorefinery takes the advantage of flexibility in choosing the plant location and expanding the production scale. If the cooperation between these technologies is realized, the overall carbon sequestration process will be more economically viable in the future.

6. Conclusions

We proposed a new process superstructure of an algal biorefinery for biological carbon sequestration and accordingly, a rigorous MINLP optimization model to minimize the unit CO2 sequestration and utilization cost. We applied a tailored branch-and-refine algorithm based on successive piecewise linear approximation to globally optimize the superstructure optimization model. The optimization results indicate the minimum unit carbon sequestration and utilization cost is \$1.48/t of CO_2 when the flue gas from a 600 MW coal-fired power plant is delivered to the biorefinery only during daytime. The optimal process design of this case employs open pond, flotation thickening, n-butanol solvent extraction, anaerobic digestion, biogas utilized to produce hydrogen and Ni-Mo as the catalyst in algal oil upgrading reactor. Cooperation between biological carbon sequestration and geological carbon sequestration is able to help realize future practice.

References

B. H. Gebreslassie, M. Slivinsky, B. L. Wang, F. Q. You, 2013a, Life cycle optimization for sustainable design and operations of hydrocarbon biorefinery via fast pyrolysis, hydrotreating and hydrocracking, Computers and Chemical Engineering, 50, 71-91.

B. H. Gebreslassie, R. Waymire, F. You, 2013b, Sustainable design and synthesis of algae-based biorefinery for simultaneous hydrocarbon biofuel production and carbon sequestration, AIChE Journal, 59, 5, 1599-1621.

M. Martin, I. E. Grossmann, 2013, Optimal engineered algae composition for the integrated simultaneous production of bioethanol and biodiesel, AIChE Journal, 59, 8, 2872-2883.

I. Quesada, I. E. Grossmann, 1995, A Global Optimization Algorithm for Linear Fractional and Bilinear Programs, Journal of Global Optimization, 6, 1, 39-76.

B. Wang, B. H. Gebreslassie, F. Q. You, 2013, Sustainable design and synthesis of hydrocarbon biorefinery via gasification pathway: Integrated life cycle assessment and technoeconomic analysis with multiobjective superstructure optimization, Computers and Chemical Engineering, 52, 55-76.

F. Q. You, I. E. Grossmann, 2011, Stochastic Inventory Management for Tactical Process Planning Under Uncertainties: MINLP Models and Algorithms, AIChE Journal, 57, 5, 1250-1277.

F. Q. You, L. Tao, D. J. Graziano, S. W. Snyder, 2012, Optimal design of sustainable cellulosic biofuel supply chains: Multiobjective optimization coupled with life cycle assessment and input-output analysis, AIChE Journal, 58, 4, 1157-1180.

F. Q. You, B. Wang, 2011, Life Cycle Optimization of Biomass-to-Liquid Supply Chains with Distributed-Centralized Processing Networks, Industrial and Engineering Chemistry Research, 50, 17, 10102-10127.

D. Yue, F. You, 2013, Planning and scheduling of flexible process networks under uncertainty with stochastic inventory: MINLP models and algorithm, AIChE Journal, 59, 5, 1511-1532.

Jiří Jaromír Klemeš, Petar Sabev Varbanov and Peng Yen Liew (Editors)
Proceedings of the 24th European Symposium on Computer Aided Process Engineering – ESCAPE 24
June 15-18, 2014, Budapest, Hungary.

Modeling and Optimization of Propylene Polymerization with Branching

Anitha Mogilicharla, Saptarshi Majumdar, Kishalay Mitra*

Department of Chemical Engineering, Indian Institute of Technology Hyderabad, Yeddumailaram 502205, Andhra Pradesh, INDIA.
kishalay@iith.ac.in

Abstract

A kinetic model has been proposed to fit the experimental data available from the open literature for branched propylene polymerization system. The present system considered is a binary catalyst system, in which the first catalyst produces the atactic polypropylene macromonomer whereas the second one grafts the atactic polypropylene macromonomers to isotactic polypropylene backbone leading to branching. The proposed kinetic model, first of its kind that has been validated with experimental data, is extended to find the optimal process conditions for the desired combination of conflicting objectives. For this purpose, multi-objective optimization technique non-dominating sorting genetic algorithm II (NSGA II) has been utilized. A wide variety of process choices have been obtained for the optimization set up which shows improvement in process performance as compared to similar process performances reported in the open literature.

Keywords: Long chain branching, polypropylene, NSGA II, multi-objective optimization

1. Introduction

Polypropylene (PP) has good properties in terms of high melting point, low density as compared to other thermoplastics. Highly linear polypropylene can be produced by Ziegler-Natta and metallocene catalysts. Due to the poor melt strength of linear PP, it cannot be processed easily. Processing techniques like thermoforming, film blowing, blow molding etc. demand high melt strength, which can be achieved by the long chain branched polypropylene (LCBPP). Due to the difficult embedded chemistry in producing LCBPP by direct synthesis methods, various techniques have been developed in the open literature. Weng et al. (2002) utilized the previously prepared polypropylene macromonomers to copolymerize with the propylene monomer leading to branching. Shiono et al. (1999) synthesized LCBPP by copolymerizing the atactic polypropylene (aPP) macromonomers with propylene monomer by using an isospecific catalyst. Ye and Zhu (2003) used two catalysts to produce LCBPP (isotactic back bones and atactic side chains). By this technique, first catalyst has the capability of producing aPP macromonomers, while the latter one copolymerizes the aPP macromonomers with the propylene monomer to produce LCBPP. By using the metallocene catalyst and T-reagent, Langston et al. (2008) synthesized LCBPP. In the present effort, we have chosen the experimental data (Ye and Zhu, 2003) from open literature to develop a kinetic model for the long chain branched polypropylene system. However, to the best of the knowledge of the authors, this is the only model for propylene polymerization system with long chain branching which has been validated with experimental data and extending this validated model to optimize and control the extent of branching rather is even rare. Multi-objective optimization techniques are excellent to find out optimal trade-off solutions which are conflicting in nature. From the perspective of branched PP system, the polymer of high grafting density (number of aPP side chains per 1000 back bone monomer units) and high weight average molecular weight (M_w) are required in less polymerization time. It is known that higher molecular weight polymer can be obtained at the higher polymerization time. Here, the main aim is to attain polymers with higher grafting density and higher molecular weight in less polymerization time.

2. Model and problem formulation

Kinetic model developed for the long chain branched polypropylene system in this study is shown in Table 1. Motivated by the work of Hustad et al. (2008), reversible chain transfer to metal has been considered for the first catalyst system to obtain polydispersity index of nearer to 1.3 instead of 2. Since we know that the catalysts with single site behavior give theoretical polydispersity index of 2 for irreversible reactions (Hustad et al., 2008), it is very difficult to obtain PDI value less than 2 without considering reversible reaction. Bimolecular deactivation has been considered for the second catalyst system (Soares and Mckenna, 2012).

Here P_n and $D_n^=$ are the live and the unsaturated dead polymers (vinyl terminated macromonomers) for aPP of chain length n, whereas, $Q_{n,i}$ and $R_{n,i}$ depict the live and the dead polymer chains of branched polypropylene having "n" numbers of chain length and "i" number of long chain branches. Direct kinetic modeling, if used for modeling polymer systems, leads to huge number of equations since the number of repeating unit in a polymer (say, n) can assume a very large value. So, the method of moments (Eqs.1 and 2) has been applied to keep the dimensional explosion under control. However, by using the overall method of moments, we can calculate total molecular weight and PDI of molecular population. Polymer properties like number average molecular weight, weight average molecular weight, polydispersity index (PDI) and grafting density (GD) are calculated by the following Eqs.3 and 4.

Table 1. Kinetic mechanism for the twin catalyst system

• Initiation

$$C_1 + M \xrightarrow{k_{i1}} P_1$$

• Propagation

$$P_n + M \xrightarrow{k_{p1}} P_{n+1}$$

• β - H elimination

$$P_n \xrightarrow{k_\beta} D_n^= + C_1^H$$

• Reversible chain transfer to metal

$$D_n^= + C_1^H \xrightarrow{k_{\beta r}} P_n$$

• Reinitiation

$$C_1^H + M \xrightarrow{k_{ri1}} P_1$$

• Catalyst activation

$$cat_2 + cocat \xrightarrow{k_{a2}} C_2$$

• Initiation

$$C_2 + M \xrightarrow{k_{i2}} Q_{1,0}$$

• Propagation

$$Q_{n,i} + M \xrightarrow{k_{p2}} Q_{n+1,i}$$

• long chain branching

$$Q_{n,i} + D_{m,0}^= \xrightarrow{\alpha k_{lcb}} Q_{n+m,i+1}$$

• Chain transfer to coctalyst

$$Q_{n,i} + cocat \xrightarrow{k_{al}} R_{n,i} + C_2^{Me}$$

• Reinitiation

$$C_2^{Me} + M \xrightarrow{k_{ral}} Q_{1,0}$$

• Bimolecular deactivation

$$2Q_{n,i} \xrightarrow{k_{d2}} 2R_{n,i} + 2C_d$$

$$\lambda_x = \sum_{n=1}^{\infty} n^x P_x \quad \mu_x^{=} = \sum_{n=1}^{\infty} n^x D_x^{=} \tag{1}$$

$$\mu_x = \sum_{n=1}^{\infty} n^x Q_x \quad \nu_x = \sum_{n=1}^{\infty} n^x R_x \tag{2}$$

$$M_n = \left(\frac{\nu_1}{\nu_0}\right) MW \quad M_w = \left(\frac{\nu_2}{\nu_1}\right) MW \quad PDI = \left(\frac{M_w}{M_n}\right) \tag{3}$$

$$GD = 1000\left(\frac{\text{Long chain branching formation rate}}{\text{Propagation rate}}\right) \tag{4}$$

where M_n and M_w are number average molecular weight and weight average molecular weight of the polymer, respectively. MW and GD represent molecular weight of monomer unit and grafting density of the polymer, respectively.

Maximization of M_w, maximization of grafting density (GD) and minimization of polymerization time (t_p) are taken as objective functions. Addition amounts of two catalysts (u_1 and u_2), cocatalyst (u_3), time gap between the two catalyst additions (u_4) and total polymerization time are taken as decision variables (represented by the superscripts min and max as lower and upper bounds). $M_{w,app}$ and PDI_{app} represents the weight average molecular weight and polydispersity index of the aPP macromonomers. All decision variables are kept within the ±10 % experimental limit to avoid possible extrapolation error from the original process. To perform multi-objective optimization, model is integrated with real coded NSGA II (Deb, 2001). Multi-objective optimization problem formulation for the LCBPP system is shown below from Eqs.5 to 14.

$$\textit{Maximize} \quad M_w \tag{5}$$

$$\textit{Maximize} \quad GD \tag{6}$$

$$\textit{Minimize} \quad t_p \tag{7}$$

$$500000 \le M_w \le 700000 \tag{8}$$

$$4500 \le \frac{u_3}{u_2} \le 8000 \tag{9}$$

$$M_{w,app} \ge 2500 \tag{10}$$

$$PDI_{app} \le 1.45 \tag{11}$$

Decision variables:

$$u_1^{min} = 14e^{-6}; u_1^{max} = 82.5e^{-6}; u_2^{min} = 9e^{-6}; u_2^{max} = 16.5e^{-6} \tag{12}$$

$$u_3^{min} = 0.045; u_3^{max} = 0.0825; u_4^{min} = 0.2t_p; u_4^{max} = 0.8t_p \tag{13}$$

$$t_p^{min} = 70\,\text{min}; t_p^{max} = 180\,\text{min} \tag{14}$$

3. Results and discussion

Polymer molecular properties such as M_w, PDI of aPP and branched polypropylene system including GD are validated with the experimental polymerization of propylene which was conducted by Ye and Zhu (2003) for a binary catalyst system at inputs (concentration of two catalysts and cocatalyst, second catalyst addition time and total polymerization time). Comparison of model predicted and experimental M_w, polydispersity index (PDI) of aPP macromonomers and branched polypropylene (iPP) is shown in Table 2. Grafting density (number of aPP side chains per 1000 iPP backbone monomer units) for various experimental runs is shown in the same table. Grafting density of the experimental (Ye and Zhu, 2003) and simulated values for the first three runs are matching quite well. Last two runs are predicted from model. These branching density data are compared with the melting points (Ye and Zhu, 2003) of the iPP copolymer. Isotactic polypropylene (iPP) copolymer melting point decreases with the increase of grafting density (Ye and Zhu, 2003).

Polymerization time and molecular weight of the polymer are conflicting objectives, similarly polymerization time and grafting density are two opposing factors. So, there is a need to perform multi-objective optimization to find the optimal process conditions for the desired combination of conflicting objective functions. Multi-objective Pareto solutions for optimization are obtained among three conflicting objectives which is given in Figure 1. Various combinations of two catalyst additions, cocatalyst addition and time gap between the two catalyst additions are possible. There are multiple numbers of solutions (as shown in Figure 1) which are equally important (i.e. non-dominated solutions). Two experimental points (which are having grafting density greater than 8, the largest grafting density reported in the experiments) represented in the Figure 1 as square points. Several Pareto optimal solutions are found to be better than the experimental points. A wide variety of process choices have been obtained for the optimization set up which shows improvement in process performance as compared to the same reported in the open literature. As opposed to single optimal solution obtained during single objective optimization, the number of solutions in multi-objective optimization is more than one and these solutions are non-dominated in nature. It is obvious that one needs to choose one solution from the set of Pareto optimal solutions. This can be calculated by the min-max method (Belegundu and Chandrupatla, 1999), where deviations from the best values such as Z_1=t-t_{min}, Z_2=GD_{max}-GD, Z_3=$M_{w,max}$-M_w can be calculated first and then from this set of points of deviations, a single Pareto solution can be calculated by using the formula of min[max{Z_1, Z_2, Z_3}]. This point is shown as a filled circular point in Figure 1.

Table 2(a). Comparison of model predictions with experimental.

Run no.	aPP Experiment		aPP Predicted		iPP Experiment		iPP Predicted	
	M_w (kg/mol)	PDI	M_w (kg/mol)	PDI	M_w (kg/mol)	PDI	M_w (kg/mol)	PDI
1	3.6	1.3	4.4	1.4	631.8	2.7	632	2.2
2	3.6	1.4	3.2	1.34	564.7	2.5	544	2.2
3	3.3	1.3	4.5	1.4	447.3	2.3	485	2.4
4	3.1	1.3	2.5	1.34	395.2	2.4	378	2.4
5	3.0	1.3	2.6	1.33	514.4	2.3	554	2.4

Table 2(b). Comparison of model predictions with experimental (continue).

Run No.	GD		Melting point
	Experiment	Predicted	
1	8.4	8.2	144.4
2	1.7	1.7	148.6
3	8.6	7.5	145.6
4		0.31	149.7
5		0.008	153.5

The corresponding decision variables have been represented as a contour like plot (in shades) is depicted from Figure 2a-d. These four plots describe the trade off solutions for the entire search space.

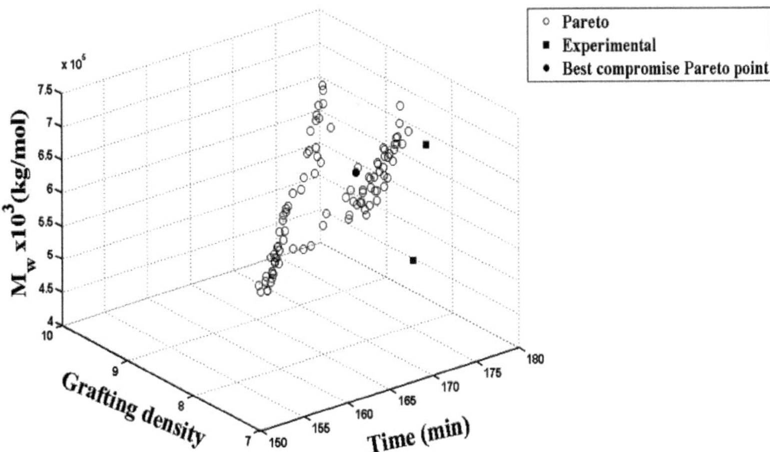

Figure 1. Pareto optimal solutions

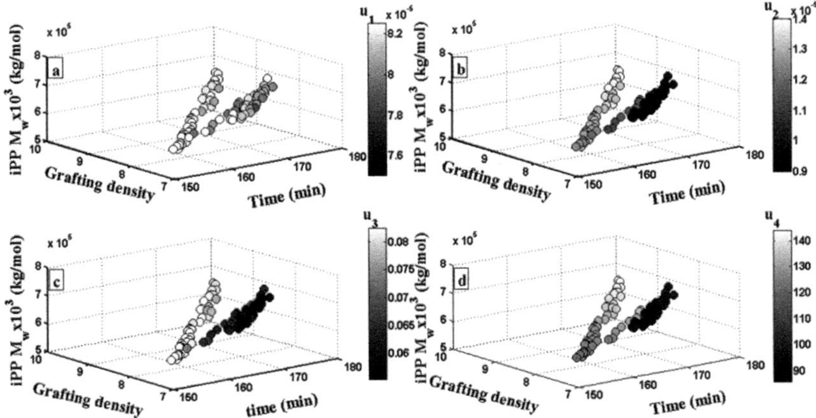

Figure 2. Pareto optimal solutions with total search space

4. Conclusions

Moment based modeling has been applied to the long chain branched polypropylene system to reduce the large set of equations. To obtain polymer with enhanced properties in less polymerization time, multi-objective optimization problem has been formulated with relevant constraints for the developed kinetic model. Real coded non-dominated sorting genetic algorithm-II is used to find the optimal process conditions. Optimization routine provided a variety of solutions in the entire search space. A decent number of solutions are found to be better as compared to the existing data from the open literature. One of the objective function grafting density strongly depends on the ratio of the two catalysts, time gap between the two catalyst additions (second catalyst addition time), and copolymerization time. Other objective function branched copolymer M_w depends on cocatalyst concentration (due to chain transfer to cocatalyst) and cocatalyst/catalyst$_2$ ratio which is due to bimolecular deactivation.

References

A.D. Belegundu, T.R. Chandrupatla, 1999, Optimization Concepts and Applications in Engineering, Prentice Hall, New Jersey, USA.

K. Deb, 2001, Multi-objective optimization using evolutionary algorithms, Wiley, Chichester, UK.

P.D. Hustad, R.L. Kuhlman, E.M. Carnahan, T.T. Wenzel, D.J. Arriola, 2008, An exploration of the effects of reversibility in chain transfer to metal in olefin polymerization, Macromolecules, 41, 12, 4081-4089.

J.A. Langston, R.H. Colby, T.C. Mike Chung, F. Shimizu, T. Suzuki, M. Aoki, 2008, Synthesis and characterization of long chain branched isotactic polypropylene via metallocene catalyst and T-reagent, Macromolecules, 40, 8, 2712-2720.

T. Shiono, S.M. Azad, T. Ikeda, 1999, Copolymerization of Atactic Polypropene Macromonomer with Propene by an Isospecific Metallocene Catalyst, Macromolecules, 32, 18, 5723-5727.

J.B.P. Soares, T.F.L. Mckenna, 2012, Polyolefin Reaction Engineering, Wiley, Weinheim, Germany.

W. Weng, W. Hu, A.H. Dekmerzian, C.J. Ruff, 2002, Long Chain Branched Isotactic Polypropylene, Macromolecules, 35, 10, 3838-3843.

Z. Ye, S.J. Zhu, 2003, Synthesis of branched polypropylene with isotactic backbone and atactic side chains by binary iron and zirconium single-site catalysts, Polym. Sci., Part A: Polym. Chem., 41, 1152-59.

Jiří Jaromír Klemeš, Petar Sabev Varbanov and Peng Yen Liew (Editors)
Proceedings of the 24th European Symposium on Computer Aided Process Engineering – ESCAPE 24
June 15-18, 2014, Budapest, Hungary.

Modeling and Optimization of an Adsorption Process for the Recovery of Catechins from Green Tea

Miguel Monsanto[a,*], Adithya Thota Radhakrishnan[a], David Sevillano[b], Nasim Hooshyar[c], J. Meuldijk[a] , E. Zondervan[a]

[a] *Department of Chemical Engineering and Chemistry, Eindhoven University of Technology , P.O. Box 513, 5600 MB Eindhoven, The Netherlands*
[b] *Department of Biotechnology, Delft University of Technology, Julianalaan 67, 2628 BC, Delft, The Netherlands*
[c] *Unilever R&D, Olivier van Noortlaan 120, 3130 AC, Vlaardingen, The Netherlands*
m.f.m.monsanto@tue.nl

Abstract
Catechins are the main polyphenols present in a green tea and have been associated to several health benefits due to the antioxidant, antimutagenic and antiviral properties. They are, therefore, regarded as desired components with several applications in a variety of areas such as foods, cosmetics and pharmaceuticals. In this study a macroporous polymeric resin is used as an adsorption medium for separating the polyphenols. Based on experimentally determined mass transfer coefficients and diffusion coefficients, a packed bed column model is developed. The highlight of this work is that we are modeling a very complex multicomponent system, where the four catechins present in green tea and caffeine are competing for the adsorption sites. This model is an axial dispersed plug flow model where the mass transfer is modeled using the linear driving force (LDF) approach. This type of predictive models allows the estimation of the adsorption amount with the contact time. The model delivers catechins and caffeine breakthrough curves for the column and it can be used to optimize the parameters in such way that the highest possible recovery yield and purity for the catechins can be obtained.

Keywords: macroporous resin, adsorption, catechins, tea, model.

1. Introduction
Tea is the most consumed beverage after water. Green tea is produced by inactivating the enzymes in the leaves from the Camellia sinensis plant by firing them. In green tea the catechins account for the majority of polyphenols (Balentine et al., 1997). The fact that it is such a popular drink together with all the potential health benefits (Dwyer and Peterson, 2013), led to several publications on the chemical and biological properties and health benefits. The increase interest in tea catechins has also been revealed by the increase number of papers published in the last 20 years: in 1993 only 8 papers where published, but 10 years later that number increased to 113 and in 2013 already 320 papers where produced (according to Scopus search).

Adsorption is a separation process commonly used to remove organic compounds from aqueous solutions. The adsorption of polyphenols from tea using resin adsorbents has shown great potential and macroporous synthetic polymeric resins have been used to isolate tea catechins (Vuong et al., 2010). Despite the fact that there are some publications on separation of green tea catechins, there is still a need for a cost effective and efficient process design, which only uses food grade solvents.

The adsorption process and separation conditions can be simulated by developing a mathematical model that describes the adsorption of tea polyphenols on a packed bed column with a macroporous resin. To model such process information about kinetics, adsorption equilibrium and adsorbent characteristics and capacity is needed. This model simulates the adsorption cycles, which are used to study the behavior of adsorbates and adsorbents, and it can be used for process optimization. The model delivers catechins and caffeine breakthrough curves. Although this data can also be obtained experimentally, it is expensive and time consuming.

There are several ways to model the adsorption kinetics that represent the mass transfer, and it can be broadly described under two main categories: based on local adsorption assumption between the solid and bulk phase or existence of mass transfer resistance between adsorbent particle and fluid phase (Siahpoosh et al., 2009).

Local adsorption models which include local equilibrium and local kinetic theories, neglect the effect of mass transfer resistance to the particle. These models are generally used for high mass transfer rates where the mass transfer resistance can be neglected. Mass transfer resistance models can include approximated and rigorous models. Rigorous models are time consuming as they account for the mass transfer inside the particle along its radius. On the other hand, approximated models are extensively used since they are numerically less time consuming to solve. The most widely used approximated method is the linear driving force (LDF) which was originally proposed by Glueckauf and Coates (1947). The adsorption kinetics in our model is described by the LDF and a lumped parameter is used to represent the overall mass transfer resistance. The thermodynamic equilibrium is modeled with the multicomponent Langmuir isotherm. This model is the base to design the column dimensions and operational parameters, and it can be used for scale-up purposes.

2. Experimental

2.1. Reagents and equipments

Acetonitrile is from Sigma–Aldrich (analytical grade) and glacial acetic acid is from Merck KGaA. Catechins standards and freeze-dried green tea powder are supplied by Unilever R&D. Deionized water (< 18.2 MΩ) is Milli-Q gradient. The ultracentrifuge is a Beckman Coulter Optima L-90K. The HPLC equipment is from Agilent (1220 Infinity LC gradient system with variable wavelength detector). The resin used is from Sigma-Aldrich (Amberlite XAD-7HP). The HPLC pump is from Knauer (Smartline Pump 1000) and the glass column (1.5 cm diameter and variable bed height) is from Omnifit.

2.2. Sample preparation

To prepare the green tea, the freeze dry tea powder is extracted with water at 85 °C in an Erlenmeyer, while stirring for 10 mins. The extract is centrifuged for 20 mins at 20,000 rpm and the two resulting phases are decanted.

2.3. Dynamic Experiments

The wet resin is filled into the glass column up to a desired bed height. The clear tea extract is pumped via the bottom of the column with an HPLC pump. Samples are then taken manually at defined intervals at the outlet of the column and analysed in the HPLC. All the experiments are performed at 20 °C.

2.4. Analytical method: HPLC analysis of catechins and caffeine

Caffeine and individual catechins (epicatechin (EC), epigallocatechin (EGC), epicatechin gallate (ECG), epigallocatechin gallate (EGCG)) concentrations are determined by HPLC analysis on an Agilent 1,220 Infinity LC gradient system equipped with a variable wavelength detector, which is set at a wavelength of 278 nm. The analysis is performed in a phenyl-hexyl column (Luna 5 μm Phenyl-Hexyl, from Phenomenex), by gradient elution (1 mL/min) at 30 °C, using 2 % acetic acid in water (v/v) (Eluent A) and 2 % acetic acid in acetonitrile (v/v) (Eluent B) as mobile phases.

3. Mathematical model

To describe the dynamic behaviour of the column, a mass balance is set up across a slice of the column and for an adsorbent particle. The flow is represented by using Ruthven's axially dispersed plug flow (Ruthven, 1984), where the differential fluid phase mass balance is given by Eq.(1). The adsorption kinetics is represented by the linear driving force approximation (Xu et al., 2013) and it is given by Eq.(2).

$$\frac{\partial c_i}{\partial t} = -v\frac{\partial c_i}{\partial x} + D_{ax,i}\frac{\partial^2 c_i}{\partial x^2} - \frac{(1-\varepsilon_b)}{\varepsilon_b}\frac{\partial q_i}{\partial t} \quad (1)$$

$$\frac{dq_i}{dt} = k_{ov,i}\left(q_{s,i} - q_i\right) \quad (2)$$

To represent the overall mass transfer coefficient $k_{ov,i}$ a lumped parameter is used, consisting of both the internal and external mass transfer resistances (Eq.(3)).

$$\frac{1}{k_{ov,i}} = \frac{1}{k_i^{int}} + \frac{1}{k_i^{ext}} \quad (3)$$

The external mass transfer resistance is found using Eq.(4), where the liquid film mass transfer coefficient is obtained by the Sherwood number and calculated using the correlation given by Wakao and Funazkri (1978), in Eq.(5). The internal mass transfer resistance is obtained using the expression presented by Glueckauf (1955) in Eq.(6).

$$k_i^{ext} = \frac{3k_{f,i}}{R_p} \quad (4)$$

$$Sh = 2 + 1.1Sc^{1/3}Re^{0.6} \qquad Sh = \frac{k_f d_p}{D_{LP}} \quad (5)$$

$$k_i^{int} = \frac{15D_{p,i}^{e}\varepsilon_p}{R_p^2} \quad (6)$$

The axial dispersion coefficient (D_{ax}) is calculated with the correlation of Gunn (Gunn, 1987), in Eq.(7). This correlation neglects the variance of the distribution of interstitial velocity in the packed bed, where $\tau = 1.4$ (for spheres).

$$\frac{vd}{D_{ax}} = \left[\frac{ReSc(1-p)^2}{\varepsilon_b\Gamma} + \frac{Re^2Sc^2p(1-p)^3}{\varepsilon_b^2\Gamma^2}\left(exp\left(\frac{-\varepsilon_b\Gamma}{p(1-p)ReSc}\right) - 1\right)\right] + \frac{\varepsilon_b}{\tau ReSc} \quad (7)$$

$$p = 0.17 + 0.33\exp\left(-\frac{24}{Re}\right) \quad (8)$$

$$\Gamma = 23.1(1 - \varepsilon_b)/\varepsilon_b \tag{9}$$

The dynamics of the adsorption are studied with an initially adsorbate free column, for a step response at the inlet of the column. This is represented by applying the Danckwerts boundary conditions given by Eq.(10), to imply continuity, and by using the initial conditions given by Eq.(11).

$$\left.\frac{\partial c_i}{\partial z}\right|_{z=0} = \frac{v}{D_{ax}}\left(c_i - c_i^{feed}\right); \quad \left.\frac{\partial c_i}{\partial z}\right|_{z=L} = 0 \tag{10}$$

$$c_i(z, t = 0) = 0 \tag{11}$$

To obtain the breakthrough curves, both the Eq.(1)-(2) are set up for every individual component and solved simultaneously. This results in a set of coupled partial differential equations (PDEs) with initial and boundary conditions. To achieve a numerical solution the PDEs are discretized using upwind finite differences.

4. Results and discussion

The lumped parameters for each component that represent the mass transfer resistance are given in Table 1 for both simulations. It can be observed that the rate of film diffusion is higher than the intra-particle diffusion and hence not the rate limiting parameter. The same conclusion can be taken by the similarity in the breakthrough curves of both simulations, at different flow rates (Figures 1 and 2). The rate of film diffusion is controlled by the flow rate and the intra-particle diffusion is an inherent property of the adsorbent particle and not dependent on the design parameters of the column. The breakthrough curves for the components are shown in Figures 1 and 2.

The sensitivity analysis shows that the model has a major dependence on both the mass transfer coefficient and the Langmuir equilibrium constant. A correction parameter is used to adjust these two parameters for each component.

Figure 1 shows that the model has a very good fitting to the experimental values for all the components. In addition, Figures 1 and 2 show that the smaller components are the first ones to break through the packed bed column and have a slight overshoot. This can be attributed to the relative speed of diffusion and affinities for the adsorbent, e.g. smaller components that diffuse faster are initially more adsorbed and are afterwards desorbed, when the bulkier components with more affinity reach the adsorption sites.

Table 1. Mass transfer resistances and liquid-phase diffusivity coefficients.

	Simulation 1				Simulation 2			
	k_i^{ext}	k_i^{int}	$k_{ov,i}$	D_{LP}	k_i^{ext}	k_i^{int}	$k_{ov,i}$	D_{LP}
EC	0.0209	0.0176	0.0095	1,442e-09	0.0434	0.0176	0.0125	1.442e-09
EGC	0.0170	0.0135	0.0075	1,450e-09	0.0359	0.0135	0.0098	1.450e-09
ECG	0.0146	0.0111	0.0063	1,209e-09	0.0312	0.0111	0.0082	1.209e-09
EGCG	0.0207	0.0174	0.0095	1,219e-09	0.0431	0.0174	0.0124	1.219e-09
Caffeine	0.0124	0.0090	0.0052	1,739e-09	0.0268	0.0090	0.0067	1.739e-09

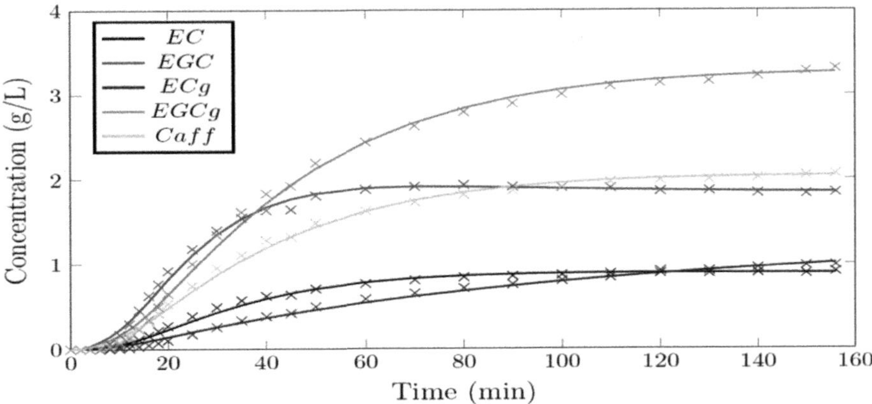

Figure 1. Modeled and experimental breakthrough curves for catechins and caffeine, for a flow rate of 1 mL/min and a column length of 0.03 m.

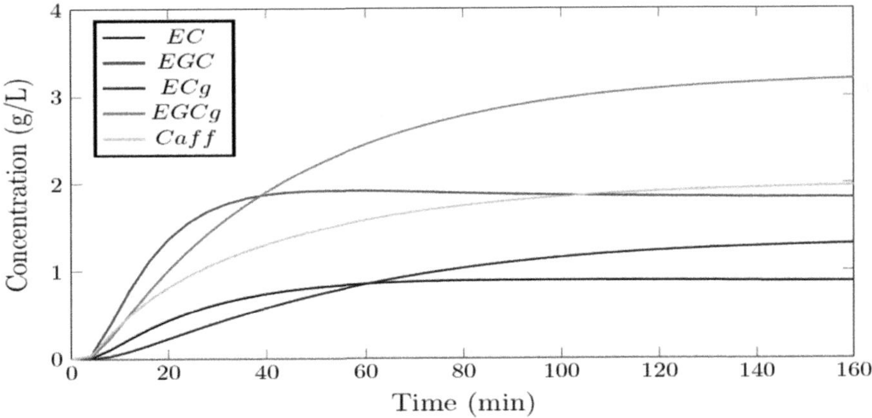

Figure 2. Modeled breakthrough curves for catechins and caffeine, for a flow rate of 5 mL/min and a column length of 0.12 m.

5. Conclusions

It is possible to model the packed bed column adsorption from a very complex system (green tea), by representing the breakthrough curves for the main components that are adsorbed (catechins and caffeine). The breakthrough curves represent the effect of competitive adsorption between the individual catechins and caffeine, and also the different affinities towards the macroporous resin.

In the model, the adsorption is considered to be instantaneous. The external mass transfer resistance accounts for the film diffusion and is dependent on the flow conditions, while the internal mass transfer resistance is only a property of the macropores of the adsorbent. This explains the differences in the external mass transfer resistance between the two simulations. Nevertheless, the intra-particle diffusion is the dominant one for the mass transfer resistance. This study is the starting point for a more complete sorption model that allows the design of an optimal adsorption column, for the recovery of catechins from green tea.

Nomenclature

τ	Tortuosity factor
ε_b	Bed porosity
c_i	Concentration of the component i, g/L
$D_{p,i}^e$	Effective pore diffusivity, m^2/s
D_{ax}	Axial dispersion coefficient, m^2/s
D_{LP}	Liquid-phase diffusivity coefficient, m^2/s
d_p	Particle diameter, m
k_i^{ext}	External mass transfer resistance, s^{-1}
k_i^{int}	Internal mass transfer resistance, s^{-1}
p	Probability of axial displacement
q_i	Concentration of component i on the adsorbent surface, g/g
v	Flow velocity, m/s
Re	Reynolds number
Sc	Schmidt number
Sh	Sherwood number

Acknowledgements

This work was supported by the ISPT (Institute for Sustainable Process Technology, The Netherlands).

References

D. A. Balentine, S. A. Wiseman, L. C. M. Bouwens, 1997, The chemistry of tea flavonoids, Critical Reviews in Food Science and Nutrition, 37, 8, 693-704.

J. T. Dwyer, J. Peterson, 2013, Tea and flavonoids: where we are, where to go next, American Journal of Clinical Nutrition, 98, 6, 1611S-1618S.

E. Glueckauf, 1955, Theory of Chromatography .10. Formulae for Diffusion Into Spheres and Their Application to Chromatography, Transactions of the Faraday Society, 51, 11, 1540-51.

E. Glueckauf, J. I. Coates, 1947, Theory of Chromatography .4. the Influence of Incomplete Equilibrium on the Front Boundary of Chromatograms and on the Effectiveness of Separation, Journal of the Chemical Society, OCT, 1315-1321.

D. J. Gunn, 1987, Axial and Radial Dispersion in Fixed-Beds, Chemical Engineering Science, 42, 2, 363-373.

D. Ruthven, 1984, Principles of Adsorption and Adsorption Processes, John Wiley & Sons, London, England.

M. Siahpoosh, S. Fatemi, A. Vatani, 2009, Mathematical Modeling of Single and Multi-Component Adsorption Fixed Beds to Rigorously Predict the Mass Transfer Zone and Breakthrough Curves, Iranian Journal of Chemistry and Chemical Engineering-International English Edition, 28, 3, 25-44.

Q. V. Vuong, J. B. Golding, M. Nguyen, P. D. Roach, 2010, Extraction and isolation of catechins from tea, Journal of Separation Science, 33, 21, 3415-3428.

N. Wakao, T. Funazkri, 1978, Effect of Fluid Dispersion Coefficients on Particle-To-Fluid Mass-Transfer Coefficients in Packed-Beds - Correlation of Sherwood Numbers, Chemical Engineering Science, 33, 10, 1375-1384.

Z. Xu, J. G. Cai, B. C. Pan, 2013, Mathematically modeling fixed-bed adsorption in aqueous systems, Journal of Zhejiang University-Science A, 14, 3, 155-176.

Jiří Jaromír Klemeš, Petar Sabev Varbanov and Peng Yen Liew (Editors)
Proceedings of the 24th European Symposium on Computer Aided Process Engineering – ESCAPE 24
June 15-18, 2014, Budapest, Hungary.

Optimal Sensor Placement for Contamination Detection and Identification in Water Distribution Networks

Venkata Reddy Palleti*, Shankar Narasimhan, Raghunathan Rengaswamy

Department of Chemical Engineering, Indian Institute of Technology, Madras, Chennai-600036, India
venki.pec@gmail.com

Abstract

Water Distribution Networks (WDN) is often exposed to either intentional or accidental contamination. In order to protect against such intrusions, an effective and efficient online monitoring system through sensors is needed. Detection of contaminants in WDN is challenging and it is not possible to place sensors at each and every potential point of intrusion, due to cost and maintenance reasons. Instead, as few sensors as possible, should be located optimally such that intrusions can be detected quickly. This is known as sensor network design problem for intrusion detection in WDNs. Several optimization models and algorithms have been proposed for intrusion detection in a WDN. In this study, we design sensor networks which satisfy the two important properties of observability and identifiability. Observability denotes the ability of the sensor network to detect the occurrence of the intrusion, whereas identifiability refers to the ability to unambiguously deduce the point (or source) of intrusion from the set of sensors affected. A hydraulic analysis of the network is first carried out for a given loading condition to determine the flow directions. The concept of a directed path is then used to construct a bipartite graph, and map the sensor network design problem to that of a minimum vertex set cover problem. Algorithms based on greedy heuristics are used to solve the set covering problem and obtain the corresponding sensor network. The proposed method is illustrated using a fairly large scale urban WDN.

Keywords: Water distribution network, Sensor network, Observability, Identifiability

1. Introduction

Water Distribution Network (WDN) is a vital part of any city. Water distribution networks consist of a network of pipes, reservoirs, pumps, valves, storage tanks and sumps. Due to its complex structure, WDNs are inherently vulnerable to either intentional or accidental contamination. Accidental contamination occurs due to the intrusion of contaminant from the ground or sewage lines through cracks in the pipelines. Accidental intrusion of chemical or biological contaminants can cause an outbreak of health related problems, which can reach epidemic proportions. Intentional contamination can be due to acts of terrorism or mischief which can pose a far greater threat to human life. A monitoring system through online sensors is needed to protect against such intrusions. Locating sensors at each and every point of intrusion is the trivial solution for protecting WDN. Obviously, such a solution is not economically feasible and maintenance of these sensors may also be difficult. Hence, it is necessary to optimally locate a limited number of sensors.

Several optimization models and algorithms are developed for identifying the strategic location of sensors in WDN. Lee and Deininger (1992) were the first to address the optimal location of monitoring stations in a water distribution system. An integer programming model was developed to maximize sensor coverage and its model is based on the steady state simulation and network connectivity. Kumar et al. (1997) and Kessler et al. (1998) improved the method proposed by Lee and Deininger (1992). Ostfeld and Solomons (2004) extended the same model by constructing the randomized pollution matrix and solved using a genetic algorithm. Watson et al. (2004) were the first to introduce a multi-objective formulation to the optimal sensor placement. The Battle of Water Sensor Network (BWSN) challenge (Ostfeld et al., 2008) highlighted the performance of the sensor network design by considering multiple objectives. Mustafa et al. (2010) developed a single-objective optimization model that incorporates the four criteria adopted in BWSN and solved it using a progressive genetic algorithm (PGA). Perelman and Ostfeld (2013) proposed a methodology using Bayesian network statistics to estimate likelihood of the injection location of a contaminant and its propagation in the water distribution system.

2. Problem Description

Despite several optimization models and algorithms, some of the basic questions are yet to be addressed for contamination detection for a given water distribution network. In this study, the two basic questions addressed are (1) what is the minimum number of sensors required to detect an intrusion for a given set of potential intrusion locations in a water distribution network? (Observability problem), and (2) what is the minimum number of sensors required to detect and identify the source of intrusion for a given set of potential intrusion locations in a water distribution network? (Identifiability or resolution problem).

The above questions have been answered in the context of locating sensors for fault diagnosis in chemical plants (Raghuraj et al., 1999). These concepts and related algorithms have been suitably adapted for designing sensor networks using a minimum number of sensors which ensures observability and identifiability of intrusions in a WDN.

A water distribution network can be represented as a graph, G = (V, E), where, E represents the edges, and V represents the vertices or nodes. Nodes are used to represent sources, such as reservoirs or tanks, from where water is supplied, as well as demand points where water is consumed. Nodes are also used to represent fire hydrants. The point where two or more pipes or a pipe divides into several branches meet is also represented as a node. Pipes, valves and pumps are represented as edges in the graph. A real life WDN can consist of several hundred nodes and pipes. Typically, nodes representing sources or fire hydrants are potentially vulnerable sites for intentional contamination, whereas unintended chemical or biological contamination can occur at any point in the WDN. In the current work, we consider only sources of WDN such as main or intermediate reservoirs, tanks, and deep wells as potential sites of intrusion, water treatment plants and pumping stations, as well as fire hydrants are also considered as potential intrusion sites. The above sites in a WDN are the most vulnerable and can be accessed relatively easily and contaminated by deliberate acts of terrorism. The nodes which are potential sites of intrusion are termed as vulnerable nodes. It is assumed that a contaminant can be introduced at any one of the vulnerable nodes of the

WDN. The contaminant is then transported along with the flow direction of water. It is also assumed that sufficient quantities of contaminant are introduced at a vulnerable node such that the concentration level of the contaminant in any pipe is above the minimum detectable level of the sensors being considered. Given a WDN and its vulnerable nodes, the problems are (a) to determine the minimum number of sensors and their location which ensures observability of the contaminant, irrespective of which vulnerable node is affected, and (b) determine the minimum number of sensors and their locations which ensures that the contaminant is observable and the contaminated vulnerable node is also identified from the sensors response.

3. Methodology

Greedy algorithm for observability:

Observability refers to the ability to detect the intrusion by at least one sensor. For a given set of sensors located in the WDN, observability condition ensures that a contaminant introduced at any vulnerable node would be observed by at least one sensor. The algorithm proposed for solving the observability problem combines graph theoretic concepts with a greedy optimization algorithm. The first phase of the algorithm is to construct a bipartite graph as follows.

Step 1: A hydraulic analysis of the WDN is carried out for a specified loading condition by considering every vulnerable node in turn as the attacked node, and the flow directions in the pipes are obtained. Based on this a directed graph of the WDN is constructed. Step 2: All directed paths from each vulnerable node to all demand points are constructed. This can be done using an efficient depth first search algorithm as described by (Deo, 1974). From the directed paths, the unions of all nodes that are present in all the directed paths corresponding to each vulnerable node are identified. These nodes are denoted as affected nodes corresponding to the vulnerable node. Step 3: The nodes are divided into two sets, one consisting of only the vulnerable nodes and the other consisting of all nodes of the graph. A bipartite graph is constructed between the two sets by adding edges from a vulnerable node to all affected nodes corresponding to the vulnerable node.

It may be noted that in Step 1 a hydraulic analysis has to be performed for each vulnerable node being considered as the attacked node. When performing a hydraulic analysis for a vulnerable node considered as the attacked node, only a single loading condition can be specified. However, when performing a hydraulic analysis for a different vulnerable node being considered as the attacked node, a different loading condition may be specified. Thus, for example, when a reservoir or other sources of water, pumping station, or treatment plant is considered as the attacked vulnerable node, the fire hydrant node can be treated as a demand node for which a demand flow rate can be specified, whereas when a fire hydrant node is considered as the attacked node, it is treated as a source node and the pressure at this node can be specified for performing the hydraulic analysis. Thus, the flow directions need not be the same for all the hydraulic analyses corresponding to different vulnerable nodes.

The observability problem is to choose the minimum number of nodes from the affected nodes on which sensors have to be located, such that there exists at least one edge from each vulnerable node to the chosen set of affected nodes. This is known as the node or set cover problem in graph theory and is known to be an NP-hard problem. A greedy algorithm for solving this problem has been developed by Raghuraj et al. (1999). The algorithm starts with an empty set of covered vulnerable nodes and repeats the following two steps.

Step 1: Choose an affected node which has maximum number of arcs incident on it. Mark this node, and add all vulnerable nodes connected to this node to the list of covered vulnerable nodes. Stop, if all vulnerable nodes are covered, else go to Step 2.
Step 2: Delete all edges from covered vulnerable nodes that are incident on the unmarked affected node and go to Step 1.

By locating sensor on all marked affected nodes, we can cover all the vulnerable nodes, which implies that if any of the vulnerable node is affected, at least one sensor with measure the response. This solves the observability problem. It should be noted that the greedy algorithm will not lead to the minimum number of sensors but is expected to give good solutions which are close to the minimum. An improved version of this algorithm is also presented in Raghuraj et al. (1999).

Greedy algorithm for identifiability
Identifiability refers to the ability to observe and identify the vulnerable node that is attacked, from the responses of the located sensors. Assuming that at most one vulnerable node is attacked, the problem of determining the minimum number of sensors for identification of the vulnerable node is formulated using an expanded bipartite graph. Let T_i be the set of affected nodes for a particular vulnerable node i. Let n be the number of vulnerable nodes. An expanded bipartite graph consisting of $n + n(n-1)/2$ vulnerable nodes is constructed as follows:

1. Define the sets $U_{ij} = U_{ji} = T_i \cup T_j - T_i \cap T_j$. The number of such sets generated is $n(n-1)/2$. Corresponding to each such set, an artificial node is added to the set of vulnerable nodes in the original bipartite graph. Thus, there are $n + n(n-1)/2$ vulnerable nodes in the expanded bipartite graph.
2. Edges are drawn from each artificial vulnerable node corresponding to the set U_{ij} to the affected nodes in the corresponding set.

The greedy algorithm described in section 3.1 is used to solve the observability problem of the expanded bipartite graph. By locating sensors on all affected nodes determined by the greedy algorithm, it is possible to observe and identify which vulnerable node is attacked. The set of sensors that covers U_{ij} is a set of sensors which respond only if vulnerable nodes T_i or T_j is affected, but not if both nodes are affected. This makes it possible to identify whether T_i or T_j is attacked. Only in the case when U_{ij} is a null set, it is not possible to distinguish whether T_i and T_j is attacked.

4. Case Study

An urban WDN taken from Mohankumar et al. (2008) is shown Figure 1. The distribution system consists of 116 pipes, 29 control valves, 3 on-off valves and 7 pumps. It has 3 source nodes each at an elevation of 100m. Hydraulic analysis of the network is carried out using EPANET 2.0 software to obtain the directed graph.

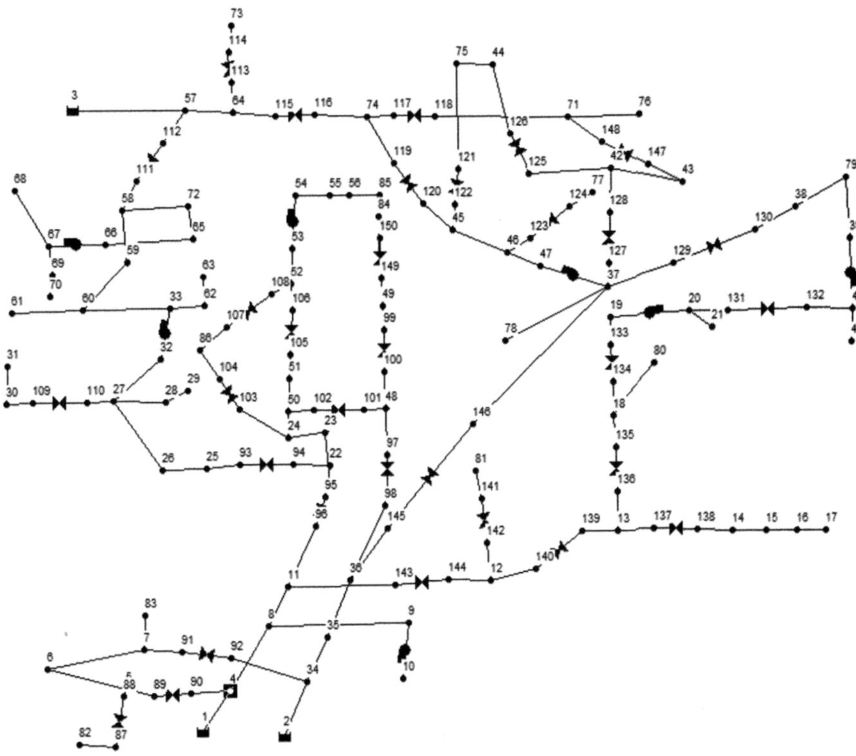

Figure 1. Layout of the water distribution network

There are 9 vulnerable nodes corresponding to nodes 1, 2, 3, 19, 32, 37, 39, 53, and 66. Nodes 1, 2, and 3 correspond to reservoirs while nodes 19, 32, 37, 39, 53, and 66 are pumping stations, and therefore these are considered as vulnerable. For simplicity, the same loadings conditions are imposed for every vulnerable node. Since there is no flow through one of the pumps (edge 155) which connects source node 10 to 9, it is not considered as a vulnerable node.

Results of the algorithm for satisfying the observability and identifiability conditions under the assumption that only one vulnerable node is attacked are shown in Table 1. The results show that for detecting whether any vulnerable node is attacked (observability condition) it is necessary to locate only three sensors at nodes 40, 54, and 67. On the other hand if it is required to identify which vulnerable node has been attacked, it is necessary to locate three additional sensors at nodes 20, 33 and 71.

Table 2 shows how the response of the sensors can be used to detect and identify the attacked vulnerable node, corresponding to the observable and identifiable sensor network designs, respectively. Row one of this table indicates for the observable sensor network design that at least one of three sensors detects a contaminant when any one of the vulnerable nodes is attacked. Second row of the table shows that different combinations of sensors detect a contaminant when different vulnerable nodes are attacked. This indicates that the attacked vulnerable node can be identified from the set of sensors that detect a contaminant.

Table 1. Results for sensor locations that satisfy observability and identifiability conditions

Criteria	Optimal sensor locations
Observability	40, 54, 67
Identifiability	40, 54, 67, 20, 33, 71

Table 2. Sensors that detect a contaminant when one of the vulnerable nodes is attacked

Attacked vulnerable node	1	2	3	19	32	37	39	53	66
Observable sensor network	40, 54, 67	40, 54	67	40	67	40	40	54	67
Identifiable sensor network	54, 20, 33	40, 71, 54	71, 67	20	33	40, 71	40	54	67

5. Conclusion

Optimal sensor network design for given water distribution network is studied. The concepts of observability and identifiability are used in the problem formulation. Greedy heuristic algorithms are proposed for the sensor network design problem using graph theory concepts. Hydraulic simulation of large scale urban water distribution system is carried out using EPANET 2.0 under various loading conditions.

References

M. A. Mustafa, J. Guan, L. M. Morris, 2010, Optimal design of sensor placement in water distribution networks, Journal of Water Resources Planning and Management, 136, 5-18.

L. Perelman, A. Ostfeld, 2013, Bayesian networks for Source intrusion detection, Journal of Water Resources Planning and Management, 139, 426-432.

A. Ostfeld, E. Salomons, 2005, Optimal layout of early warning detection stations for water distribution system security, Journal of Water Resources Planning and Management, 130, 377-385.

A. Ostfeld, J. G. Uber, 2008, The Battle of the Water Sensor Networks (BWSN): A Design Challenge for Engineers and Algorithms, Journal of Water Resources Planning and Management, 134, 556-568.

R. Raghuraj, M. Bhusan, R. Rengaswamy, 1999, Locating sensors in complex chemical plants based on fault diagnostic observability criteria, AIChE Journal , 45, 310-321.

B. Lee, R. Deininger, 1992. Optimal locations of monitoring stations in water distribution system, Journal of Environmental Engineering, 118, 4-16.

A. Kumar, A. Kansal, G. Arora, 1997. Identification of monitoring stations in water distribution system, Journal of Environmental Engineering, 123, 746-752.

A. Kessler, A. Ostfeld, G. Sinai, 1998, Detecting accidental contaminations in municipal water networks, Journal of Water Resources Planning and Management, 124, 192-198.

M. Kumar, S. Narasimhan, S. M. Bhallamudi, 2008. State estimation in water distribution network using graph-theoretic reduction strategy, Journal of Water Resources Planning and Management, 134, 395-403.

N. Deo, 1974, Graph theory with application to engineering and computer science. Prentice-Hall, Englewood Cliffs, N.J.

Jiří Jaromír Klemeš, Petar Sabev Varbanov and Peng Yen Liew (Editors)
Proceedings of the 24th European Symposium on Computer Aided Process Engineering – ESCAPE 24
June 15-18, 2014, Budapest, Hungary.

Expected Value Analysis for an Industrial Grinding Process with Fuzzy Uncertain Parameters

Nagajyothi Virivinti, Kishalay Mitra*

Indian Institute of Technology Hyderabad,Ordanance Factory Campus,Yeddumailaram, Andra Pradesh, India
kishalay@iith.ac.in

Abstract

Uncertainty in parameters, which are assumed to be known and do not change their values during the course of deterministic optimization, can have a great impact on the outcome of an optimization study. Investigations on the development and application of optimization approaches that can accommodate such kind of uncertainty in parameters during the course of optimization are, therefore, necessitated. Expected value model (EVM) is one such method which converts the uncertain optimization formulation into a deterministic problem using expected values of the objective functions and constraints based on fuzzy credibility theory. In this work, an industrial grinding model has been adopted under the credibility theory based fuzzy framework to handle several uncertain parameters and shown how the presence of uncertainty leads to an operating zone of varied risk appetite of a decision maker by defining the entire frontier of the uncertain solution region.

Keywords: Uncertainty, fuzzy, credibility, Pareto, multiobjective, FENSGA II, grinding.

1. Introduction

While modeling an industrial process, there are certain parameters appearing in the model which can be used as tuning parameters to match the performance of the model as close as to the industrial process behavior. Optimization of models with such tuning parameters assuming a constant value throughout the optimization exercise can lead to quite unrealistic results because these parameters are truly uncertain in nature.One of the methods to solve such situations by transforming the uncertain problem into an equivalent deterministic problem and then solving the equivalent problem to acquire the solution which is feasible. In this study, we are going to use the FEVM (Fuzzy Expected Value Model) approach which converts the optimization under uncertainty(OUU) problem into deterministic optimization problem. In fuzzy expected value model (FEVM), the uncertain parameters are treated as fuzzy numbers and the optimization problem uses the expected objective function and expected constraints. The expected values of the objective function and constraints can be calculated by any of the measures e.g. possibility, necessity, credibility defined above based on the different perceptions of the decision maker about the uncertain problem (Liu, 2002).

2. Formulation

2.1. Process & Model Description

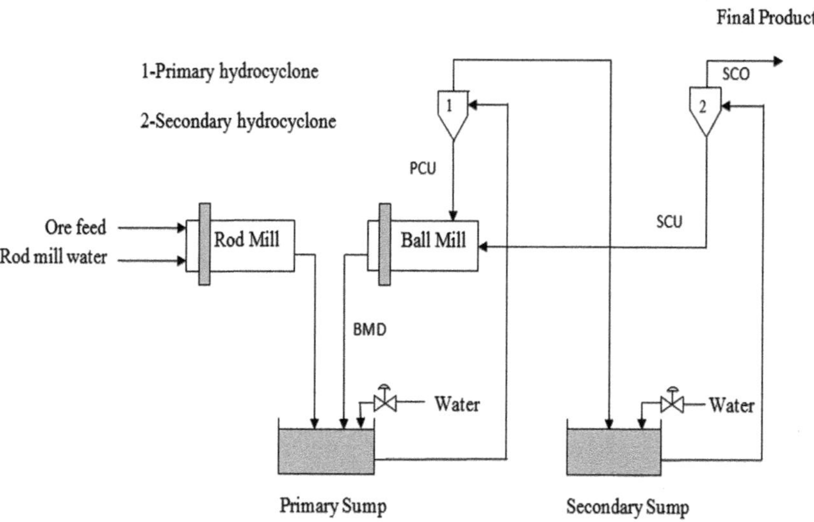

Figure 1. An industrial grinding circuit block diagram

The industrial comminution process under consideration has the following four units: Rod mill, Ball mill, hydro-cyclones, and water sumps. Fresh feed from the bin is fed to the rod mill along with water. The slurry generated from the rod mill is mixed with the slurry from the ball mill in a primary sump. The primary sump outlet stream is sent to the primary cyclone. The overflow from the primary cyclone goes to the secondary sump and the underflow is taken as a feed to the ball mill. The slurry generated in the secondary sump is taken to another hydro-cyclone which is called as secondary cyclone. The underflow of the secondary cyclone is recycled back to the ball mill for grinding and the final product is the overflow which goes to a flotation circuit as feed. Water is added to both sumps to facilitate the flow of the slurry smoothly within the circuit. Complete circuit configuration can be found in Figure 1.

Modeling of individual unit operations of the grinding circuit is performed separately using an amalgamated approach of population balance and empirical correlations. A simulation of an entire circuit is done by using a connectivity matrix which connects all the unit operations in terms of binary numbers. Here 0 denotes no connection and 1 denotes existence of a connection. Multiple simultaneous differential algebraic equations were formed using the entire set of equations which can be solved using well tested public domain software, called DASSL (Petzold, 1983). Details on these model equations can be found elsewhere (Mitra and Gopinath,2004) and not attached here for the sake of brevity.

2.2. Optimization with Fuzzy Parameters

Let us consider the following Multi-objective optimization problem

$$\text{Minimize } f_1(\mathbf{X},\xi), f_2(\mathbf{X},\xi) \ldots f_m(\mathbf{X},\xi)$$

$$\text{Subjected to } g_j(\mathbf{X},\xi)\leq 0, \quad j=1,\ldots,n$$
$$\mathbf{X}_i^L \leq \mathbf{X}_i \leq \mathbf{X}_i^U, \quad i=1,\ldots,k \tag{1}$$

where **X** and ξ are the sets of decision variables and uncertain parameters, present in both objective function and constraints.

The uncertain problem can be converted to an equivalent deterministic optimization problem by FEVM approach which uses expected values of objective functions and constraints as given below (Liu,2002)

$$\text{Minimize } E(f_1(\mathbf{X},\xi)), E(f_2(\mathbf{X},\xi))...E(f_m(\mathbf{X},\xi))$$
$$\text{Subjected to } E(g_j(\mathbf{X},\xi))\leq 0, \quad j=1,\ldots,n$$
$$\mathbf{X}_i^L \leq \mathbf{X}_i \leq \mathbf{X}_i^U, \quad i=1,\ldots,k \tag{2}$$

The expected value operator is used to calculate expected values of objective function or constraints by taking different measures such as possibility, necessity and credibility. Here, the algorithm proposed to calculate the expected values of objective function or constraints has been presented (Liu,2002).

Fuzzy Simulation Algorithm for Expected Value Model based on credibility:

$$E = E\{f(\mathbf{X},\xi)\} \text{ or } E\{g(\mathbf{X},\xi)\}$$

Step 1: Assume E = 0;
Step 2: Randomly generate N points of μ_L(L = 1, 2, …., N) from ε-set of ξ, where ε is a sufficiently small number and μ is the membership function;
Step 3: Set the two numbers $a=\min(f(\mathbf{X},\xi_1), f(\mathbf{X},\xi_2),\ldots\ldots, f(\mathbf{X},\xi_N))$ and $b=\max(f(\mathbf{X},\xi_1), f(\mathbf{X},\xi_2),\ldots\ldots, f(\mathbf{X},\xi_N))$;
Step 4: Randomly generate r between $[a,b]$;
Step 5: If $r\geq 0$, then $e=e+Cr(f(\mathbf{X},\xi)\geq r))$;
If $r<0$, then $e=e-Cr(f(\mathbf{X},\xi)\leq r))$;
Step 6: Repeat the above two steps for N' times
Step 7: $E=\max(a,0)+\min(b,0)+e.(b-a)/N'$

As mentioned above, credibility measure is used to calculate the expected value and credibility measure is defined as a weighted average of possibility and necessity measures as given below where m_1 and m_2 defined the weightage associated with possibility and necessity.

$$Cr\{f(\mathbf{X},\xi)\geq r\} = m_1 \times Pos\{f(\mathbf{X},\xi)\geq r\} + m_2 \times Nec\{f(\mathbf{X},\xi)\geq r\} \tag{3}$$

Possibility and necessity measures can be interpreted as the sign of conservative and aggressiveness, which can be clear from the way they are formulated as given below:

$$Pos\{f(\mathbf{X},\xi)\geq r\} = \max_{1\leq L\leq N}\{\mu_L | \{f(\mathbf{X},\xi_L)\geq r\}\} \tag{4}$$
$$Nec\{f(\mathbf{X},\xi)\geq r\} = \min_{1\leq L\leq N}\{1-\mu_L | \{f(\mathbf{X},\xi_L)< r\}\} \tag{5}$$

The credibility measure can, therefore, be defined accordingly to make a required balance between the possibility and necessity (e.g. an equal weightage has been given to both of them in equation 3) and based on this required balance, optimal solutions of different levels of conservativeness or aggressiveness can be obtained.

2.3. Multi-objective Optimization under Uncertainty

In industrial grinding process, in addition to goal of productivity maximization, other purposes of deterministic grinding circuit optimization have to satisfy the upper bound constraints on the control variables. We know that there lies a tradeoff between the throughput (TP) and the percent passing of midsize classes (MS) from the previous work of Mitra and Gopinath,2004. In deterministic optimization formulation, there are certain parameters which we will assume them as constant. But, in real life that may not be case. There are such six parameters in our industrial grinding process which are α_R, α_B , β_R, β_B are the grindability indices and grindability exponents for the rod mill (RMGI) and the ball mill (BMGI); and γ_P, γ_S are the sharpness indices for the primary (PCSI) and secondary cyclones (SCSI). These parameters are treated as constant in deterministic formulation. As they are going to be treated as uncertain parameters in the OUU formulation. These parameters are assumed uncertain because most of them are obtained from the regression of experimental data and thus are subject to uncertainty due to experimental and regression errors. In the next part of the section, we consider them as fuzzy numbers and solve the OUU problem by FEVM. In FEVM formulation, the uncertain parameters are considered as fuzzy numbers and the uncertain formulation is transformed into the deterministic formulation by expectation calculations for both objective function and constraints. So, the converted deterministic multi-objective optimization problem is expressed as:

Objective functions

$$\underset{S,W_1,W_2}{Max} \quad E\{TP(\alpha_R,\beta_R,\alpha_B,\beta_B,\gamma_P,\gamma_S)\}$$

$$\underset{S,W_1,W_2}{Max} \quad E\{MS(\alpha_R,\beta_R,\alpha_B,\beta_B,\gamma_P,\gamma_S)\}$$

Subject to

$$E\{CS(\alpha_R,\beta_R,\alpha_B,\beta_B,\gamma_P,\gamma_S)-CS^U\}\le 0$$
$$E\{FS(\alpha_R,\beta_R,\alpha_B,\beta_B,\gamma_P,\gamma_S)-FS^U\}\le 0$$
$$E\{PS(\alpha_R,\beta_R,\alpha_B,\beta_B,\gamma_P,\gamma_S)-PS^U\}\le 0$$
$$E\{RCL\ (\alpha_R,\beta_R,\alpha_B,\beta_B,\gamma_P,\gamma_S)-RCL^U\}\le 0$$

Decision variables bounds

$$S^L \le S \le S^U \qquad W_1^L \le W_1 \le W_1^U \qquad W_2^L \le W_2 \le W_2^U \tag{6}$$

Fuzzy Simulation Algorithm for Expected Value Model based on credibility is used to perform expectation calculations in the above equivalent deterministic formulation.

3. Results and Discussions

The case study considered here is an industrial grinding process and the results are presented here in normalized scale due to a nondisclosure agreement with the collaboration cum implementation partners. The uncertain parameters are assumed as fuzzy parameters expressed by triangular fuzzy membership functions. The triangular fuzzy functions are scalene in nature while the tip of the triangle represents the same value as the value of those parameters in deterministic formulation (Mitra and Gopinath, 2004). The span of uncertainty level is different on both sides of the deterministic value e.g. (a) 15 % on the higher side and 5 % on the lower side as in one case (type a) and (b) 5 % on the higher side and 15 % on the lower side in another case (type b). Pareto optimal (PO) fronts between two objective functions considering both triangular functions (types (a) and (b)) for equivalent deterministic as well as deterministic formulation can be observed in Figure 2. The expected value of objective function or constraint is calculated by using credibility measure where credibility is calculated with an equal weightage on possibility and necessity (i.e. m_1 = 0.5 and m_2 = 0.5). While using type (b) of scalene triangular fuzzy functions, the Pareto front is observed to shift towards the downward direction with respect to the deterministic PO front (shown as "certain" in Figure 2). On the other hand, for type (a) of scalene triangular fuzzy functions, PO front shifts towards upward direction as compared to the deterministic case. This means for a fixed value of throughput, there is an increase in mid-size fraction passing values, i.e. more finer grinding is carried out compared to that of the deterministic case. This means some values of uncertain parameters other than their nominal values can also lead to better PO front when there is variation in these uncertain parameters.

In Figure 2, the expected value of objective function/constraint is calculated by using credibility measure. In consort with credibility measure, expected value can be calculated by using possibility and necessity measures. The possibility (m_1 = 1 and m_2 = 0) measure gives extremely optimistic Pareto front while the necessity measure (m_1 = 0 and m_2 = 1) gives profoundly pessimistic Pareto front. The decision maker's attitude may vary between these two extremes and can be defined by the different combination of weights used for necessity and possibility. From equation (4) and (5), it can be observed that constraint voilation is minimum in possibility measure where as constraint voilation is maximum in necessity measure. So, possibility measure gives the Pareto which is conservative in nature and necessity measure gives the Pareto which is aggressive in nature.

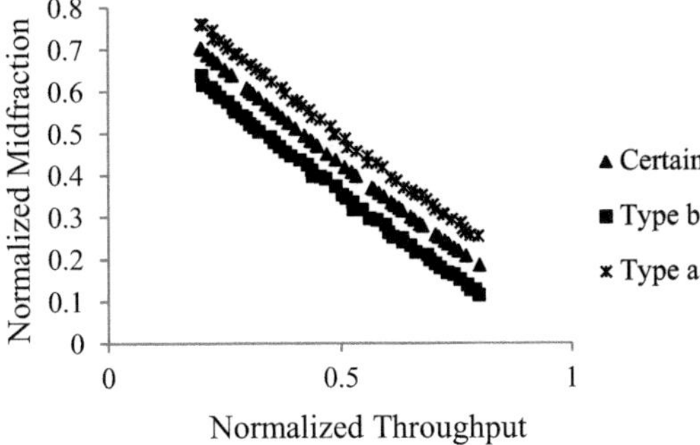

Figure 2. Pareto trade off points between normalized mid-size fraction and normalized throughput for a credibility based expected value approach for scalene triangular fuzzy function

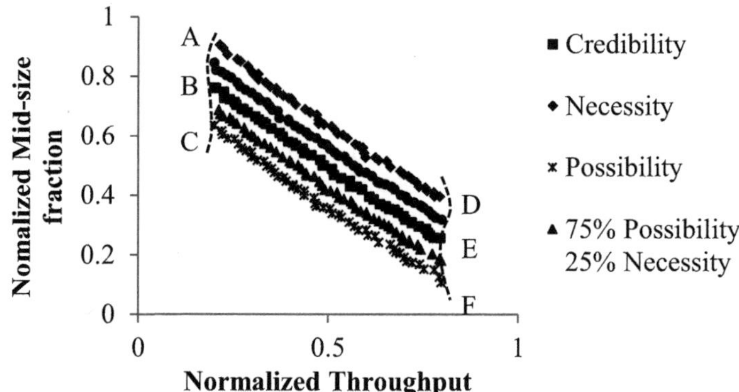

Figure 3. Pareto trade off points between normalized mid-size fraction and normalized throughput for a credibility, possibility and necessity based expected value approach for scalene triangular fuzzy function

The expected analysis has been carried out by assuming the triangular membership function of type (a) and the improvement in the PO front can be observed (represented as "Credibility" in Figure 3). Two more scenarios with different weights on possibility and necessity, one with $m_1 = 0.25$ and $m_2 = 0.75$ and the other with $m_1 = 0.75$ and $m_2 = 0.25$, have been simulated and the respective PO fronts can be observed in Figure 3. The PO front of "necessity" and "possibility" and dotted lines connecting some other boundary points such as A, B, C, D, E, F as shown in Figure 3 forms the entire solution space in which the decision maker is supposed to make decision under different scenarios.

4. Conclusions

Uncertain parameters are assumed to behave like fuzzy numbers and FEVM approach has been applied to an industrial case study of ore beneficiation process. A modified form of NSGA II, FENSGA-II has been utilized to solve the deterministic equivalent of the multi-objective optimization problem under uncertainty. Results of credibility, possibility and necessity based FEVM are presented and thoroughly analyzed. PO solutions obtained from possibility based FEVM have the optimistic attitude. Similarly, PO solutions obtained from necessity based FEVM have the pessimistic attitude. This gives a key to decision maker to select any point based on existing risk appetite.

References

K. Deb, A. Pratap, S. Agarwal, T. Meyarivan, 2002, A fast and elitist multi-objective genetic algorithms, IEEE Trans. Evo. Comp., 6, 182.

K. Mitra, R.Gopinath, 2004, Multiobjective optimization of an industrial grinding operation using elitist nondominated sorting genetic algorithm, Chem. Engg. Sci., 59, 385-396.

L.R. Petzold, 1983, A Description of DASSL: a differential/algebraic system solver, Scientific Computing, North-Holland, Amsterdam.

B. Liu, Y.K. Liu, 2002, Expected value of fuzzy variable and fuzzy expected value models, IEEE Trans. Fuzzy Syst, 10,445-450.

Jiří Jaromír Klemeš, Petar Sabev Varbanov and Peng Yen Liew (Editors)
Proceedings of the 24th European Symposium on Computer Aided Process Engineering – ESCAPE 24
June 15-18, 2014, Budapest, Hungary.

Optimization of Insulin Dosing in Patients with Type 1 Diabetes Mellitus

Stamatina Zavitsanou*, Athanasios Mantalaris, Michael C. Georgiadis, Efstratios N. Pistikopoulos

Centre for Process Systems Engineering, Department of Chemical Engineering, Imperial College London, South Kensington Campus, London SW7 2AZ, UK
stamatina.zavitsanou09@imperial.ac.uk

Abstract

Type I Diabetes Mellitus is a lifelong disease characterized by elevated blood glucose levels due to lack of insulin, resulting from autoimmune mediated destruction of the insulin-producing beta cells of the pancreas. Insulin regulates blood glucose levels by permitting glucose to enter the human cells to provide them with energy. Patients with type I diabetes require exogenous insulin administration to regulate their blood glucose concentration. Optimization of insulin dosing minimizes the risk of possible hypoglycaemia (over-dosing) and avoids hyperglycaemia (under-dosing). Rigorous optimization studies are performed for 10 patients with type 1 DM on an insulin pump, using the UVa/Padova T1DM Simulator as the process model. The insulin bolus, given to compensate for food consumption, is optimized in terms of time to peak maximum effect and also basal and bolus dosing balance during a meal is considered. These results are compared with conventional insulin dosing obtained in the literature and finally the insulin regimen that normalizes the glucose curve more effectively – maintain blood glucose concentration within the normal range – is determined. Additionally, an alternative to bolus insulin dosing is evaluated and the two dosing types are compared, again in terms of their effect on glucose concentration. This study intends to identify the most effective dosing strategy to be further used as a background guideline in closed loop studies.

Keywords: time delays, optimization, insulin delivery system

1. Introduction

The most advanced treatment in type 1 diabetes is an insulin pump. The pump delivers continuously a basal rate of insulin throughout the day and night and additional bolus doses to compensate for food consumption. Due to the nature of the treatment many complications can occur such as inappropriate insulin dosing or time plan can cause extended hyperglycaemia or hypoglycaemic episodes. These can only be prevented if insulin dosing is continuously adjusted according to the blood glucose measurements. Thus, the development of a device that continuously administers insulin and is automatically controlled by the blood glucose measurements will have a great anticipated advantage for patients with type 1 diabetes.

One of the great challenges of an automated system is the delayed insulin absorption and action. This time lag is related to the type of insulin used, the route of administration, the detection of a glucose fluctuation and patient's sensitivity to insulin. The difference in the glycaemic response produced by the same dose of insulin in different individuals indicates that there is a high intra-patient variability involved in glucose-insulin interactions. When this variability is low then a more predictable glycaemic response can be determined, which is important for a closed loop system. In order to reduce the factors that cause variability and deteriorate the prediction of the glycaemic response, open loop simulation analysis and optimization studies are performed to gain deep knowledge of the particular system and use the conclusions as a guideline for closed loop studies.

Several models describing the glucose-insulin dynamics have been reported in the literature (Zavitsanou et. al, 2011). In this study, the T1DM Uva/Padova Simulator, developed in gPROMS (Process Systems Enterprise Ltd, 2010) is used as the process model, which has been approved from the FDA to substitute animal trials in the pre-clinical testing of certain control strategies in Type 1 DM. Simulation studies are performed to quantify the delayed insulin effect on 10 adult patients. This analysis has motivated the performance of patient-specific optimization studies, to find the optimal timing of insulin dosing to maintain the patient's glycaemic target. An alternative to bolus dosing regimen is investigated in order to be incorporated in the closed loop insulin delivery strategy and the results are presented.

2. Time Delays in the system

Time delay in a system is the time that intervenes from the instant the input is applied until the instant the effect is observed. In this particular system the input is the insulin dose and the effect is the decrease in the blood glucose concentration. Assuming that the sampling time Ts is 5min (available measurements of glucose concentration in the blood from the sensor), it can be noticed that if a bolus is given at t_0=60 min insulin requires up to 15min to initiate the decrease of blood glucose concentration, practically to observe a 1mg/dl change of the concentration. This time involves the absorption of rapid acting insulin through the subcutaneous tissue and insulin action that can take up to 1-3 hours for its maximum effect.

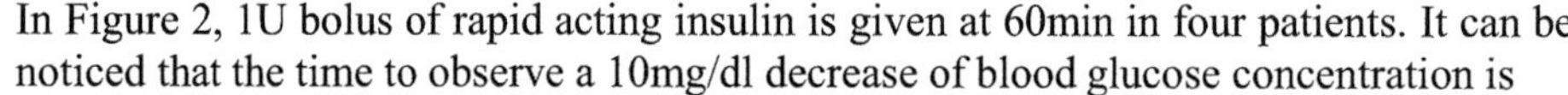

In Figure 2, 1U bolus of rapid acting insulin is given at 60min in four patients. It can be noticed that the time to observe a 10mg/dl decrease of blood glucose concentration is

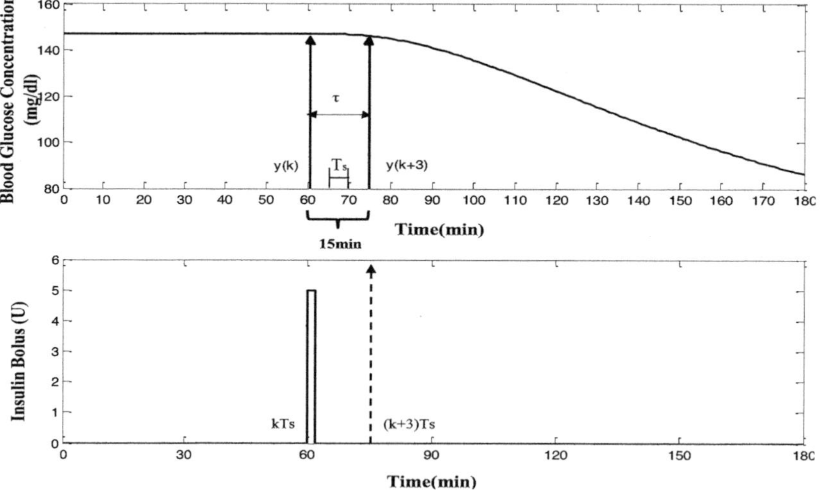

Figure 1. Delayed insulin effect

not equal for the four patients. This can be explained since every patient responds differently to insulin and has a different ability to increase the body's glucose uptake from the several tissues. This can be quantified with insulin sensitivity index. The more sensitive to insulin the patient is, the less amount of insulin is required. Patients 2 and 4 with high insulin sensitivity index require less time for their blood glucose to be decreased than patients 1 and 3.

In Figure 3 for two patients, low and high insulin sensitive, 3 bolus doses are given at 400 mins without considering meal consumption. It can be noticed that the time required for glucose to be decreased by 10 mg/dL is dependent on the amount of the bolus. The delayed insulin effect decreases while the amount of insulin bolus increases. This implies that the time delay property cannot be considered constant for an individual patient.

In conclusion, the dynamic system involves inherent, patient dependent time delays which are the delayed insulin absorption and action and also the approximately 10 mins delayed glucose appearance in the blood after food consumption due to interstitial glucose kinetics, meaning the route from the mouth to the small intestine and then to the blood. Apart from these delays, there are additional technical delays which involve the delayed detection of blood glucose concentration change because the continuous glucose monitoring devices calculate blood glucose concentration by measuring interstitial fluid glucose concentration (Keenan et al, 2009). Hence, the time lag of the displayed glucose value and the real blood glucose value consists of the time lag between ISF and blood glucose accounting for the processing requirements as well.

3. Dynamic optimization of insulin delivery

From the previous analysis, it has been evident that in order the patients to maintain their blood glucose close to their glycaemic target the timing of the bolus insulin administration must be optimally decided to achieve safe glycaemic regulation. It has also been evident that each patient presents a unique response to insulin and therefore

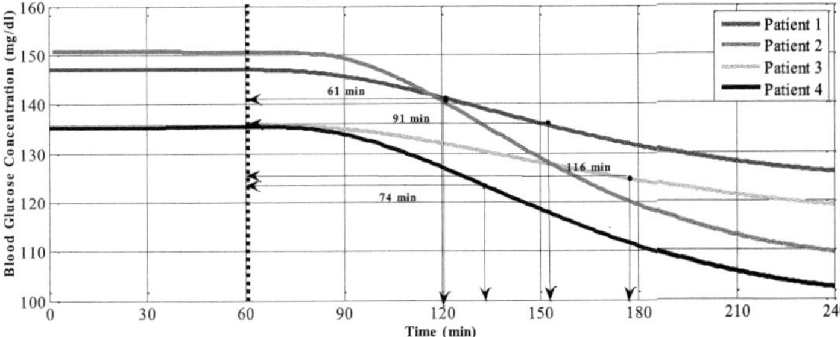

Figure 2. Patient dependent time delay

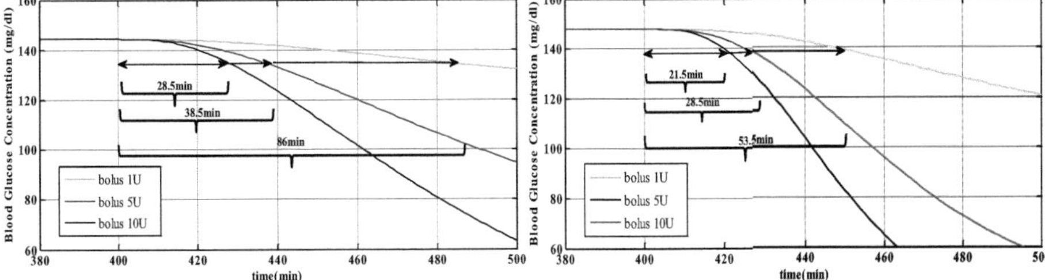

Figure 3. Time delay dependent on patient and bolus

must be treated differently. Hence, patient-specific optimization studies are performed to obtain the optimal insulin profile that minimizes the time glucose is outside of the normal range. The mathematical formulation of the optimization problem has the following general form:

$$\min_{d_i} \int_0^{t_f} (w_1 + w_2)dt \tag{1}$$

s.t.

$$\dot{G} = f(x(t), \dot{x}(t), y(t), u(t), d_i) \tag{2}$$

$$\sum_{i=1}^{N_{int}} d_i = 1, \qquad d_i \in \{0,1\} \tag{3}$$

$$w_1 \geq \varepsilon, \qquad w_1 \geq G - G_{max} \tag{4.a}$$

$$w_2 \geq 0, \qquad w_2 \geq G_{min} - G \tag{4.b}$$

where t_f is the time horizon, G is the blood glucose concentration described by the nonlinear process model specific for every patient (Kovatchev et al., 2011), G_{max} (140 mg/dL), G_{min} (70mg/dL) are the upper and lower glucose concentration bounds. Equation 4.a is a soft constraint as opposed to Equation 4.b which is a hard constraint to prevent from any severe health complications related to hypoglycemia. At t_0=400 mins a breakfast meal of 50 g of carbohydrates was given to the 10 patients. The optimal amount of insulin, appropriate to compensate for the forthcoming glucose increase due to the meal intake was provided by the Simulator when closed loop studies were performed and was chosen for every patient. The optimization studies were performed in gPROMS (Process Systems Enterprise Ltd, 2010). A window of 4h before the meal was considered to include any extreme low insulin sensitive patient and this time span was discretized every 2min, which is the time the pump requires to deliver an insulin bolus, hence, N_{int}=120. A time invariant, binary variable d_i was considered to be 0 if no bolus was given or 1 at time i if a bolus was given. The Mixed Integer Nonlinear Programming problem was solved using the approach described in (Bansal et al., 2003) as implemented in gPROMS. An augmented penalty strategy is employed to increase the possibility to obtain a global solution (Process Systems Enterprise Ltd, 2010).

The optimization results are presented in Figure 4 for 6 patients. The grey line shows the optimized glucose profile while the black line the simulated profile when bolus is given simultaneously with meal. The optimal timing of insulin administration for every patient is summarized in Table 1. When the bolus is given at the optimal time the glucose profile is improved in terms of maintenance of the concentration within the normal range for all the patients. In Table 1 the area between the upper glucose bound and the glucose profile is calculated. The difference of the values between the simulated and optimized curves indicates that a superior regulation of glucose is achieved when insulin infusion scheduling is considered. Additionally, hypoglycemic events are not observed for any of the patients, despite the considerable difference in timing between them. This is related to the sensitivity of the patient to insulin as mentioned before and for the specific optimal dose the patient would not reach the lower glucose bound, hence the lower bound is not shown in Figure 4.

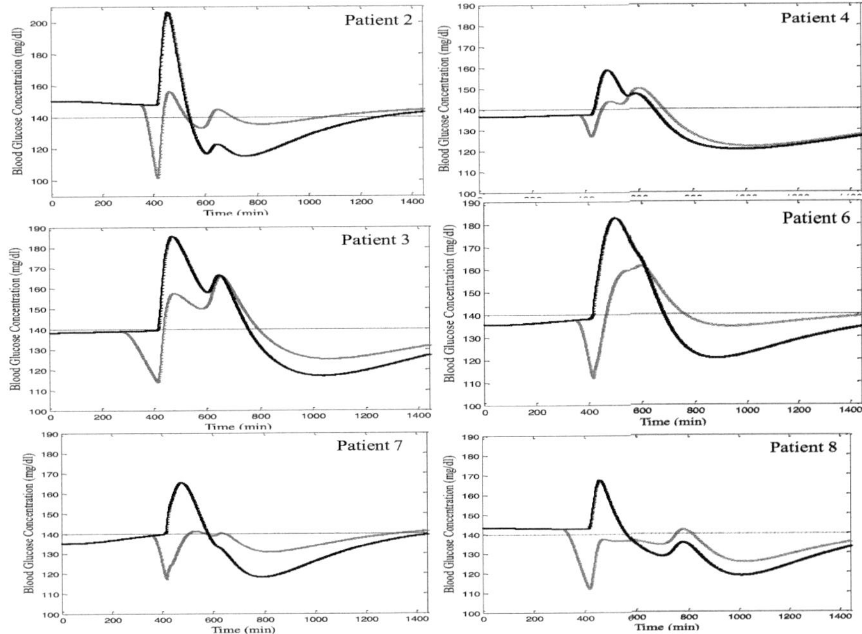

Figure 4. Optimization (gray line) and Simulation (black line) glucose profiles

Table 1. Area under the curve (outside the normal range)

	Area under the curve (outside the normal range)		
	Simulated Glucose curve	Optimized Glucose curve	Optimal Time of bolus before meal
Patient 1	5.1747×10^3	4.4825×10^3	32min
Patient 2	6.7083×10^4	5.8923×10^3	66min
Patient 3	8.3306×10^3	5.1267×10^3	140min
Patient 4	2.1919×10^3	1.3213×10^3	36min
Patient 5	4.0646×10^3	1.7180×10^3	62min
Patient 6	2.0961×10^5	3.9445×10^3	62min
Patient 7	2.0833×10^5	2.7859×10^2	52min
Patient 8	5.9726×10^4	1.2093×10^3	100min
Patient 9	1.1653×10^4	8.9137×10^3	74min
Patient 10	1.4930×10^4	1.2630×10^4	76min

4. Alternative insulin infusion

An alternative to bolus dosing is considered as a piecewise constant infusion rate that holds a specific value for 5 min time intervals. The profile is calculated with optimizing criterion the minimum range of glucose outside the normal bounds. Figure 5, for patient 1 includes the optimized glucose profile when the bolus is given at the time calculated with the previous optimization problem (a), the glucose profile when a piecewise approach is considered (d) with time frame of 32 min (Table 1) and both are compared with the glucose profile when bolus is given simultaneously with meal (b). The two approaches produce the same effect on glucose, indicating that a stepwise infusion could be considered as a possible mechanism since it provides flexibility and can be better adjusted in an automated delivery system. In Figure 5, for patient 5, in order to avoid a big time frame (62 min) which can be restricting from a control point of view, a

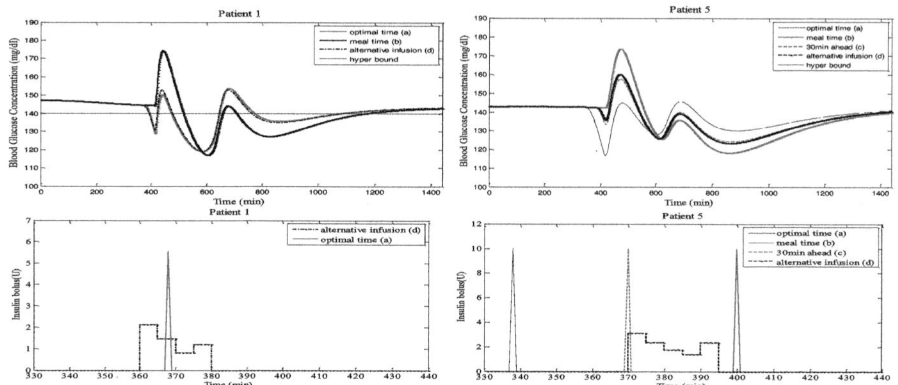

Figure 5. Optimal glucose profiles with insulin as bolus and as piecewise constant infusion

time frame of 30 min is considered. The glucose profiles are compared and additionally the profile when bolus is given 30min in advance (c) is included. The stepwise approach (d) and the 30 min bolus in advance (c) produce comparatively the same results. This approach although it is not the optimal, can still be regarded as a considerable alternative for control design.

5. Conclusions

The involved time lags caused by the patient dependent delayed insulin action were quantified for 10 patients. Therefore, patient-specific, in terms of appropriate insulin dosing for each patient, optimization studies were performed to find the optimal timing to deliver the bolus. An alternative, stepwise insulin regimen was considered and the optimization results indicate that it could provide a considerable alternative for closed loop applications. These results will be incorporated in future work into the control strategy (Dassau et al., 2006) that will be clinically evaluated.

6. Acknowledgements

The financial support from the European Research Council (MOBILE, ERC Advanced Grant, No:226462), and the CPSE Industrial Consortium is thankfully acknowledged.

References

V. Bansal, V. Sakizlis, R. Ross, J.D. Perkins, E.N. Pistikopoulos, 2003, New algorithms for mixed-integer dynamic optimization, Computers and Chemical Engineering, 27, 5, 647-668

E. Dassau, H. Zisser, R. Harvey, M.W. Percival, B. Grosman, W. Bevier, E. Atlas, S. Miller, R.Nimri, L. Jovanovič, F.J.Doyle III, 2013, Clinical Evaluation of a Personalized Artificial Pancreas, Diabetes Care, 36, 4, 801-809

D.B. Keenan, J.J. Mastrototaro, G. Voskanyan, G.M. Steil, 2009, Delays in Minimally Invasive Continuous Glucose Monitoring Devices:A Review of Current Technology, Journal of diabetes science and technology, 3, 5, 1207–1214.

B.P. Kovatchev, M.D. Breton, C. Dalla Man, C. Cobelli , 2011, In Silico Preclinical Trials: A Proof of Concept in Closed-Loop Control of Type 1 Diabetes, Journal of Diabetes Science and Technology, 3, 1, 44–55.

Process Systems Enterprise Limited (PSE), 2010, Optimization Guide, <www.psenterprise.com>, accessed on 14/02/2014.

S. Zavitsanou, N. Panoskaltsi, A. Mantalaris, M. Georgiadis, M., Pistikopoulos, E.N., 2011. Modelling of the Insulin Delivery System for patients with Type 1 Diabetes Mellitus, Computer Aided Chemical Engineering, 29, 1500-1504

Jiří Jaromír Klemeš, Petar Sabev Varbanov and Peng Yen Liew (Editors)
Proceedings of the 24th European Symposium on Computer Aided Process Engineering – ESCAPE 24
June 15-18, 2014, Budapest, Hungary.

Ternary Blends of Vegetable Oils: Thermal Profile Predictions for Product Design

Moisés Teles dos Santos,[a*] Vincent Gerbaud,[b] Galo A.C. Le Roux[a]

[a] *LSCP/CESQ Department of Chemical Engineering, Universidade de São Paulo, Av. Prof. Luciano Gualberto 380, 05508 900, São Paulo, Brazil*

[b] *Université de Toulouse, Laboratoire de Génie Chimique (LGC) UMR CNRS INP/UPS,4 allée Emile Monso, Toulouse, France*

moises.teles@usp.br

Abstract

This work deals with Product Design by means of theoretical predictions of the Solid Fat Content of different formulations using 3 vegetable oils. A Soli-Liquid Equilibrium (SLE) model was implemented and integrated into an optimization algorithm based on the Generalized Reduced Gradient method. A total of 3,696 SLE problems are solved, covering 57 binary blends, 3 pure vegetable oils and 171 ternary blends problems, before and after chemical interesterification reaction and at 8 different temperatures. A combinatorial random distribution of fatty acids in the glycerol structure is used to simulate the effect of the reaction. The results were compared with 256 experimental points, giving an average absolute error of 5.4 and 4.4 in Solid Fat Content for systems before and after reaction, respectively. Computer-aided tools can be useful to deal with the large combinatorial problem faced by product design, especially when desired product performance is related to a phase behavior in multicomponent mixtures.

Keywords: vegetable oil, product design, solid-liquid equilibrium, lipids.

1. Introduction

The interest in Chemical Product Engineering is a consequence in the shift in the chemical industry towards high value-added products, in which performance plays a major role (Hill, 2009). Among those products, cosmetics and foods are of great economic importance and have vegetable oils in their composition. In these products, the desired attributes (performance) are directly related to a solid-liquid phase behavior in a multicomponent mixture of triacylglycerols, the major compounds in vegetable oils. The use of computer-aided tools in lipid-based industry has attracted attention in Process System Engineering community. Examples of recent improvements concern property prediction models (Cunico et al., 2013), molecular dynamics (Brasiello et al., 2010), simulation of melting curves (Teles dos Santos et al., 2010) and studies about solid-liquid phase transitions in fatty compounds (Robustillo et al., 2014). Despite the increasing number of experimental and modeling studies in binary/ternary mixtures of fatty compounds, the melting behavior of multicomponent mixtures (blends of vegetable oils) is less studied in a computational point of view. This work aims to cope with this gap. When using vegetable oils for Product Design, the desired performance is related to a solid-liquid phase behavior, as in the case of the food industry where the Solid Fat Content (SFC) is a key property for match desired attributes (e.g. texture, creaminess). This work deals with theoretical predictions of SFC for Product Design using different formulations composed of 3 vegetable oils. The aim is to aid the decision-making process in choosing the best formulation in terms of desired SFC.

2. Models

2.1. Solid-Liquid Equilibrium Problem

About 95 % of vegetable oils are composed of triacylglycerols (TAGs), formed by 3 fatty acids sterified to a glycerol structure. As one TAG can be formed by 1, 2 or 3 different fatty acids, and even the position of these fatty acids leads to different TAGs, many TAGs molecules can be theoretically formed by only few fatty acids. Figure 1 shows a typical TAG molecular shape with the possible solid-liquid transitions including polymorphism in solid state (α, β' and β). To predict the solid/liquid ratio given the fraction of each vegetable oil in the blend and the temperature, a phase equilibrium problem is solved as a nonlinear programming problem searching for the minimization of the Gibbs Free Energy function (G), subject to linear material balance constraints. The problem can be stated as:

$$\min\, G(n) = \sum_{i=1}^{nc}\sum_{j=1}^{np} n_i^j \mu_i^j(n) = \sum_{j=1}^{np} n^j g^j \tag{1}$$

s.t:

$$n_i = \sum_{j=1}^{np} n_i^j \quad i = 1 \ldots nc \tag{2}$$

$$0 \le n_i^j \le n_i \; i = 1 \ldots nc;\, j = 1 \ldots np \tag{3}$$

Where nc and np are respectively the number of different TAGs and the number of phases in the mixture; n_i^j and μ_i^j represent the number of mols and the chemical potential of TAG i in phase j respectively and n_i is the total number of mols of TAG i. TAG molecules can crystallize in 3 main crystalline states: α, β' and β. When a particular polymorphic state is evaluated, another constraint is added: the number of mols of all species in the other two polymorphic states is set to zero. Then, the optimization algorithm searches for the distribution of molecules between the solid and liquid phases that minimizes the Gibbs Free Energy. The decision variables are the number of mols of each component i in each phase j (n_i^j).

2.2. Thermodynamic Model

2.2.1. Liquid Phase

Previous literature works concluded that the liquid phase can be treated as ideal, based on the Flory Huggins theory (Wesdorp, 1990). Setting the reference state of pure liquid (chemical potential zero), we have for the liquid phase:

$$g^{liquid} = RT\sum_{i=1}^{nc}(x_i^{liquid} \ln x_i^{liquid}) \tag{4}$$

2.2.2. Solid Phases

The expression of the Gibbs Energy in solid phases is given by Eq.(5) (Prausnitz et al., 1999):

$$g^{solid(j)} = RT\sum_{i=1}^{nc} x_i^{solid(j)}\left(\frac{\Delta H_{m,i}^{solid(j)}}{R}\left(\frac{1}{T} - \frac{1}{T_{m,i}^{solid(j)}}\right) + \ln\left(\gamma_i^{solid(j)} x_i^{solid(j)}\right)\right) \tag{5}$$

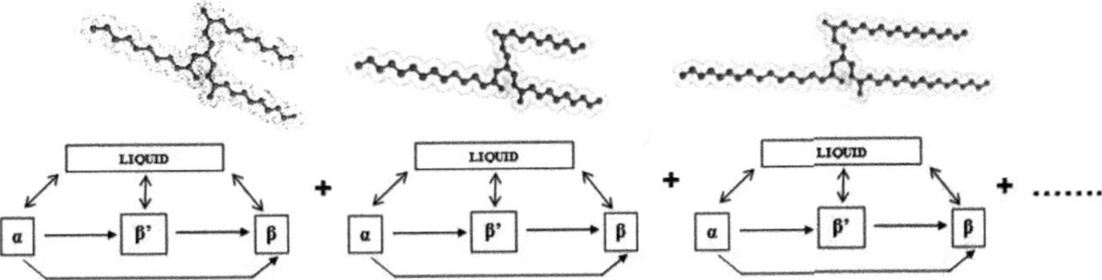

Figure 1. Typical triacylglycerol structures and possible solid-liquid phase transitions.

Where $\Delta H_{m,i}^{solid(j)}$ and $T_{m,i}^{solid(j)}$ are respectively the melting enthalpy and melting temperature of TAG i in solid state j and γ_i^j the activity coefficient of i on phase j.

2.3. Excess Gibbs Energy Model

The 2-sufixe Margules model was chosen for three reasons: 1- it is suitable for mixtures where the components have similar molar volume, shape and chemical nature (Prausnitz et al., 1999); 2-There are correlations regressed for TAGs allowing predicting the model parameters and 3-it allows flexibility/simplicity required in the optimization step. The necessary binary interaction parameters (A_{ij}) are calculated using correlations with the isomorphism in the pair of TAGs i-j (Wesdorp, 1990). The activity coefficients can be therefore estimated.

2.4. Pure Component Properties (Melting Temperature and Melting Enthalpy)

A program developed in FORTRAN 90 includes a set of experimental data. Due to the high number of TAGs that can be formed from just a few fatty acids, it is frequent that experimental data is not available for a given TAG or in all 3 polymorphic states. In these cases, the predictive methods of Zeberg-Mikkelsen and Stenby (1999) and Wesdorp (1990) are used.

2.5. Triacylglycerol Composition from Fatty Acids Data

The TAG composition is predicted from the known fatty acids data of each vegetable oil (Lida et al., 2002). Two TAG compositions are estimated: the TAG composition of the physical mixture of the oils and the TAG composition of the product of the chemical interesterification (CI) reaction among the oils. In the first case, the TAG composition of each oil is firstly estimated (by computational random distribution of fatty acids in the glycerol); then, a material balance gives the TAG composition of the mixture. In the second case, firstly a material balance of all fatty acids present in each oil gives the overall fatty acid composition; then, a computational random distribution of these fatty acids in the glycerol is done, resulting in an indirect way to simulate the effect of the CI reaction. The CI is a technique to change melting profile of vegetable oils blends. This reaction promotes a random distribution of fatty acids among the 3 positions of glycerol.

3. Solution Approach

The optimization step (Eqs. (1-3)) was implemented in GAMS (v.23) using a solver based on a Generalized Reduced Gradient method (CONOPT 3). This optimization program was then coupled (using batch files) with the main program written in FORTRAN 90, which handles the calculation of interaction parameters, melting temperature, melting enthalpy and the generation of triacylglycerols from fatty acids data. This last one is done by random distribution of fatty acids in the glycerol, generating all possible TAGs by combinatorial analysis. The results from the optimization step are the number of mols of each TAG in each phase (solid and liquid). Thus, one can compute the solid/liquid ratio (SFC) given the temperature and fraction of each vegetable oil in the blend.

4. Case Study

The method was applied to a ternary system: palm oil (PO) – sunflower oil (SFO) – palmkernel oil (PKO) before and after CI reaction. An increment of 5 % in each vegetable oil is used to cover the ternary diagram. For a given temperature, 231 optimization problems are solved (57 binary, 3 pure vegetable oil and 171 ternary problems). The same diagram is evaluated before and after CI, therefore a total of 462 SLE problems are solved in a single temperature. Spanning the procedure to 8 temperatures, 3,696 SLE problems are solved. The results were compared with experimental SFC data from Lida et al. (2002). The number of experimental points is 256: 128 before CI (16 composition x 8 temperatures) and 128 after CI (16 compositions x 8 temperatures). Only 64 experimental points refer to ternary blends.

5. Results and Discussion

The average absolute error (AAE) in SFC is indicated in Table 1, covering the points with available experimental data. The predicted thermal profile covering the ternary diagram (231 SLE problems) with corresponding temperatures and computational times are shown for simple mixtures without reaction (Figure 2) and for interesterified blends (Figure 3). Analyzing the computational results over the 256 experimental values, different model performances arise. Points with very high agreement were found. For example, for the mixture (without reaction): pure PO at 25 °C (SFC experimental = 11.3; SFC calculated = 11.0); binary PO/SFO (50/50) at 20 °C (SFC experimental = 5.2; SFC calculated = 5.0); ternary PO/SFO/PKO (1/4/1) at 5 °C (SFC experimental = 9.8; SFC calculated = 12.0). The same occurs for interesterified blends: pure PKO at 15 °C (SFC experimental = 36.3; SFC calculated = 36.0); binary SFO/PKO (50/50) at 10 °C (SFC experimental = 6.2; SFC calculated = 6.0); ternary PO/SFO/PKO (4/1/1) at 30 °C (SFC experimental = 3.3; SFC calculated = 3.0). However, large deviations were also observed.

Table 1. Average absolute error of Solid Fat Content predictions.

Mixture	5 °C	10 °C	15 °C	20 °C	25 °C	30 °C	35 °C	40 °C
Single VO	7.3	7.5	3.9	2.2	5.9	4.5	2.8	0.1
Binary blends	5.3	4.5	6.0	9.9	8.9	5.2	3.2	0.8
Ternary blends	3.7	5.7	9.9	12.2	9.1	6.1	3.5	0.5
Chemical Reaction								
Single VO	10.1	5.9	3.3	7.2	7.3	5.6	1.8	0.1
Binary blends	11.5	8.1	4.7	2.9	2.3	1.2	0.2	0.4
Ternary blends	15.6	9.4	4.1	2.1	2.1	0.6	0.0	0.0

VO: vegetable oil

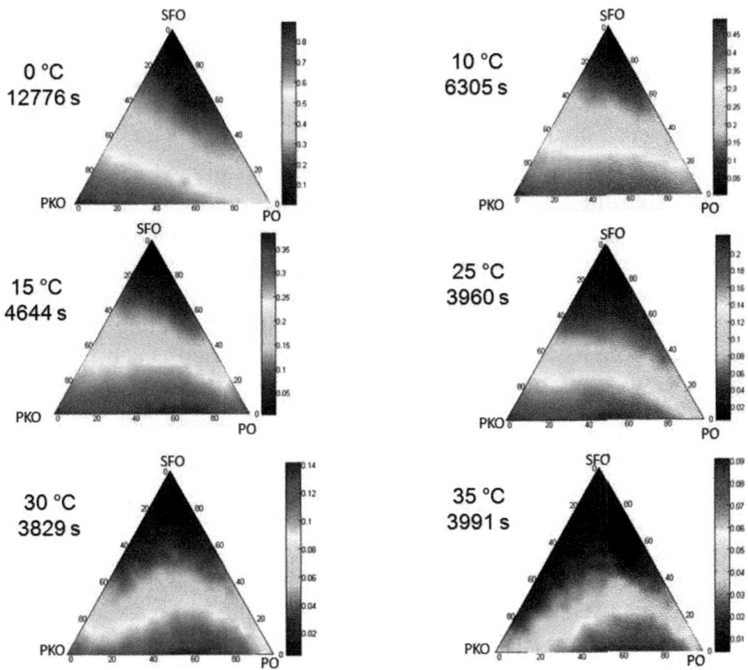

Figure 2. Predictions of Solid Fat Content for the system palm oil (PO) – sunflower oil (SFO) – palmkernel oil (PKO) without interesterification reaction.

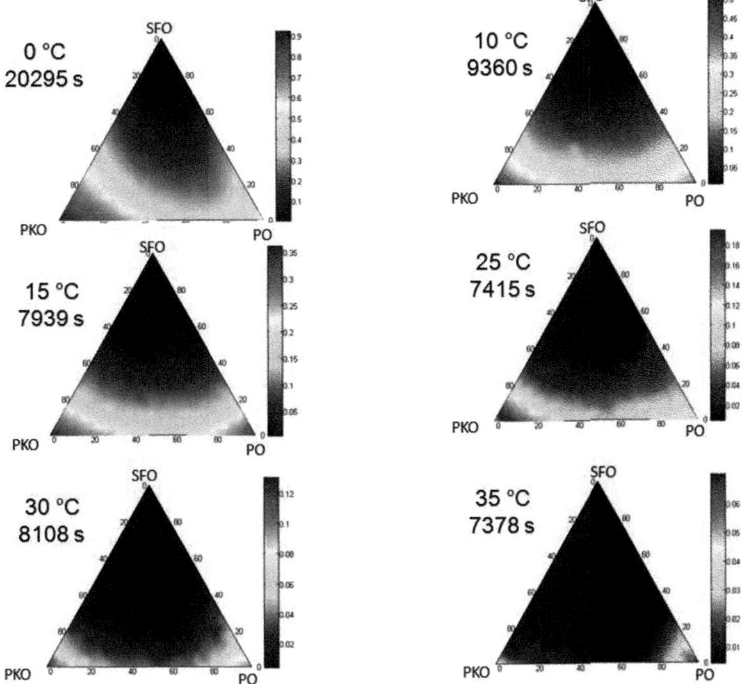

Figure 3. Predictions of Solid Fat Content for the system palm oil (PO) – sunflower oil (SFO) – palmkernel oil (PKO) with interesterification reaction.

For mixture: pure PO at 5 ºC (SFC experimental = 63.1; SFC calculated = 42.0); binary PO/PKO (50/50) at 20 ºC (SFC experimental = 7.5; SFC calculated = 31.0); ternary PO/SFO/PKO (1/1/4) at 20 ºC (SFC experimental = 5.8; SFC calculated = 22.0). For systems after reaction: pure PO at 5 ºC (SFC experimental = 62.2; SFC calculated = 42.0); binary PO/PKO (50/50) at 5 ºC (SFC experimental = 55.0; SFC calculated = 34.0); ternary PO/SFO/PKO (4/1/1) at 5 ºC (SFC experimental = 44.6; SFC calculated = 21.0). However, given the large number of SLE problems solved, the average values (Table 1) and the large combinatorial space in product formulation, the agreement between calculated and experimental data is within an acceptable tolerance. From Figures 2 and 3, it can be noted a sharp reduction in SFC after CI reaction. This is due to the reduction in the content of saturated TAGs (higher melting point). The CI reaction causes a random redistribution of fatty acids and the consequently formation of a high number of new or unsaturated TAGs with lower melting point, not present in the original blend.

6. Conclusions

Computer-aided tools are useful to observe the influence of the fraction of each vegetable oil, temperature and interesterification reaction in vegetable oils blends. When compared to experimental SFC, the model showed a similar performance with pure vegetable oils and binary bends (AAE = 4.7) and a slightly decrease in performance with ternary blends (AAE = 5.3). The main model limitations concern pure component property predictions, deviations of real systems from the simplification hypotheses of random distribution of fatty acids and limitations from the Excess Gibbs energy model.

References

A. Brasiello, L. Russo, C. Siettos, G. Milano, S. Crescitelli, 2010, Multi-Scale Modelling And Coarse-Grained Analysis Of Triglycerides Dynamics, Computer Aided Chemical Engineering, 28, 625–630.

L. P. Cunico, A.S. Hukkerikar, R. Ceriani, B. Sarup, R. Gani, 2013, Molecular structure-based methods of property prediction inapplication to lipids: A review and refinement, Fluid Phase Equilibria, 357, 2–18.

M. Hill, 2009, Chemical Product Engineering - The third paradigm, Computers and Chemical Engineering, 33, 947–953.

H. M. D. N Lida, K. Sundram, W. L. Siew, A. Aminah, S. Mamot, 2002, TAG composition and solid fat content of palm oil, sunflower oil, and palm kernel olein blends before and after chemical interesterification, JAOCS, 79, 11, 1137-1144.

J. W. Prausnitz, R. N. Lichtenthaler, G. E. de Azevedo,1999, Molecular Thermodynamics of Fluid Phase Equilibria, third ed., Prentice-Hall, NewYork.

M.D. Robustillo, D. F. Barbosa, A.J.A. Meirelles, P.A.P. Filho, 2014, Solid–liquid equilibrium in ternary mixtures of ethyl laurate, ethyl palmitate and ethyl myristate, Fluid Phase Equilibria, 361, 188– 199.

M. Teles dos Santos, G.A.C. Le Roux, V. Gerbaud, 2010, Computer-Aided Lipid Design: phase equilibrium modeling for product design, Computer Aided Chemical Engineering, 28, 271–276.

L. H. Wesdorp, 1990, Liquid – multiple solid phase equilibrium in fats, Thesis, Delft University of Technology, Netherlands.

C. K. Zeberg–Mikkelsen, E. H. Stendby, 1999, Predicting the melting points and the enthalpies of fusion of saturated triglycerides by a group contribution method, Fluid Phase Equilibria, 162, 7–17.

Jiří Jaromír Klemeš, Petar Sabev Varbanov and Peng Yen Liew (Editors)
Proceedings of the 24th European Symposium on Computer Aided Process Engineering – ESCAPE 24
June 15-18, 2014, Budapest, Hungary.

Effect of Flow Pattern on Single and Multi-stage High Temperature Proton Exchange Membrane Fuel Cell Stack Performance

Suthida Authayanun[a], Artitaya Patniboon[b], Dang Saebea[c], Yaneeporn Patcharavorachot[d], Amornchai Arpronwichanop[b,*]

[a]*Department of Chemical Engineering, Faculty of Engineering, Srinakharinwirot University, Nakhon Nayok 26120, Thailand*
[b]*Computational Process Engineering, Department of Chemical Engineering, Faculty of Engineering, Chulalongkorn University, Bangkok 10330, Thailand*
[c]*Department of Chemical Engineering, Faculty of Engineering, Burapha University, Chonburi 20131, Thailand*
[d]*School of Chemical Engineering, Faculty of Engineering, King Mongkut's Institute of Technology Ladkrabang, Bangkok 10520, Thailand*
Amornchai.a@chula.ac.th

Abstract

A high-temperature proton exchange membrane fuel cell (HT-PEMFC) is a promising clean and effective technology for power generation because of its simplified water and heat management as well as high CO tolerance. Therefore, it could be possible to directly use a reformate gas for HT-PEMFC without the need for sophisticated purification processes. Due to the non-uniform of H_2 and CO distributions within fuel cells, the stack design is one of the key factors to enhance the performance and efficiency of HT-PEMFC. In this study, a single HT-PEMFC stack is investigated by considering the CO poisoning effect. The mathematical model of HT-PEMFC based on the electrochemical reaction model coupled with the diffusion model of a gas diffusion layer and electrolyte film layer is used for simulation studies. At high fuel utilization, hydrogen is highly consumed and CO concentration increases, having a significant impact on cell performance. The multi-stack HT-PEMFC is designed to minimize the CO poisoning effect and to maximize its efficiency. The power output that is obtained from each cell stack is presented and the overall power output is compared with single cell stack. Effect of different flow patterns, i.e., co-current and counter-current flow, on the HT-PEMFC stack performance is also presented.

Keywords: HT-PEMFC, CO poisoning, Flow pattern, Stack design

1. Introduction

Nowadays, clean and effective energy technologies have been continuously developed to solve the energy crisis and environmental problems. A fuel cell is a promising source of electricity generation, due to its high efficiency and environmental friendliness (Ziogou et al., 2012). A proton exchange membrane fuel cell (PEMFC) offers the highest energy densities in comparison to other types of fuel cells. Because of its low temperature operation, approximately 60-80 °C, PEMFC can quick start and provides a good response to changes in power demand. These advantages make the PEMFC a promising candidate for transportation, portable and small stationary applications.

However, there are several difficulties associated with the operation of the PEMFC that still needs to be resolved. The intrinsic problems of PEMFCs are mainly attributed to a water management and a CO poisoning effect. In order to circumvent the issue of hydrogen infrastructure and enhance the system efficiency, a fuel cell integrated with a fuel processor allowing hydrogen generation from hydrocarbon fuels is continuously developing (Zuliani and Taccani, 2012). Nevertheless, the reformate gases obtained from the fuel processing typically contain traces of CO, which can strongly adsorb onto the surface of PEMFC catalysts (Pt) and occupy hydrogen oxidation reaction (HOR) sites. These factors cause the deterioration of PEMFC performance. To avoid the catalyst poisoning during PEMFC operation, the reformate gas has to be purified to reduce the amount of CO before use in PEMFC (Jannelli et al., 2013).

Recently, the high-temperature PEMFC (HT-PEMFC) operated at temperatures of 100-200 °C has been developed to support the use of reformate gas as a fuel for PEMFC. Under the high-temperature operation, an amount of CO that is adsorbed onto the Pt catalyst used in HT-PEMFC is reduced, which results in a high CO tolerance. Das et al. (2009) reported that the CO poisoning problem of the PEMFC operated at high temperatures is less than at low temperatures. It was found that when the PEMFC is operated at the temperature of 180 °C or above, the reformate gas with 2–5 %CO can be used with the insignificant loss of cell performance. Recently, Jiao et al. (2011) developed the non-isothermal model of HT-PEMFC by considering the effect of CO on the fuel cell performance. They found that CO has a drastic effect on the HT-PEMFC at 190 °C when the CO fraction in the hydrogen feed is higher than 10 %. They also reported that the reformate gas from methanol reformer (CO ≈ 1-2 %) can be fed directly to HT-PEMFC operated at 160 °C. Due to the high CO tolerance of HT-PEMFC, it is also possible to use the reformate gas from reformers with simplified purification process. This could make a design of the fuel processor for HT-PEMFC simpler than the conventional PEMFC. At high fuel utilization, hydrogen is highly consumed and CO concentration increases. Thus, the non-uniform of H_2 and CO distributions is occurred. The suitable stack design is important to enhance the performance and efficiency of HT-PEMFC. In this study, single and multi-stage HT-PEMFCs are investigated and compared by considering the CO poisoning effect. Effect of different flow patterns, i.e., co-current and counter-current flows, on the HT-PEMFC stack performance is presented.

2. Methodology

The HT-PEMFC stack is investigated by considering the CO poisoning effect. The design of single and multi-stack HT-PEMFCs is shown in Figure 1(a) and 1(b). The overall fuel utilization (U_f) and the total number of cells in single-stack HT-PEMFC are 0.75 and 10, respectively. For the multi-stack HT-PEMFC, the number of cells in the first, second and third stacks is specified at 5, 3 and 2. The overall fuel utilization of the multi-stack HT-PEMFC is 0.75, which equals to the single-stack HT-PEMFC. In addition, the anode feed stream consists of H_2, CO and CO_2 at different concentrations.

Mathematical models of the HT-PEMFC consist of the electrochemical reaction model coupled with the diffusion model of a gas diffusion layer and electrolyte film layer. Mass transport in a gas diffusion layer of the thin-film electrolyte is considered only in the diffusion flux direction. The Stefan Maxwell equation and the Fick's law are used to explain the diffusion of reactants in the gas diffusion layer and film electrolyte

(Mamlouk et al., 2011). The electrochemical and CO poisoning models of HT-PEMFC are shown in Table 1. The simulation was carried out by using Matlab software.

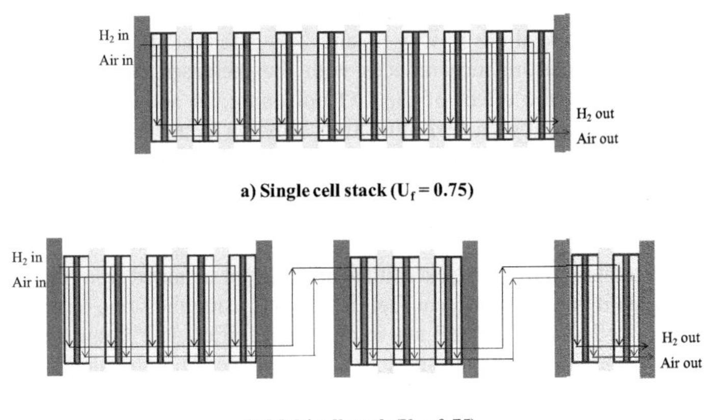

Figure 1. Cell stack design: a) Single stack and b) Multi-stack.

Table 1. Electrochemical model of HT-PEMFC (Authayanun et al., 2012)

Parameters	Model equations
Reversible cell potential	$E_r = -\left(\frac{\Delta H_T}{nF} - \frac{T\Delta S_T}{nF}\right) + \frac{RT}{nF}\ln\left[\frac{(RT)^{1.5} C_{H_2-Pt} C_{O_2-Pt}^{0.5}}{a_{H_2O}}\right]$
Anode activation loss	$\eta_{act,a} = \frac{RT}{\alpha F}\sinh^{-1}\left(\frac{i}{2i_0(1-\theta_{CO})^2}\right)$
	$i_a = i_{0,a}\left(\exp\left(\frac{-\alpha_{Rd,a}F}{RT}(\eta_{act,a})\right) - \exp\left(\frac{-\alpha_{Ox,a}F}{RT}(\eta_{act,a})\right)\right)$
	$\theta_{CO} = a * \ln\frac{[CO]}{[H_2]} + b * \ln(i) * \ln\frac{[CO]}{[H_2]} + c$
Cathode activation loss	$\eta_{act,c} = \frac{RT}{\alpha F}\sinh^{-1}\left(\frac{i}{2i_0}\right)$
	$i_0 = i_{0,c}^{ref} a_{c,c} L_{c,c}\left(\frac{C_{Pt}}{C_{ref,c}}\right)^{\gamma}\exp\left[-\frac{E_{c,c}}{RT}\left(1-\frac{T}{T_{ref,c}}\right)\right]$
Ohmic loss	$\eta_{ohmic} = \left(\frac{\sigma_m}{l_m}\right)i$
	$\sigma_m = \frac{A}{T}\exp\left(\frac{-B}{R(T)}\right)$

3. Results and discussion

In this work, the single and multi-stack HT-PEMFCs are studied and the effect of the CO poisoning on the HT-PEMFC performance is taken into account. In case of the multi-stack HT-PEMFC, the performance of each cell stack is presented. Figure 2 shows effect of the fuel utilization on the single-stack cell performance when the anode feed with different compositions of CO, H_2 and CO_2 is fed into the fuel cell. It is found that the HT-PEMFC performance reduces with the increased fraction of CO in the anode feed because of the effect of the CO poisoning. In addition, the drop in cell performance is observed at high fuel utilization, which a decrease in H_2 with increased CO fraction is observed at the outlet stream. The fuel utilization has a significant effect on the cell performance, especially when the anode feed stream contains high CO content.

Figure 3 shows a relation of the stack voltage and current obtained from the multi-stack HT-PEMFC when it is run at different fuel utilizations using the same operating current density for each cell stack. The cell active area is specified at 250 cm^2/cell. From the simulation results, it is observed the stack 1 can be operated at high voltage, whereas the lower voltage operation is needed for the stack 2 and stack 3. This is explained by high CO concentration at the anode inlet and the lower cell number of stack 2 and stack 3.

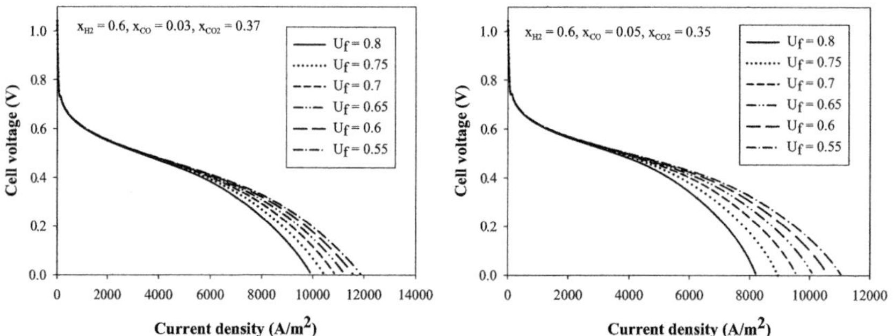

Figure 2. Effect of fuel utilization (U_f) on the single-cell HT-PEMFC performance at various anode feed composition.

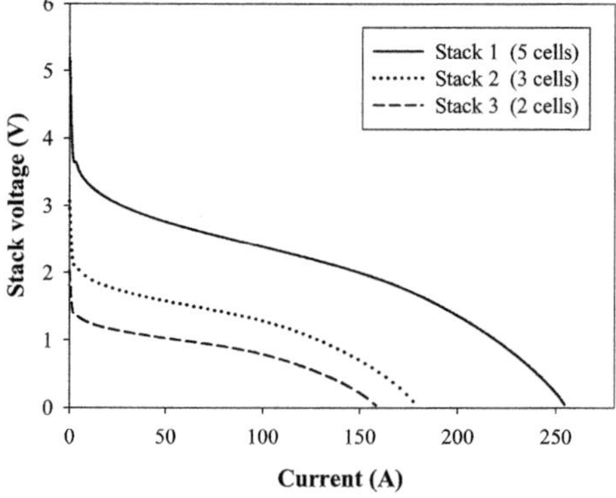

Figure 3. Stack voltage and current of the multi-stack HT-PEMFC.

The power outputs obtained from the single and multi-stack HT-PEMFCs are compared in Figure 4. It is found that the multi-stack HT-PEMFC provides higher power output than the single stack one at high density when the average fuel utilization of both the HT-PEMFC designs is 0.75 and the anode feed with the same fuel composition (CO fraction of 0.05) is applied. The raising CO fraction during the electrochemical reaction proceeding at the anode results in the CO poisoning effect, especially for the single-stack HT-PEMFC which is operated at high fuel utilization (0.75) along the entire cell stack. However, similar power output is obtained from the single and multi-stack HT-PEMFC at low current due to the high CO tolerance of HT-PEMFC at low current density operation. Figure 5 shows the effect of flow pattern on the performance of multi-stack HT-PEMFC. It indicates that at high current, the HT-PEMFC with co-current flow provides higher performance than that with counter-current flow.

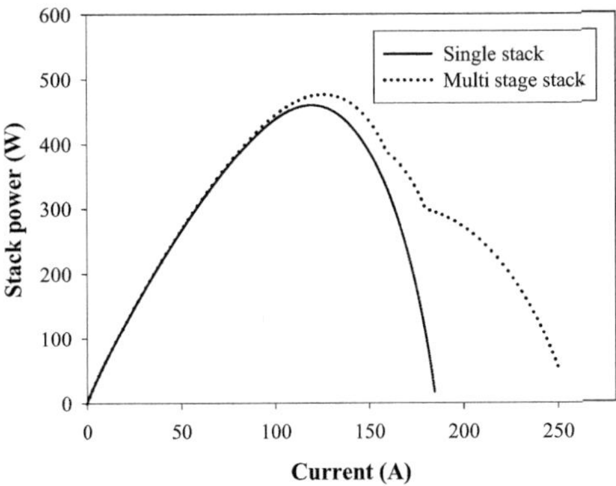

Figure 4. Power output of the single and multi-stack HT-PEMFCs.

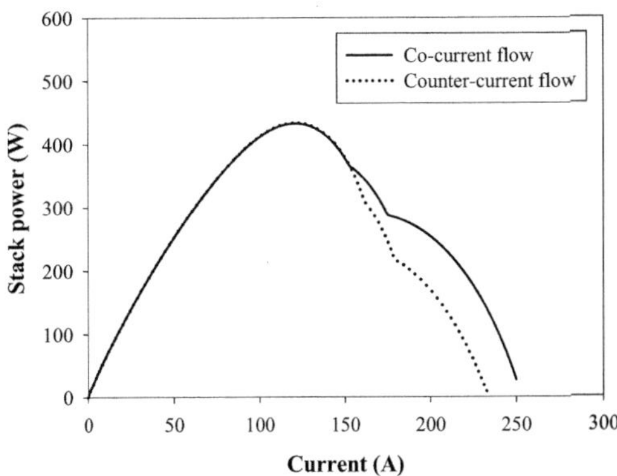

Figure 5. Power output of multi-stack HT-PEMFC with co-current and counter-current flows.

4. Conclusions

In this study, the performance of HT-PEMFC with different stack designs (i.e., single and multi-stack) is analyzed by considering the CO poisoning effect. Influence of the fuel utilization on cell performance is investigated at different anode feed compositions. When operated high fuel utilization, the HT-PEMFC gives low electrical performance. The fuel utilization has a strong effect on cell performance, especially for the anode feed stream with high CO fraction. The result shows that the multi-stack HT-PEMFC provides higher power output than the single-stack one. It is also found that the co-current flow of fuel and air is suitable for the multi-stack HT-PEMFC stack at high current operation.

Acknowledgements

Support from Srinakharinwirot University, the Ratchadaphiseksomphot Endowment Fund of Chulalongkorn University (RES560530067-EN) and the Thailand Research Fund is gratefully acknowledged.

References

S. Authayanun, M. Mamlouk, A. Arpornwichanop, 2012, Maximizing the efficiency of a HT-PEMFC system integrated with glycerol reformer, International Journal of Hydrogen Energy, 37, 6808–6817.

S.K. Das, A. Reis, K.J. Berry, 2009, Experimental evaluation of CO poisoning on the performance of a high temperature proton exchange membrane fuel cell, Journal of Power Sources, 193, 691–698.

E. Jannelli, M. Minutillo, A. Perna, 2013, Analyzing microcogeneration systems based on LT-PEMFCand HT-PEMFC by energy balances, Applied Energy, 108, 82–91.

K. Jiao, I.E. Alaefour, X. Li, 2011, Three-dimensional non-isothermal modeling of carbon monoxide poisoning in high temperature proton exchange membrane fuel cells with phosphoric acid doped polybenzimidazole membranes, Fuel, 90, 568–582.

M. Mamlouk, T. Sousa, K. Scott, 2011, A high temperature polymer electrolyte membrane fuel cell model for reformate gas, International Journal of Electrochemistry, 2011, 1–18.

N. Zuliani, R. Taccani, 2012, Microcogeneration system based on HTPEM fuel cell fueled with natural gas: Performance analysis, Applied Energy, 97, 802–808.

C. Ziogou, S. Voutetakis, S. Papadopoulou, M.C. Georgiadis, 2012, Development of a nonlinear model predictive control framework for a PEM fuel cell system, Computer Aided Chemical Engineering, 30, 1342–1346.

Jiří Jaromír Klemeš, Petar Sabev Varbanov and Peng Yen Liew (Editors)
Proceedings of the 24th European Symposium on Computer Aided Process Engineering – ESCAPE 24
June 15-18, 2014, Budapest, Hungary.

Optimal Multi-floor Plant Layout based on the Mathematical Programming

Chang Jun Lee

Department of Safety Engineering, Pukyong National University, 100 Yongdang-dong, Nam-gu, Busan 608-739, Republic of Korea

Abstract

In the fields of researches associated with plant layout optimization, the main goal is to minimizing the costs of pipelines for connecting equipment. However, what is lacking of considerations in previous researches is to handle safety distances for preventing domino impacts on a complex plant. The mathematical programming formulation can be presented as considering safety distances and economic benefits for solving the multi-floor plant layout problem. Under the risks of physical explosion, the safety distance must be considered to generate more reasonable and safe plant layouts. To consider the safety distance, a consequence analysis is employed to calculate the probability curve for the explosions of all equipment. The objective function of this study consists of two steps. The first is to minimize the costs (piping costs) connecting facilities in the process. The second is to minimize the explosion impacts under given conditions and a process. MINLP (Mixed Integer Non-Linear Programming) solvers can be performed to determine the optimal multi-floor process plant layout. The liquefaction process of an LNG-FPSO is illustrated to verify the efficacy of this study.

Keywords: Plant Layout Optimization, MINLP, LNG-FPSO.

1. Introduction

In the design of processes, one of the most important steps is to determine process plant layout based on significant engineering creativity and prior knowledge. According to plant layout, massive construction costs can be reduced. Moreover, a plant layout guarantees good maintenance accessibilities under safety requirements or regulations. To achieve this, a plant layout has to resolve the conflicting trade-off problems between costs and safety. In addition, in case of off-shore plants, multi-floor processes have to be installed in the small and limited area. This makes the plant layout problems very difficult and complex.

To solve this problem, several methods have been developed during the last two decades. Suzuki et al. (1991) developed a heuristic rules for the two-dimensional layout problems. A mixed integer linear programming model (MILP) have been employed as considering various sizes and geometries of equipment based on rectangular shapes and rectilinear distances (Georgiadis et al., 1999; Patsiatzis and Papageorgiou, 2002). But, in case of these methods, the safety issues were excluded.

A mixed integer non-linear programming (MINLP) model was implemented (Penteado and Ciric, 1996) to determine the plant layout with the consideration of protective devices and equipments. An optimization using genetic algorithms with the Mond Index was also proposed (Castell, 1998) to provide the effective solutions. In addition, an MILP model utilizing safety problems with Dow's fire and explosion index was proposed (Prugh, 1991) for the single-floor layout problems. However, since the previous researches have been focused on only single-floor problems, it is urgently needed to develop an improved method considering multi-floor plant layouts. In this study, multi-floor MILP modelling is employed with the consideration of safety devices. To consider the safety distance of equipment, the TNT equivalency method (Park et al., 2011) is used.

2. TNT equivalency model

To calculate the impact of explosion from equipments, the overpressure according to the distance can be evaluated by TNT equivalence model (Park et al., 2011). Based on the overpressure, the probability of equipment damage can be accessed. To calculate the safety distance using the TNT equivalency method, various types of explosion and their outcomes have to be investigated.

There are several types of explosion such as physical explosions, vapor cloud explosions (VCE), boiling liquid expanding vapor explosions (BLEVE) and confined explosions which may occur at a process. Since the impacts of explosions are changed due to the type of vessel, the size of rupture, chemical compounds, etc., it is really difficult to determine which type of explosion is dominant. In this study, the worst scenarios are evaluated according to explosion types and the worst case is selected. After calculating the overpressure, the probit and the probability of equipment damage can be obtained (CCPS, 2000).

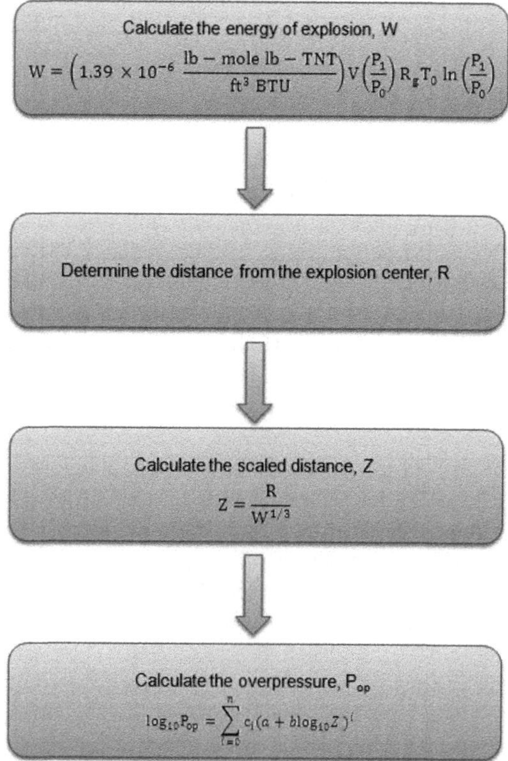

Figure 1. The procedure of calculating explosion overpressure taken from (7).

3. Optimal multi-floor plant layout: problem description

The multi-floor plant layout problem can be stated under given conditions as the following:

(1) A set of N equipment items and their size
(2) A set of potential floors and their heights
(3) The cost data
(4) PFD
(5) Probabilities of damage according to the distances

3.1. Piping costs under equipment orientation and floor constraints

It is assumed that all shapes of equipments are rectangular and are allowed to rotate by 90°. The equipment orientations are represented by the following equation;

$$l_i = a_i O_i + b_i(1 - O_i) \quad \forall i \tag{1}$$

$$d_i = a_i + b_i - l_i \quad \forall i \tag{2}$$

where O_i is the binary parameter which decides equipment length and depth. If O_i is 1, then equipment length l_i is equal to equipment dimension a_i or b_i.
Each equipment item can be located at any floor, occupying only a single floor. Two binary parameters are introduced here. The binary parameter V_{ik} has a numerical value of 1 if equipment item *i* is allocated to floor *k*; otherwise it is assigned as 0. The binary parameter F_{ij} is equal to 1 if equipment item *i* and *j* are on the same floor, but 0 if they are not. *N* is the number of floors.

$$F_{ij} = V_{ik} \times V_{jk} \quad \forall i \tag{3}$$

$$m - (ES_i + ES_j) = C_{ij} \quad \rightarrow \quad \begin{matrix} if\ C_{ij} \geq 0, S_{ij} = 1 \\ otherwise, S_{ij} = 0 \end{matrix} \tag{4}$$

ES is the distance of equipment for the maintenance. *m* is the safety distance between equipments and is determined by the regulation. Each equipment item that is allocated on the same floor should avoid overlapping against each other. The constraints for the overlapping problem follow the given equations where x_i and y_i is the location of equipment *i*;

$$m - (ES_i + ES_j) = C_{ij} \quad \rightarrow \quad \begin{matrix} if\ C_{ij} \geq 0, S_{ij} = 1 \\ otherwise, S_{ij} = 0 \end{matrix} \tag{5}$$

$$|x_i - x_j| \geq \left(\frac{l_i + l_j}{2} + (ES_i + ES_j) \times (1 - S_{ij}) + m \times S_{ij}\right) \times F_{ij} \tag{6}$$

$$|y_i - y_j| \geq \left(\frac{d_i + d_j}{2} + (ES_i + ES_j) \times (1 - S_{ij}) + m \times S_{ij}\right) \times F_{ij} \tag{7}$$

$$for\ \forall i = 1, \cdots, N-1, \forall j = i+1, \cdots, N, \forall k = 1, \cdots, F$$

To consider the size of floor, the next constrains can be generated where X_{max} and Y_{max} are the maximum size of floor.

$$x_i + \frac{l_i}{2} + ES_i \leq X_{max}, \; x_i - \frac{l_i}{2} - ES_i \geq 0 \tag{8}$$

$$y_i + \frac{d_i}{2} + ES_i \leq Y_{max},\ y_i - \frac{d_i}{2} - ES_i \geq 0 \quad (9)$$

All connections between the equipment can be possible through the geometry center of equipment. The rectilinear distance has been introduced to consider more realistic piping costs. The total rectilinear distance between equipment item *i* and *j*, TD_{ij}, is determined by considering relative distances in *x, y, z* coordinates where *z* is the height of equipment from the ground. *H* is the height of floor;

$$X_{ij} = |x_i - x_j|,\ Y_{ij} = |y_i - y_j| \quad (10)$$

$$H_{ij} = H \times \sum_{K=1}^{F} |K \times (V_{ik} - V_{jk})|,\ U_{ij} = H_{ij} + |z_i - z_j| \quad (11)$$

$$TD_{ij} = X_{ij} + Y_{ij} + U_{ij} \quad (12)$$

$$for\ \forall i = 1, \cdots, N-1, \forall j = i+1, \cdots, N$$

3.2. Safety Distance Constraints

The expected damage cost of unit *i*, DC_i, can be calculated as follows:

$$DC_{ij} = fr_i * (PC_i + \sum_f P_{ij} * PC_j) \quad (For\ \forall i \in N, \forall j \neq i) \quad (13)$$

PC is the purchase cost and fr_i is the worst accident-frequency of each potential unit. P_{ij} indicates the probability of damage of unit *j* when the unit *i* is exploded. P_{ij} according to the distance.

3.3. Objective Function

The objective function is divided into two steps. The first is to minimize the sum of pipe connection costs and the next is to minimize the expected damage costs under floor conditions, non-overlapping, land area where CC_{ij} is the connection cost per unit length of piping and CV_{ij} and CH_{ij} are the vertical and horizontal pumping cost per unit length.

$$\text{Min.} \sum_{i} \sum_{j \neq i} [CC_{ij} * TD_{ij} + CV_{ij} * U_{ij} + CH_{ij}(X_{ij} + Y_{ij})]$$

$$\text{Min.} \sum_{i} \sum_{j \neq i} DC_{ij}$$

The objective function should minimize the total cost, subject to floor, equipment orientation, non-overlapping, land area, distance and equipment damage cost constraints.

4. Case Studies

The proposed MILP model was solved by GAMS. The proposed algorithm is tested with ethylene oxide (EO) plant in Fig. 1. The EO plant is well-known due to its recent accident histories. The EO reactor, EO absorber and the CO2 absorber are selected as potential units of physical explosions in this case. The floor construction cost FC is assumed as $3,330/m^2$; the area-dependent floor construction cost FC2 is assumed as $66.7/m^2$ and the land cost LC is assumed as $26.6/m^2$. Two potential floors are assumed to be available and the floor height is assumed as 5 m. Table 1 shows basic data for the case study.

Obtained results are summarized in Table 3. Since accident frequencies vary over operation years, operation years 1, 5, and 10 are considered as simulation cases. The accident probabilities increase as the operation year is prolonged, and consequently, the optimal layout for each year is continuously changed. Evidently, the total cost of the case which includes a safety factor is much lower than that of another case which does not consider any safety factor.

In the case of no safety considerations, the layout cost is the lowest but the expected damage cost of EO reactor is significantly higher than that of the case with safety consideration. Table 3 summarizes cost changes of the case with safety consideration compared against cases without any safety considerations.

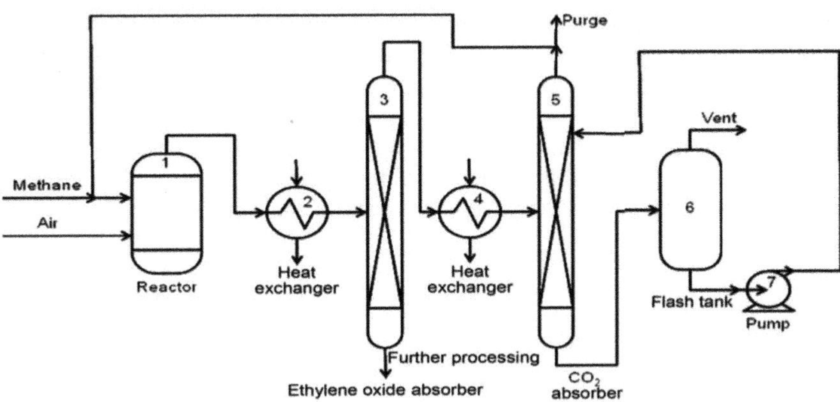

Figure 1. The PFD of EO plant

Table 1. Basic information of the EO plant.

Eq. No.	Dim. a	Dim. b	Cost	Connection	CC_{ij} (m)	CH_{ij} (m)	CV_{ij} (m)
1	5.22	5.22	335,000	2	200	400	4,000
2	11.42	11.42	11,000	3	200	400	4,000
3	7.68	7.68	107,000	4	200	300	3,000
4	8.48	8.48	4,000	5	200	300	3,000
5	7.68	7.68	81,300	1	200	100	1,000
				6	200	200	2,000
6	2.60	2.60	5,000	7	200	200	1,500
7	2.40	2.40	15,000	5	200	150	1,500

Table 2. Data for each explosion potential unit

	Reactor			EO/CO_2 absorber		
Burst Pressure (kPa)	1,013			1,013		
Accident frequency	0.6/y			0.086/y		
Distance from unit	Overpressure (kPa)	Probit	Prob. of damage (%)	Overpressure (kPa)	Probit	Prob. of damage (%)
1	3,407.05	20.12	100	2,596.44	19.33	100
4	174.19	11.44	100	125.45	10.48	100
8	43.72	7.40	99.18	33.81	6.65	95.07
12	22.63	5.48	68.40	18.11	4.83	43.18
16	14.93	4.26	23.10	12.16	3.67	9.10
20	11.04	3.38	5.29	9.06	2.81	1.41
24	8.70	2.69	1.04	7.14	2.11	0.19

Table 3. The results of a case study

	Operation year	Expected damage cost of EO reactor	Expected damage cost of EO absorber	Expected damage cost of CO_2 absorber	Layout cost	Total cost
Without the consideration of safety	1	326,641	30,123	28,479	101,230	486,473
	5	1,645,665	151,332	146,589	101,230	204,4816
	10	3,451,641	302,156	295,641	101,230	4,150,668
With the consideration of safety	1	225,746	15,123	12,331	112,310	365,510
	5	1,156,488	80,112	24,789	145,132	1,406,521
	10	2,215,646	174,445	123,156	264,897	2,778,144

5. Concluding remarks

To handle a multi-floor optimal layout problem, An MILP model with the consideration of safety is proposed. The safety problem have to be included in the presence of safety issues and TNT equivalency method is employed to predict the expected damage costs under the worst scenario. To verify the efficacy of the proposed algorithm, EO plant is tested and the results show that the proposed algorithm provide a reasonable benefits. It is expected that the proposed algorithm would contribute to reduce the costs and find the optimal layout of compact multi-floor processes such as Floating Production and Storage Offloading (FPSO).

References

C. M. L. Castell, R. Lakshmanan, J. M. Skilling, R. Banares-Alcantara, 1998, Optimisation of process plant layout using genetic algorithms, Computers and Chemical Engineering, 22, S993-S996.

CCPS, 2000, Guidelines for Chemical Process Quantitative Risk Analysis, Center of Chemical Process Safty, AIChE, New York, USA.

M. C. Georgiadis, G. Schilling, G. E. Rotstein, S. Macchietto, 1999, A general mathematical programming approach for process plant layout, Computers and Chemical Engineering, 23, 7, 823-840.

K. Park, J. Koo, D. Shin, C. J. Lee, E. S. Yoon, 2011, Optimal multi-floor plant layout with consideration of safety distance based on mathematical programming and modified consequence analysis, Korean Journal of Chemical Engineering, 28, 4, 1009-1018.

D. I. Patsiatzis, L. G. Papageorgiou, 2002, Optimal multi-floor process plant layout, Computers and Chemical Engineering, 26, 4, 575-583

F. D. Penteado, A. R. Ciric, 1996, An MINLP approach for safe process plant layout, Industrial and Engineering Chemistry Research, 35, 4, 1354-1361.

R. W. Prugh, 1991, Quantitative Evaluation of" Bleve" Hazards, Journal of Fire Protection Engineering, 3, 1, 9-24.

A. Suzuki, T. Fuchino, M. Muraki, 1991, Equipment arrangement for batch plants in multi-floor buildings with integer programming, J. Chem. Eng. Japan, 24, 2, 737-742

Jiří Jaromír Klemeš, Petar Sabev Varbanov and Peng Yen Liew (Editors)
Proceedings of the 24th European Symposium on Computer Aided Process Engineering – ESCAPE 24
June 15-18, 2014, Budapest, Hungary.

Attainment of Kinetic Parameters and Model Validation for Nylon-6 Process

Vanessa I. Funai, Delba N. C. Melo *, Nádson M. N. Lima, Ana F. Pattaro, Lamia Zuñiga Liñan, Anderson J. Bonon, Rubens Maciel Filho

Laboratory of Opmization, Design and Advanced Control - LOPCA, School of Chemical Engineering, State University of Campinas – Unicamp, Av. Albert Einstein, 500, Campinas – SP, 13083-852, Brasil
delba@feq.unicamp.br

Abstract

This work presents the simulation of the hydrolytic polymerization process of Nylon-6 in a lab-scale semi-batch reactor, using ε-caprolactam as monomer and acetic acid as monofunctional acid chain terminator. The kinetic scheme comprises 6 reactions: 3 main reactions, 2 side reactions associated with the cyclic dimer formation and one monofunctional acid termination. Operating conditions were obtained from previous definitions and kinetic parameters were estimated from experimental data. The proposed optimization problem to estimate the kinetic parameters was solved by the Sequential Quadratic Programming (SQP) and Genetic Algorithm (GA). It was shown that both methods are able to determine the final solution with good precision. The validity of the model was confirmed by comparison of the results obtained by computer simulation using the software Aspen Polymer Plus® and the process real data.

Keywords: optimization, simulation, polymerization, poliamide-6.

1. Introduction

Nylon is considered the first polymer in the category of engineering plastics and still remains as one of the most important since its discovery in 1935, its. The commercial relevance of Nylon-6 is widely known. In order to have a final product with desired properties it is necessary to have a better comprehension of the polymerization process including the reactor performance. Since plant experiments are time consuming and expensive, simulations are important means to study the process. However, the results of the simulator should be faithful to those obtained by the real process. To ensure this, it is necessary the validation of the results, performed by a comparison between the real and the simulated process outputs, which should be similar. One way to validate the simulator is estimating the reaction parameters. Optimization methods have been widely used to determine kinetic parameters (Mansoornejad et al., 2007).

The objective of this work is to simulate and to estimate the most significant kinetic parameters of the hydrolytic polymerization of Nylon-6 in order to validate a mathematic model based on a Nylon-6 polymerization reactor operated on semi-batch mode used for polymer research at Biofabris Institute/State University of Campinas/Brazil. The estimation of the parameters was performed by the use of the Sequential quadratic programming method (SQP) and Genetic Algorithm (GA). Simplified predictive models of average molecular weight (MWN) and monomer conversion (X_{CL}) were used to formulate the objective function of the problem.

2. Process description

The semi-batch polymerization reactor considered in this study consists of a jacketed vessel with a stirrer motor, one stream for vapor releasing and another to collect the final product (Figure 1). The feed consists of the monomer ε-caprolactam (*CL*), water (*W*) and acetic acid (*AA*), used as chain terminator. Vapor stream is composed by *CL*, *W* and *AA*. The process has a total operational time of 6 h and works with temperature and pressure profiles (Funai et al., 2013). To simulate the process, it was used the software Aspen Polymer Plus® (Aspentech). Equations for global reaction rates, reaction rates for species, mass balance for liquid and gas phases, energy balance for the reactor and the cooling system, mass transfer model and phase equilibrium model can be found in Funai et al. (2013).

3. Kinetics

The kinetic mechanism considered can be found in Table 1. The scheme for reactions not involving chain terminators was proposed by Arai et al. (1981) and the acetic acid chain terminator reaction is the same proposed for Gupta and Kumar (1987). All reactions in Nylon-6 polymerization takes place under two conditions: uncatalyzed or catalyzed by acid groups (-COOH), both are taking into account in the reaction rate constant (*K*) expression (Eq. (1)). The reverse rate (k_i') is calculated by using of the equilibrium constant, given by Eq. (2). In these equations, A_i^j is the pre-exponential factor, E_i^j is the activation energy, ΔH_i is the reaction enthalpy, T is the temperature and R the ideal gas constant.

$$ki = A_i^0 \cdot \exp\left(-\frac{E_i^0}{RT}\right) + A_i^c \cdot \exp\left(-\frac{E_i^c}{RT}\right) \cdot [-COOH] \quad (i = 1,2,\ldots 5); \tag{1}$$

$$Ki = \frac{k_i}{k_i'} = \exp\left(\frac{\Delta S_i}{R} - \frac{\Delta Hi}{RT}\right) \quad (i = 1,2,\ldots 5) \tag{2}$$

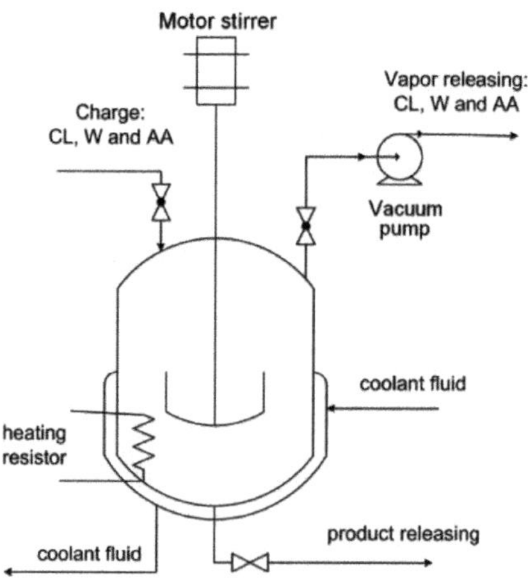

Figure 1. Schematic semi-batch reactor used for Nylon-6 hydrolytic polymerization.

Table 1. Reaction scheme for Nylon-6 hydrolytic polymerization.

1. Ring opening of ε-caprolactam:	$W + CL \underset{k_1'=k_1/K_1}{\overset{k_1}{\Leftrightarrow}} P_1$
2. Polycondensation:	$P_m + P_n \underset{k_2'=k_2/K_2}{\overset{k_2}{\Leftrightarrow}} P_{m+n} + W \quad m,n = 1,2,3...$
3. Polycondensation with acid-terminated chain:	$P_m + P_{n,x} \underset{k_2'=k_2/K_2}{\overset{k_2}{\Leftrightarrow}} P_{m+n,x} + W \quad m,n = 1,2,3...$
4. Polyaddition of ε-caprolactam:	$CL + P_n \underset{k_3'=k_3/K_3}{\overset{k_3}{\Leftrightarrow}} P_{n+1} \quad n = 1,2,3...$
5. Ring opening of cyclic dimer:	$CD + W \underset{k_4'=k_4/K_4}{\overset{k_4}{\Leftrightarrow}} P_2$
6. Polyaddition of cyclic dimer:	$CD + P_n \underset{k_{5,m}'=k_5/K_5}{\overset{k_5}{\Leftrightarrow}} P_{n+2}$
7. Acetic-acid termination:	$P_n + AA \underset{k_2'=k_2/K_2}{\overset{k_2}{\Leftrightarrow}} P_{n,x} + W \quad n = 1,2,3...$

W: water, *CL:* ε-caprolactam, P_1: aminocaproic acid, *CD*: cyclic dimer, P_n: polymer chain with *n* repeat units, $P_{n,x}$: polymer chain with *n* repeat units and acetic acid terminated.

4. Methodology

4.1. Simplified models for the molecular weight and the conversion of the monomer.

A way to obtain simplified models is using full factorial designs, which are important means to evaluate the influence of the factors on response. However, they have the inconvenience of requiring too many runs when working with a great number of factors. As the amount of runs increases exponentially with the number of involved variables, it is interesting to pick up the most significant factors before run the full factorial design when there are too many options to be studied. For screening purposes, the influence of all the 30 kinetic parameters on number average molecular weight (*MWN*) and monomer conversion (X_{CL}) were evaluated by using of a2-level fractional experimental design and a central composite design. These additional runs are used in order to generate a quadratic model for the responses. Because of the parameters E_1^c, E_3^0, E_3^c for X_{CL} and E_2^c, E_2^0, E_3^c for *MWN* were statistically most significant, these were chosen to develop the mathematical models. Even though experimental data of two process variables were considered to estimate the five parameters of the models, alternative computational tools were used to achieve satisfactory results and to validate these complex models. It is important to emphasize these statistic models were formulated in a specific behavior range of the experimental variable, thus calculations out of this range could result in less reliable results.

To obtain the simplified models, composite factorial designs were performed with the selected parameters. Level zero values were defined as the same as those estimated by Arai et al. (1981) and the variations of levels -1 and +1 were 15 % from level 0. The simplified models achieved for *MWN* and X_{CL} (variables in coded form) can be found at Eqs. (3) and (4), respectively. Analyses were carried out by using of the software

Statistica. Furthermore, the good fit Eqs. (3) and (4) provides can be confirmed by the F-test: it is almost 3 times greater than the F-tabled value for 95 % confidence level.

$$MWN = 6459.004 - 446.833E_2^0 - 93.710\left(E_2^0\right)^2 - 578.825E_2^c - 3636.732E_3^c \\ - 429.071\left(E_2^c\right)^2 - 258.096E_2^0 E_2^c + 546.275E_2^0 E_3^c + 299.598E_2^c E_3^c \quad (3)$$

$$X_{CL} = 0.889 - 0.088E_1^c - 0.101\left(E_1^c\right)^2 - 0.132E_3^0 + 0.015\left(E_3^0\right)^2 \\ - 0.242E_3^c - 0.126\left(E_3^c\right)^2 + 0.006E_1^c E_3^0 - 0.011E_1^c E_3^c - 0.219E_3^0 E_3^c \quad (4)$$

4.2. Optimization

To adjust the selected kinetic parameters, it was used the SQP optimization algorithm and the GA. SQP is a programming technique based on non-linear gradients, primarily used to solve the equations of the type Karush-Kuhn-Tucker (KKT), or simply first-order conditions. The optimum results are obtained by solving the system of nonlinear equations (Melo, 2005). In this work, the code was implemented by using of the SQP IMSL Fortran Library. It was used the subroutine DNCONF to evaluate the function at a given point. GA is a stochastic method based on natural selection, useful for solving both constrained and unconstrained optimization problems (Mansoornejad et al., 2008). GA is among the more popular evolutionary optimization techniques discussed at some works very recent as of Gupta and Garg (2013) applied in the optimization of an industrial semi-batch Nylon-6 reactor, and others as of Lima et al. (2013) in the optimization and Control of an polymerization reactors and application to PMMA. For the optimization, it was used the FORTRAN Genetic Algorithm Driver by Carroll (2001).

Through by trial-and-error method, the parameters of the GA which are significant diminution between the experimental and simulated variables (cf. Eq. (5)) were considered as the optimum. These parameters were: maximum number of generations = 80, population size = 100, jump mutation probability = 1 %, creep mutation probability = 2.4 %, uniform crossover probability = 70 %.

The statistical models obtained for *MWN* and X_{CL} were used to formulate the objective function to be achieved in these methods. The proposed optimization problem was:

Minimize: $F = (MWN_{simulation} - MWN_{experimental})^2 - [1000.(X_{CLsimulation} - X_{CLexperimental})]^2$ (5)

where: $F = f(E_1^c, E_2^c, E_2^0, E_3^c \text{ and } E_3^0)$

Because of the big order of magnitude between the data of Molecular weight and monomer conversion, it was necessary to multiply the second part of the Eq. (5) for a big arbitrary value (1,000 was chosen in this case). Thus, inconsistent results, during the optimization process were avoided.

Initially, the superior and inferior limits for parameters estimation in both methods were +1.68 and -1.68 (coded form), respectively, and no restrictions were implemented. SQP method had convergence problems depending on the initial estimative, which had to be changed from level zero values to level -1 values (see Table 3).

Also, it was found that better results were achieved in GA when applying the restriction $X_{CL} < 1.0$ and the maximum and minimum values were set as 1.0 and -1.0 (coded form), respectively. The GA has become an additional tool for validating of alternative models for optimization when compared with SQP method.

5. Results and discussion

Table 2 presents the experimental values applied in the objective function and the X_{CL} and *MWN* obtained by using of the estimated parameters in the simplified models. It can be seen that both optimization methods were efficient to achieve the objective function. In Table 3, there are the optimized parameters found by each method. Results for X_{CL} and *MWN* responses when the estimated parameters were implemented on the simulator can be found in Table 4. The differences from the calculated values and simulation results are due to limitations of the model. After this procedure, it can be noted that the results obtained by the simulator have a small error compared to the experimental values, a maximum of 5.2 % of deviation from experimental values. This difference is reasonable considering experimental errors that cannot be measured. Therefore, the mathematic model applied to the simulator can be considered validate for the studied process.

Table 2. Results obtained at the end of the optimization by SQP and GA methods.

Response	Experimental value	Calculatedvalue		Error (%)	
		SQP	GA	SQP	GA
X_{CL}	0.9636	0.9636	0.9697	0.0	0.6
MWN	10,512	10,512	10,521	0.0	0.1

Table 3. Parameters values obtained after SQP and GA optimization.

Parameter	Initial estimative (J/mol)	Estimated value after SQP optimization(J/mol)	Estimated value after GA optimization (J/mol)
E_1^c	6.6909 x 10^4	8.1554 x 10^4	6.7134 x 10^4
E_2^0	8.2798 x 10^4	8.8107 x 10^4	8.8165 x 10^4
E_2^c	7.3545 x 10^4	7.9252 x 10^4	7.6718 x 10^4
E_3^0	8.1299 x 10^4	9.1809 x 10^4	8.6885 x 10^4
E_3^c	7.1540 x 10^4	7.2724 x 10^4	7.3798 x 10^4

Table 4.Validation of the mathematical model defined from the optimization process

Response	Experimental	Simulation		Absolut Error		Error (%)	
		SQP	GA	SQP	GA	SQP	GA
X_{CL}	0.9636	0.9208	0.9209	- 0.0428	-0.0427	- 4.4	-4.4
MWN	10512	9970	10717	- 542	205	- 5.2	2.0

6. Conclusions

It was presented the estimation of kinetic parameters for the Nylon-6 polymerization process by using of two optimization techniques: Successive Quadratic Programming and Genetic Algorithm. It was shown that both methods were able to solve the optimization problem. SQP method, a deterministic method, is easier to be applied. However, it is very dependent of the initial estimative and gives a local optimal.

Genetic Algorithm is a stochastic method and requires more computational effort, but works with a global search and is independent of initial estimate, giving a global optimal. In this case, GA has showed to be more appropriate to solve our problem.

The results of the simulation after implementation of the parameters had a good agreement with experimental data, which allowed the validation of the mathematic model.

Acknowledgements

The authors acknowledge FAPESP (Fundação de Amparo à Pesquisa do Estado de São Paulo) and CNPq (Conselho Nacional de Desenvolvimento Científico e Tecnológico) for the financial support given to this work.

References

B. Mansoornejad, N. Mostoufi, F. Jalali-Farahani, 2008, A hybrid GA-SQP optimization technique for determination of kinetic parameters of hydrogenation reactions, Computer and Chemical Engineering, 32, 1447-1455.

V. Funai, D. N. C. Melo, N. M. N. Lima, R. Maciel Filho,2013,Simulation and application of response surface methodology to a nylon-6 hydrolytic polymerization in a semibatch reactor, Journal of Applied Polymer Science, 127, 2910 - 2921.

Y. Arai, K. Tai, H. Teranishi, T. Tagawa, 1981, Kinetics of hydrolytic polymerization of ε-caprolactam: 3. Formation of cyclic dimmer, Polymer, 22, 2, 273-277.

S. K. Gupta, A. Kumar, 1987, Reaction engineering of step-growth polymerization, Plenum Press, New York, U.S.

N. M. N. Lima, L.Z. Liñan,F. Manenti, R. Maciel Filho, M. Embiruçu, M. R. Wolf Maciel, 2013, Novel two-steps optimal control of batch,polymerization reactors and application to PMMA,production for the fabrication of artificial bone tissue, Computer Aided Chemical Engineering, 32, 163-168.

D. N. C. Melo, 2005, Estratégia de otimização em duas camadas: aplicação para processos de hidrogenação em reatores catalíticos trifásicos, Ph.D. Thesis, FEQ/Universidade Estadual de Campinas, Campinas, Brazil.

D.L Carroll, 2001, Fortran GA - Genetic Algorithm Driver. <www.cuaerospace.com/carroll/ga. html> Accessed on 20/07/2011.

M. Ramteke, S.K. Gupta, 2011, Kinetic Modeling and Reactor Simulation and Optimization of Industrially Important Polymerization Processes: a Perspective, International journal of chemical reactor engineering , 9, 1, 1-54.

S.K. Gupta, S.Garg, 2013, Multiobjective Optimization Using Genetic Algorithm, Advances in Chemical Engineering, 43, 205-245.

Jiří Jaromír Klemeš, Petar Sabev Varbanov and Peng Yen Liew (Editors)
Proceedings of the 24th European Symposium on Computer Aided Process Engineering – ESCAPE 24
June 15-18, 2014, Budapest, Hungary.

Simulation and Process Integration for TAME Synthesis

Olivia A. Perederic[a], Valentin Pleşu[a*], Petrica Iancu[a], Gheorghe Bumbac[a], Alexandra-Elena Bonet-Ruiz[a], Jordi Bonet-Ruiz[b], Bertram Muchan[c]

[a]*University POLITEHNICA of Bucharest, Centre for Techonology Transfer in the Process Industries, 1, Gh. Polizu Street, RO-011061 Bucharest, România*
[b]*University of Barcelona, Department of Chemical Engineering, 1, Martí i Franquès Street, 6th Floor, E-08028 Barcelona, Spain*
[c]*OMV Petrom,PETROBRAZI Refinery, 65, Trandafirilor Street, RO-100316 Brazi, Prahova County, România*
escape24@chim.upb.ro

Abstract

A new sustainable process to produce tert-amyl-methyl-ether (TAME) using as feedstock enriched C_5 fraction (LCN – light cracking naphtha) from catalytic cracking (FCC) is developed. Existing technologies are based on methanol (MeOH) separation by water extraction, combined with distillation processes (Luyben, 2011). The new process involves TAME reactor effluent, separation based only on distillation columns and liquid-liquid (L-L) separators. Unreacted MeOH is recycled. Conceptual design for separation section is presented in Perederic (2013). Process specifications are collected from an industrial plant. In this paper three case studies with specific data for separation section are presented, underlying process characteristics. Heat Integration analysis for energy savings is considered. Additionally, environmental and economic analyses are performed. Environmental Impact using WAR algorithm is assessed, considering different fuels. Elimination of water in separation section ensures good environmental performance and lower energy consumption. MeOH separation is based on L-L phase separation in C_5 hydrocarbons-MeOH mixtures and azeotropes composition variation by pressure swing. Economic indicators calculated with Aspen Process Economic Analyzer indicate an attractive process configuration, for selected Case Study.

Keywords: TAME synthesis, methanol recovery, process simulation, process integration, environmental impact, economic evaluation.

1. Introduction

TAME is one of the gasoline additives to improve performance and to achieve environmental requirements. Typical industrial technologies to produce TAME are based on reaction in liquid phase, catalyzed by cationic exchange resins. More advanced technologies involve reactive distillation. Regardless the technology, the separation of MeOH from effluent is based mainly on water extraction. This process involves water contamination of gasoline, and high heat consumption to separate MeOH-water mixture. For this reason, a new separation scheme for TAME synthesis effluent is proposed, based on pressure swing distillation and L-L separation, without using water (Perederic, 2013) Pressure swing exploits azeotropes composition variation with pressure. In certain operation conditions the mixture isoamylenes (IAs)-C_5 fraction- MeOH have

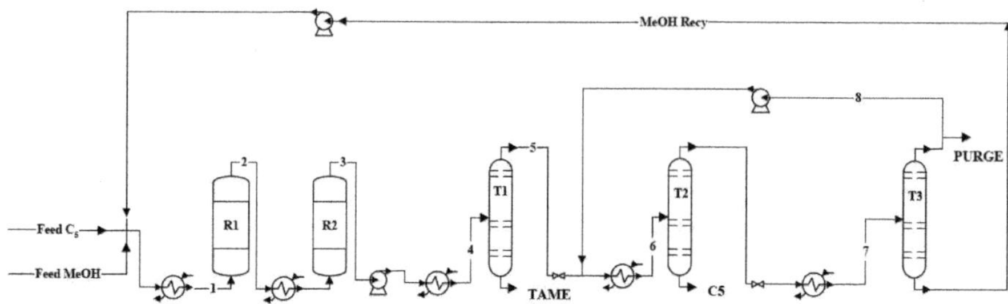

Figure 1. TAME synthesis simplified flowsheet for CS1.

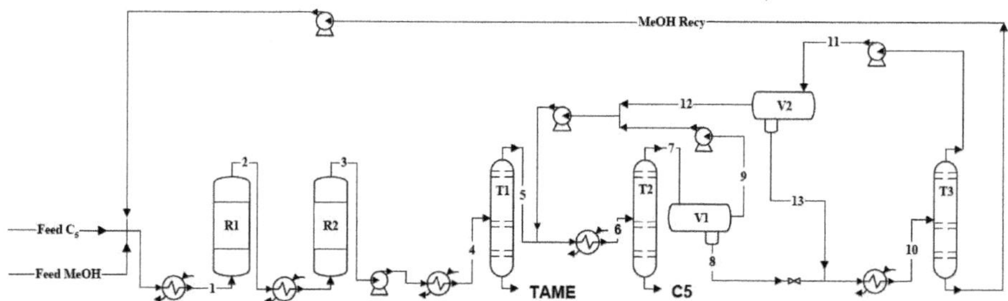

Figure 2. TAME synthesis simplified flowsheet for CS2 and CS3.

insolubility zones, which allow going over distillations boundaries, exploiting L-L equilibrium. For this analysis three case studies are considered (Figure 1 and Figure 2). Case study CS1 is based on pressure swing distillation (T1-10 bar, T2-10 bar, T3-4 bar), L-L separation is not considered. A purge (24 % from feedstock) is necessary for T3, otherwise nonreactive C_5 hydrocarbons accumulate in the system. Case study CS2 is based on pressure swing distillation (T1-10 bar, T2-10 bar, T3-2 bar) and L-L separation (V1, V2). Case study CS3is based on pressure swing distillation (T1-6 bar, T2-5 bar, T3-2 bar) and L-L separation (V1, V2). For CS2 and CS3, when L-L equilibrium is considered, MeOH separation is substantially improved compared to CS1. Consequently lower pressures (CS3), are taken into account. In this paper the analysis is based on CS3 configuration.

2. Methodology

2.1. Aspen HYSYS Process Simulation

Aspen HYSYS V.8.3 is used for flowsheet simulation. The feedstock, Table 1, is IAs enriched C_5 fraction, from FCC gasoline. For simplification, all the inert hydrocarbons (C_5 fraction without IAs) are represented by isopentane (iC5). Selected fluid package is UNIQUAC, for liquid phase, and Peng-Robinson for vapour phase. iC5-IAs-MeOH-TAME mixtures non-ideal behaviour is intensively exploited in process conceptual design. Eley-Rideal reaction kinetic model (Rihko and Krause, 1995) with Amberlyst 35 wet (Dow Chemical) cationite resin catalyst is considered. Reaction section (reactors R1 and R2) total MeOH feed is 65 kmol/h. Ideal adiabatic Plug Flow Reactor model (PFR) is selected for R1 and R2. For CS3, T1 column is aimed to separate pure TAME from R2 effluent, fed on the 5th stage, at boiling point. Consequently, bottoms product is high purity TAME, while distillate product consists of unreacted MeOH and all hydrocarbons. T1 specifications are: reflux ratio and bottoms TAME molar fraction. T2 and T3 use pressure swing coupled with L-L equilibrium separation, to obtain

Table 1. CS3 streams information.

Stream Name	Feed C_5	3	TAME	C5	MeOH Recy	7	8	9	11	12	13
T, °C	25	79	160	85	83	72	35	35	41	35	35
P, kPa	1000	939	620	520	220	480	480	480	270	270	270
iC5, kmol/h	214	214	0	214	0	125	11	114	12	1	11
2M2B, kmol/h	36	21	0	21	0	7	1	6	1	0	1
2M1B, kmol/h	18	2	0	2	0	2	0	2	0	0	0
MeOH, kmol/h	0	34	0	1	34	48	35	13	3	2	1
TAME, kmol/h	0	31	30	0	0	0	0	0	0	0	0

hydrocarbon stream C5 and pure MeOH stream. T2 column specifications are: reflux ratio, and distillate MeOH fractionThe distillate product is subcooled in V1 to separate two liquid phases (the heavy one, rich in MeOH is part of T3 feed). T3 separates MeOH high purity in bottoms, while distillate is heterogeneous azeotrope hydrocarbons-MeOH. T3 specifications are: C5 recovery in distillate product and bottoms temperature. The distillate is subcooled in V2. MeOH rich fraction is combined with V1 similar product, as T3 feed. T3 bottom product is recycled to reaction section. V1 and V2 light phase is recycled to T2 feed.

2.2. Heat Integration

Rational use of energy opportunities for CS3 flowsheet are investigated with Heat Integration analysis (Klemeš et al, 2011), using SPRINT software tool.

2.3. Environmental Impact

Process performance, regarding environmental impact is evaluated with Waste Reduction Algorithm based on WAR V.1.0.17 software. The analysis considers Potential Environmental Impact (PEI) units produced for different fuels: coal, oil, and fuel gas (Bonet-Ruiz et al, 2010), when the products are TAME and C5 streams.

2.4. Economic evaluation

Aspen Process Economic Analyzer is used considering following as assumptions: plant construction is setup within a European refinery, and 13 years plant life cycle (Perederic, 2013).

3. Results and Discussions

3.1. Aspen HYSYS Simulation

Operating conditions in reaction section are similar to industrial plant. R1 and R2 composition profiles, presented in Figure 3, show important transformation to TAME in R1, and thermodynamic limitation in R2. This behaviour is noticed despite the cooling between reactors to R1 inlet temperature (75 °C). R1 temperature increase is 17.8 °C, while R2 temperature gain is just 3.5 °C. Separation section main streams are presented in Table 1, while columns temperature and composition profiles are illustrated in Figure 4. In T1 bottoms separates high purity TAME, while the top contains 78.6 % C5 molar fraction and all amount of MeOH. T2 tower is aimed to separate MeOH-C5 azeotrope as distillate product. Bottoms stream recovers ~ 64 % of C5 compounds. T3 separates MeOH-C5 azeotrope in distillate. About 85 % of this stream is recycled in T2 feed.

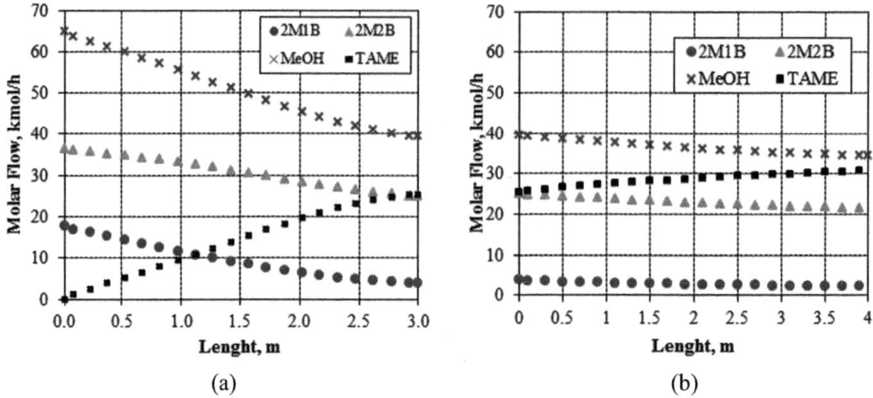

Figure 3. Composition profiles for the reactor R1 (a) and reactor R2 (b).

3.2. Heat Integration

CS3 flowsheet has small scope for process heat recovery. For ΔT_{min}=3 °C, the pinch process point temperature is 83.55 °C. Shifted Composite Curves (Figure 5a) indicate 2.7 MW, based on heat exchanger network minimum total cost . Proposed hot utilities (HU) are medium pressure steam (MP) and low pressure steam (LP) steam. Proposed cold utilities (CU) are water (28-38 °C), shaft water (5-15 °C), and boiling feed water-BFW (50-85 °C). Based on Grand Composite Curve (Figure 5b), built with SPRINT, optimal utilities placement satisfy minimum hot utilities for $Q_{H,min}$= 8,920 kW and minimum cold utilities for Q_{Cmin} = 8260 kW. It is important to underline that BFW is a good solution for heat recovery.

3.3. Environmental Impact

Figure 6 presents PEI/kg for each of three case studies and three fuels. CS1 generates large number of PEI units, because waste effluent stream Purge has important environmental impact. CS2 and CS3 have much lower environmental impact (PEI/kg) as waste streams are substantially reduced. Comparing the results of CS2 and CS3 for different fuels, a slightly lower impact is reached for coal, in CS3.

3.4. Economic Evaluation

Table 2 presents main indicators of the economic analysis: 90.5 % of operational cost is represented by raw material cost. The feasibility of the investment is given by Internal Rate of Return (IRR), which is a financial metric used in investment evaluation. IRR reasonable minimum value should be 20 %, while in Table 2, IRR= 28.95%.

4. Conclusions and future work

The work presents a systematic analysis of a new sustainable TAME synthesis process. Three case studies are analysed, to determine minimum raw material and energy consumption. Best results are achieved for CS3: practically no material loss,

Table 2. Economic analysis indicators.

Indicator	Value	Indicator	Value
Total investment cost	11.98 M€	Utility cost	2.83 M€/y
Operation cost	102.05 M€/y	Total Sales	109.77 M€/y
Raw material cost	93.35 M€/y	Internal Rate of Return	28.95 %

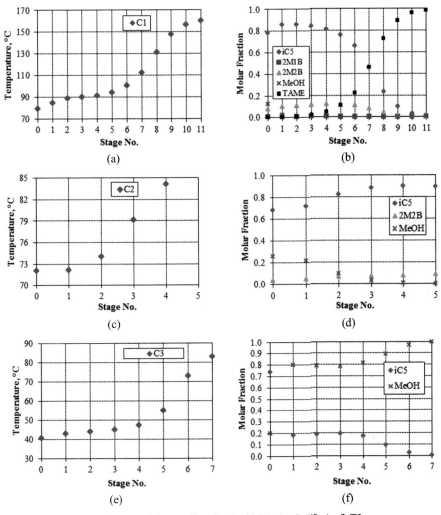

Figure 4. Temperature and composition profiles for: (a, b) T1, (c, d) T2, (e, f) T3.

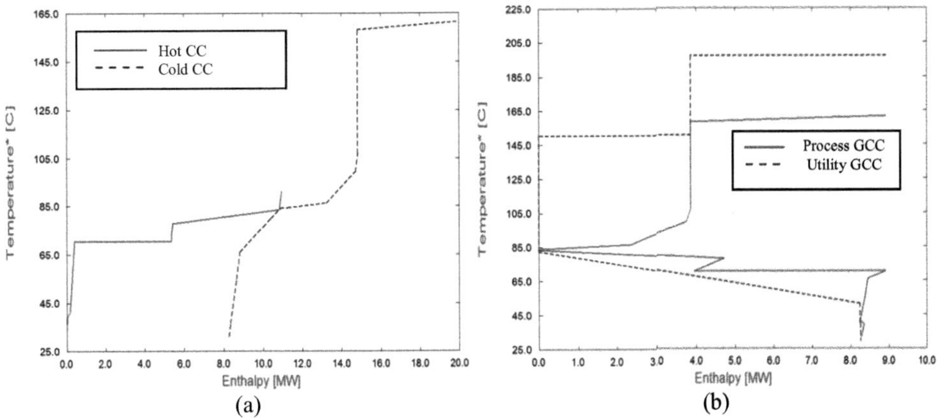

Figure 5. (a) Shifted Composite Curves (CC) and (b) Balanced Grand Composite Curves (GCC).

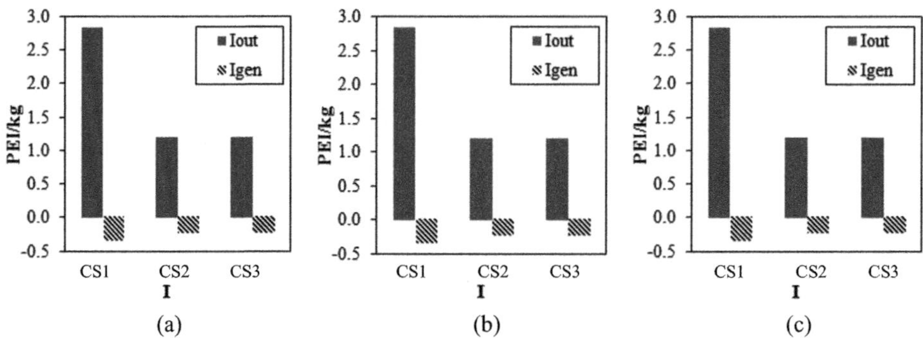

Figure 6. Comparison of PEI units for the CS1, CS2 and CS3 for coal (a), oil (b) or gas fuel (c).

minimum energy consumption, minimum environmental impact, and maximum energy recovery. CS3 economic analysis reveals an interesting solution. In the future, proposed separation method has to be taken into consideration for the process with reactive distillation. Other ethers production processes, such as tert-amyl ethyl ether and ethyl-tert butyl ether, will be analysed, based on similar methodology.

Acknowledgement

The authors acknowledge the financial support to POSCCE project ID 652.

References

A. E. Bonet-Ruiz, J. Bonet-Ruiz,V. Pleşu, G. Bozga, 2010, Environmental performance assessment for reactive distillation processes, Resources Conservation Recycling, 54, 315.

M. Enrico, B.G. Rong, 2012, New distillation sequences for bioethanol production by extractive distillation, Computer Aided Chemical Engineering, 30, Part B, Elsevier, London, 737-741.

J. Klemeš, F. Fridler, I. Bulatov, P. Varbanov, 2011, Sustainability in the Process Industry. Integration and Optimization, McGraw-Hill, New York, USA.

W. L. Luyben, 2011, Principles of distillation design and control, Principles and Case Studies of Simultaneous Design, John Wiley & Sons Inc., New Jeresy, USA.

W. Mao, 2008, Thermodynamic and kinetic study of tert-amyl, Chem. Eng. Proc., 47, 761.

O. A. Perederic, 2013, TAME Production plant from enriched C5 fraction from fluid catalytic cracking (FCC), Graduation Project, University Politehnica of Bucharest, Romania .

J. Rashed, 2009, Model-based Retrofit Design and Analysis of Petrochemical Processes, PhD Thesis, Danmarks Tekniske Universitet, Lyngby, Denmark.

L. K. Rihko, O. A. Krause, 1995, Kinetics of Heterogeneously Catalyzed tert-Amyl Methyl Ether Reactions in the Liquid Phase, Ind. Eng. Chem. Res., 34, 1172.

W. B. Su, J. R. Chang, 2000, Modelling and Simulation of Tubular Reactor in the tert-Amyl Methyl Ether Synthesis Process, Ind. Eng. Chem. Res., 39, 4140-4147.

L. Turton , R.Bailie, W. Whiting, J. A. Shaeiwitz.,1998, Analysis, Synthesis and Design of Chemical Processes, Prentice Hall PTR, New Jeresey, USA.

Amberlyst 35 wet characteristics, The Dow Chemical Company, <www.dow.com/assets/attachments/business/process_chemicals/amberlyst/amberlyst_35wet/tds/amberlyst_35wet> accessed on 08/03/2013.

Aspen Process Economic Analyzer V8.0. User's Guide, 2013, Burlington, USA.

Sprint ,<www.ceas.manchester.ac.uk/research/centres/cpi/software> accessed on 10/10/2013.

WAR V.1.0.17 Software, Environmental Protection Agency of USA (EPA), <www.epa.gov/nrmrl/std/war/sim_war.htm>, accessed on 13/03/2013.

Jiří Jaromír Klemeš, Petar Sabev Varbanov and Peng Yen Liew (Editors)
Proceedings of the 24th European Symposium on Computer Aided Process Engineering – ESCAPE 24
June 15-18, 2014, Budapest, Hungary.

Electricity Load Reduction in Hybrid Power Systems Using Power Pinch Analysis

Nor Erniza Mohammad Rozali[a], Ong Su Tin[a], Sharifah Rafidah Wan Alwi[a,*], Zainuddin Abdul Manan[a], Jiří Jaromír Klemeš[b], Mohammad Yusri Hassan[c]

[a]*Process System Engineering Centre (PROSPECT), Faculty of Chemical Engineering, Universiti Teknologi Malaysia, 81310 UTM Johor Bahru, Johor, Malaysia*
[b]*Centre for Process Integration and Intensification – CPI², Research Institute of Chemical and Process Engineering, Faculty of Information Technology, University of Pannonia, Egyetem u. 10, H-8200 Veszprém, Hungary*
[c]*Centre of Electrical Energy Systems (CEES), Faculty of Electrical Engineering, Universiti Teknologi Malaysia, 81310 UTM Johor Bahru, Johor, Malaysia*
shasha@cheme.utm.my

Abstract

Energy savings in an electrical system can be achieved through the use of energy-efficient appliances to minimise electricity consumption. This work applies the Power Pinch Analysis (PoPA) to guide electricity load reduction at the demand side of a HPS. The reduction in electricity load as well as cost can be determined from the power rating and operating hours of appliances in a HPS. Four new heuristics for load reduction have been proposed in this work. The results show that systematic efficiency improvement of the appliances has successfully reduced the total electricity consumption and cost.

Keywords: Power Pinch Analysis (PoPA), load reduction, energy efficiency

1. Introduction

The rapid growth in electricity demand has encouraged widespread energy-saving efforts especially in the industrial, commercial and domestic sectors. Energy-saving measures in an electrical power system include the use of energy-efficient equipment and appliances, abiding by the energy-efficiency regulations and implementation of good housekeeping techniques. Opportunities to reduce electricity consumption can be specifically achieved through the improvement of lighting, electric motors and heating, ventilating and air conditioning (HVAC) systems. Popovic-Gerber et al. (2012) reported that lighting consumes over 20 % of all electricity generated in the U.S, while electric motors account about for 30–80 % of the total industrial energy use according to Hasanuzzaman et al. (2011). Improvement of energy efficiency in industrial systems through the use of energy-efficient technology has become an important demand side management strategy (Du Plessis et al., 2013). Some typical measures to enhance the industrial energy efficiency include replacing inefficient incandescent lights with the more efficient compact fluorescent lamps (e.g. change T8 to T5 or LED) and the use of the high efficiency motors or variable speed drives (VSD) as alternatives for the standard motors in motor driven systems (e.g. conveyors, fans, pumps and chillers). A total implementation of energy-efficient appliances in electrical systems is not always economically feasible due to the additional costs incurred. However, given the correct strategies and magnitude of reduction, this extra cost would be a worthwhile investment in exchange for the potential reduction in electricity bills over time, as a result of the use of the energy-efficient appliances.

Studies to investigate electricity savings potential by improving appliance efficiency in industrial systems have been conducted extensively. Electricity saving potentials in the German paper industry are scrutinised by Fleiter et al. (2012). Technology-specific information is integrated in a bottom-up model to identify the energy efficiency potentials and to evaluate their cost-effectiveness. Du Plessis et al. (2013) developed a novel real-time energy management system to improve the electricity and cost efficiency of cooling systems. In situ experiments on various cooling systems were carried out and 33.3 % electricity saving is realised. Bortoni et al. (2013) presented a model development for the energy consumption estimation as well as peak demand reduction. Motor efficiency curves, annual working hours and efficiency loading are taken into account in the model construction.

Pinch Analysis concept has been widely used for heat (Klemeš and Varbanov, 2013), mass and water minimisation (Klemeš, 2013). Its application has been recently extended to power systems – see e.g. Wan Alwi et al. (2012) and Mohammad Rozali et al. (2013). However, the use of Pinch Analysis to explore the electricity savings potential in power systems has not been reported. Power Pinch Analysis (PoPA) has been applied by Wan Alwi et al. (2013) to reduce the storage capacity and the maximum demand in a Hybrid Power System (HPS). The total electricity load reduction has been achieved by performing load shifting. Load reduction through energy efficiency improvement however is not considered. In this paper, PoPA is applied to provide insights on the electricity allocations in HPS to guide load reduction in the total end-use electricity consumption. The reduction in electricity load as well as cost can be determined from the power rating and operating hours of appliances in a HPS.

2. Methodology

The baseline (using the standard level of appliance energy efficiency) power allocation at each time interval is determined using the graphical PoPA tool called the Outsourced and Storage Electricity Curves – OSEC (Wan Alwi et al., 2013). Figure 1 shows the OSEC combination during start up and continuous 24 h operation for the Illustrative Case Study data as tabulated in Table 1.

Table 1. Limiting power sources and demands for Illustrative Case Study.

No.	Power Type	Description	Time, h		Power rating, kW
			From	To	
S1	Source	Solar	8	18	70
S2	Source	Wind	2	10	50
S3	Source	Biomass	0	24	80
D1	Demand	Fans	0	24	40
D2	Demand	Compressors	8	18	60
D3	Demand	Lighting	0	24	30
D4	Demand	Pumps	8	18	50
D5	Demand	Conveyors	8	20	50

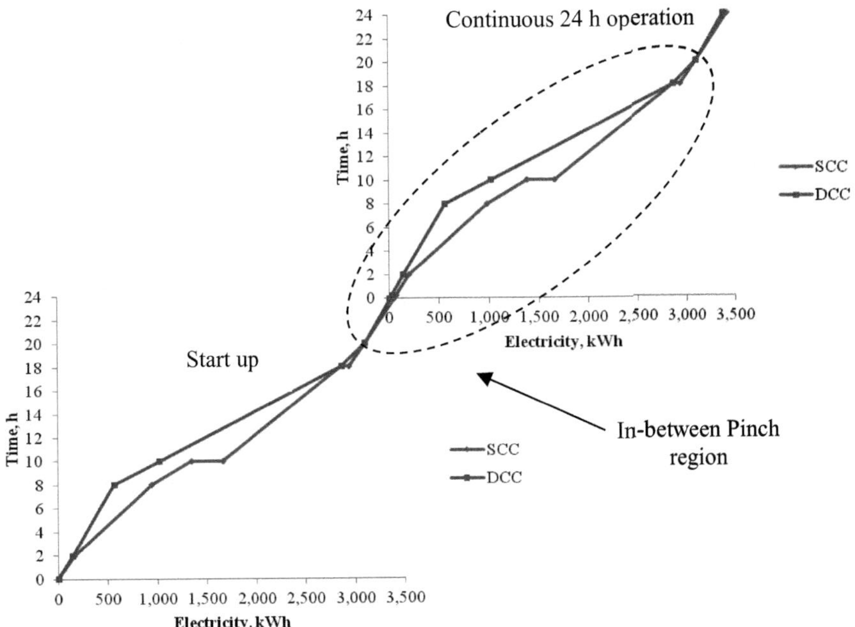

Figure 1. OSEC for start up and continuous 24 h operation

The OSEC is constructed by allocating the Source Composite Curve (SCC) directly to the Demand Composite Curve (DCC) within each time interval (Wan Alwi et al., 2013). Prior to the load reduction, the total electricity consumption is 3,380 kWh with minimum outsourced electricity supply (MOES) requirement of 360 kWh during continuous 24 h operation. In order to determine the load and magnitude of reduction, the outsourced electricity allocations are identified. The OSEC plot shows that 280 kWh of outsourced electricity is required between time intervals 10 and 18 h. Between time intervals 18 and 20 h, 80 kWh is needed, which represents the maximum demand of 40 kW for the system. Electricity is stored during the rest of other time intervals, with the maximum storage capacity occurs between time intervals 2 and 8 h (420 kWh).

As mentioned earlier, load reduction via appliance efficiency improvement involve a trade-off between the appliance cost and electricity bill. While the reduction of load consumption can lead to electricity bill payment reduction, it may also increase the storage size, and thereby increase the cost of storage system. Besides, reduction limit should also be specified in order to avoid electricity excess, where the available excess electricity for the next day (AEEND) is higher than the MOES. Bearing in mind these factors, four heuristics are proposed to guide the load reduction;

i. Reduction of load demand operating when the MOES and maximum demand occurs to reduce the total outsourced electricity requirement.
ii. Reduction of load demand operating within the in-between Pinch region to avoid storage capacity increment.
iii. Reduction of load demand operating across the Pinch location is not favoured to avoid storage capacity increment.
iv. Reduction magnitude should not exceed the amount of MOES to avoid electricity excess.

Referring to the OSEC plot, it is found that all demands operated within the MOES occurrence i.e. 10 to 20 h (Heuristic 1). Based on Heuristic 3, consumption of D1 and D3 are not feasible to be reduced because they operate across the pinch location at t=20 h. Following the second heuristic, the loads that are left for the load reduction procedure are D2 (compressors), D4 (Pumps) and D5 (conveyors). These loads are driven by electric motors. Therefore, VSD installation is considered as an alternative to improve the efficiency, and consequently to reduce the electricity consumption. Based on Heuristic 4, the magnitude of reduction is determined. As can be seen, the total MOES for a 24 h operation is 360 kWh (280 + 80 = 360 kWh). The limit of the reduction is therefore set to 360 kWh. A constant 0.25 speed reduction ratio, S_R is considered in the load reduction for all the three demands.

2.1 Reduction of D2 consumption

The 60 kW compressors operate between time intervals 8 and 18 h, with total daily consumption of 600 kWh. After the installation of VSD with S_R of 0.25, the new rated power of the compressors is calculated using Eq.(1) (Abdelaziz et al., 2011) to give 34 kW. This alternative comply with Heuristic 4 because the magnitude of reduction is 260 kWh ((60 kW – 34 kW) × 10h).

$$EC_{VSD} = EC_i \times (1 - S_R)^2 \quad (1)$$

Where the EC_{VSD} is the electricity consumption after VSD installation, EC_i is the baseline electricity consumption, S_R is the speed reduction ratio.

The effect of this load reduction is visualised using OSEC and is illustrated in Figure 2. It can be observed that the MOES requirement has been reduced to 120 kWh, which gives a reduction of 67%. The maximum demand however are not affected (40 kW).

2.2 Reduction of D4 consumption

To reduce the electricity consumption of the 50 kW pumps, VSD with S_R of 0.25 is installed. Using Eq.(1), the new rated power of the pumps after the energy efficiency improvement is calculated as 28 kW. It indicates a total reduction magnitude of 220 kWh. Figure 3 presents the effect of D4 reduction. 61 % of total MOES reduction (from 360 kWh to 140 kWh) has been successfully achieved by this option, but the maximum demand remains at 40 kW.

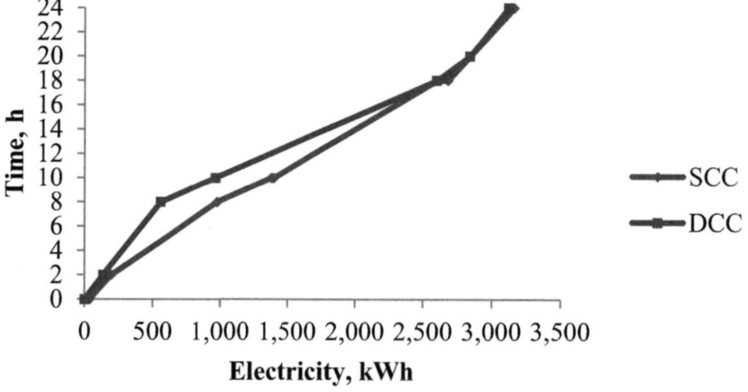

Figure 2. OSEC for continuous 24 h operation after the reduction of D2 consumption

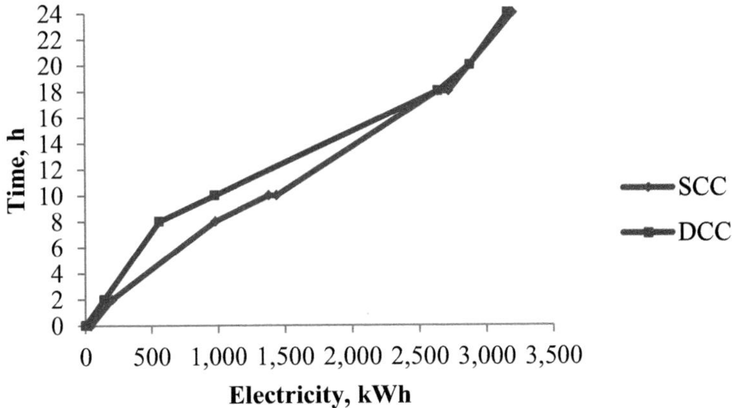

Figure 3. OSEC for continuous 24 h operation after the reduction of D4 consumption

2.3 Reduction of D5 consumption

The efficiency of the conveyors is also improved by installing the VSD with 0.25 S_R. The magnitude of the reduction is 264 kWh, because the rated power of the conveyors after the efficiency improvement is 28 kW. The OSEC visualising the effect of this load reduction is shown in Figure 4. Reduction of D5 consumption has reduced the MOES to 96 kWh (73% reduction). Besides, this alternative also contributes to a total 55% reduction in the maximum demand.

The results from the consumption reduction of the three demands show that the maximum capacity of the storage is successfully maintained at its initial size (420 kWh). The reduction of the maximum demand cannot be achieved after the D2 and D4 reduction because these demands operate between time intervals 8 and 18 h. The maximum demand on the other hand occurs between time intervals 18 and 20 h, and can only be reduced after the D5 (operating between 8 and 20 h) consumption is reduced.

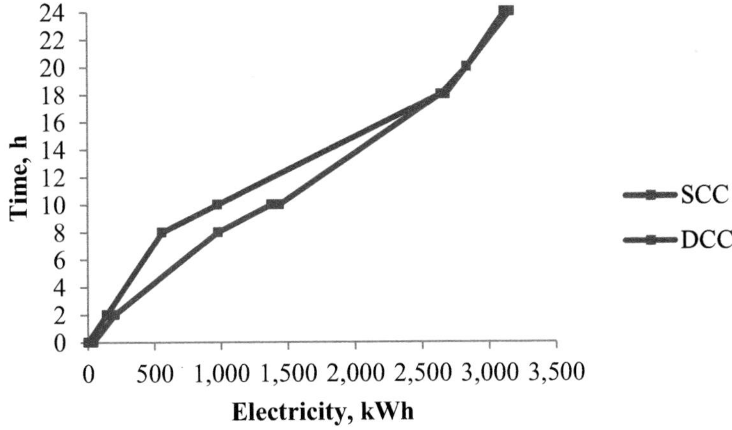

Figure 4. OSEC for continuous 24 h operation after the reduction of D5 consumption

3. Conclusions

PoPA has been successfully applied to guide load reduction via appliance efficiency improvement in a HPS. Considering various factors including the amount of MOES, storage size and amount of electricity excess, four heuristics have been developed to ensure the appropriate and feasible load reduction strategies. Results show that load reduction using PoPA has successfully reduced the total consumption and the MOES requirement of the system. Further studies are required to include the economic assessment to evaluate the economic feasibility. Besides, effects of the implementation of other alternatives such as the energy-efficient motors could also contribute to energy efficiency improvement in the system.

Acknowledgements

The authors would like to thank the Universiti Teknologi Malaysia (UTM) for providing the financial support through the Research University Grant under the Vote No. Q.J130000.2544.03H44 as well as the Hungarian State and the European Union under project TAMOP-4.2.2.A-11/1/KONV-2012-0072 — Design and optimisation of the modernisation and efficient operation of energy-supply and the utilisation systems using renewable energy sources and ICTs.

References

E. Abdelaziz, R. Saidur, S. Mekhilef, 2011, A review on energy saving strategies in industrial sector, Renewable and Sustainable Energy Reviews, 15, 150-168.

E. C. Bortoni, L. a. H. Nogueira, R. B. Cardoso, J. Haddad, E. P. Souza, M. V. X. Dias, R. A. Yamachita, 2013, Assessment of the achieved savings from induction motors energy efficiency labeling in Brazil, Energy Conversion and Management, 75, 734-740.

G. E. Du Plessis, L. Liebenberg, E. H. Mathews, J. N. Du Plessis, 2013, A versatile energy management system for large integrated cooling systems, Energy Conversion and Management, 66, 312-325.

T. Fleiter, D. Fehrenbach, E. Worrell, W. Eichhammer, 2012, Energy efficiency in the German pulp and paper industry–A model-based assessment of saving potentials, Energy, 40, 84-99.

M. Hasanuzzaman, N. Rahim, R. Saidur, S. Kazi, 2011, Energy savings and emissions reductions for rewinding and replacement of industrial motor, Energy, 36, 233-240.

J. J. Klemeš (ed.) 2013. Handbook of Process Integration (PI), Minimisation of energy and water use, waste and emissions, Cambridge, UK: Woodhead/Elsevier.

J. J. Klemeš, P. S. Varbanov, 2013, Process Intensification and Integration: an assessment, Clean Technologies and Environmental Policy, 15, 417-422.

N. E. Mohammad Rozali, S. R. Wan Alwi, Z. Abdul Manan, J. J. Klemeš, M. Y. Hassan, 2013, Process integration of hybrid power systems with energy losses considerations, Energy, 55, 38-45.

J. Popovic-Gerber, J. A. Oliver, N. Cordero, T. Harder, J. A. Cobos, M. Hayes, S. C. O'mathuna, E. Prem, 2012, Power electronics enabling efficient energy usage: Energy savings potential and technological challenges, IEEE Transactions on Power Electronics, 27, 2338-2353.

S. R. Wan Alwi, N. E. Mohammad Rozali, Z. Abdul-Manan, J. J. Klemeš, 2012, A process integration targeting method for hybrid power systems, Energy, 44, 6-10.

S. R. Wan Alwi, O. S. Tin, N. E. M. Rozali, Z. A. Manan, J. J. Klemeš, 2013, New graphical tools for process changes via load shifting for hybrid power systems based on Power Pinch Analysis, Clean Technologies and Environmental Policy, 15, 459-472.

Jiří Jaromír Klemeš, Petar Sabev Varbanov and Peng Yen Liew (Editors)
Proceedings of the 24th European Symposium on Computer Aided Process Engineering – ESCAPE 24
June 15-18, 2014, Budapest, Hungary.

Energy Minimization in Cryogenic Distillation Columns Through Intermediate Side Heat Exchangers

J. Rafael Alcántara-Avila,[a*] Fernando I. Gómez-Castro,[b] J. Gabriel Segovia-Hernández,[b] Ken-Ichiro Sotowa,[a] Toshihide Horikawa[a]

[a]*Department of Chemical Science and Technology, The University of Tokushima, 2-1 Minami Josanjima-cho, Tokushima 770-8506, Japan*
[b]*Departamento de Ingeniería Química, Universidad de Guanajuato, Noria Alta s/n, Guanajuato 36050, Mexico*
alcantara@chem.tokushima-u.ac.jp

Abstract

Cryogenic distillation is very similar to other distillation systems except it is used to separate chemicals with very low boiling points (e.g. propylene/propane mixture). In the case of cryogenic distillation, a refrigeration system must be coupled with the condenser, which is at the lowest possible temperature. Therefore, the temperature difference between the inlet and outlet of the working fluid in the refrigeration system is at its largest possible value thereby it leads to high energy consumption. Therefore, the aim of this research is to propose a new synthesis procedure to enumerate optimal heat-integrated cryogenic distillation structures through the installation of heat exchangers at intermediate locations in the column. The synthesis procedure combines superstructure representation, rigorous simulations and mixed-integer linear programming (MILP) optimization techniques. The results for the separation of a propylene/propane mixture showed that the installation of intermediate side heat exchangers can reduce the energy consumption up to 75 % in comparison with conventional distillation.

Keywords: cryogenic distillation, heat integration, process synthesis, MILP, propylene.

1. Introduction

Cryogenic distillation is widely used in the chemical and petrochemical industry. Representative applications of cryogenic distillation can be found in liquefied natural gas (LNG) plants, air separation units (ASU), ethylene manufacturing plants, etc. In case of propylene, because it has a very low boiling point (e.g. -47.6 °C), there are two options to separate it from propane: (1) operate the distillation column at high pressure as well as temperature to ensure the use of water as cooling medium, and (2) operate the distillation column at low pressure as well as temperature to use a refrigerant as cooling medium. Regardless of these options, the energy consumption is inevitably high, which makes this separation a very energy-intensive process.

To reduce the energy consumption in cryogenic distillation, vapor recompression columns (VRC) and heat-integrated distillation columns (HIDiC) have been proposed. Olujic et al. (2006) compared VRC and HIDiC in terms of energy consumption and capital cost for a propylene-propane splitter at steady state while Schmal et al. (2006) did it at dynamic state. Both results showed that the HIDiC structure exhibited economic and energy savings, and faster control when a model predictive control

(MPC) was used. Contrarily in a later work, Chen et al. (2013) performed economic and energy comparisons between them, and their results showed that VRC attained the lowest cost and energy consumption.

Another way to reduce energy is through the diabatic distillation (DDC). It is the separation process in which heat is supplied or removed in the trays of a distillation column. Hirata (2009) researched the DDC and his results showed that an ideal DDC was superior to VRC and HIDiC. Bisgaard et al. (2013) studied the effect of diabatization in distillation column through dynamic controllability analysis and closed-loop performance. They mentioned that diabatization increase the input-output interaction.

This research aims to find distillation structures which embed a set of refrigeration cycles to realize heat integration not only at the condenser or reboiler, but at any location in a distillation column for the separation of a propylene/propane mixture. The proposed synthesis problem combines superstructure formulation, rigorous simulations and the solution of mixed integer optimization (MILP) problems.

2. Simulation procedure

2.1. Simulation of distillation columns

Given the feed conditions and product specifications, the number of stages in a distillation column can be determined as a function of its operating pressure and reflux ratio. For conventional columns (CC), the number of stages is calculated from short-cut simulations, then the design of the column is done through rigorous simulations. In addition, for VRC, a pseudo stream leaving the column connects the compressor and then a heat exchanger. The compressor work duty and heat exchanged are calculated by setting a design specification where the compressor outlet pressure is varied.

Figure 1 summarizes the simulated distillation columns in this research. In Figure 1, A denotes the light component, and B the heavy component. CW denotes cooling water and STM steam, which are used in CC as shown in Figure 1a. VRC is shown in Figure 1b. The dotted lines in Figure 1c represent the energy transfer through all the stages in DCC. Figure 1d shows one exchanger in the rectifying section as a representative example for one possible structure, however, the number of intermediate exchangers, the exchanged amount of heat and their locations in the process side will be determined through optimization techniques. q_{so} (Q_{si}) stands for heat source (sink) in the refrigeration side.

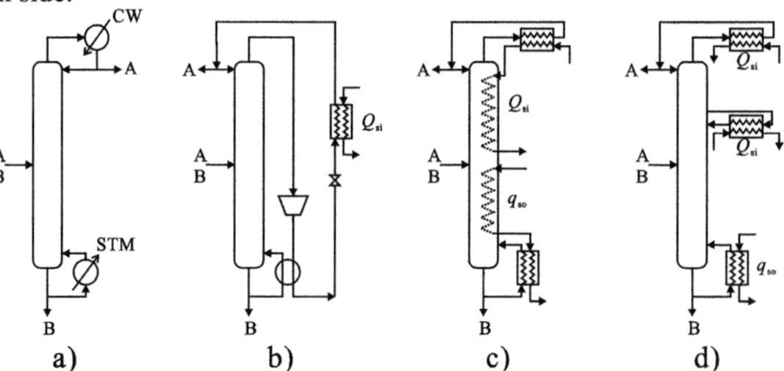

Figure 1. Candidate distillation structures and heat integration techniques.

2.2. Simulation of refrigeration cycles

Figure 2 shows the conceptual representation of a refrigeration cycle in this work. The working fluid leaves the compressor as superheated vapor at high pressure P_{out} and temperature T_0 and it is cooled down to T_{m} by removing the heat $q_{\text{so},1}$ through $q_{\text{so},m}$. Then, the fluid is decompressed by means of a throttling valve and it is heated from t_0 to t_n by supplying the heat $Q_{\text{si},1}$ through $Q_{\text{si},n}$. A vapor stream at low pressure P_{in} and temperature t_n is increased to P_{out} and T_0 by adding the work duty, W, at the compressor. This closes the refrigeration cycle.

Refrigeration cycles are simulated with m heat exchangers in the hot side, and n heat exchangers in the cold side with a compressor and throttling valve as in Figure 2. By fixing the outlet temperature, $q_{\text{so},1}$ to $q_{\text{so},m}$ and $Q_{\text{si},1}$ to $Q_{\text{si},n}$ can be calculated. The compressor work duty is calculated when t_n, P_{in}, and P_{out} are known. The relationships between W, $q_{\text{so},m}$, and $Q_{\text{si},n}$ are very important to determine the necessary amount of heat exchanged by the refrigeration cycle, and they are included in the optimization procedure.

3. Synthesis problem

3.1. Superstructure formulation

A candidate distillation column and a set of refrigeration cycles can be embedded in a superstructure to determine the optimal locations for heat exchangers. Figure 3 shows the proposed superstructure in this research for the separation of a binary mixture.

The superstructure in Figure 3 is a state task network representation. In the process side, a distillation column at a fixed pressure and number of stages represents the task while the circles represent the states of the original feed and the product specifications. In the refrigeration side, each different refrigeration cycle represents a different utility. If necessary, CW and STM provide cooling and heating to satisfy the energy balance.

3.2. Installation of intermediate heat exchangers

Since the amount of heat exchanged at an intermediate heat exchanger (q_i or Q_j) is not equal to the heat reduced at the condenser or reboiler (q_{con} or Q_{reb}), it is very important to estimate the changes in condenser and reboiler duty. One of our previous researches have addressed the relationships between q_i, Q_j, q_{con}, and Q_{reb} by developing the concept of *compensation terms* (Alcántara–Avila et al., 2013). Eqs.(1) and (2) show the compensation terms for the rectifying and stripping sections in a distillation column

$$\Delta q_{\text{tot}} = \sum_{i \in REC} \Delta q_i = \sum_{i \in REC} q_i - (q_{\text{con0}} - q_{\text{con}}) \tag{1}$$

$$\Delta Q_{\text{tot}} = \sum_{j \in STR} \Delta Q_j = \sum_{j \in STR} Q_j - (Q_{\text{reb0}} - Q_{\text{reb}}) \tag{2}$$

where Δq_i (ΔQ_i) is the compensation term at stage i (j) in the rectifying (stripping) section. Δq_{tot} (ΔQ_{tot}) is the overall compensation term in the rectifying (stripping) section. *REC* (*STR*) is the set of stages in the rectifying (stripping) section. Finally, q_{con0} (Q_{reb0}) is the condenser (reboiler) heat duty prior heat integration at any stage.

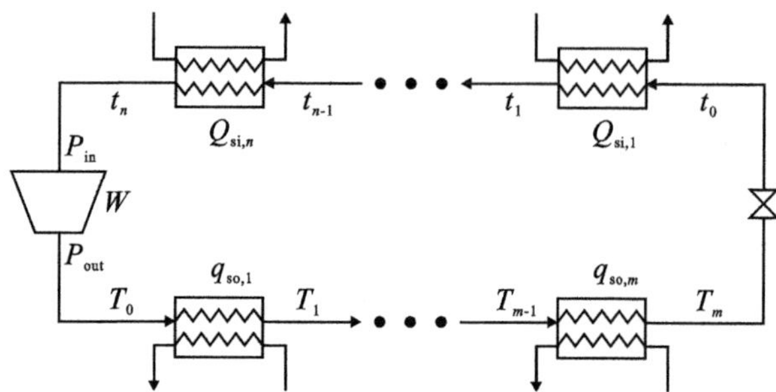

Figure 2. Representation of a refrigeration cycle.

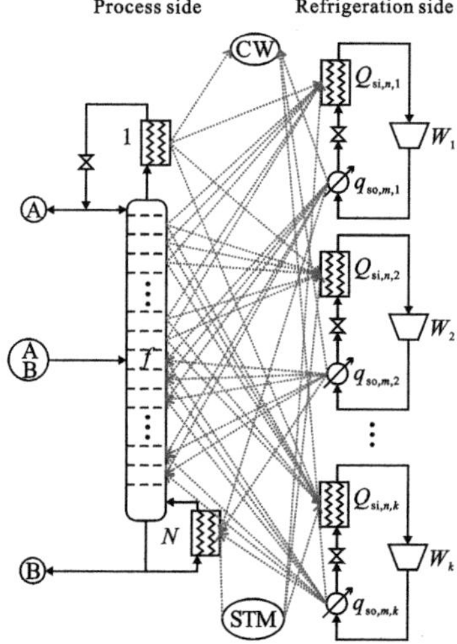

Figure 3. Superstructure formulation.

3.3. Heat integration through intermediate side heat exchangers

The intrinsic non-linearity in distillation columns and refrigeration cycles can be treated by rigorous simulation procedures in section 2, and the obtained results of Δq_i, ΔQ_i, Δq_{tot}, ΔQ_{tot}, q_{con0}, Q_{reb0}, W, $q_{\text{so},m}$, and $Q_{\text{si},n}$ can be input in an optimization problem. The adopted optimization approach is the solution of a mixed-integer linear programming (MILP) problem. This formulation is valid when the operating pressure and number of stages is fixed in the process side, and the temperature levels of each q_m and Q_n in the refrigeration side are known. Eq.(3) shows the objective function, which minimizes the steam and electricity energy consumption in a cryogenic distillation column

$$\min ENERGY = \sum_{\substack{i \in HU \\ j \in STR}} Q_{i,j}^{ex} + \sum_{\substack{i \in HU \\ j \in RSI}} Q_{i,j}^{ex} + \eta \sum_{i \in RSI} W_i \tag{3}$$

where η is a parameter which relates the consumption of primary energy sources per unit amount of electricity generated. In this research, η was equal to 2.73.

The constraints for this problem can be summarized in the following equation

$$g(Q_{i,j}^{ex}, W_j, Y_i^{rec}, Y_j^{str}, q_{\text{con0}}, Q_{\text{reb0}}, \Delta q_{\text{tot}} \Delta Q_{\text{tot}}, q_{\text{so},i}, Q_{\text{si},j}, \alpha_i, \beta_j, \gamma_j, UB) \geq 0 \tag{4}$$

where Q^{ex} is the energy exchange between heat sources and heat sinks and W_j is the compressor work duty in cycle j, and Y^{rec} (Y^{str}) is the binary variable that becomes one if a heat exchanger is installed at stage i (j), and zero otherwise. α defines the relation between the heat supplied to a reference heat source, $Q_{si,ref}$ and the heat removed from $q_{so,m}$, β defines the relation between $Q_{si,ref}$ and the heat supplied to another $Q_{si,n}$, and γ defines the relation between $Q_{si,ref}$ and the work duty W supplied to the refrigeration cycle. *UB* denotes upper bound for internal heat integration at each stage.

3.4. Synthesis procedure

The synthesis procedure proposed in this research is as follows:

1. Execute short-cut and rigorous simulations of the candidate distillation columns.
2. Execute simulations for all the candidate refrigeration cycles.
3. Calculate the condenser and compensation terms for the distillation column subject to heat integration through intermediate heat exchangers.
4. Solve the MILP problem to find the best DCC.
5. Perform a sensitivity analysis for *UB*, Y^{rec} and Y^{str} and obtain several optimal structures with heat integration at intermediate locations in a column.
6. Calculate the energy consumption of the base case CC and VRC. Then, compare all the results in terms of the energy consumption.

4. Results and discussion

4.1. Case study

The separation of 100 kmol/hr of an equimolar propylene/propane mixture, which enters the column at 12 bar as saturated liquid, is taken as case study. Propylene and propane are desired with 99.5 %mol purity. Simulations of the base case CC at 16 bar, and VRC at 12 bar were executed to calculate *ENERGY*. The selected refrigerant was isobutane, and the minimum temperature difference was set to 6 °C.

4.2. Results

The MILP problem was solved in IBM ILOG CPLEX Optimization Studio 12.5. The size of the problem was 7207 continuous variables and 72 binary variables, and it was solved in about 5 s in an Intel Core @ 3.40 GHz. The executed sensitivity analysis also had similar computing time. Figure 4 shows the results of the sensitivity analysis which *UB* and the number of possible heat exchangers in the rectifying and stripping section (m,n). In addition, it shows the optimal DDC and VRC. When the upper bound for heat integration at each side heat exchanger is unconstrained (*UB*= 30), the minimum energy consumption is achieved regardless the number of m and n. DDC is obtained when the number of possible side heat exchangers is unconstrained (m,n = 30). For the same number of possible heat exchange locations, the more energy can be exchanged per location, the less the overall energy consumption. For the same allowed heat exchanged per location, the more side heat exchangers, the less the overall energy consumption. In addition, IHX-DC1 and IHX-DC2 are structures that removes energy at one and two locations in the rectifying section (i.e. condenser and stage 12), which has embedded one and three refrigeration cycles, respectively. There is a gap of 0.1 MW between IHX-DC1 and DDC, and within this gap a set of optimal distillation columns shows a trade-off between energy consumption and complexity of heat integration networks.

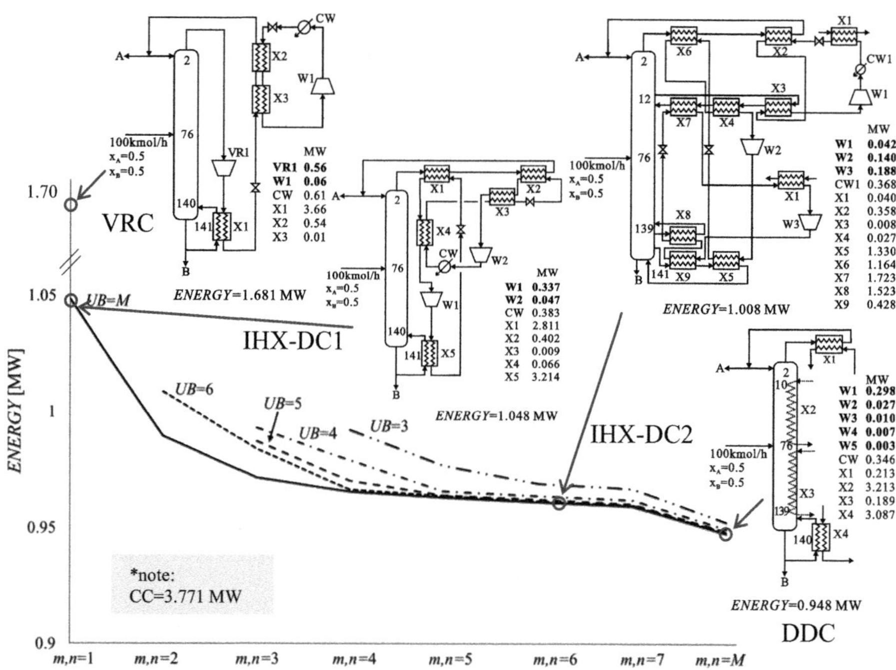

Figure 4. Sensitivity analysis for IHX-DC.

5. Conclusions

This work addressed the problem of cryogenic distillation when the propylene/propane separation was taken as case study. Conventional distillation, vapor recompression, and several diabatic distillation columns were compared in terms of energy consumption. The vapor recompression column and the diabatic distillation column were able to reduce 55 % and 75 % the energy consumption, respectively. The results from sensitivity analyses showed that by worsening 10 % the energy consumption in the diabatic distillation column, optimal cryogenic distillation structures can be found with easier (less integrated) heat exchange networks and still attain energy savings over 72%.

References

J. R. Alcántara–Avila, M. Kano, S. Hasebe, 2013, New synthesis procedure to find the optimal distillation sequence with internal and external heat integrations, Industrial and Engineering Chemistry Research, 52, 4851–4862.

T. Bisgaard, J. K. Huusom, J. Abildskov, 2013, Dynamic effects of diabatization in distillation columns, Computer Aided Process Engineering, 32, 1015-1020.

D. Chen, X. Yuan, L. Xu, K. T. Yu, 2013, Comparison between different configurations of internally and externally heat-integrated distillation by numerical simulation, Industrial and Engineering Chemistry Research, 52, 5781–5790.

K. Hirata, 2009, Heat integration of distillation column, Chem. Eng. Trans., 18, 39–44.

Ž. Olujić, L. Sun, A. de Rijke, P.J. Jansens, 2006, Conceptual design of an internally heat integrated propylene-propane splitter, Energy, 31, 3083–3096.

J. P. Schmal, H. J. Van Der Kooi, A. De Rijke, Ž. Olujić, P.J. Jansens, 2006, Internal versus external heat integration operational and economic analysis, Chemical Engineering Research and Design, 84, A5, 374–380.

Jiří Jaromír Klemeš, Petar Sabev Varbanov and Peng Yen Liew (Editors)
Proceedings of the 24th European Symposium on Computer Aided Process Engineering – ESCAPE 24
June 15-18, 2014, Budapest, Hungary.

Premises for a combined Exergy and Pinch Optimization within ProSimPlus® simulator

Stéphane Gourmelon[a]*, Raphaële Hetreux[a], Pascal Floquet[a], Philippe Baudet[b], Olivier Baudouin[b]

[a] *Université de Toulouse ; INPT, UPS ; Laboratoire de Génie Chimique; 4 allée Emile Monso, F-31030 Toulouse, France*
[b] *ProSim SA ; Immeuble Stratège A, 51 rue Ampère, F-31670 Labège France*
stephane.gourmelon@ensiacet.fr

Abstract

The recent increase in fossil fuel prices and the more and more stringent environmental regulations have stimulated the search for further improvements. A short term and sustainable solution consists in improving energy efficiency of industrial processes. To tackle this challenge, a combined exergy and Pinch Analysis has been developed for industrial process' optimization. To summarize the presented methodology, the Exergy Analysis firstly aims at making a diagnosis of the existing process by identifying the major inefficiencies; then based upon this diagnosis; the Pinch Analysis enables to give concrete solutions to improve its energy efficiency. Moreover, the strength of this work relies in the implementation of this Exergy Analysis and Pinch Analysis methodologies in the process simulation software ProSimPlus® which provides an efficient support to the engineer.

Keywords: Exergy Analysis, Pinch Technology, Process optimization, Process simulation.

1. Introduction

Industrial sector accounts for one third of global energy consumption. The recent increase in fossil fuel prices and the more and more stringent environmental regulations have stimulated the search for further improvements. A short term and sustainable solution consists in improving energy efficiency of industrial processes. Process Integration may be used to tackle this challenge (Klemeš et al., 2013). Among the several methodologies of process integration, one can find the Pinch Technology and the Exergy Analysis. While the latter (Ghannadzadeh et al., 2012) can be applied to identify thermodynamic imperfections (exergy losses) of a given process and to propose some hints to reduce such losses, Pinch Technology (Klemeš and Kravanja, 2013) aims at improving heat-exchanger network of a process, solely dealing with heat transfers, excluding chemical or pressure changes. To overcome these limitations, it seems appropriate to implement a methodology combining Exergy Analysis and Pinch Technology as shown in the literature (Marmolejo-Correa and Gundersen, 2012).

The purpose of this paper is to present a new general approach for optimizing an industrial process from an exergy point of view as well as an energy efficiency view point. More emphasis is placed on the retrofitting and improvement of existing processes operating under steady-state conditions. The concepts of exergy load, and exergy efficiency are combined to the Pinch methodology. The general procedure for process optimization and improvement is described through a very simple cogeneration case study. This paper is part of the COOPERE ANR project involving several partners (Veolia Environnement Recherche et Innovation, Prosim SA, AgroParisTech' and Laboratoire de Génie Chimique).

2. Methodology

The Computer-aided Exergy and Pinch Analysis (PA) methodology (CEPA) is primarily based on the ProSimplus® environment's ability to make Pinch and exergy calculations. Therefore, the studied process needs first to be modeled and simulated in ProSimPlus®.

2.1. Exergy Analysis

The Exergy Analysis, which has been proved to be an efficient tool for the energy diagnosis of industrial processes, especially relies on the computation of internal losses and exergy efficiencies. The Exergy Analysis first enables to perform an energy diagnosis of the existing process by evaluating several efficiencies representing the thermodynamic performance from different points of view. By offering the possibility to make automatic calculation of exergy of material and heat streams, ProSimPlus® simulation software (ProSim S.A., 2014) facilitates Exergy Analysis of industrial processes (Ghannadzadeh et al., 2012). As a reminder, the amount of exergy destroyed, I, also known as irreversibilities or exergetic internal losses, of a system is obtained by a simple exergy balance – Eq (1) – where B_{in} and B_{out} respectively represent the whole exergy entering and leaving the system.

$$I = B_{in} - B_{out} \tag{1}$$

An in-depth study of exergy based efficiencies has been undertaken. It highlighted that the intrinsic efficiency – Eq (2) - (Sorin et al., 1998) is the general way to compute a significant exergy efficiency.

$$\eta = \frac{Exergy\ produced}{Exergy\ consumed} \tag{2}$$

The intrinsic efficiency must be combined to the exergy load concept in order to compute an exergetic efficiency of a multiple unit operation system – Eq (3).

$$\eta = \sum_{i=1}^{N_{UO}} \left[\lambda_i^p . \eta_i - \lambda_i^{1-p} . (1 - \eta_i) \right] \tag{3}$$

The computation of the intrinsic efficiency η_i, exergy load coefficients λ_i^p and λ_i^{1-p} which rely on a general methodology is beyond the scope of the study, thus the reader is recommended to consult references (Gourmelon et al., 2013). For a given unit operation, it is also possible to define the relative exergy loss as the ratio of exergy loss and exergy consumed – Eq (4).

$$I_{rel} = \frac{Exergy loss}{Exergy\ consumed} \tag{4}$$

All of these coefficients are part of the exergy based tools package used by engineer to make a process energy diagnosis.

2.2. Complementarity between Pinch and Exergy Analysis

The analysis of these thermodynamic criteria permits to suggest modifications aimed at reducing irreversibilities (exergy internal losses) and to maximize the reuse of external losses (waste streams). The decomposition of exergy into thermal, mechanical and chemical terms enables to get a clear vision of the potential of reuse of waste streams. The way of using such waste streams depends on the contribution of each term (T, P, z) in the exergy balance.

As presented in Figure 1, thermal exergy losses should be recovered as hot or cold streams. For chemical exergy losses, some recycling solutions could be considered such as methanisation or combustion. In the case of high mechanical exergy loss, it might be possible to produce power.

Pinch Analysis provides an efficient tool to generate a heat exchanger network in order to maximize the internal heat load reuse. However it is sometimes difficult to decide which heat exchanger, heat pump… represents the best investment for a more efficient energy use in the industrial process. Finally, calculation of the exergetic efficiency and other exergy based coefficients of the different configurations can help the process manager to make a choice between several solutions.

3. Case study description

Air entering the cogeneration system (Figure 2) is compressed up to 25 atm and is sent to the combustion chamber. Natural gas (NG), supplied by stream S03, is burnt to produce hot gases. The latters are expanded down to 1 atm and recycle to produce steam (E101). The power produced by the turbine T101 is partly used to fulfill the needs of the compressor C101. The rest is sent to another system.

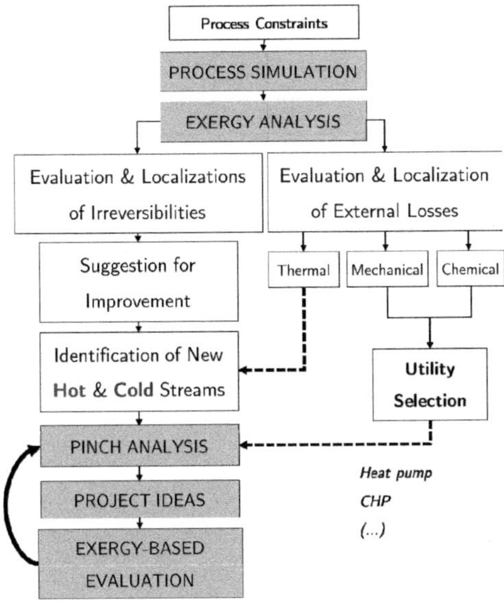

Figure 1. CPEA methodology diagram

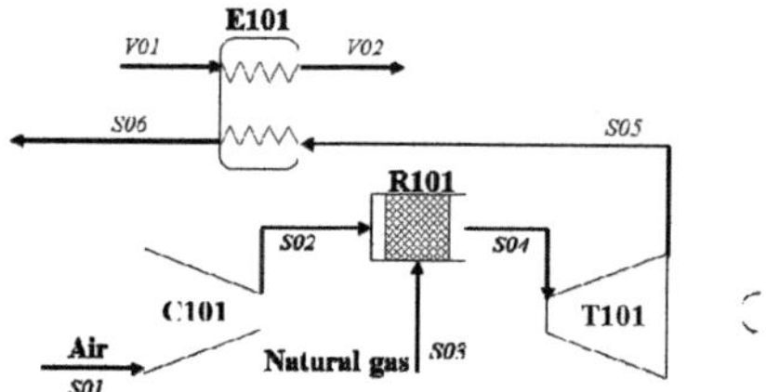

Figure 2. Heat and power cogeneration system

The natural gas and air flowrate are computing according to equation (5). The temperature of steams leaving the evaporator E101 is equal to 773.15 K. Stream S06 is assumed to be a waste stream.

$$F_{Natural\,Gas} = 0.047.F_{Air} \tag{5}$$

4. Heat and power cogeneration system analysis

4.1. Exergy analysis

The first step of the methodology consists of proceeding to an Exergy Analysis of the studied process. Exergy balance is reported in Table 1 and Figure 3 summarizes the results of the exergy analysis by detailing the irreversibility and the exergy efficiency on unit operations. The overall efficiency is 55.22 %.

As shown in Figure 3, even though the exergy destroyed represents about 30 % of the exergy consumed by the combustion chamber, chemical reaction is the most significant source of exergy destruction in the cogeneration system. As noticed by Cziesla et al. (Cziesla et al., 2006), the thermodynamic inefficiencies may be reduced by preheating

Table 1: Exergy balance of the cogeneration system

Streams	S01	S02	S03	S04	S05	S06	V01	V02
Temperature (K)	298.15	797.17	298.15	1762	915.03	520.71	298.15	773.15
Pressure (atm)	1	25	25	24.5	1	1	15	15
Total exergy (MW)	0.40	74.06	202.86	224.09	53.32	13.53	1.06	26.92
Physical exergy (MW)	0.00	73.66	1.90	220.99	50.22	10.43	0.03	25.89
Thermal exergy (MW)	0.00	32.69	0.00	182.13	50.22	10.43	0.00	25.86
Mechanical exergy (MW)	0.00	40.96	1.90	38.86	0.00	0.00	0.03	0.03
Chemical exergy (MW)	0.40	0.40	200.96	3.10	3.10	3.10	1.03	1.03

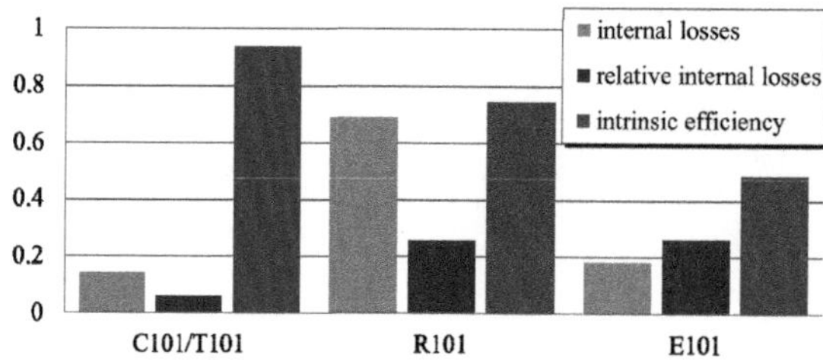

Figure 3. Exergy efficiencies and internal losses on unit operations

the air or increasing the fuel/air ratio. Consequently, a heat exchanger dedicated to the preheating of air should be introduced in the flowsheet after the compressor. The maximum input temperature is set at 947 K in order to keep the output temperature below 1,900 K.

As the stream S06 is a waste stream, and despite the low relative internal losses, the exergy efficiency of the heat exchanger E101 is very low. In fact, the formulation of intrinsic efficiency allows taking into account the difference between waste and utilized streams. When analysing the values of the three components of exergy of the stream S06, it would be interesting to reuse the thermal exergy rather than reject it to the environment.

4.2. Pinch analysis

The new process flowsheet with the air preheater, the updated fuel/air ratio and the cooling down of the stream S06 to the ambient temperature is modeled using ProSimPlus®.Then, applying the automatic Pinch calculation, the process Composite Curve and the Grand Composite Curve are drawn in Figure 4. As illustrated in Figure 4, the S05 hot stream leaving the T101 turbine is sufficient to meet the global hot utility requirement of the cogeneration system. It can be concluded from the design of the new heat exchanger network that a preheater has to be placed before the E101 heat exchanger in the S05 stream flow.

4.3. Retrofitted process

The retrofitted cogeneration system, represented in Figure 5, has been simulated in ProSimPlus® modeling and simulation software.

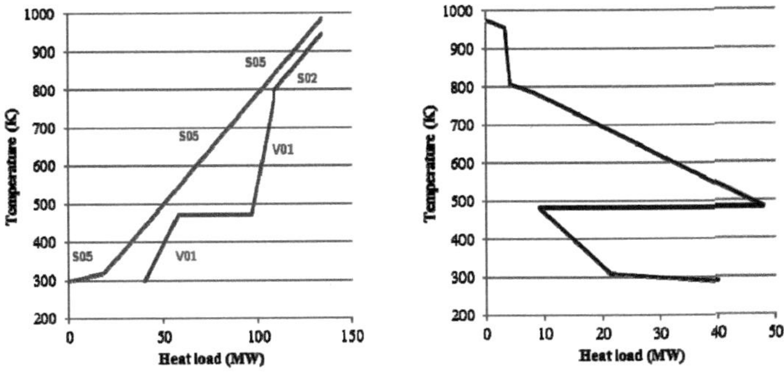

Figure 4. (a) Composite curve and (b) grand composite curve of the cogeneration system

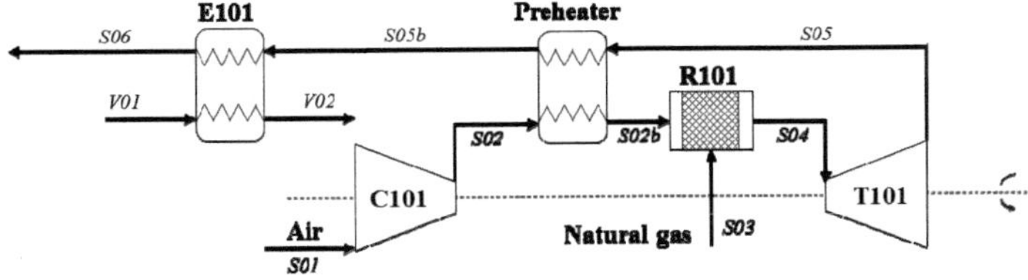

Figure 5. Retrofitted cogeneration system

Table 2: Base case vs. Retrofitted case

	Base case process	Retrofitted process
Generated Power (MW)	86.39	98.20
Overall exergy efficiency (%)	55.22	61.03
Overall internal losses (MW)	76.42	69.23
Overall relative internal losses (%)	37.60	34.06
External losses (MW)	13.53	8.90

Table 2 compares the performances of the retrofitted process with the base case cogeneration system. The increase of generated power and the decrease of irreversibilities are obvious. In addition, exergy efficiency is increased as external is reduced by recycling the thermal exergy loss.

5. Conclusions

This paper presents a general methodology for computer-aided process improvement tool combining the Pinch Technology and the Exergy Analysis. The Exergy Analysis first enables to make a diagnosis of a process proposing then solutions to recover external losses or to reduce internal losses. Here, with the cogeneration system, we have illustrated the case of thermal losses. In such a case the concerned streams become hot or cold streams for the Pinch Analysis. A more in-depth study could have been done to determine the best input temperature and air/fuel ratio of the combustion chamber. Then starting from cold and hot streams, power sinks and sources deduced from a previous Exergy Analysis, the Pinch methodology proposes different solutions to optimize both process and utility. The next step is to extend the scope of this methodology to industrial scale processes.

Acknowledgement

Financial support of the French National Agency (ANR) is gratefully acknowledged.

References

F. Cziesla, G. Tsatsaronis, Z. Gao, 2006, Avoidable thermodynamic inefficiencies and costs in an externally fired combined cycle power plant, Energy, 31, 1472–1489.

A. Ghannadzadeh, R. Thery-Hetreux, O. Baudouin, P. Baudet, P. Floquet, X. Joulia, 2012, General methodology for exergy balance in ProSimPlus® process simulator, Energy, 44, 38–59.

S. Gourmelon, R. Hetreux, P. Floquet, P. Baudet, O. Baudouin, 2013, General procedure for the computing of exergy efficiency□: a first step of a complete exergy analysis methodology within ProSimPlus process imulation software, Presented at the SFGP, Ed. SFGP, Lyon.

J.J. Klemeš, Z. Kravanja, 2013, Forty years of Heat Integration: Pinch Analysis (PA) and Mathematical Programming (MP), Current Opinion in Chemical Engineering, 2, 461–474.

J.J. Klemeš, P.S. Varbanov, Z. Kravanja, 2013, Recent developments in Process Integration, Chemical Engineering Research and Design, 91, 2037–2053.

D. Marmolejo-Correa, T. Gundersen, 2012, A new procedure for the design of LNG processes by combining Exergy and Pinch Analyses, Proceedings of ECOS, 24-39, Perugia, Italy.

ProSim S.A., 2014, Software and services in Process Simulation, <www.prosim.net> accessed on 28/01/2014.

M. Sorin, J. Lambert, J. Paris, 1998, Exergy Flows Analysis in Chemical Reactors, Chemical Engineering Research and Design, 76, 389–395.

Jiří Jaromír Klemeš, Petar Sabev Varbanov and Peng Yen Liew (Editors)
Proceedings of the 24th European Symposium on Computer Aided Process Engineering – ESCAPE 24
June 15-18, 2014, Budapest, Hungary.

Integrating the Concept of Bio-Refinery onto the Biogas Field: the BIOREFILL Strategy

Flavio Manenti,[a,]* Fabrizio Adani[b,c]

[a]*Politecnico di Milano, Dipartimento di Chimica, Materiali e Ingegneria Chimica "Giulio Natta", Piazza Leonardo da Vinci 32, 20133 Milano, Italy*
[b]*Università degli Studi di Milano, DISAA, Gruppo Ricicla, Lab. Agricoltura e Ambiente, Via Celoria 2, 20133 Milano, Italy*
[c]*Parco Tecnologico Padano, Lab. Biomasse e Agroenergia, Cascina Codazza, Via Einstein, 26900 Lodi, Italy*
flavio.manenti@polimi.it

Abstract

The paper illustrates the redefinition of the concept of biorefinery and its application onto the biogas field, which is the topic of BIOREFILL, a project funded by Lombardy Region and Fondazione CARIPLO. The layout of the biorefinery is given and compared to the state-of-the-art of biorefineries and biogas plants. The specific focus on the optimal conversion of biomass to syngas and the improvement of carbon conversion ratio using one-step technologies for methanol and dimethylether synthesis is discussed in detailed.

Keywords: biorefinery; biogas; biomethane; biomethanol; carbon conversion.

1. Introduction

The energy field is one of the main authors involved in the developing of sustainability in the European Community and abroad, because of its relationship with both environmental and economic development issues as well as because it constitutes a core business in providing the solution for the different economic sectors requirements (Pirola et al., 2010b). The BIOREFILL (BIO-REFinery Integrated Lombardy Labs) project represents an operative strategy to recover energy and molecules from non-food-competing vegetables and from lignocellulosic residues of second generation biomass, a current requirement that has to quickly come true in Lombardy Region, where about 400 biogas plants are counted in 2013 with one third of the entire Italian bioenergy production in terms of forest residues and wastes conversion, leading to technological advances for the incoming European challenges of Horizon 2020 (European Commission, 2011) and Energy RoadMap 2030 and 2050. In the last few years, biogas has been appeared as the main biofuel to sustain the growth of the bioenergy field due to its more mature technology, which could provide directly industrial applications, respect to the other biotechnologies that need more research activity in order to be industrially attractive. In this context, the general aim of the paper is to broach the concept of bio-refinery onto the biogas framework as schematically reported in Figure 1. The key point is the generation of different commodities in order to exploit at best the biomass potential as well as to couple the existing technologies of second and third generation resulting in the reduction of the environmental impact and in the significant lowering of production costs (Boffito et al., 2013a;b). In particular, Arundo Donax and lignocellulosic wastes will be used as feedstock for conversion processes, as they allow reducing feedstock cost to about 1/3 partially resolving the food vs. no-food crop conflict. In order to achieve the economic sustainability, the main bioenergy production chain will be supported by the development of parallel sub-processes able to convert efficiently the bioenergy wastes/by-products into valuable products, resulting in the greed parity of the integrated biorefinery. The specific aim of the paper is to show the conversion of the solid lignocellulosic residues first into biosyngas and next into biomethanol and biodimethylether (bio-MeOH, bio-DME) as fuels and energy carriers with high carbon conversion ratio. Section 2 briefly describes the state of art for the biogas field with focus on the Lombardy region; section 3 shows the CAPE advances to achieve to optimal conversion of lignocellulosic residues to syngas; section 4 describes the improvement in bio-MeOH/bio-DME synthesis.

2. State of the art – Biogas

Biogas is nowadays a well-developed sector in Lombardy Region that count for 363 biogas agricultural, i.e. 268 MW installed. Biogas has strongly developed in rural area in the last 6 years on the wave of the government incentive, i.e. 0.28 c€/kW produced; nevertheless other drivers played a role in the diffusion of biogas in agriculture. In the Lombardy Region exist about 1.5 x 10^6 cows, 4.5 x 10^6 pigs and 18 x 10^6 poultries, producing manure/slurry that represent a problem for their use and disposal, because of nitrate directive that limited the use of slurry on land. Moreover emissions from animals (GHGs and NH_3) have to be controlled because of their great contribution to air and water pollution. Therefore the necessity to manage animal slurries pushed both farmer and regional policymakers to adopt biogas to both transform slurry in valuable fertilizers and remove surplus N (Ledda et al., 2013). The large use of animal biomasses led to a sustainable develop of biogas in Lombardy that is characterized by the absence of competition between food crop and energy crop, differently by other countries (e.g., Germany) (Britz and Delzeit, 2013). In a recent survey, Adani et al. (2013) described the average diet of biogas plant (w/w) that was composed by 49 % of animal slurry, 31 % of crop energy (maize + winter crops) and 20 % of agro-industrial wastes. This diet led to a total crop energy surface used of about 35,000 Ha, which is less than 4 % of the total available agricultural area of the region (about 900,000 Ha). In the future the

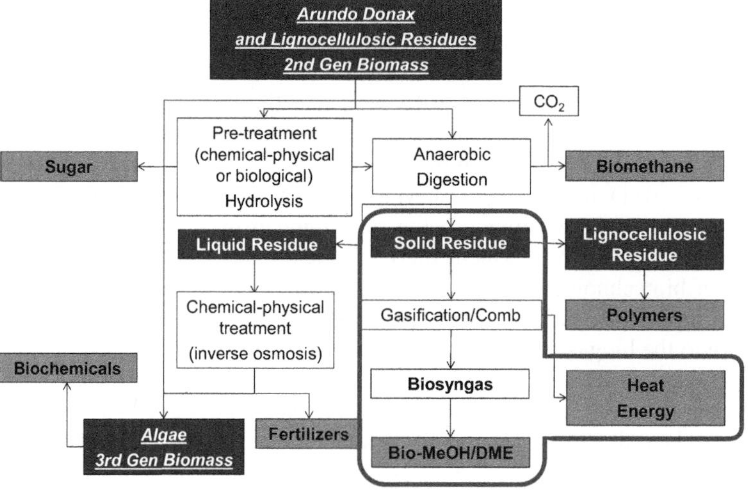

Figure 1. Concept of effective energy-sustainable bio-refinery (red circle: paper focus).

introduction of high productive no-food energy crop, i.e. Arundo donax, and the recovery of lignocellulose wastes will allow to improve biogas sustainability reducing land surface used in a new biorefinery context.

3. Optimal conversion of solid lignocellulosic residues

According to the picture above, there is a strong interest in tools to characterize the chemical-physical phenomena that govern the transformation process from biomasses to added-value commodities for design purposes and plant operations as well. Some transformations such as the devolatilization, thermal degradation, and pyrolysis of the main components of the biomass are carried out at high temperatures. Thus, the well-established methodology to model traditional processes based on detailed kinetic schemes (Manenti et al., 2013) could be successfully adopted also in the case of bioprocesses. Four steps are needed: (1) reliable characterization of biomasses; (2) development of ad hoc detailed multi-step kinetic schemes, (3) implementation of the schemes into a multi-phase and multi-scale reactor model; and (4) solution of complex and large-scale systems.

3.1. Biomass characterization

For general characterization, biomass can be modelled by considering its three main components: cellulose, hemicellulose, and lignin. The left-hand side of Figure 1 shows some biomasses within such a ternary plot. The easiest way to do so is to adopt a van Krevelen-like plot (right-hand side of Figure 1), where the biomasses are classified according to their content in hydrogen and carbon, and define some reference compounds (for more details, please refer to Ranzi et al., 2013).

3.2. Kinetic scheme

A lumped multis-tep kinetic scheme for biomass pyrolysis with 26 reactions (including 3 reactions for bio-char gasification/combustion) and related kinetic parameters was already proposed in the literature (Ranzi et al., 2013) and adopted in the present study.

3.3. Reactor model

The GASDS tool (GASDS, 2014) has been developed to solve different configurations of biomass gasifiers/combustors. It is based on dynamic mass and energy balances and it consider the gas-solid multi-phase nature of systems as well as the different scales of interest (biomass particle scale, biomass layer scale, biomass stack scale, and overall process scale). Both the gas and solid reactions are considered.

3.4. Numerical tools

The aforementioned multi-phase and multi-scale structure leads to large-scale, highly-

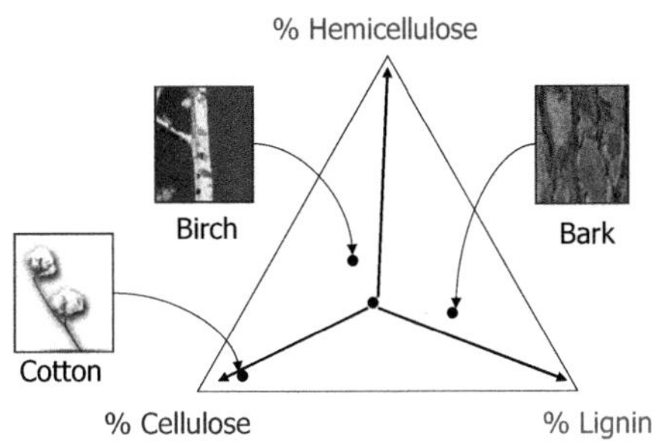

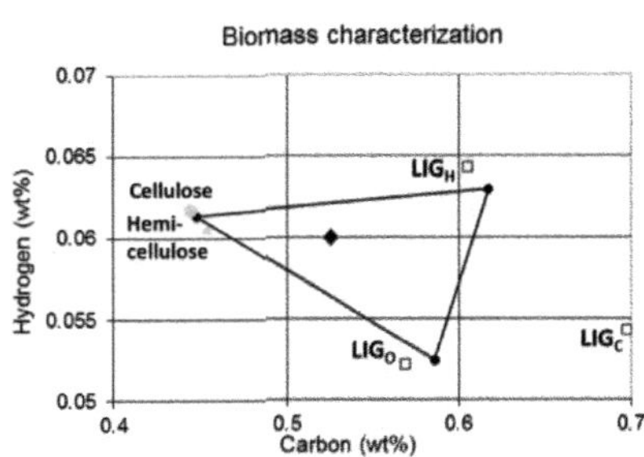

Figure 2. Main elements of biomass (left-hand side); van Krevelen-like diagram for biomass characterization (right-hand side).

sparse, partially-structured systems which need dedicated numerical solvers to be efficiently and accurately integrated. Parallel algorithms for differential and algebraic systems belonging to BzzMath are adopted (Buzzi-Ferraris and Manenti, 2012).

3.5. Optimal conversion

Thanks to the combination of the tools above, it is possible to design processes for the optimal conversion biomass as well as to operate them preserving this optimal conversion also during the common operations, which are subject to strong variability of the feedstock composition and load. In the specific case of this work, it is possible to select the best H_2/CO ratio of bio-syngas to favour the conversion to bio-MeOH/DME.

4. Improvements in bio-MeOH/bio-DME synthesis

Syngas is the basis for the production of key chemical and industrial compounds such as ammonia and methanol but also of fuels by means of gas-to-liquid (biomass-to-liquid) technology (Pirola et al., 2010b). The BIOREFILL target is to transform the syngas obtained from biomass treatment into bio-MeOH/DME, both considered as major energy carriers (Olah et al., 2009). The methanol synthesis is usually carried out using two successive fixed-bed tubular reactors (Mayra and Leiviska, 2009): water-cooled and gas-cooled reactor (see left-hand side of Figure 3). The syngas is fed to the shell side of gas-cooled reactor, where it is pre-heated by the hot process stream flowing in the fixed-bed tube bundle. The pre-heated syngas is then fed to the catalytic bed of the tube side of water-cooled reactor for methanol conversion. The methanol synthesis is particularly exothermic and the shell side is filled of boiling water to preserve the desired operating conditions of the water-cooled reactor. Phenomena occurring within in the first part of water-cooled reactor are kinetic limited, whereas the thermodynamic equilibrium is usually achieved after 1-2 m along the longitudinal axis. The outflow of water-cooled reactor is fed to the tube side of gas-cooled reactor where the methanol synthesis continues. The outflow of gas-cooled reactor is sent to the downstream process where methanol is recovered and unreacted syngas is recycled back except for a purge to remove incondensable by-products. Methanol is produced from three main reactions:

$$CO + 2H_2 \leftrightarrow CH_3OH \tag{1}$$

$$CO_2 + H_2 \leftrightarrow CO + H_2O \tag{2}$$

$$CO_2 + 3H_2 \leftrightarrow CH_3OH + H_2O \tag{3}$$

Exothermic reactions (1) and (3) are favoured at low temperature despite the reaction rate; moreover, it is necessary to operate at high pressure (i.e. 80 bar) to improve the equilibrium conversion. Typically, the synthesis of methanol is conducted over commercial $Cu/ZnO/Al_2O_3$. Since catalyst deactivation occurs at temperatures above the 550 K, the operating range of temperature is 484 K to 540 K. Typical feed composition is: $CO = 0.046$; $CO_2 = 0.094$; $H_2 = 0.659$; $H_2O = 0.0004$; $CH_3OH = 0.005$; $N_2 = 0.093$; $CH_4 = 0.1026$. It is worth underlining that the following relevant side reactions are inhibited by the high selectivity of modern catalysts:

$$CO + 3H_2 \leftrightarrow CH_4 + H_2O \text{ (methanation reaction)} \tag{4}$$

$$nCO + 2nH_2 \leftrightarrow [CH_2]_n + nH_2O \tag{5}$$

$$2CH_3OH \leftrightarrow CH_3OCH_3 + H_2O \text{ (synthesis of DME)} \tag{6}$$

Contrarily to traditional processes that transform fossil sources (i.e. natural gas) into syngas and, thereafter, syngas into methanol, the reaction (6) assumes relevant interest, in the case of bio-source as feedstock. Actually, although the DME has a less appealing market price with respect to methanol, it has a very high carbon conversion, stated as:

$$\text{Carbon Conversion} = 1 - \left(F_{CO} + F_{CO_2}\right)_{out} / \left(F_{CO} + F_{CO_2}\right)_{in} \tag{7}$$

Thus, the so-called one-step technologies are very promising in the case of biomass-to-DME, but the current best practice for MeOH/DME synthesis must be deeply redefined. The systematic staging design defined by Hillestad (2010) has been adopted to assess the existing reactor network for MeOH/DME synthesis and revise it according to the above peculiarities related to the use of bio-sources. The models adopted for the optimization of the reactor network are already discussed elsewhere (Manenti et al., 2013). The objective function for systematic staging optimization is stated as follows:

$$\max_{\substack{water/gas-cooled\ reactor\ ratio\\ water-cooled\ shell\ temperature\\ inlet\ molar\ feed\ flow}} \quad y_{MeOH} + F_{steam}\left(+y_{DME} + Carbon\ Conv.\right)_{\substack{only\ if\ DME\\ is\ considered}} \tag{8}$$

$$s.t.: model\ equations\ for\ MeOH\ (and\ DME)\ synthesis$$

The application of the systematic staging design leads to the results of Table 1 and Figure 3. Net additional income of about 2M€/y and significantly improved carbon conversion are both expected from the novel configuration of the one-step technology for the conversion of bio-syngas into bioMeOH/DME.

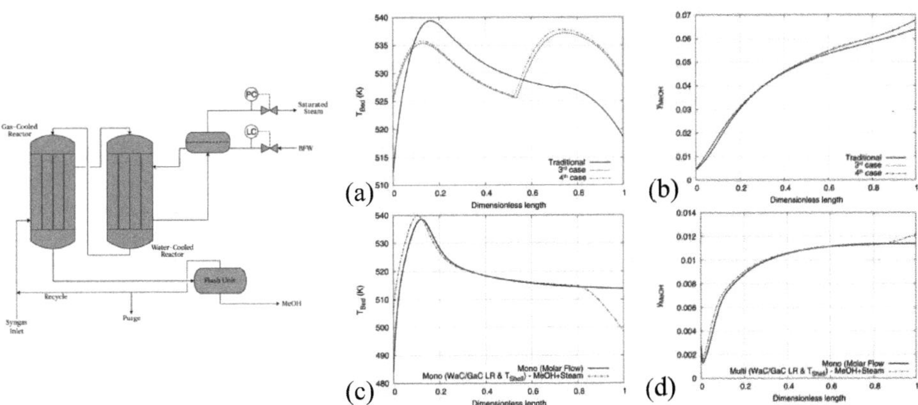

Figure 3. Reactor network for MeOH/DME synthesis (left-hand side); improved yield with revised network (left-hand side): a) (MeOH case) temperature profile, b) (MeOH case) MeOH molar fract., c) (MeOH/DME case) temperature profile, d) (MeOH/DME case) MeOH molar fract..

Table 1. Techno-economic comparison of traditional and proposed processes for bio-MeOH/DME synthesis.

	Units	MeOH	New MeOH	MeOH/DME	New MeOH/DME
Length ratio	-	0.7/0.3	0.53/0.47	1.0/0.0	0.78/0.22
Shell side temp.	K	524	520	513	513.4
Carbon conversion	-	0.2149	0.2977	0.5038	0.5087
MeOH mole fract.	-	0.063922	0.06782	0.011388	0.012150
DME mole fract.	-	-	-	0.069311	0.069612
Steam produced	GJ/y	190,295	193,736	207,021	212,312
Total revenue	€/y	45,844,440	47,580,869	34,701,633	35,014,810

5. Conclusions

A novel concept of integrated biorefinery is going to be developed at the laboratory scale and adopted for the biogas field. The paper has broached the general overview of this concept of biorefinery. Moreover, advances dealing with conversion of solid lignocellulosic residues to bio-methanol and bio-dimethylether, which is one of the targets of the biorefinery, have been reported highlighting the differences with traditional processes fed by fossil sources.

Acknowledgments

The authors gratefully acknowledge the partners of the BIOREFILL project Actygea Srl, Bict Srl, Lombardatrading Srl, National Research Council (CNR-ICRM), Parco Tecnologico Padano, Resindion Srl, The Enzyme Factory, Università degli Studi dell'Insubria, Università degli Studi di Milano Bicocca as well as Biochemtex - Mossi&Ghisolfi SpA and Industria e Innovazione SpA for their endorsements. Authors are grateful for the funding supplied by Fondazione CARIPLO and for the selection of the project by Lombardy's Green Chemistry cluster.

References

F. Adani, A. Manca, T. Guarneri, 2013, La digestione anaerobic nel contesto agriolo lombrado. Università degli Studi di Milano, Milano, Italy.

W. Britz, R. Delzeit, 2013, The impact of German biogas production on European and global agricultural markets, land use and the environment, Energy Policy, 62, 1268–1275.

D.C. Boffito, C. Pirola, F. Galli, A. Di Michele, C.L. Bianchi, 2013a, Free Fatty Acids esterification of waster cooking oil and its mixtures with Rapeseed oil and diesel, Fuel, 108, 612-619.

D.C. Boffito, V. Crocella, C. Pirola, B. Neppolian, G. Cerrato, M. Ashokkumar, C. L. Bianchi, 2013b, Ultrasonic enhancement of the acidity, surface area and free fatty acids esterification catalytic activity of sulphated ZrO2-TiO2 systems, Journal of Catalysis, 297, 17-26.

G. Buzzi-Ferraris, F. Manenti, 2012, BzzMath: Library Overview and Recent Advances in Numerical Methods, Computer Aided Chemical Engineering, 30, 2, 1312-1316.

European Commission, COM/2011/0808 Horizon 2020 - The Framework Programme for Research and Innovation - Communication from the Commission, 2011.

GASDS, 2014, <www.super.chem.polimi.it> , accessed on 18/01/2014.

F. Manenti, S. Cieri, M. Restelli, G. Bozzano, 2013, Dynamic Modelling of the Methanol Synthesis Fixed-Bed Reactor, Computers and Chemical Engineering, 48, 325-334.

F. Manenti, D. Papasidero, A. Frassoldati, G. Bozzano, S. Pierucci, E. Ranzi, 2013, Multi-scale modeling of Claus thermal furnace and boiler using detailed kinetics and reactor network. Computers and Chemical Engineering, 59, 219-225.

O. Mayra, K. Leiviska, 2009, Modelling in methanol synthesis, Chem Eng Trans, 17, 1413-1418.

C. Ledda, A. Schievano, S. Salati, F. Adani, 2013, Nitrogen and water recovery from animal slurries by a new integrated ultrafiltration, reverse osmosis and cold stripping process: A case study, Water Research, 47, 6157-6166.

C. Pirola, C. L. Bianchi, D. C. Boffito, G. Carvoli, V. Ragaini, 2010a, Vegetable oils de-acidification by Amberlyst: study of catalyst lifetime and a suitable reactor configuration, Industrial and Engineering Chemistry Research, 49, 10, 4601-4606.

C. Pirola, C. L. Bianchi, A. Di Michele, P. Diodati, D. C. Boffito, V. Ragaini, 2010b, Ultrasound and microwave assisted synthesis of high loading Fe-supported Fischer Tropsch catalysts, Ultrasonic Sonochemistry, 17, 610-616.

G.A. Olah, A. Goeppert, G. K. Surya Prakash, 2009, Beyond Oil and Gas: The Methanol Economy, Wiley-VCH, Weinheim, Germany.

E. Ranzi, M. Corbetta, F. Manenti, S. Pierucci, 2013, Kinetic modeling of the thermal degradation and combustion of biomass, Chemical Engineering Science, DOI: 10.1016/j.ces.2013.08.014.

Jiří Jaromír Klemeš, Petar Sabev Varbanov and Peng Yen Liew (Editors)
Proceedings of the 24th European Symposium on Computer Aided Process Engineering – ESCAPE 24
June 15-18, 2014, Budapest, Hungary.

Sustainable Integration of Heat Exchanger Networks and Utility Systems

Luis Fernando Lira-Barragán,[a] José María Ponce-Ortega, [a]* Medardo Serna-González, [a] Mahmoud M. El-Halwagi[b]

[a]*Chemical Engineering Department, Universidad Michoacana de Sán Nicolás de Hidalgo, Morelia, Michoacán, 58060, México*
[b]*Chemical Engineering Department, Texas A&M University, College Station, TX, 77843, USA*
jmponce@umich.mx

Abstract

This work deals with the problem of synthesizing sustainable trigeneration systems (i.e. heating, cooling and power generation cycles) integrated with heat exchanger networks accounting simultaneously for economic, environmental and social issues. The trigeneration system is comprised of steam and organic Rankine cycles and an absorption refrigeration cycle. Multiple sustainable energy sources such as solar energy, biofuels and fossil fuels are considered to drive the steam Rankine cycle. The model is aimed to select the optimal working fluid to operate the organic Rankine cycle and to determine the optimal system to drive the absorption refrigeration cycle. The residual energy available in the steam Rankine cycle and/or the process excess heat can be employed to run both the organic Rankine cycle and the absorption refrigeration cycle to produce electricity and refrigeration below the ambient temperature, respectively.

Keywords: Sustainability, trigeneration, renewable energies, multi-objective optimization.

1. Introduction

Nowadays energy is one of the most important resources and at the same time one of the most relevant concerns around the world owing to fast depletion of non-renewable fuels, the global warming and the climate change. For these reasons, several governments have promoted the use of cleaner energies through tax credits and there have invested significant economic resources to searching for alternative energies to mitigate the environmental issues. In this sense, power plants and industry consumes an enormous amount of fossil fuels to satisfy the electricity and utilities demands. Several methodologies have been reported to minimize the external utilities for the heat exchanger networks (HEN). This way, Morar and Agachí (2010) carried out an extensive review of the most important contributions for synthesizing HEN. Additionally, other methodologies minimize the energy requirements for the industry; in this sense, Klemeš et al. (2013) reported an overview of recent achievements in process integration and Alwi et al. (2012) introduced a numerical algorithm to address the total site heat integration involving variable supply and demand. Nonetheless, previous approaches have considered the energy interactions among utility systems and the HEN.

On the other hand, power plants involve very inefficient processes and a considerable amount of energy is wasted through the condenser without reusing this residual heat;

however, it can be reused for other subsystems that provide external utilities to the HEN (i.e. hot and cold utilities and refrigeration) as well as to produce electricity in an organic Rankine cycle (ORC). In this context, the objective of this paper is to present a mathematical programming formulation for the simultaneous synthesis of sustainable trigeneration systems and heat exchangers networks, where the optimal working fluid to operate the ORC is determined as well as the optimal system to run an absorption refrigeration (AR) cycle, considering the energy connections among the different accounted subsystems. The problem takes into account a set of hot process streams (HPS) and a set of cold process streams (CPS), as well as three thermodynamic cycles: single-effect AR to supply below ambient cooling, a steam Rankine cycle (SRC) and an ORC to produce electricity. The proposed mathematical model is based on a superstructure that includes all feasible heat integration options and connections between the system components (to obtain the proposed configuration an analysis of all the feasible energy interactions among the subsystems has been carried out). The synthesis problem is formulated as a multi-objective mixed integer nonlinear programming problem with economic, environmental and social concerns of sustainability. The environmental objective is evaluated by the overall greenhouse gas emissions (GHGE), and the social objective is quantified by the number of jobs generated. The multi-objective optimization model is solved with the constraint method. The optimal solutions lead to the Pareto set for the problem that shows the tradeoffs between the total annual profit, the GHGE and the number of generated jobs in the entire life cycle of the integrated energy system. Figure 1 shows the general scheme for the problem considered by this work; where, the primary energy sources only are provided to the SRC, which produces electricity and low pressure steam (LPS). This steam is divided to be supplied to the evaporator that belongs to the ORC, as well as it can be provided to the AR cycle to satisfy the refrigeration demands of HPS in the HEN and finally it can be reused as hot utility in the HEN. Additionally, the HPS inside the HEN can transfer their excess heat to the AR cycle and to the ORC. Finally, it is also allowed (if the temperatures permit it) the heat exchange among the ORC and the CPS.

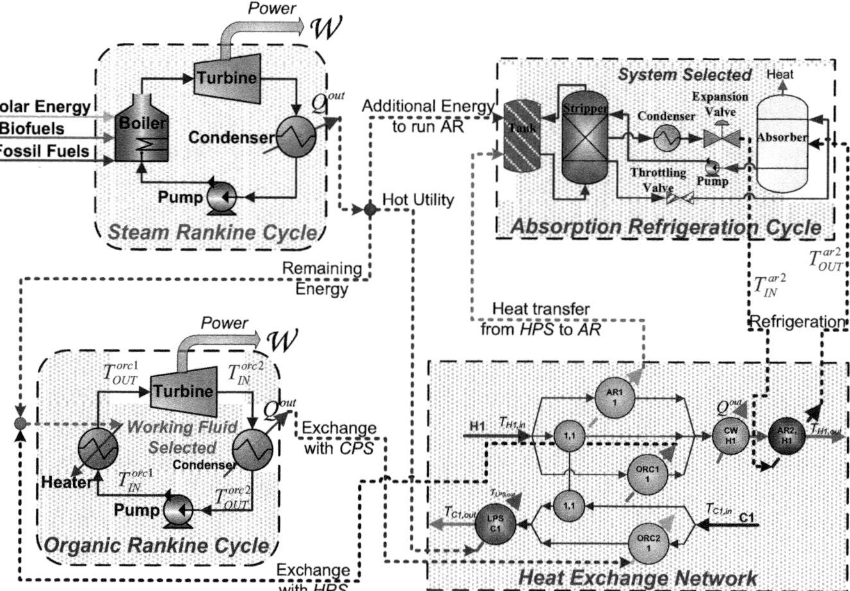

Figure 1. Schematic representation of the proposed integrated system

2. Model formulation

The proposed approach contains the mathematical formulation to model all the heat exchanger units shown in Figure 2, a couple of disjunctive models for the selection of the working fluid in the ORC and the optimal system to run the AR cycle; in addition, the mathematical programming model for the thermodynamic cycles (SRC, ORC and AR) and their interactions are considered, the solar collector model to determine its optimal size (if it is required) and the restrictions for maximum availabilities of biofuels and fossil fuels. Finally, the objective functions considered in this work are described.

2.1. Model for the heat exchanger network.

The proposed superstructure (shown in Figure 2) considers the heat exchange for any match in each stage between HPS and CPS, as well as the heat transfer from HPS to the AR cycle (AR1 units) and the ORC (ORC1 units). The HPS can satisfy their cooling demands using cooling water (CW) and, when they require refrigeration below room temperature, heat transfer units located at the cold-end (AR2 units) of the superstructure can carry out this task. On the other hand, CPS have the possibility of heat exchange with the ORC (ORC2 units) and HPS in any stage of the superstructure; finally, CPS can complete their heating using steam from the SRC (LPS units). The required equations to model the heat exchanger network must be included in the mathematical formulation.

2.2. Optimal selection of working fluids.

This work considers the selection of the working fluid to operate the ORC as well as the model determines the optimal system to run the AR cycle. It is important to remark that in each optimal solution it is determined if the ORC is required or not; whereas the AR cycle is always needed because of the proposed methodology considers the existence of cooling requirements. All mentioned constraints must be added to the formulation.

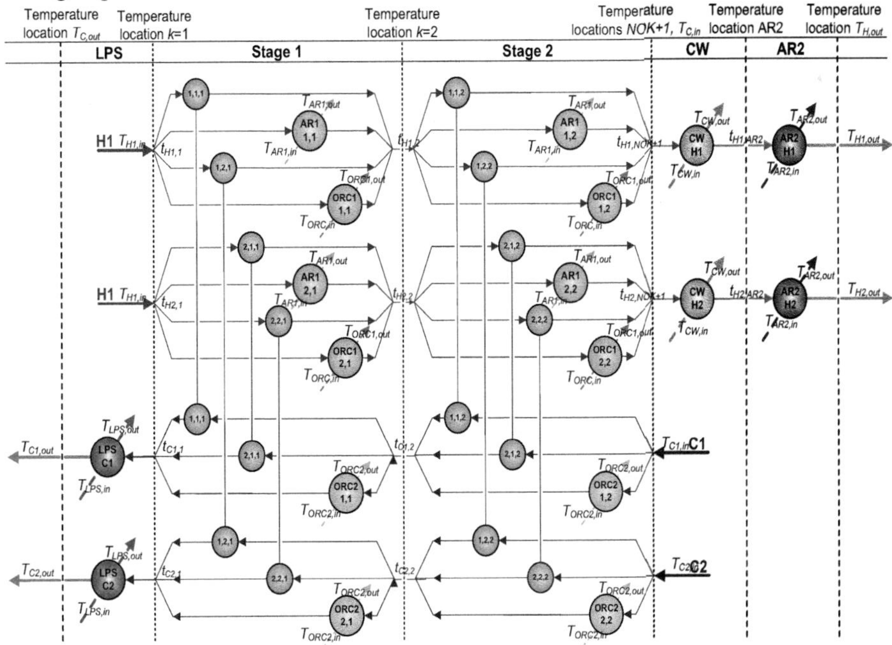

Figure 2. Proposed superstructure for energy integration.

2.3. Thermodynamic cycles and their interactions.

To model the operation of the AR cycle, it is considered a coefficient of performance (COP); whereas the modelling for thermodynamic cycles is carried out through efficiency factors. Additionally, it must be established that the available heat in the condenser in the SRC (residual energy) can be taken to be used in the ORC, AR cycle and in the HEN (as hot utility). These relationships are included in the methodology.

2.4. Optimal size for solar collector and maximum availability of biofuels.

The proposed formulation considers external energy sources to provide the external energy requirements such as the solar collector, biofuels and fossil fuels. In this sense, the solar collector can exist or not in the optimal solution (owing to it represents the most expensive energy source); then, if the solar collector is required, it must determine its optimal area. Furthermore, an important limitation that must be considered in the use of biofuels is the variation for their production during the year.

2.5. Objective functions.

The proposed problem is a multi-objective MINLP problem that simultaneously considers economic, environmental and social issues (which are important criteria included in the sustainability), which are stated as follows.

Economic objective function. The economic objective function consists in maximizing the profit associated to the project, which is composed by the sum of selling of power (*SP*), tax credits reduction (*TCR*) minus the capital costs (*CaC*), fixed costs (*FiC*), operational costs (*OC*) and the energy sources costs (*ESC*). This is stated as follows,

$$Max\ Profit = SP + TCR - CaC - FiC - OC - ESC \tag{1}$$

It should be noted that depending on the values for the revenues and costs, for some cases the profit can be positive, while for other cases it can have a negative value.

Environmental objective function. The environmental impact assessment is carried out through the overall quantification of the GHGE ($NGHGE^{Overall}$) because of fossil fuels and biofuels release carbon dioxide when they are burned,

$$Min\ NGHGE^{Overall} = \sum_{t \in T} \sum_{f \in B} \left[GHGE_f^{Fossil} Q_{f,t}^{Fossil} D_t \right] + \sum_{t \in T} \sum_{b \in B} \left[GHGE_b^{Biofuel} Q_{b,t}^{Biofuel} D_t \right] \tag{2}$$

Notice that the individual GHGE are determined through the life cycle analysis.

Social objective function. The social objective function consists in maximizing the number of jobs created by the project ($NJOBS^{Overall}$) for the production of fossil fuels, biofuels and for the operation of the solar collector. To quantify the number of jobs created it is employed the JEDI (jobs and economic development impact) model (see Bamufleh et al., 2013),

$$\begin{aligned} Max\ NJOBS^{Overall} = & \sum_{t \in T} \sum_{f \in B} \left[NJOB_f^{Fossil} Q_{f,t}^{Fossil} D_t \right] + \sum_{t \in T} \sum_{b \in B} \left[NJOB_b^{Biofuel} Q_{b,t}^{Biofuel} D_t \right] \\ & + \sum_{t \in T} \left[NJOB^{Solar} Q_t^{Solar} D_t \right] \end{aligned} \tag{3}$$

The main contribution and the novelty of the proposed mathematical approach are the energy integration of all systems considered, as well as the optimal selection of the working fluids. These depend strongly on the operational temperatures.

3. Results and discussion.

The applicability of the proposed methodology is shown through an example.

3.1. Case study.

A new industrial plant will be located at Morelia, México. This complex requires external utilities such as electricity, hot and cold utilities and refrigeration (see Table 1). The fluids available to operate the ORC are R123, R245fa and Isobutane with efficiency factors equal to 0.169, 0.163 and 0.145, respectively; however between more efficient is the fluid, the turbine inlet temperature is higher (this represents an inconvenient to take advantage of the heat available in the HPS). The efficiency factor for the SRC is 0.33 and the maximum power production is 3.2 MW. Also, Vélez et al. (2012) reported that the maximum production for ORC is 2 MW.

Once the methodology is applied to this example, it obtains the solutions shown in Figure 3. As can be seen, there are two Pareto curves; one corresponding to the optimal solutions when the power generation is equal or lower than 3.2 MW (continuous line), and the dashed line illustrates the best solutions when the power production is strictly equal to 3.2 MW. It should be noted that each optimal point shows the number of jobs created by the project and the fluid selected to run the ORC; thus the number 1 represents the selection of R123, number 2 for R245fa, number 3 for Isobutene and when appears an N means that the ORC does not exist in the solution. In this sense, the fluid 1 (R123) does not appear in the solutions of the continuous line. This is explained as follows; for some cases is more useful to have a turbine inlet temperature relatively low (allowing the heat exchange between HPS and the ORC) than a higher efficiency for the ORC. For all the solutions, the chosen system to run the AR is H_2O-LiBr.

Table 1. Streams data for the example considered.

Stream	Inlet temperature [K]	Outlet temperature [K]	*FCp* [kW/K]
H1	368	288	33.15
H2	483	358	15.25
H3	398	283	18.5
C1	338	468	24.55
C2	291	363	27.85
C3	293	383	39.75

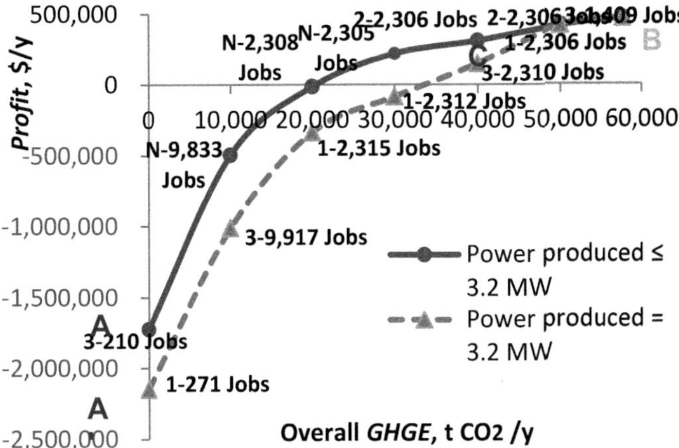

Figure 3. Pareto solutions for the example considered.

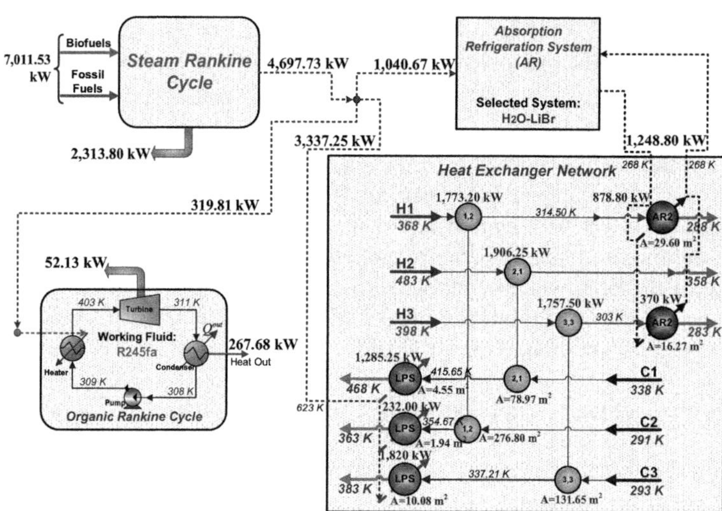

Figure 4. Configuration for solution C.

On the other hand, Points A and A′ represent solutions with zero emissions and the opposed case is represented by solution B, which is the best economic solution but it emits the maximum amount GHGE (57,710.77 t CO_2/y). Additionally, Point C was selected owing to it balances the three goals. In this regard, Figure 4 illustrates the optimal design for point C. Notice that there is no heat exchange between HPS and the ORC as well as the ORC runs using residual energy from the SRC.

4. Conclusions

Results highlight the benefits of considering the energy integration of the heat available in the SRC, where the residual energy available in the SRC can be reused for different applications. Other relevant point consists in the optimal selection of the fluid to operate the ORC; in fact, the results emphasize the importance of including the optimal selection for the working fluid owing that it can be more useful to have a set of operational temperatures that allows the heat exchange to maximize the reuse of heat and reduce the consumption of primary energies than a more efficient fluid. Since Pareto curves show the tradeoffs among the economic and environmental goals, the social function can be the decisive criteria to decide the best feasible solution.

References

F. Vélez, J.J. Segovia, M.C. Martín, G. Antolín, F. Chejne, A. Quijano, 2012, A technical, economical and market review of organic Rankine cycles for the conversion of low-grade heat for power generation, Renewable and Sustainable Energy Reviews, 16, 6, 4175-4189.

H.S. Bamufleh, J.M. Ponce-Ortega, M.M. El-Halwagi, 2013, Multi-objective optimization of process cogeneration systems with economic, environmental, and social tradeoffs, Clean Technologies and Environmental Policy, 15, 1, 185-197.

J.J. Klemeš, P.S. Varbanov, Z. Kravanja 2013, Recent developments in process integration, Chemical Engineering Research and Design, 91, 10, 2037-2053.

M. Morar, P.S. Agachi, 2010, Review: Important contributions in development and improvement of the heat integration techniques, Computers and Chemical Engineering, 34, 8, 1171-1179.

S.R. Wan Alwi, P.Y. Liew, P.S. Varbanov, Z.A. Manan, J.J. Klemeš, 2012, A numerical tool for integrating renewable energy into total sites with variable supply and demand, Computer Aided Chemical Engineering, 30, 1348-1351.

Jiří Jaromír Klemeš, Petar Sabev Varbanov and Peng Yen Liew (Editors)
Proceedings of the 24th European Symposium on Computer Aided Process Engineering – ESCAPE 24
June 15-18, 2014, Budapest, Hungary.

Energy Supply Chain Optimisation: Special Considerations for the Solution of the Energy Planning Problem

Christiana Papapostolou[a], Emilia M. Kondili[b*], John K. Kaldellis[c]

[a] *Sch. of Eng. and Ph. Sciences, Heriot-Watt University, Edinburgh EH14 4AS, UK*
[b]*Optimisation of Production Systems Laboratory, TEI of Piraeus, 20 P. Ralli and Thivon St., Athens 12244, Greece*
[c]*Soft Energy Applications and Environemntal Protection Laboratory, TEI of Piraeus, 20 P. Ralli and Thivon St., Athens 12244, Greece*
ekondili@teipir.gr

Abstract

The present work is a part of a major research project aiming to the development of the methodology and the corresponding integrated tool for the economic, social and environmental evaluation of various alternative energy and fuel Supply Chains (SCs). With special consideration of the energy supply options and dimensions, the applicability of the present modelling approach to the energy systems planning is examined. The energy system of an isolated area consists of a set of energy inputs – supply sources, storage facilities as well as a certain profile of energy demand. The optimisation model may include various economic, environmental or optimisation criteria such as cost minimisation, environmental impacts minimisation, profit maximisation as well as a set of constraints expressing the design, operation and limits of the system. A very interesting issue of the present research work is that it introduces an approach that may be followed equally well in energy as well in water systems with the same characteristics, i.e. in isolated areas with a variety of supply sources and users as well as with various criteria and considerations such as technical, environmental, social and economic.

Keywords: optimisation, energy supply chains, modelling

1. Introduction

Nowadays, security of energy supply has become a very important dimension of the contemporary socio-economic global regime, as its constrained availability in many areas of the world sets significant barriers for development, economic and technological progress, as well as for social prosperity. Energy supply, in complete accordance to water (supply) should be available, affordable, technologically adaptive (being able to respond to new challenges through the research and development of the sector), socially and environmentally sustainable (minimising the per-case environmental aspects and the impacts on human health) and institutionally (regulations and governance) compliant (Sovacool and Mukherjee, 2011). Either under the realistic conceptualisation, according to which energy is considered as constrained resource and states should emerge to control the strategic resources and find solutions and pathways towards community autonomy and diversification of the existing fuel mix, or under the normal commodity conceptualisation (Blum and Legey, 2012), under which the resources should be considered as normal commodities and not as strategic points of decisions, one should not argue that energy and development are inextricably interrelated.

As an intuitive response to the energy supply problem, with special emphasis in isolated areas, alternative fuels and supply options like biomass for heating and electricity, wind and PVs for power generation, natural gas for heating and transportation purposes, have been introduced to the associated markets, in most of the cases with limited penetration rates. Owing that to the intermittent character of the renewable supply options as well as to other techno-economic and social oppositions and environmental parameters i.e. landscape visual impacts and land intensiveness, many RES-related projects failed to dominate in diversification of the supply. However economic barriers related to price fluctuations, especially in oil-based fuels and also to environmental quality constraints for GHGs' limitations, have reinforced the adoption of renewable-based supply options. In any case, these types of decisions i.e. selecting over different alternative supply routes is a very complex and multi-parametrical problem since in each option there are conflicting goals i.e. minimisation of environmental impact vs. profit maximisation and priorities.

This multi-stakeholder and interacting environment has initiated the research community to address the problem of energy supply and planning under the systemic perspective of supply chain management and optimisation. Biomass and biofuels SCs, natural gas, hydrogen and water SCs (Kondili et al., 2010), have been extensively studied and modelled in respect to: technical feasibility (Almansoori and Shah, 2009) economic viability -profit maximisation and/or cost minimisation- (Papapostolou et al., 2011), as well as in respect to key challenges and major barriers (Mafakheri and Nasiri, 2013). However, the integration of all the dimensions into an evaluation, uniform scheme has not yet been widely achieved.

In this content, the present work seeks to develop the basic principles for an evaluation framework of multiple and conflicting supply chain options by combining economic, technical, environmental and social criteria. The assorted tool for the optimisation of these SCs will have its origin in mathematical programming so as to prove the optimality of each alternative point of decision. Before that, in the following section a concise overview of the novel concept of ESCs on top of the conventional ones will be presented along with the emerging issues and complexities followed in the present approach. Furthermore the typical representation of the SC will be cited in accordance to the major/critical parameters of the optimisation problem. As quoted above, the present research will try to identify all the implications of energy and fuel SCs in respect to electricity as end use, as this SC superstructure involves the maximum combination of raw materials, production technologies, and has actually the very significant social and environmental impacts on the level of strategic planning (i.e. installation of a large scale wind park). By this kind of analysis, the interactions of the parameters imbedded in the decision making process in terms of social, environmental, economical and technological aspects will be identified (qualitative analysis) and quantified.

2. Energy supply chains

2.1. Basic conceptualization and emerging issues

Owing that to similar demand and supply characteristics, the basic conceptualisation of product SC which entails the suppliers, the logistics /transportation network, the producers and the consumers, as well as time-variant demand and supply characteristics (multi and/or single echelon) was early adopted by the chemical industry for the optimal operation of batch processes (Kondili et al., 1993). More recently, energy policy makers seeking to identify the optimum configuration of specific energy supply streams like hydrogen (Almaraz et al., 2012), biomass-based (Pinto-Varela et al., 2011; Yue et al., 2014) and more end-product oriented ones like bioelectricity SCs (Palander, 2011; Pérez-Fortes et al., 2012), embraced the SC representation along with its implications and sustainability-specific dimensions (Heffron and McCauley, 2014). Typically, the main structure of the SC consists of raw material, feedstock production (supply side) - (inventory-storage), distribution / logistics (raw materials), manufacturing / production process (inventory-storage), distribution /logistics (end product), and finally the demand side (retailers, customers).

Building under the idea of homogeneity and uniform evaluation of these energy and fuel SCs, the Resource-Task-Network (RTN) representation was adopted. Looking at the background of the work, as acknowledged by Kondili et al. (1993), batch processes in multipurpose plants can be modeled and optimised in terms of State-Task Networks (STN), whereas both individual batch operations "tasks" and the feedstocks, intermediate and final products "states" can be explicitly included as network nodes. The term plant is very similar to the concept of the SC since, plants in chemical industries maybe characterised as multi-product facilities, where the products follow exactly the same production pathways (i.e. the biofuels SC) and as multipurpose facilities in which different products may follow different production pathways (i.e. the biomass SC). All these, are driven by demand requirements and capacity constraints under a short-term horizon (scheduling) or a long-term, strategic planning. In 1994 Pantelides (Pantelides, 1994) presented an integrated framework based on a Resource-Task Network (RTN) representation of the process in which all resources (equipment items, storage, utilities etc.) are treated uniformly. This generic approach (Figure 1) facilitates the conceptualisation of energy and fuel SCs in the case under examination, taking into account that complicated production features and differentiated SC activities exist, all in a unified and consistent manner.

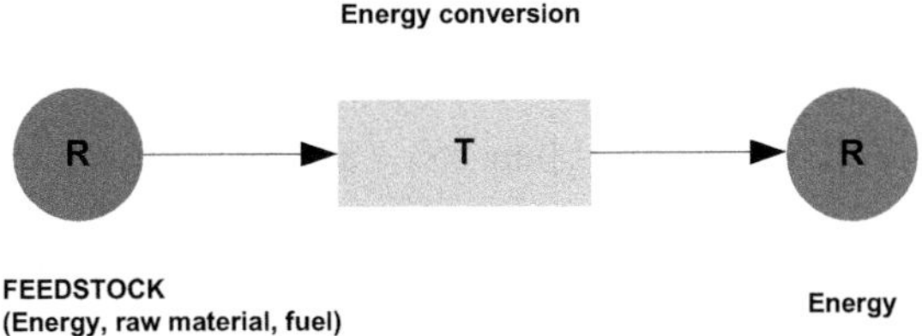

Figure 1. The RTN-generic representation of ESCs

3. The proposed mathematical model

3.1. Basic Characteristics and Structure of the Proposed Model

The proposed mathematical model, maybe in its most simple form approached by a Mixed Integer Linear Programming model, mainly due to the easiness of its solutions. In any case, there is no conceptual limitation of the present work to Non Linear Programming problem-formulations as well. As quoted above, the progress towards modelling of these novel energy and fuel SCs has reached a point where very detailed and case-specific, explicit and complicated (i.e. fuzzy, multi-objective optimisation problems) modelling schemes exist. However, the present approach due to its primary scope, which is to implicitly model in a uniform way the alternative energy SC options, is focused on developing a deterministic approach, which will make modelling easier, accessible and very structured, too. Owing that to its generic and adaptable nature and structure, the solution is sensitive to the parameters taken into consideration for the model testing. This sensitiveness of the model parameters imposes the need for preciseness, as much as possible, of the selected values; otherwise the optimisation maybe rendered out of scope.

Interesting to be acknowledged is that the present work has actual implementation possibilities to the level of decision acquired being also special focused both on the role of stakeholders and on the associate/representative parameters of decision, like:

- Legislative schemes
- Environmental characteristics and limitations
- Socially just communities
- Technological choices
- Economic opportunities

Whilst, the types of decisions that are supported by the model comprise:

- Selection of specific resources / energy inputs
- Selection over specific SCs networks and configurations (in some cases seasonal specific according to particular priorities and needs)
- Selection of (domestic) production capacity and/ or expansion of existing and /or imports (0-1) types of decisions
- Possibility of switching over different optimisation targets depending on the regional character of the proposed configuration and the stakeholders interests

Thus, for a selected set of resources and production technologies the optimisation criterion is, Maximisation of the Total Value of the ESC:

Max [a_1×(Turnover–Total Costs) – a_2×(Environmental Impacts) + a_3×(Social Benefits)], where,

- $a_{1,2,3}$: Appropriate weighted – normalisation factors of the different dimensions considered.
- Turnover: Incomes received from electricity production- technology oriented sales (if trade-exchange options are applicable in the system under consideration)
- Total Costs: Costs related to energy production (investment, maintenance and operational costs).
- Environmental Impacts: Negative environmental impacts of the ESCs in Life Cycle Assessment in terms of energy input/output ratio, CO_2 emissions, land and noise footprint, water consumption.

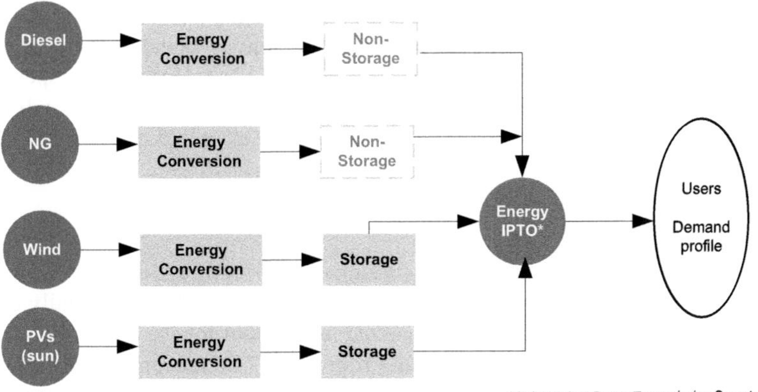

Figure 2. The RTN- generic representation of the energy planning problem under consideration

- Social Benefits: Positive social impact of the ESCs (in LCA view) in terms micro (jobs creation) and macro (security of energy supply) economic benefits.

All these subjected to technical and physical limitations like resources availability, plants' capacity limitations, storage-stations capacity limitations and energy demand satisfaction (under conflicting and high important priorities).

4. An indicative example of energy planning

The progress of the work at the moment is in the state of the RTN formulation and optimisation modelling for specific energy planning cases in order to validate:

- The SC approach
- The various involving parameters
- The optimisation problem definition.

To that effect, a particular remote-autonomous energy system is considered, where there are specific energy users as well as supply energy sources. The potential energy planning issues are regarded as emerging in this specific case e.g. energy storage, environmental impacts, various stakeholders and a conflicting set of optimisation criteria and constraints. In an effort to develop the RTN of this particular system, the following scheme maybe shown in Figure 2.

5. Conclusions

In the present work, the basic characteristics and typology of the energy SCs and their uniform representation is presented. The innovative element of this research relies on a twofold approach: the holistic consideration of different but interrelated aspects, economic, technical, environmental and social parameters and criteria, all incorporated into an optimisation criterion, as well as to the implicit representation of the fossil and alternative energy and fuel (SCs) in a generic/ comparable topology. Following this type of representation alternative and fossil based SCs can be easily treated and modelled under the same principles/ guides of comparability. The proposed model can also be implemented apart from state level for strategic type of decisions, also for supporting any type of energy decision planning, even at the level of consumer and/or of a small isolated/autonomous community. The adaptability of the optimisation criterion with the weighted factors in each special dimension, economic, environmental and social, provides the flexibility to the user to adjust his decision considering the special characteristics and needs of each energy planning problem e.g. special emphasis will be given to the environmental criterion if the area under examination implies an environmental degraded profile.

Acknowledgements

This work is part of the Ph.D. research thesis entitled “Social, environmental and economic impacts of alternative energy and fuel supply chains” which is financially co-supported by the “Bursary Program of individualized assessment for the academic year 2012-2013” from resources of the Operational Programme "Education and Lifelong Learning" of the European Social Fund and from the National Strategic Reference Framework (2007-2013).

References

A. Almansoori, N. Shah, 2009, Design and operation of a future hydrogen supply chain: Multi-period model, International Journal of Hydrogen Energy, 34, 19, 7883-7897.

S.D-L Almaraz, C. Azzaro-Pantel, L. Montastruc, L. Pibouleau, O.B. Senties, 2012, Design of a hydrogen supply chain using multiobjective optimisation, Computer Aided Chemical Engineering, 30, 292-296.

H. Blum, L.F.L. Legey, 2012, The challenging economics of energy security: Ensuring energy benefits in support to sustainable development, Energy Economics, 34, 6, 1982-1989.

R. J. Heffron, D. McCauley, 2014, Achieving sustainable supply chains through energy justice, Applied Energy, DOI:10.1016/j.apenergy.2013.12.034.

E. Kondili, J.K. Kaldellis, C. Papapostolou, 2010, A novel systemic approach to water resources optimisation in areas with limited water resources, Desalination, 250, 1, 297-301.

E. Kondili, C.C. Pantelides, R.W.H. Sargent, 1993, A general algorithm for short-term scheduling of batch operations-I.MILP formulation, Computers and Chemical Engineering, 17, 2, 211-27.

T. Palander, 2011, Modelling renewable supply chain for electricity generation with forest, fossil, and wood-waste fuels, Energy, 36, 10, 5984-5993.

C.C. Pantelides, 1994, Unified frameworks for optimal process planning and scheduling, In Proceedings of 2nd Foundations of Computer-Aided Process Operations, FOCAPO, New York, Cache Publications, 253.

F. Mafakheri, F. Nasiri, 2013, Modeling of biomass-to-energy supply chain operations: Applications, challenges and research directions, Energy Policy, DOI:10.1016/j.enpol.2013.11.071.

C. Papapostolou, E. Kondili, J.K. Kaldellis, 2011, Development and implementation of an optimisation model for biofuels supply chain, Energy, 36, 10, 6019-6026.

M. Pérez-Fortes, J.M. Laínez-Aguirre, P. Arranz-Piera, E. Velo, L. Puigjaner, 2012, Design of regional and sustainable bio-based networks for electricity generation using a multi-objective MILP approach, Energy, 44, 1, 79-95.

T. Pinto-Varela, A.P.F.D. Barbosa-Póvoa, A.Q. Novais, 2011, Bi-objective optimization approach to the design and planning of supply chains: Economic versus environmental performances, Computers and Chemical Engineering, 35, 8, 1454-1468.

B.K. Sovacool, I. Mukherjee, 2011, Conceptualizing and measuring energy security: A synthesized approach, Energy, 36, 8, 5343-5355.

D.Yue, F. You, S.W. Snyder, 2014, Biomass-to-bioenergy and biofuel supply chain optimization: Overview, key issues and challenges, Computers and Chemical Engineering, DOI:10.1016/j.compchemeng.2013.11.016.

Jiří Jaromír Klemeš, Petar Sabev Varbanov and Peng Yen Liew (Editors)
Proceedings of the 24th European Symposium on Computer Aided Process Engineering – ESCAPE 24
June 15-18, 2014, Budapest, Hungary.

Multi-objective Optimization of Heat Integrated Water Networks in Petroleum Refineries

Shivom Sharma, Gade Pandu Rangaiah*

Department of Chemical & Biomolecular Engineering,
National University of Singapore, Engineering Drive 4, Singapore 117585,
chegpr@nus.edu.sg

Abstract

Heat and water integrations for large scale chemical processes have become important due to economic and environmental reasons. These reduce consumption of both fresh water and energy, thus improving the sustainability of industrial processes. In chemical and related industries, water is used as a reactant, separation solvent and heating/cooling medium. An optimal water network reduces the consumption of fresh water by efficient reuse and recycling of water in the plant itself. In this work, onepetroleum refinery water network is optimized for two objectives: quantity of fresh water and total flow at the inlet of regenerator units simultaneously, using the ε-constraint method. Then, selected optimal water network designs are studied for heat integration, using Aspen Energy Analyzer. The proposed approach gives better insights by providing a range of alternative designs, which is useful in the final selection of one optimal network design.

Keywords: water network, heat exchanger network, multi-objective optimization.

1. Introduction

Most of the existing chemical plants have been designed for once through water use, and end-of-pipeline treatment of wastewater is carried out to meet the environmental restrictions. In a chemical plant, some process units require nearly pure water, whereas slightly contaminated water can be used in many others. If required, wastewater from a process unit can be partially purified using a treatment unit, and then it can be reused in the plant (El-Halwagi, 2012). Treatment units can reduce the concentration of selected contaminants below certain limits, and treated water is cheaper than fresh water. Water requirement, for different process units, varies in terms of flow rate, temperature and contaminant concentration. The mixing of water from different process units with fresh water fulfills the flow rate and contaminant concentration requirements of the process (Bogataj and Bagajewicz, 2008). In order to achieve the target temperature, the water stream to a process unit exchanges heat with hot/cold utility or other process streams (Karuppiah and Grossmann, 2006). In the literature, heat integrated water networks are designed using pinch analysis (Manan et al., 2009) and/or mathematical approach (Bogataj and Bagajewicz, 2008; Karuppiah and Grossmann, 2006).

In the design of heat integrated water networks, multi-objective optimization (MOO) did not receive much attention in spite of its many applications in chemical engineering (Sharma and Rangaiah, 2013). Boix et al. (2012) have simultaneously minimized the water and energy/utility consumptions in a water network, using mathematical programming. Then, selected design is further improved for energy consumption by indirect heat exchange (i.e., heat integration) in the water network. Hence, the broad objective of the present work is to further investigate the potential of MOO for the design of heat integrated water networks. Here, mathematical approach is used for the water network design, and direct mixing of different water streams is allowed to achieve the required flow rates and contaminant concentration.

In this work, the water network is first optimized for quantity of fresh water and total flow at the inlet of regenerator units, simultaneously. For this, ε-constraint method along with GAMS based solver is used to obtain the Pareto-optimal front. After that, selected optimal water network designs are considered for heat integration, where heat can be exchanged between different process water streams, regenerator water streams and wastewater stream. If necessary, hot and cold utilities can be used to achieve the target temperatures of process water streams, regenerator water streams and wastewater stream. Total annual cost is considered as the objective in the heat integration of water network, using pinch analysis. This MOO procedure is applied to one petroleum refinery example, from the literature.

The following section deals with modeling of water networks. Section 3 describes a water network case study from a petroleum refinery. Section 4 presents MOO problem formulation and results for the water network; after that, results for heat integration in selected water networks are discussed. Finally, conclusions of this work are presented in the last section.

2. Water Network Model

In the water network (shown in Figure 1), water using processes (P_i) and regeneration units (R_j) are interconnected using mixers (MIX) and splitters (SPT). Fresh water (FW) is free of contaminant, and can only be used in water using processes. The waste water (WW) from a process or regeneration unit can be used in any other process and/or regeneration unit, but no recycling is allowed. The interconnections recycle both water and heat to other processes and regeneration units. All the processes and regeneration units may produce waste water, and the contaminant concentration in the mixed waste water stream should be below the discharge limit. The outlet stream from each mixer must satisfy the flow rate and contaminant requirements of respective water using processes, whereas heaters/coolers (HE) are used to achieve the target temperature. In Figure 1, P-P_i and R-P_i are respectively water recycling from other processes and regeneration units to i^{th} process, whereas P_i-P and P_i-R are water flow from i^{th} process to other processes and regeneration units, respectively. In the water network model, balances around processes, regeneration units, mixers and splitters are considered; details on these balances can be found in Bogataj and Bagajewicz (2008).

- Processes: concentration balance; no change in flow rate and temperature
- Regeneration units: concentration balance; no change in flow rate and temperature
- Mixers: mass, energy and concentration balances
- Splitters: mass balance; no change in concentration and temperature

3. Refinery Case Study

In this work, an example from a petroleum refinery is used to demonstrate the benefits of MOO in water network design (Faria and Bagajewicz, 2011). It has six processes and four contaminants; details of these and limiting data for different processes are presented in Table 1. There are three regenerations units: (1) reverse osmosis (which reduces salts to 20 ppm), (2) API separator followed by ACA (Ammoniacal Copper Arsenate) (which reduces organics to 50 ppm), and (3) Chevron waste water treatment (which reduces H_2S and NH_3 to 5 and 30 ppm, respectively).

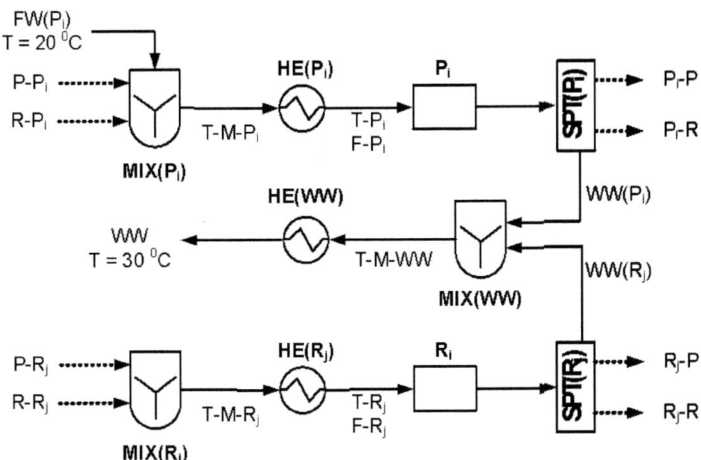

Figure 1. Water allocation network

Table 1. Operating data for water network in a petroleum refinery (Faria and Bagajewicz, 2011)

Process	Contaminant	Mass load (kg/h)	$C^{in, max}$ (ppm)	$C^{out, max}$ (ppm)
Caustic treating	salts	0.18	300	500
$T\text{-}P_1 = 38^0C$	organics	1.2	50	500
$F\text{-}P_1 = 2.667$ t/h	H_2S	0.75	5,000	11,000
	NH_3	0.1	1,500	3,000
Distillation	salts	3.61	10	200
$T\text{-}P_2 = 90^0C$	organics	100	1	4,000
$F\text{-}P_2 = 25$ t/h	H_2S	0.25	0	500
	NH_3	0.8	0	1,000
Amine sweetening	salts	0.6	10	1,000
$T\text{-}P_3 = 38^0C$	organics	30	1	3,500
$F\text{-}P_3 = 8.751$ t/h	H_2S	1.5	0	2,000
	NH_3	1	0	3,500
Merox-I sweetening	salts	2	100	400
$T\text{-}P_4 = 38^0C$	organics	60	200	6,000
$F\text{-}P_4 = 10.084$ t/h	H_2S	0.8	50	2,000
	NH_3	1	1,000	3,500
Hydrotreating	salts	3.8	85	350
$T\text{-}P_5 = 45^0C$	organics	45	200	1,800
$F\text{-}P_5 = 191.481$ t/h	H_2S	1.1	300	6,500
	NH_3	2	200	1,000
Desalting	salts	120	1,000	9,500
$T\text{-}P_6 = 90^0C$	organics	480	1,000	6,500
$F\text{-}P_6 = 191.481$ t/h	H_2S	1.5	150	450
	NH_3	0	200	400

All the regeneration units operate at 30 ^{0}C temperature. Faria and Bagajewicz (2011) reported a minimum fresh water consumption of 33.571 t/h (water flow rate through regeneration units = 550.06 t/h). Also, there were no discharge limits on different contaminants present in waste water. In this study, discharge limits for all contaminant is assumed to be 400 ppm, and so end-of-pipe treatment may be required before discharge. Further, suitable operating temperatures for water using processes and regeneration units are chosen, and these numbers are confirmed by our contact in a petroleum refinery.

4. MOO Problem Formulation and Results for Water Network

The water network in Figure 1 is optimized for minimizing both the quantity of fresh water (OF_1) and total flow rate at the inlet of regenerator units (OF_2), simultaneously. These objectives affect investment and operational costs of water network, and hence they are important. The optimization problem is as follows:

Objectives: $$\text{Min.}OF_1 = \sum_{i=1}^{6} FW(P_i) \quad (1)$$

$$\text{Min.}OF_2 = \sum_{j=1}^{3} F\text{-}R_j \quad (2)$$

Decision variables: Flow rate of various water streams
Interconnections between processes and/or regeneration units

Constraints: Material and energy balances
Concentration limits for contaminants
Logical constraints

The above two-objective optimization problem was transformed into single objective optimization problem (SOO) by the ε-constraint method. The resulting SOO problem is a mixed integer non-linear (MINLP) problem, having 205 continuous variables, 72 integer variables and 291 constraints. It was solved using BARON solver in GAMS.

Figure 2 shows the Pareto-optimal front obtained for two objectives, using the ε-constraint method (see closed circles); open circles are dominated solutions, obtained for different limits on the total flow rate through regeneration units, and they are not discussed further. Solvers in GAMS require gradients of objective function and constraints, so they are sensitive to the starting point. For different ε values, the solver may give non-dominated solutions, dominated solutions or no solution yet all. In Figure 2, only non-dominated solutions and selected dominated solutions obtained from many trials are presented. The water network obtained for each non-dominated solution is different. As expected the fresh water flow rate is conflicting with the total flow rate through the regenerations units (Figure 2). Table 2 provides more details for these non-dominated solutions, such as stream flow rate, number of interconnections and stream temperature. The minimum fresh water consumption is 33.755 t/h, which requires 400 t/h of total water flow rate through the regenerations units (solution G in Table 2); this is close to the solution reported in Faria and Bagajewicz (2011). Additionally, minimum fresh water consumption requires larger number of interconnections (see Table 2), and a small decrease in fresh water consumption is accompanied by a large increase in total water flow rate through regeneration units (see solutions F and G in Figure 2).

Each solution on the Pareto-optimal front (Figure 2) is equally good for the objectives in the optimization problem, and decision maker can select one solution based on his/her requirements. In this work, all 7 non-dominated solutions obtained are considered for indirect heat integration to achieve the target temperatures of different streams. For this, Aspen Energy Analyzer was used, and the results are shown in the bottom half of Table 2, for different water network designs in Figure 2.

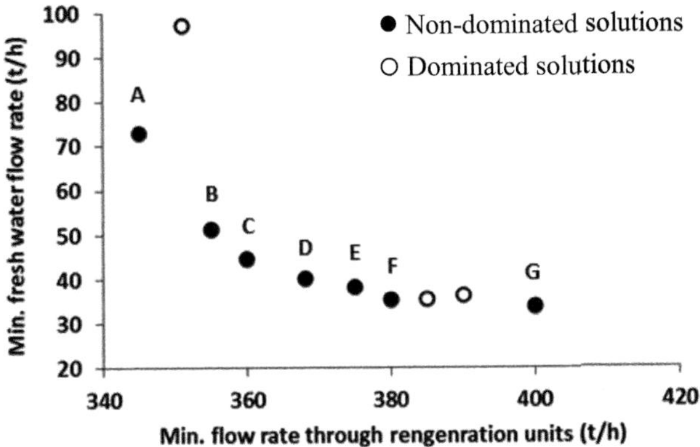

Figure 2. Results for simultaneous minimization of fresh water flow rate and total flow rate through regeneration units

Table 2. Design and operating variables for the non-dominated solutions in Figure 2

	A	B	C	D	E	F	G
OF_1	72.956	51.254	44.667	40.095	38.154	35.317	33.755
OF_2	345	355	360	368	375	380	400
$F\text{-}R_1$ (t/h)	137.78	158.6	163.01	170.38	157.44	201.36	175.83
$F\text{-}R_2$ (t/h)	198.47	196.4	196.99	197.62	198.07	5.08	217.44
$F\text{-}R_3$ (t/h)	8.751	0.0025	0.0006	0.0013	19.5	35.32	6.735
Number of interconnections	11	14	15	16	17	14	17
$T\text{-}M\text{-}P_1$ (^{0}C)	20.0	20.0	22.9	30.0	30.0	30.0	30.0
$T\text{-}M\text{-}P_2$ (^{0}C)	20.0	20.0	20.0	20.0	20.0	20.0	20.0
$T\text{-}M\text{-}P_3$ (^{0}C)	20.0	20.0	20.0	20.0	20.0	20.0	20.0
$T\text{-}M\text{-}P_4$ (^{0}C)	21.3	23.8	23.8	23.7	25.7	28.4	30.0
$T\text{-}M\text{-}P_5$ (^{0}C)	28.6	30.0	30.4	30.4	30.3	30.5	30.5
$T\text{-}M\text{-}P_6$ (^{0}C)	49.9	50.7	50.7	50.7	50.1	50.9	47.5
$T\text{-}M\text{-}R_1$ (^{0}C)	30.0	30.0	30.0	30.0	30.0	30.0	30.0
$T\text{-}M\text{-}R_2$ (^{0}C)	87.3	88.2	88.2	88.2	88.3	87.4	86.4
$T\text{-}M\text{-}R_3$ (^{0}C)	38.0	42.0	30.0	39.4	45.0	30.0	30.0
T-M-WW (^{0}C)	40.4	40.6	41.2	42.0	37.7	41.1	40.0
Q-h (10^3 kJ/h)	54,522	52,591	52,225	52,137	52,686	51,805	54,486
Q-c (10^3 kJ/h)	51,444	50,429	50,341	50,445	51,077	50,315	53,062
Area of HE, m^2	1,935	1,837	1,828	1,831	1,881	1,828	2,162
Number HE	10	9	9	9	10	9	9
Capital cost ($)	903,849	826,731	808,339	838,634	890,280	786,002	930,209
Operating cost (10^3 $/y)	1,980	1,932	1,939	1,933	1,924	1,975	1,858
Annual cost (10^3 $/y)	2,214	2,146	2,149	2,150	2,155	2,179	2,099

The physical properties and other relevant data used in Aspen Energy Analyzer are: ΔT_{min} = 10 ^{0}C, Cp (water) = 4.183 kJ/kg-^{0}C, latent heat for steam condensation = 2,196 kJ/kg-^{0}C, h (water) = 4,088.4 kJ/h-m^2-^{0}C, h (steam) = 8,177 kJ/h-m^2-^{0}C, plant life = 10 years, rate of return = 10%, plant operation = 8,765.76 hours per year, cost of water (5 to 15 ^{0}C) = 4.43 \$/GJ, and cost of low pressure steam = 13.28 \$/GJ. Three solutions, namely, B, C and D are comparable based on number of interconnections, number of heat exchanges (HE) and total annual cost of heat exchange network (see Table 2), but solution C has relatively lower values of both objectives (i.e., quantity of fresh water and total flow rate through regeneration units). Hence, solution C can be selected for implementation.

5. Conclusions

This study optimizes a water network for both fresh water consumption and total water flow rate at the inlet of regeneration units, simultaneously. The obtained Pareto-optimal front gives better insights by providing a range of alternative designs. The optimal water network designs are further studied for indirect heat integration, using Aspen Energy Analyzer. The methodology is illustrated using a case study from a petroleum refinery. Apart from the shape of the Pareto-optimal front, number of interconnections between different processes and regenerations units in the water network, number of heat exchangers and total annual cost of heat exchange network are also important. These are considered in the final selection of one water network design in the case study.

Acknowledgement

The authors are grateful for the financial support provided by the Public Utilities Board, Singapore, for the research reported in this paper.

References

D.C. Faria, M.J. Bagajewicz, 2011, Global optimization of water management problems using linear relaxation and bound contraction methods, Industrial and Engineering Chemistry Research, 50, 7, 3738-3753.

M. Bogataj, M.J. Bagajewicz, 2008, Synthesis of non-isothermal heat integrated water networks in chemical process, Computers and Chemical Engineering, 32, 12, 3130-3142.

M. Boix, L. Pibouleau, L. Montastruc, C. Azzaro-Pantel, S. Domenech, 2012, Minimizing water and energy consumptions in water and heat exchange networks, Applied Thermal Engineering, 36, 442-455.

M.M. El-Halwagi, 2012, Sustainable design through process integration, Butterworth-Heinemann Ltd./Elsevier, Oxford, UK.

R. Karuppiah, I.E. Grossmann, 2006, Global optimization for the synthesis of integrated water systems in chemical process, Computers and Chemical Engineering, 30, 4, 650-673.

S. Sharma, G.P. Rangaiah, 2013, Multi-objective optimization applications in chemical engineering, Multi-objective Optimization in Chemical Engineering, Wiley, Chichester, UK.

Z.A. Manan, S.Y. Tea, S.R.W. Alwi, 2009, A new technique for simulataneous water and energy minimization in process plant, Chemical Engineering Research and Design, 87, 1509-1519.

Jiří Jaromír Klemeš, Petar Sabev Varbanov and Peng Yen Liew (Editors)
Proceedings of the 24th European Symposium on Computer Aided Process Engineering – ESCAPE 24
June 15-18, 2014, Budapest, Hungary.

Study of Integration of Cryogenic Air Energy Storage and Coal Oxy-fuel Combustion through Modelling and Simulation

Kelvin André Pacheco[a], Yongliang Li[b], Meihong Wang[a, *]

[a]*School of Engineering, University of Hull, UK, HU6 7RX*
[b]*Institute of Particle Science and Engineering, University of Leeds, Leeds, LS2 9JT, UK*
Meihong.Wang@hull.ac.uk

Abstract

Energy storage acts as an important tool in balancing energy supply and demand across the electricity grid. With low carbon policy, renewable energy sources play an important role. Thermal energy storage can be performed using a cryogen (liquid air), which is produced during off-peak time and stored in order to be used according to the demand. The liquefaction of liquid air, operating at high pressure and low temperatures, requires a significant amount of electricity. In order to improve the thermal efficiency, it is proposed to integrate the cryogenic energy storage (CES) with coal oxy-fuel combustion and carbon capture. This study presents a process simulation in Aspen Plus® and performance analysis of such an integrated process. The study suggested that there are many opportunities for heat recovery and re-use in such a complex process. The whole integrated system efficiency can be improved significantly.

Keywords: Coal Oxy-fuel Combustion, Cryogenic Energy Storage, Thermal Energy Storage, Carbon Capture, Process Simulation, Process Integration.

1. Introduction

1.1. Overview of Energy Storage

Energy storage is one of the pillars for the expected revolution to make the world's energy supply clean. With low carbon policy, renewable energy plays an important role, particularly solar and wind energy. Driven by concerns about climate change and the levels of oil reserves increasingly low, it becomes necessary to find an efficient way to store the energy produced. According to DTI (2007), there is a binding target of increasing the overall EU consumption of renewable resources by 20 % by 2020, therefore a significant proportion of electricity will come from intermittent sources.

Chen et al (2009a) classified the energy storage technologies for electricity into 4 categories: Electrical energy storage, Mechanical energy storage, Chemical energy storage, and Thermal energy storage. Thermal energy storage can be performed in two approaches: cold (e.g. cryogenics) or hot (e.g. molten salt). Using cryogen as a mean to store energy, a much higher energy density can be reached using liquid air (Li et al., 2010a).

1.2. Features of Liquid Air

Liquid air shows a high liquid density and it is important regarding the physical restrictions in some places. Moreover, liquid air has significant potential benefits as a future energy carrier (Li et al., 2010b). To recover the energy from cryogen, there are basically four main methods proposed for power generation: direct expansion (cryogen is pumped to high pressure and heated before expanding), Rankine cycle (the cryogen energy is transferred to the working fluid by heat exchangers, driving force is the temperature difference), Brayton cycle (cryogen cools the gas of a compressor, the gas is then heated and expands to generate power through a turbine) and combination of these methods. According to Li et al (2010a), the direct expansion-Brayton hybrid cycle is the most efficient method to extract the exergy, and when carbon capture is considered, the Rankine cycle is better because of its lower power consumption.

1.3. Air Separation Unit (ASU) and Liquefaction

ASU uses multi-column cryogenic distillation process to produce gaseous oxygen and nitrogen (at above atmospheric pressure and near ambient temperature). The gas liquefaction is a process to form liquid from a gas through compression and cooling. To produce a liquid product (i.e. liquid nitrogen), it requires two to three times the electricity compared with producing gaseous product (Smith and Klosek, 2001). Large scale gas liquefaction is important in the energy field and is vital in the development of an efficient energy storage process (Li et al., 2012). Ameel et al. (2013) reported that the exergy loss during heating in Rankine cycle can be recovered in the Linde cycle, thus improving efficiency.

In ASU, the feed stream (i.e. air) is compressed to high pressure in a compressor, passes through heat exchangers to cool down. The stream will further go to distillation columns to produce gaseous oxygen and nitrogen. Gaseous oxygen can be used for oxy-fuel combustion. Gaseous nitrogen can be used for liquefaction through a series of heat exchangers and compressions. Liquid nitrogen is stored at2.26 bar and around -188 °C. When we need electricity, the liquid nitrogen will be pumped to increase pressure to around 200 bar and cooled to around -187 °C. After gaining heat through heat exchangers, liquid nitrogen will become vapour. This gaseous nitrogen will be expanded near-isentropically with turbines to generate electricity. Advantages of the CES are rapid, simple start-ups and shutdowns, and more stable in performance.

1.4. Oxy-fuel Combustion with Carbon Capture

In the oxy-fuel combustion, coal is combusted in an environment rich in oxygen. There are three main blocks in such a power plant: ASU, combustion process and CO_2 capture. The basic characteristic is that the combustion takes place in an environment rich in oxygen and flue gas has to be recycled. CO_2 capture in the context of oxy-fuel combustion is based on refrigeration separation.

1.5. Aim of the paper and its novel contribution

The aim of this study is to integrate three different processes to improve the efficiency available for energy storage and oxy-fuel combustion with carbon capture. Casana (2009) adopted a flowsheet for ASU and reported simulation of ASU. However, the products from ASU are in a gaseous phase. Li et al. (2012) and Dubar et al. (1998) reported air liquefaction processes to produce liquid nitrogen. The integration of these two processes (ASU and Liquifaction) provides chances for heat recovery of the cold from nitrogen and cooling down the inlet air stream. Carbon capture in coal-fired power plants can be made through pre-combustion, post-combustion or oxy-fuel combustion. The oxy-fuel combustion technology is attractive for CO_2 capture due to higher thermal efficiency. Hu (2011) simulated oxy-coal power plant with CO_2 capture, focused on determining operational parameters (e.g. recycle ratio) for different configurations. In this paper, the integration of an oxy-coal power plant with CO_2 capture and CES using ASU and liquefaction was proposed. For such an integrated process, it is vital to evaluate whether the thermal efficiency is improved and why. Process modelling and simulation can facilitate the performance analysis and improving the understanding of this integrated process.

2. ProcessModelling

2.1. Modelling of integrated ASU and Liquefaction Process

The flowsheet for ASU was adopted from Casana (2009). The flowsheet for liquefaction process was adopted from Dubar et al. (1998). Figure 1 shows the flowsheet for ASU and liquefaction. In ASU (left part of Figure 1), the air is compressed (ASUCOMP) to 4 bar at stream AIR2, cooled to -173.5 °C at stream AIR4 (through HE1 and HE2). The stream enters the separation column ASUHP. The oxygen rich stream OXYGEN1 goes to another distillation column ASULP. The stream OXYGEN3 provide cooling in HE1 and goes to oxy-fuel combustion process. The nitrogen rich stream N2AR mixes with stream N2. STREAM5 provides further cooling in HE2 and HE1 to become INCOMP1 for liquefaction process. In liquefaction (right half of Figure 1), INCOMP1 is compressed in two compressors (COMP1 and COMP2) to 50 bar (i.e. STREAM3). The stream is spitted into two streams to be further compressed by COMP3 and COMP4 to get streams OUTCOMP3 and OUTCOMP4 at 75 bar. These two streams are mixed together and cooled from 58 °C to 5 °C in OUTCOOL before entering HE1. STREAM6 at -15°C is split into INT1 and STREAM7. STREAM7 goes through HE2 to become INT2 at -90°C. INT1 is expanded in TURB1 to provide power for COMP3. The stream OUT1 is returned to MIXER2. Similarly INT2 is expanded in TURB2 to provide power for COMP4, the outlet stream OUTT2 at -188°C with vapour fraction 0.91. OUTT2 is split and cooled in CHILLING to get LIQUIDN2. This liquid nitrogen is stored in the TANK.

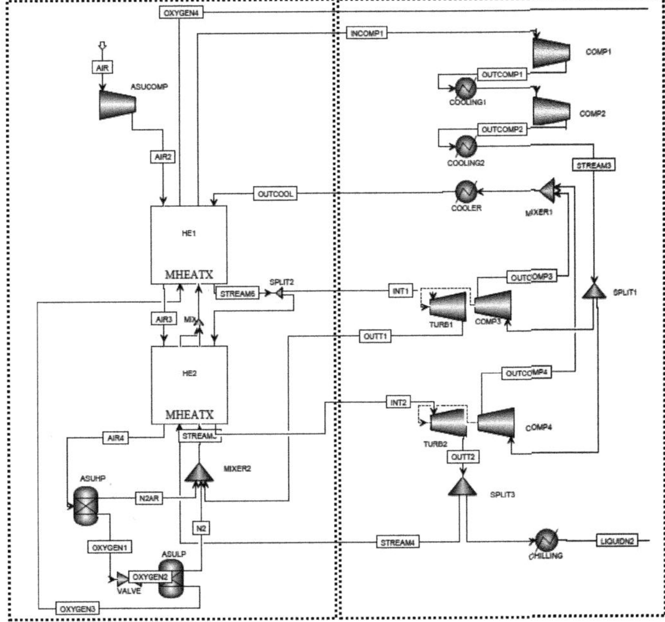

Figure 1. ASU and liquefaction process model in Aspen Plus®

2.2. Modelling of Oxy-fuel Combustion and CO_2 capture

The flowsheet (Figure 2) for oxy-fuel combustion and carbon capture was adopted from Casana (2009) with some improvements. Since coal is a non-conventional component in Aspen Plus, RYield block (DECOMP) is used to decompose coal into constituent elements (Table 1) before it is sent to RGibbs block (BOILER) to simulate combustion of coal in oxygen rich stream (Aspentech, 2009). Here for simplicity, it is assumed that there is no radiation. All energy in stored in flue gas, therefore flue gas temperature is very high (2040 °C). The stream FLUEGAS is used to generate steam in HeatX (STEAMG). The STEAM (at 75 bar and 773 °C) will drive steam turbine Comp block – Turbine option (TURBNE) for electricity generation. With outlet condition at 0.07 bar and 42 °C, 825.522 MWe can be generated. Due to high flame temperature in oxy-fuel combustion, some flue gas is recycled. The stream FLUEGAS3 goes through COOLEROX and H2OSEPAR (a Flash2 block). FLUEGAS5 stream is compressed to 25 bar and is cooled in CO2COOL1 and CO2COOL2 to 25 bar and -30 °C. The two columns (Flash 2 block) CO2SEPAR and CO2SEPA2 separate CO_2 from non-condensables.

2.3. Modelling of CES

The flowsheet (Figure 3) for CES was adopted from Chen et al. (2009b). Liquid nitrogen leaving storage TANK to PUMP to increase pressure to 200 bar (at -187 °C). SN2-LIQ2 stream goes to SHE2 and SHE1 (MHeatX block) to gain heat. INTURB stream is obtained at 200 bar and 127 °C, which is expanded in a Comp block – Turbine option (TURB-STO) to generate electricity.

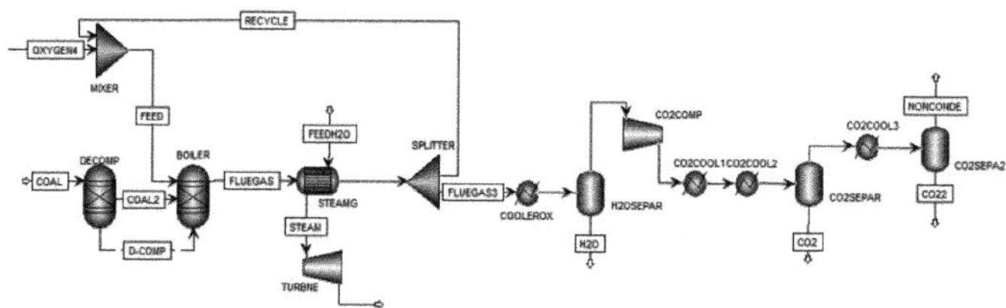

Figure 2. Flowsheet in Aspen Plus® for Oxy-fuel combustion and CO_2 capture model

Table 1. Coal Parameters used in this simulation (modified from Hu, 2011)

Moisture (wt.%)	10.80	Ultimate (wt.%) (dry)	
Proximate (wt.%) (dry)		Carbon	72.09
Ash	11.00	Hydrogen	5.20
Volatile matter	33.44	Nitrogen	2.00
Fixed carbon	55.56	Sulphur	0.33
		Oxygen	9.37

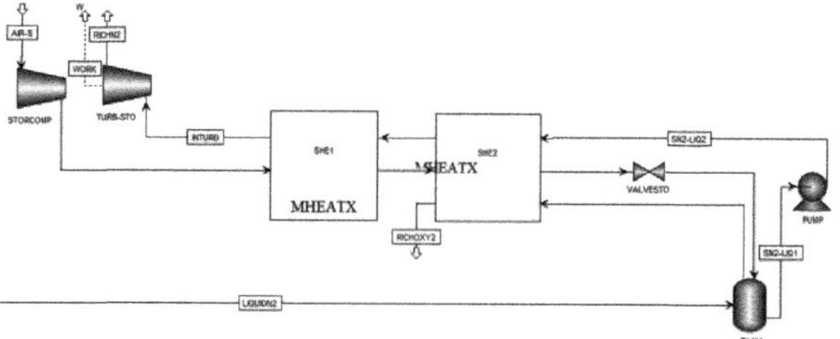

Figure 3. Flowsheet in Aspen Plus® for Energy Storage

3. Process Simulation and Analysis of the integrated system

3.1. Simulation results for integrated process

Using the coal presented in Table 1, the integrated process is simulated in Aspen Plus®. Table 2 shows the simulation results. From ASU, the key process variables are oxygen purity (95.4 wt%) and oxygen flowrate (122.22 kg/s). These will be provided to oxy-fuel combustion. From liquefying section, the key process variables are liquid nitrogen temperature (-188 °C), liquid nitrogen pressure (2.26 bar) and flowrate (390.78 kg/s). From oxy-fuel combustion and carbon capture section, the key process variables are electricity generated (875.74 MWe), captured CO2 flowrate (132.59 kg/s) and its purity (95.3 mol%). From CES, the key process variable is electricity generated (215.33MWe) from stored liquid nitrogen.

3.2. Process analysis

In the proposed integrated process, ASU generated gaseous oxygen and nitrogen. The gaseous oxygen is mainly used for coal combustion. The gaseous nitrogen from ASU is further liquefied using excess electricity at off-peak time. There are many chances to

Table 2. Simulation results for the integrated system

Stream Name or Block Name	Physical Meaning/Units	Value
OXYGEN3	O_2 purity (wt%)	95.40
OXYGEN3	O_2 flowrate (kg/s)	122.22
LIQUIDN2	Stream temperature (°C)	-188
LIQUIDN2	Stream pressure (bar)	2.26
LIQUIDN2	Stream flowrate (kg/s)	390.78
FLUEGAS	CO_2mol% in flue gas (directly after combustion)	60.20
FLUEGAS	H_2O mol% in flue gas(directly after combustion)	32.60
FLUEGAS8	CO_2 purity before cryogenic cleaning (mol%)	83.90
CO22	Captured CO_2 purity (mol %)	95.30
CO22	Captured CO_2 flowrate (kg/s)	132.59
COAL	Coal (Feedstock) HHV (MWth)	1474.24
ASUCOMP	ASU compressor power consumption (MWe)	106.29
CO2COMP	Captured CO_2 – compression electricity consumption (MWe)	61.10
TURBNE	Oxy-fuel plant (Steam turbine) power output (MWe)	825.52
	Net Thermal efficiency of Oxy-fuel power plant (%)	44.64
COMP1	Liquefaction – Compressor electricity consumption (MWe)	875.74
COMP2	Liquefaction – Compressor electricity consumption (MWe)	244.52
TURB-STO	Electricity generated (MWe) from stored liquid nitrogen	215.33
	Net Thermal Efficiency for CES (%)	19.22

utilize heat integration in this complex process, which help the thermal efficiency improvement.

4. Conclusions and Future Work

In this paper, the integration of a coal oxy-coal power plant with CO_2 capture and CES using ASU and liquefaction was proposed with the aim to improve the thermal efficiency. The integrated process is simulated in Aspen Plus®. The integration of these processes provides chances for heat recovery and utilisation. Further work is needed to optimise the heat integration and further improve the thermal efficiency.

Acknowledgement

The first author would like to acknowledge the financial support from CNPq, Brazil.

References

A.M. Casana, 2009, Study of Oxy-fuel power plant with CO_2 capture, MSc Dissertation, Cranfield University, UK.

A.R. Smith, J. Klosek, 2001, A review of air separation technologies and their integration with energy conversion processes, Fuel Processing Technology, 70, 115-134.

Aspentech, 2009, Aspen Plus Tutorial: Getting started modelling process with solids, Version Number: V7.1, Aspentech Plc. USA.

B. Ameel, C. T'Joen, K. De Kerpel, P. De Jaeger, H. Huisseune, M. Van Belleghem, M. De Paepe, 2013, Thermodynamic analysis of energy storage with a liquid air Rankine cycle, Applied Thermal Engineering, 52, 130-140.

C. Dubar, T. Forcey, V. Humphreys, H. Schmidt, 1998, A competitive offshore LNG scheme utilising a gravity base structure and improved nitrogen cycles, Proceedings of the LNG 12, Institute of Gas Technology, Perth, WA, Australia.

DTI, 2007, Meeting the Energy Challenge: a White Paper on Energy, The Stationery Office, UK Government.

H. Chen, T.N. Cong, W. Yang, C. Tan, Y. Li, Y. Ding, 2009a, Progress in electrical energy storage system: a critical review, Progress in Natural Science, 19, 291-312.

H. Chen, Y. Ding, T. Peters, F. Berger, 2009b, Energy Storage and Generation, US Patent 2009/0282840 A1.

Y. Hu, 2011, CO2 capture from oxy-fuel combustion power plants, Licentiate dissertation, Stockholm, KTH Royal Institute of Technology, Sweden.

Y. Li, H. Chen, X. Zhang, C. Tan, Y. Ding, 2010b, Renewable energy carriers: Hydrogen or liquid air/nitrogen?, Applied Thermal Energy, 30, 1985-1990.

Y. Li, H. Cheng, Y. Ding, 2010a, Fundamentals and applications of cryogen as a thermal energy carrier: A critical assessment, International Journal of Themal Sciences, 49, 941-949.

Y. Li, X. Wang, Y. Ding, 2012, An optimal design methodology for large-scale gas liquefaction, Applied Energy, 99, 484-490.

Jiří Jaromír Klemeš, Petar Sabev Varbanov and Peng Yen Liew (Editors)
Proceedings of the 24th European Symposium on Computer Aided Process Engineering – ESCAPE 24
June 15-18, 2014, Budapest, Hungary.

Process Design Analysis for the Valorisation and Selection of Integrated Micro-algae Biorefineries

Melina Psycha*, Kostantinos Pyrgakis, Antonis C. Kokossis

School of Chemical Engineering, National Technical University of Athens, Zografou Campus, 9, Iroon Polytechniou Str., GR-15780 Athens, Greece
melpsycha@mail.ntua.gr

Abstract

The paper discusses the development of an integrated process that addresses the co-production of glycerol, β-carotene and proteins using a multitude of solvents and scoping to reduce energy consumption. Process integration is applied to target efficiency scoping reviewing thermal integration, and the use of alternative separation schemes. The analysis reviews economic benefits as well as the impact of process integration in securing the viability of the incentive.

Keywords: glycerol; β-carotene; micro-algae; thermally coupled distillation; biorefinery

1. Introduction

Biorefineries typically refer to lignocellulosic feedstock as they are available from agricultural activities, residues, waste organics or forestry supplies. There is much less attention to water substrates from micro-algae and macro-algae systems that feature alternative paths to products, involve competitive chemistries and require co-production of chemicals to remain feasible. A notable case relates to halophytic Dunaliella cultures capable to convert CO_2 into a multitude of products. One needs to select Dunaliella for its extraordinary tolerance to salt stress establishing it as one of the few organisms that can survive in extreme environments.

2. Integrated designs of a micro-algae biorefinery

The use of a simultaneous approach is not possible due to practicalities and limitations. Therefore, an evolutionary approach is taken which starts with a single-product flowsheet and evolves to multi-product flowsheets with a gradual selection of products keeping integration in mind. The production of glycerol from the halophytic alga Dunaliella is described by the single-product flowsheet (Figure 1). The cultivation occurs in an open pond, where CO_2, seawater and nutrients are added. The CO_2 is used by the microalgae for their growth. Additionally, paddle wheels are attached to the pond, so that all the layers will absorb the same amount of solar radiation. The next step is to stress the algae by increasing the salt concentration. As a reaction, Dunaliella accumulates glycerol for the purpose of maintaining the suitable osmotic pressure inside the cells. Subsequently, glycerol is separated from the cells and obtained as the main product.

In the next series of process engineering flowsheets, some design specifications change and assumptions are made. The target is to study the extent of process modifications required and the potential to co-produce.

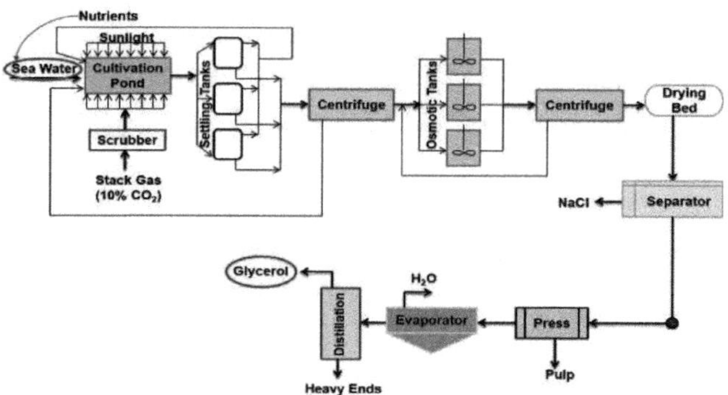

Figure 1. Single-product reference flowsheet

In general, the stages of the process are as followed:

- Cultivation of Dunaliella: The cultivation of the algae takes place in a cultivation pond. The culture is enriched with sea water and nutrients (mostly NaCl), since Dunaliella has the ability to thrive in media with high salt concentrations. The CO_2 added to the culture is being used as feed for the algae and increases their growth.
- Harvesting: Algae are harvested from the cultivation pond and processed, in order to accumulate glycerol and β-carotene. Usually, this is achieved by osmoregulation (the mechanism by which an organism adapts to various salt concentrations). The response to glycerol is rapid, unlike to β-carotene, which is a slow response. The residence time in the stage of the osmotic shock for glycerol is 2 d as for β-carotene is 5 days.
- Oil extraction: This is the stage where produced glycerol and β-carotene are extracted from the algae biomass in order to obtain them as final products. There are many ways an oil extraction can occur and one of them is solvent extraction.
- Product recovery: The final products are separated from the mixture. Some byproducts such as lipids and carbohydrates also exist in the extracted mixture. Thus, the desired products have to be purified.

The first attempt to a multi-product flowsheet uses trichloroethane ethanol, cyclohexane and alum/ferric chloride as solvents (Figure 2 left).

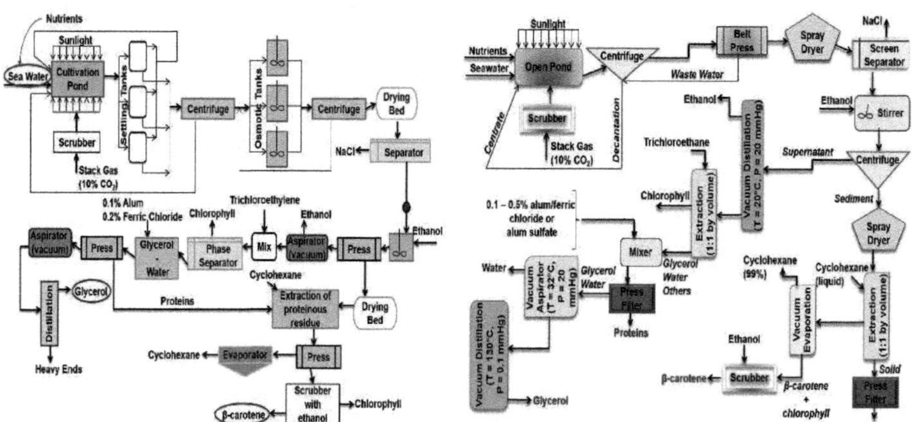

Figure 2. First multi-product flowsheet (left) and optimized multi-product flowsheet (right)

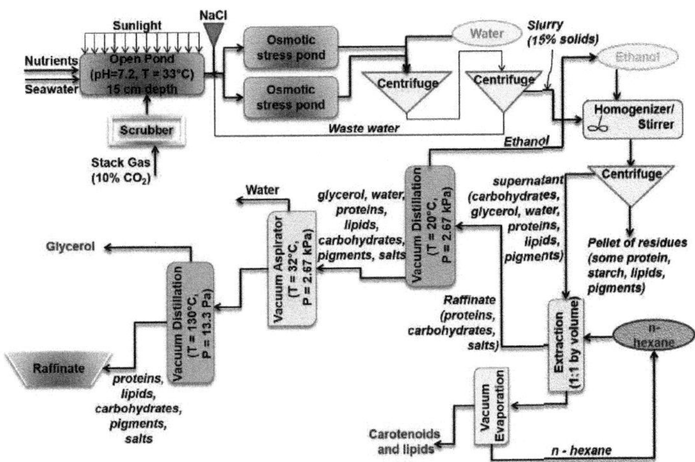

Figure 3. Final flowsheet (proteins as co-product)

The general concept is to extract glycerol and β-carotene from the algal biomass and, consequently, separate them using the solvents mentioned above and a wide range of devices. As a result, the operating cost increases, but the additional production of β-carotene raises the profit. The second attempt to a multiple-product flowsheet (Figure 2 right) is an optimization regarding operating conditions, which are not preferable for co-production. Namely, the conditions that prevail in the osmotic shock tanks do not favour the osmoregulation of Dunaliella, as glycerol is not accumulated well in the dark.

The final flow sheet (Figure 3) depicts a more accurate design, considering that a number of devices were redundant and the solvents being used (cyclohexane, trichloroethane and alum/ferric chloride) were not suitable, bearing in mind the requirement for protein meal as a feed supplement for e.g. fish. Thus, n-hexane is used instead. In the open pond (0.5 ha), algae feed from CO_2, nutrients, NaCl and sunlight in order to grow. The production reaches 3.5 t of biomass per year. Following, Dunaliella is induced in osmotic shock by the rapid increase of salt concentration (from 2M to 4M). In response to the osmotic shock, the cells accumulate glycerol. Harvesting is achieved by the use of two centrifuges to remove the waste water and the damaged cells. The next stage is to add ethanol in order to extract produced glycerol and β-carotene as well as other components. First, β-carotene (4.474 kg/h) is separated from the mixture by using n-hexane. The remaining mixture of ethanol/water/glycerol is distilled and glycerol is recovered (24.213 kg/h). The residue could find use as animal feed. It is worth mentioning that after the distillation, ethanol is recycled for the purpose of operating cost reduction and is reused.

3. Energy integration

As concerned to the final flowsheet, distillation is the most energy intensive operation unit establishing this process unsustainable. Energy integration is a powerful tool able to secure the feasible and sustainable margins for energy efficiency improvement. Thermally coupled distillation columns are used as promising alternatives offering important energy and capital cost savings compared with conventional distillation columns (even higher than 30 % in total annual cost).

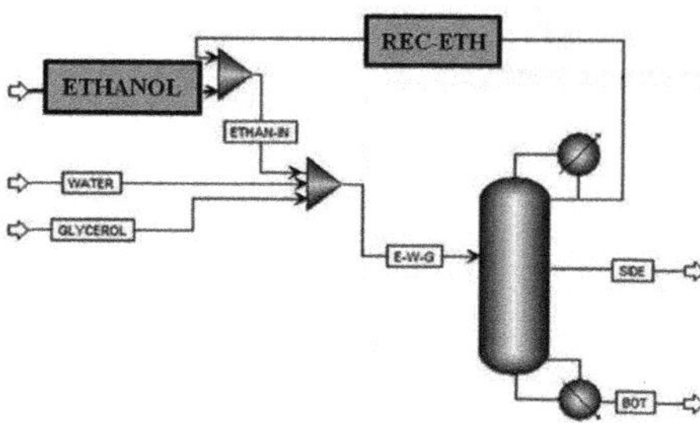

Figure 4. Representative flowsheet of the ethanol/water/glycerol distillation: REC-ETH: ethanol recovery; ETHANOL: ethanol feed

The degrees of freedom of this study are the configurations (conventional tasks and thermally coupled distillation columns) and the distillation design specifications. The configurations are: direct simple task, indirect simple task, prefractionator, side rectifier, sloppy split and side stripper. The distillation design specifications are ethanol recovery and ethanol feed as shown in Figure 4. It should be noted that the valorization of every configuration refers to the optimized distillation design specifications. In this paper two cases are studied. The first addresses the production of glycerol as a single product and the second one the parallel production of glycerol and β-carotene. The required ethanol/water fraction for the extraction of glycerol in the first case is 66 % w/w, as opposed to the second case where the fraction of ethanol/water for the extraction of glycerol and β-carotene is 95 % w/w. In both cases, ethanol is being recycled and the pressure of the distillation columns is set up to 2.67 kPa in order to avoid the appearance of the ethanol/water azeotrope which is encountered in higher pressures.

4. Results and discussion

Table 1. Results regarding single-product process (66 %).

Configurations	Annual cost ($)	Cost sav. (%)	Utilities HOT Units (MW)	HOT Energy sav. (MW)	COLD Units (MW)	COLD Energy sav. (MW)	Ethanol feed (kg/h)	Ethanol recovery (%)
Direct Simple	50,228		0.250		-0.240		1	99.97
Prefractionator	101,519	-102.1	0.370	-50.3	-0.380	-59.2	1	99.96
Side Rectifier	53,890	-7.3	0.350	-39.0	-0.230	3.6	1	99.98
Side Rectifier	50,228	0.0	0.310	-24.3	-0.220	9.0	22.54	99.44
Sloppy Split	75,596	-50.5	0.261	-4.9	-0.334	-40.3	1	99.96
Indirect Simple	73,846	-47.0	0.315	-26.6	-0.305	-28.1	1	99.96
Side Stripper	122,055	-143.0	0.865	-247.6	-0.332	-39.4	1	99.96
Direct Simple	35,349	29.6	0.158	36.7	-0.155	35.0	217.78	90.80
Prefractionator	57,243	-14.0	0.181	27.2	-0.250	-5.5	91.70	96.12
Side Rectifier	33,450	33.4	0.090	63.9	-0.161	32.3	152.83	95.24
Sloppy Split	49,885	0.7	0.165	33.9	-0.230	4.8	135.25	94.04
Indirect Simple	35,207	29.9	0.156	37.3	-0.154	35.4	221.60	90.35
Side Stripper	58,196	-15.9	0.410	-64.7	-0.159	33.3	126.08	94.67

Table 2. Results regarding multi-product process (95 %).

Configurations	Annual cost ($)	Cost sav. (%)	Utilities HOT Units (MW)	HOT Energy sav. (MW)	COLD Units (MW)	COLD Energy sav. (MW)	Ethanol feed (kg/h)	Ethanol recovery (%)
Direct Simple	275,301		1.19		-1.12		1	99.97
Prefractionator	664,124	-141.2	2.34	-96.4	-2.35	-110.9	1	99.96
Side Rectifier	306,144	-11.2	2.27	-90.2	-1.10	1.1	1	99.97
Side Rectifier	275,301	0.0	1.69	-42.0	-0.94	16.0	423	87.99
Sloppy Split	478,994	-74.0	1.45	-21.9	-1.99	-78.3	1	99.96
Indirect Simple	449,856	-63.4	1.81	-51.6	-1.75	-56.9	1	99.96
Side Stripper	520,091	-88.9	3.66	-207.4	-1.42	-27.0	1	99.96
Direct Simple	190,692	30.7	0.74	38.1	-0.73	34.1	2,060	14.34
Prefractionator	325,212	-18.1	0.84	29.6	-1.33	-18.9	1,030	56.80
Side Rectifier	169,078	38.6	0.37	68.6	-0.70	36.9	1,717	39.71
Sloppy Split	299,951	-9.0	0.75	37.4	-1.26	-12.7	1,144	52.04
Indirect Simple	215,953	21.6	0.83	30.0	-0.83	25.5	2,060	14.34
Side Stripper	274,871	0.2	1.89	-59.0	-0.74	33.8	1,144	52.04

Tables 1 and 2 show the results of the two cases studied for 66 % and 95 % of ethanol concentration, respectively. The upper part of the tables refers to ethanol feed minimization and the lower part to energy minimization. The configurations are listed in the first column with direct simple task being the base case configuration. The tables present the hot and cold utilities as well as the energy savings for each configuration under optimum design specifications (4th-7th column). The second and third column refer to the total annual energy cost and the cost savings of hot and cold utilities compared to the base case. The values of the optimized distillation design specifications are listed in the last two columns.

As shown in Tables 1 and 2, the energy and ethanol costs are competitive. For both case studies, the side rectifier gives the lowest annual utility cost, although this happens at the expense of ethanol feed's cost. Nonetheless, even if direct simple gives higher annual utility cost, it is considered to be the best solution, since the feed ethanol cost is kept in a lowest price resulting to a sustainable solution. This is important especially for the case of 66 % ethanol/water fraction where the high profit of β-carotene is missing. More specifically, both cases display a glycerol profit of 56,000-64,000 $/y, but in Case 2 the profit from β-carotene, 18,195,566 $/y, is more than enough to cover the losses due to energy costs and ethanol feed cost. The conclusion that can be drawn from the results is that the energy is possible to be reduced, but this will cause an increase in ethanol cost. However, the configuration of the side rectifier seems to be quite promising from an energy point of view, if the remaining and non-recycled ethanol was to be used from another process.

It is noteworthy that the main characteristic affecting the economic viability of the process is the low pressure of the distillation columns (2.67 kPa), thus avoiding the appearance of the ethanol/water azeotrope. As a result, ethanol is distilled under very low temperatures leading to high cost refrigeration levels. A pressure increase close to the atmospheric pressure would cause an increase in cooling temperatures reducing the operating cost. This deduction is raising questions regarding the existence of the optimal solution in the current study or in a future work related to the azeotropic mixture.

5. Conclusions

With biorefineries being in the spotlight for the last decade, it is of high importance to secure their feasibility and sustainability. This study proves that multiple-product processes can achieve both goals. On one hand, energy integration combined with a design specifications optimization procedure is obligatory to secure the sustainability of a single-product (glycerol) process. On the other hand, the development of a multi-product (glycerol, β-carotene and proteins) process is sufficient to secure the sustainability of the biorefinery, due to the introduction of products with high profitability such as β-carotene. Nevertheless, a process integration procedure is still significant to detect the appropriate margins of energy savings and offer new non-conventional, design perspectives.

References

A. Ben-Amotz, A. Shaish, M. Avron, 1991, The Biotechnology of Cultivating Dunaliella for Production of β-Carotene Rich Algae, Bioresource Technology, 38, 2-3, 233-235

A.C. Kokossis, A. Yang, 2010, On the use of systems technologies and a systematic approach for the synthesis and the design of future biorefineries, Computers and Chemical Engineering, 34, 9, 1397-1405

A. Prieto, J.P. Canavate, M. García-González, 2011, Assessment of carotenoid production by Dunaliella salina in different culture systems and operation regimes, Journal of Biotechnology, 151, 180-185

G. P. Agarwal, 1990, Glycerol, Advances in Biochemical Engineering/Biotechnology, 41, 95-128

J.A. Caballero, I.E. Grossmann, 2004, Design of distillation sequences: from conventional to fully thermally coupled distillation systems, Computers and Chemical Engineering, 28, 11, 2307-2329

P.J. Harvey, M. Psycha, A. Kokossis, A.L. Abubakar, V. Trivedi, R. Swami, A.K. Cowan, D. Schroeder, A. Highfield, G. Reinhardt, S. Gartner, J. McNeil, P. Day, M. Brocken, J. Varrie, A. Ben-Amotz, 2012, Glycerol production by halophytic microalgae: Strategy for producing industrial quantities in saline water, Conference proceedings, 20th European Biomass Conference and Exhibition, Milan, Italy, 85-90

R. Raja, S. Hemaiswarya, R. Rengasamy, 2007, Exploitation of Dunaliella for β-carotene production, Applied Microbiology and Biotechnology, 74, 517-523

R. Vogt Alves da Cruz, C. Augusto Oller do Nascimento, 2012, Process modelling and economic analysis of microalgal systems for CO_2 capture and production of chemicals, Computer Aided Chemical Engineering, 31, 490-494

Jiří Jaromír Klemeš, Petar Sabev Varbanov and Peng Yen Liew (Editors)
Proceedings of the 24th European Symposium on Computer Aided Process Engineering – ESCAPE 24
June 15-18, 2014, Budapest, Hungary.

A Design Methodology for Retrofit of Crude Oil Distillation Systems

Víctor M. Enríquez-Gutiérrez*, Megan Jobson, Robin Smith

Centre for Process Integration, School of Chemical Engineering and Analytical Science, The University of Manchester, Manchester, UK
victormanuel.enriquezgutierrez@postgrad.manchester.ac.uk

Abstract

Retrofit of crude oil distillation systems is a non-trivial problem with many degrees of freedom and constraints. This work proposes a systematic retrofit methodology for increasing the throughput to crude oil distillation systems, embedded in a computational tool with mass and energy balance results from rigorous simulations, hydraulic correlations for valve trays and structured packings and a retrofit model for heat exchanger networks. The feasibility of retrofit options is assessed against constraints related to product specifications, jet flooding and liquid load per weir length in the main fractionator and side strippers and the required area for heat exchangers in the heat exchanger network (HEN). The methodology is applied to an existing crude oil distillation system; the results show the impact of increasing throughput on column hydraulics and heat transfer area requirements. Retrofit solutions are proposed for relieving hydraulic bottlenecks and minimizing impact on the HEN by varying column operating conditions.

Keywords: Crude oil distillation retrofit, HEN retrofit, hydraulic design

1. Introduction

The crude oil distillation system consists of an atmospheric distillation unit, in which crude oil is separated into more valuable products, and a heat exchanger network (HEN) which pre-heats the crude oil before it enters the column. The atmospheric distillation unit and the HEN interact with each other, making the retrofit of crude oil distillation systems a complex problem requiring analysis of column hydraulics and HEN performance.

Retrofit aims to increase the profitability of the process by maximizing the use of existing equipment. Examples of retrofit objectives are increasing the throughput, changing the feedstock, increasing the production or the quality of the products and reducing the energy demand or atmospheric emissions. (Liu and Jobson, 2004).

Gadalla et al. (2003a) developed a retrofit methodology for atmospheric crude oil distillation columns and associated HENs. The distillation columns are evaluated using shortcut models for retrofit design (Gadalla et al., 2003b) and retrofit models were used for the HEN. However, the shortcut distillation models cannot identify bottlenecks within the main column and side strippers. Although the diameter required to avoid entrainment flooding is used as hydraulic indicator, the effect of pressure drop and liquid loads inside the column are neglected. In the HEN retrofit model constant stream properties were assumed. Smith et al. (2010) extended and modified the HEN retrofit methodology by considering temperature dependent thermal properties.

Liu and Jobson (2004) developed a hydraulic indicator, the "fractional utilization of area" (FUA), defined as the ratio between the area required for vapour flow in the column and the available area. A useful graphical tool was developed to identify capacity bottlenecks for distillation columns and screen retrofit solutions. This parameter was applied to evaluate alternative solutions with respect to capacity enhancement. Wei et al. (2012) proposed the utilization of FUA together with a new hydraulic indicator, the maximum capacity expansion (x_{max}), to screen hydraulic bottlenecks when increasing capacity. Determining the FUA and x_{max} requires rigorous distillation simulation results. The key shortcoming of these methods is that they only account for jet flooding.

Thernesz et al. (2010) used process design software to evaluate retrofit modifications in crude oil distillation systems. PRO II v7.1 (2005) was used to simulate the distillation column, SULCOL v1.0 (2005) and KG-TOWER v2.02 (2005) evaluated the hydraulic design and SUPERTARGET v6.0 (2005) analyzed the performance of the HEN. However, the software was applied sequentially for each proposed modification, requiring significant engineering resources to screen the many design options.

Kamel et al. (2013) developed a retrofit methodology for crude oil distillation systems in which rigorous simulation and optimisation procedures are used to optimise the process conditions and to explore structural modifications to the flowsheet in order to increase the capacity and the energy efficiency of the system. However, this methodology does not account the effects of the capacity enhancement to the column hydraulics.

Therefore, the retrofit of heat- integrated crude oil systems needs to consider both the distillation columns and the HEN and their capacity constraints. Furthermore, the impact of changing distillation operating conditions or equipment on the HEN should be assessed. This work develops a systematic retrofit methodology, considering the interactions between operating parameters, the hydraulic performance of the distillation column and the heat transfer performance of the HEN for crude oil distillation systems. This work focuses on increasing throughput, where capacity limits (jet flooding and downcomer flooding) in the column and heat transfer area constraints in the HEN are avoided.

2. Retrofit methodology

Figure 1 represents the proposed methodology which employs converged simulations of the atmospheric distillation column (using Aspen HYSYS v7.3, 2012) and Matlab code which can exchange inputs and outputs with the simulator.

The column is simulated at the desired increased throughput. Then the simulation results (stage-by-stage flow rates and physical properties) are read by Matlab and used as inputs for column hydraulic calculations. Next, the stream data (temperatures, flow rates and enthalpy changes) are used as inputs to the HEN retrofit model, which is also embedded in Matlab. Feasibility is checked in terms of product specifications, hydraulic constraints and heat exchange area requirements in the HEN. The simulation inputs are then modified to address infeasibilities and this sequence of calculations is repeated.

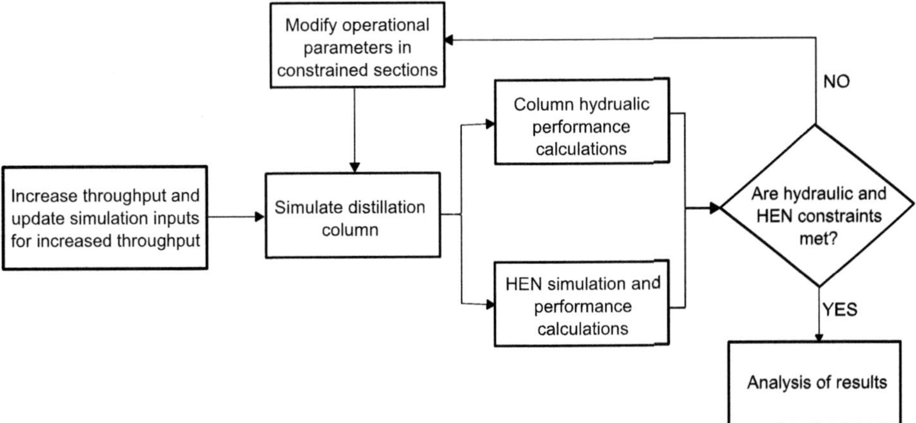

Figure 1. Proposed retrofit methodology for crude oil distillation systems

2.1. Hydraulic methodology

Distillation columns containing trays can operate efficiently only within certain limits. The upper limit of the vapour flow rate is related to jet flooding, which occurs when the vapour rate is high enough to carry over liquid to the stage above. The upper limit of the liquid flow rate is related to downcomer flooding: in this case, the liquid flow rate in the downcomer is too high to allow the vapour in the downcomer to disengage, leading to entrained vapour being carried to the tray below (Stichlmair, 1998, Chap. 8.2).

The percent of flooding is defined in Eq. (1) as the ratio of the C-factor at the operating conditions of interest to that under flooding conditions (Kister et al., 2007). A maximum value of 80 % is assumed in line with design practice. To predict jet flooding, the correlation of Kister and Haas (1990) is used to predict the flooding C- factor $C_{sb(flooding)}$. Downcomer flooding is evaluated in terms of liquid load per weir length L_w using Eq. (2) (Stichlmair, 1998, Chap. 8.2) where V_L is the volumetric flow rate of the liquid in m^3 h^{-1}, l_w is the weir length in m and N_p is the number of passes per tray. A limit of 110 m^3 m^{-1} h^{-1} is assumed, as this value is typically applied in practice (Resetarits, 2010).

$$\%Flooding = \left(C_{sb}/C_{sb(flooding)}\right)\cdot 100\% \tag{1}$$

$$L_w = \frac{V_L}{l_w N_p} \tag{2}$$

For distillation columns containing structured and random packings, the flood point is defined by the pressure drop at which the liquid is no longer able to flow (Stichlmair, 1998, Chap. 8.3). In this work, to estimate the capacity parameter at flooding conditions $CP_{flooding}$ a correlation is proposed, regressed from the pressure drop correlation chart for structured and random packings of Kister and Gill (cited by Kister et al., 2007). The regressed model is given in Eq. (3), where A and B are functions of the pressure drop, estimated using Eqs. (4) and (5) for structured packings and Eqs. (6) and (7) for random packings. The definitions of the capacity parameter $CP_{flooding}$ and flow parameter F_{lv} are presented in Kister et al. (2007). Eq. (1) is also applied in order to predict the percent of flooding. The pressure drop is predicted using the correlation of Rocha et al. (1993).

$$CP_{flooding} = A\ln(F_{lv}) + B \tag{3}$$

$$A = -7.31x10^{-11}\Delta P^3 + 2.18x10^{-7}\Delta P^2 - 2.19x10^{-4}\Delta P - 0.0124 \tag{4}$$

$$B = 1.28x10^{-10}\Delta P^3 - 3.15x10^{-7}\Delta P^2 + 2.62x10^{-4}\Delta P + 0.0826 \tag{5}$$

$$A = 6.82x10^{-8}\Delta P^2 - 1.48x10^{-4}\Delta P - 0.0063 \tag{6}$$

$$B = 2.55x10^{-10}\Delta P^3 - 6.09x10^{-7}\Delta P^2 + 4.70x10^{-4}\Delta P + 0.0882 \tag{7}$$

Eq. (3) is only valid between flow parameters from 0.03 to 0.3. The pressure drop is given in Pa m^{-1}.

2.2. HEN retrofit methodology

This work simulates the HEN using the model of Ochoa-Estopier et al. (2013) which extends the approach of de Oliveira Filho et al. (2007) by specifying each heat exchanger in terms of heat load and considering heat capacities as temperature-dependent and uses the approach of Smith et al. (2010) is applied to identify and evaluate HEN retrofit options.

3. Case Study

The distillation system used to illustrate the proposed methodology comprises an atmospheric distillation column and its corresponding HEN (Figure 2). The atmospheric distillation unit consists of a main fractionator, three side-strippers (SS), three pump-arounds (PA) and one condenser. The column processes 100,000 bbl d^{-1} (0.23 m^3 s^{-1}) of Venezuela Tía Juana Light crude (Watkins, 1979) into five products: residue (RES), light naphtha (LN), heavy naphtha (HN), heavy distillate (HD) and light distillate (LD). The operating conditions, stage distribution and product specifications of the atmospheric distillation unit are those presented by Chen (2008, Chap. 6.1). The HEN has 22 heat exchangers with a total heat transfer area of 5325 m^2; the demand for fired heating is 55.4 MW. Heat exchanger details and process and stream data are given by Chen (2008, Appendix C). Column internals are assumed to be standard valve trays for all sections except for Section 3 which is assumed to use Flexipac 3.5Y structured packing. The retrofit methodology was applied stepwise for throughput increases of 5% until the flooding or liquid load limits were reached. Pump-around flow rates in constrained sections were varied and the impact of these modifications on the HEN were analysed. Throughout the study, product specifications, expressed in terms of TBP5 and TBP95, were maintained.

4. Results

Figure 3 presents hydraulic profiles for the atmospheric distillation column for the base case and for throughput increases of 5 % to 25 %.

It is observed that a 25 % increase creates two hydraulic bottlenecks: jet flooding in Section 2 (82 % of flooding) and downcomer flooding in Section 1 (liquid load per weir length is 110.5 m^3 m^{-1} h^{-1}). The HEN was simulated and optimised; results show that

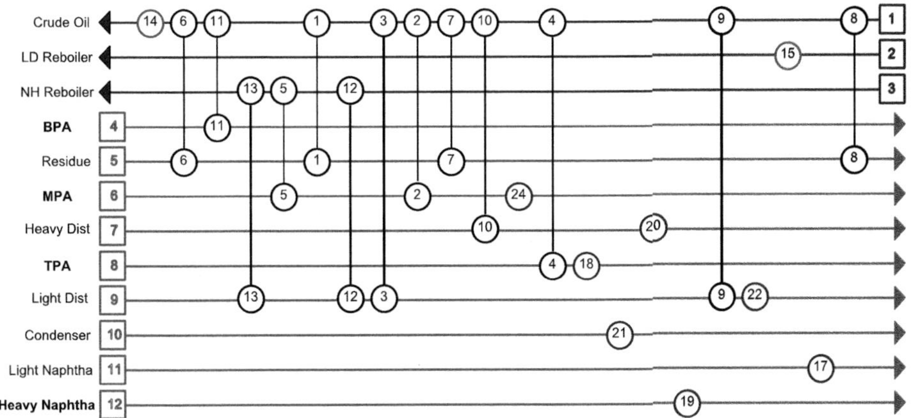

Figure 2. Case study: Existing heat exchanger network (Chen, 2008).

fifteen heat exchangers will require additional area (2012 m^2 in total). After HEN optimisation, the demand for fired heating increases by 32 % to 73.5 MW.

To debottleneck the column for a throughput increase of 25 %, two scenarios were considered, namely changing the flow rates of pump-arounds MPA and BPA. It is found that a 10 % reduction in the flow rate of MPA reduces flooding in Section 2 to 79.7 %, but the modification had no significant effect on Section 1. However, reducing the flow rate of TPA by 10 % relieves both bottlenecks (79.6 % flooding in Section 2 and a liquid load per weir length of 102.2 m^{-1} h^{-1} in Section 1). At this new operating condition, 13 heat exchangers require additional area (2678 m^2 in total) and the demand for fire heating increases slightly, to 74.8 MW. It is observed that the modified pump-around flow rate have little effect on the hydraulic performance of the side strippers.

5. Conclusions

The case studied illustrates the benefit of the proposed methodology to screen and evaluate retrofit options to increase the throughput of crude oil distillation systems.

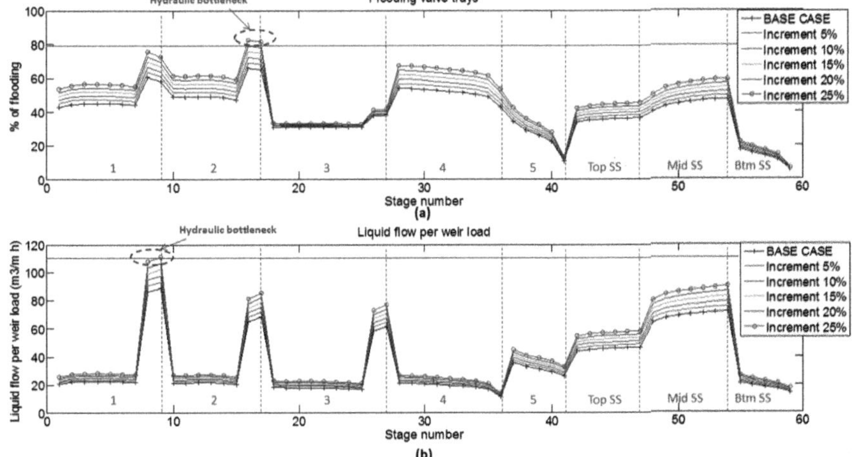

Figure 3. Hydraulic profiles: (a) Flooding profile in main column and side strippers; (b) Liquid loading profile in main column and side strippers.

The methodology can be applied to distillation columns containing trays and/or structured packings, and accounts for the impact of operational changes on the HEN. In this case study, the distillation column could accommodate throughput increases less than 25 % without encountering hydraulic bottlenecks. However, the HEN would require some retrofitting.

It was observed that reducing the pump-around flow rate in constrained sections can reduce flooding and the liquid load per weir length, but reduce heat recovery; as a result, the HEN require more additional area. The methodology also assessed impact of the operational changes on the hydraulic performance in other parts of the column too. Cost- benefit analysis would be needed to further evaluate the retrofit solutions.

References

L. Chen, 2008, Heat-integrated crude oil distillation system design, PhD. Thesis, The University of Manchester, Manchester, UK.

L. O. de Oliveira Filho, E. M. Queiroz, A. L. H. Costa, 2007, A matrix approach for steady-state simulation of heat exchanger networks, Applied Thermal Engineering, 27, 14-15, 2385-2393.

D. Kamel, M. Gadalla, F. Ashour, 2013, New retrofit approach for optimisation and modification for a crude oil distillation system, Chemical Engineering Transactions, 35, 1363-1368

M. Gadalla, M. Jobson, R. Smith, 2003a, Optimization of existing heat-integrated refinery distillation systems, Chemical Engineering Research and Design, 81, 1, 147-152.

M. Gadalla, M. Jobson, R. Smith, 2003b, Shortcut models for retrofit design of distillation columns, Chemical Engineering Research and Design, 81, 8, 971-986.

H.Z. Kister, J. R. Haas, 1990, Predict entrainment flooding on sieve and valve trays, Chemical Engineering Progress, 86, 9, 63-69.

H. Z. Kister, J. Scherffius, K. Afshar, E. Abkar, 2007, Realistically predict capacity and pressure drop for packed columns, Chemical Engineering Progress, 103, 7, 28-38.

Z. Liu, M. Jobson, 2004, Retrofit design for increasing the processing capacity of distillation columns: 1. A hydraulic performance indicator, Chemical Engineering Research and Design, 82, 1, 3-9.

L. M. Ochoa-Estopier, M. Jobson, R. Smith, 2013, Retrofit of heat exchanger networks for optimising crude oil distillation operation, Chemical Engineering Transactions, 35, 133-138.

M. Resetarits, 2010, Propelling distillation research, Chemical Engineering, 117, 6, 26-27.

J.A. Rocha, J.L. Bravo, J. R. Fair, 1993, Distillation columns containing structured packings: A comprenhensive model for their performance. 1. Hydraulic models, Industrial and Engineering Chemistry Research, 32, 4, 641-651.

R. Smith, M. Jobson, L. Chen, 2010, Recent development in the retrofit of heat exchanger networks, Applied Thermal Engineering, 30, 16, 2281-2289.

J. Stichlmair, 1998, Distillation: Principles and practice, Wiley-VCH, New York, USA.

A. Thernesz, Z. Varga, I. Rabi, Z. Czaltig, M. Lörincova, 2010, Applying process design software for capacity increase and revamp of distillation units, Clean Technologies and Environmental Policy, 12, 2, 97-103.

R.N. Watkins, 1979, Petroleum Refinery Distillation, Gulf Pub. Co., Houston, USA.

Z. Q. Wei, B. J. Zhang, S. Y. Wu, Q. L. Chen, C. W. Hui, 2012, A hydraulics-based heuristic strategy for capacity expansion retrofit of distillation systems and an industrial application on a light-ends separation plant, Chemical Engineering Research and Design, 90, 1527-153.

Jiří Jaromír Klemeš, Petar Sabev Varbanov and Peng Yen Liew (Editors)
Proceedings of the 24th European Symposium on Computer Aided Process Engineering – ESCAPE 24
June 15-18, 2014, Budapest, Hungary.

Biomass Drying for an Integrated Power Plant: Effective Utilization of Waste Heat

Tesfaldet Gebreegziabher[a], Adetoyese Olajire Oyedun[b], Zhang Yu[b], Wang Maojian[b], Zhu Yi[b], Liu Jin[b], Chi Wai Hui[b,*]

[a]*Department of Environmental Engineering, The Hong Kong University of Science and Technology, Clear Water Bay, Kowloon, Hong Kong.*
[b]*Department of Chemical and Biomolecular Engineering, The Hong Kong University of Science and Technology, Clear Water Bay, Kowloon, Hong Kong.*
kehui@ust.hk

Abstract

Unlike fossil fuels, biomass offers potential benefits due to its low cost and presumed zero-carbon emission for power generation. However, raw biomass contains high moisture level that reduces combustion temperature and causes certain operational problems and due to this reason biomass is often dried prior to combustion. Having multiple advantages however, drying biomass is an energy intensive and relatively low efficiency process. Hence, for making drying process more economical, reasonable waste heat from some other industries or processes should be assessed and extracted for drying purpose. Biomass power plant is one of the process industries where the existing waste heat can be utilized for drying the feedstock before combustion for improved operations. In this work, heat integration studies are performed to a 12.5 MW capacity biomass power plant that burns empty fruit bunches (EFB) as fuel. A multi-stage drying process that combines, hot air dryer (HAD), superheated steam dryer (SSD) and flue gas dryer (FGD) is considered. Pinch analysis is used to show the effectiveness of the heat integration of different design options. The result of this study shows that, when compared with a system with no drying, nearly 10 % improvement in overall efficiency is achievable by proper integration of the dryers with the power plant.

Keywords: Heat integration, biomass power plant, biomass drying.

1. Introduction

Biomass is one form of renewable energy source used for both heat and power generation through direct combustion. The combustion process is largely affected by moisture content of the fuel. A biomass with high moisture content is not suitable for direct combustion. In order to sustain the combustion in a boiler, biomass is often burnt at a moisture level below 55 – 65 wt% while the optimum moisture content could be as low as 10 – 15 wt% (Ross, 2008). Using dry fuel in combustion systems improves efficiency and boiler operation. Having multiple advantages however, drying biomass is an energy intensive process and can account for up to 15 % of the overall industrial energy usage with relatively low thermal efficiency ranging between 25 – 50 % (Chua et al, 2001). One of the possible economic ways of drying is to utilize the existing waste heat sources like low pressure steam and flue gas from a power plant. Utilization of steam or waste-heat from a power plant for drying can significantly reduce the energy cost (Li et al, 2012). The effectiveness of heat integration options among the drying and the steam power plant can be studied by pinch analysis.

2. Heat Integration of Biomass Power Plant

Heat integration approach, namely "Pinch Analysis" was introduced by Linnhoff and Flower (1978) to target, design and optimize heat exchanger networks in chemical processes. This work was then extended to designing commercial power plants (Linnhoff and Alanis, 1989) and to integrate chemical and utility plants (Hui and Ahmad, 1994). Until recently, researchers are still using these techniques for improving the efficiency of different kind of power plants (Fu and Gundersen, 2010). So far, applying pinch analysis to design and optimize a biomass power plant is rarely discussed in literature.

Most of the latest biomass power plants are often integrated with drying facilities of which biomass is shredded and/or thermally dried before sending it to the boiler plant. Le Lostec et al. (2008) suggested that, using waste heat of a power plant is an economical solution for drying wood chips. Three different drying methods namely steam drying, flue gas drying and vacuum drying were studied by Andersson et al. (2006) in a process where the drying and pelletizing of biofuel is integrated to pulp mill. Their study showed the possibility of energy recovery and reduction in CO_2 emissions compared to stand-alone pellets production. Song et al. (2012) studied the effect of integrating drying process into a biomass power plant. Flue gas from the boiler plant was used to dry the biomass feedstock and their result shows 3.1 % increase in overall efficiency. Their work demonstrated that the integration of the drying process with the power plant is beneficial.

In this study, a biomass power plant that burns empty fruit bunch (EFB) is used to illustrate the integration of a multi-stage drying process with the power plant. Mathematical models of the steam power plant and the drying process are used for designing and optimizing the energy efficiency of the overall plant. Pinch analysis is used to show the effectiveness of the heat integration of different design options and to identify further improvements.

3. Process description

For illustrating on how the concept of pinch analysis can give insight on improvement of heat integration process an EFB based power plant targeting an output power, P_{out}, of 12.5 MW is considered as in Figure 1.

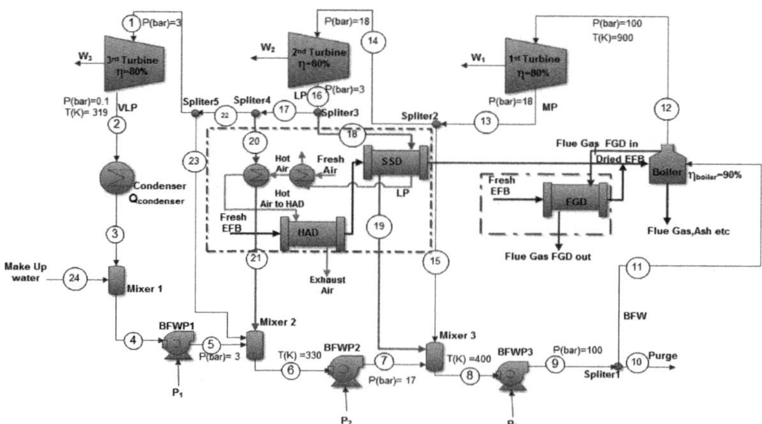

Figure 1. Schematic diagram of the process.

The process flow diagram given in Figure 1 describes the Base Case along with four possible integration cases. In the base case fresh EFB with a moisture content of 70 wt% is fed directly to the boiler and the units in the dashed line were not considered in simulation study. The steam level and the BFW water preheating temperatures are selected arbitrarily. Next in case 2 an attempt was made on possible overall efficiency increment by optimizing the steam pressure and boiler feed water preheating levels. The next three cases are comprised of different drying schemes either with only HAD, only SSD, only FGD and simultaneous usage of HAD and SSD in multi-stage manner. When considering the last three cases only the dryers in question are integrated in the simulation study. When using HAD or SSD only drying, LP steam is extracted from the power plant to reduce the moisture content of moist EFB from 70 % to some value at the inlet of the boiler. While in simultaneous usage of HAD and SSD for drying LP steam from the power plant is used in SSD and LP steam generated at SSD along with LP from the power plant is used to preheat the air for later usage in the HAD. In the case of only FGD, flue gas coming out from the boiler is used as a drying medium.

4. Modelling the steam power plant

Mathematical modeling of the steam cycle is based on conservation of mass and energy principles. Eq.(1) and Eq.(2) describes the mass and energy balance respectively.

$$\sum_i m_{in} = \sum_i m_{out} \tag{1}$$

$$\sum_i E_{in} = \sum_i E_{out} + \Delta E \tag{2}$$

where $\sum_i m_{in}$ and $\sum_i m_{out}$ respectively are mass in and mass out of a unit (kg/h), $\sum_i E_{in}$ and $\sum_i E_{out}$ respectively are energy flow in and out of a unit (kJ/h), and ΔE is the change (e.g. power output of a turbine) in energy of a unit (kJ/h).

The energy flow rate, E (kJ/h), is the product of the specific enthalpy, e (kJ/kg), of each stream and the mass flow rate, m (kg/h). The specific enthalpy and other properties of water or vapor stream such as specific entropy, s (kJ/kg-K), saturation temperature, T_{sat} (K), are calculated by Water97. Water97 is an Add-In for MS Excel which provides a set of functions for calculating thermodynamic and transport properties of water and steam using the industrial standard IAPWS-IF97 (Spang, 2002). The boiler feed water pumps are assumed to operate at 100 % isentropic efficiency, η_{pump}, defined by Eq.(3).

$$\eta_{pump} = \frac{(e_{out,s} - e_{in})}{(e_{out} - e_{in})} \times 100\% \tag{3}$$

where $e_{out,s}$ is enthalpy of the outlet stream of the pump at 100 % isentropic efficiency and e_{out} is the actual enthalpy of the stream at η_{pump}. The turbines are assumed to operate at 80 % isentropic efficiency. The isentropic efficiency, η_{turb}, is define by Eq.(4)

$$\eta_{turb} = \frac{(e_{in} - e_{out})}{(e_{in} - e_{out,s})} \times 100\% \tag{4}$$

e_{in} and e_{out} are the enthalpy values of the inlet and outlet streams of the turbine at the given isentropic efficiency respectively.
For the boiler, its heat duty depends on the lower heating value (LHV) of the fuel to be used and the boiler efficiency. The efficiency of the boiler, η_{boiler}, is assumed to be 90 % and the boiler duty, Q_{boiler} (kJ/h), can be calculated as in Eq.(5).

$$Q_{boiler} = \frac{(E_{12}-E_{11})}{\eta_{boiler}} \tag{5}$$

The LHV (kJ/kg) of EFB depends on the moisture content, X (%), and is estimated by using the data provided by the ERCN, Netherland (2012) as in Eq.(6).

$$LHV_{EFB} = 15820 - X * 181.99 \tag{6}$$

When EFB is totally dried (i.e. 0 % moisture), the LHV_{EFB} is 15,820 (kJ/kg). Hence, the feed rate of moist EFB, m_{EFB} (kg/h), required to generate a specific amount of boiler heat duty, Q_{boiler} (kJ/h), can be calculated by Eq.(7).

$$m_{EFB} = \frac{Q_{boiler}}{LHV_{EFB}} \tag{7}$$

The total power output, P_{out} (MW), for the closed cycle of the power plant in figure 1 for a given amount of EFB feed can be calculated by Eq.(8) using the W_i (the power output of the three turbines) and P_i (the pumping represents pumping power of the pumps.

$$P_{out} = (W_1 + W_2 + W_3) - (P_1 + P_2 + P_3) \tag{8}$$

5. Modelling of Dryers

We recently proposed a mathematical model to determine the optimum drying level of biomass (Gebreegziabher et al., 2013). The model incorporates material and energy balances as well as heat transfer and drying kinetics to determine the optimum moisture content for calorific value enhancement of wood where the drying medium is air. Besides, we recently developed a methodology for simulating drying process of EFB using air and super-heated steam for power generation using basic mass and energy balance (Luk et al., 2013). Hence the models of both HAD and SSD of this study are based on our previous works. Unlike HAD and SSD, the mathematical model of flue gas based dryer is based on combustion analysis of EFB. The material and energy balanced model for flue gas drying proposed by Yarnal and Puranik (2010) is used in this study. The ultimate analysis for EFB is 45.53 % C, 5.46 % H, 43.4 % O, 0.45 % N, and 5.12 % ash on a moisture free basis. The combustion products are estimated by assuming complete combustion of EFB with 50 % excess air and enthalpy values within the boiler, at the inlet and outlet of dryer were calculated using Eq.(9).

$$H^o - H^o_{298.15} = At + B\,{t^2}/{2} + C\,{t^3}/{3} + D\,{t^4}/{4} - {E}/{t} - H \tag{9}$$

H^o is standard enthalpy (kJ/mol) and A, B, C, D, E, H are constant values and the data for all product gases is readily available in any hand books. t is a function of the temperature of the flue gas, T (K), and is given by equation (10).

$$t = T/1000 \tag{10}$$

6. Objective function

The objective function is to maximize the overall efficiency, $\eta_{overall}$, defined by Eq.(11).

$$\eta_{overall} = \left(\frac{P_{out}}{(1-X_{F,d})m_{EFB}*LHV_{EFB\ at\ 0wt\%\ moisture}}\right)*100\% \quad (11)$$

The overall efficiency defined in Eq.(11) was maximized by changing the feed rate of air, the air preheat temperature, the temperature and relative humidity of the exhaust air, low pressure steam flow rate and flue gas outlet temperature with regard to water dew point temperature. Excel 2010 Standard GRG Non-linear Solver with Water 97 add-in was used to solve the optimization problem. For all cases stream data was extracted and composite curves are drawn.

7. Results

The results of the five case studies are summarized in Table 1. It shows that the integration of drying to power generation from EFB increases the overall energy efficiency. After taking drying into consideration, the overall energy efficiency increased from 22.08 % to 29.92 %. The main reason leading to the exceptionally low efficiency achieved by the Base Case is due to its high moisture content. Heat integration studies were performed for all cases to indicate the shortfalls in the integration. The composite curves of the studies as shown in Figure 2 indicates the tightest coupling of the hot and cold composite curves for HAD and SSD integrated plant using LP among all cases, indicating the heat is properly integrated.

8. Conclusions

A material and energy balance model of a 12.5 MW biomass steam power plant that utilizes EFB as fuel is presented in this paper. Water and steam properties in this model

Table 1. Summary of the effect of drying on the overall process efficiency

System	EFB Requirement kg/hr	Air for drying kg/hr	Final moisture (%)	Efficiency %
Base Case	45,589	-	70	20.08
Base Case preheat and optimum P	42,934	-	70	22.08
Integration with FGD	37803	-	14	26.59
Integration with HAD	34322	958544	4.5	27.36
Integration with HAD and SSD using LP	31576	355110	4.5	29.92

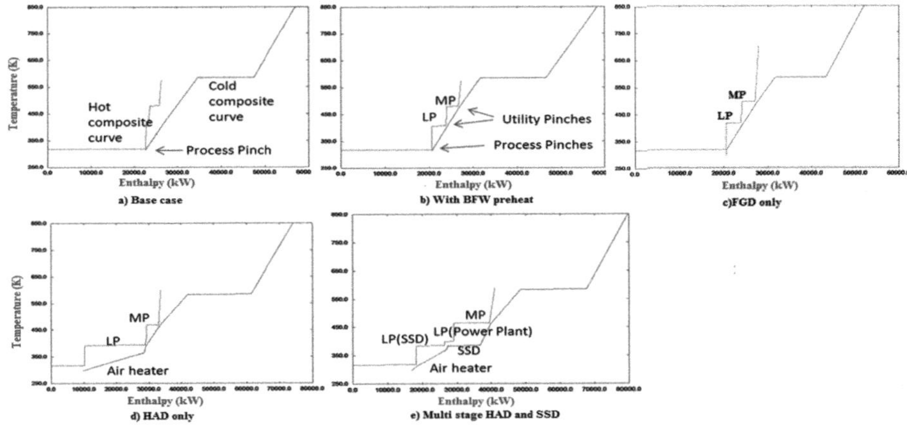

Figure 2. Composite curves of Case studies

were calculated using Water97 in Excel making the model be able to simulate and optimize the energy efficiency of the overall process. To obtain the optimal solution, the model simultaneously varied the flow rates, pressures and temperatures of the streams in the power plant as well as the drying process. Composite curves of the overall plant are plotted for each case to indicate the effectiveness of heat integration and to provide insights for further improvement. Results showed that huge improvement in energy efficiency can be achieved by proper drying of the biofuel. Innovative design of integrating a hot air dryer, a superheated steam dryer and flue gas dryer is proposed in this study. By proper integrating HAD and SSD together in to the power plant in multi-stage manner, energy efficiency can be improved by nearly 10 % comparing to the case where EFB was not dried.

Acknowledgements

The authors would acknowledge the financial support from the Hong Kong RGC-GRF grant (613513), the UGC-Infra-Structure Grt. (FSGRF13EG03), the Studentship from EVNG program, the International Studentship from the School of Engineering at HKUST and the PhD Fellowship to Oyedun A.O. from Hong Kong RGC (PF09-05997).

References

B. Le Lostec, N. Galanis, J. Baribeault, J. Millette, 2008, Wood chip drying with an absorption heat pump, Energy, 33, 500-512.

B. Linnhoff, F. Alanis, 1989, A systems approach based on pinch technology to commercial power station design, ASME Advanced Energy Systems, 85, 10-15.

B. Linnhoff, J.R. Flower, 1978, Synthesis of heat exchanger networks: I. Systematic generation of energy optimal networks, AIChE Journal, 24, 633-642.

B. Spang, 2002, Water97_v13.xla – Excel Add-In for Properties of Water and Steam in SI-Units, Hamburg, Germany.

C. Fu, T. Gundersen, 2010, Heat integration of an oxy-combustion process for coal-fired power plants with CO2 capture by pinch analysis, Chemical Engineering Transactions, 21, 181.186.

C. J. Ross, 2008. Biomass Drying and Dewatering for Clean Heat & Power, North West CHP Application Center, Olympia WA.

C. W. Hui, S. Ahmad, 1994, Total site heat integration using the utility system, Computers and Chemical Engineering, 18, 729-742.

E. Andersson, S. Harvey, T. Berntsson, 2006, Energy efficient upgrading of biofuel integrated with a pulp mill, Energy, 31, 1384-1394.

ERCN, 2012. Phyllis2; Database for Biomass and Waste, Energy Research Centre of the Netherlands, Netherlands.

G. S. Yarnal, V. S. Puranik, 2009, Energy Management Study in Sugar Industries by Various Bagasse Drying Methods, Strategic Planning for Energy and the Environment, 29, 56-78.

H. N. Li, Q. Chen, X. H. Zhang, K. N. Finney, V. N. Sharifi, J. Swithenbank, 2012, Evaluation of a biomass drying process using waste heat from process industries: A case study, Applied Thermal Engineering, 35, 71-80.

H. Song, F. Starfelt, L. Daianova, J. Y. Yan, 2012, Influence of drying process on the biomass-based polygeneration system of bioethanol, power and heat, Applied Energy, 90, 32-37.

H. T. Luk, T. Y. Lam, A. O. Oyedun, T. Gebreegziabher, C. W. Hui, 2013, Drying of Biomass for Power Generation: A Case Study on Power Generation from Empty Fruit Bunch (EFB), Energy, 63, 205-215.

K. J. Chua, A. S. Mujumdar, M. N. A. Hawlader, S. K. Chou, J. C. Ho, 2001, Batch drying of banana pieces - effect of stepwise change in drying air temperature on drying kinetics and product colour, Food Research International, 34, 721-731.

T. Gebreegziabher, A. O. Oyedun, C.W. Hui, 2013, Optimum biomass drying for combustion – A modeling approach, Energy, 53, 67-73.

Jiří Jaromír Klemeš, Petar Sabev Varbanov and Peng Yen Liew (Editors)
Proceedings of the 24th European Symposium on Computer Aided Process Engineering – ESCAPE 24
June 15-18, 2014, Budapest, Hungary.

An Improved Linear Programming Approach for Simultaneous Optimization of Water and Energy

Maziar Kermani[b], Zoé Périn-Levasseur[b,]*, Marzouk Benali[b], Luciana Savulescu[b], Francois Maréchal[a]

[a]*EPFL/Industrial Processes & Energy Systems Engineering Group (IPESE), Lausanne, Switzerland*
[b]*Natural Resources Canada/CanmetENERGY, Varennes, Quebec, Canada*
zoe.perin-levasseur@nrcan.gc.ca

Abstract

An optimization method based on Mixed Integer Linear Programming (MILP) has been developed for simultaneous optimization of water and energy (SOWE) in industrial processes. The superstructure integrates process thermal streams and optimizes the consumption of water while maximizing internal heat recovery to reduce thermal utility consumption. In this paper, additional concepts have been implemented in the superstructure to target the issues of the pulp and paper processes. Non-Isothermal Mixing (NIM) has been considered at different locations in order to reduce the number of thermal streams and decrease the investment cost by avoiding unnecessary investment on heat exchangers. The concepts of restricted matches and water tanks have been added to the superstructure to adapt it to the pulp and paper case studies. The Integer-Cut Constraint (ICC) technique has been combined with the MILP model to generate systematically a set of optimal solutions to support the decision-making for cost-effective configurations.

Keywords: combined water and energy; process integration; linear programming.

1. Introduction

Improving the energy efficiency of pulp and paper mills is strongly interconnected to the optimal management of water, which underlines the development of a methodology that can address water and energy reduction simultaneously. Reported state-of-the-art publications on water and energy optimization can be categorized into two groups: conceptual and mathematical methods. Conceptual methods are generally insight-based approaches such as Savulescu and Alva-Argaez (2013). They provide a good vision of the whole procedure using powerful visualization tools. However, these approaches may result in an arduous path to reach the minimum water and energy consumption. On the other side, non-linear mathematical approaches such as Ahmetovic and Kravanja (2014) are complex and less popular among experienced engineers due to their difficult applications in practical contexts. These methods cannot guarantee the global optimum. A further barrier when developing a combined water-energy optimization is the unavailability of measured water contamination levels, which makes it difficult to target water reuse opportunities. This paper provides a novel simultaneous optimization of water and energy (SOWE) method built on a MILP model overcoming these barriers. The NIM concept and multi-contaminant problem as well as the simultaneous integration of the water network and process energy streams have also been addressed by linear programming.

2. Methodology

2.1. SOWE superstructure definition

The SOWE method is based on a mathematical formulation of the superstructure optimization, including a heat cascade and a source/sink model. A set of water sources N_S and demands N_D are available. Each source produces a specific amount of water $\dot{m}_S$ at a given temperature T_S with a maximum allowed contamination level(s) C_S^{max}. Each demand needs an amount of water $\dot{m}_D$ with a specific temperature T_D and maximum level(s) of contamination C_D^{max}. Besides, a list of process thermal streams N_{th} is also provided consisting of hot and cold streams. Each stream is characterized by an inlet (outlet) temperature, $T_{in}(T_{out})$ together with a heat load Q_{th}. Thermal utilities (i.e. hot or cold utilities) are also available in case that energy within the system is not sufficient to satisfy the energy demands. The existing wastewater treatment system processes wastewater at a fixed temperature and any contamination level. Figure 1 illustrates the SOWE superstructure with two sources and two demands. All sources-demands interconnections are considered as well as the NIM concept. Since SOWE is based on MILP, an innovative linearized formulation of the NIM has been integrated in the superstructure. This is done by replacing unknown temperature levels at which NIM can take place with pre-defined levels through the concept of sub-units. These temperature levels are the ones available in the water network.

2.2. Mathematical formulation

The objective function of the MILP corresponds to minimizing the total cost:

$$\min_{R_r, y_w, f_w} \left(\sum_{w=1}^{N_w} c_w \times f_w \right) \times time + \frac{i(1+i)^{n_y}}{(1+i)^{n_y} - 1} \sum_{w=1}^{n_w} (ICF_w \times y_w + ICP_w \times f_w) \tag{1}$$

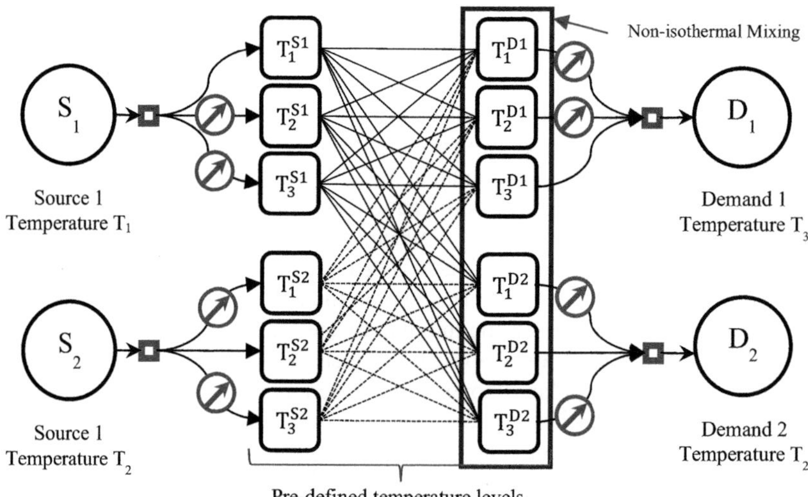

Figure 1. Linear SOWE superstructure for 2 sources, 2 demands, and 3 levels of temperature.

Subjected to:

1. Existence of a system (e.g. utility of fresh water, sub-units, hot utility …):

$$y_w f_w^{min} \leq f_w \leq y_w f_w^{max} \qquad y_w \in \{0,1\}, \forall\, w = 1, \dots, N_w \tag{2}$$

2. Heat cascade model (Maréchal and Kalitventzeff, 1996)
3. Source/Sink model,
4. Temperature constraint on mixers before water demands: The weighted average temperature of all inlet mass streams i to demand j should be equal to its temperature multiplied by its mass flow rate. This is the non-isothermal constraint at the inlet of each mixer.

$$\sum_{i=1}^{N_{sub-units}} T_i \times f_{i,j} = T_j \times f_j \qquad \forall\, j = 1, \dots, N_D \tag{3}$$

5. Contamination constraint on mixers before water demands: A concentration of total suspended solids measured in ppm is selected as the water contaminant. The weighted average of the contamination level of all mass streams inlet to the demand should be equal or less than the maximum allowed contamination demand. For multi-contaminant problems, Yang and Grossmann (2013) proved that the minimum fresh water target by Eq. (4) is the same as the optimum predicted value by nonlinear formulation under a specific condition, i.e. at least one contamination reaches its maximum level at all the process units with nonzero water reuse streams.

$$\sum_{i=1}^{N_{sub-units}} C_{i,max} \times f_{i,j} \leq C_{j,max} \times f_j \tag{4}$$

With:

R_r	the heat cascaded from the temperature interval r to the lower temperature intervals (r=1, n_r + 1) [kW]
C_i^{max}	maximum contamination level allowed.
c_w	operating cost of utility w , [USD/s/unit of w]
f_w	level of utilization of subsystem w (e.g. the heat load of a thermal utility unit)
$time$	operating time [s]
i	interest rate
ICF_w	fixed investment cost [USD/y]
ICP_w	proportional investment cost [USD/y/unit of w]
$f_{i,j}$	mass transfer from unit i to unit j [kg/s]

3. Benchmarking analysis

The improved MILP-based SOWE approach has been evaluated using several examples from the literature (Bagajewicz et al. (2002), and Dong et al. (2008)). The benchmarking analysis was done using key performance indicators based on energy and water targets, network complexity, and operating and investment costs.

3.1. Addressing a multi-contaminant problem

Dong et al. (2008) example is a multi-contaminant problem solved via a MINLP algorithm. Fresh water (0 ppm) is available at 80 °C. Hot and cold utilities are steam at 160 °C, and cooling water at 10 °C.

As shown in Table 1, SOWE methodology reaches the same targets as Dong's approach, which indicates a correct formulation of multi-contaminant problem with linear programming. Moreover, it shows that the new linear formulation of NIM allows reducing the investment cost by almost 10 %. This can be explained by the selected streams lowering the surface area of heat exchangers.

3.2. Comparing two MILP approaches

In Bagajewicz et al. (2002) example, the MILP approach relies on two sequential LP problems to target the water and energy consumptions. A MILP transshipment model is used to build the HEN having the utility targets as constraints.

Bagajewicz et al. (2002) only consider heat exchange among fresh water and wastewater streams while SOWE method includes water reuse streams in the heat exchange network. The results indicate that the number of thermal streams is reduced by 20 % due to the higher number of NIMs (12 compared to 10).

4. SOWE adjustment for pulp and paper industry

The concept of restricted matches between process unit operations (PUOs) aims to:

1. Address economic and process topology limitations; i.e. recycling between specific processes or a heat exchange among certain streams can be beneficial or disadvantageous depending on economic, material and geographical constraints.
2. Avoid the use of contamination levels, which are often difficult to have access in the pulp and paper processes.

Table 1. Performance, complexity and economic indicators

Related Article		Example of Dong		Example of Bagajewicz	
		Dong et al. 2008	SOWE	Bagajewicz et al. 2002	SOWE
Approach		Mathematical		Mathematical	
Mathematical programming		MINLP	MILP	MILP	MILP
Objective/Objective function		Total cost	Total cost	Nb. of matches	Total cost
HEN design		YES	NO	YES	NO
Key Performance Indicators (KPIs)					
Vapor	kW	1254	1254	5265	5265
Cooling water	kW	7106	7106	0	0
Clean water	kg/s	70	70	126	126
Contaminated water	kg/s	70	70	126	126
Network Indicators					
Nb. of thermal streams	-	7	6	10	8
Heat exchangers	-	6	6	12	7
Total area of HEs	m^2	181	114	788	760
Nb. of mixers (NIM)	-	4 (2)	6 (3)	13 (10)	21 (12)
Financial Indicators					
Operating cost	\$/yr	1,157,518	1,157,518	1,349,553	1,349,553
Investment cost	\$/yr	82,015	74,355	196,289	129,828
Total cost	\$/yr	1,239,533	1,231,873	1,545,841	1,479,381

A level of restriction is defined for each stream using binary variables. Eq.(5) allows or prevents connections among PUOs:

$$\sum_{i=1}^{N_{sub-units}} RM^k{}_i \times f_{i,j} \geq RM^k{}_j \times f_j \tag{5}$$

Water tanks have also been added to the superstructure to assess their temperature variation influence on utility consumption. They act as hubs in which water streams from outlet of heat exchangers can be mixed non-isothermally to reach a fixed temperature and then can be used in any other process units or cooling duties. In a real industrial process, water streams and process thermal streams are often combined, i.e. process thermal streams can interact with water thermal streams for energy target reduction. SOWE method has the ability to address this aspect, which has never been addressed explicitly in the literature. ICC can also be used to generate automatically the ordered set of solutions (Fazlollahi et al., 2012). This allows comparing the solutions with regard to different criteria, which has not been taken into account in the objective function. These SOWE features are applied to a pulp and paper case study.

4.1. Pulp and paper case study

SOWE method has been applied to a simplified kraft pulp process. The water system and the main thermal process streams from which heat can be recovered are shown in Table 2. Fresh water is considered as process and cooling water resulting in simultaneous minimization of water and energy consumptions.

Restricted matches concept is applied using the following restrictions:

1. Outlet of recausticizing, washing and bleaching cannot be reused.
2. Outlet of the pulp machine can only be reused in washing section.
3. Outlet of the stock preparation can only be reused in bleaching section.
4. No fresh water can be used to dilute the wastewater streams,
5. No recycling can take place within each tank.
6. A connection is possible from cold water tank to warm water tank either directly or through a heat exchanger.

The use of binary variables to allow or prevent a match is used in the superstructure model. Table 3 shows that by using SOWE method the total water consumption will be reduced by 17 % while no thermal hot utility is used. The investment cost is increased by 10 % due to a lower approach temperature in heat exchangers. Though total cost

Table 2. Operating data and conditions of the kraft process case study.

PUOs	T_{in}	T_{out}	Flow	Process thermal streams	T_{in}	T_{out}	Load
	°C	°C	kg/s		°C	°C	kW
Pulp machine	50	50	10	Surface condenser	65	64	7,560
Bleaching	70	70	20	Turpentine condenser	95	50	10,920
Washing	65	65	35	Effluent	75	40	2,205
Stock preparation	62	62	25	Dryer exhaust	59	30	1,050
Recausticization	35	35	20	Contaminated condensate	80	65	630
Source and sink				Utility thermal streams			
Fresh water	-	10	-	Hot utility	120	120	-
Waste water	-	30	-	Cold utility	10	35	-
Water tanks							
Hot water tank	62	62	-	Warm water tank	35	35	-

Table 3. Results of the case study

			Reference Case	SOWE
Key Performance Indicators	Fresh water	kg/s	137	104 (-24 %)
	Hot utility	kW	3,392	0
	Cold utility*	kW (kg/s)	14,257 (136)	12,795 (122)
	Total water consumption[1]	kg/s	273	227 (-17 %)
	Waste outlet temperature	°C	59	59
Network Indicators	Nb of thermal streams	-	13	8
	Nb of heat exchangers	-	7	7
	Total area of HEs	m^2	310	462.6
Financial Indicators	Operating cost	$/yr	774,635	243,645 (-69 %)
	Investment cost	$/yr	104,287	114,673 (+10 %)
	Total cost	$/yr	878,922	358,318 (-60 %)

* Cold utility required to cool down waste streams to 30°C.

[1] Sum of fresh water and water needed to cool down the waste.

decreases by 60 %. When compared to the actual operating condition of the total kraft mill, this corresponds to a 5 %-reduction of the total cost. Sensitivity analysis can also be performed on tank temperature to investigate its impact on utility consumption.

5. Concluding remarks

A linear modified definition of non-isothermal mixing has been included in a linear mathematical model for simultaneous optimization of water and energy to reduce the number of thermal streams in the network. Hence, it reduces the number of heat exchangers and decreases the investment cost. To respond to the pulp and paper industry needs, the SOWE method was improved by including the concepts of restricted matches, temperature flexibility of water tanks, and integer-cut constraint technique. As a result, a spectrum of cost-effective decision-making solutions is obtained. The MILP/ICC-based SOWE method has been satisfactorily applied to a kraft mill resulting in a complete elimination of the steam used for hot water production through water reuse, equivalent in lowering water intake by 24 %.

References

E. Ahmetovic, Z. Kravanja, 2014, Simultaneous optimization of heat-integrated water networks involving process-to-process streams for heat integration, Applied Thermal Engineering, 62, 302-317.

M. Bagajewicz, H. Rodera, M. Savelski, 2002, Energy efficient water utilization systems in process plants, Computers and Chemical Engineering, 26, 59-79.

H.-G. Dong, C.-Y. Lin, C.-Y. Chang, 2008, Simultaneous optimization approach for integrated water-allocation and heat-exchange network, Chemical Engineering Science, 63, 3664-3678.

S. Fazlollahi, P. Mandel, G. Becker, F. Maréchal, 2012, Methods for multi-objective investment and operating optimization of complex energy systems, Energy, 45, 12-22.

F. Maréchal, B. Kalitventzeff, 1996, Targeting the minimum cost of energy requirement: A new graphical technique for evaluating the integration of utility systems, Computers and Chemical Engineering, 20, S225-S230.

L. Savulescu, A. Alva-Argaez, 2013, Process Integration Concepts for Combined Energy and Water Integration, Handbook of Process Integration (PI): Minimisation of Energy and Water Use, Waste and Emissions, 461-483, Woodhead Publishing Limited, Cambridge, UK.

L. Yang, I. E. Grossmann, 2013, Water targeting Models for Simultaneous Flowsheet Optimization, Industrial and Engineering Chemistry Research, 52, 3209-3224.

Jiří Jaromír Klemeš, Petar Sabev Varbanov and Peng Yen Liew (Editors)
Proceedings of the 24th European Symposium on Computer Aided Process Engineering – ESCAPE 24
June 15-18, 2014, Budapest, Hungary.

The Total Site Approach as a Synthesis Tool for the Selection of Valorization Paths in Lignocellulosic Biorefineries

Michail E. Stefanakis, Konstantinos A. Pyrgakis, Aikaterini D. Mountraki, Antonis C. Kokossis*

School of Chemical Engineering, National Technical University of Athens, Heroon Polytechniou 9, Athens 15780, Greece
akokossis@mail.ntua.gr

Abstract

This paper deploys Total Site Analysis as a process synthesis methodology for the valorization and selection of chemical paths in order to integrate under studied biorefineries. As a results, it is able to screen numerous and complex candidate chemical paths and select the best integrated product portfolios. The methodology offers the rules to collocate and integrate plants together securing the feasible margins of maximum energy efficiency and sustainability of the biorefinery. The proposed methodology applied to integrate a lignocellulosic biorefinery converting biomass to three chemical intermediates: Lignin, C5 and C6 Sugars. Then, a set of chemical paths is branched to convert these intermediates to the final products through 8 chemical paths. The purpose of this process synthesis approach is to valorize and select the best integrated combination of plants that subject to minimum energy consumption and offer the highest energy savings. As a result, the methodology offered high reduction to the energy consumption and high energy savings of up to 83.3 % and 84.4 % of heating and cooling duties, respectively.

Keywords: Biorefinery, Lignocellulosic, Process Integration, Pinch Analysis, Total Site Analysis.

1. Introduction

In this paper, a scheme of energy intensive chemical production paths that convert biomass to intermediate and final products are possible to enter in an understudy biorefinery. Since these chemical paths constitute a significant degree of freedom, it is proposed that a Process integration procedure should be upgraded into a process synthesis tool.

Process Integration (Kemp, 2007) is significant to secure the feasible and sustainable margins for energy efficiency improvement of chemical processes. Total Site Analysis (Dhole and Linnhoff, 1993a) is a powerful tool of Process Integration procedure able to consider and manage the complexity of energy interactions among plants. In that context, methodologies and tools, applying Total Site Analysis, have been developed to assess sensitivity analysis (Liew et al., 2012) and optimize energy costs (Maréchal and Kalitventzeff, 1998). Recently, Total Site Analysis has been applied to target process modifications (Chew et al., 2013) and regional integration for the selection of energy sources optimizing energy targets and environmental footprints (Čuček et al., 2013). However, Total Site Analysis has been exclusively addressed for energy targeting and optimization of a Total Site including known and specifically selected processes and not to cases that candidate processes are possible to enter, or not, in a new refinery.

The contribution of this concept is that candidate chemical production lines are integrated within different Total Sites managing the number of the included processes as a degree of freedom. The valorization and screening procedure of separate Total Sites targets to the optimal selection of the appropriate process combinations that subject to maximum energy savings. Indeed, this process to process synthesis methodology proved that the selection of appropriate processes to collocate and integrate them together can offer huge energy benefits for the understudied biorefinery than integrating them individually. The proposed methodology has been applied in the course of BIOCORE project to assess an understudied lignocellulosic biorefinery and contributed for the selection of the appropriate product portfolios, among a scheme of 8 candidate and energy intensive processes, offering maximum energy savings of up to 83.3 % and 84.4 % of heating and cooling duties, respectively.

All candidate processes were simulated in Aspen Plus V7.2. The energy targets have been detected to Background process needs (Heat Exchangers) and physical separations (distillation columns and evaporators). Pinch Analysis (Dhole and Linnhoff, 1993b) was used for the integration of distillation columns and evaporators by adding separation effects and changing operating temperatures and pressures.

2. Methodology approach

So that, given a generic scheme (Figure 1) of chemical production paths, there are processes possible to enter in a biorefinery. The target of this methodology is to select the appropriate combination of processes that subject to minimum energy consumption and offer the highest energy savings using Total Site Analysis upgraded in a process synthesis approach. This purpose gives the guidelines for the development of clusters of processes – each of which represents a Total Site – that are integrated together and include all possible combinations depending on the number of the selected processes each time. The clusters that are developed include processes that use different feedstocks. For the scheme of Figure 1, where four feeds are included, there are detected four different types of clusters. These are Type 1 (8 different clusters), Type 2 (23 different clusters), Type 3 (28 different clusters) and Type 4 (12 different clusters) including 1, 2, 3 and 4 processes, respectively.

Thus, each process can be integrated individually (Type 1) or together with other processes (Types 2, 3 and 4) according to the number of processes selected to be involved in a cluster. The great advantage of process to process integration is that high available energy of a process is able to be used to cover the energy duties of other incoming processes making them very promising. This energy benefit even augments as long as more processes are selected to get integrated together in one cluster. The proposed synthesis approach offers the answers about which processes seem to be the most promising and should be included in the final biorefinery. For example, a synthesis procedure that involves four processes in the final solution may conclude to the selection of different types of clusters such as Type 2 and Type 2 or Type 3 and Type 1 or only Type 4.

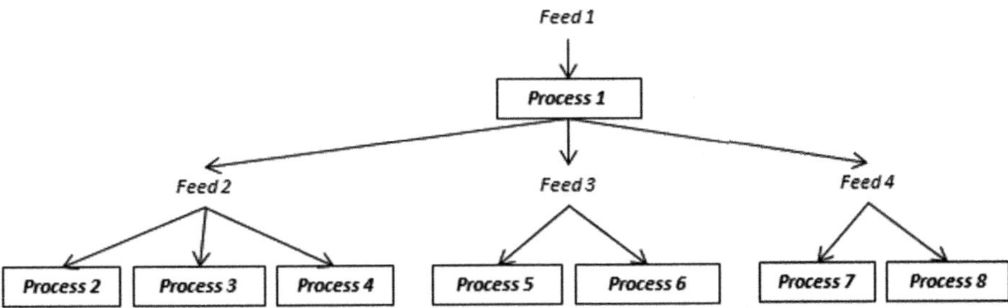

Figure 1. Generic scheme of chemical production paths

The final solution is explicitly affected by two synthesis constraints which are feed availability and the total number of the desired processes. The capacities of the plants are fixed and selected based on the conversion rates of the chemical paths. As a result, on one hand, if the problem is constraint by feed availability then each feed should be used at once and since a process (e.g. Process 2) uses one feed (e.g. Feed 2) then no other competitive processes, which use the same feed, are able to be involved in the final solution (e.g. Processes 3 and 4). Example 1 (Section 3.2) presents the effect of feed availability constraint to the final solution. On the other hand, there is studied the case that all chemical plants are desired to be included in the final biorefinery independently of feedstock supply. Example 2 (Section 3.3) presents the effect of the desired processes constraint to the final solution.

3. Results and Examples

3.1. The understudied lignocellulosic biorefinery

The proposed methodology has been applied within BIOCORE project scoping to the optimal synthesis of an integrated lignocellulosic biorefinery. The candidate chemical production paths consist of the main process, Organosolv, for the fractionation of biomass to its main components: C5 Sugars, C6 Sugars and Lignin. These intermediate products constitute available feeds for a range of other chemical processes. As a result, a set of chemical paths, each of which constitutes an individual plant, are branched to convert these intermediates to the final products which are PF Resins, PolyUrethanes, Ethanol, Xylitol (biological and catalytic process) and Itaconic Acid (Figure 2). As a result, there are eight candidate processes that are possible to enter to the final lignocellulosic biorefinery. The valorized heating and cooling duties before and after integration and the respective energy savings are presented in Table 1. Specifically, there are presented the top three clusters of each Type that result the highest energy savings. The screening results of Table 1 prove that higher energy savings are succeeded as more process are collocated and integrated together.

3.2. Example 1: Feed availability constrained problem

In this example, there is presented the synthesis procedure for the selection of the appropriate processes (Figure 2) for a lignocellulosic biorefinery. This example constrained by feed availability rules the usage of each feed only at once. As a result, competitive processes are forbidden to be included in the final solution. Thus, the synthesis methodology will select four processes supplied by the four available feedstocks and possibly tended to be integrated together in one Total Site of Type 4. However, since each cluster is ruled to include non competitive plants, the necessity of the other Types 1, 2 and 3 is still being important for cases where competitive processes should be included in the final solution.

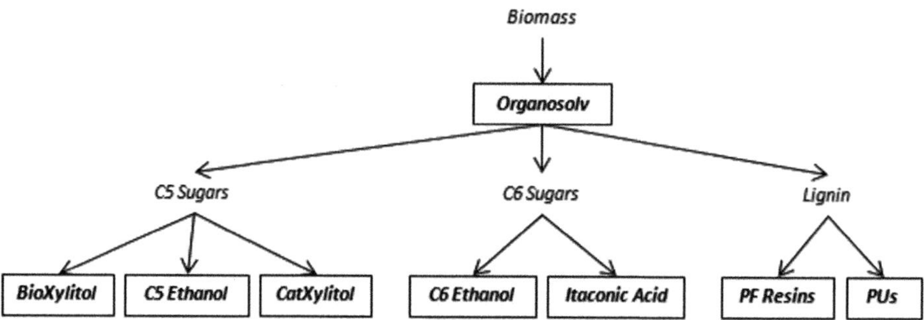

Figure 2. Scheme of chemical production paths of BIOCORE lignocellulosic biorefinery

Demonstrative results of the synthesis procedure are presented in Table 2 in order to show the contribution of the concept of using and combining different Total Sites. The same procedure is apparently conducted for all other possible combinations to detect the best ones. The fact that collocation offers higher energy benefits is being proved through Selections 1 to 3 (Table 2), where more processes are introduced in the same cluster. Nevertheless, this synthesis approach offers the opportunity to valorize the competitiveness among processes and screen which incoming process seems to be more or less profitable. This is shown in Selections 3 and 4 (Table 2), where the introduction of C5 Ethanol (Selection 4) increases energy duties and reduces energy savings. The selected processes, for the feed constrained problem, are Organosolv, BioXylitol, Itaconic Acid and PF Resins in one Total Site (Type 4) reducing the energy consumption of heating and cooling duties, respectively, from 226.4 and 228.6 MW to 37.8 and 35.8 MW, offering the highest energy savings of 83.3 % and 84.4 %.

Table 1. Energy duties and energy savings of clusters before and after integration.

	Processes included in cluster	Hot Utilities before/after integration [MW]	Hot Utility savings [%]	Cold Utilities before/after integration [MW]	Cold Utility savings [%]
Type 1	CatXyl	3.4 / 0.6	82 %	4.5 / 1.7	62 %
	Itac	42.1 / 8.5	80 %	53.7 / 20.2	62 %
	Organ	152.1 / 37.9	75 %	139.0 / 22.7	84 %
Type 2	CatXyl - PU	4.2 / 0.6	85 %	5.2 / 1.6	69 %
	Itac – PF Res	45.3 / 8.8	81 %	58.8 / 24.1	59 %
	Organ - BioXyl	181.1 / 37.9	79 %	169.8 / 24.4	86 %
Type 3	Organ - BioXyl - Itac	223.2 / 37.8	83 %	223.5 / 35.9	84 %
	Organ - CatXyl - Itac	197.6 / 37.8	81 %	197.2 / 35.3	82 %
	CatXyl - Itac - PF Res	48.7 / 9.8	80 %	63.3 / 24.4	61 %
Type 4	Organ - BioXyl - Itac - PF Res	226.4 / 37.8	83 %	228.6 / 35.8	84 %
	Organ - CatXyl - Itac - PU	198.5 / 37.8	81 %	197.9 / 35.3	82 %
	Organ - C5 Eth-Itac- PF Res	226.9 / 58.7	74 %	226.3 / 53.8	76 %

Table 2. Representation of synthesis procedure constrained by the feed availability.

Total Biorefinery	Utilities [MW] Heating/Cooling	Recovery [%] Heating/Cooling
Organ, BioXyl, Itaconic, PF Res: Initial Duties	226.4 / 228.6	-
Selection 1	56.7 / 56.9	75 % / 75 %
Organosolv, BioXyl, Itaconic, PF Resins: all Type 1		
Selection 2	46.7 / 48.5	79 % / 79 %
Organosolv + BioXyl:Type 2 and Itaconic +PF Resins:Type 2		
Selection 3	37.8 / 35.8	83 % / 84 %
Organosolv + BioXyl + Itaconic + PF Resins : Type 4		
Organ, C5 Eth, Itaconic, PF Res:Initial Duties	223.5 / 226.3	-
Selection 4	58.7 / 53.8	74 % / 76 %
Organosolv +C5 Ethanol +Itaconic +PF Resins : Type 4		

3.3. Example 2: Problem constrained by the desired processes

This example is constrained by the use of all processes in the final lignocellulosic biorefinery. The results and the structure of such a procedure are presented in Table 3. The conduction of the proposed synthesis approach, including all processes in the biorefinery, concluded to the selection of Organosolv, XylBIO, Itaconic Acid and PF Resins (Type 4) in the first Total Site, C5 Ethanol, C6 Ethanol and PolyUrethanes (Type 3) in the second Total Site and XylCat to be integrated individually. Using all processes, the total energy consumption of heating and cooling duties, respectively, reduced from 279.8 and 281.9 MW to 79.1 and 76.1 MW, offering the highest energy savings of 71.6 % and 73.0 %.

Table 3. Representation of synthesis procedure constrained by the desired processes.

Total Biorefinery	Utilities [MW] Heating / Cooling	Recovery [%] Heating / Cooling
All processes included: Initial Energy Duties	279.8 / 281.9	-
Organ + C5 Eth + C6 Eth + PU:Type 4 BioXyl + Itaconic + PF Resins: Type 3 XylCat: Type 1	98.8 / 95.8	65 % / 66 %
Organosolv + XylCat + C6 Eth + PF Resins:Type 4 BioXyl + Itaconic: Type 2 C5 Eth + PU: Type 2	102.0 / 98.1	64 % / 65 %
Organosolv + BioXyl + Itaconic + PF Resins:Type 4 C5 Eth + C6 Eth + PU: Type 3 XylCat: Type 1	79.5 / 76.1	72 % / 73 %

4. Conclusions

In this paper, it is proposed a Total Site Analysis procedure upgraded into a process synthesis tool for the valorization, screening and selection of the appropriate chemical production paths to enter in an understudied biorefinery. The proposed methodology is able to detect promising product portfolios among numerous and complex chemical production paths and find the best way of plant collocation that offers the highest energy savings for the final biorefinery. The results prove that collocating and integrating more processes together offers higher energy savings than integrating them individually. The methodology has been applied in the context of BIOCORE project and contributed to detect the best integrated product portfolios and the best way to collate them together. As a result, there are proposed two different structures for a lignocellulosic biorefinery which offer high energy savings of up to 83.3 % and 84.4 % of heating and cooling duties, respectively.

Acknowledgements

Financial support from the European Research Program BIOCORE (FP7-241566) is gratefully acknowledged.

References

K.H. Chew, S.R. Wan Alwi, J.J. Klemes, Z.A. Manan, 2013, Process Modification Potentials for Total Site Heat Integration, Chemical Engineering Transactions, 35, 175-180

L. Čuček, P.S. Varbanov, J.J. Klemeš, Z. Kravanja, 2013, Multi-Objective Regional Total Site Integration, Chemical Engineering Transactions, 35, 97-102

V.R. Dhole and B. Linnhoff, 1993a, Total site targets for fuel, co-generation, emissions, and cooling, Computers and Chemical Engineering, 17, 101-109

V.R. Dhole and B. Linnhoff, 1993b, Distillation columnn targets, Computers Chemical Engineering, 17, 549-560

I.C. Kemp, 2007, Pinch Analysis and Process Integration: A User Guide on Process Integration for the Efficient Use of Energy, Elsevier Butterworth-Heinemann, Oxford, UK

P.Y. Liew, S.R.Wan Alwi, P.S. Varbanov, Z.A. Manan, J.J. Klemes, 2012, A numerical technique for Total Site sensitivity analysis, Applied Thermal Engineering, 40, 397-408

F. Maréchal and B. Kalitventzeff, 1998, Energy integration of industrial sites: tools, methodology and application, Applied Thermal Engineering, 18, 921-933

Jiří Jaromír Klemeš, Petar Sabev Varbanov and Peng Yen Liew (Editors)
Proceedings of the 24th European Symposium on Computer Aided Process Engineering – ESCAPE 24
June 15-18, 2014, Budapest, Hungary.

Screening Curve Method for Optimum Source Sizing to Satisfy Time Varying Demand

Krishna Priya G.S., Santanu Bandyopadhyay*

Department of Energy Science and Engineering, Indian Institute of Technology Bombay, Powai, Mumbai 400076, INDIA

santanub@iitb.ac.in

Abstract

Screening curve method was originally proposed for sizing various power plant capacities to satisfy time varying power demand. Though screening curve methods are normally used for power system planning, they can be applied on a wide range of process systems related problems. In this paper the concept of screening curve methodology is extended to determine optimal sizing of various sources to satisfy time varying demands. Applicability of the proposed methodology is illustrated with various examples: cost optimal sizing various pumps to satisfy time varying water demand, energy optimal sizing of various reciprocating compressors to deliver time varying compressed air requirement, and cost optimal sizing of various air conditioning systems to satisfy time varying cooling requirement.

Keywords: screening curve; optimisation; time varying demand; system sizing.

1. Introduction

In any electrical power system, electrical power demand varies over time. The power is supplied by various types of power plants, e.g., coal based power plant, nuclear power plant, natural gas fired gas turbine power plant, hydroelectric power plant, etc. Investment and operating costs of these power plants also varies significantly. For example, investment cost of a coal based power plant is significantly higher than that of the gas turbine based power plant. On the other hand, operating cost of a coal based power plant is much lower than that of the gas turbine based power plant. Because of these two competing costs, coal based power plant is cheaper if it runs for longer duration of time and a gas turbine power plant is cheaper if it runs for a short duration of time. It is one of the most important problem in power system design is to decide appropriate sizing of various power plants to satisfy time varying power demand most economically. Screening curve methodology was originally proposed to address this problem (Fitzpatrick and Gallagher, 1962) and continues to find applications in the field of power system planning to this day as by Batlle and Rodilla (2013) where screening curve method is used for thermal expansion planning.

In many process systems problems, a large number of demands are time varying. The demands for electricity, cooling requirements, water, etc. are common examples. Typically, single source with the capability of supplying the maximum demand is chosen to meet the time varying demand. This results in part load operation of the source for predominant period. Most equipment operates with significantly lower efficiency at part load condition and oversized large supply equipment typically operates at much higher operating cost. There may also be significant capital investment related to high capacity of the source. It is therefore important to identify an optimum source mix for meeting the time varying demand. In this paper the concept of screening curve methodology, usually used in power system planning, is extended to other systems. Applicability of the proposed methodology is illustrated with various examples: energy optimal sizing of various reciprocating compressors to deliver time varying compressed air requirement, cost optimal sizing various pumps to satisfy time varying water demand, and cost optimal sizing of various air conditioning systems to satisfy time varying cooling requirement. These examples prove that the screening curve method is simple, versatile, and yet a powerful methodology for appropriately sizing various equipments to satisfy time varying demands.

2. Problem statement and solution methodology

Consider a time varying demand $d(t)$ over a time interval $0 \le (t) \le T$. Now, consider various sources capable of meeting this demand. Let the incremental cost associated with each of these sources be:

$$C_i = F_{Ci} + V_{Ci} * CF \qquad \forall i \tag{1}$$

where CF is the capacity factor (or, normalized time as a fraction of time horizon of interest), F_{Ci} is the annualised fixed cost and V_{Ci} is the variable cost associated with i^{th} source. Let demand D_i , which persists for time CF_i be met by source S_1, D_2 by source S_2, D_i by source S_i and D_n by source S_n where n is the total number of sources available. The objective here is to meet the total demand requirements using the available sources at the lowest possible cost. The total cost function can be written as,

$$C_{tot} = \sum_{i=1}^{i=n} D_i \times F_{Ci} + \sum_{i=1}^{i=n} D_i \times CF_i \times V_{Ci} \tag{2}$$

where the first term is the fixed costs component and the second is the variable component. It should be noted that the fixed component of total cost depends on the sizing of each source, while the variable cost also depends on how long the source is in use. The demand can be plotted as a load-duration curve (LDC) by depicting the demand as a function of its duration. The LDC is obtained by arranging all load levels in descending order of magnitude and plotting them against the duration for which they occur. In other words, it represents the percentage (or number) of hours of a given time frame at which the load is at or above a given value. In other words it is a plot of D vs. CF. To minimize cost, it is important to make use of the cheapest source at each capacity factor. Plotting equation 1 for each available source will give a set of lines called screening curves. Using these two graphs, it is possible to graphically obtain the cost optimal source mix.

3. Diversifying screening curve method

3.1. Compressed air systems

The screening curve method is typically used in power system planning. It can however, have a much wider range of application. For example, consider a typical compressed air requirement of a steel plant. The data for a steel plant provided by Bureau of Energy Efficiency (2009) is used for this case study. From the data available in, a load duration curve can be obtained for the compressed air requirement. Such a load duration curve is shown in figure 1. Multiple types of compressors can be used for meeting this load. However, compressors tend to consume energy even on no load conditions, i.e., they have certain fixed energy consumption, which is independent of the amount of air they are supplying. In short, the incremental energy change for supplying unit volume of compressed air is affine. The screening curve method is applicable here. The data for energy requirement is given in table 1. The data is adapted from BEE hand book on compressed air systems (Bureau of Energy Efficiency, 2012a). Slight changes have been made to highlight the methodology. The screening curves for these compressors can now easily be obtained as in Figure 2. It can be seen that up to a capacity factor of 0.4, compressor A is cost effective. From 0.4 to 0.7, compressor B is cost effective and the rest is best supplied by compressor C. From the load duration curve, it can be seen that at a capacity factor of 0.4, the air flow needed is 87 units. So, a total of 6 units need to be supplied by compressor A and the rest should be supplied by compressor B. In this particular example, compressor C need not be used as there are no loads to be supplied in that range of capacity factors.

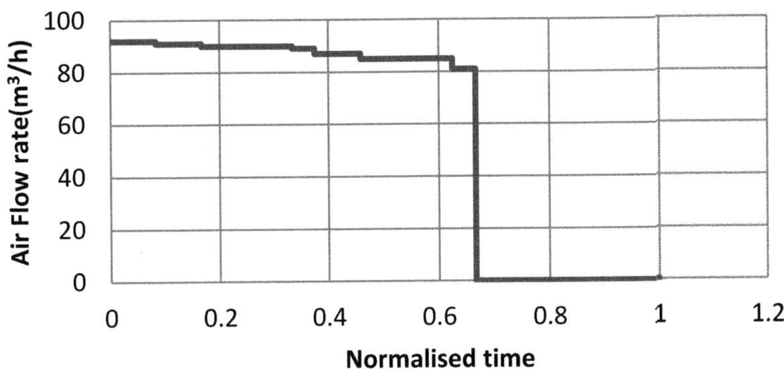

Figure 1. Load duration curve for compressed air requirement

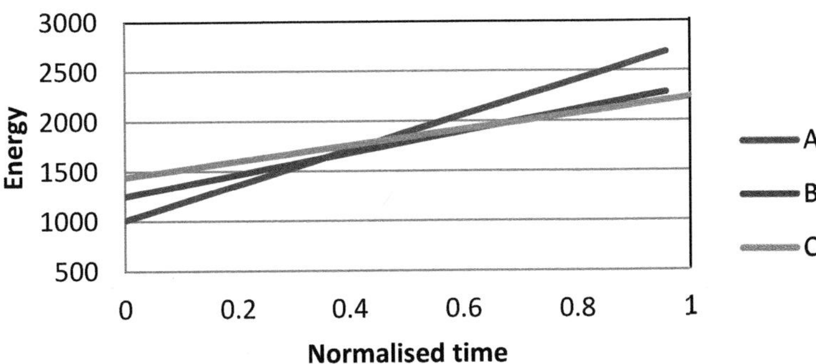

Figure 2. Screening curve for compressors

Table 1. Characteristics of compressors

Type	A	B	C
Fixed component : No load power (kW/cycle)	1,008	1,248	1,800
Variable component: Variable power (kW)	73	45	33

3.2. Refrigerating system

Consider applying the screening curve method to a refrigeration system. The load pattern is adapted from Ashok and Banerjee (2003) and is that of a typical office complex in Mumbai, India. It has been taken as a representative load pattern for a year. For demonstrating the method, three types of air conditioners, each of different 'star rating' as per the Bureau of Energy Efficiency specifications have been chosen. The ones with higher star values are more energy efficient, but have a higher capital cost. The values used are given in Table 2. A discount rate of 10 % and a lifetime of 20 y have been assumed for calculation. The energy consumption rates for various star ratings are given by the Bureau of Energy Efficiency (2012 b) and the electricity charge is considered to be Rs. 8 per kWh. The capital costs are the representative market prices of air conditioners available in the Indian market. The rating of all three units chosen is 1 TR. After plotting the screening curves and load duration curve as shown in figure 3, an optimum mix of air conditioners is obtained. As expected, a large portion of the load is best supplied by a 5 star (most energy efficient) air conditioner. However, interestingly, at the peak load region, the air conditioner with the lowest capital investment (1 star) and least energy efficiency is preferred.

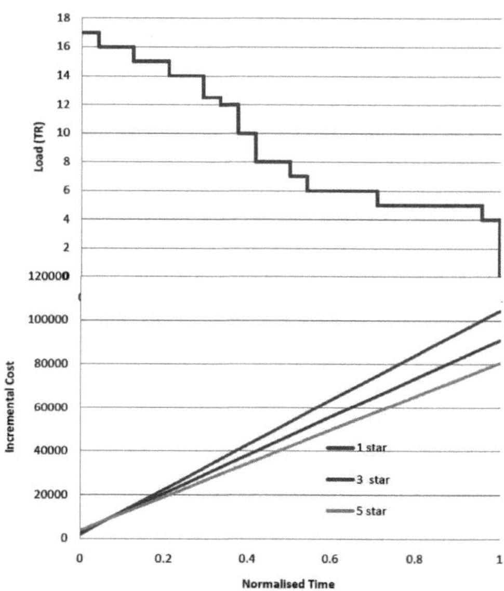

Figure 3. Load duration curve and screening curve for refrigerating system

Table 2. Air conditioner specifications

Type	1 star	3 star	5 star
Capital Cost (Rs.)	15,000	25,000	30,000
Annualised Fixed cost (Rs.)	1,761.89	2,936.49	3,523.78
Power/TR (kW)	1.46	1.25	1.1
Variable cost (Rs/TR-h)	11.73	10.05	8.8

For this particular problem, it is best to obtain 1 TR from a 1 star AC and the rest of the cooling requirement (16 TR) from a 5 star unit. As the values used for calculation are purely representative, these figures are only indicative. However, it is safe to conclude that the most energy efficient system need not always be the answer. There is scope for a mixture of low capital and low operating cost systems if the objective is overall cost minimisation.

3.3. Water pumping systems

As a third case study, the method has been applied to a water pumping system. The thermal load pattern is of a residential building in Pune, India, as given by Pillai and Banerjee (2007). The peak load is taken as 6,000 LPH. The load duration curve is obtained for the same. Here, three different pumps, each of 0.5 HP power rating and a capacity to pump 1,000 LPH are chosen as possible options. The pumps have different efficiencies and capital costs. Representative values for the same were obtained after a market survey. The values used are given in table 3. The LDC and screening curves are given in figure 4. A discount rate of 10 % and a life of 20 y have been assumed for calculations. It can be seen that, the screening curves of pumps 2 and 3 govern the solution. These two lines intersect at around a capacity factor of 0.12. Reading off the load duration curve, it can be seen that around 4,000 LPH of the flow should be supplied by pumps of type 3 and the rest (2,000 LPH) by pumps of type 2. As a 0.5 HP pump is capable of handling 1,000 LPH of flow, we can conclude that 4 pumps of type 3 and 2 of type 2 will constitute the ideal solution for this particular load. It should be noted that for calculations, only the variable cost of electricity tariff has been considered. Other fixed quantities like meter rent are present. However, as they do not influence the solution, such costs have been ignored.

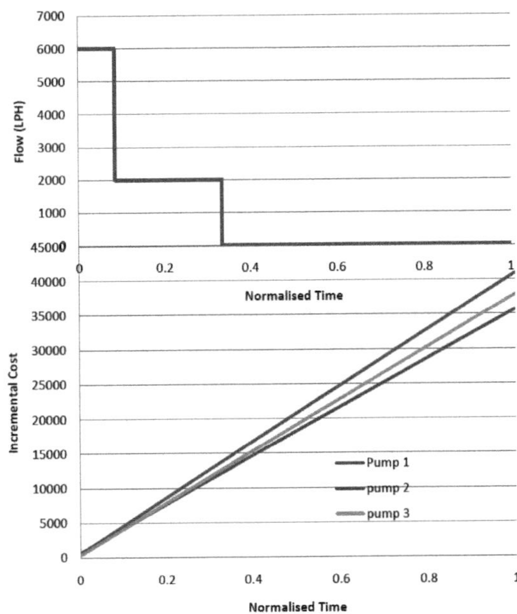

Figure 4. Load duration curve and screening curve for water pumping systems

Table 3. Characteristics of pumps

	Pump 1	Pump 2	Pump 3
Capital Cost (Rs.)	4,500	5,600	2,750
Annualised Fixed Cost (Rs/yr)	528.57	657.78	323.01
Efficiency (%)	65	75	70
Variable cost (Rs/1000 LPH)	4.62	4	4.29

4. Conclusions

In this paper, the classical screening curve method, which is usually used for power system planning, is applied to other process engineering problems with diverse applications. It can be seen that this methodology can be used to solve a wide variety of problems. It is simple yet effective methodology for optimally sizing source equipments to satisfy time varying demands. The examples presented here are to illustrate the versatility of the method. The scope of this method is not limited to these in any way. It should also be noted that this method has been used to optimise a different quantities, like energy consumption in case of compressed air system, and cost in the other two cases. Also, system specific characteristics like efficiency of pumping systems and star rating of refrigerating systems can also be accounted for.

References

Bureau of Energy Efficiency, 2009, One Day Technical Workshop on Adoption of Energy efficient process technologies & practices and implementation of Energy Conservation Act 2001 in Iron & Steel Sector, <www.emt-india.net/Presentations2009/3L_2009May9_IronSteelRe-Rolling/03-Godrej.pdf > accessed on 21/01/2014.

Bureau of Energy Efficiency, 2012a, Handbook on compressed air systems, < www.energymanager training.com/GuideBooks/3Ch3.pdf> accessed on 21/01/2014.

Bureau of Energy Efficiency, 2012b, Air Conditioner Labeling, <http://beeindia.in/awareness_and_outreach/documents/neap/Annexure_III.pdf> accessed on 21/01/2014.

C. Batlle, P. Rodilla, 2013, An Enhanced Screening Curves Method for Considering Thermal Cycling Operation Costs in Generation Expansion Planning, IEEE Transactions on Power Systems, 28, 4, 3683-3691.

I.R. Pillai, R. Banerjee, 2007, Methodology for estimation of potential for solar water heating in a target area, Solar Energy, 81, 162–172.

R.J. Fitzpatrick, J.W. Gallagerr, 1962, Determination of an optimized generation expansion pattern, Power apparatus and systems, part iii, Transactions of the American Institute of Electrical Engineers, 8, 3, 1052-1057.

S. Ashok, R. Banerjee, 2003, Optimal cool storage capacity for load management, Energy, 28, 115–126.

Jiří Jaromír Klemeš, Petar Sabev Varbanov and Peng Yen Liew (Editors)
Proceedings of the 24th European Symposium on Computer Aided Process Engineering – ESCAPE 24
June 15-18, 2014, Budapest, Hungary.

Multi-objective Heat Exchanger Networks Synthesis Considering Economic and Environmental Optimization

Mauro A. S. S. Ravagnani[a,*], Thiago B. Mano[a], Esdras P. Carvalho[a], Aline P. Silva[a], Caliane B. B. Costa[b]

[a] *State university of Maringá, Av. Colombo, 5790, CEP 87020-900, Maringá, Paraná, Brazil*

[b] *Federal University of São Carlos, Rodovia Washington Luís, Km 235, CEP 13565-905, São Carlos, São Paulo, Brazil*

ravag@deq.uem.br, mauro.ravagnani@hotmail.com

Abstract

In the present paper it is presented a model for the synthesis of HEN considering both economic and environmental features. The model presents a multi-objective mixed-integer non-linear programming (MINLP) formulation. The optimization problem aims to find the optimal HEN considering the total cost as well as the environmental impact minimization. Environmental aspects are incorporated to the objective function by considering Life Cycle Assessment (LCA), using SIMAPRO software. ReCiPe methodology is used and 18 impact categories from midpoint to endpoint are evaluated. An algorithm based on Particle Swarm Optimization (PSO) was developed to solve the model and a superstructure that considers the number of stages as an optimization variable is proposed. A literature case was chosen to test the model applicability. Results are better than the previously published ones, even considering environmental impacts. Furthermore, not all impact metrics are in conflict with the cost function.

Keywords: Heat Exchanger Network Synthesis, Life Cycle Assessment, ReCiPe, Particle Swarm Optimization, Multi-objective optimization.

1. Introduction

In industrial processes many studies have been developed to solve the problem of minimizing the use of hot and cold utilities as well as gas and liquid pollutant emissions from burning fossil fuels. In this way, Heat Exchanger Networks (HEN) synthesis is a very studied subject during the last 50 years and the majority of published papers relate different methodologies and techniques to achieve both of the objectives. Some recent interesting papers focused on the minimization of economic and environmental aspects. In Jin et al. (2013) a mathematical model is proposed considering the environmental impact as a factor of the objective function using proper quantitative weight attributes. The maximum benefits of the economy and the environment are obtained by trading off between the two indices.

In Vaskan et al. (2012) the problem of synthesizing HEN including environmental features is considered and its solution is posed in mathematical terms as a multi-objective mixed-integer non-linear programming (MINLP) problem, in which life cycle assessment (LCA) principles are used to quantify the environmental impact. Ten impact categories, as defined by the Eco-indicator 99, were considered. The problem is solved using the □-constrain method, which relies on formulating an auxiliary model in which one objective is kept as main objective while the rest is transferred to auxiliary constraints that impose epsilon bounds on their values. These single-objective problems are solved for several epsilon values, generating in each run a different Pareto solution. A heuristic-based approach is used in order to reduce the computational burden of the epsilon constraint method by solving a series of bi-criteria models in which the main objective is optimized against each single secondary objective separately.

Life cycle assessment (LCA) is a methodological tool used to quantitatively analyze the life cycle of products, services, processes or activities in all its life cycle. The use of LCA allows good choices in the actions that aim to minimize pollution emissions and to adequate material, human and economic resources distribution. Initially emissions and raw material necessary to the process must be calculated. This information is converted into environmental impacts relative to distinct damage categories. These impacts can be used in a multi-objective optimization structure to improve the process environmental performance (Azapagic and Clift, 1999). A generic framework is provided by ISO 14040 and 14044.

In López-Maldonado et al. (2011), a mathematical programming formulation for the synthesis of heat exchanger networks minimizing simultaneously the total annual cost and the environmental impact is presented. The proposed model consists of a multiobjective MINLP problem that considers the optimal location and use of different types of hot and cold utilities available through disjunctive formulations.

In the present paper it is presented a model formulation for the synthesis of HEN considering, economic and environmental features, in a multi-objective MINLP formulation. Two objective functions are considered, cost and environmental impact. Environmental aspects are incorporated to the objective function by considering Life Cycle Assessment (LCA) tool and ReCiPe methodology is used (Hauschild et al., 2013), considering 18 impact categories from midpoint to endpoint. An algorithm based on Particle Swarm Optimization (PSO) was developed to solve the model.

2. Model Development

The model presents a multi-objective MINLP formulation. A superstructure based on the paper of Vaskan et al. (2012), is proposed, but, differently from that work, the number of stages is considered as an optimization variable. Two objective functions are proposed, cost and environmental impact. The cost objective function is the summation of capital cost and the operational cost (utilities consumption). Capital cost considers manufacturing cost as well as area cost equations. Binary variables are used to identify if the heat transfer equipment (heat exchanger, heater or cooler) exists or not.

Constraints are the equations for global energy balance, energy balance at each stage and at each branch of the superstructure. Eq. (1) presents the cost objective function, in which $A_{i,j,k}$, A_i^{CU} and A_j^{HU} are the heat transfer area, $FC_{i,j}$, $FC^{CU}{}_i$ and $FC^{HU}{}_j$ are the fixed costs and $AC_{i,j}$, $AC^{CU}{}_i$ and $AC^{HU}{}_j$ are the area costs and qcu_i and qhu_j are hot and cold utilities demand.

$$Cost = \sum_{i\varepsilon HP}\sum_{j\varepsilon HP}\sum_{k\varepsilon SK} FC_{i,j} z_{i,j,k} + \sum_{i\varepsilon HP} FC_i^{CU} zcu_i + \sum_{j\varepsilon HP} FC_j^{HU} zhu_j +$$
$$\sum_{i\varepsilon HP}\sum_{j\varepsilon HP}\sum_{k\varepsilon SK} AC_{i,j}(A_{i,j,k})^{\beta_{i,k}} + \sum_{i\varepsilon HP} AC_i^{CU}(A_i^{CU})^{\beta_i^{CU}} + \sum_{j\varepsilon CP} AC_j^{HU}(A_j^{HU})^{\beta_j^{HU}} \quad (1)$$
$$+ \sum_{i\varepsilon HP} CUCqcu_i year + \sum_{j\varepsilon CP} HUCqhu_i year$$

The environmental objective function is presented in Eq. (2). Environmental charges in the present paper are given by the heat exchangers stainless steal mass and by the utilities consumption. Life cycle inventory (LCI) is given by:

$$LCI_b = \sum_{i\varepsilon HP} qcu_i \omega_b^{CU} + \sum_{j\varepsilon CP} qhu_j \omega_b^{HU} + mass\omega_b^{M} \quad (2)$$

In Eq. (2) ω_b^{CU}, ω_b^{HU} and ω_b^{M} are LCI inlets (emissions liberated to the environment or resources extracted from a determined region or ecosphere) relative to a chemical b per mass flux of activity of reference (mass of generated steam, used cooling water and mass of produced steal, for example). These parameters are obtained from ecoinvent, a specific databank on LCA. The impact quantification of a set of damage categories can be made by ReCiPe methodology. Inventory results can be translated from the category of environmental impact in the midpoint level (Eq. 3) and endpoint level (Eq. 4):

$$MI_m = \sum_b LCI_b \theta_{b,m} \quad (3)$$
$$MI_e = \sum_b LCI_b \theta_{b,e} \quad (4)$$

where MI_m and MI_e are the results of the impact indicator at midpoint and endpoint levels, respectively, $\theta_{b,m}$ and $\theta_{b,e}$ are the characterization factor linking LCI results of the chemical b to the midpoint and endpoint level impact categories, respectively.

LCA results must be analysed and a set of conclusions and recommendations for the system is formulated. In the present case, decisions are defined after the Pareto Front analysis.

A Particle Swarm Optimization (PSO) algorithm was developed to solve the model, based on the work of Silva et al. (2008).

3. PSO multi-objective optimization algorithm

PSO can be adapted to be used in multi-objective optimization problems to obtain a Pareto Front with high quality. The great difficulties are associated with finding the social and cognitive leader of each particle. In this case, there are several non-dominated solutions and some of them can be a possible leader.

In the present paper the PSO developed algorithm is based on three works: the elitist-mutated multi-objective Particle Swarm Optimization (EM-MOPSO), Reddy and Kumar (2007), the Time Variant Multi-Objective Particle Swarm Optimization (TV-MOPSO), Tripathi et al. (2007) and the Particle Swarm Algorithm With Discrete

Binary, Kennedy and Eberhart (1997). It incorporates the concept of Pareto domain; the mechanism of density analysis, similar to the Crowding distance from EM-MOPSO; the variation with time of the parameters w and acceleration coefficients of the TV-MOPSO; the external repository, ERP, that is limited to minimize the excessive generation of solutions in a determined region of the space; and for the binary variables, an adaptation following the method changes of probabilities, Kennedy and Eberhart (1997). The developed algorithm is named VPAD-MOPSOB.

4. Case study

A literature case presented in Huang and Karimi (2013) is used to test the applicability of the developed model. Table 1 presents streams data. To apply the developed model, all solutions must be divided by the maximum value found among all Pareto solutions to normalize the results obtained from each objective function. Heat exchangers material is stainless steal 176 with density equal to 7900 kg/m³. Ecopoints at midpoint and endpoint for steam, water, stainless steal mass (kg) were obtained from SIMAPRO software.

The parameters used in PSO are: c_1 = 2.5 to 0.5 and c_2 = 0.5 to 2.5; w = 0.9 to 0.4; Number of particles: 25; Number of iterations: 50; ERP size: 200 particles.

Table 2 presents the results for costs and the LCI at midpoint level. It can be observed that not all environmental impact categories conflict with the minimum cost HEN. Results for environmental impacts at endpoint level are not presented in this paper due to pages limit. It is interesting to say that all the impact categories should be evaluated at midpoint and endpoint levels to verify the impact of each category in the final HEN.

For the results presented in Table 2 the category of particulate formation was chosen to show the synthesized HEN. Figure 1 presents the HEN considering the cost and particulate formation minimization. Huang and Karimi (2013) achieved the optimum value of $ 76.327,00 with three heat exchangers, without heaters or coolers, considering just cost minimization. The HEN presented in Figure 1, besides minimizing the particulate formation, has a cost of $ 74,564.84, better than the cited results.

Other HEN can also be synthesized, considering the studied impact categories. The identification of the best HEN is not a trivial task. Considering the complexity of the problem and the number of variables, the incorporation of environmental impacts to the optimization problem makes it difficult because a large amount of alternatives needs to be evaluated.

Table 1. Streams data (Huang and Karimi, 2013)

Streams	T_{inlet}(°C)	T_{outlet}(°C)	F (kW/°C)	h(kW/m^2°C)	Cost ($/kW-year)
H1	167	77	22	2.0	-
C1	76	157	20	2.0	-
C2	47	95	7.5	0.67	-
HU	227	227	-	1.0	120
CU	27	47	-	1.0	20
Min. App. Temp. = 2°C			Heat exchanger cost ($) = 6600+670(Area)$^{0.83}$		

Table 2. Results for costs and the LCI at the midpoint level

Impact categories	Maximum total cost ($)	Minimum impact (-)	Minimum total cost ($)	Maximum impact (-)
Climate change – human health	75,110.90	5.02	75,110.90	5.02
Ozone depletion	74,807.82	0.04	74,807.82	0.04
Human toxicity	78,170.55	603.01	78,170.55	603.01
Photochemical ozone formation	76,928.68	2.26	76,928.68	2.26
Particulate formation	74,564.84	10.30	74,564.84	10.30
Radiation	74,704.34	4.03	74,704.34	4.03
Marine eutrophication	74,909.37	0.81	74,909.37	0.81
Territorial acidification	74,811.26	3.57	74,811.26	3.57
Fresh water eutrophication	75,074.05	48.89	75,074.05	48.89
Territorial Eco-toxicity	74,772.70	2.46	74,772.70	2.46
Fresh water Eco-toxicity	97,706.12	231.45	76,685.50	275.10
Marine Eco-toxicity	74,799.79	1,298.10	74,799.79	1,298.10
Agricultural land occupation	74,822.03	0.14	74,822.03	0.14
Urban occupation	74,730.56	0.58	74,730.56	0.58
Natural land transformation	74,623.31	0.22	74,623.31	0.22
Mineral depletion	145,346.79	106.90	77,425.78	217.89
Fossil fuel depletion	74,946.09	6.27	74,927.01	6.27
Water depletion	200,383.78	0.00	77,102.41	0.00

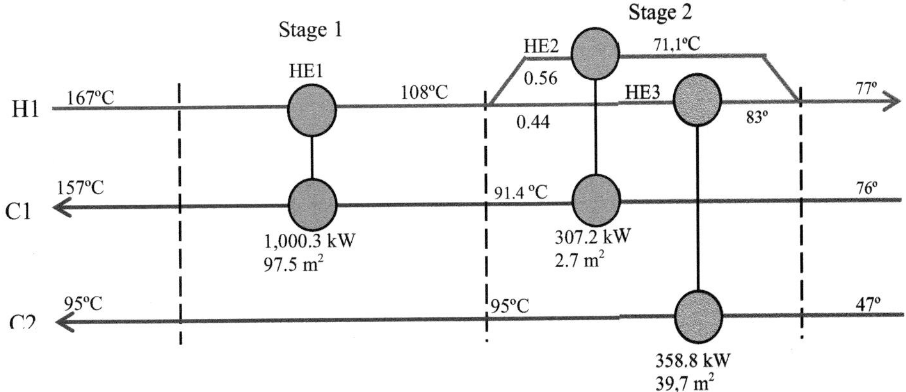

Figure 1. HEN with minimum cost and particulate formation at midpoint level

5. Conclusions

In the present paper it was proposed a model for HEN synthesis incorporating cost and environmental impact evaluation. The model has a formulation of a multi-objective MINLP optimization problem. LCA techniques and ReCiPe methodology for the LCI were used and 18 impact categories were evaluated. VPAD-MOPSOB algorithm was proposed to solve the problem and the results confirm that it is very effective in the achievement of optimal HEN with multiple objectives. A literature example was chosen to test the model applicability and a HEN with lower cost was obtained, even considering particulate formation minimization. However, the identification of the best HEN is not a trivial task because of the complexity of the problem, the number of involved variables and because of the large amount of alternatives to be evaluated. Moreover, it was demonstrated that not all impact metrics are in conflict with the cost function.

References

A. Azapagic, R. Clift, 1999, Application of life cycle assessment to process optimization, Computers and Chemical Engineering, 23, 1509–26.

M. Z. Hauschild, M. Goedkoop, J. Guinée, R. Heijungs, M. Huijbregts, O. Jolliet, M. Margni, A. De Schryver, S. Humbert, A. Laurent, S. Sala, R. Pant, 2013, Identifying best existing practice for characterization modeling in life cycle impact assessment, The International Journal of Life Cycle Assessment, 18, 683-697.

K. F. Huang, I. A. Karimi, 2013, Simultaneous synthesis approaches for cost-effective heat exchanger networks, Chemical Engineering Science, 98, 231–245.

Z. Jin, X. Chen, Y. Wang, M. Liu, 2013, Heat exchanger network synthesis based on environmental impact minimization, Clean Technology and Environmental Policy, 16, 1, 183-187.

J. Kennedy, R. Eberhart, 1997, A discrete binary version of the particle swarm algorithm, IEEE International Conference on Neural Network, 4104-4108.

L. A. López-Maldonado, J. M. Ponce-Ortega, J. G. Segovia-Hernández, 2011, Multiobjective synthesis of heat exchanger networks minimizing the total annual cost and the environmental impact, Applied Thermal Engineering, 31, 1099-1113.

M. J. Reddy, D. N. Kumar, 2007, An efficient multi-objective optimization algorithm based on swarm intelligence for engineering design, Engineering Optimization, 39, 1, 49–68.

A. P. Silva, M. A. S. S. Ravagnani, E. C. Biscaia Jr., 2008, Particle Swarm Optimisation in Heat Exchanger Network Synthesis Including Detailed equipment Design, Computer Aided Chemical Engineering, 25, 713-718.

P. K. Tripathi, S. Bandyopadhyay, S. K. Pal, 2007, Multi-Objective Particle Swarm Optimization with time variant inertia and acceleration coefficients, Information Science, 177, 5033 – 5049.

P. Vaskan, G. Guillen-Gosalbez, L. Jimenez, 2012, Multi-objective design of heat-exchanger networks considering several life cycle impacts using a rigorous MILP-based dimensionality reduction technique, Applied Energy, 98, 149–161.

Jiří Jaromír Klemeš, Petar Sabev Varbanov and Peng Yen Liew (Editors)
Proceedings of the 24th European Symposium on Computer Aided Process Engineering – ESCAPE 24
June 15-18, 2014, Budapest, Hungary.

Comparison among Proposals for Energy Integration of Processes for 1G/2G Ethanol and Bioelectricity Production

Cássia M. Oliveira,[a] Antonio J. G. Cruz,[a] Caliane B. B. Costa[a*]

[a]*Department of Chemical Engineering, Federal University of São Carlos, Rodovia Washington Luiz Km 235, 13565-905, São Carlos, São Paulo, Brazil*
caliane@ufscar.br

Abstract

Brazil has an important role in the world market of ethanol production and the implementation of technologies of second generation ethanol will intensify its production. In this work Pinch Analysis was used in order to perform energy integration of processes for first and second generation (1G/2G) ethanol and bioelectricity production, using hydrothermal and diluted acid pretreatments of sugarcane bagasse, both including and not including pentoses fermentation step. Processes that include pentoses fermentation step, for both considered pretreatments, have higher ethanol production when compared to the ones that do not make use of hemicellulose fraction of bagasse to produce ethanol, but steam consumption increases in the same order of magnitude of ethanol production. For the four evaluated scenarios the application of energy integration demonstrated a reduction in energy consumption of more than 50% when compared to the corresponding cases without any energy integration and of more than 30% when compared to partially integrated processes, as commonly found in Brazilian industrial plants. Besides the economical advantage, due to the decrease in costs of hot and cold utilities, energy integrated processes increase bagasse availability for production of second generation ethanol.

Keywords: Energy integration, Pinch, Biorefinery, Sugarcane bagasse and Ethanol.

1. Introduction

The increase in demand for biofuels has driven the development of new technologies such as ethanol production from sugarcane bagasse hydrolysis. Consequently many studies have been conducted in this area in order to evaluate the technological difficulties concerning the effects of pretreatments on sugarcane bagasse (Abo-State et al., 2013), perspectives of production (Cardona et al., 2010), different technological routes (Dantas et al., 2013), flexibility of electricity and bioethanol production (Furlan et al., 2013), effects of different scenarios for first and second generation (1G and 2G) ethanol and electricity production (Dias et al., 2013) and the integrated production of 1G and 2G bioethanol from sugarcane (Furlan et al., 2012). Brazil is the second largest producer of ethanol and the development of second generation ethanol technology will intensify ethanol production in industrial plants.

Process integration techniques provide important advantages for the industrial processes in terms of process improvement, increased productivity, energy resources management and conservation, pollution prevention, and reductions in the capital and operating costs of chemical plants (Morar and Agachi, 2010). Energy integration in a sugarcane biorefinery can provide economical advantage, environmental benefits and increased ethanol production. The last factor is related to lower steam consumption in the plant due to energy integration and, consequently, less bagasse need to be burnt in the cogeneration system and its surplus can be made available for the production of second generation ethanol. In this context, this work performed energy integration in a sugarcane biorefinery using Pinch Analysis.

Pinch Analysis consists of a set of techniques for the systematic application of the First and Second Law of Thermodynamics and allows that process engineers obtain intuition needed in thermal interactions among chemical processes and utility systems (Panjeshahi et al. 2008). In recent years several studies have shown the application of Pinch Analysis in processes to produce biodiesel (Sánchez et al., 2011), biomethane (Modarresi et al., 2012) and bioethanol from lignocellulosic biomass (Dias et al., 2011), demonstrating the importance of the technique in processes of biofuels production. Other techniques more robust for energy integration may be cited as methods of simultaneous optimization. However, Pinch Analysis is one of the most important methods for energy integration due to its simplicity and achievement of good results, which justifies the use of this technique.

The biorefinery used in this work is the process for 1G/2G ethanol and bioelectricity production by computer simulation (virtual biorefinery) performed on free software EMSO (Environment for Modeling, Simulation, and Optimization). Four different scenarios were considered in these biorefineries, since two different types of pretreatment for bagasse (hydrothermal and diluted acid) and inclusion or not of pentoses fermentation step were considered.

2. Methods

Initially, a study of the four different scenarios of biorefinery was conducted to identify possible streams for energy integration, considering streams requirements of heating or cooling and possible restrictions of process.

Pinch Analysis requires streams data such as initial and final temperature, mass flow and definition of stream type (hot or cold). Information was obtained from simulations in the free software EMSO, which has been used in the development of virtual biorefinery performed by the research group of Simulation and Process Control of the Department of Chemical Engineering, Federal University of São Carlos, Brazil. For each identified possible stream heat capacity, enthalpy change and mass flowrate were calculated.

A minimum temperature difference (ΔT_{min}) equal to 10 °C was defined between hot and cold streams, a value commonly adopted in literature. The value of ΔT_{min} could be optimized in order to obtain more accurate values of energy savings, but, as it will be demonstrated on next section, the adopted value already shows that great savings can be attained. Since the aim of this work was to demonstrate that energy integration has a great potential to, together with other studies, make second generation ethanol viable, due to increased availability of bagasse, optimization was out of the scope, and different values of ΔT_{min} were not analyzed. To assist in the calculations the free software Hint (Martín and Mato, 2008) and the spreadsheet available at Elsevier Ltd (2007) were used. With the assistance of those tools heat exchangers networks (HEN) were proposed that reduce the consumption of utilities. In the final step comparisons were made among the biorefinery with energy integration, without energy integration and partially integrated. The term partially integrated refers to process commonly found in Brazilian bioethanol plants, in which some degree of energy integration is already present involving few process streams.

3. Results and discussion

The biorefinery presented in this paper has a processing capacity of 12,000 t/d of sugarcane for all evaluated scenarios. Table 1 presents process information. There is often some degree of energy integration in the process, which depends on the design of each plant. The simulated biorefinery has energy integration between streams of wine and vinasse and between the juice stream coming out of sugarcane mills and the concentrated juice stream (i.e. juice stream that comes out of evaporator). This type of energy integration is commonly found in Brazilian plants and is named in this work partially integrated biorefinery (see Figure 1). For the processes without any energy integration, every heating and cooling of streams is provided by the use of hot and cold utilities. Figure 1 shows simplified diagram of processes for 1G/2G ethanol and bioelectricity production. For Scenarios 2 and 4 pentoses (from hemicellulose fraction) fermentation step shown in Figure 1 is absent. All scenarios have a boiler in the cogeneration system of 65 bar.

Table 1. Data of biorefinery process for the four considered scenarios.

Scenario	Pretreatment	Pentoses Fermentation	Bag. Cog.[1] (t/d)	Bag. 2G[2] (t/d)	L+ C Cog.[3] (t/d)	Ethanol Produced (m^3/d)
1	Hydrothermal	Yes	2,655	350	110	1,144
2	Hydrothermal	No	2,655	350	110	1,123
3	Diluted acid	Yes	733	2,272	1,120	1,382
4	Diluted acid	No	650	2,355	1,161	1,253

[1] Bag. Cog. - bagasse availability for cogeneration system; [2] Bag. 2G - bagasse availability for production of second generation ethanol; [3] L + C Cog. - lignin and not hydrolyzed cellulose availability for cogeneration system.

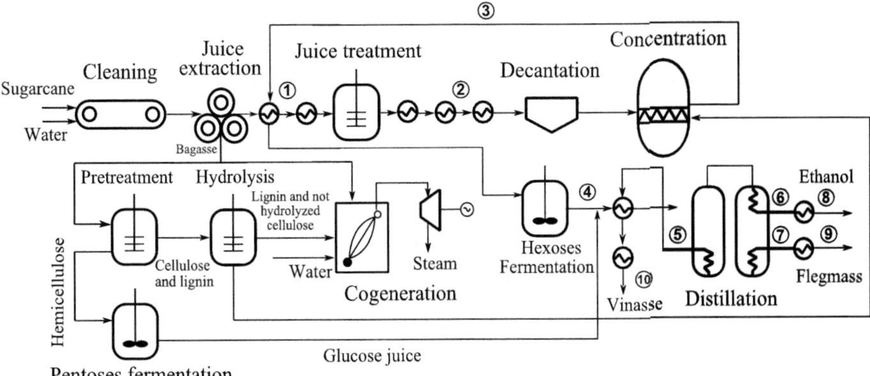

Figure 1. Schematic representation of the general sugarcane biorefinery process

The amount of bagasse available for the cogeneration system (responsible for thermal and electric energy production) is greater in processes with hydrothermal pretreatment due to the use of turbine extraction steam in pretreatment step. Processes with diluted acid pretreatment require less turbine extraction steam, thus greater fraction of bagasse can be diverted to production of second generation ethanol, which implies greater ethanol production and consumption of utilities.

Lignin and cellulose that was not hydrolyzed in hydrolysis reactor are available for the cogeneration system, increasing the capacity of producing energy when compared to the use of only bagasse as boiler fuel. The fractions of lignin and not hydrolyzed cellulose are greater in scenarios that use diluted acid pretreatment, because the fraction of bagasse available for production of second generation ethanol is far superior to the one in processes with hydrothermal pretreatment. Since both lignin and not hydrolyzed cellulose come from the fraction of bagasse that was sent to 2G sector of the plant (Pretreatment + Hydrolysis + Pentoses Fermentation blocks in Figure 1), availability of these additional boiler fuels are greater in processes with diluted acid pretreatment.

Ten streams participate in the energy integration network, which are identified in Figure 1 by numbers. To synthesize heat exchangers networks it was necessary to split stream 2 into two parallel branches. If the split was not performed, the proposed network would exceed the minimum energy demand. However, splitting the stream may not be compatible with the process and its restrictions. Therefore, a second network without split streams was proposed. For all evaluated scenarios two networks of heat exchangers were proposed, except for scenario 3, for which it was possible to propose a heat exchangers network that fulfills the minimum energy demand without the need to split any process stream. Table 2 shows the consumption of utilities of processes without energy integration and the achieved economy with both heat exchangers networks proposals in relation to process without integration and to partially integrated process, as commonly found in Brazilian plants. Due to conciseness reasons, heat exchangers networks proposals are not shown.

The savings of utility in relation to processes without energy integration approximate 60% for the 1st HEN and range between 40 % and 50 % for the 2nd HEN. When compared to partially integrated processes, these values range between 30 % and 40 % for the 1st HEN and between 10 % and 30 % for the 2nd HEN. Processes with the 2nd

Table 2. Consumption and savings of utilities

Scenario	Hot utility[4] (MW)	Cold utility[5] (MW)	Hot/cold utility saving (without integration, %)[6]		Hot/cold utility saving (part. integrated, %)[7]	
			1st HEN	2nd HEN	1st HEN	2nd HEN
1	117.3	106.9	58.2/63.9	41.5/45.5	37.1/43.0	11.9/14.0
2	113.0	102.1	58.7/65.0	51.8/57.5	38.0/44.4	27.8/32.5
3	148.2	143.9	54.8/56.5	-	30.6/32.0	-
4	122.1	116.5	57.9/60.6	41.8/43.8	36.5/39.2	12.2/13.1

[4] Hot utility - demand of hot utility in process without energy integration; [5] Cold utility - demand of cold utility in process without energy integration; [6] Hot/cold utility saving (without integration, %) - saving hot/cold utility of processes with the proposed networks in relation to process without energy integration, in %; [7] Hot/cold utility saving (part. integrated, %)- saving hot/cold utility of processes with the proposed networks in relation to partially integrated process, in %.

HEN have greater amplitude in the range of economy due to attempts to propose networks that were feasible from a practical point of view, resulting in an increase in energy demand to greater or lesser degrees depending on the evaluated scenario.

Table 3 shows the number of heat exchange units and consumption of utilities for the proposed heat exchangers networks in each evaluated scenario. The number of heat exchange units ranges between 14 and 17 for processes with the 1st HEN and 13 and 15 for processes with the 2nd HEN. The consumption of vegetal steam in processes without energy integration varies little among evaluated scenarios, from 3.1 to 3.4 kg steam/L hydrous ethanol. Vegetal steam is the term used to designate steam produced in the evaporator due to concentrating sugarcane juice, which is used in the processes as hot utility. The consumption of steam varies from 1.3 to 1.5 kg steam/L hydrous ethanol in processes with the 1st HEN. The saving is lower with the 2nd HEN, with consumption varying from 1.5 to 1.9 kg steam/L hydrous ethanol. There are advantages and disadvantages among the proposed heat exchanger networks. The first ones have superior utilities saving, but have more heat transfer units and split streams, which can be infeasible from a practical point of view. The second networks provide fewer saving in utilities, but have less heat exchange units and have no split streams. The reduction of utilities consumption in biorefinery, besides reducing operating costs, can lead to an increase in the production of second generation ethanol.

In the studied process the bagasse for cogeneration is burned, providing steam at 65 bar. Then, this steam drives the turbine, generating turbine extraction steam at 2.5 bar, that is used in the evaporator for concentrating sugarcane juice. The vegetal steam at 2.1 bar generated in the evaporator is used as hot utility. The saving of vegetal steam achieved with the energy integration can reduce the consumption of bagasse in cogeneration system. Thus, the surplus can be made available for production of second generation ethanol. However, for effective implementation of this, the single evaporator used in synthesizing this process must be replaced by a multiple-effect evaporator, in order for the juice to be concentrated on the same specifications using less steam and generating less vegetal steam, but enough to meet the thermal energy demand of the plant. Consequently, less bagasse is driven to the cogeneration system and the surplus is destined for 2G ethanol, increasing ethanol production.

Table 3. Number of heat exchange units and consumption of vegetal steam

Scenario	NHEU[8]		Steam consumption (without energy int., kg steam/L hydrous ethanol)[9]	Steam consumption (with energy int., kg steam/L hydrous ethanol)[10]	
	1st HEN	2nd HEN		1st HEN	2nd HEN
1	17	13	3.3	1.4	1.9
2	17	15	3.2	1.3	1.5
3	14	-	3.4	1.5	-
4	15	13	3.1	1.3	1.8

[8] NHEU - number of heat exchange units; [9] Steam consumption (without energy int., kg steam/L hydrous ethanol) - vegetal steam (2.1 bar) consumption of process without energy integration; [10] Steam consumption (with energy int., kg steam/L hydrous ethanol) - vegetal steam (2.1 bar) consumption of process with both networks proposals.

4. Conclusions

The presented results indicate that energy integration provides considerable reduction in energy consumption and consequently in operating costs of the plant for all evaluated scenarios. However, the choice of the best network of heat exchangers to be implemented into process is not straightforward, since the proposed HENs exhibit pros and cons when number of units, achieved economy and splitting of streams are considered. Besides the economical aspect, due to the decrease in utility costs (hot and cold ones), there are environmental benefits and the possibility of increasing bagasse availability for production of second generation ethanol.

Acknowledgement

The authors acknowledge the support from CTBE, DEQ/UFSCar, FAPESP and CNPq.

References

M.A. Abo-State, A.M.E. Ragab, N.S. El-Gendy, L.A. Farahat, H.R. Madian, 2013, Effect of different pretreatments on egyptian sugar-cane bagasse saccharification and bioethanol production, Egyptian Journal of Petroleum, 22, 161–167.

C.A. Cardona, J.A. Quintero, I.C. Paz, 2010, Production of bioethanol from sugarcane bagasse: Status and perspectives, Bioresource Technology, 101, 4754–4766.

G.A. Dantas; L.F.L. Legey, A. Mazzone, 2013, Energy from sugarcane bagasse in Brazil: An assessment of the productivity and cost of different technological routes, Renewable and Sustainable Energy Reviews, 21, 356–364.

M.O.S. Dias, T.L. Junqueira, O. Cavalett, M.P. Cunha, C.D.F. Jesus, P.E. Mantelatto, C.E.V. Rossell, R. Maciel Filho, A. Bonomi, 2013, Cogeneration in integrated first and second generation ethanol from sugarcane, Chemical Engineering Research and Design, 91, 1411–1417.

M.O.S. Dias, M. Modesto, A.V. Ensinas, S.A. Nebra, R. Maciel Filho, C.E.V. Rossell, 2011, Improving bioethanol production from sugarcane: evaluation of distillation, thermal integration and cogeneration systems, Energy, 36, 3691-3703.

Elsevier Ltd, 2007, Pinch Analysis and Process Integration: Spreadsheet, <www.elsevierdirect.com/v2/companion.jsp?ISBN=9780750682602> Accessed on: 02/07/2013.

F.F. Furlan, R.J. Tonon Filho, F.H.P.B. Pinto, C.B.B. Costa, A.J.G. Cruz, R.L.C. Giordano, R.C. Giordano, 2013, Bioelectricity versus bioethanol from sugarcane bagasse: is it worth to be flexible?, Biotechnology for Biofuels, 6, 142.

F.F. Furlan, C.B.B. Costa, A.J.G. Cruz, A.R. Secchi, R.P. Soares, R.C. Giordano, 2012, Integrated tool for simulation and optimization of a first and second generation ethanol-from-sugarcane production plant, Computer Aided Process Engineering, 30, 81-85.

A. Martín, A.F. Mato, 2008, Hint: An educational software for heat exchanger network design with the pinch method, Education for Chemical Engineers, 3, e6-e14.

A. Modarresi, P. Kravanja, A. Friedl, 2012, Pinch and exergy analysis of lignocellulosic ethanol, biomethane, heat and power production from straw, Applied Thermal Engineering, 43, 20-28.

M. Morar, P.S. Agachi, 2010, Review: Important contributions in development and improvement of the heat integration techniques, Computer Chemical Engineering, 34, 1171-1179.

M.H. Panjeshahi, E.J. Langeroudi, N. Tahouni, 2008, Retrofit of ammonia plant for improving energy efficiency, Energy, 33, 46–64.

E. Sánchez, K. Ojeda, M. El-Halwagi, M.V. Kafarov, 2011, Biodiesel from microalgae oil production in two sequential esterification/transesterification reactors: Pinch analysis of heat integration, Chemical Engineering Journal, 176-177, 211-216.

Jiří Jaromír Klemeš, Petar Sabev Varbanov and Peng Yen Liew (Editors)
Proceedings of the 24th European Symposium on Computer Aided Process Engineering – ESCAPE 24
June 15-18, 2014, Budapest, Hungary.

Design of Optimal Reactive Distillation Processes for ETBE Production using Rigorous Thermodynamic Models

Gisela N. Durruty, M. Soledad Diaz, Patricia M. Hoch*

Universidad Nacional del Sur, Chemical Engineering Department, Planta Piloto de Ingeniería Quimica, 8000 Bahía Blanca, ARGENTINA
p.hoch@plapiqui.edu.ar

Abstract

In this work we propose a model for the design of a reactive distillation unit for ETBE synthesis from ethanol and isobutene, with both rigorous thermodynamic models (UNIFAC and SRK) and hydraulic constraints, in an equation oriented environment within GAMS. The objective is to minimize total annual cost. The main contribution of this paper is the estimation of binary interaction parameters yet unavailable for the system being considered, using experimental data taken from literature, within a reactive distillation column optimization environment.

Keywords: Reactive Distillation, Process Intensification, Thermodynamics.

1. Introduction

Most successful commercial process intensification applications at industrial scale include reactive distillation, microreactors, rotating packed bed systems, simulating moving bed reactors, thus the importance of developing reliable methods for the optimal design of such systems. In particular, reactive distillation (RD) is a simultaneous implementation of sequential reaction and distillation in a countercurrent column. The industrial application of these processes is motivated by significant reductions in capital and operating costs, as compared to the equivalent conventional reaction-separation processes. Reactive distillation has also significant advantages when chemical equilibrium limits the conversion, the reason being that continuous removal of products enhances overall conversion. Other benefits include reduced downstream processing and higher energy efficiency due to the utilization of the reaction heat for evaporation of the liquid phase when reaction is exothermic.

ETBE (ethyl tert-butyl ether) is an octane enhancer additive used in gasoline as a replacement for MTBE (methyl tert-butyl ether), which showed some drawbacks as contamination of ground water reservoirs nearby the petrol stations due to leakage from small fractures of the containing underground vessels, and its use was discontinued since 2006. ETBE synthesis can be efficiently carried out through reactive distillation to achieve high conversion and low capital and operating costs. The conventional process for ETBE synthesis basically consists of pretreatment of the C_4 hydrocarbon feed flow, reaction, purification, and recovery of non-reacted products (Domingues et al., 2012), which renders high capital and operating costs. The design of RD for ETBE synthesis, requiring good kinetic models integrated to reliable thermodynamic predictions still requires further analysis and it was not thoroughly explored in literature yet. A review on the evolution of ETBE and its future prospects is presented by Yee et al. (2013).

2. General description of the model

The RD unit model formulation is based on MESH equations. Special attention is given to the thermodynamic model. The model includes an activity coefficient approach for the liquid phase, UNIFAC, and a cubic equation of state for the vapor phase, SRK with quadratic mixing rules with a k_{ij} on a and l_{ij} on b. To the best of our knowledge, there are not SRK binary interaction parameters for all the components in the RD unit studied. Thus, k_{ik} and l_{ik} had to be estimated using parameter estimation techniques with experimental data taken from literature. Sources for the data are shown in Table 1. Having PTxy data for each binary set and proposing the desired thermodynamic model it is possible to find the adjusted k_{ik} and l_{ik}. The parameters were checked predicting the V-L equilibria with GPEC (Cismondi et al., 2008). All three binary mixtures with ethanol present azeotropic compositions.

3. Thermodynamic model

3.1 UNIFAC

$$\ln \gamma_{s,i} = \ln \gamma^{C}_{s,i} + \ln \gamma^{R}_{s,i} \tag{1}$$

$$\ln \gamma^{R}_{s,i} = \sum_j \upsilon^i_j \cdot (\ln \Gamma_{s,j} - \ln \Gamma^i_{s,j}) \tag{2}$$

$$\ln \gamma^{C}_{s,i} = \ln(\phi_{s,i}/x_{s,i}) + z/2 \cdot q_i \cdot \ln(\theta_{s,i}/\phi_{s,i}) + l_i - (\phi_{s,i}/x_{s,i}) \cdot \sum_k x_{s,k} \cdot l_k \tag{3}$$

$$\ln \Gamma_{s,j} = Q_j \cdot [1 - \ln(\sum_m \Theta_{s,m} \cdot \Psi_{s,m,j}) - (\sum_m (\Theta_{s,m} \cdot \Psi_{s,m,j} / \sum_n \Theta_{s,n} \cdot \Psi_{s,n,m}))] \tag{4}$$

$$\Theta_{s,m} = Q_m \cdot X_{s,m} / \sum_n Q_n \cdot X_{s,n} \tag{5}$$

$$\phi_{s,i} = r_i \cdot x_{s,i} / \sum_k r_k \cdot x_{s,k} \tag{6}$$

$$\theta_{s,i} = q_i \cdot x_{s,i} / \sum_k q_k \cdot x_{s,k} \tag{7}$$

$$X_{s,m} = \sum_k \upsilon^k_m \cdot x_{s,k} / \sum_k \sum_n \upsilon^k_n \cdot x_{s,k} \tag{8}$$

$$\Psi_{s,n,m} = \exp(-a_{n,m} / T_s) \tag{9}$$

$$r_i = \sum_j \upsilon^i_j \cdot R_j \tag{10}$$

$$q_i = \sum_j \upsilon^i_j \cdot Q_j \tag{11}$$

$$l_i = z/2 \cdot (r_i - q_i) - (r_i - 1) \tag{12}$$

Where z=10. R_j and Q_j are group surface area and volume contributions, respectively, and $a_{m,n}$ is a group interaction parameter (Pretel, 1997). υ^i_j is the number of ocurrences of group j in molecule i. Eq. (4) is also valid for $\ln \Gamma^i_{s,j}$.

3.2 SRK

$$zmix_s^3 - zmix_s^2 + (A_s - B_s - B_s^2) \cdot zmix_s - A_s \cdot B_s = 0 \tag{13}$$

$$A_s = P \cdot (\sum_i \sum_k y_{s,i} \cdot y_{s,k} \cdot \alpha_{s,i,k}) / (T_s \cdot R)^2 \tag{14}$$

$$B_s = P \cdot (\sum_i\sum_k y_{s,i} \cdot y_{s,k} \cdot \beta_{i,k}) / (T_s \cdot R) \qquad (15)$$

$$\alpha_{s,i,k} = [(ac{\cdot}\alpha)_{s,i} \cdot (ac{\cdot}\alpha)_{s,k}]^{1/2} \cdot (1 - k_{ik}) \qquad (16)$$

$$[\alpha_{s,i}]^{1/2} = 1 + mc_i \cdot (1 - [T_s/Tc_i]^{1/2}) \qquad (17)$$

$$ac_i = 0.42747 \cdot (R \cdot Tc_i)^2 / Pc_i \qquad (18)$$

$$bc_i = 0.08664 \cdot R \cdot Tc_i / Pc_i \qquad (19)$$

$$mc_i = 0.48 + 1.574 \cdot w_i - 0.176 \cdot w_i^2 \qquad (20)$$

$$\beta_{i,k} = (bc_i + bc_k)/2 \cdot (1 - l_{ik}) \qquad (21)$$

$$\ln \varphi_{s,i} = bc_i/(\sum_i\sum_k y_{s,i} \cdot y_{s,k} \cdot \beta_{i,k}) \cdot (zmix_s - 1) - \ln(zmix_s - B_s) + A_s/B_s \cdot [bc_i/(\sum_i\sum_k y_{s,i} \cdot y_{s,k} \cdot \beta_{i,k}) - 2 \cdot \sum_k (y_{s,k} \cdot \alpha_{s,i,k})/(\sum_i\sum_k y_{s,i} \cdot y_{s,k} \cdot \alpha_{s,i,k})] \cdot \ln(1 + B_s/zmix_s) \qquad (22)$$

UNIFAC and SRK are related in the equilibrium calculations in each stage of the column. Discrimination of cubic roots is not a trivial task. A methodology to find the vapor root is implemented within the model, taking into account that in Eq. (13) $f(zmix_s)=0$ can be differentiated to yield the desired roots at the values where $f'(zmix_s)>0$.

4. Column model

For the model of the column, blocks for condenser, reboiler and stages (either reactive or non-reactive) are written as MESH equations using molar compositions and mole flow rates. In particular,

$$FL_s \cdot xF_i + L_{s-1} \cdot x_{s-1,i} + v_{s+1} \cdot y_{s+1,i} - L_s \cdot x_{s,i} - V_s \cdot y_{s,i} + Fv_{s+1} \cdot yF_i + r_{s,i} = 0 \qquad (23)$$

Where $r_{s,I}$ is the generation or consumption due to reaction rate. For the reactive stages, the value of the term $r_{s,i}$ depends on the existence of catalyst in the stage. Within the optimization, the catalyst amount $Mcat_s$ (mass in [g]) is defined for each reactive stage as shown in the following section.

4.1 Reaction kinetics (Al-Arfaj and Luyben, 2002)

$$r_{s,i} = krate_s \cdot g_s \cdot Mcat_s \qquad (24)$$

$$krate_s = 7.418E12 \cdot \exp(-60.4E3/(R \cdot T_s)) \quad Y \qquad (25)$$

$$g_s = act_{s-1,Ethanol} \cdot (act_{s-1,Isobutene} - act_{s-1,ETBE}/KETBE_s)/(1 + KA_s \cdot act_{s-1,Ethanol})^3 \qquad (26)$$

$$KETBE_s = 10.4 + 4060/T_s - 2.9 \ln T_s - 0.02\, T_s + 5.3E\text{-}5\, T_s^2 - 5.3E\text{-}8\, T^3 \qquad (27)$$

$$KA_s = \exp(-1.0707 + 1323.1/T_s) \qquad (28)$$

$$act_{s,i} = \gamma_{s,i} \cdot x_{s,i} \qquad (29)$$

4.2 Hydraulic constraints

$$\rho_g = P \cdot MW_g / (R \cdot Tsf) \qquad (30)$$

$$u_g = F^{1/2} / \rho_g^{1/2} \quad (31)$$

$$V_g = V_{sf} * MW_g / \rho_g \quad (32)$$

$$A_{COL} = V_g / u_g \quad (33)$$

$$D_{COL} = (4 \cdot A_{COL} / \pi)^{1/2} \quad (34)$$

$$Psi = 0.000265 \cdot (1/D_{COL})^2 - 0.018827 \cdot (1/D_{COL}) + 0.559770 \quad (35)$$

$$V_l = l_{sf} \cdot MW_l / \rho_l \quad (36)$$

$$u_l = V_l / A_{COL} \quad (37)$$

$$u_l < u_{lmax} \quad (38)$$

$$CAT_{LIM} = \tfrac{1}{4} \cdot \pi \cdot D_{COL}^2 \cdot \Delta Z \cdot Psi \cdot (1 - 0.3) \cdot \rho_{CAT} \quad (39)$$

$$M_{CAT} < CAT_{LIM} \quad (40)$$

5. Numerical results

Estimation of binary interaction parameters for the system is important for the correct simulation of the process, due to the binary azeotropes present. Data taken from literature were used to estimate the values of k_{ij} and l_{ij}, thus obtaining reliable VLE predictions for all the components present in the system. A parameter estimation problem was posed in order to find such binary data.

There is good agreement between experimental and predicted data. Table 1 shows the interaction parameters estimated for the system. Using the same binary interaction coefficients for iC4-EtOH and nC4-EtOH yields a good prediction of VLE.

Plots showing the agreement between the proposed thermodynamic model and experimental data are shown for the systems containing ETBE in Figures 1 and 2. They are not shown for the other binary sets due to lack of space, but they also show good agreement with experimental data.

Table 1. Estimated binary interaction parameters k_{ij} and l_{ij}

		k_{ij}	l_{ij}	Experimental data from:
ETBE	Ethanol	0.3728	0.4006	Kammerer et al. (1999)
	i-butene	-0.0068	-0.005	Leu et al. (1999)
	n-butene	-0.0068	-0.005	Id.
Ethanol	i-butene	0.1826	0.1254	Ouni et al. (2005)
	n-butene	0.1724	0.1203	Laakkonen et al. (2003)
Isobutene	n-butene	0	0	--

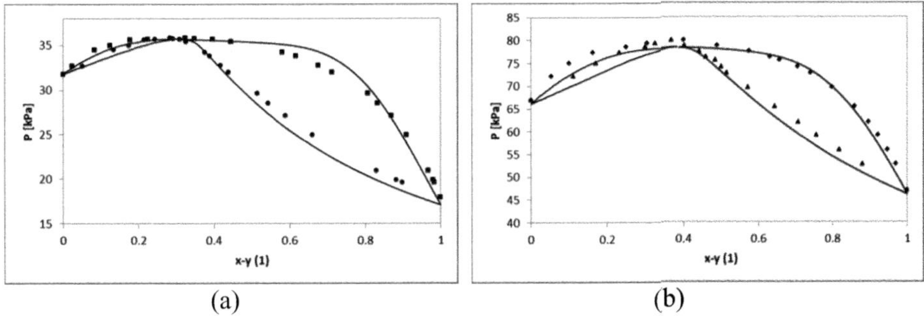

Figure 1. Ethanol (1) – ETBE (2) equilibrium at (a) 313.15K and (b) 333.15K. ▪ and ● equilibrium data for liquid and vapor phase, respectively (Kammerer et al. 1999). — Prediction.

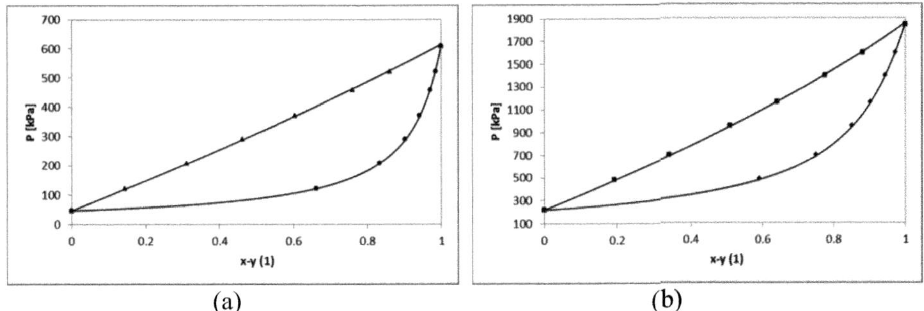

Figure 2. Isobutene (1) – ETBE (2) equilibrium at (a) 323.15K and (b) 373.15. ▲ and ● equilibrium data for liquid and vapor phase, respectively (Leu et al. 1999). — Prediction.

Optimization of the reactive distillation system is carried out using GAMS, for minimizing the total annualized cost (See Appendix) with constraints on purity of ETBE in the bottom stream (>95 % mole basis) and an isobutene conversion (> 90 %). The cost of the process is reduced by roughly 30 % compared to the traditional ETBE process scaled to match for this column capacity (Sneesby, 1998).

6. Conclusions

In this work, optimization of a reactive distillation column is carried out. The model is implemented in GAMS, including rigorous thermodynamic model and hydraulic constraints. Parameters required for simulating this system were unavailable in literature, thus they were estimated from experimental data taken from different sources. The fact of using a cubic equation of state within an equation oriented modelling environment made necessary to discriminate correct roots. This task was performed with an algorithm embedded in the optimization environment that evaluates derivatives of the function in order to find the correct roots.

Reactive distillation poses a challenge for process control (Nikacevic et al, 2011) which will be addressed in future work, within a dynamic optimization environment.

7. Appendix: Column Costs

$$ATC = 0.2\,(C_{COL} + C_{REB} + C_{COND} + C_{CAT}) + C_{STEAM} + C_{WATER} + \tag{41}$$

$C_{C4} + C_{ETHANOL} - C_{PRODUCT}$

$$C_{COL} = 17640D^{1.066}L^{0.802} \ [\$, D \ and \ L \ in \ m] \text{ (Sharifzadeh, 2013)} \tag{42}$$

$$C_{REB} = 7296 \, A_{REB}^{0.65} \ [\$, A \ in \ m^2] \text{ (Sharifzadeh, 2013)} \tag{43}$$

$$C_{COND} = 7296 \, A_{COND}^{0.65} \ [\$, A \ in \ m^2] \text{ (Sharifzadeh, 2013)} \tag{44}$$

$$C_{STEAM} = 0.0019 \ (\$/kg) \ (P=9.4bar, \ T=451.7K) \tag{45}$$

$$C_{WATER} = 0.0414 \ (\$/kg) \ (P=7bar, \ T_{supply}=451.7K) \tag{46}$$

$$C_{C4} = 29.65 \ (\$/kmol) \tag{47}$$

$$C_{ETHANOL} = 39.67 \ (\$/kmol) \tag{48}$$

$$C_{ETBE} = 118.25 \ (\$/kmol) \tag{49}$$

$$C_{CAT} = 10.16 \ (\$/kg, Amberlyst \ 15) \tag{50}$$

References

L. Domingues, C. I. C. Pinheiro, N. M. C. Oliveira, J. Fernandes, A. Vilelas, 2012, Model Development and Validation of Ethyl tert-Butyl Ether Production Reactors Using Industrial Plant Data, Industrial and Engineering Chemistry Research, 51, 15018–15031.

K. Kammerer, S. Schnabel, D. Silkenbaumer, R. N. Lichtenthaler, 1999, Vapor – liquid equilibria of binary mixtures containing an alcohol and a branched ether . Experimental results and modeling, Fluid Phase Equilibria, 162, 289–301.

M. Laakkonen, J.-P. Pokki, P. Uusi-Kyyny, J. Aittamaa, 2003, Vapour–liquid equilibrium for the 1-butene + methanol, + ethanol, + 2-propanol, + 2-butanol and + 2-methyl-2-propanol systems at 326 K, Fluid Phase Equilibria, 206, 1-2, 237–252.

A. Leu, D. B. Robinson, A. Tg, 1999, Vapor-Liquid Equilibrium for Four Binary Systems. Journal of Chemical Enginnering data, 44, 398–400.

N. M. Nikacevic, A. E. M. Huesman, P. M. J. Van Den Hof, A. I. Stankiewicz, 2011, Opportunities and challenges for process control in process intensification, Chemical Engineering and Processing - Process Intensification, 52, 1–15.

T. Ouni, A. Zaytseva, P. Uusi-Kyyny, J.-P. Pokki, J. Aittamaa, 2005, Vapour–liquid equilibrium for the 2-methylpropane+methanol, +ethanol, +2-propanol, +2-butanol and +2-methyl-2-propanol systems at 313.15K, Fluid Phase Equilibria, 232, 1-2, 90–99.

M. Sharifzadeh, 2013, Implementation of a steady-state inversely controlled process model for integrated design and control of an ETBE reactive distillation, Chemical Engineering Science, 92, 21–39.

M.G. Sneesby, Simulation and Control of Reactive Distillation, PhD Thesis, Curtin University of Technology, Australia.

G. Soave, 1972, Equilibrium constants from a modified Redlich-Kwong equation of state, Chemical Engineering Science, 27, 6, 1197-1203

K. F.Yee, A. R. Mohamed, S. H. Tan, 2013, A review on the evolution of ETBE and its future prospects, Renewable and Sustainable Energy Reviews, 22, 604–620.

Jiří Jaromír Klemeš, Petar Sabev Varbanov and Peng Yen Liew (Editors)
Proceedings of the 24th European Symposium on Computer Aided Process Engineering – ESCAPE 24
June 15-18, 2014, Budapest, Hungary.

Systematic Approach to Factory Acceptance Test Planning

Michal Kopcek*, Tomas Skulavik, Pavol Tanuska, Dusan Mudroncik

Institute of Applied Informatics, Automation and Mathematics MTF STU, Paulinska 16, Trnava 91724, SlovakiaFirst affiliation, Address, City and Postcode, Country
michal.kopcek@stuba.sk

Abstract

This paper deals with proposal of the basic frame of systematic approach to factory acceptance tests (FAT). The motivation of the presented research is briefly and concisely introduced in connection with relevant standards. Presented systematic approach to FAT is exhaustively explained using a case study example. The main results could be summarized as follows. In the first place is the analysis of approaches in the relevant research area, which is the life cycle of control systems on process level. Next is the proposal of the basic frame of systematic approach to planning, execution, evaluation and documenting of FAT and finally the detailed FAT plan specification. It is obvious that the presented proposal provide engineers with effective uniform methodics to deal with FAT, which could consequently lead to shortening the implementation phase of project life cycle.

Keywords: factory acceptance test, control system.

1. Introduction

Control systems with hierarchical structure are very complex systems from the point of hardware and software. The bottom level of these systems so called process level, where the process data are acquired and control actions are executed, plays a key role in the technological process control. The design, development, implementation, commissioning, maintenance and servicing has to be done according to valid international standards e.g. GAMP4 (2001) or GAMP5 (2008), ISO 15504 and others. Many control system applications are of the category safety relevant control systems, where the development requirements are much stricter in compliance with ISO 61508 and ISO 61511 as reported by Galik and Mudroncik (2009). Modifications of the safety critical control systems life cycle were proposed in Trnovsky and Tanuska (2013).

2. Factory acceptance tests

All the stages of project life cycle are ensured by processes related to the design, implementation, commissioning and maintenance of control system. Very important stage of control system life cycle is planning, execution, evaluation and documenting of Factory Acceptance Tests (FAT). The primary purpose of FAT is to minimize the occurrence of faults during the commissioning, which are typically detected by on-Site Acceptance Tests (SAT). Since FAT falls in the competence of control system supplier, they are executed without interconnection between control system with controlled technology. This implies that in the processes of FAT methods of modeling and simulation of hardware and software of the controllers and controlled dynamic process must be applied. Let us note, that these tests cover also the input and output signals processing, alarms processing and PID parameters verification. Standards (e.g. IEC 62337, IEC 62381 and IEC 62382) present the procedures of FAT execution too broadly therefore each supplier currently deals with this problem using internal guidelines on implementation of FAT. This contribution deals with the systematic approach to planning, execution, evaluation and documenting of FAT for the Control Systems on Process Level, hereinafter CSPL.

3. Basic frame

The originally proposed basic frame of systematic approach supposes processing of this documentation:

- User Requirements Specification (URS) – this is specified by customer itself or by dedicated representative and defines customers' expectations from CSPL.
- Functional Specification (FS) – this is formulated based upon the agreement between customer and supplier and describes the detailed functions of the CSPL i.e. what the system will do.
- FAT plan specification
- FAT realization
- FAT evaluation
- Processing of nonconformities
- FAT documentation

The proposal assumes, for all items except the last one, encoding of every specification such, that principles of Traceability Matrix (TM) may be used, as recommended by GAMP4 (2001).

Processing of nonconformity presents a very complex problem. In case of nonconformity occurrence it is necessary to develop a plan of tests for every corrective action executed. This involves a lot of work, because all the parts of specifications, which could be affected by executed corrective actions, must be tested again, even if they were tested before corrective actions. Described process is called as Change Management and it has to be performed during the whole life cycle of CSPL.

Let's look a bit closer on the most important item of the before mentioned proposal, which is the FAT Plan Specification (FATPS) for CSPL and is addressed by this contribution. As is generally known, the CSPL are implemented using industrial programmable controllers. We have proposed the FATPS in sequence as follows:

3.1. Input tests

These tests serve for verifying of the correctness of connection of the hardware analog input signals with the corresponding software address, for checking A/DC converting to engineering units and for testing of the filtering time according to given type of controller.

The verification of address correctness and the way of configuration of the binary inputs according to the physical value and logical one is done as well.

3.2. Output tests

The check of correctness of the analog outputs configuration including the check of threshold and limit values and verification of the binary outputs are performed within these tests.

3.3. PID tests

Testing of PID requires appropriate theoretical knowledge and know-how. The presented proposal involves a methodic of testing of the three fundamental types of PID algorithms, which are ISA, ideal parallel and interactive algorithm. Taking into account the type of controller (according to producer and assortment), there are possibly tens auxiliary parameters of the given PID algorithm, that have to be tested too.

3.4. Alarms tests

Planning of alarms tests is the simplest one. Alarms could be technological or safety and these are usually the alarms of I/O signals, Set Point (SP), Process Variable (PV), Deviation (DEV), etc.

3.5. Optimal control parameter setting tests

These tests are more complex than the others, because they require a physical or software model of the controlled system. They are focused to proving, that the settings of control parameters meet the requirements of the FS. It is obvious that in case of complex control structures, e.g. cascade control, ratio control, feedforward control and so on, suitable testing strategies must be used.

4. FAT for validation of control parameters

Because of limited scope of this paper, only an illustrative example of the implementation of FAT for validation of the optimal control parameters setting is presented. Note that the implemented PID algorithm could be in one of the following three forms:

1. Standard or so called ISA algorithm:

$$GAIN.\left(1+\frac{1}{s.T_i}+s.T_d\right) \tag{1}$$

where:

GAIN - proportional gain of the PID algorithm, it could be expressed also as proportional band PB=100/GAIN,

T_i - integral time constant,

T_d - derivative time constant.

2. Ideal parallel algorithm:

$$P+\frac{I}{s}+s.D \tag{2}$$

where:

P - gain of proportional part of the control algorithm,

I - gain of integral part of the control algorithm,

D - gain of derivative part of the control algorithm.

3. Interactive algorithm:

$$PB.\left(1+\frac{1}{s.T_i}\right).\left(1+\frac{s.T_d}{1+\alpha.T_d}\right) \tag{3}$$

where

PB - proportional band

T_i - integral time constant
T_d - derivative time constant
$\alpha < 1$ – derivative action's filtering coefficient

Testing the PID algorithm of given type of controller has to be planned depending on the implemented PID algorithm. In addition, some manufacturers of industrial controllers insufficiently document the type of PID algorithm and the meaning of its parameters in manuals. Most often the parameters PB with GAIN or T_i with REPEAT (time units) or I with RESET (inverse time units) are interchanged. The time constant T_d is always in time units, but the algorithm of numerical differentiation may be very different. In terms of processing of the set point (SP) is the PID algorithm standardly configurable in following modifications:

- PID algorithm applies all types of control action on the SP as well as on the process variable (PV).
- PI.D algorithm does not apply derivative of SP, other features are the same as PID.
- I.PD algorithm applies only integral control action on the SP.

The industrial controller could be implemented as a so-called discreet or as a continuous. The discreet algorithm offers the option to change the value of the sampling period (SCAN or sample time). The controller output (OUT) values are displayed with a frequency of SCAN. A time test table of controller output is used in this case. The continuous algorithm may have predefined sampling period. Outwardly, it behaves as a continuous analog controller. For recording of the controller output an analog signals data logger has to be used while the analog signal of the controller output after the D/A conversion is recorded.

4.1. Discrete PID algorithm tests

A test table with at least two rows is planned in this case. The values of time are listed in the first row while the values of the PID output are in the second row. The values depend on the structure of the algorithm, which may be P, PI, PD, PID.

PI algorithm testing

Let's assume that PI algorithm is in ISA form Eq.(1). The difference equation of this algorithm is as follows:

$$OUT_k = OUT_{k-1} + GAIN.\left(1 + \frac{T_v}{T_i}\right).e_k - GAIN.e_{k-1} \tag{4}$$

where:

OUT_k – current value of output,
OUT_{k-1} – previous value of output,
e_k – current value of deviation,
e_{k-1} – previous value of deviation,
T_v – sampling period.

Eq. (4) shows that the proportional part of control action is:

$$P_{PART} = GAIN.DEV \tag{5}$$

and the integral part of control action is:

$$I_{PART} = GAIN.\frac{T_v}{T_i}.DEV \tag{6}$$

In the first step, after changing the deviation (DEV) is the value of the control action (OUT) obtained as a sum of P_{PART} and I_{PART}. In the next steps is the output signal incremented only by the I_{PART}. Continuing the experiment without time limit, the final value of OUT will reach lower limit or higher limit according to the control action direction.

4.2. Test table design

According to expressions Eqs.(5), (6) and the controller parameters setting, which are noted in Table 1, the separate parts of PI algorithm are calculated as follows:

$$P_{PART} = 2.5 = 10\ \%\ and\ I_{PART} = 2.\frac{1}{10}.5 = 1\ \% \tag{7}$$

The designed table suitable for documentation is shown in Table 1 and the time response characteristic of the controller output is shown in Figure 1.
The change of DEV value was made from 0 to 5 e.u. in the time t = 2 s, regarding to this, the control action value OUT was calculated as:

$$OUT_0 + P_{PART} + I_{PART} = 61\ \% \tag{8}$$

In the next steps the output increases by each sampling period, i.e. about 1 % until the value OUT reaches the maximum limit value OUT_{max}.

Table 1. PI algorithm FAT table

Parameters:	SCAN = 1 s, GAIN = 2, Ti = 10 s, OUT_0 = 50 %, OUT_{min} = 0 %, OUT_{max} = 100 %									
Time [s]	0	1	2	3	4	5	6	...	42	43
DEV [e.u.]	0	0	5	5	5	5	5	...	5	5
OUT [%]	50	50	61	62	63	64	65	...	100	100

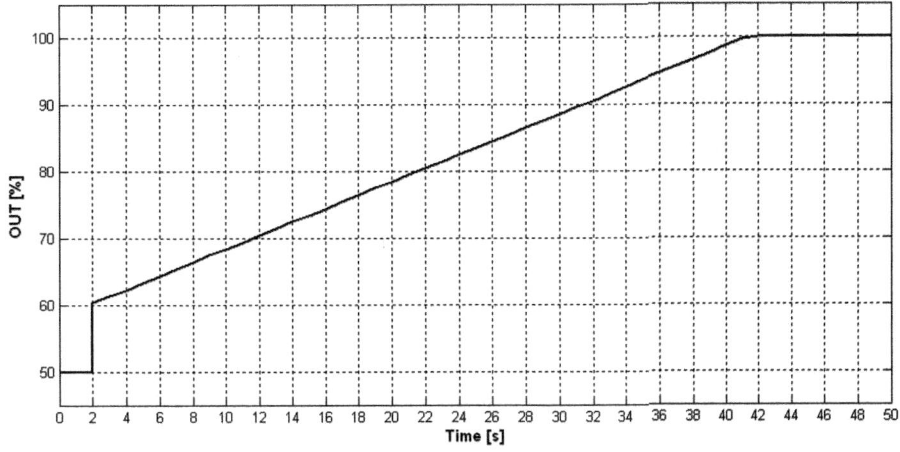

Figure 1. PI controller output time response.

4.3. Test evaluation

Several cases of wrong OUT value in time t = 2 s could occur due to misinterpretation of separate parameters:

- the increment of 1 % is right, but the OUT value is wrong, means misinterpretation of parameter GAIN,
- the increment of 1 % is wrong, indicates misinterpretation of parameter Ti,
- another case is misinterpretation of both mentioned parameters.

The other algorithms (P, PD, PID) are tested in a similar way and similar procedures are used during FATPS for other tests mentioned above. The presented case study example was performed using the virtual model of industrial controller Honeywell UDC3300, which was developed on the authors' workplace. More details about the virtual controller could be found in Tanuska and Mudroncik (2003).

5. Conclusions

The main results of presented research could be summarized into these three highlights. The first is the analysis of approaches in the relevant research area, which is the CSPL life cycle. The second is the proposal of the basic frame of systematic approach to planning, execution, evaluation and documenting of FAT for CSPL. The third is the detailed FAT plan specification.

Methods of realization of the FAT for CSPL were developed within the presented research on the authors' workplace. The results of the research are already applied in education process, where the students are familiarized with the systematic approach to FAT as a whole. Further research is oriented to development of another methodics dedicated to the FAT in compliance with the aforementioned basic framework.

References

M. Galik, D. Mudroncik, 2009, Standards for the control systems software development, Automa, no. 4, FCC Public, Praha, Czech republic, 22-25, ISSN 1210-9592 (in Slovak).

GAMP 4, 2001, Good Automated Manufacturing Practice (GAMP) Guide for validation of automated systems, version 4, ISPE, Tampa, Florida.

GAMP 5, 2008, Good Automated Manufacturing Practice (GAMP) Guide for validation of automated systems, version 5, ISPE, Tampa, Florida.

IEC 62337, Commissioning of electrical, instrumentation and control systems in the process industry - Specific phases and milestones.

IEC 62381, Automation systems in the process industry - Factory acceptance test (FAT), site acceptance test (SAT), and site integration test (SIT).

IEC 62382, Control systems in the process industry - Electrical and instrumentation loop check

ISO 15504, Information technology - Process assessment.

ISO 61508, Functional Safety of Electrical/Electronic/Programmable Electronic Safety-related Systems.

ISO 61511, Functional safety - Safety instrumented systems for the process industry sector.

P. Tanuska, D. Mudroncik, 2003, Virtual controller UDC 3300 honeywell, In: Process Control 2003, 14th International Conference, Strbske Pleso, Slovak Republic.

P. Trnovsky, P. Tanuska, 2013, Modified proposal of life cycle for safety critical control systems, International Journal of Innovation, Management and Technology, 4, 1, 73-75.

Jiří Jaromír Klemeš, Petar Sabev Varbanov and Peng Yen Liew (Editors)
Proceedings of the 24th European Symposium on Computer Aided Process Engineering – ESCAPE 24
June 15-18, 2014, Budapest, Hungary.

Optimal Integration of a Concentrated Solar Plant Facility with a Biomass Based Polygeneration System

Marta Vidal, Lidia Martín, Mariano Martín*

Department of Chemical Engineering, University of Salamanca, 37008, Salamanca, Spain
mariano.m3@usal.es

Abstract

In this paper we address the integration of a polygeneration system based on biomass with a concentrated solar power facility for the constant production of electricity over a year long. The process is modeled as a superstructure embedding two different gasification technologies, direct and indirect, and two reforming modes, partial oxidation or steam reforming, followed by gas cleaning and three alternatives for the syngas use, water gas shift reactor (WGSR) to produce hydrogen, a furnace for thermal energy production and an open Brayton cycle. We couple this system with a concentrated solar plant that uses tower technology, molten salts energy storage, and a regenerative Rankine cycle. The problem is formulated as a multi-period mixed-integer non linear programming problem (MINLP). The optimal integration involves the use of indirect gasification and steam reforming using the Brayton cycle to produce 340 MW of electricity and 97 kt/yr of hydrogen. The electricity cost is 0.073 €/kWh.

Keywords: Solar energy, Biomass, Polygeneration, Hydrogen.

1. Introduction

Solar irradiation is a promising source of energy due to large amount that the Earth recevies dayly, enough to supply on its own the needs of the entire planet. So far most of the analysis on concentrated solar power evaluate stand alone plants from a simulation point of view (Palenzuela et al., 2013) or simplified optimization models (Richer et al., 2011). Only lately, detailed equation based modeling has been presented (Martín and Martín, 2013). The main problem with solar based systems is their variable nature which results in the fact that storage systems or supplementary sources of energy are needed to maintain the production level and meet the demand. Yaun et al. (2012) presented an overview of integration possibilities as a perspective on the future promising use of a combination of different energy sources, fossil and renewable ones.In this paper we address the integration of a polygeneration system based on biomass with a concentrated solar power facility for the constant production of electricity over a year long operation. The process is limited by the irradiation of solar and the availability of biomass within 50 km of the CSP facility. We locate the plant in Almería, where high solar irradiation is available (Martín and Martín, 2013) as well as forest and grassy biomass (Alcamo and Onigkeit, 2006).

2. Modeling Assumptions

In this section we describe the two processes that are being integrated.

2.1. Polygeneration system

The biomass is first preprocessed to eliminate solids and water. Later, gasification produces raw syngas from the biomass. Gasification can be atmospheric or pressurized, direct or indirect, resulting in very different gas compositions. The Renugas gasifier, pressurized direct oxygen fired gasifier, produces a gas rich in CO_2, while the fraction of hydrocarbons can be further reformed to hydrogen. Gasification at high pressure allows a large throughput per reactor volume, and reduces the need for pressurization downstream, so that less overall power is needed. However, the gasifier efficiency is lower and more steam is needed. Furthermore, the Renugas gasifier requires pure oxygen to avoid diluting the gas and to reduce the downstream equipment size. The low pressure gasifier, Battelle Columbus (Ferco), is indirectly heated so that it is possible to use air to combust the char. The gasifier produces a gas with low CO_2 content, but contains heavier hydrocarbons. The reactor is fast fluidized, allowing throughputs equal to the bubbling fluidized Renugas gasifier despite the nearly atmospheric operation. Working at lower pressure decreases the operating cost. The next step is syngas reforming to remove hydrocarbons. We consider either steam reforming, which is endothermic but generates higher yield to hydrogen, or partial oxidation, that is exothermic but whose yield to hydrogen is lower. Subsequently, the gas must be cleaned. We consider either cold or hot cleaning. Cold cleaning uses a water scrubber to remove solids and NH_3. Alternatively, hot gas cleaning uses ceramic filters at high temperature. In the case of high pressure operation the hot cleaning is selected, while for low pressure the cold cleaning process is considered. Finally, a multi bed PSA system is used to remove the last traces of hydrocarbons, H_2S and CO_2, in that order.Once the syngas is purified, we consider three alternatives. On the one hand, we can use a water gas shift reaction to produce hydrogen. The second alternative is the use of the syngas for thermal energy production that is used to heat up the molten salts in the concentrated solar plant. Finally, an open Brayton cycle with multiple stage compression for the air is proposed. Figure 1 shows the superstructure, where Q represents excess of thermal energy available while E corresponds to electricity production.

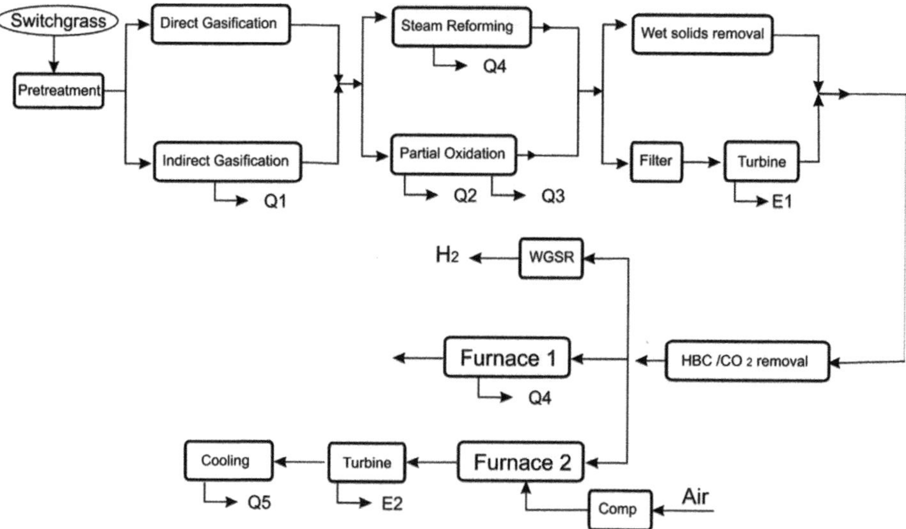

Figure 1. Scheme of a Biomass based polygeneration system; Q: Thermal energy; E: Electricity.

2.2. Concentrated Solar Plant

The concentrated solar plant facility consists of three parts, the heliostat field including the tower collector and the molten salts storage tanks, a regenerative Rankine cycle that includes the steam turbine and the cooling tower, see Figure 2. The steam is generated in a system of three heat exchangers where it is first heated up to saturation and then evaporated using the total flow of molten salts. A fraction of the flow of salts is used to superheat the steam before it is fed to the first body of the turbine. The rest is used to reheat up the steam before it is fed to the second body. In the second body of the turbine, a fraction of the steam is extracted at a medium pressure and it is used to heat up the condensate. The rest of the steam is finally expanded to an exhaust pressure, condensed and recycled. A cooling tower is used to condensate this exhaust steam, see Martín and Martín (2013).

2.3. Integration

We use the energy available in the flowsheet given by Figure 1, either in the form of electricity produced in Expand2 or the Brayton cycle, E1, E2, or the thermal energy in excess in certain heat exchangers within the flowsheet, Q1, Q2, Q3, Q5 or produced in a furnace, Q4, to produce electricity to meet the demand or to provide energy to heat up the molten salts of the concentrated solar plant so as to maintain constant electricity production.

2.4. Optimization procedure

The process integration is formulated as a multiperiod mixed-integer non linear programming problem (MINLP). We evaluate the year long operation of the combined facility to maintain a production of 340 MW of electricity depending on the solar irradiation and the climatic conditions of the location. The problem as a whole is more than 26,000 eqs and 30,000 var. We first solve the concentrated solar plant, 3,000 equations and 3,300 variables (Martín and Martín, 2013), to compute the monthly energy needs for a production capacity of 340 MW. Based on these results we optimize the superstructure of the polygeneration system on a monthly basis to determine the energy needed to maintain 340 MW along the year. A total enumeration of alternatives has been applied due to the small number of 0-1 variables which model the direct or indirect gasification and the partial or steam reforming. Therefore, the MINLP is decomposed into four subproblems, one per each gasifier, and one per each reforming

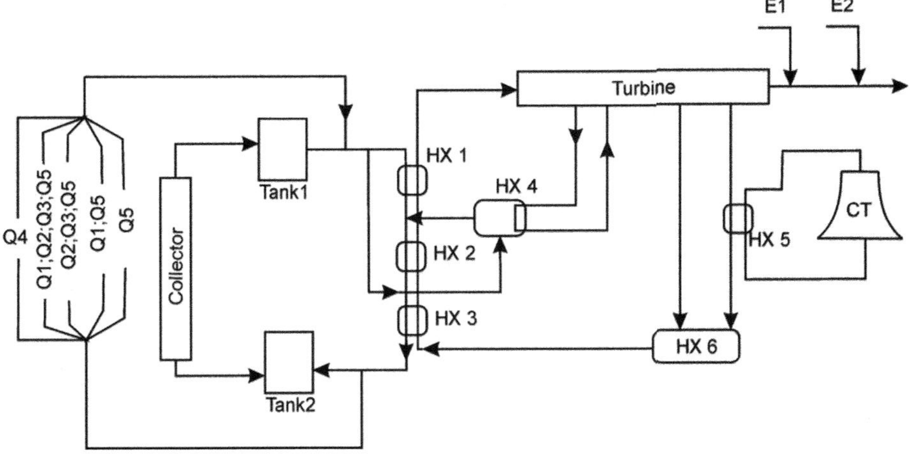

Figure 2. Scheme of a concentrated solar plant facility integrated with power and heat from biomass Q: Thermal energy; E: Electricity; CT: Cooling Tower; HX: Heat exchanger.

mode so that we solve four NLP problems consisting of 23,500 eqs. and 28,700 variables. Due to the complexity of solving a multi-period optimization problem with this size and due to the independency among the months for the polygeneration system, we solve a problem per month consisting of 2,000 eqs. and 2,400 variables each. The objective function is as given by Eq.(1) where Ci is the cost of the different items, i, where Electr, HX and WGSR represent electricity, heat exchangers and water was shift reactor:

$$Z = -C_{Electr}\sum W_{turbines} - C_{Electr}\sum W_{compressors} - C_{Steam}\Big(\sum_{Furnace,HXi,} Q - \sum_{WGSR,Gasifier} Q\Big) + fc(H_2)C_{H_2}$$
$$-C_{biomass}\cdot fc(biomass) - \sum_{Gasifier,Re\,forer} fc(O_2)C_{O_2} \quad (1)$$

3. Results

3.1. Optimal Integration

In Figure 3 we present the comparison of the design options for the design as an example for different biomass cost. The optimal integration involves the use of indirect gasification followed by steam reforming, cold cleaning and a gas turbine to be coupled with the concentrated solar plant facility for constant electricity production (340 MW) and variable production of hydrogen. Within typical range of biomass and byproduct costs, the use of the Ferco indirect gasifier and the steam reforming is recommended due to the availability of streams a high temperature from the combustor and the slightly higher production of hydrogen as compared to the partial oxidation. In terms of further integration, this solution is interesting since it matches the ones presented for the FT-fuels and hydrogen production even though it is not the same as for bioethanol production (Martín and Grossmann, 2013).

3.2. Economic evaluation

The investment cost of such a plant is based on equipment sizing for maximum production of hydrogen, July, during summer period, maximum production of electricity from biomass in winter and the maximum solar energy production in July. The advantage of the integrated facility is that most of the plant is operating at full capacity but for the WGSR or the Brayton cycle increasing the efficiency compared to the solar plant alone.The investment cost is estimated based on Sinnot's method (Sinnot, 1999), land and buildings cost are estimated to be 110 M€, and we pay for the salts (0.665 €/kg). These items add up to the fix cost (2,305 M€), see Figure 4 for the breakdown. The fees represent 3 % of the fix cost, other administrative expenses and overheads and the plant layout represent 10 % of the direct costs (fees plus fix capital)

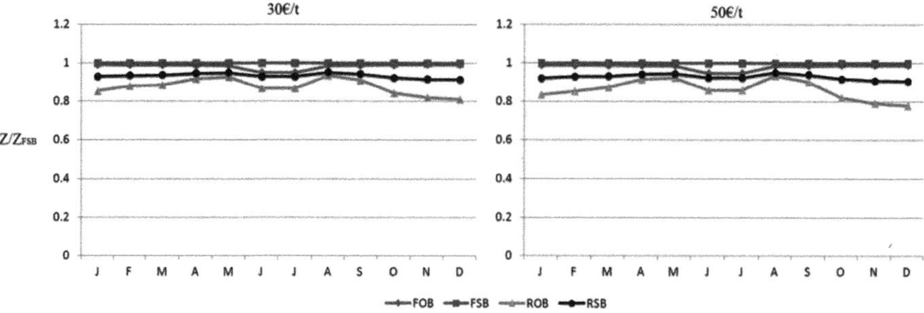

Figure 3. Biomass cost sensitivity on the topology selection: F: Ferco Gasifier; R: Renugas Gasifier, O: Partial Oxidation, S: Steam reforming, B: Brayton cycle

and 5 % of the fix cost respectively. The plant start up cost represents 15 % of the investment. The investment adds up to 3,225 M€.

Furthermore, we estimate the production cost of the electricity considering the hydrogen as a credit. The advantage is that we can store the hydrogen produced or generate energy out of it. We assume $1.58/kg since the Department of Energy of the U.S.A. (Spath et al., 2005) has established this value as a target (1.2 €/kg). Based on Sinnot's method, Figure 5 presents the contribution of the different items to the production cost of electricity before credits. We see that the biomass, at 50 €/t, represents 23 % of the production costs, while the equipment cost and maintenance represents 45 % altogether. The total hydrogen production along the year reaches 97 kt, resulting in an electricity cost of 0.073 €/kWh.

Finally we present a sensitivity study of the effect of the price of biomass and hydrogen on the electricity production cost, see Figure 6. In order to maintain electricity costs below 0.1 €/kWh we need to assure biomass costs below 100 €/t and /or hydrogen prices above 0.58 €/kg.

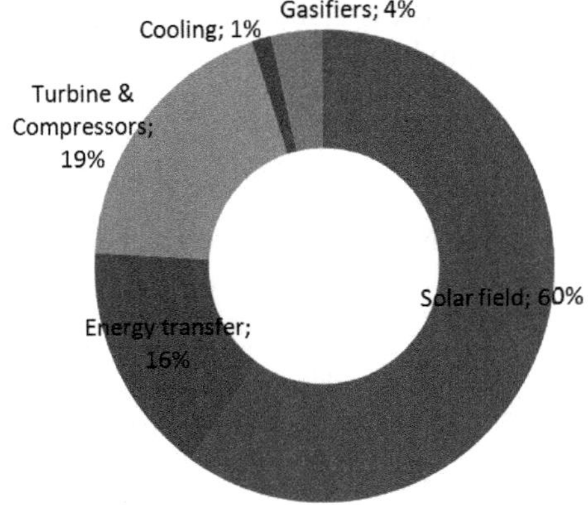

Figure 4. Breakdown of equipment costs

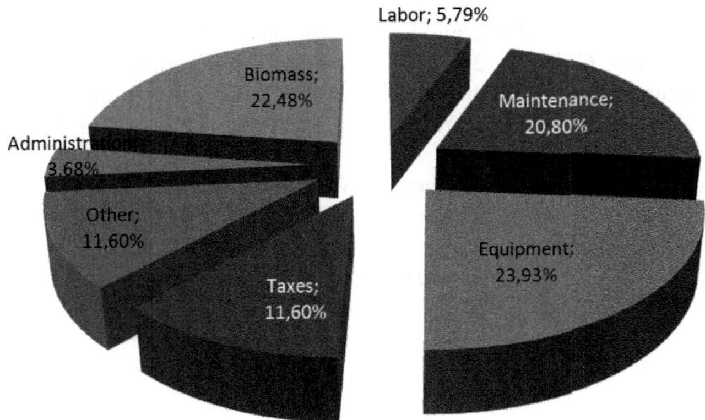

Figure 5. Production cost break down

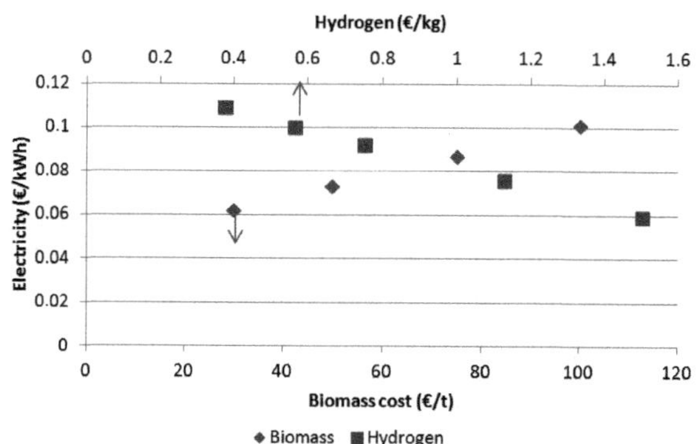

Figure 6. Sensitivity analysis on hydrogen and biomass prices

4. Conclusions

The optimal integration involves the use of indirect gasification followed by steam reforming, cold cleaning and a gas turbine to be coupled with the concentrated solar plant facility for constant electricity production (340 MW) and variable production of hydrogen. The total investment cost is 3,200 M€ and the production cost for electricity, assuming that the hydrogen produced, 97 kt, is a credit (1.2 €/kg), results in 0.073 €/kWh.

Acknowledgments

Salamanca Research and MICINN for a starting research fellowship to Ms. M. Vidal.

References

J. Alcamo, J. Onigkeit, 2006, Miscanthus yields in tons of dry matter per ha throughout the EU-25 <www.usf.uni-kassel.de/cesr/images/project/jet-set_miscanthus.jpg>, Accesed on 01/01/2014.

L. Martín, M. Martín, 2013, Optimal year-round operation of a Concentrated Solar Energy Plant in the South of Europe, Applied Thermal Engineering, 59, 627-633.

M. Martín, I.E. Grossmann, 2013, On the systematic synthesis of sustainable biorefineries, Industrial Engineering Chemistry Research, 52, 9, 3044-3064

P. Palenzuela, G. Zaragoza, D.C. Alarcón-Padilla, J. Blanco, 2013, Evaluation of cooling technologies of concentrated solar power plants and their combination with desalination in the Mediterranean area, Applied Thermal Engineering 50, 1514-1521.

P. Richter, E. Abraham, G. Morin, 2011, Optimisation of concentrating solar thermal power plants with neural networks, Adaptive and Natural Computing Algorithms, 6593, 190-199.

R.K. Sinnot, 1999, Coulson and Richardson's Chemical Engineering, 3ªEd, Butterworth Heinemann, Singapore.

P. Spath, A. Aden, T. Eggeman, M. Ringer, B. Wallace, J. Jechura, 2005, Biomass to Hydrogen Production Detailed Design and Economics Utilizing the Battelle Columbus Laboratory Indirectly-Heated Gasifier, Technical Report NREL/ TP-510-37408.

Z. Yuan, B. Chen, 2012, Process Synthesis for Addressing the Sustainable EnergySystems and Environmental Issues, AIChE J., 58, 11, 3370-3389.

Jiří Jaromír Klemeš, Petar Sabev Varbanov and Peng Yen Liew (Editors)
Proceedings of the 24th European Symposium on Computer Aided Process Engineering – ESCAPE 24
June 15-18, 2014, Budapest, Hungary.

Pinch Analysis of an Industrial Batch Process for the Refining of Vegetable Oil

Bruno S. Custódio[a,c], Henrique A. Matos[a]*, Fernando G. Martins[b], António L. Oliveira[c]

[a]*CPQ/CERENA, DEQ, Instituto Superior Técnico, Universidade de Lisboa, 1049-001 Lisboa, Portugal;*
[b]*LEPABE, Departamento de Engenharia Química, Faculdade de Engenharia, Universidade do Porto, Rua Dr. Roberto Frias, 4200-465 Porto, Portugal;*
[c]*FIMA Produtos Alimentares, Sociedade Anónima, Marinhas de D. Pedro, 2690-361 Santa Iria de Azóia, Portugal.*
henrimatos@tecnico.ulisboa.pt

Abstract

This work addresses the application of a detailed Pinch Analysis modelling technique, developed in Excel/VBA, for a multipurpose refinery batch plant. This application is focused on developing a tool that enables a quick analysis of Heat Integration to improve the energy-efficiency by rescheduling the operations. The developed tool was used with a real case study process data of a vegetable oil's refining plant. Several scenarios of re-scheduling were used to still accomplish the demand from the downstream plant production. This study show that a reduction of about 15 % in both utilities consumption can be achieved by some scenarios compared to the current vegetable refining scheduling. Also the results show that the integrated approach leads to better synchronization between production plant and the utility system. Thereby, the integrated approach leads to significant reduction in energy costs and gas emissions, showing advantages for future improvements based on rescheduling and indirect/direct heat exchange opportunities. Also the results of this work indicate a great potential of the use of HENs in real Batch Process systems for refining vegetable oils and present an important enhancement on the industrial plant thermal energy efficiency.

Keywords: Pinch Analysis; Batch processing; Time Slice Model (TSM); Rescheduling; Refining Vegetable Oil.

1. Introduction

For batch systems, Pinch Analysis and the development of direct heat recovery projects are much more difficult to perform than for continuous processes. For example, in these systems, many streams are present for only certain time periods, which restrict the possibilities for heat exchange. In addition they usually do not evolve at constant temperatures with constant heat capacity flow rates. In many situations, much heating and/or cooling are done in situ in vessels were the contents gradually change the temperature. Nonetheless, Pinch Analysis can be applied to batch processes, with suitable modifications.

Such Heat Integration approach and Pinch Analysis techniques have been initially establish by Kemp and Deakin in 1989 to obtain the energy targets for the batch operation, were they expanded the concept of the Time Slice Model (TSM) of Kemp and MacDonald (1987, 1988). The TSM takes the schedule of streams into account and split into several time intervals, where each sub-process is associated to each time slice. Ian Kemp in 2007 described the basic procedures of using TSM for Heat Integration of Batch Processes.

Some recent works have been developed applying several programming techniques to improve the integration of Batch Processes (Friedler, 2010). Mixed Integer Linear Programming (MILP) has also been considered to improve Batch Processes by attempting Rescheduling (Jia, 2013).

In this work an Excel/VBA application is presented based on Pinch Analysis procedures for batch processes. The main goal of this application is to create an advanced software tool of data manipulation In\Out, analysis, and displaying of the energy saving potentials in a Batch Process system and also to give the incentive to improve the direct Heat Integration through quick rescheduling. The energy targets calculated by this tool are based on the time – temperature cascade analysis methodology (Kemp, 2007). In general this methodology gives targets for maximum heat recovery within a batch system and for a TSM, from which rescheduling opportunities can be obtained. Moreover, the created application takes the schedule of streams into account for Batch Process systems and split into several time intervals, where each sub-process is associated to each time slice.

The Pinch Analysis method was implemented in FIMA refinery plant in St. Iria, Portugal, a multipurpose refinery batch plant. The plant produces in batch mode about 36,000 t/y of vegetable oils, which creates a real industrial case study for the implementation of this kind of analysis. In this way, opportunities for Heat Integration were explored.

2. The Pinch Analysis and the Excel/VBA tool

The evaluation of the optimal energy saving potential by rescheduling in a Batch Process system is a difficult task because the existence of a large number of possibilities. The Excel/VBA tool proposed in this work was developed for helping to define the rescheduling opportunities of the operating process with savings in energy consumption. The main features of this tool are presented in Figure 1.

The algorithm is described as follows:
Step 1: Define the number of stream j max in the case study process.
Step 2: Insert the steams data from the case study process (j=1; j=2; j=3;...; j max) and choose the specific minimum temperature difference ΔTmin.
Step 3: If the time event of each stream are independent from each other insert the desired time deviation td and the corresponding number of feasible iteration i max otherwise select first the stream that are dependent on each other.
Step 4: Start the Pinch Analysis modelling simulation considering the methodology of Kemp (2007).
Step 5: Creation of the table of results of the required hot utility and cold utility in the process for each iteration and the corresponding graphs.

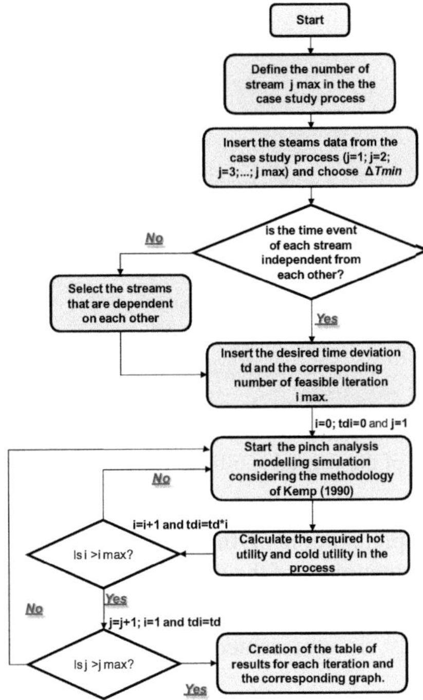

Figure 1. Flowchart for the Pinch Analysis modelling with Excel/VBA programming

The user has to provide the data time intervals of all operations and the streams source data (until a maximum of 10 streams).
The target values calculated by the Excel/VBA tool indicate automatically the best opportunities of rescheduling to minimize the energy consumption.

3. Case study

The methodologies described above are applied to a real industrial case of a refinery of vegetable oil.

3.1. Process description.

The first step of the production process in the refinery is the preparation of the vegetable oil. The oil arrive in raw or semi-refined state to the plant from tanks or vessels, being subjected to prior treatment at the refinery.
The raw materials are: Sunflower, Corn, Soybeans (non-genetically modified) Palm oil and its derivatives such palm stearin or palm olein and coconut oil.
These raw materials are firstly subject to a control quality and after they proceed to three different processing operations in the refinery:

- Neutralization to remove the impurities and the acidity of the oil, with a solution of caustic soda;
- Bleaching to remove all natural colours of the oil by taking out all pigments, such as chlorophyll and carotenoids;
- Deodorization to eliminate the taste and odour of the natural oil by heating the oil up to a temperature in the range (230-260 °C) under a vacuum pressure of 2 to 10 mm Hg absolute.

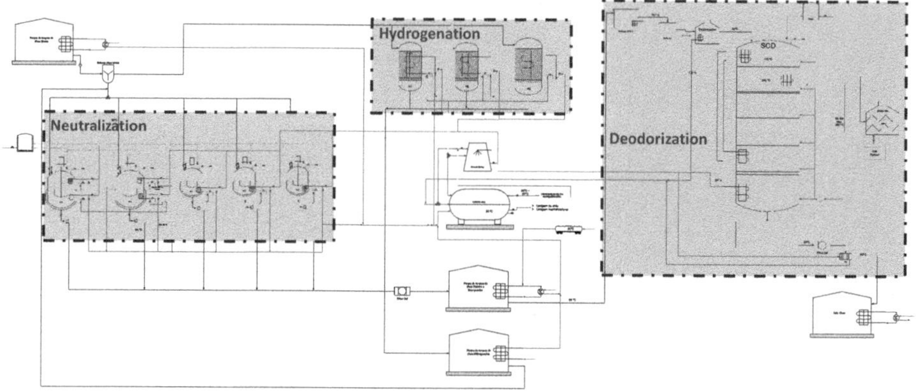

Figure 2. Process flowsheet of the vegetable oil's refinery.

Finally, the pre-treated oil are sent to margarine plant, more properly to the storage room for the finalizing preparation of the oil (the fat phase). Figure 2 presents the process flowsheet for the treatment of the oil at the refinery.

3.2. Analysis of the neutralization process.

The data of the case study are represented in the Table 1, this represents a part of the refining process.

The plant production scheduling was used for the products (A1) and (A2) in the neutralization process. Each product occupies, respectively, the reactors N5 and N4. The products hold also distinct process operations. For example the product A1 is heated first from 50 °C to 110 °C, then the product is cooled to 95 °C, and then heated to 105 °C. Finally the product is cooled to 50 °C (Stream 1, 2, 3 and 4 of Table 1). For the product A2 the process is more simplified. The product is heated first from 50 °C to 85 °C and finally cooled to 60 °C.

The neutralization reactors operate under reduced pressure. They are cylindrical vessels and their height is approximately 1.5 times the diameter. The two reactors contain Heat Transfer Systems. Steam or cold water can be passed through that coils system to obtain the target values of the temperatures.

The cycle time of the process is 1.5 h and the streams exist during the following time periods: Cold stream 1: 0–0.2 h; Hot stream 2: 0.4–0.6 h; Cold stream 3: 0.7–1 h; Hot stream 4: 1.1–1.3 h; Cold stream 5: 0.5–0.9 h and Hot stream 6: 1.2–1.5 h

Through the heat cascades it was possible to obtain for each time interval placed side by side the visualization of the heat load and the wanted targets. The targets obtained are the Maximum Energy Recovery (MER) within that time interval by direct heat exchange. The TSM targets are 1087 kWh hot utility and 1125 kWh cold utility.

Table 1. Data for the existing case in the refinery

									Operational times		
	Stream	Type	Ti	Tf	Ti′	Tf′	Cp (kW/K)	Q (kW)	Start (h)	End (h)	Q (kWh)
N5 A1	1	cold	50	110	55	115	-58.3	-3500	0	0.2	-700
	2	hot	110	95	105	90	58.3	875	0.4	0.6	175
	3	cold	94	105	99	110	-38.9	-428	0.7	1	-128
	4	hot	105	50	100	45	58.3	3208	1.1	1.3	642
N4 A2	5	cold	50	85	55	90	-24.6	-862	0.5	0.9	-345
	6	hot	100	60	95	55	32.8	1314	1.2	1.5	394

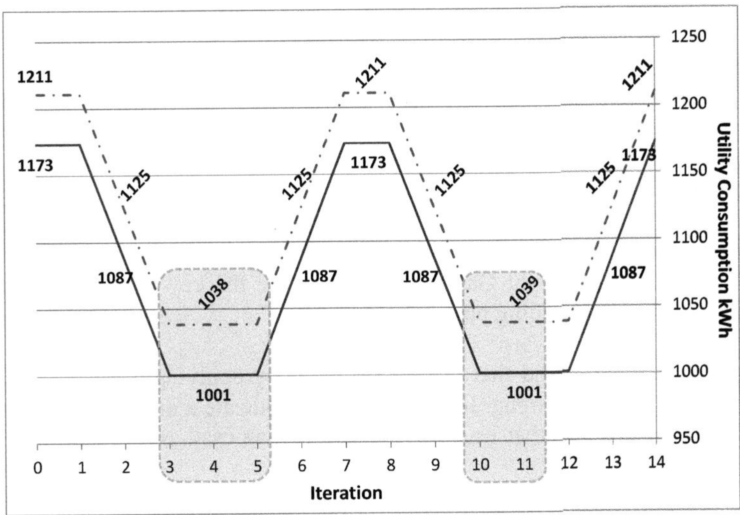

Figure 3. Graphical representation of the consumption of the process utilities obtained by the Excel/VBA tool for 15 scheduling scenarios/iterations. (---- Cold Utility; — Hot Utility)

3.3. Results of Excel/VBA software tool.

The results are given automatically in a graphical representation, allowing for an easy assessment of rescheduling opportunities (Figure 3 and 4).

It can be seen that the opportunities for rescheduling exist. From the several TSM iterations, we obtain five opportunities (Iteration 3; 4; 5; 10 and 11), which implements time deviation for the streams 5 and 6 (-0.3 h; -0.2 h; -0.1 h; 0.4 h and 0.5 h), respectively. The iteration twelve was not considered due to violation of the specific minimum temperature difference ΔTmin. The best result introduces requirements of 1,001 kWh of hot utility and 1,038 kWh of cold utility. These streams (5 and 6) are mutually dependent of the time scheduling of the reactor N4 and the remaining streams to the reactor N5. The corresponding heat recovery is a potential value of 172.4 kWh. This saving of about 15 % is obtained for each utility compared with the former requirements without heat integration (1,173 kWh and 1,211 kWh).

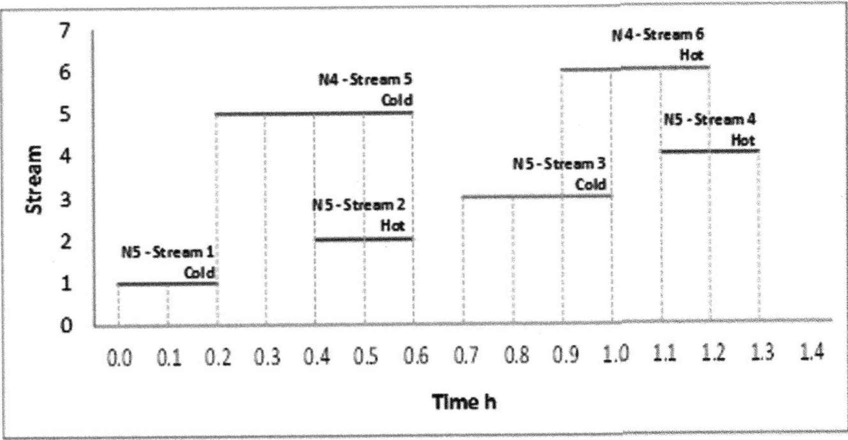

Figure 4. New time event diagram from the iteration 3 with saving of 15 % in each utility.

4. Conclusions

Heat recovery in batch processes is possible, but generally gives lower absolute savings than for continuous processes, because energy use is generally lower and there are major constraints on whether hot and cold streams coexist at the same time. The case study shows that Pinch Analysis can identify substantial benefits on batch processes, and also on other time-dependent situations.

The two most commonly useful techniques for batch and time-dependent processes are the TSM and the time event Gantt chart. These are the key points in evaluating heat exchange and for rescheduling possibilities.

This work was able to find that these techniques by applying a framework developed with Excel/VBA programming. It was possible to indicate a direct target saving near 15 %, and also demonstrate that was possible through an easy assessment of rescheduling opportunities.

Further work will be focused on the operational issues for applying this results and new studies about the opportunities created by including the indirect heat storage strategy.

References

F. Friedler, 2010, Process integration, modelling and optimisation for energy saving and pollution reduction, Applied Thermal Engineering, 30, 16, 2270-2280.

I.C. Kemp, 2007, Pinch Analysis and Process Integration: A User Guide on Process Integration for the Efficient Use of Energy, Second Edition, Elsevier, UK

I.C. Kemp, 1990, Application of the time-dependent cascade analysis in process integration, Journal of Heat Recovery System and CHP, 10, 4, 423-425.

I.C. Kemp, A.W. Deakin, 1989, The cascade analysis for energy and process integration of batch processes, Part 1: Calculation of energy targets, Chemical Engineering Research and Design 67, 495-509.

I.C. Kemp, E.K. Macdonald, 1987, Energy and process integration in continuous and batch processes, IChemE Symposium Series, 105, 185-200, Institution of Chemical Engineers, Rugby, UK.

I.C. Kemp, E.K. Macdonald, 1988. Application of pinch technology to separation, reaction and batch processes. IChemE Symposium Series, 109, 239-257, Institution of Chemical Engineers, Rugby, UK.

Y. Jia, W. Xiao, G.H. He, 2013, Petri Net Methodology for Optimization of Heat Integration and Batch Process Scheduling, Proceedings of the 6th International Conference on Process Systems Engineering (PSE ASIA), Kuala Lumpur, Malaysia.

Jiří Jaromír Klemeš, Petar Sabev Varbanov and Peng Yen Liew (Editors)
Proceedings of the 24th European Symposium on Computer Aided Process Engineering – ESCAPE 24
June 15-18, 2014, Budapest, Hungary.

Electric Field Driven Separation of Oil-water Mixtures: Model Development

Wilma Wallau, Raj Patel, Iqbal Mujtaba, Harvey Arellano-Garcia*

School of Engineering, University of Bradford, West Yorkshire BD7 1DP, UK
H.Arellano-Garcia@bradford.ac.uk

Abstract

Coalescence enhancement of water droplets in oil emulsions is commonly contemplated for the separation of an aqueous phase dispersed in a dielectric oil phase with a considerably lower dielectric constant than that of the dispersed phase. The characteristics and geometry of the electrode system have a large impact on the performance of an electrostatic coalescer and are actually strictly linked to the type of the applied electric field and the emulsion used. Furthermore, addition of chemicals and heating has also been revealed to further enhance the electrocoalescence of water droplets. In this work, the coalescence of two water drops sinking in a dielectric oil phase at an applied high voltage, pulsed dc electric field, in particular with regards to the effects of pressure and temperature on coalescence performance is investigated. The developed model should help to recognise and prove approaches to electrocoalescence mechanisms, the dispersion flow direction with respect to the applied electric field, as well as the electric field configuration.

Keywords: modelling, process analysis, electrical field, coalescence

1. Introduction

Electrocoalescence describes the phenomenon by which coalescence of an electrically conducting phase, dispersed in an insulating phase, is achieved by applying an electric field between a high voltage and a ground electrode. In separation technology, electro-coalescers help to enhance the performance of common sedimentation units. Since larger particles sink faster, coalescence of small droplets is desired so as to decrease the residence time, and thus, separator sizes. Although electro-coalescers are broadly applied in industry, i.e. for water-crude oil separation, the system behaviour is not yet fully understood. However, electrocoalescence has been studied extensively over the last decades. Theoretical and empirical simulation approaches deal with a wide range of electrocoalescence effects such as drop deformation (Raisin et al., 2009), attraction and repulsion of drops (Eow and Gharidi, 2003), drop-drop (Mohammadi et al., 2012) and (Shahhosseini et al., 2014) as well as drop-interface coalescence in vertical or horizontal electric fields, dipole-induced-dipole mechanism and film thinning. Following up the comprehensive research of Bailes et al. in the 1980's at the University of Bradford, which was investigating the coalescence performance of emulsions at test-size scale, the examination of electro-coalescence will be expanded exemplary to the coalescence of two single droplets at a micro meter scale. The impact of temperature has indirectly been investigated by (Chiesa et al., 2006), when analysing the role of viscosity, which was adjusted by temperature variation.

Coalescence performance depends among others on electric field parameters such as field strength, frequency, wave form, electrode insulation, electrode design, and substance parameters such as density, viscosity, dielectric constant, electric conductivity, and surface tension, the existence of surface active additives, drop size, and drop position.

2. Problem statement

Since the introduction of the concept of pulsed DC electric fields together with insulated electrodes, this has become more common in the electro-coalescence technology. Moreover, the characteristics and geometry of the electrode system influence the performance of the electrostatic coalescer and are in fact closely related to the emulsion used. For the development of a high-grade electrocoalescer design, which is tailored to a particular system, a precise simulation is particularly indispensable as drop-drop-coalescence depends on a large number of parameters. Apart from the substantial modelling work, the model-based analysis of the influential parameters such as pressure and temperature is pursued. The simulation results and corresponding experiments are to be integrated in multi-drop systems. In order to allow the application of commonly used tools to further process optimization, the simulation in this work is first conducted in MATLAB.

3. Experimental set-up

An experimental set-up, shown in Figure 1, with two vertically placed electrodes inside a test-cell has been arranged. The dielectric organic liquid dodecane is filled into the cell. Temperature and pressure can be controlled. By applying a high dc voltage, a homogeneous electric field is then set up at an adjustable pulse frequency. Two water droplets are injected simultaneously at the top of the test-cell and then sink in the lighter, stagnant oil phase. Optical measurement of the particle tracks and drop deformation allows the evaluation of coalescence performance for varied parameters of interest.

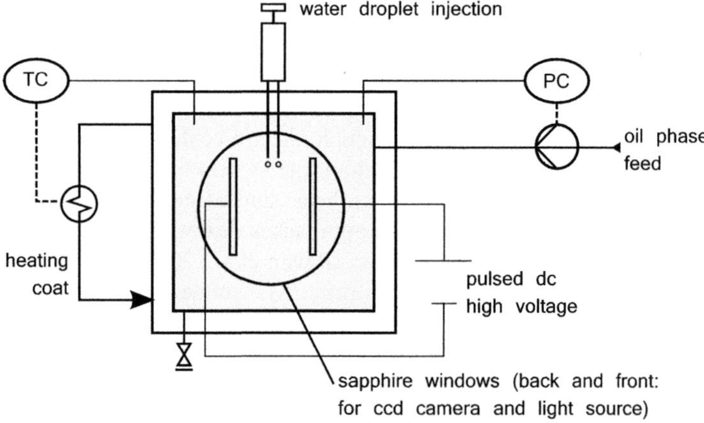

Figure 1. Sketch of the test cell set-up

4. Modelling

A number of different forces, which are applied to the water drops, have been investigated in previous research; see e.g. (Chiesa et al., 2005). Figure 2 sketches the forces, which are being considered in this work.

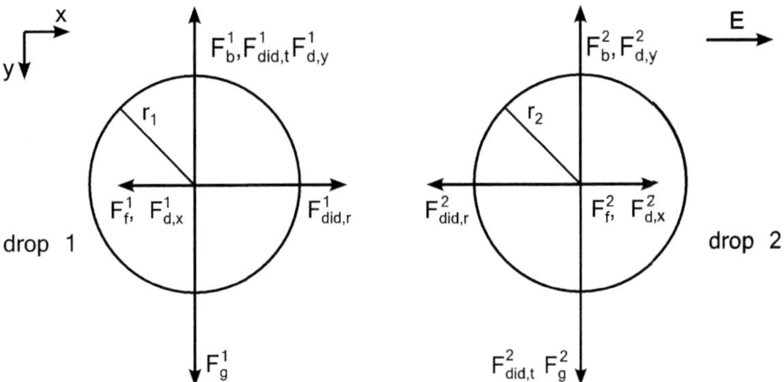

Figure 2. Forces applying on adjacent drops sinking orthogonally in an electric field

The buoyancy force F_b and gravity force F_g are included as well as the drag force

$$F_d = \frac{\pi}{8} d_d{}^2 C_D \rho_c v^2 F_d = \frac{\pi}{8} d_d{}^2 C_D \rho_c v^2 \ , \tag{1}$$

with the drop diameter d_d, its velocity v, the continuous phase density ρ_c, and the drag coefficient C_D, which may be estimated by the Hadamard-Rybczynski formula:

$$C_D = \frac{24}{Re} \frac{\lambda+2/3}{\lambda+1} C_D = \frac{24}{Re} \frac{\lambda+2/3}{\lambda+1} \ , \tag{2}$$

where $\lambda=\mu_c/\mu_d$ represents the viscosity ratio of continuous and dispersed phase, see (Chiesa et al., 2005). Due to drop deformation and surfactants, the surface tension at the water-oil interface may vary, which provokes internal dispersed phase circulation. For first simulations this effect on the drag coefficient is neglected for the sake of simplicity.

The mechanism of attraction of two adjacent uncharged water drops, which are oriented along the field lines of a uniform electric field, is called dielectrophoresis. The effect of induced dipoles to the polar water droplets can be described by the so called dipole-induced-dipole forces in tangential and radial direction:

$$F_{did,t} = \frac{12\pi\beta^2 \varepsilon_c \varepsilon_{vac} E^2 r_1^3 r_2^3}{d^4} (3K_1 \cos^2\theta - 1) \tag{3}$$

and

$$F_{did,r} = \frac{12\pi\beta^2 \varepsilon_c \varepsilon_{vac} E^2 r_1^3 r_2^3}{d^4} K_2 \sin(2\theta) \ , \tag{4}$$

which are depending on the distance between the drop centers d, the electric field strength E, the constant

$$\beta = \frac{\varepsilon_d - \varepsilon_c}{\varepsilon_d + 2\varepsilon_c} \beta = \frac{\varepsilon_d - \varepsilon_c}{\varepsilon_d + 2\varepsilon_c}, \tag{5}$$

the dielectric constant of the continuous phase ε_c, and the dispersed phase ε_d, the vacuum permittivity ε_{vac}, the angle between the line on which the two drop centers lie and the direction of the electric field θ, with the two coefficients K_1 and K_2 depending on β, the radii and inter-drop distance, see (Chiesa et al., 2005).

Once the drops approached each other closely enough for the gap between the drops h to be $h<<a=r_1r_2/(r_1+r_2)$, the drainage and stability of the trapped continuous phase film becomes a controlling mechanism for drop coalescence, see (Melheim et al., 2004) and (Eow et al., 2001). The film-thinning force F_f may be calculated from a formula set up by Vinogradova

$$F_f = \frac{6\pi\, \mu_c a^2 (\bar{v_r}\cdot\bar{e_r})}{8}\frac{2h}{6b}\left(\left[1+\frac{h}{6b}\right]\ln\left(1+\frac{6b}{h}\right)\text{-}1\right)\bar{e_r}, \qquad (6)$$

with the relative velocity between the drops $\bar{v_r}$ and the origin vector of the relative motion direction $\bar{e_r}$. The slip distance b characterizes the effect of slip, occurring for very close non-rigid particles and can be chosen with respect to droplet size (Chiesa et al., 2005).

For each drop, with the respective mass m, a momentum balance caon be solved by applying a simple numerical solver. Experimental results by (Chiesa et al., 2005) could be reproduced for the transient inter-drop distance between two larger drops, sinking perpendicularly in a pulsed electric field. Further validation by identification of the critical skew angle of drops which are not aligned with the electric field shall be pursued, see (Eow and Gharidi, 2003).

5. Simulation

The parameters density and dynamic viscosity of dodecane and water are estimated by temperature-dependant correlations, presented by Huber and Laesecke (2004), Lemmon and Huber (2004), Kleiber and Joh (2006) and Jeffery and Austin (1999). With regard to possible future applications in micro-emulsion breaking, the experimentally investigated

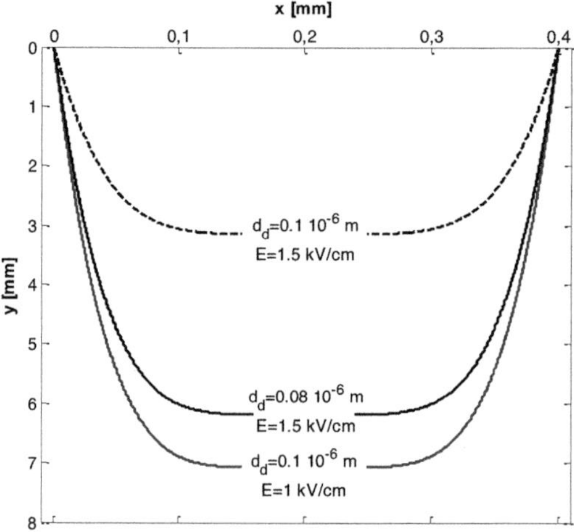

Figure 3. Simulated drop motion trajectories for varied electric field strength and drop diameter

and simulated drop sizes shall be kept small. Since small droplets sink slower, a longer residence time in the gap between the electrodes can be realized. Although the time, within coalescence has to occur, then is not too limited, a small enough initial inter-drop distance is to be implemented. The exemplary simulation results presented below are obtained assuming a slip distance of $b=10^{-5}$m, in a non-pulsed electric field.

5.1. Electric field strength and drop diameter

Results of a first simulation are presented in Figure 3, which illustrates a cross-section of the inter-electrode gap along the field lines. The droplet trajectories from their injection at y=0 (θ=0°; both drop centers are lying on the same field line) to their assumed coalescence at $h\leq0$ are shown for varied drop diameters d_d and electric field strengths E. In the simulation, the direct current electric field is implemented without pulsation. The initial distance between the centers of the drops is kept constant.

With an increased electric field strength, drops coalesce at lower vertical path lengths and therefore faster. A decrease in drop size, meaning a larger initial relative inter-drop-distance h/d_d to be overcome, demands longer residence time. For test-cell design considerations simple simulations can help especially for an appropriate dimensioning.

5.2. Temperature

Since density, viscosity and surface tension of the involved substances are implemented as depending on temperature, its effect can be simulated.

Figure 4 shows the time-dependant behavior of the inter-drop surface distance h at varied temperature. Coalescence is assumed to happen when h drastically declines. At a system temperature of T = 50 °C, coalescence occurs clearly faster in comparison to a simulation at ambient conditions. Although the electric permittivity of water and dodecane are not implemented as temperature-dependant parameters, the dependence of coalescence performance on temperature can be assumed.

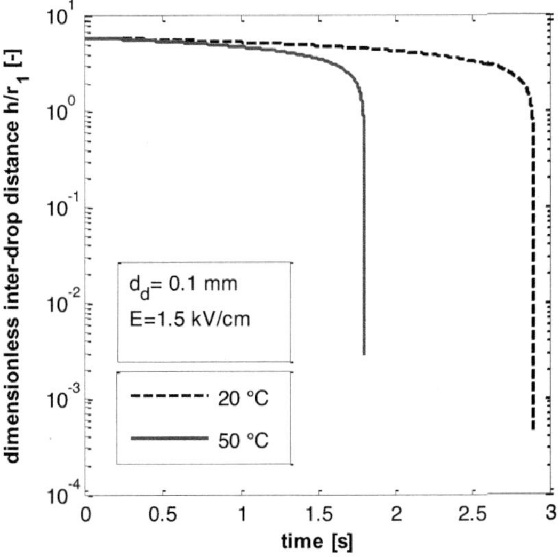

Figure 4. Inter-drop distance over residence time at varied temperature

6. Conclusions

Experimental work and mathematical modelling of the coalescence process have both been carried out. In particular, a model has been developed from momentum balances of two droplets and from forces, which have presented and verified with the open literature so as to suit the design of an experimental set-up. Based on the model-based analysis, it can be shown that the process parameter temperature has a strong influence on the electro-coalescence time. The simultaneous development of the experimental set-up and a describing model has been promoted to gain further insights to electro-coalescence of adjacent water droplets. Therefore, the magnitude of the applied electric field and the pulsing frequency is optimised to match the liquid–liquid system.

Current works emphasize on the implementation of a pulsed electric field so as to confirm the modelling of drop behaviour just before coalescence allowing also a detailed description of the effects of relevant system parameters on droplet behaviour.

References

M. Chiesa, J. A. Melheim, A. Pedersen, S. Ingebrigtsen, G. Berg, 2005, Forces acting on water droplets falling in oil under the influence of an electric field: numerical predictions versus experimental observations, European Journal of Mechanics B/Fluids, 24,717-732.

M. Chiesa, J. A. Melheim, A. Pedersen, S. Ingebrigtsen, G. Berg, 2006, Forces acting on water droplets falling in oil under the influence of an electric field: numerical predictions versus experimental observations, European Journal of Mechanics B/Fluids, 24, 717-732.

J. S. Eow, M. Gharidi, 2003, Drop-drop coalescence in an electric field: the effects of applied electric field and electrode geometry, Colloids and Surfaces A: Physicochem. Eng. Aspects, 219, 253-279.

J. S. Eow, M. Ghadiri, A. O. Sharif, T. J. Williams, 2001, Electrostatic enhancement of coalescence of water droplets in oil: a review of the current understanding. Chemical Engineering Journal, 54, 173-192.

M. L. Huber, A. Perkins, R. Laesecke, 2004, Transport Properties of n-Dodecane, Energy and Fuels, 18, 960 - 967.

P. H. Jeffery, C. A. Austin, 1999, A new analytic equation of state for liquid water, Journal of Chemical Physics, 110, 484 - 496.

M. Kleiber, R. Joh, 2006, Stoffwerte von sonstigen chemisch einheitlichen Flüssigkeiten und Gasen, VDI-Wärmeatlas (English: Physical properties of other standard liquids and gases), by VDI-Gesellschaft Verfahrenstechnik und Chemieingenieurwesen, Dca. Berlin Heidelberg, Germany, Springer-Verlag (in German).

E. W. Lemmon, M. L. Huber, Thermodynamic Properties of n-Dodecane, 2004, Energy and Fuels, 18, 960 - 967.

J. A. Melheim, M. Chiesa, S. Ingebrigtsen, G. Berg, 2004, Forces between two water droplets in oil under the influence of an electric field, 5th International Conference on Multiphase Flow, Yokohama, Japan, No. 126.

M. Mohammadi, S. Shahhosseini, M. Bayat, 2012, Direct numerical simulation of water droplet coalescence in the oil, International Journal of Heat and Fluid Flow, 36, 58-71.

J. Raisin, J. L. Reboud, P. Atten, 2009, Electrocoalescence of two water drops in oil: Experiment and modeling, International Journal of Plasma Environmental Science and Technology, 3, 2, 127-132.

S. Shahhosseini, M. Bayat, M. Mohammadi, 2014, Numerical Study of the Collision and Coalescence of Water Droplets in an Electric Field, Chemical Engineering and Technology, 37, 1, 27-35.

Jiří Jaromír Klemeš, Petar Sabev Varbanov and Peng Yen Liew (Editors)
Proceedings of the 24th European Symposium on Computer Aided Process Engineering – ESCAPE 24
June 15-18, 2014, Budapest, Hungary.

Reconfiguration of an Oilseed Processing Plant into a Whole-crop Biorefinery

José F.O. Granjo[a], Belmiro P.D. Duarte[b], Nuno M.C. Oliveira[a]*

[a]*CIEPQPF, Department of Chemical Engineering, University of Coimbra, Rua Sílvio Lima – Pólo II, 3030-790 Coimbra, Portugal*

[b]*Department of Chemical and Biological Engineering, ISEC Polytechnic Insitute of Coimbra, Rua Pedro Nunes, 3030-199 Coimbra, Portugal*

nuno@eq.uc.pt

Abstract

We consider the integration of biodiesel and bioethanol production processes with an existing oilseed processing industry to expand the value chain associated with the original raw materials, with multiple advantages from the economic and sustainability perspectives. This process integration task provides several opportunities for the application of systematic decision making methodologies. However, to be implemented in a significant extension, it also places many demands at the levels of the development of accurate models for the thermodynamic and kinetic description of the operations considered, and optimization based design methods for the units to be included in the processing structure. An overview of recent developments in each of these levels is considered in the first part of this work. This is followed with the presentation of an optimal design methodology for the specification of a "De Smet" horizontal solid-liquid extractor, commonly used by the industry to leach out the oil from the flakes. A comparison of the performance of the optimal design with a reference unit is given.

Keywords: process design, biorefinery, soybean, oil extraction.

1. Introduction

In the last decade and at a global scale, climate change concerns and fossil resources depletion led to reinforced efforts on R&D of technologies associated with the production of bioenergy and bioproducts from biomass. Numerous agricultural and forest feedstocks are continuously screened to identify promising chemicals, fuels and energy that can be produced from these raw materials. Bioproducts and biofuels are currently fast paced markets representing globally more than \$200 billion (10^9) and \$83 billion of dollars in value, respectively (Navigant Research, 2011). In this field, systematic process and product systems development have been recently applied to assist decision-making in each development stage: design of bioproduct portfolios; product design; logistics planning; optimal process and unit operations design with sustainability metrics (e.g. TCA, LCA); "brownfield", "greenfield", and "retrofit" projects for biorefineries implantation; and heat, mass and biorefinery process integration. Stuart and El-Halwagi (2012) present several reviews with many contributions in this area.

The current work exemplifies the application of some of these methodologies in the reconfiguration of an oilseed processing plant (soybean) into a whole-crop biorefinery, where the production of biofuels is added up to the original plant setup. The technology of oilseed processing industries is well established and mature, with decades of experience. However, environmental pressures and oilseed market instabilities have prompted the need to reduce energy and material requirements, promote the integration among processing units and expand the value chain associated with the industrial operation. To accommodate these requirements, decisions involving the operation of individual processes must consider their impact on the whole factory. Although a significant number of studies are available regarding the analysis of individual parts of the "new" biorefinery (*e.g.*, bean preparation, solvent extraction, meal preparation, oil refining, biodiesel and bioethanol for several feedstocks), works addressing the integration of these various processes together within the scope of an integrated biorefinery are still scarce in the open literature. In this context various PSE tools were applied to this problem, to assist in the decision making process. Section 2 presents the framework within which ongoing work is being done, and in Section 3 systematic methodologies are applied to the optimal design of an industrial solid-liquid extractor for the separation of soybean oil from flakes, using hexane as leaching agent.

2. Framework

Figure 1 shows a generic diagram block of an oil processing and livestock meal production plant coupled with biodiesel and bioethanol production processes forming a whole-crop biorefinery. Only mass flows of main input and outputs are shown. Data regarding typical operating conditions, energy and material consumptions, and product yields in industry was collected from Freitas (2009) and Santos (2012), among others. A production base of 150 kt/y of biodiesel was considered.

The operations in process areas 1 and 2, with minor changes, are common among oilseed processing plants. Oilseeds are first cleaned by removing the foreign matter, adjusting the moisture, cooking and cracking the cell structure to make the oil more available to be extracted from the meat. This step is energy intensive and its economy is dictated by the efficiency of the crushing equipment and the amount of spent vapor. The flakes are then defatted by solvent extraction (2) using hexane as percolation agent, and the oil goes through various refining steps – solvent stripping, degumming, filtration and deacidification – to remove contaminants. The main challenging here is to reduce the solvent and energy consumptions while reducing oil losses, which typically represent 6% of the total mass of the crude oil processed. The soybean bagasse then goes through desolventizing, toasting and drying to remove hexane and decrease moisture. The final soybean meal has a protein content above 40 % and is marketed as livestock meal. Another alternative is to produce protein concentrate for human consumption, by ethanol extraction of the untoasted and flash-desolventized meal. The extract is enriched with oligo-, polysaccharides and simple sugars that can be hydrolyzed and fermented to produce bioethanol.

The application spectrum of PSE tools to improve and integrate the resources within the whole process is broad. To improve the economic performance of biodiesel process (3), a wide range of data and thermo physical properties of the components and mixtures involved was gathered, modeled and included in the design of operating units. Granjo et al. (2005) and (2009) presented preliminary economical assessments and kinetic studies of the transesterification reaction, where simple unit models where used to study the economic performance of both alkaline and acid catalysis for both batch and continuous operation mode. Moreover, Granjo (2008) modeled and estimated the parameters for the

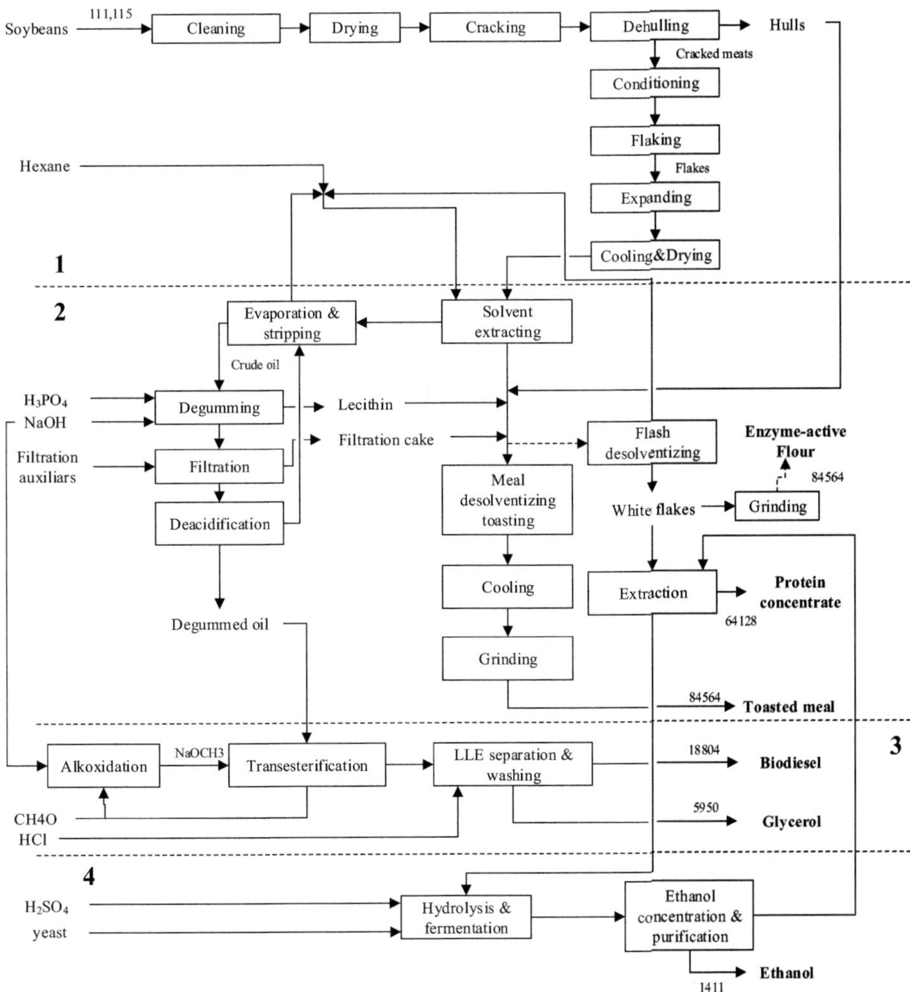

Figure 1. Block diagram of a whole-crop biorefinery based on soybean (mass flows in kg/h).

eNRTL model to describe electrolyte solutions in the production of sodium methoxide (a common biodiesel catalyst). Latter, an alternative process based upon reactive distillation was designed, showing greater economic performance than the traditional method, i.e. methanolysis of metallic sodium. In the bioethanol process (4), an alternative scheme proposed by Neves et al. (2012) was also adopted, based on (i) extractive fermentation using a phosphonium-based ionic liquid as a solvent (ii) and pervaporation for bioethanol dehydration.

Following these modular studies, the information collected was brought together to consider the integration of the whole biorefinery system. In a first approach, simple unit models were used to analyze the process globally, identifying bottlenecks and opportunities to integrate materials and utilities between the sub-systems, increasing efficiency and reducing costs. This grass-root design was then incorporated in a process simulator for more detailed economical assessment, and to produce a feasible design that could be used as a starting point for the optimization of the entire process. This process configuration will be later used to build a very detailed global process model, capable of being used with an optimization based design methodology, to determine the best operating regions for the fully integrated process.

3. Optimal design of a solid-liquid extraction unit

As an example of the development of detailed models for the process units to be considered in the integrated process, we consider the optimal design of the solid-liquid extraction units, since solvent extraction is a critical step in oilseed processing. Sharper oil separation and its higher recovery from flakes are required to guarantee higher meal quality and to reduce costs in the desolventizing and miscella distillation steps. There are essentially three types of industrial solid-liquid extractors commonly used – "Rotocell, "De Smet" horizontal extractor, and "Crown Model". These extractors share the same counter-current cross flow pattern in the extraction area; they present a loading section where the fresh solvent is charged and the spent flakes exit to the desolventizer, and a drainage section where the full miscella exits to the solvent recovery section. The extraction in these units can be modeled as a sequence of stages where the solvent is charged at the top of a moving bed of flakes, flows through the bed leaching the oil and is collected at the bottom. The resulting partial miscella is then pumped again to the top of the bed in the following stage and so forth, until exiting in the drainage section. The leaching process involves a sequence of phenomena: a) transfer of the solvent to the bulk of the solid, b) diffusion of the solvent into the solid matrix, c) dissolution of the solute into the solvent inside the solid, d) diffusion of the solute across the solid-solvent environment to the surface of the particles, and e) diffusion of the solute to the bulk solution (Geankoplis, 2008).

We consider the optimal design of an industrial "De Smet" horizontal extractor comprising a drainage zone, a loading zone and a pre-defined set of trays, where the solvent circulating in counter-current is pumped from the vessel below the mth section to the top of the $(m\text{-}1)^{\text{th}}$. The corresponding dynamic model used is based on Veloso et al. (2005), describing the oil concentration profile along the axial coordinate (x) and vertical coordinate (z) that results from gradients due to the movement of the bed transporting the flakes and to the movement of the miscella across the bulk. Dimensionless oil concentrations in the bulk (C) and (C_p) pore phases are given by Eqs. (1) and (2), respectively.

$$\frac{\partial C}{\partial \tau} = -V_m \frac{\partial C}{\partial z} + Es\left(\frac{\partial^2 C}{\partial x^2} + \frac{\partial^2 C}{\partial z^2}\right) + \frac{(1-\varepsilon_b)}{\varepsilon_b} K_f a_p (C_p - C) - u_h \frac{\partial C}{\partial x} \tag{1}$$

$$\frac{\partial C_p}{\partial \tau} = \frac{K_f a_p (C_p - C)}{\varepsilon_p + (1-\varepsilon_p) E_d^v} - u \frac{\partial C_p}{\partial x} \tag{2}$$

$$\frac{d\overline{C}_m}{d\tau} = \frac{\varepsilon_b H V_m \int_{X_n}^{X_k} C(x, L_s, \tau) dx - \overline{C}_m(\tau) Q_T}{V_b} \tag{3}$$

Here $x = 0,\dots,X_1$, if $m = 1$ and $x = (X_1 + (m-2)\cdot X_s),\cdots,(X_1 + (m-1)X_s)$, if $m = 2,\cdots,(m_s - 1)$. Also, Vm represents the velocity of the porous media (m/s); Es is the dispersion coefficient (m/s); u is the velocity of solvent (m/s); u_h is the miscella velocity in the horizontal direction (m); τ is the dimensionless time; ε_b is the outer porosity of the porous media; ε_p is the internal porosity of the porous media; K_f is the mass transfer coefficient between the pore and the bulk phases (m/s); a_p is the contact surface area per unit of volume (1/m). Eq. (3) represents the conservation balance in mth tray and $\bar{C}_m$ the dimensionless oil media concentration in mth tray; Q_T is the miscella vertical volumetric flow through section (m^3/s); E_d^v is the equilibrium volumetric coefficient; X_n and X_k start and end edge of a tray (m), respectively; V_b is the tray oil volume (m^3); H is the bed thickness (m); and L_s is the height of the porous media layer (m).

The miscella flow rate entering in the loading zone (Q_p) and the oil media concentration in the last section ($\bar{C}_{ms}$) are given by Eqs. (4) and (5):

$$Q_p = HL_s\left(u_h\varepsilon_b + u(1-\varepsilon_b)\varepsilon_p\frac{1-C_p^{in}}{1-\bar{C}_2}\right) \tag{4}$$

$$\frac{d\bar{C}_{ms}}{d\tau} = \frac{\varepsilon_b H\left[V_m\int_{X_n}^{X_k} C(x,L_s,\tau)dx + u_h\int_0^{L_s} C(X_f,Z,\tau)dz\right] - \bar{C}_m(\tau)Q_T}{V_b} \tag{5}$$

The boundary and initial conditions are given by Eqs. (6):

$C(0,z,\tau) = \bar{C}_2(\tau), \quad z = 0,\ldots,L_s; \quad \tau > 0$ (6a)

for the sections $m = 1,\ldots,(m_s - 1)$: $C(x,0,\tau) = \bar{C}_{m+1}(\tau) \quad \tau > 0$ (6b)

for the drainage zone: $\partial C(X_f,z,\tau)/\partial x = 0, \quad z = 0,\cdots,L_s; \quad \tau > 0$ (6c)

for section m_s: $C(x,0,\tau) = C_{in}, \quad x = (X_f - X_{ms}),\cdots,X_f$ (6d)

bottom boundary: $\partial C(x,L_s,\tau)/\partial z = 0, \quad x = 0,\cdots,X_f; \tau > 0$ (6e)

loading zone: $C^p(0,z,\tau) = C_{in}^p(\tau), \quad z = 0,\cdots,L_s; \tau > 0$ (6f)

initial values: $C(x,z,0) = C_0(x,z)$; $C^p(x,z,0) = C_0^p(x,z)$, $x = 0,\ldots,X_f$, $z = 0,\ldots,L_s$ (6g)

The system of Eqs. (1-6) was implemented in GAMS and solved using a finite difference (FD) scheme, with the continuity of the concentrations in the bulk and in the pores and their respective time derivatives. The optimal design of this unit was formulated as a NLP, where the PDE system was solved at steady-state conditions:

$$\begin{aligned} Z = \min_{V_m,H,L,u} \quad & C_{op} + C_{cap} \\ \text{s.t} \quad & \text{model eqs. (FD discretized)} \\ & C_u^s \ge C^d, \quad L^L \le L \le L^U \\ & u^L \le u \le u^U, \quad V_m^L \le V_m \le V_m^U \\ & H^L \le H \le H^U \end{aligned} \tag{NLP1}$$

The objective function (Z) is the overall sum of operating ($C_{op} \propto Q_T$ and power for pumps) and capital costs ($C_{cap} \propto L\times W$). A target oil concentration of $C^d = 0.580$ was established. Experimental parameter values for a reference industrial extractor were retrieved from Veloso et al. (2005). The numerical results of NLP1 are presented in Table 1, where a significant reduction of the overall costs relative to the reference design (circa 30 %) can be observed.

Table 1. Summary of numerical results.

Parameter	Reference	Optimal	Parameter	Reference	Optimal
Vm / (m/h)	36	37.54	u / (m/h)	72	54
H /m	2.0	1.946	*C*	0.49	0.58
L / m	10.8	6.943			
Z / (€/day)	319.421	224.150			

4. Conclusions

This work addresses the integration of biodiesel and bioethanol production processes with an oilseed processing industry, to achieve economic and sustainability gains. Since specific decisions regarding the final process structure and the portfolio of products to be marketed depend largely on the chemical composition of the oilseeds in consideration, namely their protein and oil contents, PSE tools have here a broad field of application in the analysis of these systems. An optimization based design methodology for the design of a "De Smet" horizontal extractor unit commonly used is described. Results show that a cost reduction of 30 % could be achieved for this unit.

Acknowledgement

The authors acknowledge financial support provided by Fundação para a Ciência e a Tecnologia (Portugal) through the Ph.D. Grant SFRH/BD/64338/2009 of José F.O. Granjo.

References

B.P. Duarte, M.J. Moura, F.J. Neves, N.M. Oliveira, 2008, A mathematical programming framework for optimal model selection/validation of process data, Computer Aided Chemical Engineering, 25, 343-348.

S.C.B. Freitas, 2009, Auditoria energética da fábrica de óleos e bagaços da Iberol, Master's thesis, Chemical Engineering Department, University of Coimbra, Coimbra, Portugal.

C.J. Geankoplis, 2008, Transport processes and separation process principles, PHI Learning, New Jersey, USA.

J.F.O. Granjo, D.C.M. Silva, F.J.M. Neves, N.M.C. Oliveira, J.M.S. Rocha, 2005, Economical assessment for biodiesel production, Proc. ChemPor 2005, Coimbra, Portugal.

J.F.O. Granjo, 2008, Study of the production of sodium methylate, Master's thesis, University of Coimbra, Coimbra, Portugal (in Portuguese).

J.F.O. Granjo, B.P.M. Duarte, N.M.C. Oliveira, 2009, Kinetic models for the homogeneous alkaline and acid catalysis in biodiesel production, Computer Aided Chemical Engineering, 27, 483-488.

Navigant Research, 2011, <www.navigantresearch.com/newsroom/global-biofuels-market-value-to-double-to-185-billion-by-2021>, Accessed on 04/11/2013.

C. Neves, J.F.O. Granjo, M.G. Freire, A. Robertson; N.M.C. Oliveira, J.A.P. Coutinho, 2011, Separation of ethanol–water mixtures by liquid–liquid extraction using phosphonium-based ionic liquids, Green Chemistry, 13, 6, 1517-1526.

S.M. Santos, Reconversão de uma unidade de pré-tratamento de óleos para biodiesel,Master's thesis, Department of Chemistry, University of Aveiro, Aveiro, Portugal (in Portuguese).

P.R. Stuart, M.M. El-Halwagi, Eds., 2012, Integrated biorefineries: design, analysis, and optimization, CRC Press, USA.

G. Veloso, V. Krioukov, H. Vielmo, 2005, Mathematical modeling of vegetable oil extraction in a counter-current crossed flow horizontal extractor, J. of Food Engineering, 66, 4, 477-486.

Jiří Jaromír Klemeš, Petar Sabev Varbanov and Peng Yen Liew (Editors)
Proceedings of the 24th European Symposium on Computer Aided Process Engineering – ESCAPE 24
June 15-18, 2014, Budapest, Hungary.

Advantages of Process Integration Evaluated by Gibbs Energy: Biodiesel Synthesis Case

Valentin Pleşu[a], Jordi Bonet[b], Alexandra E. Bonet Ruiz[a,b*], Joan Llorens[b]

[a] *UniversityPOLITEHNICA of Bucharest, Centre for Technology Transfer in Process Industries (CTTPI), 1, Gh. Polizu Street, Bldg A, Room A056, RO-011061 Bucharest, Romania*

[b] *University of Barcelona, Department of Chemical Engineering, 1,Martí I Franquès Street, 6th Floor, E-08028 Barcelona, Spain*

a_bonet@chim.upb.ro

Abstract

The present study shows that the potential for process integration is easily evaluated by the Gibbs energy change between input and output streams assuming isotherm and isobaric units. The minimum energy requirements to get the streams to the desired temperature at the entrance and output of the units for the overall process can be later evaluated by the second thermodynamic principle, i.e. Pinch Analysis. In the case study of biodiesel synthesis from oils, a single hybrid reactive extraction unit substitutes a reactor, one extractive column and three distillation columns and therefore avoids the residual streams.

Keywords: process intensification, evaluation of classical process, energy saving.

1. Introduction

Although there are a great number of industrial processes available, the number of unit operations is limited to a few ones, whose models are quite well known and studied. An overall process is made of the unit operation models whose validity does not depend on which compounds are present or the type of process. The unit operations become interdependent in the overall process and the interlinking variables must be optimized taking into account the overall process as a whole. The traditional way to design a chemical process was to define first of all the reactor units considered the heart of the process. All the remaining units were designed according to the reactor output for products recovery and recycle of unreacted compounds. However, this approach does not foresee the possible synergic integration of the reaction unit with the remaining units. Furthermore, without an overall vision of the global process, an improvement in a unit can decrease the overall process performance. In certain circumstances, the process integration joining several unit operations in the same unit is very advantageous. For instance joining reactor and distillation column leads to reactive distillation. Unfortunately, when a well-known unit operation is integrated with another well-known operation in the same unit, the behavior of the resulting unit becomes unknown and not directly predictable from both unit operations separately. Neither, there is not any guideline of how to check if it could be advantageous or to quantify the potential improvement of integrating units. This fact is one of the main reasons that despite the successful examples of process integration available, nowadays it is not used all the potential and synergies of process integration to generate novel processes.

For the design of a novel process, the first step is to check if the novel process proposed is feasible. A process design is feasible only if the mass and energy balances and thermodynamic principles are fulfilled (e.g. conservation of mass and energy). Some additional conditions are specific for some units such as for distillation, a composition column profile between the distillate and bottoms must exists, e.g. infinite/infinite analysis. Usually, multiple feasible alternatives can be proposed and a detailed study of all them would be very time consuming and therefore simplified models are often used. The second step is therefore to check the potential of each one and discard the worst ones. For instance, to determine the minimum hot and cold services required for a process, it is not necessary to define a detailed heat exchanger network but just to take into account the second thermodynamic principle, e.g. Pinch Analysis (Chew et al., 2013).

Novel process designs can be proposed when the study departs from the conservation and thermodynamic principles and not from assumptions and previous industrial designs. Most commercial simulators provide temperature, entropy and enthalpy information in the stream results and therefore all the data required to calculate the Gibbs energy of the stream is readily available. For instance, AspenPlus® has implemented a Gibbs reactor which estimates the output stream of the reactor just minimizing the Gibbs energy. A non-spontaneous process ($\Delta G>0$) does not imply it is unfeasible, but that additional energy is required. For instance, a distillation column decreases the entropy of the streams by consuming energy with efficiency according to the Carnot efficiency, i.e. a distillation column is a thermal machine that instead of work produces a decrease of entropy (Pleşu et al., 2013). A reactive distillation column can reach total conversion to products although the minimum Gibbs energy is for a certain concentration of equilibrium at a reactor output. A non-spontaneous process can become feasible when energy is provided or when it is combined with a spontaneous process, the latter can compensate the first one and the overall process can become spontaneous.

One of the first examples of process integration is the Leblanc process (patented in 1791). The process manages to obtain soda ash from calcium carbonate and sodium chloride which is thermodynamically unfavorable. For instance, in the first step combines reaction with separation (HCl evaporation) to obtain a total reaction conversion. However, the most well-known example is the Eastman Kodak process to produce methyl acetate, where a single reactive distillation column was able to substitute a reactor, an extraction column, 8 distillation columns and one decanter.

In this paper, biodiesel synthesis is presented to illustrate the use of Gibbs energy and thermodynamics to determine the usefulness of process integration. An intense research is performed nowadays to provide biodiesel in the best process conditions, fact reflected by the great number of papers available in literature. The biodiesel synthesis example available in AspenPlus® version 8.0 is used to show how to evaluate quantitatively the advantages of unit operations integration.

2. Materials and method

Mass balances, temperature, entropy and enthalpy of the streams are calculated using AspenPlus®8.0 simulation environment, departing from the flowsheet readily available. From this data, the Gibbs energy for each stream is calculated. Duplicators (Manipulators) are inserted to maintain the process scheme and allow for changes in temperature, providing the variation of Gibbs energy at isothermal and isobaric conditions around the units or process regions. The change of entropy is used to determine when a (reactive) distillation can be placed in the scheme or when it can be avoided.

3. Results

For the start, the entropy and enthalpy of the process streams are determined and the variation of Gibbs energy around each unit operation is calculated taking into account the operating conditions of each unit (Figure 1). The Gibbs energy variations for the distillation processes are positive (not spontaneous) and very low in comparison with the reaction. The Gibbs energy for neutralization should be negative (spontaneous) but the implemented reaction has a main simplification: the components not present in the database were implemented as water and then some of their thermodynamic properties are modified such as the molecular weight and vapour pressure. For the same reasons, the filtration operation is not spontaneous either. The Gibbs energy for the extraction unit should be slightly negative, but as in AspenPlus® was implemented as an adiabatic unit, the isothermal conditions make it slightly positive. However, in Figure 2 illustrating the variation of Gibbs energy calculated for all the process at 25 °C and 1 bar, the extraction column becomes slightly negative as expected. From the results it can be stated that when the reaction is integrated with other parts of the process, then the integrated unit becomes spontaneous without energy consumption. Due to the importance of the reactor unit operation, it is further studied.

The Gibbs Reactor available in AspenPlus® is used to determine the thermodynamic chemical equilibrium. When a stoichiometric mixture of triolein and methanol is fed to the reactor at 25 °C (and at higher temperatures), a total conversion to products is observed. This fact is in agreement with the results of Yancy-Caballero and Guirardello (2013). Therefore, the excess of methanol required in all the literature experimental studies is not justified to shift the reaction towards products. It promotes the mixing of reactants and avoids the phase split of products that would slow down the reaction. However, the energy cost to recover the excess is very high.

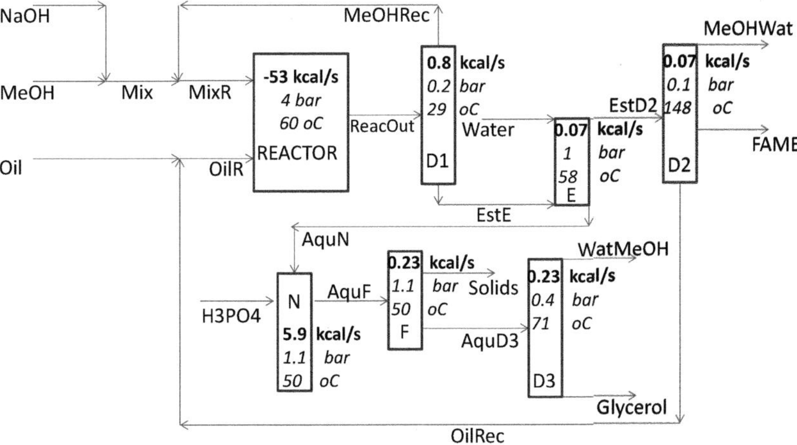

Figure 1. Gibbs energy variation for each unit.

An unexpected result is obtained when feeding pure triolein (instead of palm oil) and pure methanol as reactants to the Gibbs reactor. The list of compounds coming out of the Gibbs reactor provides other oils and their related species whose missing Gibbs energies of formation have been previously estimated. Then more than three moles of methanol for each mole of triolein are required (2.38 ratio methanol-oil in excess) but the conversion of reactants is total providing mainly methyl palmitate and glycerol. As there is not experimental evidence of this fact so far, the original kinetic reactor of the example will be used instead of the Gibbs reactor to proceed with the free Gibbs energy analysis for the rest of the process. In the next section, the process is discussed in more detail from the point of view of integration and compared with literature results.

3.1. Process Integration

3.1.1. Integration of Mixing and Reaction

Mixing oil with alcohol is not a spontaneous operation, but the reaction is spontaneous. When combining the mixing of reactants with the reaction operation in a single unit, then the mixing-reacting process can become spontaneous. Mono and diglycerides are chemical compounds with chemical characteristics between oil and glycerine and therefore their presence favour their miscibility. The experimental results of Agarwal et al (2013) demonstrate the suitability of integrating the mixing and the reaction: the residence times in a helical tube reactor and a reactive distillation column were 4 and 8 min, respectively, but in a batch reactor for the same yield was 1 h.

3.1.2. Reactive Distillation

The reaction and distillation operations can be integrated in a single unit called reactive distillation. The reactive distillation is thermodynamically advantageous. The enthalpy of reaction is directly used as heat source for the distillation. When the entropy derived by the reaction is favourable, it decreases the consumption of the distillation column and when it is unfavourable then the distillation column offers a way to overcome the unfavourable conversion by providing energy. The reaction and distillation work in synergy.

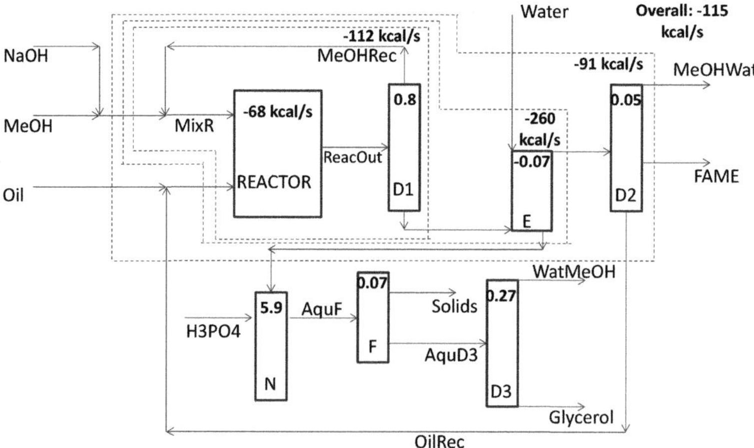

Figure 2. Gibbs energy variation taking into account integration, calculated at 25°C and 1 bar.

The reaction can be also at the service of the separation, two components that would form an azeotrope but are involved in a reaction, cannot be separated by distillation but by reactive distillation. In Fig. 2 the reactive distillation integration would correspond to the zone including the reactor and the column D1. In this case, the Gibbs energy is of -112 kcal/s. As indicated previously, the distillation column is a thermic machine that produces a decrease of entropy instead of work. But in this case, the process is already spontaneous and the use of reactive distillation has no meaning (the entropy is already favourable to the product formation). This fact is in agreement with the result that when the required reflux is optimized by rigorous simulation, it tends to zero (Machado et al, 2013). No energy is required for the separation but to recover the excess of methanol. As a conclusion, the distillation operation is not required.

3.1.3. Extractive reaction

Another option is to integrate the reaction with the extraction column, which corresponds to the zone in Figure 2 that includes the reactor and extraction column. The increase of Gibbs free energy is very high, -260 kcal/s. The reason is the flow rate of pure water that is impurified by the system generating a high amount of entropy. As the reaction products are already immiscible and the energy of Gibbs without water is already favourable, the use of water is not required. This fact is in agreement with the results of Cadavid et al (2013) that proved experimentally that a high conversion of oil is attained in a reactive extraction column. As demonstrated previously in the Gibbs reactor, thermodynamically the oil conversion is total when there is enough methanol available. Some methanol is lost due to its appreciable miscibility with FAME and the excess of methanol that is not collected in FAME stream is collected in the glycerol stream. Then the distillation columns used to separate methanol from FAME and from glycerol are still present.

3.1.4. Feasibility for the overall system integration

The integration proposed above still requires the use of two distillation columns. Further calculation of the Gibbs energy point out that both distillation columns are not really required because the entropy change is already favourable and no external source of energy is required. Including the FAME-methanol distillation column, the Gibbs energy is -91 kcal/s and when both distillation columns are included, then the Gibbs energy is -115 kcal/s. The Gibbs energy does not provide directly how the best process should be, however it is indicating clearly that biodiesel can be produced without spending energy for distillation operations since the overall process is favourable. Calculating the variation of Gibbs energy at 25 °C and 1 bar between the input reactant streams (MeOH and Oil) and the output reactant streams (FAME and Glycerol), the value obtained is -43 kcal/s which confirms an overall favourable process without requiring other components or additional energy. Due to analysis of the biodiesel synthesis process using the Gibbs energy value as described in the present paper, recently a new process able to transform the reactants in pure products has been proposed (Jurado et al., 2013): a hybrid reactive extraction column. Oil and methanol are fed at stoichiometric ratio and circulate counter currently in the reactive section. Pure glycerol is collected and used as extractive agent in the non-reactive section of the column to avoid methanol presence in FAME stream.

As a final remark, it is important to notice that all the above analysis was performed taking into account pure oils, pure palm oil was implemented in AspenPlus®.

Nevertheless, the presence of free fatty acids in residual oils will influence the results since the reaction of a free fatty acid with methanol can be of equilibrium, and in this case reactive distillation becomes justified to overcome this limitation. Furthermore, water is also generated. Therefore, the recommendable process can depend on the quantity of free fatty acids present.

4. Conclusions

The paper shows that the optimization of the reactor without taking into account the overall process provides schemes that could greatly improve when process integration is considered. The paper shows that Gibbs energy is very useful to determine when certain process integration is worth. Gibbs energy calculation is straightforward but does not provide the path to achieve the corresponding integration. The case study of biodiesel synthesis from oils shows that for this particular case the reactive distillation is not recommended. A simple Gibbs energy calculation checking the spontaneity of the overall process provides the hint that no distillation is required and that a process without energy consumption is feasible to convert oils to biodiesel. The classical process for biodiesel synthesis provided as example in AspenPlus® consisting of a reactor, an extraction column and three distillation columns operated at extreme values of low pressure and high temperatures, with residual streams of water and methanol (classical scheme) can be substituted by a single hybrid reactive extraction column operated at atmospheric pressure and ambient temperature without residual streams and very low energy consumption (integrated scheme). Nowadays, some of the industrial simulators include the option of reactive distillation but no simulator includes the option of reactive extraction column. The integrated processes provide a higher performance than the classical schemes consisting of a reactor followed by a separation train. However, the possibilities of integration must be evaluated for each case, as the nature of reactants (oil or free fatty acids) can be of great influence. Therefore, Gibbs energy evaluation provides a useful tool to identify when process integration is advantageous. Similar case-studies can be performed based on this approach.

References

K.H. Chew, S.R.W. Alwi, J.J. Klemeš, Z.A. Manan, 2013, Process modification potentials for total site heat integration, Chemical Engineering Transactions, 35, 175-180.

V. Pleşu, A.E. Bonet Ruiz, J. Bonet, J. Llorens, P. Iancu, 2013, Minimum number of transfer units and reboiler duty for multicomponent distillation columns, Applied Thermal Engineering, 61, 1, 67–79.

D.M. Yancy-Caballero, R. Guirardello, R., 2013, Thermodynamic simulation of transesterification reaction by Gibbs energy minimization, Fluid Phase Equilibria, 341, 12-22.

M. Agarwal, S. Soni, S., K. Singh, S.P. Chaurasia, R.K. Dohare, 2013, Biodiesel yield assessment in continuous-flow reactors using batch reactor conditions, International Journal of Green Energy, 10, 1, 28-40.

G.D. Machado, F.L.P. Pessoa, M. Castier, D.A.G. Aranda, V.F. Cabral, L. Cardozo-Filho, 2013, Biodiesel production by esterification of hydrolyzed soybean oil with ethanol in reactive distillation columns: Simulation studies, Industrial and Engineering Chemistry Research, 52, 27, 9461-9469.

J.G. Cadavid, R.D. Godoy-Silva, P.C. Narvaez, M. Camargo, C. Fonteix, 2013, Biodiesel production in a counter-current reactive extraction column: Modelling, parametric identification and optimization, Chemical Engineering Journal, 228, 717-723.

M.B.G. Jurado, V. Pleşu, J.B. Ruiz, A.E.B. Ruiz, A. Tuluc, J.L. Llacuna, 2013, Simulation of a hybrid reactive extraction unit. Biodiesel synthesis, Chemical Engineering Transactions, 33, 205-210.

Jiří Jaromír Klemeš, Petar Sabev Varbanov and Peng Yen Liew (Editors)
Proceedings of the 24th European Symposium on Computer Aided Process Engineering – ESCAPE 24
June 15-18, 2014, Budapest, Hungary.

Process Simulation and Analysis for CO_2 Transport Pipeline Design and Operation – Case Study for the Humber Region in the UK

Xiaobo Luo[a], Ketan Mistry[b], Chima Okezue[a], Meihong Wang[a, *], Russell Cooper[b], Eni Oko[a], Julian Field[b]

[a]*School of Engineering, the University of Hull, Cottingham RD, Hull, United Kingdom*
[b]*CCS Research Group, National Grid, Birmingham, United Kingdom*
Meihong.Wang@hull.ac.uk

Abstract

Carbon Capture and Storage (CCS) will play a vital role for carbon dioxide (CO_2) emissions reduction. Pipelines are considered the preferred method for both onshore and offshore large volumes of CO_2 transported. In the Humber region in the UK, there are two advanced proposals for CCS power station developments: the Don Valley project and the White Rose (Drax) CCS project, which were expected to provide a basis to develop a pipeline supporting a CCS cluster in this area. This paper presents a case study of the pipeline network for the Don Valley and the White Rose CCS projects, representing the possibilities in the Humber area. A model of the pipeline network was developed using the computer software package Aspen HYSYS® and three different operating strategies were compared and discussed regarding their energy and utilities requirement. For all three operating strategies, simulation results show that energy consumption ranges from 96 to 103 kWh/t-CO_2 and cooling duty range from about 140 to 147 Mcal/t-CO_2 in a wide range of the flow rate of the CO_2-rich stream.

Keywords: CCS, CO_2 transport, Pipeline design/operation, Process simulation

1. Introduction

Reducing CO_2 emission is a big challenge both technically and commercially. CCS is regarded as a crucial mitigation technology and will contribute to reducing the global CO_2 emissions by about 7 Gt/y in 2050 (IEA, 2012). CCS is the process of capturing CO_2 from large industrial emitters and transporting it to a storage site, to mitigate CO_2 emissions to the atmosphere. Pipelines are the preferred method for large volumes of CO_2 transport (IPCC, 2005). Recent study of Roussanaly et al. (2013) shows pipeline method has 10% lower cost than the shipping method for a typical CO_2 transportation network. Pipelines have been used to transport CO_2 in gaseous and dense (i.e. liquid or supercritical) phases. The dense phase is regarded as the energy-efficient condition due to its high density and low viscosity (Zhang et al., 2006). However, two-phase flow may occur as the pressure will change with the transient flow of CO_2. Relevant process simulations have been conducted about the changes of the CO_2 physical properties along pipelines (Zhang et al., 2006) and the performance of pipeline network including injection well (Nimtz et al., 2010) using steady state models. Some dynamic models were also developed to evaluated the scenarios of load change, start-up, shout down and compressor trip(Liljiemark et al., 2010) and to examine the hydraulic parameters of the CO_2 pipelines(Chaczykowski and Osiadacz, 2012). However, the pipeline model in

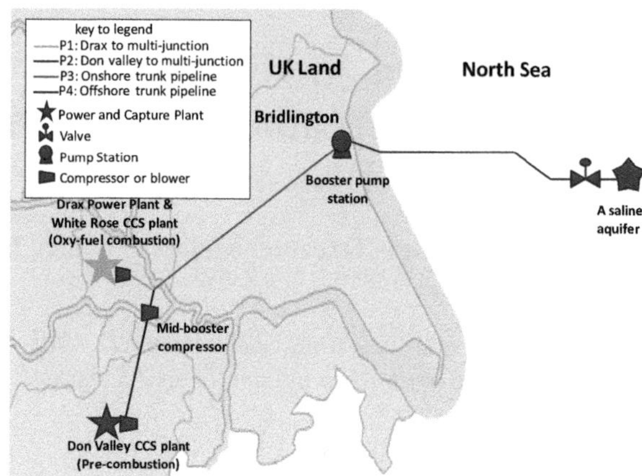

Figure 1. The pipeline sketch for the Humber case study

these studies are relatively simple, with a single emitter or without booster stations. This may not reflect realistic operating scenarios for a typical CO_2 pipeline network system. In this paper, the authors consider a multi-source case study with booster station and onshore and offshore trunk pipelines. The model was developed using commercial computer software package Aspen HYSYS®. Three possible operating strategies were discussed and their potential energy and utilities requirements were estimated.

2. Pipeline network scheme in the Humber region

The Humber region in the UK offers a good opportunity to deploy CCS in the UK (Lazic et al., 2013). In this area, the Don Valley power project and the White Rose CCS project were approved in 2009 and 2013 respectively, which were expected to provide a basis to develop a pipeline supporting a CCS cluster. Figure 1 shows an example route corridor of the pipeline network. The CO_2 captured from Don Valley power plant is transported in gaseous phase at a maximum allowable operating pressure (MAOP) of 35 bar, and then is boosted to dense phase by a compressor near the multi-junction site, before joining the dense phase CO_2-rich stream from Drax power plant. The combined CO_2-rich stream will then be transported in dense phase via a pipeline with a MAOP of 136 bar. A pumping station located near the coast will boost the pressure of the CO_2-rich stream to a saline aquifer storage site more than 1 km beneath the bed of the North Sea via an offshore pipeline with a MAOP of 186 bar.

An entry specification for the CO_2-rich stream is needed to define the acceptable range of composition, taking into account safety, impact on pipeline integrity and hydraulic efficiency (Race et.al, 2012). In this case study, the entry specification was defined to be 96 mole% CO_2 and a mixture of nitrogen, oxygen, hydrogen, argon and methane with hydrogen limited to 2.0 mole% and oxygen limited to 10 ppmv.

Table 1. Parameters of the pipelines

Emitter	Flow rate range	Collecting pipeline		Onshore trunk pipeline		Offshore trunk pipeline	
		Length	ID	Length	ID	Length	ID
	Mt/y	km	mm	km	mm	km	mm
Don Valley	0.91-6.27	15	738.2	71	571.8	91	559.2
White Rose	0.61-2.65	5	295.5				

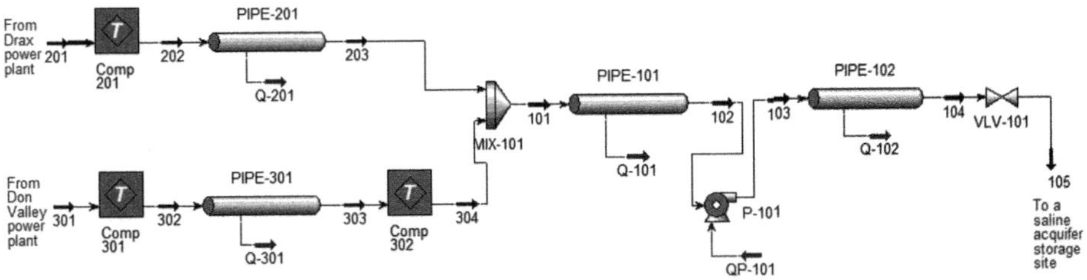

Figure 2. Process flowsheet of the pipeline network

3. Simulation method

3.1. Process flow diagram

The steady state model for this case study was developed using Aspen HYSYS®. Figure 2 shows the process flowsheet.

3.2. Physical property

The cubic equation of state (EOS) and other more complex EOS have been widely used to calculate the physical properties of CO_2 for pipeline transport modeling and simulations. There is no consensus in the literature regarding the best EOS for the design of CO_2 pipelines. Diamantonis et al. (2013) compared the results of several EOS with experimental data, which shows the Peng-Robinson (PR) (Peng and Robinson, 1976) EOS is of comparable accuracy even compared with other advanced EOS, when binary interaction parameters are used. In this study, PR EOS has been selected considering both the accuracy and the simplicity.

3.3. Base case

The maximum entry flow rate from both the White Rose and the Don Valley projects and the highest ambient temperature were chosen as the base case. This is considered as the worst case scenario, since it would require the highest entry pressure and the greatest boosting pressure at the pump station. The assumptions made for the simulation are as follows: 1) 330 operating days per year for each power plant; 2) the pressure drops across valves and other fittings are neglected; 3) the adiabatic efficiencies of compressors and pumps used in this model are 75 %.

The pressure settings of key sections are based on two operational constraints: 1) the entry pressure (i.e the outlet pressure of the compressor at each capture plant) should be high enough to maintain a minimum pipeline operating pressure of 101 bar, to avoid two phase flow in the dense phase pipelines; 2) a constant injection pressure of 126 bar is specified to satisfy the injection rate, which requires a minimum arrival pressure of 126 bar at the storage site. The input and boundary conditions for the base case were specified in Table 2.

4. Process analysis of different operating strategies

It is important to study daily operation for determining the best strategy to operate the system economically, safely and efficiently. In this case study, the two emitters are fossil fuel power plants. Typical daily operating scenarios involve variation of the flow rate of the CO_2-rich stream due to fluctuations in energy demand. The pressure profile of the pipeline network relies on the CO_2-rich stream flow rate. When there is fluctuation in the flow rate in response to changes in electricity demand, there are several possible operating scenarios, all based on different pressure settings. In this

Table 2. Input and boundary conditions for the base case

	Unit	White Rose	Don Valley
Capture technology	-	Oxy-fuel	Pre-combustion
Entry composition	mole%	96%CO_2, 2%N_2, 2%Ar	96%CO_2, 2%N_2, 2%H_2
Flow rate	kg/h	334,596	791,667
Entry pressure	bar	120.50	35.00
Differential pressure of mid-compressor	bar	-	86.92
Numbers of compressor stages	-	5-stages	3 stages
Numbers of mid-compressor stages	-	-	2 stages
Entry temperature	°C	20.0	20.0
Pump boosting pressure	bar	43.00	
Offshore platform arrival pressure	bar	126.00	

section, a case study was performed to compare power consumption and cooling duty for each operating strategy. For the modelled CO_2 pipeline system, three possible operating scenarios are:

Case1: To maintain the same entry pressure and the same pump boosting pressure, so that the arrival pressure at the offshore storage site would vary with the flow rate of CO_2-rich stream.

Case2: To maintain the same entry pressure and adjust the pump boosting pressure.

Case3: To adjust both the entry pressure and pump boosting pressure, while maintaining a constant injection pressure.

A throttle valve would be added at the end of the offshore pipeline to maintain a constant injection pressure of 126 bar when the arrival pressure at the storage site is higher than 126 bar for each case. Table 3 presents the different pressure settings at the different flow rates in each case.

Figure 3 and Figure 4 respectively illustrate the energy consumptions and cooling duties per tonne of CO_2-rich fluid transported in each case, as a function of the flow rate from the power stations. As can be seen in Figure 4, in cases 1 and 2 the cooling duties per ton of CO_2 are the same at each of the three flow rates considered.

Table 3. Pressure settings in difference cases

Case Name	Flow rate from White Rose	Flow rate from Don Valley	Entry pressure at White Rose	Entry pressure at Don Valley	DP of mid-compressor for Don Valley	Pump boosting pressure	Arrival pressure
	kg/h	kg/h	bar	bar	bar	bar	bar
Case 1a	334,596	791,667	136	35	102.52	26.8	126
Case 1b	205,808	453,283	136	35	102.52	26.8	147
Case 1c	77,020	114,899	136	35	102.52	26.8	157
Case 2a	334,596	791,667	136	35	102.52	26.8	126
Case 2b	205,808	453,283	136	35	102.52	5.9	126
Case 2c	77,020	114,899	136	35	102.52	0	130.3
Case 3a	334,596	791,667	120.5	35	86.92	43.0	126
Case 3b	205,808	453,283	114.9	35	80.12	25.8	126
Case 3c	77,020	114,899	112.4	35	77.23	17.1	126

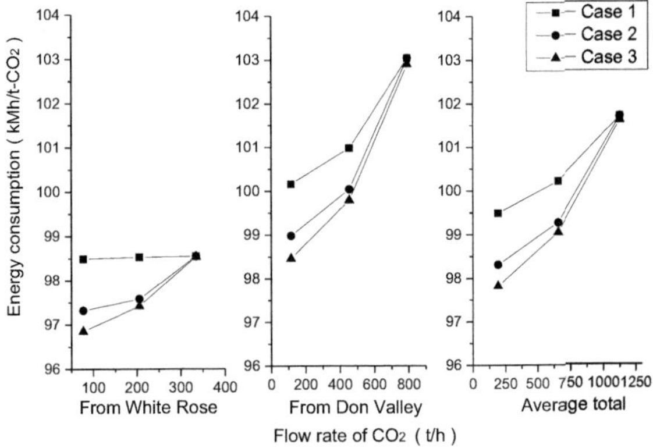

Figure 3. Energy consumptions with the variation of the flow rate

Figure 3 and Figure 4 show that the trends of energy consumption and cooling duty are relatively gradual when the flow rate changes sharply. For all three cases, energy consumption ranges from 96 to 103 kWh/t-CO_2 and cooling duty ranges from 140 to147 Mcal/t-CO_2 when the flow rate varies from 190 t/h to 1,250 t/h. This is due to the relatively high entry pressure (as shown in Table 4) which is required to maintain a minimum operating pressure of 101 bar in the trunk pipelines regardless of the flow rate. This also indicates that a large part of the compressor energy is required to maintain the dense phase flow inside truck pipelines. Additionally the pressure needs to be sufficient enough to overcome the pressure drop associated with an elevation profile increase of approximately 140 m along the pipeline route whilst maintaining a minimum operating pressure of 101 bar.

In this case study, the energy consumption and cooling duty is lowest in Case 3. The energy consumption per tonne of CO_2 in case 3 is about 1.67 kWh less than in case 1 at the lowest flow rate and 1.16 kWh less than in case 1 at the medium flow rate. With the industrial electricity price of 0.0847 £/kWh (UK Government, 2013) in 2012 in the UK, the total energy cost per year in Case 3 is about £514,938 cheaper than in case 1, based on an average flow rate. Due to its lower energy requirement, the operating strategy described as Case 3 is the preferred option. However, for determining the best operating strategy for a real project, additional factors should be considered, such as:

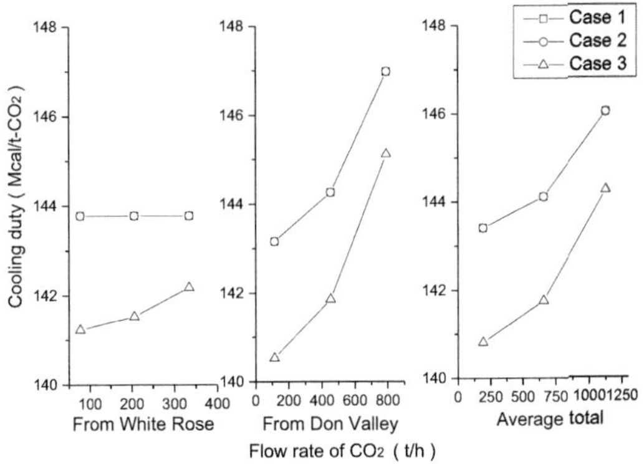

Figure 4. Cooling duties with the variation of the flow rate

1) The capital investment costs and maintenance costs may be higher for compressors and pumps with adjustable discharge pressures.
2) From a control philosophy perspective, a stable or fixed operating pressure for the trunk pipelines may be preferred under normal operating conditions.

5. Conclusions

The physical characteristics of a potential pipeline network for CO_2 transportation, in the Humber area have been described. An example pipeline network model was developed in Aspen HYSYS® and simulations were performed for different operating strategies over a wide range of flow rates of the CO_2-rich stream. For all three operating strategies, simulation results show that the energy consumption ranges from 96 to 103 kWh/t-CO_2 and the cooling duty ranges from 140 to 147 Mcal/t-CO_2. The preferred operating strategy is to adjust both the entry pressure and pump boosting pressure as this requires the lowest energy consumption and cooling duty compared to the other strategies. However determining the strategy to be adopted in a real system may be more complicated as the costs of capital investment and maintenance, along with other factors, must be taken into account.

References

M. Chaczykowski, A.J. Osiadacz, 2012, Dynamic simulation of pipelines containing dense phase/supercritical CO_2-rich mixtures for carbon capture and storage, International Journal of Greenhouse Gas Control, 9, 446-456.

N.I. Diamantonis, G.C. Boulougouris, E. Mansoor, D.M. Tsangaris, I.G. Economou, 2013, Evaluation of cubic, SAFT, and PC-SAFT equations of state for the vapor-liquid equilibrium modeling of CO_2 mixtures with other gases, Ind Eng Chem Res, 52, 10, 3933-3942

International Energy Agency (IEA), 2012, Energy Technology Perspectives, Paris, France.

IPCC, 2005, IPCC Special Report on Carbon Dioxide Capture and Storage, Prepared by Working Group III of the Intergovernmental Panel on Climate Change, Cambridge University Press, Cambridge, United Kingdom and New York, USA.

T. Lazic, E. Oko, M. Wang, 2013, Case study on CO_2 transport pipeline network design for Humber region in the UK, Proceedings of the Institution of Mechanical Engineers, Part E, Journal of Process Mechanical Engineering, DOI: 10.1177/0954408913500447.

S. Liljemark, K. Arvidsson, M.T.P. Mc Cann, H. Tummescheit, S. Velut, 2011, Dynamic simulation of a carbon dioxide transfer pipeline for analysis of normal operation and failure modes, Energy Procedia, 4, 3040-3047.

M. Nimtz, M. Klatt, B. Wiese, M. Kühn, H. Joachim Krautz, 2010, Modelling of the CO_2 process- and transport chain in CCS systems—Examination of transport and storage processes, Chemie der Erde - Geochemistry, 70, 185-192.

D.Y. Peng, D.B. Robinson, 1976, A new two-constant equation of state, Industrial and Engineering Chemistry Fundamentals, 15, 1, 59–64.

J.M. Race, B. Westenhall, P.N. Seevam, M.J. Downie, 2012, Towards a CO_2 pipeline specification: defining tolerance limits for impurities, Journal of Pipeline Engineering, 11, 3, 173–190.

S. Roussanaly, G. Bureau-Cauchois, J. Husebye, 2013, Costs benchmark of CO_2 transport technologies for a group of various size industries, International Journal of Greenhouse Gas Control, 12, 0, 341-350.

UK Government, 2013, Industrial electricity prices in the EU and G7 countries (QEP 5.3.1), <www.gov.uk/government/statistical-data-sets/international-industrial-energy-prices> accessed on 28/01/2014.

Z.X. Zhang, G.X. Wang, P. Massarotto, V. Rudolph, 2006, Optimization of pipeline transport for CO2 sequestration, Energy Conversion and Management, 47, 6, 702–715.

Jiří Jaromír Klemeš, Petar Sabev Varbanov and Peng Yen Liew (Editors)
Proceedings of the 24th European Symposium on Computer Aided Process Engineering – ESCAPE 24
June 15-18, 2014, Budapest, Hungary.

Reliability and Availability Analysis of Process Systems under Changing Operating Conditions

Soo Hyoung Choi*

School of Semiconductor and Chemical Engineering, Chonbuk National University, Jeonju, 561-756, Korea
soochoi@jbnu.ac.kr

Abstract

Quantitative risk analysis for process safety often requires reliability and availability analysis of process systems. Although most systems are operated under changing conditions, conventional methods use reliability models with constant parameters only, and thus average operating conditions should be applied. Furthermore, a simplified availability equation is frequently used. Case studies indicate that using an average operating condition for reliability or using a simplified availability equation can cause a serious error. A rigorous method is proposed in this work which is suitable for solving the exact availability equation using the reliability under changing operating conditions.

Keywords: reliability, availability, operating condition, Weibull distribution

1. Introduction

Many methods for reliability, availability, and maintainability (RAM) analysis are now available for project managers and engineers (Department of Defense, 2009). The analysis of reliabilities of process systems often uses models based on the Weibull distribution, for which the cumulative distribution function for reliability, i.e. probability of survival is as follows.

$$R(t) = e^{-\left(\frac{t}{\eta}\right)^{\beta}} \tag{1}$$

where $\beta > 0$ is the shape parameter, and $\eta > 0$ is the scale parameter. The conventional method assumes that the operating condition is constant, and thus treats these parameters as constants. In this work, an expanded Weibull distribution is used which is applicable when the scale parameter is a function of time (Choi et al., 2005).

$$R(t) = e^{-z(t)^{\beta}} \tag{2}$$

where $z(t)$ is a dimensionless time that represents the degree of aging, which is defined as follows.

$$z(t) = \int_0^t \frac{dt}{\eta(t)} \tag{3}$$

where $\eta(t)$ is a finite positive function that depends on the operating condition that changes with time.

Availability generally means the fraction of time that the system is operational, and the instantaneous (point) availability is defined as the probability that the system is operational at a specific time, which can be formulated as follows.

$$A(t) = R(t) + \int_0^t A(t-\tau)dQ(\tau) \tag{4}$$

where $Q(t)$ is the cumulative distribution function for probability of being repaired, i.e. probability of failure, wait, and repair, which can be calculated as follows.

$$P(t) = \int_0^t F(t-\tau)dG(\tau) \tag{5}$$

$$Q(t) = \int_0^t P(t-\tau)dH(\tau) \tag{6}$$

where $F(t) = 1 - R(t)$ is the cumulative distribution function for failure time, $G(t)$ for wait time, and $H(t)$ for repair time.

Yang et al. (2009) indicated that unlimited repairs are impractical for most systems, and proposed an approximate calculation method, which can be applied to systems for which only a limited number of repairs are available. Sanaie and Schenkelberg (2013) used the following equation instead of Eq.(4).

$$A^1(t) = R(t) + \int_0^t R(t-\tau)dQ(\tau) \tag{7}$$

This equation is explicit for availability, so relatively easy to calculate, and thus popularly used. However, it is correct only when the system can be repaired only once.

Eq.(4) belongs to Volterra integral equation of the second kind, for which numerical methods are available (Press et al., 2007). The objective of this work is to propose a rigorous method for solving Eqs.(4) to (6) in conjunction with Eqs.(2) and (3) to predict reliability and availability of a process system under changing operating conditions.

Volterra integral equations are also used in stochastic models that can deal with not only changing operating conditions but also process uncertainties as proposed by Deng et al. (2013). Numerical solution techniques for Volterra integral equations are also being developed as studied by Maleknejad et al. (2014).

2. Proposed Method

For time t_i, $i = 0,\ldots, n$, the dimensionless time defined by Eq.(3) can be calculated using the trapezoid rule as follows ($z_0 = 0$).

$$z_i = \frac{1}{2}\sum_{k=0}^{i-1}\left[\frac{1}{\eta(t_{k+1})} + \frac{1}{\eta(t_k)}\right](t_{k+1} - t_k), i = 1,\ldots,n \tag{8}$$

where z_i represents $z(t_i)$.

The convolutions are calculated as follows ($P_0 = Q_0 = 0$).

$$P_i = \frac{1}{2}\sum_{k=0}^{i-1}\left[F(z_{i-k}) + F(z_{i-k-1})\right]\left[G(t_{k+1}) - G(t_k)\right], i = 1,\ldots,n \tag{9}$$

$$Q_i = \frac{1}{2}\sum_{k=0}^{i-1}\left(P_{i-k} + P_{i-k-1}\right)\left[H(t_{k+1}) - H(t_k)\right], i = 1,\ldots,n \tag{10}$$

where P_i and Q_i represent $P(t_i)$ and $Q(t_i)$ respectively, and $F(z) = 1 - R(z)$ where $R(z) = \exp(-z^\beta)$.

The availability is calculated as follows ($A_0 = 1$).

$$A_i = \frac{R(z_i) + \frac{1}{2}\left[A_{i-1}(Q_1 - Q_0) + \sum_{k=1}^{i-1}(A_{i-k} + A_{i-k-1})(Q_{k+1} - Q_k)\right]}{1 - \frac{1}{2}(Q_1 - Q_0)}, i = 1,\ldots,n \tag{11}$$

where A_i represents $A(t_i)$.

The above equations may be modified for a Simpson's rule for better precision, or reformulated for better efficiency as a differential transform method such as proposed by Seiheii et al. (2013) or as a Galerkin method such as proposed by Rahman (2013).

3. Case Study

3.1. Limited Repairs

Yang et al. (2009) presented the following example of failure, wait, and repair functions.

$$F(t) = 1 - e^{-(0.40t)^{8.0}} \tag{12}$$

$$G(t) = 1 - e^{-(0.99t)^{1.2}} \tag{13}$$

$$H(t) = 1 - e^{-(0.95t)^{1.5}} \tag{14}$$

where time t is in days.

Fig. 1 shows the result of the proposed method where $A(t)$ represents the availability, $A^1(t)$ the availability when the system can be repaired only once, and $R(t)$ the reliability. Although the solution of $A(t)$ is based on the assumption that the system can be repaired infinitely many times, the result is still meaningful because impractical situations such as rare cases of many repairs within a short period of time will have low probabilities, and thus affect the final solution very little. Furthermore, the steady state availability is an important factor for a system design.

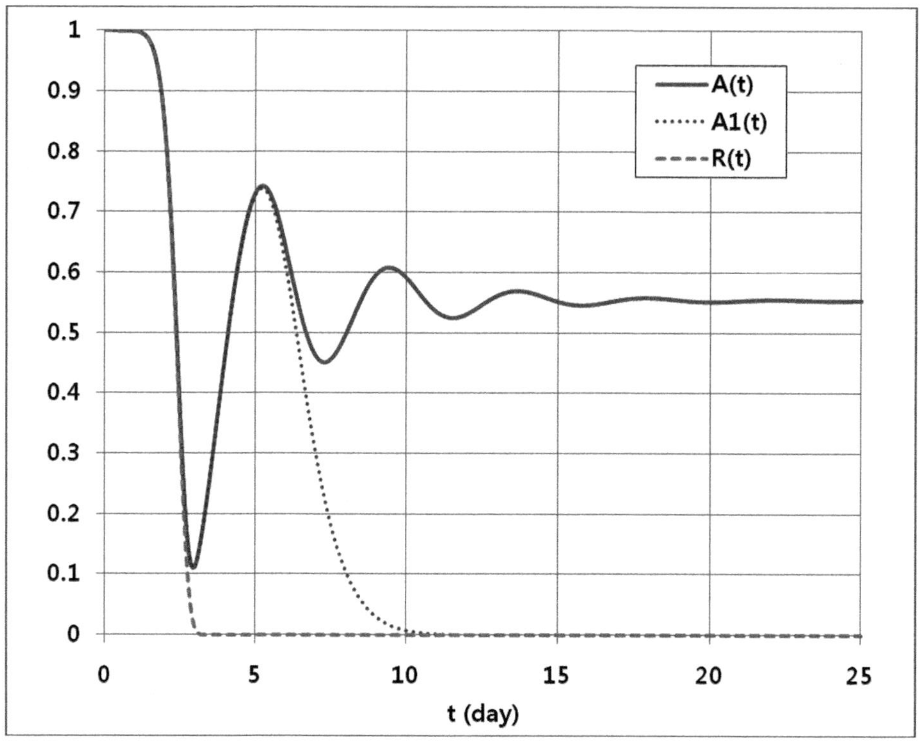

Figure 1. Availability and reliability functions.

3.2. Changing Operating Conditions

Sanaie and Schenkelberg (2013) presented a system that uses a cooling fan that has the following reliability function.

$$R(t) = e^{-\left(\frac{t}{\eta}\right)^{3.0}} \tag{15}$$

where η = 95,933 h at the operating temperature T = 45 °C. For different temperatures, the life acceleration factor can be calculated as follows.

$$\frac{\eta}{\eta_0} = 1.5^{-\left(\frac{T-T_0}{10}\right)} \tag{16}$$

They used this equation, but assumed that the operating temperature is constant. In this work, it is assumed that the operating temperature changes with time as follows.

$$T = T_0 + \Delta T \sin\frac{2\pi t}{8766} \tag{17}$$

where time t is in hours, so the operating temperature T oscillates between $T_0 \pm \Delta T$ with a period of one year.

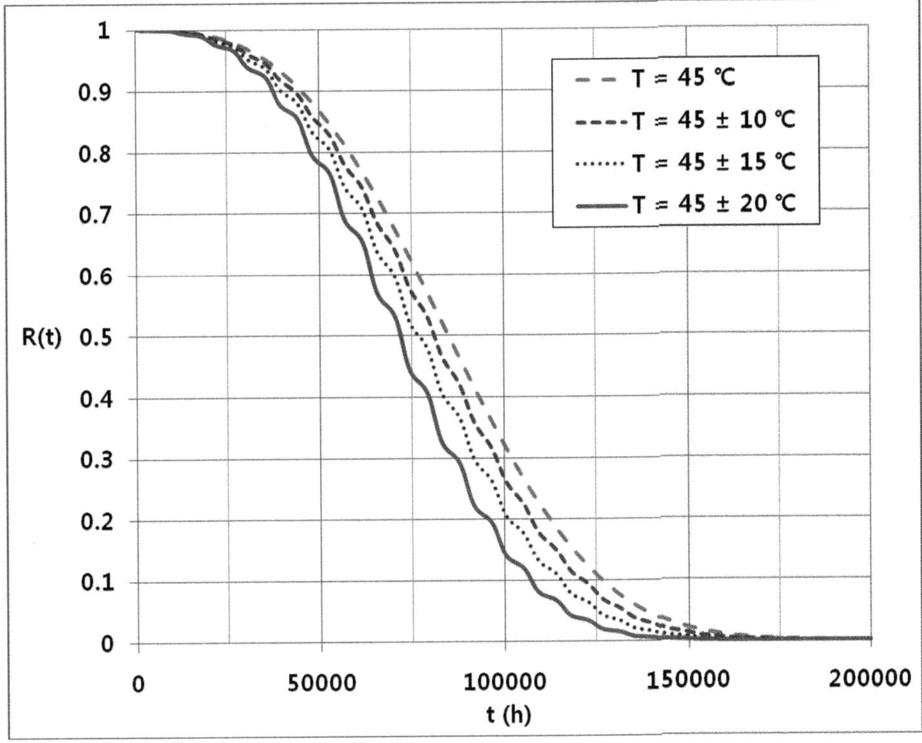

Figure 2. Reliability functions under changing operating conditions.

Figure 2 shows the result of the proposed method for $T_0 = 45$ °C, $\Delta T = 10$, 15, and 20 °C. Note that the life can be significantly shortened if the operating condition oscillates even though the average condition is the same. If we applied daily oscillations also, the reliability would be further lowered.

4. Conclusions

A numerical method based on the trapezoid rule has been proposed for calculation of reliability and availability functions under changing operating conditions. More precise integration techniques are considered unnecessary unless the operating condition changes very rapidly, because the failure, wait, and repair functions are already very approximate in most cases.

The simplified availability model equation is being popularly used, but caution is necessary because it is based on the assumption that the system can be repaired only once. It is shown in this work that the actual availability can be very different from that. Caution is also required when using an average operating condition because it can result in overestimation of reliability as shown in this work.

It is expected that the proposed method can give more accurate reliability and availability analysis of various process systems under changing operating conditions than conventional methods that use average operating conditions.

Acknowledgement

The wholehearted support from Prof. En Sup Yoon at Seoul National University is gratefully acknowledged.

References

S. H. Choi, B. Lee, C. B. Chung, 2005, An expanded Weibull distribution model for reliability analysis of process facilities under changing operating conditions, Proceedings of PSE Asia 2005: The 3rd International Symposium on Design, Operation and Control of Chemical Processes, P096.

Y. Deng, A. Barros, A. Grall, 2013, Residual useful life estimation based on a time-dependent Ornstein-Uhlenbeck process, Chemical Engineering Transactions, 33, 325-330.

Department of Defense Reliability, Availability, Maintainability, and Cost Rationale Report Manual, 2009, Office of the Secretary of Defense, Washington, DC, USA.

K. Maleknejad, R. Mollapourasl, P. Mirzaei, 2014, Numerical solution of Volterra functional integral equation by using cubic B-spline scaling functions, Numerical Methods for Partial Differential Equations, 30, 699-722, DOI: 10.1002/num.21837.

W. H. Press, S. A. Teukolsky, W. T. Vetterling, B. P. Flannery, 2007, Numerical Recipes: The Art of Scientific Computing, 3rd ed., Cambridge University Press, New York, NY, USA.

M. M. Rahman, 2013, Numerical solutions of Volterra integral equations using Galerkin method with Hermite polynomials, Proceedings of the 2013 International Conference on Applied Mathematics and Computational Methods in Engineering, 276-281.

G. Sanaie, F. Schenkelberg, 2013, Using reliability modeling and accelerated life testing to estimate solar inverter useful life, Proceedings of Reliability and Maintainability Symposium (RAMS), DOI: 10.1109/RAMS.2013.6517651.

H. Seiheii, M. Alavi, F. Ghadami, 2013, Numerical method for solving a kind of Volterra integral equation using differential transform method, Journal of Mathematics and Computer Science, 6, 220-229.

Y. Yang, L. Wang, Y. Yu, R. Kang, 2011, Approximate instantaneous availability and its error analysis, Proceedings of the 9th International Conference on Reliability, Maintainability and Safety (ICRMS), 339-343, DOI: 10.1109/ICRMS.2011.5979288.

Jiří Jaromír Klemeš, Petar Sabev Varbanov and Peng Yen Liew (Editors)
Proceedings of the 24th European Symposium on Computer Aided Process Engineering – ESCAPE 24
June 15-18, 2014, Budapest, Hungary.

Dynamic Modeling and Validation of Post-combustion Calcium-looping Process

Ana-Maria Cormos*, Abel Simon

Babes-Bolyai University of Cluj-Napoca, Faculty of Chemistry and Chemical Engineering, Arany Janos 11, RO-400028 Cluj-Napoca, Romania
cani@chem.ubbcluj.ro

Abstract

Chemical looping systems became competitive solutions within CCS technologies to reduce CO_2 capture energy penalty. The paper presents a 1D dynamic mathematical of calcium-looping process to be used for carbon capture in fossil fuel-based power plants. The modeling includes transfer processes: conservation equations for mass, energy and conversion degree for both interconnected fluidized bed reactors of the calcium looping process. The developed model of carbon dioxide capture by Ca-looping cycle has been validated with data collected from pilot plant published in literature (INCAR-CSIC, Spain). The developed model predicts the overall CO_2 capture efficiency taking into consideration the deactivation of the sorbent.

Keywords: CO_2 Capture, Calcium looping processes, Dynamic Mathematical Modeling

1. Introduction

Carbon capture and storage (CCS) technologies are mitigation measures aimed to reduce CO_2 emissions from energy and other energy-intensive sectors (e.g. cement, metallurgy, petro-chemical etc.). CCS applied to a modern conventional power plant could reduce CO_2 emissions to the atmosphere by approximately 80–90 % compared to a plant without CCS. The first generation of CCS technologies, i.e. scrubbing with amines, is energy intensive. Second and third generation CCS technologies such as carbonate looping or chemical looping combustion has been proposed to reduce costs (IEA, 2012). In case of Ca-looping process (Rodriguez et al., 2010) two fluidized columns is used (Figure 1). In first fluidized bed reactor (carbonator) the CO_2 in the flue gas of a coal-fired power plant is captured by its reaction with calcium oxide and the limestone converted back into CaO and gaseous CO_2 in other fluidized bed reactor (calciner). After heat recovery, decarbonized flue gas is vented to the atmosphere (Grasa and Abanades, 2006).

Many studies have been done recently regarding the characteristics of this process (Peltola et al. 2013) some studies on plant modeling and simulation have also been published to estimate the performance of complete power plants. Earlier studies related to Ca-looping process modeling the researchers have concentrated on stationary cases and in some cases only one of the reactors is modelled. Nevertheless, steady state analysis does not correctly represent neither issues related to daily operations nor the transient behavior of the plants. The dynamic CO_2 capture evaluation is considered of a paramount importance for establishing optimal operation procedure for power plants equipped with CCS.

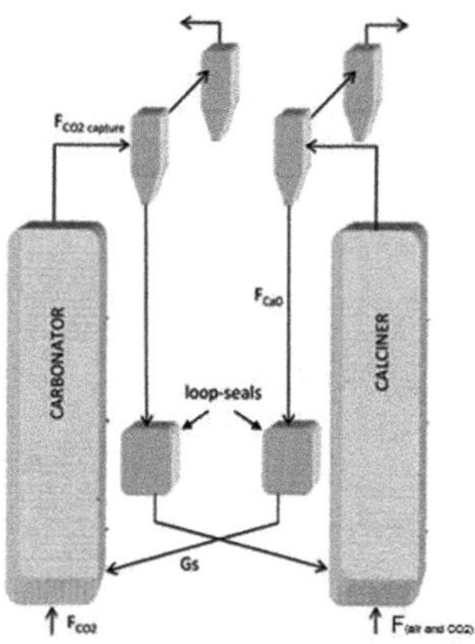

Figure 1. Scheme of the Ca-looping process

It is widely known that fossil power plants are required to be operated in dynamic scenario due to the timely variation of the grid demand (Kvamsdal et al., 2009). The novelty of our work is the development of a dynamical model for CO_2post-combustioncalcium looping process. So, it can be followed, not only the effect of the disturbance, separately, on each parts of the process but also the interactions between the carbonator and calciner. Based on a carbonator/calciner dynamic model it is estimated the link between the fundamental Ca-looping process parameters (carbonator inventory, sorbent make-up and sorbent recycle rate) and CO_2 capture efficiency.

2. Mathematical model

2.1. Balance equations

The developed dynamic mathematical model of carbonator (Cormos and Simon, 2013, Romano, 2012) and calciner (Cormos et al., 2005) includes partial differential equations (PDE) to describe the time and space dependent of the investigated parameters. Carbonation reaction rate is modeled with a correlation presented by Grasa and Abanades (2006). A shrinking core model was used to describe $CaCO_3$ granules decomposition. The sorbent particle has been assumed to be spherical and isothermal. The shrinking core model considers the decomposition of $CaCO_3$ at a well-defined CaO–$CaCO_3$ interface around the particle and the diffusion of CO_2 released through the porous CaO to the particle surface.

The total mass balance for the gas and solid phases are:

$$\frac{dQ_j}{dt} = -v_j \frac{dQ_j}{dz} \pm S_{carb/calc} \quad (1)$$

Where: j represents solid or gas phase, v_j is the solid/gas velocity, Q_j is solid/gas flow, $S_{carb/calc}$ is the source term of CO_2 from chemical reaction. The sign ± shows the direction of CO_2 mass transfer.

The component mass balance for the solid and gas phases are:

$$\frac{d[Q_j(x_i - x_{i,eq})]}{dt} = -v_j \frac{d[Q_j(x_i - x_{i,eq})]}{dz} \pm S_{carb/calc} M_i \quad (2)$$

where: i is component: CO_2, O_2, N_2 from gas phase, and $CaCO_3$ and CaO from solid phase, x_i – mass fraction of component i, in j solid/gas phase, $M_i$is the molecular mass of component I, S_{carb}andS_{calc} is equal 0 for O_2 and N_2 component mass balance.

The model proposed by Grasa et al., (2008) which describes the reaction rate of cycled particles was used here.

$$S_{carb} = \frac{\xi V_S k_{carb} Q_G (C_{CO_2} - C_{CO_2,eq}) M_i v_j}{1000 V_G \rho_G v_G} \quad (3)$$

A reaction rate correlation for the calcinations reaction was presented by Garcia-Labiano et al. (2002) and depends on the properties of the limestone.

$$S_{calc} = \frac{Q_S V_S}{v_S V_G} x_{CaCO_3} k_{calc} \frac{M_i v_j}{M_{CaCO_3}} \tag{4}$$

The heat balance for the solid and gas phase:

$$\frac{dT_j}{dt} = -v_j \frac{dT_j}{dz} + \frac{v_j \left(H_{GS} - H_{Pj} - H_{R_{carb/calc}}\right)}{Q_j c_{P_j}} \tag{5}$$

Where $H_{R\ carb/calc}$ is the reaction term, H_{GS} heat flux from gas to solid and $H_{P,j}$ heat fluxes from gas/solid to wall.

2.2. The hydrodynamics of circulating fluidized beds

Following the 1D model for turbulent fluidization presented by Kunii and Levenspiel (1997), the fluidized bed reactors can be divided into a dense bottom zone with a higher solid concentration with a core-annulus radial distribution and a lean upper zone (Romano, 2012). In the dense zone volume fraction of solids, ε_{sd} is constant and depends on the fluidization regime u_0. Ranges of 0.2–0.4 (Kunii and Levenspiel, 1997) have been suggested and a value of 0.25 was assumed. In the lean region the volume fraction of solids decreases exponentially with height. Knowing the dimensions of the reactor (H_t, D) it is possible to calculate the height of the lean H_l and dense zone H_d:

$$H_l = \frac{1}{a} ln\left(\frac{\varepsilon_{sd} - \varepsilon_S^*}{\varepsilon_{se} - \varepsilon_S^*}\right) \tag{6}$$

Mass of solids in each region:

$$W_l = A_t \rho_s H_l \left(\frac{G_S^*}{u_0 * \rho_s} + \frac{\varepsilon_{sd} - \varepsilon_{se}}{H_l a}\right), \ W_d = A_t \rho_s H_d \varepsilon_{sd} \tag{7}$$

Where A_t is cross-sectional area and $au_0 = 4\ s^{-1}$. The volume fraction of solids at the reactor exit ε_{se}, could be determinate by following equation:

$$\varepsilon_{se} = \frac{G_S^*}{(u_0 - u_T) * \rho_S} \tag{8}$$

The solid solid circulation rate at the exit of the riser, G_S^* can be calculated from Eq.(9) as an exponential function of terminal and superficial gas velocity u_T, u_0, (Johansson et al., 2007).

$$G_S^* = 23.7 \rho_g u_0 exp(-5.5 \frac{u_T}{u_0}) \tag{9}$$

The terminal free-fall velocity u_T depends on the particle diameter d_p, solid and gas density ρ_s, ρ_g and the viscosity μ of the gas under the given conditions (Kunii and Levenspiel, 1997).

$$u_T = \left[\frac{18}{(d_p^*)^2} + \frac{0.591}{(d_p^*)^{1/2}}\right]^{-1} \left[\frac{\mu(\rho_s - \rho_g)g}{\rho_g^2}\right]^{1/3} \quad \text{where} \quad d_p^* = d_p \left[\frac{\rho_g(\rho_s - \rho_g)g}{\mu^2}\right]^{1/3} \tag{10}$$

3. Results and discussion

The partial differential equations of the mathematical model were transformed in ordinary ones, by discretization, and all mathematical equations used in this model have been implemented in the equation oriented process simulator Matlab/Simulink 2008.

A summary of the fluidization columns (INCAR-CSIC, Spain) characteristics and operating data, used in this work is presented in Table 1 (Caritos et al.,2011; Romano, 2012).

The developed model of carbon dioxide capture by Ca-looping cycle has been validated with data collected from pilot plant published in literature. Temperature profiles and composition within the columns are predicted successfully by the model, illustrating the predictive capabilities of the model (Figure 2 and 3).

The Figure 2 shows the gas phase output CO_2 concentration values, for every carbonation-calcinations cycle; obtained by simulation vs. experimental values published by Charitos et al., (2011), R value is 0.988. The differences of the temperature profile from the experimental values come from the empirical equations to estimate the heat transfer coefficients. A good correlation between temperature carbonator profiles obtained by simulation and experimental could be observed too in Figure 3 (R value is 0.824).

In order to analyze the dynamic behavior and to evidence the interactions between the parts of a CO_2 capture process (carbonator and calciner) a dynamic study has been realized. The dynamic simulation results have showed that the height of the dense region decreases with increasing of the superficial velocity of the gas, from 4.8 m to 3.2 m for changing of gas velocity from 1.1 m/s to 2 m/s in carbonator case (Figure 4). And

Table 1. Parameters of the model

Parameter	Carbonator	Calciner
Mean particle size, d_p [μm]	155	155
Height, H_t [m]	6.5	6
Diameter, D [m]	0.1	0.1
Gas velocity, u_0 [m/s]	1.1-2.5	1.1-2.5
Inlet CO_2 concentration, x_{in} [% vol.]	10	50
Temperature, T [K]	923	1,173
Pressure, p [bar]	1	1
Solid density, ρ_s [kg/m^3]	1,660	1,660
Inlet gas density, ρ_g [kg/m^3]	0.3956	0.3735
Solid fraction in dense region, ε_{sd} [-]	0.25	0.25

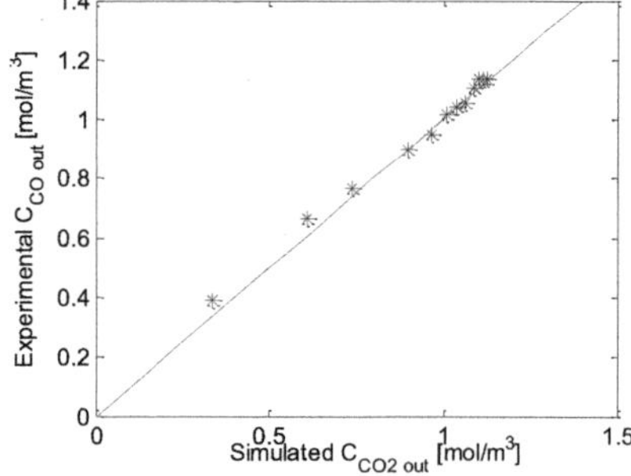

Figure 2. Experimental vs. simulated CO_2 concentration

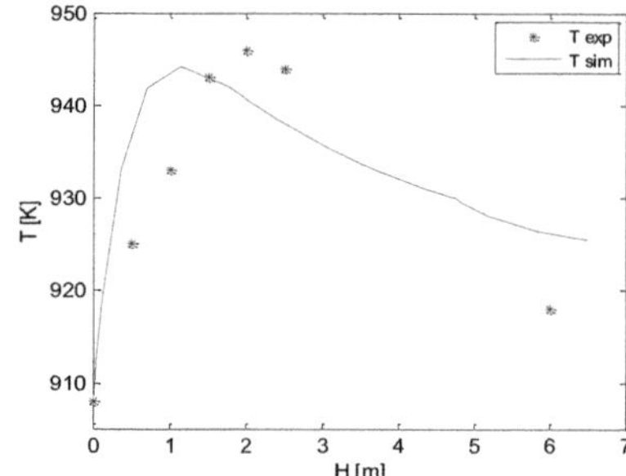

Figure 3. Carbonator solid temperature profile

the most part of the carbonation/decarbonation reaction takes place in the dense region, therefore at smaller superficial gas velocities much higher carbonation degree can be achieved. The gas phase in carbonator stabilizes almost immediately at the new steady-state value, after the disturbance, but in term of solids phase the effect of the disturbance propagates with delay (Figure 5). As is expected, simultaneously with the exhaust gas flow, CO_2 molar concentration is increasing (Figure 4).

The effect of the disturbance propagates with delay, from the carbonator to the calciner Figure 6 and 7 show the effect of changing of the gas velocity on the CO_2 concentration profile and solid flow profile along the column's height, in time. As is expected, in case of calciner the CO_2 molar concentration is decreasing and solid flow is increasing.

The results of the simulation shows that more than 90 % of the total CO_2 capture has occurred in the lower dense region of the carbonator. And 75 % of CO_2 is released into the dense region of the calciner. In terms of CO_2 capture efficiency, the model predicted that in every carbonation-calcinations cycle the sorbent capacity decreases significant with the number of cycles, in accordance with experimental data.

4. Conclusions

The simulation results have showed that the height of the dense region decreases with changing of the superficial velocity of the gas and solid particle diameter. And the most part of the carbonation/decarbonation reaction takes place in the dense region, therefore at smaller superficial gas velocities much higher carbonation degree can be achieved.

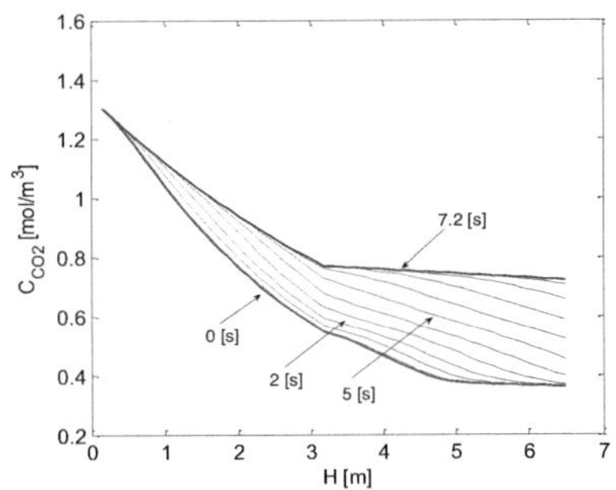

Figure 4. Carbonator CO_2 concentration profile

Figure 5. Carbonator solid temperature profile

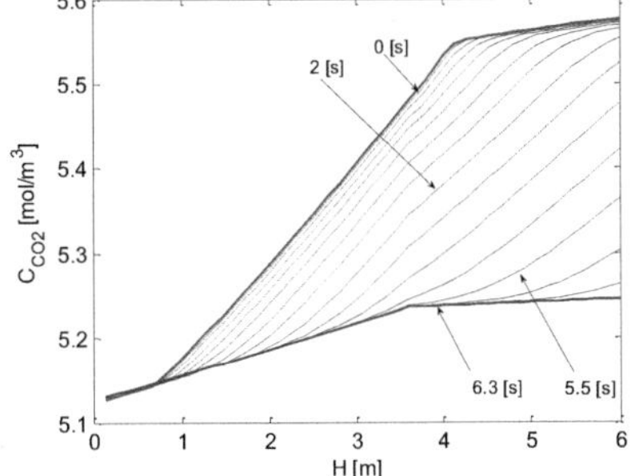

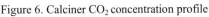

Figure 6. Calciner CO_2 concentration profile

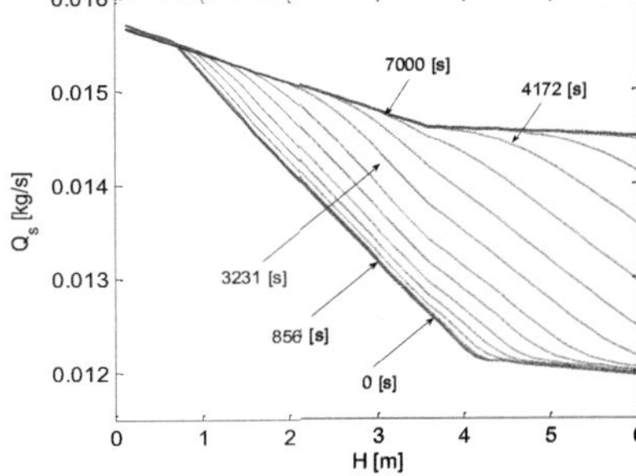

Figure 7. Calciner solid flow profile

The originality of dynamic behavior analyses consist in the fact that the carbonator and claimer are connected between them and the only input parameters are necessary: gas and solid input flow, composition and temperature of these streams. In accordance with simulation results the effect of the disturbance propagates with delay, from the carbonator to the calciner. The developed mathematical model would be used for analyzing CO_2 capture efficiency and understanding of micro level interaction of various processes taking place inside of fluidized columns. Also, model would be used in evaluation of various operation conditions for optimization of technical indicators of carbon dioxide capture process.

Acknowledgement

This work was supported by the Romanian National Authority for Scientific Research UEFISCDI, grant number ID-PCE-2011-3-0028: "Innovative methods for chemical looping carbon dioxide capture applied to energy conversion processes for decarbonized energy vectors poly-generation".

References

A. Charitos, N. Rodríguez, C. Hawthorne, M. Alonso, M. Zieba, B. Arias, G. Kopanakis, G. Scheffknecht, J. C. Abanades, 2011, Experimental Validation of the Calcium Looping CO_2 Capture Process with Two Circulating Fluidized Bed Carbonator Reactors, Ind. Eng. Chem. Res., 50, 16, 9685–9695.

A. M. Cormos, C. C Cormos, S. Agachi, 2005, Modeling and simulation of thermal decomposition of limestone in a vertical lime kiln, Studia Chemia L, 2, 50-56.

A.M. Cormos, A. Simon, 2013, Dynamic Modelling of CO_2 Capture by Calcium-Looping Cycle, Chem. Eng. Trans., 35, 421- 426.

F. Garcıa-Labiano, A. Abad, L. F. deDiego, P. Gayan, J. Adanez, 2002, Calcination of calcium-based sorbents at pressure in a broad range of CO_2 concentrations, Chem. Eng. Sci., 57, 2381–2393.

G.S. Grasa, J. C. Abanades, 2006, CO_2 capture capacity of CaO in long series of carbonation/ calcination cycles, Ind. Eng. Chem. Resources, 45, 8846–8851.

G.S. Grasa, J. C. Abanades, M. Alonso, B. Gonzalez, 2008, Reactivity of highly cycled particles of CaO in a carbonation /calcination loop, Chem. Eng. J., 137, 561-567.

International Energy Agency (IEA) GHG R&D Programme, 2013, High temperature solid looping cycles network, <www.iea.org>, accessed on 10.09.2013.

A. Johansson , F. Johnsson, B. Leckner, 2007, Solid back-mixing in CFB boilers, Chem. Eng. Sci., 62, 561-573.

D. Kunii, O. Levenspiel, 1997, Circulating fluidized-bed reactors, Chem.Eng.Sci., 52, 2471–82.

H.M. Kvamsdal, J.P. Jakobsen, K.A. Hoff, 2009, Dynamic modeling and simulation of a CO_2 absorber column for post-combustion CO_2 capture, Chem. Eng. Process, 48, 135–144.

N. Rodríguez,M. Alonso, J. C.Abanades, 2010, Experimental investigation of a circulating fluidized-bed reactor to capture CO_2 with CaO,AIChE J., 57, 1356–1366.

M. C. Romano, 2012, Modeling the carbonator of a Ca-looping process for CO_2 capture from power plant flue gas, Chem. Eng. Sci., 69, 257-269.

P. Peltola, J. Ritvanen, T. Tynjälä, T. Pröll, T. Hyppänen, 2013, One-dimensional modelling of chemical looping combustion in dual fluidized bed reactor system, International Journal of Greenhouse Gas Control, 16, 72-82.

Jiří Jaromír Klemeš, Petar Sabev Varbanov and Peng Yen Liew (Editors)
Proceedings of the 24th European Symposium on Computer Aided Process Engineering – ESCAPE 24
June 15-18, 2014, Budapest, Hungary.

Effect of Liquefaction Plant Performance and Location on the Cost of CO_2 Transport

Umer Zahid, Jinjoo An , Ung Lee, Chonghun Han *

School of Chemical and Biological Engineering, Seoul National University,Seoul 151-744, Korea.

chhan@snu.ac.kr

Abstract

Carbon capture and storage (CCS), a key technology for addressing global warming is in between demonstration to commercialization phase. Transportation of CO_2 is required since storage sites are not necessarily present under the source sites. Ships can be used for long distance transport of CO_2; liquefaction being a vital component in ship transportation. In this study, a state of art CO_2 liquefaction process has been designed by taking account of source facilities (i.e. post-combustion and pre-combustion). The proposed liquefaction process offers lower liquefaction energy requirement compared with other available literature. Three different scenarios for post-combustion and pre-combustion each have been studied on the basis of liquefaction plant location. The considered scenarios are categorized as: a) capture site, liquefaction plant and shipping terminal are located close to each other; b) capture site and liquefaction plant are far from shipping terminal; c) capture site is far from liquefaction plant and shipping terminal. Finally, an economic analysis is performed in order to evaluate the feasibility of CO_2 transport from source sites to ship loading terminal including liquefaction plant.

Keywords: CO_2 liquefaction, CO_2 transport, economic analysis.

1. Introduction

Based on the experience from LNG and LPG industry, ships can be used for long distance transport of CO_2. Ship transportation becomes important as it offers flexible routes between sources and sink sites. Also, many sources are located along the coasts and storage sites are often offshore. Currently, small size ships up to 1,500 m^3 are being used for CO_2 transport at (-27 °C, 16 bar). However, these small ships are not suitable for large-scale ship based transport of CO_2. Lower pressure is required for enlarged storage and ship tanks. Most of the recent studies were focused on specific ship transportation without taking account of the preceding pipeline and liquefaction section. Some of the studies included CO_2 liquefaction plants but resulted in high liquefaction energy leading to high costs. For example, Yoo et al. (2013) results correspond to liquefaction energy of 115 kWh/tCO_2; Aspelund and Jordal (2007) simulated the CO_2 liquefaction design resulting in liquefaction energy of 105 kWh/tCO_2. Also, most of the reference studies considered CO_2 source sites near loading terminal, which don't show the complete picture for the commercialized large scale CO_2 transport network. All the previous studies considered CO_2 source as post-combustion facility and none of the researches study about the CO_2 transport from a pre-combustion source facility. Moreover, none of the previous studies considered the optimum location of liquefaction plant. The objective of this paper is to develop liquefaction design by taking account of source facilities and decide its location based on specific scenario.

2. Liquefaction System

Liquefaction is a vital component for ship transportation of CO_2. There are basically two processes in practice to compress and liquefy CO_2 commercially. The first one is the low pressure process making use of an external refrigeration system to achieve the required cooling for condensation of the gaseous CO_2 after it is dried and compressed to about 17 bars. The second method to liquefy CO_2 is high pressure compression with free liquid expansion. This process uses self-refrigeration to liquefy the CO_2 that is compressed beyond the critical point. Once the CO_2 reaches the critical pressure (73.8 bar), it is cooled below its critical temperature (31.1 ^oC). It is then expanded adiabatically where approximately 50 % of the total expanded flow is liquefied, while the cold CO_2 vapor is returned back to the respective compression stage and is maintained in a closed, recycle loop. This study will stay focused on high compression with free liquid expansion process. The liquefaction processes in this study has been simulated by using the Aspen Plus® software. Soave Redlich Kwong (SRK) equation of state is used as a property method. Final liquid CO_2 specifications are set at -52 ^oC and 6.5 bars.

2.1. Liquefaction System for Post-Combustion Source

The base design studied in this work for CO_2 liquefaction from post combustion facility was proposed by Lee et al. (2012) which was a modified design from Aspelund and Jordal (2007). The basic theme of design is to compress CO_2 in four stages up to 52 bars with inter-cooling between each stage. The compressed CO_2 free from water and volatiles is then expanded through multi-stage Joule-Thompson valves to produce liquid CO_2 at -52 ^oC and 6.5 bars. At each expansion stage, cold CO_2 vapors are generated which after exchanging heat with incoming CO_2 are directed back to appropriate compression stage as shown in Figure 1. Two process heat exchangers are utilized for the purpose of heat transfer between cold CO_2 vapor and incoming high temperature CO_2. However, the design proposed by Lee et al. (2012) can be further modified and optimized in order to improve the liquefaction energy requirement. In the base-case design, there are two major approaches that can be applied to reduce the operating energy. First, the cold CO_2 vapor produced from last stage of expansion have pressure energy which can be extracted by using a turbo expander. Expansion through an expansion valve does not remove energy from the gas but moves the molecules father apart under the influence of intermolecular forces. On the other hand, an expansion through an expansion turbine can remove energy from the gas as an external work. Also, an isentropic expansion through an expander would always be the most effective means of lowering the temperature of a gas. Between any two given pressures, an isentropic expansion will always result in lower final temperature than will an isenthalpic expansion from the same temperature. Second, the process heat exchanger employed to exchange cold energy available from flashed CO_2 vapor can be optimized to improve the overall energy consumption of liquefaction process. The work input to compressor basically depends on two parameters, the compression ratio and the inlet temperature of the compressor. The higher the inlet temperature to compressor, the more work input is required. Therefore, it is necessary to utilize the cold energy available from the flashed CO_2 vapor at the right place in order to attain the least compressors work requirements. The result shows that in contrast to the base design liquefaction energy of 98.1 kWh kWh/tCO_2, the modified design has lower liquefaction energy requirement of 97.3 kWh/tCO_2.

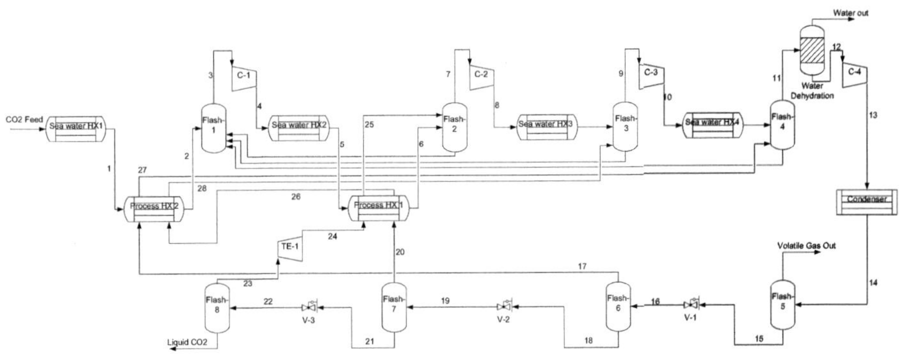

Figure 1. Flow Diagram for Post-combustion Source Liquefaction Process

2.2. *Liquefaction System for Pre-Combustion Source*

The flue gas temperature, pressure and composition from pre-combustion source facility differs from that of post combustion source in a way the CO_2 is captured at the capture plant. Pre combustion CO_2 capture often employs the physical solvent which on multiple recovery stages produces CO_2 streams at different pressure and temperature. Hence, a new liquefaction process for pre-combustion source facility is proposed in this study as shown in Figure 2. The temperature, pressure and composition of CO_2 feed streams are taken from the KRW gasification process. The KRW gasification process employs the glycol as a physical solvent for the removal of CO_2 from the flue gas. CO_2 can be recovered by flashing the rich solvent in three stages. The details of the process can be found in report by Doctor et al. (1997). Since the rich solvent is flashed in three stages for CO_2 recovery, the input to liquefaction system consists of three CO_2 streams at different thermodynamic conditions. The process description is similar to that for post-combustion source; however, the location of process heat exchangers is different in this process because of different CO_2 feed condition. The result shows that liquefaction energy of 71.89 kWh/tCO_2 is required for pre-combustion source facility.

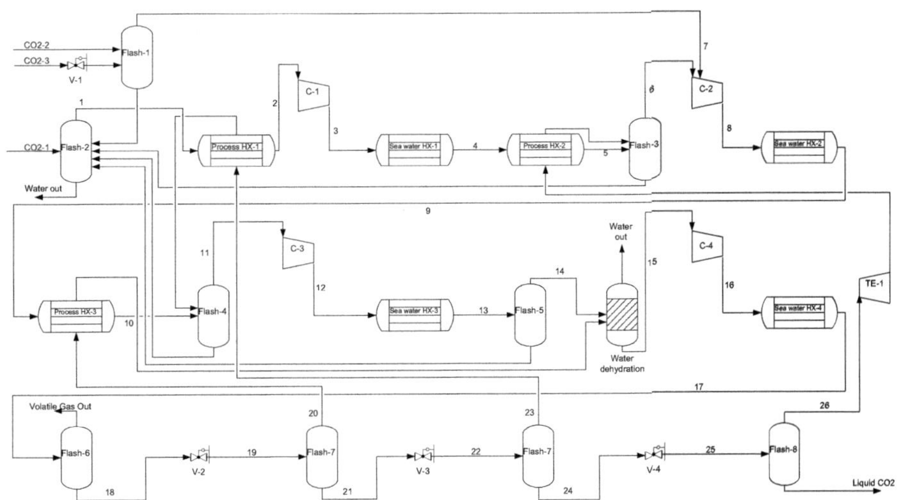

Figure 2. Flow Diagram for Pre-combustion Source Liquefaction Process

3. Transport Scenarios

The CO_2 transport scenarios in this work are based on the type of CO_2 source facility and location of liquefaction plant. The scope of CO_2 source facilities in this study is limited to post-combustion and pre-combustion type. The location of liquefaction plant is categorized in the following three cases as shown in Figure 3. In order to ensure a fair evaluation of analysis, a consistent and transparent methodology has been followed.

3.1. Case 1

Capture plant, liquefaction plant and intermediate storage are located near the ship loading terminal. This case assumes all the above mentioned facilities to be located near the sea shore where loading terminal is located. Captured CO_2 at the source site is sent to liquefaction plant present in the same location. Depending on the type of source facility (post-combustion or pre-combustion), CO_2 is liquefied by the process mentioned in previous section 2. It is then sent to storage tanks at the loading terminal site where liquefied CO_2 is stored till the ships come on their defined schedule.

3.2. Case 2

Capture and liquefaction plant are located far from the intermediate storage and ship loading terminal. In this case, capture unit and liquefaction plant are assumed to be close to each other but far from the loading terminal. The liquefied CO_2 at -52 °C and 6.5 bars is transported via insulated pipeline to the loading terminal where it is stored in intermediate storage tanks. Once liquefied, pumps can be used to transport liquid CO_2 through the pipeline to the loading terminal site. However, CO_2 pipeline transportation in liquid phase requires pipelines to be insulated and operating conditions should be well controlled in order to ensure safe pipeline operation. Although the pipeline is insulated, some heat influx leaks into the pipeline from the surroundings causing an increase in CO_2 temperature. In order to ensure no vapor formation and safe pipeline operation, a concept of re-chilling and pumping has been evaluated in this study for the transport of CO_2 in liquid phase.

3.3. Case 3

Capture plant is located far from the ship loading terminal, while liquefaction plant is located at ship loading terminal. In this case, CO_2 transport from capture plant to loading terminal site is done in supercritical phase. Captured CO_2 is compressed using multistage compressor to a pressure higher than 73.8 bars across supercritical region and then transported through a pipeline as shown in Figure 3. In this study, the compressed CO_2 is assumed to be delivered at liquefaction plant at 52 bars and 15 °C. The high pressure CO_2 can then be liquefied by expansion in three stages. The CO_2 vapor produced at each expansion stage is sent for recompression at the appropriate pressure.

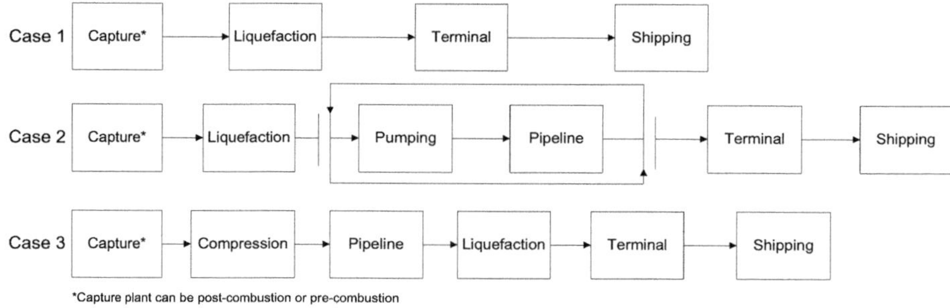

Figure 3. Transport Chains Based on the Liquefaction Plant Location

4. Results and Discussions

4.1. Economics

The cost of transporting CO_2 for different cases has been calculated by using information on both the capital investment and operation cost from a number of references available in literature. The economic depreciation was assumed to be 5 % over a project of 30y. Three different transport capacities of 1Mt, 5Mt and 10Mt have been selected for the transport distance of up to 500 km. Figure 4 shows the cost results for different transport scenarios based on the type of capture facility and liquefaction plant location as described in above cases. Zero distance along the horizontal axis represents the case 1 result in which capture facility and liquefaction plant are located near the loading terminal site. As the transport distance increases, the transport cost for smaller capacities increase significantly compared with larger capacities. The results showed that increasing transport capacity for a certain distance decreases the unit cost. However, increasing the distance for certain capacity increases the unit cost.

4.2. Liquefaction Plant Location Decision

The location of liquefaction plant can be decided on the basis of amount of CO_2 to be transported and distance. Figure 5a and 5b show the cost comparison between case 2 and case 3 for post-combustion and pre-combustion capture facilities respectively for different capacities. The CO_2 transport in liquid phase offers low cost for short distances, however after certain distance supercritical transport may become more economical. In other words, it is better to locate liquefaction plant near capture facility for short transport distances and smaller capacities to be transported. On the other hand, locating liquefaction plant near storage and loading terminal is beneficial for larger distances and higher capacities.

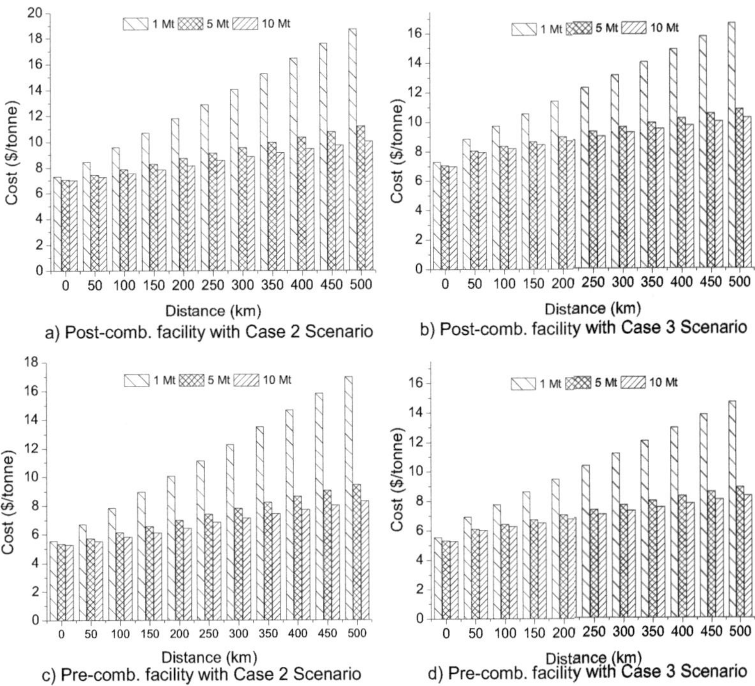

Figure 4. Cost Analysis for Various Transport Scenarios

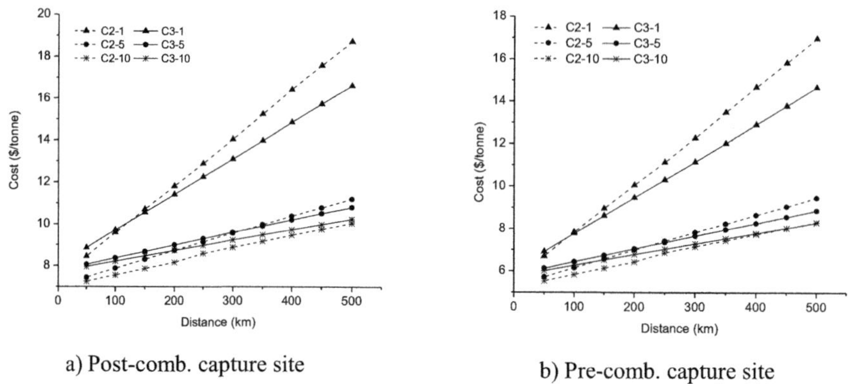

a) Post-comb. capture site

b) Pre-comb. capture site

Figure 5. Cost Comparison for Deciding Liquefaction Plant Location

5. Conclusions

Liquefaction processes are designed for captured CO_2 from post-combustion and pre-combustion source facilities. The liquefaction energy of 97.3 and 71.89 per kWh/tCO_2 is required for post-combustion and pre-combustion sources respectively. These liquefaction processes are then integrated with various transport scenarios to study the optimum location of the liquefaction plant.

Acknowledgment

This research was supported by the second phase of the Brain Korea 21 Program in 2013, Institute of Chemical Processes in Seoul National University, Energy Efficiency & Resources Development of the Korea Institute of Energy Technology Evaluation and Planning (KETEP) grant funded by the Ministry of Knowledge Economy (MKE) and grant from the LNG Plant R&D Center funded by the Ministry of Land, Transportation and Maritime Affairs (MLTM) of the Korean government.

References

A. Aspelund, K. Jordal, 2007, Gas conditioning- The interface between CO_2 capture and transport, International Journal of Greenhouse Gas Control, 1, 3, 343-354.

B. Y. Yoo, D. K. Choi, H. J. Kim, Y. S. Moon, H. S. Na, S. G. Lee, 2013, Development of CO_2 terminal and CO2 carrier for future commercialized CCS market, International Journal of Greenhouse Gas Control, 12, 323-332.

R. D. Doctor, J. C. Molburg, P. R. Thimmapuram, 1997, Oxygen-blown gasification combined cycle: carbon dioxide recovery, transport, and disposal, Energy conversion and management, 38, S575-S580.

U. Lee, S. Yang, Y. S. Jeong, Y. Lim, C. S. Lee, C. Han, 2012, Carbon Dioxide Liquefaction Process for Ship Transportation, Industrial and Engineering Chemistry Research, 51, 46, 15122-15131.

Jiří Jaromír Klemeš, Petar Sabev Varbanov and Peng Yen Liew (Editors)
Proceedings of the 24th European Symposium on Computer Aided Process Engineering – ESCAPE 24
June 15-18, 2014, Budapest, Hungary.

Optimal Control Strategies for Wastewater Stabilization Ponds

María P. Ochoa, Vanina Estrada, Patricia M. Hoch*

Universidad Nacional del Sur, Chemical Engineering Department, Planta Piloto de Ingeniería Química, 8000 Bahía Blanca, Argentina

p.hoch@plapiqui.edu.ar

Abstract

In this work, we address the control problem of wastewater stabilization ponds by formulating an optimal control problem considering electrical motor power for mixers and nutrient addition rate as control variables (degrees of freedom of the problem). Nitrogen and phosphorus are the added nutrients. Constraints are embedded in the DAE model and boundaries on the control variables. As the specification on biochemical oxygen demand (BOD) in the outlet stream is far from the target one, the objective is to minimize the offset between the desired value and the current one, along a time horizon of a year. As a result of the dynamic optimization problem the optimal time profiles of motor power and nutrient addition rates (phosphorus and nitrogen) are obtained for the time horizon of a year, while the BOD is kept below the required level.

Keywords: Optimal Control, Stabilization Ponds, Wastewater Treatment.

1. Introduction

There are impacts on freshwater and coastal ecosystems associated to urban and industrial growth, and wastewater treatment processes are key to minimize their major adverse effects. Currently, activated sludge processes are the most widely used biological processes for sites where the size of land is an issue. Stabilization ponds, in turn, are large lagoons where wastewater is stored for long periods to allow a wide range of microorganisms to break down organic matter and sludge is not returned. These systems have not received great attention in literature, yet they are widely used. To highlight a few characteristics of these ponds, they present aerobic, facultative and anaerobic zones, and different chemical and biochemical processes take place within the different zones. Relationships between microalgae, heterotrophic bacteria and fungi are taken into account, which greatly influence the pond efficiency in biological wastewater treatment. We present the formulation of a detailed mechanistic model for a system of three stabilization ponds in series (two aerobic and one facultative) for control purposes within a control vector parameterization framework (PSEnterprise, 2011).

Waste stabilization ponds or lagoons offer the simplest solution for treatment of wastewater streams and are widely used in developing countries especially in rural areas. Wastewater treatment in stabilization ponds mainly results from settling and complex symbiosis of bacteria and algae where the oxidation of organic matter is accomplished by bacteria in presence of dissolved oxygen supplied by algal photosynthesis and surface re-aeration (Kargi, 2005). The major aim of wastewater treatment is to convert the waste materials into stable oxidised end products which can be safely discharged to inland or coastal waters without any adverse ecological effect. The quality of the final effluent and its volume determine the unit processes selected in the design of a wastewater treatment plant (Gray, 2004).Dynamic optimization of large size waste water treatment plants constitutes a great challenge because of the complexity of the biological process, with a heavy computational burden, and its large variations of influent in flow rate and composition. Contributions regarding dynamic optimization of wastewater treatment ponds are scarce (Luo and Biegler, 2011).

In the present work, we address the formulation of a detailed mechanistic model of a system of aerobic and facultative ponds in series, based on first principles of mass conservation. Dynamics mass balances for biomass, nutrients, dissolved oxygen and biochemical oxygen demand concentrations are formulated. The most relevant parameters of the developed model were calibrated in a previous work (Iturmendi et al. 2012) from experimental data provided by an apple and pear juice plant in Villa Regina (Argentina). It allows representing the process dynamics to be used in estimating the effluent quality under different operating conditions. Furthermore, an optimal control problem is formulated taking the engine power of the aerators' motors and nutrient dosage rate as control variables. The main objective is the minimization of the offset between the desired and real value of the biochemical oxygen demand along the time horizon of a year. Numerical results provide useful information about the complex relationships between microorganism, nutrients and organic matter concentration, as well as the optimal operation of the pond's systems.

2. Model Stabilisation Ponds

Stabilisation ponds are generally classified by the type of biological activity in anaerobic lagoon, aerobic lagoon and oxidation pond, within the latter one there are facultative pond, maturation pond, high-rate algal lagoon and Purification Lake.The main biological processes that take place in these lagoons are:

Organic matter oxidation due to respiration of aerobic bacteria.

$$C_6H_{14}O_2N + 3.35\ O_2 \rightarrow 0.12\ NH_4^+ + 0.12\ OH^- + 1.6\ CO_2 + 0.88\ C_5H_7NO_2 + 3.62\ H_2O$$

Photosynthetic oxygen production performed by algae.

$$106\ CO_2 + 16\ NH_4^+ + HPO_4^{-2} + 100\ H_2O \xrightarrow{\text{(sunlight)}} C_{106}H_{263}O_{110}N_{16}P + 103\ O_2 + 2\ H^+$$

Anaerobic digestion of organic matter.

$$CHONS + H_2O \rightarrow CH_4 + CO_2 + C_5H_7NO_2 + NH_3 + H_2S + Q$$

Factors as organic load, degree of mixing, pH, nutrients availability, solar radiation and temperature determine the biomass predomination in the different zones of the lagoons. The model takes into account dynamic mass balances of the main groups of phytoplankton: cyanobacteria (C), diatom (D) and chlorophyta (G), bacteria (B), yeast (Y), nitrate (NO_3), ammonium (NH_4), phosphate (PO_4), organic phosphorous (OP) and nitrogen (ON), dissolved oxygen (DO) and biochemical oxygen demand (BOD). This results in a complex system of differential and algebraic equations. However, homogeneous conditions are supposed in the aerobic lagoon due to the aerators, whereas two horizontal layers describe the facultative pond. Balances include inlet and outlet flows, generation, consumption, transfer between layers and volume variation terms.

$$\frac{dC_{Uj}}{dt} = \frac{Q_{IN}}{V_U} C_{IN_{Uj}} - \frac{Q_{OUT}}{V_U} C_{Uj} + r_{Uj} - \frac{k_d A}{\Delta h\, V_U}\left(C_{Uj} - C_{Lj}\right) - \frac{C_{Uj}}{h_U}\frac{dh_U}{dt} \tag{1}$$

$$\frac{dC_{Lj}}{dt} = r_{Lj} + \frac{k_d A}{\Delta h\, V_U}\left(C_{Uj} - C_{Lj}\right) \tag{2}$$

j= C, D, G, B, Y, NO_3, NH_4, PO_4, OP, ON, DO, BOD.

Where *C* represents the concentration of *j* component in the upper (*U*) an lower (*L*) layer, Q_{in} and Q_{out} represent the inlet and outlet flow respectively, r_{Uj} and r_{Lj} correspond to net generation of j in each layer, k_d is the diffusion rate between layers, *h* is the water column height, *A* is the pond transversal area, *V* is the pond volume, Δh is the sum of the middle height of each layer. An overall mass balance is also formulated, where contributions of rain (Q_{rain}) and evaporation (Q_{evap}) are considered.

$$\frac{dh_T}{dt} = \frac{1}{A}\left(Q_{in} - Q_{out} + Q_{rain} - Q_{evap}\right) \tag{3}$$

Where h_T is the total water column height. The external forcing functions for the model were temperature, solar radiation, precipitation, evaporation, inlet flow, inlet concentration of nitrogen and phosphorous. Sinusoidal functions were used to approximate them. Other algebraic equations correspond to generation and consumption of modelled biomass. They consider production and loss due to basal metabolism (respiration, excretion and natural mortality), settling and grazing (Estrada, 2008).

$$r_{ij} = R_{ij,growth} - R_{ij,met} - R_{ij,sett} - R_{ij,graz} \tag{4}$$

j= C, D, G, B, Y.
i= Upper layer, Lower layer.

Nutrients availability, temperature, pH and light intensity impact on biomass growth and are included thought limiting functions using a multiplicative model. This type of functions decrease the maximum growth rate by taking values between 0 and 1.

$$R_{ij,growth} = k_{ij,growth} f(T)_{ij} f(N)_{ij} f(pH)_{ij} f(I)_{ik} f(BOD)_{il} \tag{5}$$

j= C, D, G, B, Y. *k*= C, D, G.*l*= B.
i= Upper layer, Lower layer.

Physical, chemical and biochemical reactions are highly influenced by temperature. In general, organic matter degradation rate increases with temperature. On the other hand, light intensity plays a fundamental role in the photosynthetic activity. Steele's equation with Beer's law is used to model its effect though the water column depth.
Nutrient limitation is modelled in different ways depending on the type of biomass. Monod type kinetics is used to model internal phosphorous concentration as limiting nutrient for algae groups and to model ammonium concentration as limiting nutrient for yeast. In the case of bacterial growth, nutrient limitation is calculated using a Monod type kinetic and Liebig's "Law of the minimum" that the extent of growth is determined by the nutrient in least supply. Biochemical oxygen demand limits bacterial growth. It is also assumed to be a Monod type.

In addition, the pH in stabilization ponds tends to rise depending on the rate of phytoplankton's photosynthetic activity and utilization of bicarbonate ions. Its dependency of biomass growth is assumed to be a Monod type, except for yeast growth where an experimental equation is used. Biomass basal metabolism includes all internal processes that decrease biomass concentration. It is assumed to increase exponentially with temperature, following an Arrhenius' type behaviour.

3. Control Strategies

The main objective of a wastewater treatment plant is to keep the BOD concentration in the effluent at an acceptable level. This must be achieved without releasing an excessive amount of nutrients in the receptor body.

Wastewater treatment at insufficient nutrient levels often results in poor quality effluent. Generally, carbon adsorption rate is greater than other nutrients uptake rate leading to phosphorous and nitrogen deficiency in the biomass. This imbalance can only be overcome by increasing the concentration of these deficient nutrients. So, to operate the biological process, phosphorous and nitrogen must be added to the nutrient deficient wastewater (Lindblom, 2003). Nitrogen is added in the form of urea ($(NH_2)_2CO$). Urea dissolves slowly when diluted in water and ends up as ammonium and CO_2. Phosphorous is added in the form of NP granules. This salt consists of NH_4-N (14%), NO_3-N (12%) and PO_4-P (6%). Furthermore, the supply of oxygen provided by mechanical aerators is taken into account to ensure the necessary amount of oxygen. Oxygen transfer rate is assumed to be proportional to power engine of aerator's motors and inversely proportional to stabilization pond volume.

4. Dynamic Optimisation: Optimal Control

We consider processes described by mixed differential and algebraic equations of the form:

$$f((x(t), \dot{x}(t), y(t), u(t), v) = 0 \qquad (6)$$

Here $x(t)$ and $y(t)$ are the differential and algebraic variables in the model while $\dot{x}(t)$are the time derivatives of the$x(t)$ (i.e.,$\dot{x}(t) = dx/dt$). $u(t)$ are the control variables and v the time invariant parameters to be determined by the optimisation (PSEnterprise, 2011).Dynamic optimisation seeks to determine the values of the time invariant parameters, v, and the time variation of the control variables, $u(t)$, over the entire time horizon so as to minimise the final value of a single variable z.

$$z = \int_0^{t_f} (C_{BOD} - C_{BOD\ setpoint})^2\, dt \qquad (7)$$

We have formulated a dynamic optimisation problem in an equation oriented control vector parameterization environment. In this approach, control variables (degrees of freedom that are time dependent, if any) are approximated by piecewise-constant, piecewise linear or, in general, polynomial functions, over a specified number of control intervals, and optimization parameters (time independent degrees of freedom, like parameters in a parameter estimation problem) are also approximated. Therefore, an NLP is formulated at the outer level, with coefficients of these polynomials (if any) and parameters as optimization variables. In the inner level, with fixed values for parameters, there are no degrees of freedom and the differential algebraic equations

(DAE) system can be integrated with a BDF (Backward Differentiation Formulae) strategy, with sparse matrix techniques in the DASOLV routine. At this step, also the partial derivatives of differential and algebraic equations with respect to the optimization variables (parameters to be estimated) have to be determined along the integration horizon. They are obtained by integrating the sensitivity equations, along with the original DAE system. Information on objective function, constraints and sensitivities (the gradients of the constraints and the objective function with respect to parameters to be estimated at each instant of time) is transferred to the external NLP problem, in which parameter values are updated in the NLP and new values for parameters are proposed to proceed with the inner DAE system solution.

5. Numerical Results

In this section, results of the optimal control are presented. Our main objective is to minimise BOD concentration in the effluent. In Figure 1(a) are shown the inlet and outlet BOD concentration of the system of 3 lagoons, whereas in Figure 1(b) the same variables are presented after implementing the control strategies.

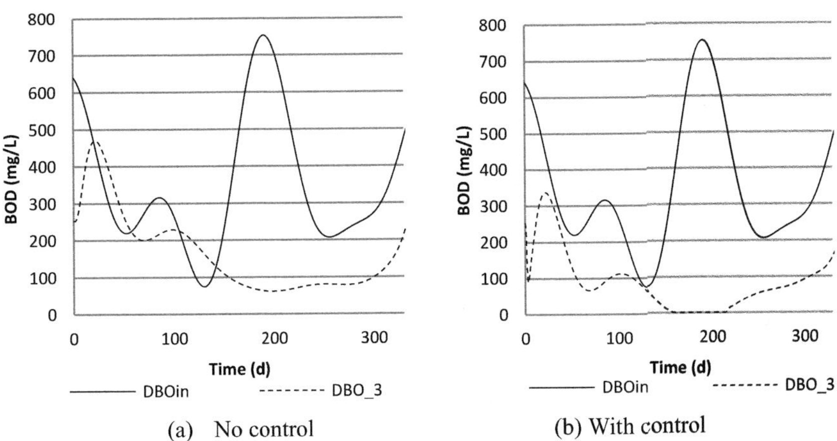

Figure1. Biochemical Oxygen Demand concentration: inlet stream (in), outlet stream the facultative pond (3).

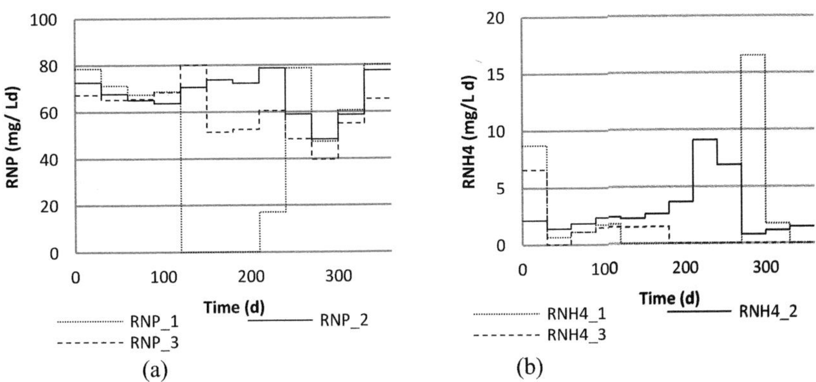

Figure 2. (a) NP dosage rate profiles. (b) Ammonium dosage rateprofiles.

The optimal dosage rate profiles are shown in Fig 2 for the three lagoons. Aerator motor power's profiles are not shown but results indicate that they must operate at maximum power.

Peak on inlet BDO at approximately t=200 is due to the higher amount of organic contents of the plant effluent at such time, which corresponds to summertime. Strategies are being developed to increment the size of the treatment facility in order to keep this value at a lower level.

6. Conclusions

We presented the formulation of a detailed mathematical mechanistic model for a system of stabilization ponds for control purposes within a control vector parameterization framework, obtaining optimal profiles for the control variables: motor power and nutrient addition rates. The model parameters are found for a system of stabilization ponds within an industrial facility of juice production. The amount of organic waste in the effluents of the plant requires an optimal control strategy for nutrient addition and mixing in the aerobic lagoons.

Numerical results provide useful information on the complex relationship among microorganisms, nutrients and organic matter concentration, as well as optimal management of the system of ponds. Another aerobic lagoon could allow for lowering this value. It is worth pointing out that the outlet BDO from the system is always lower than the inlet BDO after implementing the control strategies, as expected. It is suggested that agitators operate at maximum power all the time, while optimal profiles of nutrient inlet flow rates that minimize the DBO have been found for a time horizon of one year.

References

A. Alvarado, M. Vesvikar, J.F. Cisneros, T. Maere, P. Goethals, I. Nopens, 2013, CFD study to determine the optimal configuration of aerators in a full-scale waste stabilization pond, Water Research, 47, 13, 4528-4537.

D. Dochain, S. Gregoire, A. Pauss, M. Schaegger, 2003, Dynamic modelling of a waste stabilization pond, Bioprocess and Biosystems Engineering, 26, 19–26.

V.G. Estrada, E. Parodi, M.S. Diaz, 2008, Developing a Lake Eutrophication Model and Determining Biogeochemical Parameters: A Large Scale Parameter Estimation Problem, Computer Aided Chemical Engineering, 25, 1113-1119.

N.F. Gray, 2004, Biology of wastewater treatment, World Scientific Publishing Company, Ireland.

F. Iturmendi, V.G. Estrada, M.P. Ochoa, P.M Hoch, M.S. Diaz, 2012, Biological Wastewater Treatment: Dynamic Global Sensitivity Analysis and Parameter Estimation in a System of Waste Stabilization Ponds, Computer Aided Chemical Engineering, 30, 212-217.

F. Kargi, B. Beran, 2005, A dynamic mathematical model for wastewater stabilization ponds, Ecological Modelling, 181, 39-57.

S. Kayombo, T.S.A. Mbwette, A.W. Mayo, J. Katima, S.E. Jorgensen, 2000, Modelling diurnal variation of dissolved oxygen in waste stabilization ponds, Ecol. Modelling, 127, 21–31.

Lalzad, 2007, An Overview of Global Water Problems and Solutions, London, UK.

E. Lindblom, 2003, Dynamic modelling of nutrient deficient wastewater treatment processes, Master Tesis, Dept Ind. Electrical Engineering and Automation, Lund University, Sweden.

J. Lou, L. Biegler, 2011, Dynamic Optimization of Aeration Operations for a Benchmark Wastewater Treatment Plant, Proceedings of the 18th IFAC World Congress, Milan, Italy, 14189-14194.

J.G. Manga, R. Molinares Nelson, E. Orlando Soto, J. Arrieta, J. Escaf Germa, A. Hernandez Gustavo, 2004, Influence of inlet-outlet structures on the flow pattern of a waste stabilization pond, Proceedings 6th International Conference of Waste Stabilization Ponds, Avignon, France.

PSEnterprise, 2011, gPROMS User guide, Process Systems Enterprise Limited, London, UK.

A.N. Shilton, D.D. Mara, 2005, CFD (computational fluid dynamics) modelling of baffles for optimizing tropical waste stabilization pond system, Water Science and Technology, 51,103–106.

Jiří Jaromír Klemeš, Petar Sabev Varbanov and Peng Yen Liew (Editors)
Proceedings of the 24th European Symposium on Computer Aided Process Engineering – ESCAPE 24
June 15-18, 2014, Budapest, Hungary.

Decision Support System for Effective Use of Woody and Herbaceous Biomass

Yasuto Kawashima, Shinji Hasebe*

Department of Chemical Engineering, Kyoto University, Katsura Campus, Nishikyo-ku, Kyoto 615-8510 JAPAN
hasebe@cheme.kyoto-u.ac.jp

Abstract

As the available biomass depends on the region, the best process structure processing the biomass also depends on the region. This suggests the importance of the decision support system which can easily be used by researchers who are not familiar with the optimization. By taking the above point into account, a support system which can derive the best biomass processing system is developed. In the proposed support system, biomass transformation processes comprising the total system, such as the harvesting, drying and chipping of biomass and various final transformation processes of biomass, are modelled in advance as individual modules. Then, as a combination of these modules, a site superstructure is generated. Site superstructures are assigned to all locations which are candidates of biomass generation area, depot, and transformation processes, and unavailable modules are removed from the site superstructure. By assigning the transportation cost among the sites, the total site superstructure can be obtained. If the generation rate of biomass and the demands depend on the season, a multi-period superstructure is generated by duplicating the total site superstructure. Finally, the optimization problem formulated as MILP is solved to derive the best system. By adopting such a hierarchical structure, the engineer can easily combine the site superstructures to make an original model which is adequate for the problem. The developed system has been applied to the design problem of a biomass processing system of the local area in a prefecture of Japan, and the effectiveness of the system was validated through case studies.

Keywords: Biomass, process synthesis, facility location problem, superstructure.

1. Introduction

Dominant features of a biomass processing system are the diversity of the biomass resources and their wide distributions. Thus, the selection of raw material is one of the decision variables. Not to use the biomass at some area may be the best result when considering the harvesting and transportation costs. Furthermore, the best combination of products and the types of transformation processes and their locations are treated as decision variables, and the problem of finding the best biomass processing system is formulated as a combination of the supply chain design, process synthesis, and facility location problems. From that viewpoint, many researchers have discussed the supply chain problems as well as the problems of the effective use of biomass. Tatsiopoulos and Tolis (2003) proposed a model of the cotton biomass supply chain. Dunnett et al. (2007) adopted the state task network to model the supply chain and embedded the period-specific harvest tasks in the formulation. For the synthesis and design problems of biorefineries, Kokossis and Yang (2010) stressed the importance of systematic approach. Bowling et al. (2011) discussed the optimal production planning and facility placement problems of a biorefinery, and considered the nonlinear economy-of-scale behaviour of the capital cost. Kim et al. (2011) discussed the biomass supply chain for biofuels under uncertainty. Lam et al. (2013) used a P-graph for an open-structure biomass network synthesis. Most of the works however treat a specific problem, and it is difficult for practical engineers to apply the proposed methods to their own problems. It is desirable that the engineers who face the real problems can model their own problem and solve it by themselves. Like a process simulator, if practical engineers can modify the combination of modules to fit their problem, the system can be applied to a wide range of problems. In this research, as a first step in the development of such a flexible system, a module-based modelling procedure is proposed. In addition, it is demonstrated that the problem of finding the desirable biomass processing system is formulated by hierarchically combining the processing modules and superstructures.

2. Problem description

2.1. Given data and design variables

In this research, the problem optimizing the allocation of biomass transformation processes and the supply chain of biomasses is treated. The following data are assumed to be given in advance.

1. Districts of biomass generation, and the available amount of each biomass,
2. Locations of sites available for depot and biomass transformation processes,
3. Types of transformation processes assignable to each site, and their fixed and operational costs,
4. Transportation costs among the districts supplying biomass and the depot, and those among the depot and the site of the transformation process.

When seasonal variation is discussed, some of the parameters mentioned above take different values at different seasons. In this case, storage costs are also assigned to each material.

The following are decision variables used to derive the optimal biomass system.

1. Amount of each biomass supplied from biomass generation district to depot,
2. Amount of each biomass transferred from depot to processing site, and among the processing sites,
3. Processing modules which are adopted at the processing site, and their production capacities.

When seasonal variation is discussed, season-related variables are optimized as a function of the seasons. In such a case, the production rate of each module is optimized seasonally under the constraint of production capacity. By the changes of production rate, the amount of storage of each material is also changed.

2.2. Biomass and transformation processes

There are many types of woody and herbaceous biomasses, such as lumber from thinning at the forest, saw dust and rice straw. And for each of those biomasses, various transformation processes have been developed. In this study, to make the explanation clearer, only the biomasses and their transformation processes which are used in Section 5 are explained. It is possible to add new types of biomasses and processes without changing the structure of the problem formulation.

Lumber from thinning remaining in cedar and cypress forests and the wood pieces spun off in a lumber mill are taken up in this research. The moisture rate depends on the biomass type. As the transformation processes, gasfication cogeneration system, direct combustion generation, and ethanol production are discussed. To supply biomass to these processes, chipping and drying are necessary for some cases, so chipping and drying are also regarded as transformation processes.

3. Mathematical formulation

3.1. Process flows

There are two types of expressions on the stream. One way is to use a vector, the component of which is the flow rate of each material or energy. The other way is to distinguish the flows one by one if the compositions are different. In the former expression, the mixing of two flows can be treated as a simple addition of the vectors. But the expression of flow split becomes non-linear. In the latter expression, though the flow split can be treated by simple equation, a large number of flows must be defined when a precise model is requested. In this study, the mixing of flows seldom appears because the materials treated in the research are solid. Thus, the latter method is adopted. There are some restrictions on the input and output flows of each transformation process. To consider such restrictions, all the flows are classified by wood species, moisture rate, bulk density and size. As the combinations of these types, a variety of flows appears in the biomass processing systems. In addition to the flow of biomasses, electricity, steam and CO2 are also used in the problem formulation.

3.2. Processing modules

The performance of the transformation process depends on the input flows and the capacity. When the relationship among the input, $\boldsymbol{x}^i$, and output, $\boldsymbol{y}^i$, of a process is expressed by Eq.(1), it is treated as a module (module *i*). Many modules are generated from one transformation process.

$$\boldsymbol{y}^i = \mathrm{A}^i \boldsymbol{x}^i + \delta^i \boldsymbol{b}^i \tag{1}$$

where A^i and $\boldsymbol{b}^i$ are parameter matrix and vector, respectively. δ^i is a zero-one variable which takes 1 when module *i* is used. The dimensions of $\boldsymbol{x}^i$ and $\boldsymbol{y}^i$ are N^i_{in} and N^i_{out}, respectively.

In many cases, Eq.(1) is valid for a limited range of input flow. So, the restrictions on the lower bound, $\delta^i c^i_{\min}$, and the upper bound, $\delta^i c^i_{\max}$, are added to the capacity of module *i*, C^i (Eq.(2)).The total amount of input is restricted by the capacity of the module, and the relationship is expressed by Eq.(3).

$$\delta^i c^i_{\max} \geq C^i \geq \delta^i c^i_{\min} \tag{2}$$

$$\sum_{k=1}^{N^i_{\mathrm{in}}} e^i_k x^i_k \leq C^i \tag{3}$$

where x^i_k is the *k*-th element of $\boldsymbol{x}^i$, and e^i_k is the predetermined coefficient.

4. Superstructure of Biomass Processing System

4.1. Site Superstructure and Total Site Structure

There are many trade-off relationships among the assignment of modules to site. For example, if the chipping operation is executed at the depot, the bulk density is increased and as a result the transportation cost can be decreased. Similarly, if the drying operation is executed at the depot, the transportation cost decreases because of the decrease of the weight of biomass. However, these operations at the depot require smaller processes, whose efficiencies are worse than those of larger plants. To discuss the trade-off between the distributed and concentrated processing, the superstructure having all processing function is allocated to all of the candidate sites of biomass generation, depot and processes. An example of the site superstructure is shown in Figure 1.

Various modules are prepared for each type of transformation process. For example, when the moisture rates of product biomass are different, these drying process are regarded as different modules. Thus, a box in the figure expresses the set of modules whose processing types are the same, and the arrow between the boxes expresses the set of material flows. The generation of biomass is treated as a module, and it does not have input flows. The final transformation processes such as the ethanol production do not have output flows.

The site superstructure has two characteristic modules: storage and transportation. The output of each module does not become the input of other processes but the input of the storage module, and the input of each process comes from the storage module. As explained above, each process consists of many similar modules, the outputs of which are the same. Figure 2 shows the case where the outputs of five modules are connected with the inputs of five other modules. By introducing the storage module, the number of flows in the superstructure can be drastically reduced as shown in the bottom of Figure 2. The transportation module connects a site superstructure to other site superstructures. For each material, the transportation costs between the sites are formulated by this module. By assigning the transportation cost among the sites, the total site superstructure can be obtained. If the generation rate of biomass and the demands do not depend on the season, the total site superstructure can be used for optimization.

4.2. Multi-period Superstructure

The growing rate of herbaceous biomass depends on the seasons, and some transportation routes may not be able to be used in the winter season. In such cases, a multi-period superstructure is generated by duplicating the total site superstructure. In this case, the operating rate of each facility is treated as a function of seasons, though the production capacity of each operation does not depend on the season. The storage unit works effectively to formulate the problem, i.e., the amount of storage at the end of

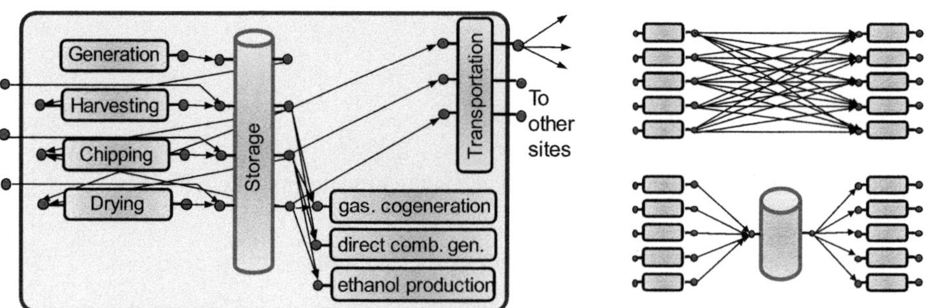

Figure 1. Site superstructure

Figure 2. Role of storage module

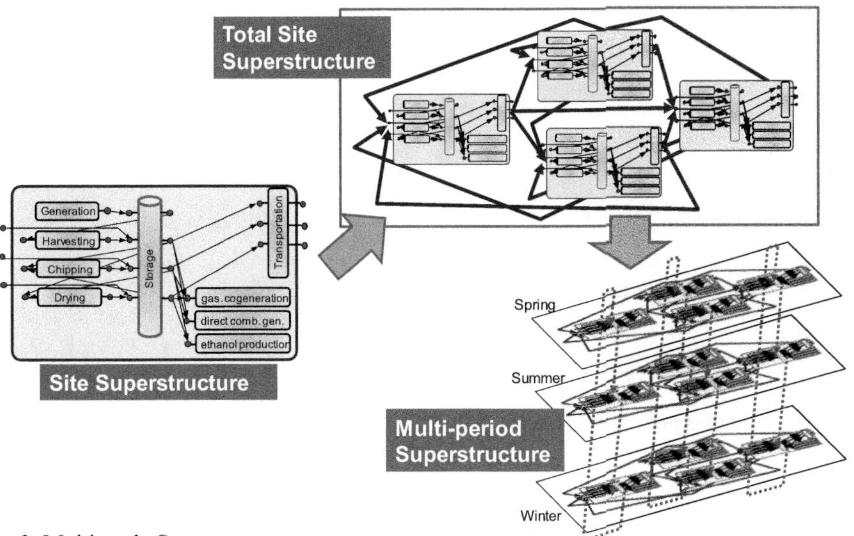

Figure 3. Multi-scale Superstructures

a season is transferred to the same storage unit of the next season, and is treated as the initial amount of storage. Three levels of superstructures are shown in Figure 3. The extension from the total site superstructure to the multi-period superstructure just adds the flows between the storage modules. In the multi-period superstructure in Figure 3, the periodic boundary condition is adopted in the formulation of the multi-period problem.

5. Case studies

The developed system has been applied to the design problem of a biomass processing system of an area of the Yamaguchi prefecture in Japan. As the final transformation processes, gasfication cogeneration system, direct combustion generation, and ethanol production are taken, and the chipping and drying processes are also embedded in the model. It is assumed that the wood pieces spun off in a lumber mill can be used at all processes without executing the chipping and drying operations. It is also assumed that the production cost of the ethanol highly depends on the capacity, i.e., the production at smaller plant is ineffective. The data of biomass was obtained from the Statistics handbook of forests and forestry at Yamaguchi prefecture (Forest Planning Division, 2009).

Two case studies have been executed: A derivation of the most economical system and the derivation of an environmentally benign system. For deriving the latter system, 10^4 times higher penalty is assigned to the emission of CO_2. The results are shown in Figure 4. Sites A to F are biomass generation areas, and sites G to J are candidates where transformation processes are assigned. Arrows indicate the transfer roots obtained from the optimization system, and simple lines are routes which have not been selected.

For the case of maximizing the profit, relatively small gasfication cogeneration systems were assigned to sites G, H and J. For the site generating a large amount of biomass, the chipping and drying operations were executed at that site. By increasing the penalty of CO_2 emission, the structure was changed to the right-side graph in Figure 4. In this

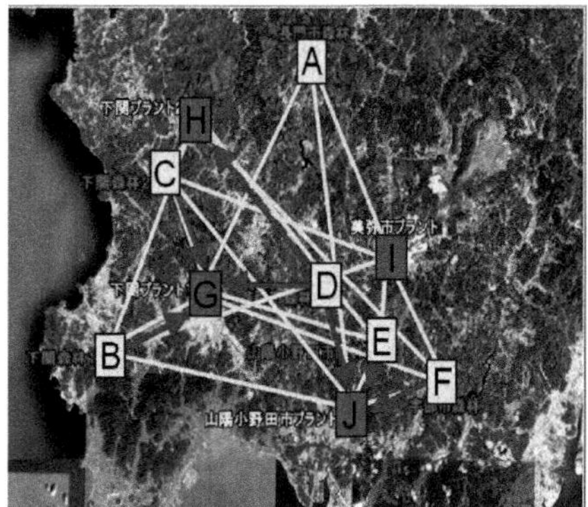

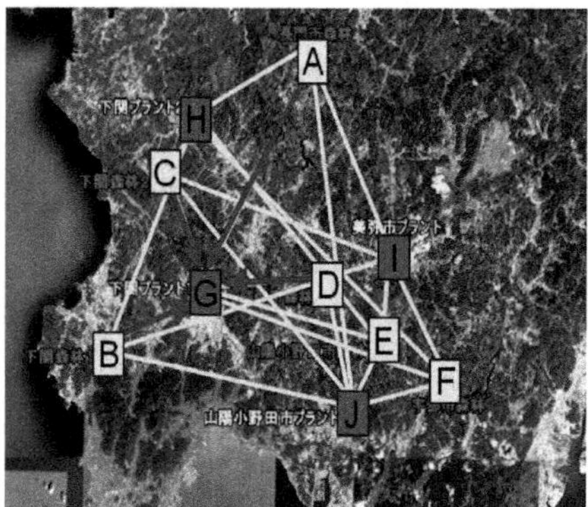

Figure 4. Biomass processing system (Left: Profit maximum, Right: CO2 generation minimum)

result, the biomasses having high moisture rate were not used at any sites so as to reduce the CO_2 emission from the drying processes. By constructing a large ethanol plant, cost merit can be obtained.

6. Conclusions

A decision support system for effective use of woody and herbaceous biomass has been proposed. The proposed system consists of three layers: site superstructure, total site superstructure and multi-period superstructure. The key feature is that the site superstructure is the template of the processes which execute various types of processing. Thus, by constructing the site superstructure in advance, the system can be applied to a wide range of problems. By introducing the storage module in the site superstructure, the number of variables in the problem can be drastically reduced. The storage module is also effective when a multi-period problem is discussed. The model of a multi-period problem can easily be derived by duplicating the total site superstructure and the addition of the material balance equations around the storage modules. The effectiveness of the proposed system was verified by case studies. Future work includes the development of a good human-machine interface and the application of relatively large multi-period problems.

References

I. P. Tatsiopoulos, A. J. Tolis, 2003, Economic aspects of the cotton-stalk biomass logistics and comparison of supply chain methods, Biomass and Bioenergy, 24, 199-214.

A. Dunnett, C. Adjiman, N. Shah, 2007, Biomass to heat supply chains applications of process optimizations, Process Safety and Environmental Protection, 85, B4, 419-429.

A. C. Kokossis, A. Yang, 2010, On the use of systems technologies and a systematic approach for the synthesis and the design of future biorefineries, Comp. and Chem. Eng., 34, 1397-1405.

I. M. Bowling, J. M. Ponce-Ortega, M. M. El-Halwagi, 2011, Facility Location and Supply Chain Optimization for a Biorefinery, Ind. Eng. Chem. Res., 50, 6276-6286.

J. Kim, M. J. Realff, J. H. Lee, 2011, Optimal design and global sensitivity analysis of biomass supply chain networks for biofuels under uncertainty, Comp. and Chem. Eng., 35, 1738-1751.

H. L. Lam, J. J. Klemeš, P. S. Varbanov, Z. Kravanja, 2013, P-Graph Synthesis of Open-Structure Biomass Networks, Ind. Eng. Chem. Res., 52, 172-180.

Forest Planning Division at the Department of Agriculture, Forestry and Fisheries, Yamaguchi Prefecture (Edited), 2009, Statistics handbook of forestsand forestryat Yamaguchi prefecture for fiscal 2007.

Jiří Jaromír Klemeš, Petar Sabev Varbanov and Peng Yen Liew (Editors)
Proceedings of the 24th European Symposium on Computer Aided Process Engineering – ESCAPE 24
June 15-18, 2014, Budapest, Hungary.

Mathematical Modelling of Coal and Biomass Gasification: Comparison on the Syngas H_2/CO Ratio under Different Operating Conditions

Michele Corbetta,[a] Flavio Manenti,[a,*] Fiona Soares,[b] Zohreh Ravaghi-Ardebili,[a] Eliseo Ranzi,[a] Carlo Pirola,[c] Guido Buzzi-Ferraris,[a] Sauro Pierucci[a]

[a] *Politecnico di Milano, Dipartimento di Chimica, Materiali e Ingegneria Chimica "Giulio Natta", Piazza Leonardo da Vinci 32, 20133 Milano, Italy*
[b] *INPT-ENSIACET, Génie des procédés, 4 allée Emile Monso 31000 Toulouse, France*
[c] *Università degli Studi di Milano, Dipartimento di Chimica, Via Golgi 13, 20133 Milano, Italy*
flavio.manenti@polimi.it

Abstract

Gasification is a thermo-chemical process aiming at the production of high heating value syngas, starting from a solid fuel such as biomass or coal. From a chemical point of view the process results in a partial oxidation by means of sub-stoichiometric air or oxygen and/or steam. According to the solid fuel used as a feedstock and to the operating parameters of the process, the quality and the chemical composition of the produced syngas is differently affected. This gas is mainly composed by carbon monoxide and hydrogen, while carbon dioxide, water, methane and small hydrocarbons are minor components. The final applications of syngas include the power generation and the production of chemicals, with special reference to methanol synthesis and Gas-to-Liquid technologies. For these last catalytic processes it is necessary to provide syngas with a specific H_2/CO ratio, and for this reason in the present work we apply our comprehensive mechanistic approach to the description of the gasification process, highlighting the sensitivity of the key operating parameters on syngas quality. Moreover a comparison between coal and biomass gasification is proposed, as well as the validation of the kinetic model with some experimental data.

Keywords: coal gasification, biomass gasification, detailed kinetics, syngas.

1. Introduction

The gasification of cheap solid fuels is gaining more attention, due to the possibility to efficiently exploit the calorific value of solid fuels in a greener fashion. Beyond the applications in the power generation field, the syngas produced from this kind of processes could provide an interesting platform for the production of fuels and chemicals with a lower environmental footprint. Actually, several Gas-to-Liquids technologies are available for the production of hydrocarbons (e.g. Fischer-Tropsch synthesis (Pirola et al., 2009)) and oxygenated chemicals (e.g. MeOH/DME synthesis, (Manenti et al., 2013)), and for these applications it is crucial to focus the attention on the quality of the syngas produced, mostly in terms of H_2/CO ratio. In fact the downstream catalytic processes need to be fed with a syngas with a proper composition, usually in the range of $H_2/CO \approx 1\text{-}2$. For this reason it is of utmost importance to be able to predict the performance of a gasifier, not only in terms of the overall efficiency but also in relation to the chemical characterization of the syngas produced. In this work we aim to describe a mathematical modeling approach, which is based on the solution of a multi-scale problem spanning from the particle scale up to the full reactor scale. The novelty of the proposed approach, on the contrary of a conventional thermodynamic and equilibrium approach (Emun et al., 2010), consists in a greater chemical detail of the pyrolysis and devolatilization process of coal and biomass, considering a large number of lumped tar and gas species. In fact, both for coal and biomass feedstocks a multi-step kinetic model for the pyrolysis of solid fuels was developed and embedded within the particle model, along with gas-solid reactions of char gasification and secondary gas-phase reactions of the released volatiles (Ranzi et al., 2013). The chemical evolution of the system is predicted with a mechanistic approach, and it is thus possible to infer the behavior of gasification units also in case of scarce experimental data availability. On the other hand, the mathematical model is applied to the case of coal and biomass gasification in order to find out the sensitivity of the system to the key operating parameters (e.g. oxygen/fuel and steam/fuel ratios, temperature, composition, etc.). An additional comparison is made between the responses of the two different kind of solid fuels keeping constant the geometry of the gasifier and the energy flux associated with the solid feed stream. With respect to coal gasification, biomass gasification occurs at lower temperatures, due to the higher reactivity of the feedstock. On the other hand biomass is more heterogeneous and difficult to characterize, leading to a demanding flexibility of reactors and processes. We also provide some comparisons of the model predictions with the experimental data on the available literature in order to validate the consistency of our approach for both biomass (Di Blasi et al., 1999) and coal (Grieco and Baldi, 2011) gasification.

2. Kinetic models

During the gasification process, the chemical evolution of the system has been described by means of detailed kinetic schemes for solid fuel devolatilization and pyrolysis, residual solid (char) gasification with steam, CO_2 and oxygen, and finally, secondary gas phase reactions, as outlined in Figure 1. At first, the solid fuel, either biomass or coal, is heated up until devolatilization and pyrolysis occur.

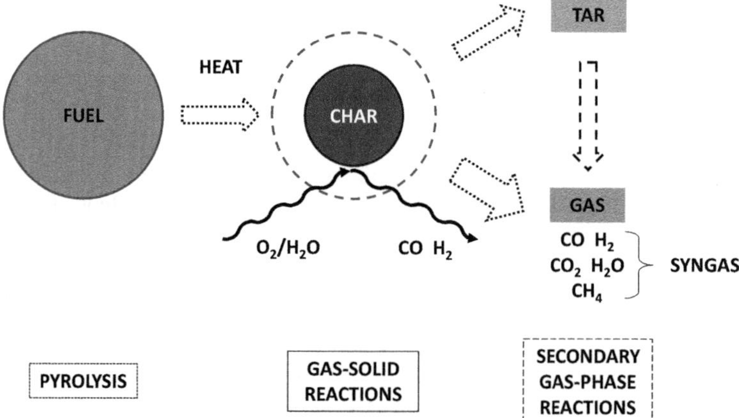

Figure 1. Solid fuel devolatilization and gasification. Pyrolysis: dotted box and arrows; Gas-solid reactions: solid box and arrows; secondary gas-phase reactions: dashed box and arrow.

During this first stage the solid fuel is progressively converted to three main product groups: light gases, tar species and a residual solid, mainly composed by ashes and char, with a residual content of volatiles trapped within the porous matrix (i.e. metaplastic phase). In the model this stage is described using the multi-step kinetics reported in (Ranzi et al., 2013) for biomass pyrolysis and in (Sommariva et al., 2011) for coal pyrolysis. For both kinetic schemes, the solid feedstock is characterized as a mixture of reference lumped species, for which first-order kinetics are provided. After this first step, the carbonaceous residual solid is partially subject to gas-solid gasification reactions with steam and oxygen, with the preferential production of carbon monoxide and hydrogen. Moreover, volatiles, especially heavy tar species, as soon as are released in the gas phase, are cracked to lighter gaseous species through gas-phase secondary reactions (Ranzi et al., 2012). A detailed kinetic scheme has been adopted, the POLIMI_1310, available on the creckmodeling.chem.polimi.it website. This kinetic scheme, including the pyrolysis and combustion of tar and oxygenated species and successive reactions of aromatic and polycyclic-aromatic species, involves more than 450 species and about 15,000 reactions.

3. Particle and reactor model

In order to model and simulate the gasification process, a suitable particle and reactor model is mandatory for the description of both kinetic and transport phenomena aspects. This lead to the solution of a multi-scale dynamic system, spanning from the description of kinetic and transport aspects at the particle scale, up to the description of mass and energy transfer as well as secondary reactions at the reactor scale (Ranzi et al., 2013). To further increase the complexity, the system is intrinsically multi-phase, due to the combined presence of a gas, liquid and solid phase, which can exchange mass and energy among themselves (Mettler et al., 2012). The structure of the system is outlined in Figure 2, where it is possible to highlight the presence of three main scales. At the particle scale, the system evolves along the radial coordinate, as well as through time.

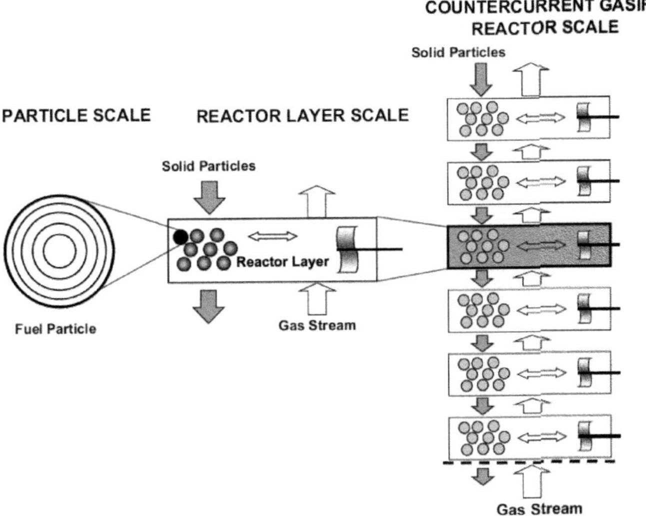

Figure 2. Multi-scale gasifier

The successive scale (elementary reactor layer) accounts for the coupling between isotropic solid particles with an external gas phase, considered homogeneous and perfectly mixed. Finally, at the reactor scale, several elementary reactor layers are adopted and interconnected to reproduce different reactor configurations. For instance the counter-current fixed bed gasifier (i.e. updraft) is reproduced through a cascade of elemental reactor layers. In this configuration, which has been selected for the successive studies below in the paper, the solid fuel is fed from the top of the reactor where it encounters a rising gas stream, fed from the bottom of the tower. During the residence within the gasifier, particles are progressively dried, pyrolyzed and gasified, leading to a residual solid stream withdrawn from the bottom and to a gas stream rich in hydrogen and carbon dioxide exiting from the top. The complete set of model equations is provided elsewhere (Ranzi et al., 2013).

4. Results

4.1. Validation of the model

The mathematical model has been validated with some available experimental data from the scientific literature, mainly in terms of gas composition (H_2/CO ratio).

4.2. Comparisons between coal and biomass gasification model predictions

Following the partial validation of the model, a comparison has been performed between coal and biomass gasification, keeping constant in the two case studies both the gasifier geometry and the inlet solid energy flux (in terms of heating value multiplied by the mass flowrate). For sake of conciseness, we report below (Figure 3) just the complete summary of the simulation of coal gasification, considering a reactor 4 m high with a section of 1 m^2, and a coal flowrate of 10,000 kg/h. In the following Table 2 we summarize the main results and comparisons between the two different simulations for coal and biomass gasification. In Table 2, cold gas efficiency (CGE) is considered as the heating value of the produced syngas at room temperature multiplied by its flowrate all divided by the heating value of the solid fuel multiplied by its flowrate.

$$CGE = \frac{\dot{m}_{SYNGAS} HHV_{SYNGAS}}{\dot{m}_{FUEL} HHV_{FUEL}} \tag{1}$$

Table 1. Comparison between coal (Grieco and Baldi, 2011) and biomass (Di Blasi et al., 1999) gasification experimental data; and model predictions

	Coal			***Biomass***		
	EXP	MODEL	Deviation	EXP	MODEL	Deviation
H_2/CO	0.58	0.70	-0.12	0.24	0.36	-0.12
CO_2	4.1 % dry	4.60	-0.54	7.0 % mol	8.2 % mol	-1.20
CH_4	1.4 % dry	0.00	1.30	1.8 % mol	2.0 % mol	-0.20

Table 2: Comparison between coal and biomass gasification

	Coal	***Biomass***
Fuel mass flowrate	10,000 kg/s	18,000 kg/s
H_2/CO	0.820	0.906
CGE	0.70	0.59

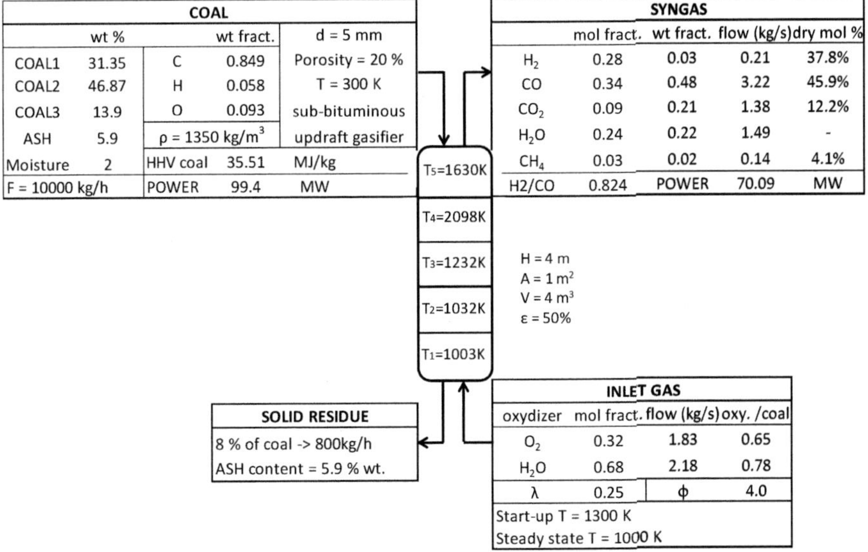

Figure 3. Summary of the coal simulation

4.3. Sensitivity analysis

In order to exploit the possibilities of the proposed methodology, we performed some sensitivity analysis on the key operating parameters, such as inlet gas temperature. Here we propose just a few results referring to the case study of the coal gasification reported above. After reaching a steady-state hot solution of the gasifier, summarized in Figure 3, the simulation was restarted with stepwise input changes on some operating conditions. For instance, in Figure 4 it is possible to see the effect of the inlet oxidizing gas temperature on temperature profiles, mass flowrates of the produced gas components and residual solid. From Figure 4 it is possible to point out that increasing the temperature of the oxidizing gas, the amount of produced gas increases, leading to a lesser solid residue. However the quality of the gas decreases because CO increases more than hydrogen. Moreover axial thermal profiles show a decrease in the temperature gradient increasing the inlet gas temperature.

5. Conclusions

We outlined a multi-scale mathematical model for the simulation of solid fuels thermochemical conversion processes. The novelty of this approach relies on a kinetic modelling approach, which can characterize, with a reasonable detail, also the devolatilization and pyrolysis steps, as well as the secondary gas phase reactions. The best characteristic of the present model relies on an intrinsic flexibility to handle different feedstock and to account for new available experimental data. This model has been here applied to the gasification process of biomass and coal, considering the counter current fixed-bed reactor. Comparisons with experimental data show the viability of the approach although some further comparisons should be done in order to improve the reliability of the model. Finally, the sensitivity analysis shows the strong effect of operating parameters on the quality of the produced syngas, and could provide a tool to optimize them in order to reach the desired target.

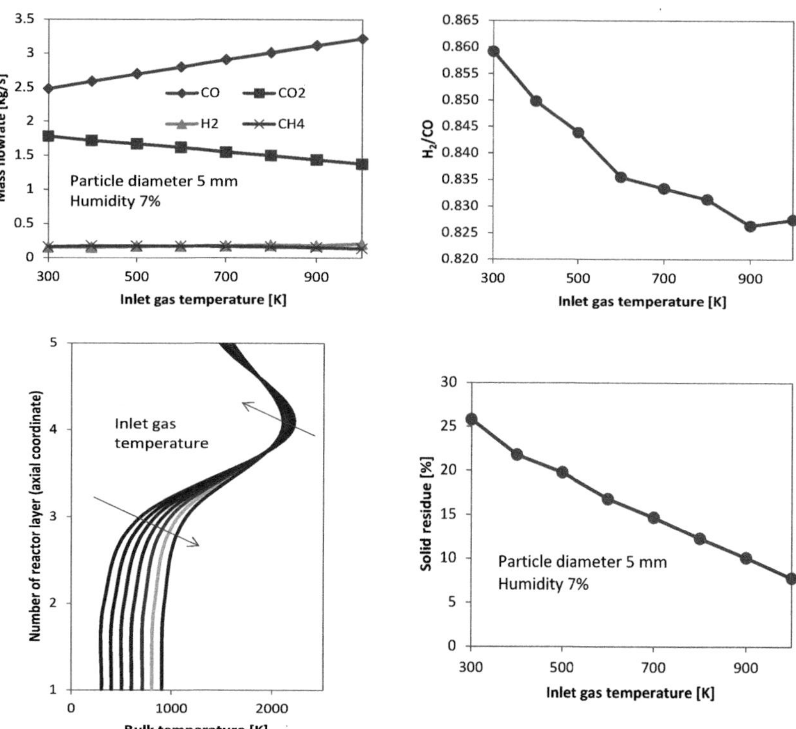

Figure 4. Sensitivity analysis. Effect of the inlet gas temperature on the gasifier bulk temperature, composition, and residual solid percentage.

References

C. Di Blasi, G. Signorelli, G. Portorico, 1999,Countercurrent fixed-bed gasification of biomass at laboratory scale, Industrial Engeneering Chemical Research, 38, 2571-2581.

F. Emun, M. Gadalla, T. Majozi, D. Boer, 2010, Integrated gasification combined cycle (IGCC) process simulation and optimization, Computers & Chemical Engineering, 34, 3, 331-338.

E. M. Grieco, G. Baldi, 2011, Predictive model for countercurrent coal gasifiers, Chemical Engineering Science, 66, 5749-5761.

F. Manenti, A. R. Leon-Garzon, G. Bozzano, 2013, Energy-Process Integration of the Gas-Cooled/Water-Cooled Fixed -Bed Reactor Network for Methanol Synthesis, Chemical Engineering Transactions, 35, 1243-1248.

M. S. Mettler, D. G. Vlachos, P. J. Dauenhauer, 2012, Top ten fundamental challenges of biomass pyrolysis for biofuels, Energy Environmental Science, 5, 7797-7809.

C. Pirola, C.L. Bianchi, A. Di Michele, P. Diodati, S. Vitali, V. Ragaini, 2009, High Loading Fe-supported Fischer–Tropsch Catalysts: Optimization of the Catalyst Performance, Catalysis Letters, 131, 294-304.

E. Ranzi, M. Corbetta, F. Manenti, S. Pierucci, 2013, Kinetic modeling of the thermal degradation and combustion of biomass, Chemical Engineering Science, DOI: 10.1016/j.ces.2013.08.014.

E. Ranzi, A. Frassoldati, R. Grana, A. Cuoci, T. Faravelli, A.P. Kelley, C.K. Law, 2012, Hierarchical and comparative kinetic modeling of laminar flame speeds of hydrocarbon and oxygenated fuels, Progress in Energy and Combustion Science, 38, 4, 468-501.

S. Sommariva, R. Grana, T. Maffei, S. Pierucci, E. Ranzi, 2011, A kinetic approach to the mathematical model of fixed bed gasifiers, Computers and Chemical Engineering, 35, 928-35.

Jiří Jaromír Klemeš, Petar Sabev Varbanov and Peng Yen Liew (Editors)
Proceedings of the 24th European Symposium on Computer Aided Process Engineering – ESCAPE 24
June 15-18, 2014, Budapest, Hungary.

Simultaneous Optimization Models for Heat Exchanger Network Synthesis with Multiple Utilities: A New Strategy by Using Utility Sub-stage

Jonggeol Na, Jaeheum Jung, Chansaem Park, Chonghun Han*

School of Chemical and Biological Engineering, Seoul National University, Gwanak-ro 1, Gwanak-gu, Seoul 1515-742, South Korea
chhan@snu.ac.kr

Abstract

In simultaneous method area of heat exchanger network synthesis (HENS), a mixed integer nonlinear programming (MINLP) model with stagewise superstructure is developed to minimize the total annualized cost (TAC). However, most of the preceding researches do not allow to consider the multiple utilities. Unlike previous superstructure, the utility sub-stage is located between the stages and multiple utilities are arranged in series. The heuristic, the optimal utility position should not be located in splitting stream, increase the searching area by expanding the number of stage and reduce the model size which is related to convergence of model. To verify the model, two examples are proposed and they show the effectiveness by deducing a network superior to any reported methodology.

Keywords: heat exchanger network synthesis (HENS); simultaneous; multiple utilities; optimization; mixed-integer nonlinear programming (MINLP).

1. Introduction

During last 50 years, heat exchanger network synthesis designed for economic benefit through energy has been one of the most important field of research regarding process synthesis. The methodology can be divided into the sequential method that applies heuristics after dividing a problem into sub-problems; represented by pinch technology, and the simultaneous method that simultaneously optimizes operating and capital cost using MINLP model (Furman and Sahinidis, 2002). Recent trend of research is focused on expanding the simultaneous model, which optimizes TAC without using heuristics, to model that can consider non-isothermal mixing, bypass stream that used to be considered only by sequential method.

Conventional methodologies cannot form a multiple utility-applied network because they consider single utility when composing HEN (Yee and Grossmann, 1990). However, in actual procedures, it's generally more lucrative in terms of cost to design the heat exchanger network using various utilities such as refrigerants and different pressure steams. Moreover, since they could place utilities only at the end sites, they failed to consider situations in which utilities exist between heat exchangers. Therefore, necessity to consider multiple utilities situations and form the most efficient network via its arrangement came up.

Methodology such as multiple utilities targeting(it forms multiple pinch point considering multiple utilities based on newly developed cheapest utility principle and calculates the minimum total annual cost entailing the minimum approach temperature) were developed based on pinch method (Shenoy et al., 1998). However, they inherited critical limitations of pinch method; inability to consider forbidden stream matches or disallowed heat flows cross the pinch point.

In simultaneous method section, multiple utilities were applied to interval based MINLP model in attempt to overcome such limitation, but couldn't place utilities anywhere else than end sites, like conventional superstructures (Isafiade and Fraser, 2008). Ponce-Ortega et al. (2010) developed modified superstructure that expands stagewise superstructure, adds stream splitting each time, and considers the utility at each part. However, utilities generally don't consist of a splitting at a single stage, so even a small increase in the number of stream considerably expands the model size, thereby rendering it inefficient and hard to converge. The method's another shortcoming is that its utility selection part's constraint can only consider a single utility, thereby making it necessary to increase the number of stages to analyse a structure that contains subsequently arranged utilities. Huang and Karimi (2013) introduced generalized stagewise superstructure with cross flows, but even with the application of four simplification constraints for utility, model size had lots of discrete variables and constraints. By setting time limitation on a solver of branch and bound concepts, such as BARON, it led to the false result of equalizing upper bound solution to optimal solution.

In this paper, a simultaneous optimization models for HENS with multiple utilities by using utility sub-stage is proposed. Our proposal makes it possible to consider the existence of utility not only at the end sites but also in between stages by introducing utility sub-stage that serially connects multiple utilities in the middle of conventional superstructure. Also, it can introduce more than one utility to a single sub-stage and generates the expediency of being able to selecting the number and kind of constraint by controlling it. Unlike previous models, assumption that usually utility location does not exist in the splitting stream is considered and utility sub stages belongs to the single streamline. Therefore, it has a reduced model size and can procure converging quality optimal solutions, compared to existing models.

2. Utility Sub-stage Superstructure and Model Formulation

Basic assumptions and constraints of utility sub-stage superstructure are derived from conventional one which was proposed by Yee and Grossmann (1990). For considering multiple utilities with simultaneous method, our formulation includes a utility sub-stage shown in Figure 1. To formulate the alternative superstructure with utility sub-stage, the following sets are specified. The stream set are divided into a HP and CP as defined previous researches (Yee and Grossmann, 1990). The superstructure stage set used in this paper is made of 2 types: conventional stream based stage (ST) set and utility sub-stage set for considering multiple utilities (STM: hot utility, STN: cold utility). If the process design were defined, number of stage (NOK, NOM, NON) should be fixed. Those three sets were connected organically for notating temperatures, heats, and binary variables.

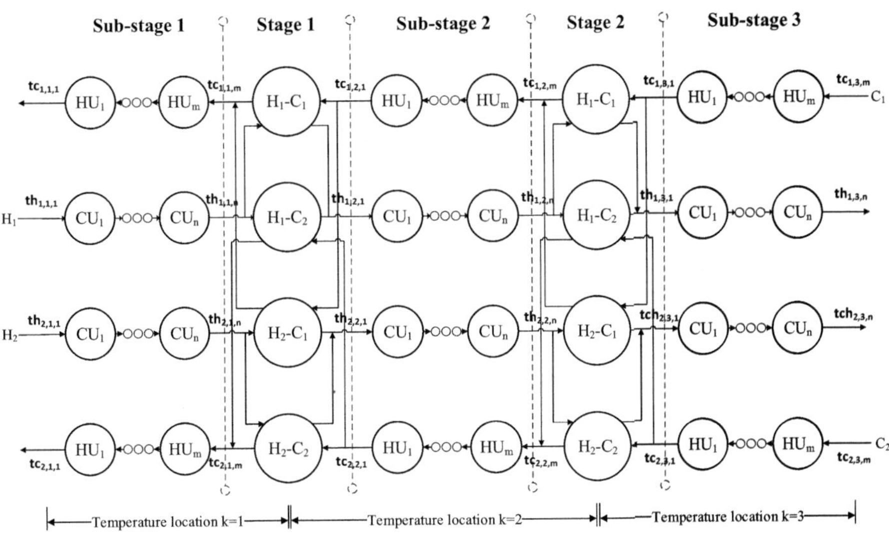

Figure 1. Utility sub-stage superstructure

Although sub-stage locates between stages, it is possible to describe all temperatures in modified superstructure by using only two types of temperature, $th_{i,k,n}$ (hot stream), $tc_{j,k,m}$ (cold stream) because sub-stage set and stream set are connected for defining the temperature. Hence, design variables do not increase extremely even multiple utilities are considered. For expressing approach temperature sequentially, it is divided pivot on heat exchanger and they are described as $dtl_{i,j,k}$ and $dtr_{i,j,k}$.

Especially, utility sub-stage set contains all utilities in series which are used in the system. Because the location of utilities in series type sub-stage is defined by the temperature order, it is possible to reduce the discrete variable than disjunction constraint with Boolean variable. Furthermore, proposed superstructure do not need to increase the number of stage for calculating solution when optimal network shows that each utility locates one after another because of series connection in sub-stage. Thus, the more we consider the multiple utilities, the better efficient than other algorithm because of less model size. Moreover, it is possible to select the number of utilities in single utility sub-stage by binary variable constraint which reduces the model size.

The Eqs. (1) and (2) denote the design variables and the feasible searching space for minimizing objective function. At last, utility sub-stage HENS formulation is completed by setting several conditions such as positive variable constraint and slightly modifying objective function proposed by Yee and Grossmann (1990).

The mathematical programming formulation for minimizing the TAC which consists of utility cost and heat exchanger investment cost, can be established as follows:

$$x_H \equiv \left\{ \begin{array}{c} z_{ijk}, zcu_{i,k,n}, zhu_{j,k,m}; \quad th_{i,k,n}, tc_{j,k,m}; \quad q_{i,j,k}, qcu_{i,k,n}, qhu_{j,k,m}; \\ dtl_{i,j,k}, dtr_{i,j,k}, dtcu_{i,k,n}, dthu_{j,k,m}; \\ \forall i \in HP, j \in CP, k \in ST, n \in STN, m \in STM \end{array} \right\} \tag{1}$$

$$\Omega_H = \left\{ x_H \left| \begin{array}{l} \left.\begin{array}{l} (TIN_i - TOUT_i)F_i = \sum_{i\in HP}\sum_{k\in ST} q_{i,j,k} + \sum_{k\in ST'}\sum_{m\in STM} qhu_{j,k,m} \\ (TOUT_j - TIN_j)F_j = \sum_{j\in CP}\sum_{k\in ST} q_{i,j,k} + \sum_{k\in ST'}\sum_{n\in STN} qcu_{i,k,n} \end{array}\right\} \text{overall heat balances} \\ \left.\begin{array}{l} (th_{i,k,NON+1} - th_{i,k+1,1})F_i = \sum_{j\in CP} q_{i,j,k} \\ (tc_{j,k,NOM+1} - tc_{j,k+1,1})F_i = \sum_{i\in HP} q_{i,j,k} \\ (th_{i,k,n} - th_{i,k,n+1})F_i = qcu_{i,k,n} \\ (tc_{j,k,m} - tc_{j,k,m+1})F_i = qhu_{j,k,m} \end{array}\right\} \text{stagewise heat balances} \\ \left.\begin{array}{l} th_{i,1,1} = TIN_i \\ tc_{j,1,1} = TOUT_j \\ th_{i,NOK+1,NON+1} = TOUT_i \\ tc_{j,NOK+1,NOM+1} = TIN_j \end{array}\right\} \text{temperature assignment} \\ \left.\begin{array}{l} th_{i,k,n} \geq th_{i,k,n+1} \\ tc_{j,k,m} \geq tc_{j,k,m+1} \\ th_{i,k,NON+1} \geq th_{i,k+1,1} \\ tc_{j,k,NOM+1} \geq tc_{j,k+1,1} \end{array}\right\} \text{feasibility of temperature} \\ \left.\begin{array}{l} q_{i,j,k} - \Omega z_{i,j,k} \leq 0 \\ qcu_{i,k,n} - \Omega zcu_{i,k,n} \leq 0 \\ qhu_{j,k,m} - \Omega zhu_{j,k,m} \leq 0 \end{array}\right\} \text{logical contraint} \\ \left.\begin{array}{l} dtl_{i,j,k} \leq th_{i,k,NON+1} - tc_{j,k,NOM+1} + \Gamma(1 - z_{i,j,k}) \\ dtr_{i,j,k} \leq th_{i,k+1,1} - tc_{j,k+1,1} + \Gamma(1 - z_{i,j,k}) \\ dtcu_{i,k,n} \leq th_{i,k,n} - TOUTcu_n + \Gamma(1 - zcu_{i,k,n}) \\ dtcu_{i,k,n+1} \leq th_{i,k,n+1} - TOUTcu_n + \Gamma(1 - zcu_{i,k,n}) \\ dthu_{j,k,m} \leq TINhu_m - tc_{j,k,m} + \Gamma(1 - zhu_{j,k,m}) \\ dthu_{j,k,m+1} \leq TINhu_m - tc_{j,k,m+1} + \Gamma(1 - zhu_{j,k,m}) \end{array}\right\} \text{approach temperature} \end{array} \right. \right\} \quad (2)$$

3. Examples

Two problems which have been used for checking the performance of proposed method for multiple utilities network are presented to demonstrate the advantages of the utility sub-stage. The solver BARON in the general algebraic modeling system (GAMS) were used.

3.1. Example 1

The first example was presented by Shenoy et al. (1998) and also solved by Huang and Karimi (2013). This example is consist of two hot streams and one cold stream with three hot utilities, high, medium and low pressure steam and one cold water as cold utility. Figure 2 shows the optimal network obtained by utility sub-stage algorithm. From this new algorithm, we can get 44,816 \$/y for investment cost and 51,541 \$/y for utility cost to yield a TAC of 96,357 \$/y which is about 0.60 % lower than the best solution by Huang and Karimi (2013). A remarkable result from this research is that the optimal solution appeared where lower bound met upper bound. This is due to the fact that it has lesser model complexity than reported algorithms, thereby being able to consider more binary variables even with more stages. Table 1 compares the sizes of Ponce-Ortega et al. (2010) model and the proposed model, and we can deduce from this table that constraint and variable were reduced by 45 % and 70 %, respectively.

3.2. Example 2

Ponce-Ortega et al. (2010) used this example for handling isothermal process streams with multiple utilities. There are four hot streams and three cold streams with three types of hot utilities and two types of cold utilities. Figure 3 shows optimal solutions obtained by utility sub-stage algorithm. Although solution prints same utility cost (40,374 \$/y), it shows decreased investment cost (32,700 \$/y vs. 34,417 \$/y). As a result, TAC is reduced as 2.3 % with same number and types of exchangers and utilities. Notice that optimal network is considerably different from that of literature because simple structure of utility sub-stage gives possibility to consider more stages with lower number of continuous and discrete variables.

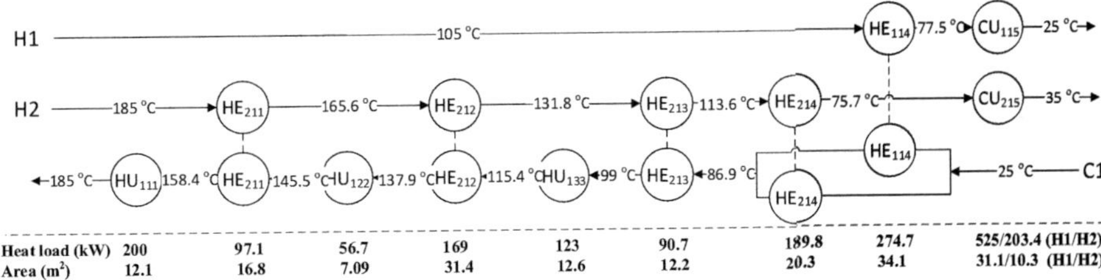

Figure 2. Optimal HEN for example 1

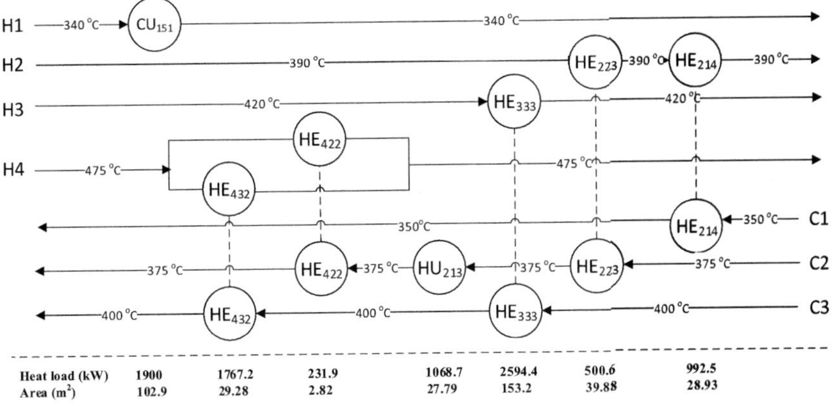

Figure 2.Optimal HEN for example 2

Table 1. Result comparison for examples

Method	Example 1		Example 2	
	this paper	Best in reported	this paper	Best in reported
HU load (kW)	44,254	45,476	21,374	21,374
CU load (kW)	7,287	7,406	19,000	19,000
Number of units	10	8	7	7
TAC (\$/y)	96,357	96,937	73,074	74,791
Continuous variables	169	501	674	861
Discrete variables	33	120	168	216

4. Conclusion

We proposed a simultaneous MINLP model for solving HENS with multiple utilities by using utility sub-stage. Utility sub-stages are serially connected between existent stages, enabling the composition of linear and continuous constraint, thus we could conduct programming with smaller model size. By assuming that utility does not fit in a stream-split part, we could get closer to global optimum by considering more stages. Additionally, through two examples, we could verify the effectiveness by deducing a network superior to any reported methodology. They demonstrated that the new method decreased the TAC as 0.6 % and 2.3 % respectively which is the most important object for network decision making. Moreover, our method reduced the continuous and discrete variables which related to the calculation time.

References

K. F. Huang, I. A. Karimi, 2013, Heat exchanger network synthesis with multiple utilities using a generalized stagewise superstructure with cross flows, Proceeding of the 6th International Conference on Process Systems Engineering, Kuala Lumpur, Jun 25–27, 44-49.

K. C. Furman, N. V. Sahinidis, 2002, A critical review and annotated bibliography for heat exchanger network synthesis in the 20th century, Industrial and Engineering Chemistry Research, 41, 2335-2370.

A. J. Isafiade, D. M. Fraser, 2008, Interval-based MINLP superstructure synthesis of heat exchange networks, Chemical Engineering Research and Design, 86, 245-257.

J. M. Ponce-Ortega, M. Serna-González, A. Jiménez-Gutiérrez, 2010, Synthesis of Heat Exchanger Networks with Optimal Placement of Multiple Utilities, Industrial and Engineering Chemistry Research, 49, 2849-2856.

U. V. Shenoy, A. Sinha, S. Bandyopadhyay, 1998, Multiple Utilities Targeting for Heat Exchanger Networks, Chemical Engineering Research and Design, 76, 259-272.

T. F. Yee, I. E. Grossmann, 1990, Simultaneous optimization models for heat integration—II. Heat exchanger network synthesis, Computers and Chemical Engineering, 14, 1165-1184.

Jiří Jaromír Klemeš, Petar Sabev Varbanov and Peng Yen Liew (Editors)
Proceedings of the 24th European Symposium on Computer Aided Process Engineering – ESCAPE 24
June 15-18, 2014, Budapest, Hungary.

Techno-economic Analysis of a Thermochemical Lignocellulosic Biomass-to-Butanol Process

Chinedu O. Okoli, Thomas A. Adams II*

Department of Chemical Engineering, McMaster University, 1280 Main Street West, Hamilton, L8S 4L8, Canada
tadams@mcmaster.ca

Abstract

Biobutanol production through the thermochemical route allows the use of a wide variety of feedstocks (including lignocellulosic biomass) and is a potentially superior alternative to the biochemical route. However the thermochemical route is poorly understood and no techno-economic studies of the thermochemical route exist in the peer-reviewed literature to our knowledge. To address this issue, this work focuses on the use of CAPE tools in modelling a novel thermochemical lignocellulosic biomass-to-butanol process and an assessment of its economic feasibility. This goal is achieved with a three-step methodology comprising of process simulation, heat integration, and an economic analysis. The application of this methodology results in a minimum butanol selling price (MBSP) which is competitive with biobutanol via the biochemical route. A sensitivity analysis on different design and cost parameters confirm that this process is quite promising under a large range of uncertain market conditions.

Keywords: biobutanol; lignocellulosic biomass; minimum butanol selling price; techno-economic analysis; thermochemical.

1. Introduction

Biofuels from second generation feedstocks have benefits over first generation sources as they generally do not compete with food for land use. These second generation feedstocks are typically cellulosic or lignocellulosic biomass such as agricultural residue, wood chips and switchgrass. In Canada, about 5.1×10^{15} J of forest and agricultural residue are produced annually, which is equivalent to 62 % of the country's fossil fuel combustion derived energy (Wood and Layzell, 2003). This potential for cellulose/lignocellulose-to-biofuels technology is further highlighted by the U.S. congress mandate of a minimum of 79.5×10^{9} L of cellulosic biofuels production by 2022 (US Congress, 2007). Though bioethanol has received a lot of attention in the past decade, biobutanol is increasingly seen as its potential replacement as a gasoline substitute because biobutanol offers advantages such as a lower miscibility with water, higher energy content, good blending ability and better compatibility with internal combustion engines and fuel pipeline networks (Ranjan and Moholkar, 2012). Biobutanol production is grouped into biochemical and thermochemical routes. The Acetone-Butanol-Ethanol (ABE) fermentation process is the primary pathway for the biochemical route. In the ABE process biomass is converted to butanol via fermentation with Clostridial bacteria (Kumar and Gayen, 2011). The ABE process faces difficulty in handling lignocellulosic biomass because of is high lignin content, and has other challenges such as the low productivity of the fermentation process and the highly energy intensive separation of the butanol product from the dilute fermentation broth (Kumar and Gayen, 2011). Thermochemical routes, however, allow the handling of a wider range of feedstocks as they proceed through the gasification route which allows the conversion of the carbonaceous compounds (including lignin in lignocellulose) into syngas. This syngas is subsequently cleaned and catalytically converted to butanol over an alcohol synthesis catalyst. Another advantage of the thermochemical route is the easier separation step as the butanol is present at a higher concentration in the alcohol synthesis reactor product. Despite the potential advantage of the thermochemical route over the biochemical route for biobutanol production from lignocellulosic feedstock, it is poorly understood, and recent reviews of thermochemical biofuel technologies (Haro et al. 2013) confirm that no techno-economic studies or detailed process design studies exist in the peer-reviewed literature. A techno-economic study of the thermochemical biobutanol process will be very important as past research has shown that key process parameters such as the product yield and choice of feedstock are highly correlated to the cost of production of biofuels (Klein-Marcuschamer and Blanch, 2013). The objective of this work is thus to use CAPE tools and a techno-economic methodology to design and analyse a novel thermochemical lignocellulosic biomass to butanol process. Furthermore, the product yields, the overall energy efficiency of the process, and the economics of the process are determined and compared to the ABE butanol process.

2. Process description

This study evaluates the production of butanol with 2,000 dry t per day of woody biomass feedstock as the design basis. The ultimate analysis of the feedstock is obtained from Dutta et al. (2011). The block flow diagram in Figure 1 illustrates the major steps in the process.

Biomass feedstock is dried and then sent to an indirect fluidized bed gasification system consisting of an interconnected gasifier, char combustor and cyclones. The produced raw syngas contains impurities such as tars and acid gas (CO_2 and H_2S). The removal of these impurities is critical as at low temperatures the tars in the syngas condense and clog process equipment, while the acid gas poisons the alcohol synthesis catalyst. The tars are reformed to syngas in a tar reformer, while the acid gas is removed by amine scrubbing and ZnO polishing. The clean syngas is compressed and sent to the alcohol synthesis section where it is converted to alcohols (primarily C_1 to C_6 alcohols).

The alcohol synthesis catalyst is a modified low pressure methanol catalyst which has high selectivity to butanol (Herman, 2000).

Table 1. Main design assumptions

Unit	Technology	Operating condition
Gasifier system	Indirect, low pressure, circulating fluidized bed gasifier	Gasifier: 2.28 bar, 868 °C Char combustor: 2 bar, 995 °C
Tar reformer	Catalytic, indirect, low pressure, circulating fluidized bed reformer	Tar reformer: 1.86 bar, 910 °C Catalyst regenerator: 2 bar, adiabatic
Acid gas removal	Monoethanolamine (MEA) absorption system	MEA concentration: 35 wt% Absorber: 31 bar; Stripper: 4.12 bar Outlet syngas spec.: 10 ppm H_2S, 5 wt% CO_2
Syngas polishing	ZnO adsorption bed	Outlet syngas spec.: 0.1 ppm H_2S
Alcohol synthesis reactor	Double bed reactors in series	CO/H_2 ratio of inlet syngas: 1.1 - 1.3 First bed: 76 bar, 324 °C Second bed: 76 bar, 340 °C
Alcohol separation	Zeolite molecular sieve and distillation columns	Outlet water content of mol. sieve: 0.5 wt% Distillation col. tray efficiency: 60 % Outlet butanol purity: 99.5 wt%

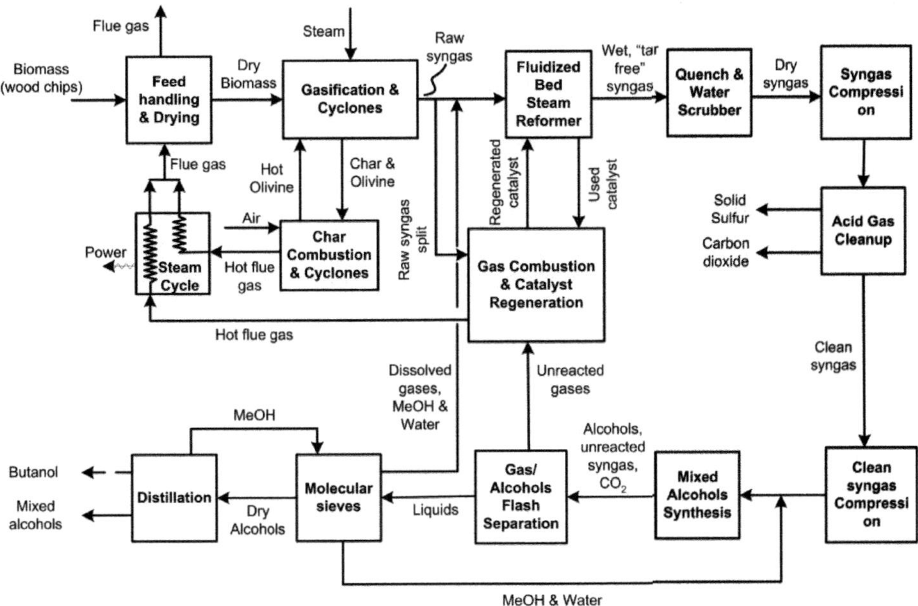

Figure 1. Block flow diagram of the thermochemical biobutanol process

The alcohols are sent to an alcohol separation section in which molecular sieves (for water removal), and three distillation columns in series are used to obtain butanol and mixed alcohols as products. The main design assumptions for the process are shown in Table 1.

3. Methodology

The techno-economic evaluation was performed through a three step methodology comprising of process simulation, heat integration, and an economic analysis. The process was simulated using Aspen Plus® V.8. The Redlich-Kwong-Soave equation of state with Boston-Mathias modifications was used for most of the simulation, except for the steam cycle and cooling water sections where ASME 1967 steam table correlations were used, and the alcohol separation section where the non-random, two-liquid activity coefficient model with Redlich-Kwong modifications was used. A heat integration analysis was carried out in conjunction with the design of the steam cycle and cooling water sections with the goal of improving the energy efficiency of the process. The first step in the heat integration analysis is the extraction of cold and hot stream data from the material and energy balance results from the process simulation. This information is used to construct composite curves which are used to determine maximum energy recovery targets. Finally, a heat exchanger network is designed from these targets. Aspen Energy Analyzer® software was the key tool used for the heat integration analysis. The goal of the economic analysis is to determine the MBSP, defined as the selling price of the butanol product over the plant's life time at which the net present value is zero. Material and energy balance results from the process simulation are used to size the process equipment. The equipment cost is then estimated based on a combination of the Aspen Capital Cost Estimator® software and literature data (Dutta et al., 2011). Equipment cost estimates obtained from literature were scaled using the capacity power law expression, and updated to current (2012) US dollars with the Chemical Engineering Plant Cost Index. The total capital investment is then determined with the use of Lang factors (Peters et al., 2003). Correlations for fixed (Seider et al., 2009), variable operating costs (Dutta et al., 2011), and current energy prices (US EIA, 2013) are obtained from the relevant literature. The capital and operating cost results are then used to determine the MBSP using a discounted cash flow rate of return (DCFROR) analysis and an assumption of nth plant costs.

4. Results and discussions

4.1. Process results

The process yields butanol and mixed alcohols as products with an overall product yield of 228 kg/dry t of biomass. Butanol makes up 54 % of the overall liquid product, with mixed alcohols as the remainder (46 %), highlighting the importance of its valuation on the MBSP. One of the goals of this study was to design a self-sufficient plant were no external utilities are required except for cooling water. Thus, char combustion in the indirect gasification system and combustion of un-reacted syngas are used to meet the energy demands of the process, resulting in a process carbon efficiency of 31 %. Besides improving the energy efficiency of the process, another benefit of the heat integration analysis is the net production of 9 MW of power as a result of extra steam generation and its subsequent expansion in steam turbines. This power is considered as a co-product which can be sold to the grid to offset some of the butanol production costs. The overall energy efficiency of the process is 46 % (dry biomass lower heating value basis) which is comparable to a thermochemical lignocellulosic biomass-to-ethanol process (Dutta et al., 2011).

4.2. Economic results

These results are intuitive, as the feedstock cost makes up a major percentage of the variable operating cost while the mixed alcohols co-product makes up almost half of the products. In order to consider the effects of multiple parameters which change at the same time, different scenarios in which the most significant parameters vary simultaneously are considered as shown in Table 3. The results show that in the “optimistic” to “pessimistic” scenario range of 0.55 - 1.17 $/L the process remains competitive, especially in comparison to ABE-derived butanol prices which range from 0.59 $/L (Kumar et al., 2012) to 1.05 $/L (Qureshi et al., 2013). An important assumption in this study is the alcohol synthesis catalyst CO-conversion of 40 %. This value is in line with the National Renewable Energy Laboratory target of greater than 50 % CO-conversion for alcohol synthesis catalysts, achievable from future research adva-

Table 2. Breakdown of capital cost

Capital cost calculations	$ Million
Total Installed Equipment Cost	214
Total Indirect Cost	114
Total Depreciable Capital	328
Royalties	7
Land	6
Fixed Capital Investment	341
Working Capital	17
Total Capital Investment	358

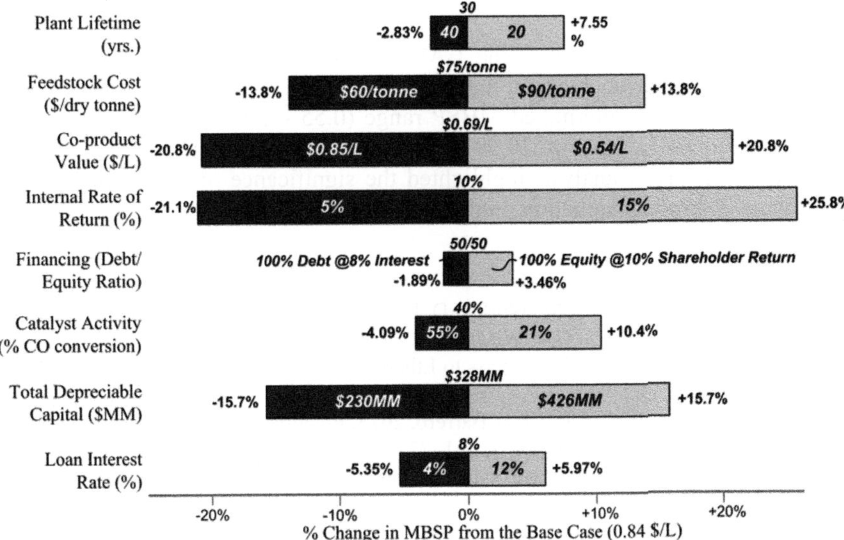

Figure 2. Sensitivity of the MBSP (base case of 0.84 $/L) to changes in key parameters

nces (Phillips et al., 2007). However the catalyst used in this study has a CO-conversion of 8.5 % (Herman, 2000), a value that results in an MBSP of 1.60 $/L which is unlikely to be competitive. Furthermore, the base case MBSP result of 0.84 $/L in comparison to the gasoline price of 0.82 $/Lbeq is intuitive, as the MBSP should be worse than the gasoline price except for high crude oil price situations. Thus this process provides a method of producing 2nd generation biofuels at only a small premium over petroleum-derived gasoline, assuming the achievement of the target alcohol synthesis catalyst CO-conversion. In addition, it is important to note that the lignocellulose biomass-to-butanol ABE process has only been demonstrated at the laboratory scale, and thus the wide range of prices for ABE-derived butanol is highly uncertain as it is unlikely to be better than gasoline.

Finally, an area to consider in future research is the impact of cheaper feedstocks, such as switchgrass and wheat straw, on the thermochemical biobutanol MBSP. These feedstocks will have different performance metrics, as they will form different syngas compositions with undetermined ripple effects through the process which will have to be evaluated.

Table 3. Impact of different economic scenarios on the MBSP

Scenarios – Parameter Values Considered	Very Optimistic	Optimistic	Base Case	Pessimistic	Very Pessimistic
Internal Rate of Return	5	7.5	10	12.5	15
Feedstock costs ($/dry t)	60	68	75	83	90
Mixed Alcohol value ($/L)	0.85	0.77	0.69	0.62	0.54
Total Depreciable Capital	230	279	328	377	426
Resulting MBSP ($/L)	0.29	0.55	0.84	1.17	1.54

5. Conclusions

A techno-economic methodology using CAPE tools has demonstrated the economic feasibility of a novel thermochemical lignocellulosic biomass-to-butanol process. It has been established that the determined MBSP range (0.55 - 1.17 $/L) of this process is competitive with ABE butanol (0.59 - 1.05 $/L) and gasoline (0.82 $/Lbeq). Furthermore, a sensitivity analysis highlighted the significance of feedstock costs and mixed alcohols co-product valuation on the process economics.

References

A. Dutta, M. Talmadge, J. Hensley, M. Worley, D. Dudgeon, D. Barton, P. Groenedijk, D. Ferrari, B. Stears, E.M. Searcy, C.T. Wright, J.R. Hess, 2011, Process Design and Economics for Conversion of Lignocellulosic Biomass to Ethanol, National Renewable Energy Laboratory, Golden, CO, USA.

P. Haro, P. Ollero, A.L.V. Perales, F. Vidal-Barrero, 2013, Potential routes for thermochemical biorefineries, Biofuels Bioprod Bioref, 7, 551–72.

R.G. Herman, 2000, Advances in catalytic synthesis and utilization of higher alcohols, Catal Today, 55, 3, 233–45.

D. Klein-Marcuschamer, H.W. Blanch, 2013, Survival of the Fittest: An Economic Perspective on the Production of Novel Biofuels, AIChE Journal, 59, 12, 4454–60.

M. Kumar, K. Gayen, 2011, Developments in biobutanol production: new insights, App Energy, 88, 6, 1999–2012.

M. Kumar, Y. Goyal, A. Sarkar, K. Gayen, 2012, Comparative economic assessment of ABE fermentation based on cellulosic and non-cellulosic feedstocks, App Energy, 93, 193–204.

M.S Peters, K.D. Timmerhaus, R.E. West, 2003, Plant Design and Economics for Chemical Engineers, McGraw-Hill Science/Engineering/Math, Massachusetts, USA.

S. Phillips, A. Aden, J. Jechura, D. Dayton, T. Eggeman, 2007, Thermochemical Ethanol via Indirect Gasification and Mixed Alcohols Synthesis of Lignocellulosic Biomass, National Renewable Energy Laboratory, Golden, CO, USA.

N. Qureshi, B.C. Saha, M.A. Cotta, V. Sing, 2013, An economic evaluation of biological conversion of wheat straw to butanol: A biofuel, Energy Conversion and Management, 65, 456–62.

A. Ranjan, V.S. Moholkar, 2012, Biobutanol: science, engineering, and economics, Int J Energ Res, 36, 3, 277–323.

W.D. Seider, J.D. Seader, D.R. Lewin, 2009, Product & Process Design Principles: Synthesis, Analysis and Evaluation, 3rd ed., John Wiley & Sons, New Jersey, USA.

US Congress, 2007, Energy Independence and Security Act, Public Law, 2, 110–40

US EIA, 2013, U.S. Gasoline and Diesel Fuel Prices, <www.eia.gov>, accessed on 31/07/2013.

M.S. Wood, D.B. Layzell, 2003, A Canadian Biomass Inventory: Feedstocks for a Bio-based economy, BIOCAP Canada Foundation, 18–24.

Jiří Jaromír Klemeš, Petar Sabev Varbanov and Peng Yen Liew (Editors)
Proceedings of the 24th European Symposium on Computer Aided Process Engineering – ESCAPE 24
June 15-18, 2014, Budapest, Hungary.

Design and Exergy Analysis of Combined Rankine Cycle Using LNG Cold Energy

Ung Lee*, Chonghun Han

School of Chemical and Biological Engineering, Seoul National University, Gwanak-ro 599, Gwanak-gu, Seoul 151-742, South Korea

Abstract

In this study, a 90 MW_e combined Rankine cycle utilizing LNG cold exergy was proposed. Utilizing LNG cold exergy and waste heat from the conventional steam cycle, this process was able to generate additional power in the CO_2 organic Rankine cycle (ORC). A conventional steam cycle generates only 42 MW electric power; this combined Rankine cycle produced more than twice as much power as the conventional steam cycle while consuming the same amount of fossil fuel. Through parameter sensitivity analysis and exergy analysis, the optimum design and operating conditions were also determined. Finally, reduction of the power plant de-rate by introducing a CO_2 capture process was also analyzed.

Keywords: LNG, CCS, ORC, Combined Cycle

1. Introduction

The recent climate change and related consequences have attracted worldwide attention and increased global efforts to reduce the emission of greenhouse gases, particularly CO_2. Among the various sources of the CO_2 emission, power plants combusting fossil fuel such as coal, oil and gas contribute to the CO_2 emission the most. Several methods of removing CO_2 from power plant flue gas have been proposed, and amine-based CO_2-absorbing systems are considered to be one of the most suitable options because they have been demonstrated to be mature and less expensive technologies. However, high energy consumption and corresponding electricity cost increment have been pointed out as an obstacle of the commercialization. Abu-Zahra et al. indicated that the estimated electricity production cost increase from introducing a CO_2 capture process is 40–85 % for a supercritical pulverized coal (PC) power plant (Abu-Zahra et al., 2007). To reduce the energy penalty, several studies have been conducted on more-efficient power generation processes with CO_2 capture. Research on minimizing the de-rate of the power cycle includes optimization of the steam extraction point for the CO_2 stripper reboiler. Romeo et al. indicated that steam for the CO_2 stripper can be extracted from midway through the low-pressure (LP) section of the turbine (Romeo et al., 2008). Despite steam extraction optimization, the plant de-rate ranged from 17 % to 30 % in these studies compared to similar plants without a capture process.

In order to improve conventional power processes, various thermodynamic cycles such as organic Rankine cycle, supercritical Rankine cycle, Kalina cycle and Goswami cycle have been proposed to produce electricity from low grade heat. Among these cycles, Chen et al. insisted the organic Rankine cycle as the most efficient low temperature heat recovery method because of its high efficiency and simplicity (Chen et al. 2013). Numbers of studies proposed different type of combined cycle with ORC as the bottom cycle as well as ORC with different working fluids. Chacartegui et al. proposed an alternative combined power cycle with ORC bottoming cycle (Chacartegui et al., 2009) and Shengjun et al. demonstrated cycle performance with different working fluids (Shengjun et al., 2011). Technical and economical analysis of the ORC were also carried out (Kosmadakis et al., 2009) Although the advantage of ORC with steam cycle is obvious for low grade waste heat recovery, the cycle efficiency of the ORC itself is not as high as conventional steam cycle due to its small pressure ratio. As an alternative to the conventional ORC, transcritical Rankine cycles using CO_2 are proposed which has higher pressure ratio and efficiency, but efficiency of these processes can be further improved when its condensation process is took place at sub ambient temperature.

To improve the cycle efficiency, cryogenic exergy utilization of liquefied natural gas (LNG) has been receiving attention, including an LNG direct expansion cycle, Brayton cycle, or Rankine cycle. In a proposal by Zhang, an LNG evaporation system was integrated into a gas–steam combined power plant for CO_2 liquefaction, and liquefied CO_2 was used as a working fluid for the Rankine cycle (Zhang et al., 2006). Deng et al. also proposed a combined cycle that utilized CO_2 from the gas turbine operation (Deng et al., 2004). These processes were mainly focused on integration of the Brayton cycle with the CO_2 ORC. Power generation from these gas turbine cycles not only requires installation of air separation units, but costs >20 % more than from conventional steam cycles.

In this study, a complete combined Rankine cycle is proposed and modeled using Aspen Plus. The basecase of the power generation process is composed of coal fired steam generator, steam cycle, CO_2 capture process, CO_2 treating process and CO_2 ORC. Exergy analysis is done on each process unit of the power cycle in order to analyze the and optimize the process. Using the basecase design and exergy analysis the optimum design of the power generation system can be presented and the optimized process is able to produce twice as much power as the conventional steam cycle by utilizing wasted LNG cold exergy and latent heat of low pressure steam discharge from steam turbine.

2. Process Scheme

The layout of the thermal-power plant considered in the present work is shown in Figure 1. It is mainly consisted of five parts; Coal fired steam generator, Steam cycle, CO_2 capture process, CO_2 treating process and CO_2 ORC. The coal fired boiler in this study was modeled using Illinois No. 6 bituminous coal. The steam generator is comprised of coal dryer, burner, steam generators, particulate control, and flue gas desulfurization (FGD). Since the aim of this study is primarily focused on the exergy analysis and optimization of the power generating system, the coal feed pulverizer which consumes negligible energy in comparison with the CO_2 capture process are not took into account and component separator models are used for SOx and NOx removal. The flue gas generated from the boiler is directed to the post-combustion capture process to recover the CO_2-rich stream. The CO_2-rich stream is then pressurized and dried in the gas conditioning process for high-purity CO_2 recovery. The composition of the flue gas and design coal characteristic are shown in Table 1.

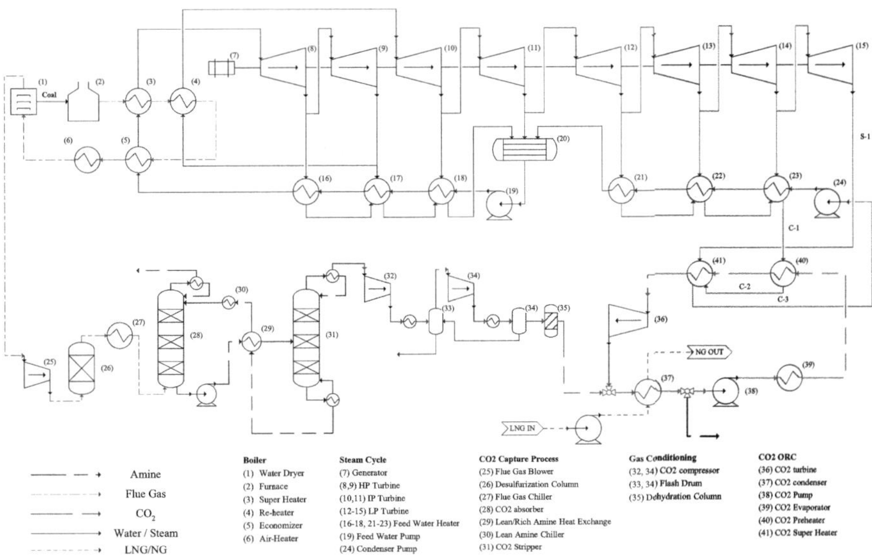

Figure 1. Process flow diagram of combined Rankine cycle

Table 1. Flue gas and Illinois No. 6 bituminous coal composition

Proxanal Analysis (Dry wt %)		Ultanal Analysis (Dry wt %)		Flue Gas Composition (Mass Frac)	
MOISTURE	11.12	ASH	10.91	H2O	0.053
FC	49.72	CARBON	71.73	N2	0.70
VM	39.37	HYDROGEN	5.06	O2	0.023
ASH	10.91	NITROGEN	1.41	H2	4.3E-05
		CHLORINE	0.33	CO2	0.22
		SULFUR	2.82	Ash	0.0093
		OXYGEN	7.74		

The steam cycle consists of two high-pressure (HP), two intermediate-pressure (IP), and four low-pressure (LP) steam turbines with a gross efficiency of 46.5 %. It was assumed that the steam cycle employed a standard vacuum condensing cycle. The low-pressure steam from the LP turbine is expanded to 0.25 bar. Seven feed water heaters (FWH) are used to preheat the water delivered to the steam-generating boiler. Preheating the feed water reduces the irreversibility involved in steam generation and thus improves the thermodynamic efficiency of the system. The CO_2 capture and conditioning process are designed to remove about 92 % of the CO_2 in the flue gas, purify, compress and dry it to the suitable condition for the liqufaction. The CO_2 capture and conditioning processes are comprised of CO_2 absorption system, solvent stripping, CO_2 compression and drying system. They employ monoethanolamine (MEA) as a CO_2 capturing solvent and a two stage compressor with dehydration unit for CO_2 conditioning. The CO_2 capture process is designed based on the pilot plant operation data which is installed in Boryeong coal power plant.

For the ORC, CO_2 was selected as the working fluid because high-purity CO_2 can be readily supplied from the CO_2 capture and gas conditioning process. As opposed to the steam cycle, condensation in the CO_2 ORC generally takes place at sub-ambient temperatures. Consequently, external coolant is required for condensation. For this study, the CO_2 ORC utilized the cryogenic exergy of LNG as a cold sink to condense CO_2 near the triple point. The temperature and pressure at which CO_2 condensation takes place are -49.7 °C and 7 bar, respectively. In this process liquid CO_2 can only be pressurized to 52 bar to avoid possible liquid generation within the CO_2 turbine while expansion. The liquid CO_2 is then heated to 20 °C with water supplied at 25 °C. After the CO_2 is vaporized using water, it is further heated using low pressure steam discharged from the LP turbine. In this manner, CO_2 working fluid can be superheated and more work can be recovered from the CO_2 turbine. To recover maximum power from the cycle, the lowest possible turbine discharge pressure is always favourable. However, CO_2, in contrast to water, has a triple point higher than atmospheric pressure. It was assumed in the present study that CO_2 could be expanded to 7 bar. After expansion, the low-pressure CO_2 stream is merged with CO_2 from the gas conditioning process and reintroduced to the CO_2 condenser. A portion of the liquefied CO_2 stream is purged through the splitter, and the purged stream (R-7) can be sent to a pipeline or a CO_2 carrier for sequestration.

3. Exergy Analysis

Exergy is composed of two parts: physical exergy and chemical exergy. In this study, the kinetic and potential part of the exergy is assumed negligible. The exergy balance of the control volume can be defined using Eq. (1)

$$E_Q + \sum_i m_i e_i = \sum_e m_e e_e + E_W + I \tag{1}$$

Where e is the total specific exergy and I is the exergy loss rate.

$$E_Q = (1 - \frac{T_0}{T_i}) Q_i \tag{2}$$

$$E_W = W \tag{3}$$

$$e = (h - h_0) - T_0 (S - S_0) \tag{4}$$

The chemical exergy of the mixture and can be define as follows

$$e_{mix}^{ch} = [(\sum_{i=1}^{n} x_i e^{ch} + RT_0 \sum_{i=1}^{n} x_i \ln x_i + G^E)] \tag{5}$$

The evaluation of the fuel exergy is not included in this study, because the optimization of the fuel combustion system is beyond the scope of this study. In this study, the exergy analysis is more focused on each process unit composing power cycle and calculated irreversibility in order to identify the energy and exergy loss of the system.

4. Result and Discussion

Figure 2 indicate the result of exergy analysis. As indicated in the figure the LNG gasifier and CO_2 evaporator contribute system irreversibility the most. The high irreversibility of LNG gasifier is resulted from the LNG cryogenic characteristics. Since the initial temperature of the LNG is resigned at near -150°C, high irreversibility is unavoidable due to high due point temperature difference between CO_2 and LNG. As oppose to the LNG gasifier, the irreversibility of the CO_2 evaporator can be reduced by changing process scheme. When pressurized CO_2 at 20 bar is utilized for CO_2 ORC heat source instead of using 25°C water, the irreversibility of the unit process can be lowered because the CO_2 dew point at 20 bar is far less than the water at ambient pressure. In this manner, the cold exergy of the LNG is solely used for CO_2 working fluid liquefaction, the amount of working fluid circulating CO_2 ORC cycle is also increased. Consequently both thermal efficiency and power generation of the entire process is increased. The optimized process flow diagram of combined Rankine cycle is presented in Figure 3.

Finally, the power reduction of the combined Rankine cycle due to installation of the CO_2 capture process is evaluated. Both the conventional power plant and combined Rankine cycle consume the same amount of the fossil fuel; thus the CO_2 generation of 32.6 t/h, is identical for both cases. The energy consumption of the CO_2 capture process is 3.81 GJ/ ton CO_2, reducing power reduction by 38 % in a conventional process. However, it is reduced to 18 % for the combined Rankine cycle. The decrease in power reduction is due to additional power generation from the CO_2 ORC and can be maximized with the steam extraction location selection and exergy optimization. Despite power reduction in the combined Rankine cycle due to the CO_2 capture process installation, net power generation for the combined Rankine cycle is higher than that for

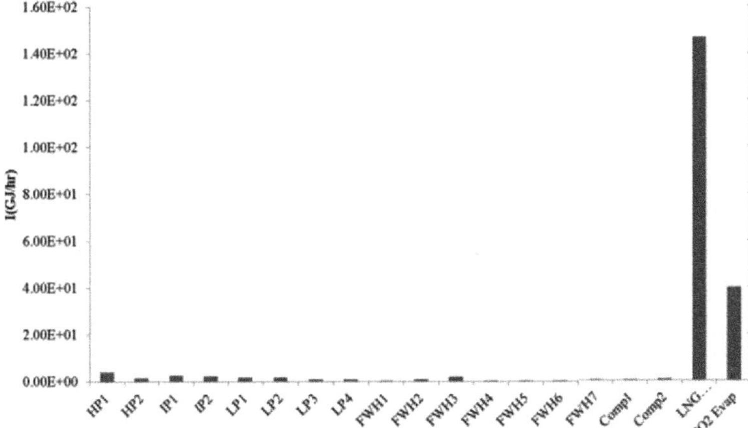

Figure 2. Exergy analysis of combined Rankine cycle

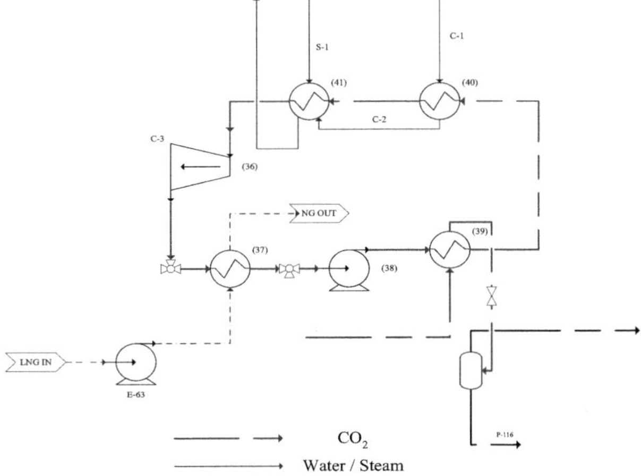

Figure 3. Optimized process design of combined Rankine cycle

a conventional process even without CO_2 capture. The power generation increments of the combined Rankine cycle are about 80 % compared to the conventional process without CO_2 capture and it can reach up to 190 % when they are compared with the conventional process with CO_2 capture. According to the decrease in power reduction and power generation increment, this combined Rankine cycle can make it more economically feasible to install the CO_2 capture process on the power plant and eventually lower the power generation cost.

5. Conclusion

A combined Rankine cycle utilizing LNG cold exergy and the wasted latent heat of steam was proposed and modeled in this study. The primary merit of the system is that both power generation and exergy efficiency of the cycle can be enhanced without consuming additional fossil fuel. The combined Rankine cycle utilized CO_2 from the flue gas as a working fluid by treating it with a CO_2 capture and gas conditioning process. Through the energy anaylsis of the process the irreversibility of entire system is identified. Among the highly irreversible processes, the CO_2 evaporating system is modified and the thermal efficiency and power generation can be improved from the basecase. Power reduction due to CO_2 capture process installation is also decreased from 38 % to 18 % in the combined Rankine cycle. The amount of net power generation in the combined Rankine cycle is about 80 % higher than that of the conventional power generation process even without CO_2 capture.

References

C. F. Alie, 2004, CO_2 capture with MEA: integrating the absorption process and steam cycle of an existing coal-fired power plant, Master Thesis, University of Waterloo, Canada.

G. Kosmadakis, D. Manolakos, S. Kyritsis, G. Papadakis, 2009, Economic assessment of a two-stage solar organic Rankine cycle for reverse osmosis desalination, Renewable energy, 34, 6, 1579-1586.

H. Chen, D. Y. Goswami, E. K. Stefanakos, 2010, A review of thermodynamic cycles and working fluids for the conversion of low-grade heat, Renewable and Sustainable Energy Reviews, 14, 9, 3059–3067.

L. M. Romeo, I. Bolea, J. M. Escosa, 2008, Integration of power plant and amine scrubbing to reduce CO_2 capture costs, Applied Thermal Engineering, 28, 8, 1039-1046.

M. R. Abu-Zahra, J. P. Niederer, P. H. Feron, G. F.Versteeg, 2007, CO_2 capture from power plants: Part II. A parametric study of the economical performance based on mono-ethanolamine, International Journal of Greenhouse Gas Control, 1, 2, 135-142.

M. Ystad, A. Lakew, O. Bolland, 2013, Integration of low-temperature transcritical CO_2 Rankine cycle in natural gas-fired combined cycle (NGCC) with post-combustion CO_2 capture, International Journal of Greenhouse Gas Control, 12, 213-219.

N. Zhang, N. Lior, 2006, A novel near-zero CO_2 emission thermal cycle with LNG cryogenic exergy utilization, Energy, 31, 1666-1679.

R. Chacartegui, D. Sánchez, J. Muñoz, T. Sánchez, 2009, Alternative ORC bottoming cycles for combined cycle power plants, Applied Energy, 86, 10, 2162-2170.

S. Deng, H. Jin, R. Cai, R. Lin, 2004, Novel cogeneration power system with liquefied natural gas (LNG) cryogenic exergy utilization, Energy, 29, 4, 497-512.

Z. Shengjun, W. Huaixin, G. Tao, 2011, Performance comparison and parametric optimization of subcritical Organic Rankine Cycle (ORC) and transcritical power cycle system for low-temperature geothermal power generation, Applied Energy, 88, 8, 2740-2754.

Jiří Jaromír Klemeš, Petar Sabev Varbanov and Peng Yen Liew (Editors)
Proceedings of the 24th European Symposium on Computer Aided Process Engineering – ESCAPE 24
June 15-18, 2014, Budapest, Hungary.

Stochastic Optimization of the Strategic Planning Supply Chain of Biorefineries: Large Scale Models

Pablo A. Rodríguez-González, Sergio Frausto-Hernández*, Ulises I. Bravo-Sánchez

Instituto Tecnológico de Aguascalientes, Chemical and Biochemical Department, Ave. Adolfo López Mateos No. 1801 Ote., Fracc. Bona Gens, Aguascalientes, Ags., C.P. 20256, Mexico
serfraher@yahoo.com.mx

Abstract

This paper addresses the strategic planning of the supply chain of biorefineries by using a model of optimization problem formulated as a two-stage mixed-integer linear stochastic programming with recourse, in which the uncertainties are considered in the product demand and the availability of the raw materials. The study case presented here was developed for the southeastern region of the USA, resulting in a mathematical optimization problem of large scale, with a lot of constraints and decision variables, and more than a hundred uncertain parameters. The dimensions of the resulting problem are greater than those of the problems that have so far been solved with Stochastic Decomposition Algorithm, for which it was necessary to modify the computational implementation proposed by Frausto-Hernández et al. (2010). The resulting solution was determined not only the maximum economic benefit, but also the most suitable processing route, location and optimal production capacities of the facilities involved in the process of biorefinament. The results show the usefulness of the solution algorithm and computational implementation improvements and robustness in solving large-scale problems.

Keywords: Biorefineries, supply chain, stochastic decomposition, two stages problems.

1. Introduction

Increasing trend in the consumption of fossil resources, the cost of resources, and consequently the increase in carbon dioxide emissions from anthropogenic sources indicate that a reduction in the use fossil resources would be needed to address climate change. This has prompted search for alternative ways to obtain energy, fuels, and chemicals. The life cycle of fossil show that coal, oil and natural gas are all from biomass decomposed on the surface of the earth trapped in geological formations. Therefore the biomass to be a precursor to conventional non-renewable resources can be used as fuel and can generate energy and chemicals with some modifications of existing processes (Sengupta and Pike, 2013).

Today, for the synthesis optimization and supply chain a biorefinery, the models that have been considered are deterministic in nature, because all the parameters that influence the optimization task are well known in advance (see Santibañez-Aguilar, 2013). However, there are situations where the uncertainties should not be ignored because they are present in a large proportion of important parameters in the problem of production planning of a biorefinery (Subrahmanyam et al., 1994). For example, are not known with certainty the supply and cost of the various sources of biomass supply and productivity, as they relate to agriculture, subject to weather and environmental conditions, as well as not known exactly the relationship between the amount of ground with the quantity and quality of production. While the demand for biofuels is directly affected by the prices of fossil fuels and environmental policies. The assumption that these parameters are known with certainty limits the usefulness of the approach, so do not consider their uncertainty can lead to non-optimal decisions or not feasible to apply them to real situations, leading to economic losses of great magnitude (Birge and Louveaux, 1994).

Problems of this type are often modeled by Stochastic Programming techniques and referred to as Two-Stage Stochastic Programs with Recourse, being resolved in a formal way through Stochastic Decomposition Algorithm (Higle and Sen, 1991). However, by attempting to solve this kind of problems are some limitations, such as large computational requirements arising from the complexity of addressing the problems under the explicit consideration of uncertainties (Sahinidis, 2004). So far, the application of computational developments for stochastic troubleshooting has been limited to problems of not more than 300 constraints, and 300 decision variables, 40 uncertain parameters, due to the large computational requirements of memory and processing speed, which were previously easily exceeded (Frausto-Hernández et al., 2010). Therefore, with the improvements and advances in computer technology, along with stochastic techniques available, this paper seeks to overcome existing limitations for solving large stochastic model resulting from the strategic planning problems of supply chain of biorefineries (Rodríguez-González et al., 2012), through improvements in computational implementation proposed by Frausto-Hernández et al. (2010).

2. Strategic planning supply chain of biorefineries

2.1 Mathematical model

The mathematical model of optimization which is used for strategic planning of the supply chain of biorefineries was proposed by Rodríguez-González et al. (2012); this model consists of a two-stage stochastic linear programming problem with recourse (see Eqs. 1-11). The problem of the first stage is Mixed-Integer Linear Programming (MILP), and it involved making capital investment decisions with constraints that determine the size and location of the processing plants. The linear problem of the second stage are determined matter flows through restrictions on availability of raw material, mass balances, product demand and limits the production capacity of the facilities. Considering both uncertainties in the availability of raw materials and the demand for the products represented by a uniform probability distribution function.

First stage problem:

$$\min f_1 = capital \cos ts \tag{1}$$

Production capacity restrictions:

$$Fcap_j \le F_j^{\max} x1_j \tag{2}$$

$$Kcap_k \le K_k^{\max} x2_k \tag{3}$$

Second stage problem:

$$\max f_2 = \text{Product sales} - \text{Raw material costs} - \text{Transportation costs} - \text{Panalty costs} \quad (4)$$

Raw material availability:

$$\sum_j f_{irj} \leq u1_{ir} \quad \forall\, i,r \quad (5)$$

Maximum flow restrictions:

$$\sum_r \sum_i f_{irj} \leq Fcap_j \quad \forall\, j \quad (6)$$

$$\sum_l^r \sum_j^i g_{jlk} \leq Kcap_k \quad \forall\, k \quad (7)$$

Material Balances:

$$\sum_k g_{jlk} + Ppre_{jl} - \sum_r apre_{rlj} \sum_i f_{irj} = 0 \quad \forall j,l \quad (8)$$

$$\sum_m^k Pcen_{kpm} - \sum_l acen_{lpk} \sum_j g_{jlk} = 0 \quad \forall\, k,p \quad (9)$$

Product demand:

$$\sum_j Ppre_{jl} + Mpre_l = u2_l \quad \forall\, l \quad (10)$$

$$\sum_m^j \sum_k Pcen_{kpm} + Mcen_p = u3_p \quad \forall\, p \quad (11)$$

2.2 Solution algorithm and computational implementation

The resulting model is solved using the Stochastic Decomposition Algorithm (Higle and Sen, 1991), which consists of an iterative procedure that uses a sampling technique to generate a given number of uncertain variables observations. The algorithm begins by solving the problem of the second stage in its dual form for optimality cuts, which are linear constraints that are added to the problem of the first stage during the resolution process. Then solve the problem of the first stage will provide the new values would use the following problem of the second stage. The algorithm continues until it meets the stop criterion, e.g. until the objective function value of the first stage is less than or equal to an error.

Based on computational implementation proposed by Frausto-Hernández et al. (2010), improvements were made to the parts of the sampling techniques and master program. These consisted of changes in the source codes to increase the ability to generate a greater number of uncertain parameters for the case of sampling techniques and increased handling capacity of the RAM, in the case of the master program. Both modifications coupled with computational advances are expected to exceed the limiting sizing problem.

3. Illustrative example

We considered the problem proposed by Kim et al. (2011), which includes biomass as sources of logging residues, thinning waste, garden waste, energy crops and wood waste, such as vegetable oil products, coal and gas as main products biogasoline and biodiesel. Furthermore, as shown in Figure 1 includes a set of 30 possible agricultural areas producing feedstock, 29 geographical areas where build possible pre-processing facilities, 10 zones likely to install central processing facilities, as well as 10 final distribution sites, geographically distributed in south eastern USA.

The resulting model consists of 39 constraints and 78 variables in the first stage, of which 39 are binary variables. In the second stage we obtain a system of 316 equations and 5,716 variables. The problem is considered as uncertain variables to the availability of biomass in each agricultural area and to the demand for major products in each market, for a total of 104 uncertain parameters, of which 84 correspond to the availability of raw materials and the remaining claims. The values of these parameters are presented in Tables 1 and 2, corresponding to an average value for a uniform probability distribution of ± 10 %.

The results of stochastic and deterministic way are shown in Tables 3 and 4 respectively. The optimal configuration of the problem is presented in Figure 2. Table 3 shows that all land areas are required as a raw material supplier that send to the pre-processing facilities closest to them. In addition, four core processes facilities are required to meet the demands of biofuels in the region: The biorefinery 2 oil receives pre-processes the 3, 9 and 21, and provides markets 1, 2 and 5, the biorefinery 5, receives oil from the pre- process 7 and 25, and provides the market 5; biorefinery 8 receives oil from the pre-process 4, 12 and 13, and provides markets 3 and 6, and the biorefinery 9 receives oil pre-processes of 1, 2, 4, 15 and 28 and provides markets 4, 9 and 8.

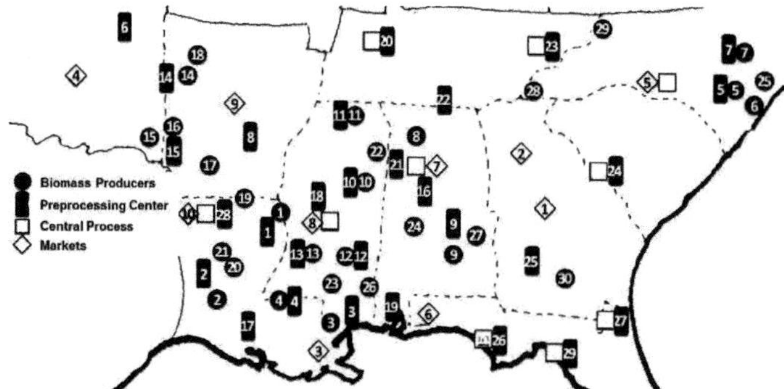

Figure 1. Geographical distribution.

Table 1. Product demand for Study Case.

Product	Market (t)									
	1	2	3	4	5	6	7	8	9	10
Gasoline	222.1	813.8	786.5	918.7	590.5	331.2	400.2	307.7	343.9	319.1
Biodiesel	111.1	406.9	393.3	459.4	295.3	165.6	200.1	153.9	172.0	159.6

Table 2. Availability of biomass for the Study Case.

Biomass	Producer (t)									
	1	2	3	4	5	6	7	8	9	10
1	-	-	103.6	155.4	184.8	-	168.0	-	319.0	139.3
2	116.6	116.6	-	-	-	50.4	-	100.1	-	-
3	38.9	38.9	25.9	38.9	46.2	16.8	42.0	33.4	79.8	34.8
4	-	-	621.6	932.4	-	-	-	-	-	835.9
5	305.0	297.0	188.0	202.0	291.0	198.0	186.0	198.0	221.0	246.0
Biomass	Producer (t)									
	11	12	13	14	15	16	17	18	19	20
1	77.4	-	77.4	-	-	-	561.6	-	-	-
2	-	-	-	-	189.0	231.0	-	105.3	155.4	77.7
3	19.4	-	19.4	-	63.0	77.0	140.4	35.1	51.8	25.9
4	464.4	-	-	-	-	-	-	-	1243.2	621.6
5	228.0	301.0	297.0	285.0	192.0	-	-	-	-	-
Biomass	Producer (t)									
	21	22	23	24	25	26	27	28	29	30
1	-	116.1	38.7	92.9	-	131.6	-	100.6	100.6	100.6
2	116.6	-	-	-	105.0	-	95.7	-	-	-
3	38.9	29.0	9.7	23.2	35.0	32.9	31.9	25.2	25.2	25.2
4	932.4	696.6	-	557.3	-	789.5	-	603.7	603.7	603.7
5	-	-	-	-	-	-	-	-	-	-

Table 3. Stochastic solution for the Study Case.

Preprocessing ($t\ 10^6$)													
1	2	3	4	5	6	7	8	9	10	11	12	13	14
1.91	2.37	0.94	1.33	-	-	2.05	-	0.82	1.25	0.87	1.30	0.43	-
Preprocessing ($t\ 10^6$)													
15	16	17	18	19	20	21	22	23	24	25	26	27	28
1.14	.	-	-	-	-	2.35	-	-	-	0.80	-	-	0.77
	Central process ($t\ 10^6$)										Net profit ($\$\ 10^6$)		
29	1	2	3	4	5	6	7	8	9	10			
-	-	4.53	-	-	1.62	-	-	3.08	4.60		1,320.2		

Table 4. Deterministic solution for the Study Case.

Preprocessing ($t\ 10^6$)													
1	2	3	4	5	6	7	8	9	10	11	12	13	14
1.91	2.26	0.94	1.33	1.32	-	-	-	0.75	1.26	0.79	1.30	0.39	-
Preprocessing ($t\ 10^6$)													
15	16	17	18	19	20	21	22	23	24	25	26	27	28
1.88	.	-	-	-	-	1.85	-	-	-	0.73	-	-	-
	Central Process ($t\ 10^6$)										Net profit ($\$\ 10^6$)		
29	1	2	3	4	5	6	7	8	9	10			
-	-	3.59	-	-	1.48	-	-	3.03	4.49		1,444.7		

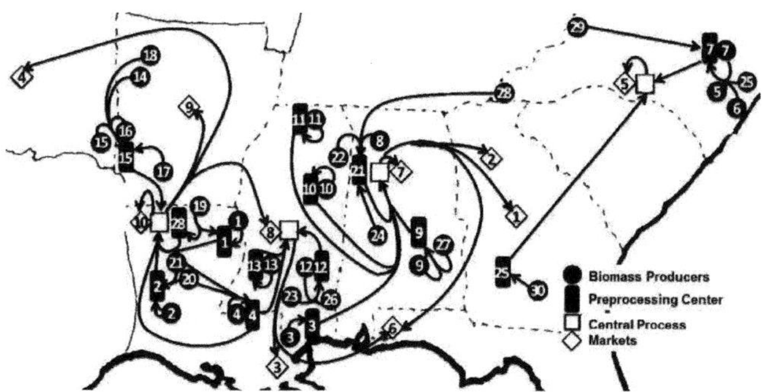

Figure 2. Optimal configuration.

4. Conclusions

The improvements made to the proposed computational implementation Frausto-Hernández et al. (2010) allowed to solve the model proposed by Rodriguez-González et al. (2012) for a case study developed for the southeastern USA. In this case we used a lot of continuous and binary variables, constraints and uncertain parameters, as in other conditions had hampered their solution.

For the particular case study, the biofuel demand is high enough to provide all the raw material from all agricultural areas. The cost of transport is an important decision, because in each agricultural area is favored those facilities (both pre-process and central process) and markets that are closer together. The uncertain nature of the demand for the products, and the availability of raw materials are parameters that significantly affect the optimal configuration of the problem, highlighting differences between stochastic and deterministic solution.

References

J. R. Birge, A. Louveaux, 1997, Multicut Algorithm for Two Stage Stochastic Linear Programming, European Journal of Operations Research, 34, 384-392.

S. Frausto-Hernández, V. Rico-Ramírez, I.E. Grossmann, 2010, Strategic Capacity Allocation under Uncertainty by Using a Two-Stage Stochastic Decomposition Algorithm with Incumbent Solutions, Industrial and Engineering Chemical Research, 49, 2812–2821.

J. L. Higle, S. Sen, 1991, Stochastic Decomposition: An Algorithm for Two-Stage Linear Programs with Recourse, Mathematics of Operations Research, 16, 650-669.

J. Kim, M.J. Realff, J.H. Lee, 2011, Optimal Design and Global Sensitivity Analysis of Biomass Supply Chain Networks for Biofuels under Uncertainty, Computers and Chemical Engineering, 35, 738–1751.

P. T. Rodríguez-González, S. Frausto-Hernández, U.I. Bravo-Sánchez, 2012, Stochastic Optimization of Strategic Planning for a Supply Chain of a Biorefinery, Primer Congreso Iberoamericano de Biorefinerías, Los Cabos, Baja California, Mexico, Memorias-2012.

N. V. Sahinidis, 2004, Optimization under Uncertainty: State-of-the-Art and Opportunities, Computers and Chemical Engineering, 28, 971–983.

J. E. Santibañez-Aguilar, J. B. González-Campos, J. M. Ponce-Ortega, M. Serna-González, M. M. El-Halwagi, 2013, Optimal Planning and Site Selection for Distributed Multiproduct Biorefineries Involving Economic, Environmental and Social Objetives, Journal of Cleaner Production, dx.doi.org/10-1016/j.jclepro.2013.08.004.

D. Sengupta, R. W. Pike, 2013, Chemicals from Biomass, Integrating Bioprocesses into Chemical Production Complexes for Sustainable Development, CRC Press, United States of America.

S. Subrahmanyam, J.F. Peknyt, G.V. Reklaitis, 1994, Design of Batch Chemical Plants under Market Uncertainty, Industrial and Engineering Chemical Research, 33, 2688–2701.

Jiří Jaromír Klemeš, Petar Sabev Varbanov and Peng Yen Liew (Editors)
Proceedings of the 24th European Symposium on Computer Aided Process Engineering – ESCAPE 24
June 15-18, 2014, Budapest, Hungary.

Performance Analysis of a Biomass Supercritical Water Gasification Process under Energy Self-sufficient Condition

Amornchai Arpornwichanop[a], Nathapol Boonpithak[a], Soorathep Kheawhom[a], Pimporn Ponpesh[a], Suthida Authayanun[b,*]

[a]*Computational Process Engineering, Department of Chemical Engineering, Faculty of Engineering, Chulalongkorn University, Bangkok 10330, Thailand*
[b]*Department of Chemical Engineering, Faculty of Engineering, Srinakharinwirot University, Nakhon Nayok 26120, Thailand*
suthidaa@g.swu.ac.th

Abstract

Depletion of fossil fuel and environmental concerns stimulate the use of clean and renewable energy. Biomass is regarded as a potential energy source and can be efficiently converted to a useful synthesis gas via incomplete combustion in a gasification process. However, the thermal gasification causes a tar formation and requires high energy input when wet biomass is used. The objective of this study is to investigate the performance of an autothermal biomass gasification process in supercritical water. A flowsheet model of the gasification process is developed and validated with experimental data. Thermodynamic analysis is performed based on the minimization of total Gibbs free energy. Simulations are performed to study effects of key operational parameters on the supercritical water gasification process at an energy self-sufficient condition, which a total net heat energy can be zero. Hydrogen in the synthesis gas product and thermal efficiency of the gasification process are also considered and suitable operating conditions of the autothermal biomass gasification for hydrogen production are identified.

Keywords: Supercritical water gasification, Autothermal operation, Hydrogen production, Performance analysis.

1. Introduction

An energy shortage problem is foreseen for the next few decades as a result of increasing worldwide population and economic growth. A global warming problem is also a critical issue caused by usage of fossil fuel. Many researchers have presently searched for alternative and more environmentally friendly energy sources. Biomass derived from organic and agricultural matters is considered an attractive, renewable energy resource (Maxim et al., 2011). However, due to its low energy density, the direct use of biomass is inconvenient and inefficient.

Gasification technology is likely to be the most effective energy conversion process of fuel sources in a solid form (Sadhwani et al., 2013). However, traditional gasification technologies have encountered a number of major difficulties hindering their development. First of all, the quality of the product gas obtained is usually low. Because a large portion of biomass is wet, this causes high drying costs in the gasification process. The biomass gasification in supercritical water is a promising technology to handle with these problems, especially for very wet biomass or organic waste. At supercritical condition, a significant change in the thermophysical properties of water is observed and causes the supercritical water gasification (SCWG) to avoid the formation of tar and char, thereby improving the product gas quality (Basu, 2010).

Although a number of experimental and simulation investigations in the biomass gasification with supercritical water have been performed, most of these studies used a biomass model compound (Withag et al., 2012). In addition, a high temperature operation of the gasification processes leads to high operating cost. The objective of this study is to investigate the performance of biomass gasification process in supercritical water. To minimize external heat requirement, the gasification operated at energy self-sufficient condition is considered. A thermodynamic analysis is performed to study effects of key operating parameters on the gasification performance. Hydrogen yield in the synthesis gas (syngas) product and thermal efficiency are also considered.

2. Model of supercritical water gasification process

Modeling of the supercritical water gasification for syngas production is performed using Aspen Plus simulator (Aspen Plus 2004.1). Equilibrium composition of the syngas is predicted based on the minimization of Gibbs free energy. Figure 1 shows a typical process of the supercritical water gasification consisting of a feed storage for wet biomass, a high pressure pump to increase the slurry pressure to a supercritical condition, a heat exchanger, a supercritical water gasification reactor, a cooler and high and low pressure separators. Simulation model of the biomass gasification process is divided into five sections (Figure 2): (1) fuel feed preparation, (2) air supply, (3) biomass decomposition, (4) gasification and (5) product gas separation. In this study, the RYIELD module is used to change the non-conventional stream "BIOMASS" into the conventional components based on a biomass composition. Char and volatile products consisting of H_2, CO, CO_2, CH_4 and H_2O are sent to the gasification section. The RGIBBS module is employed to simulate the partial oxidation and gasification steps. High and low pressure phase separators (SEP module) are used to separate the product gas. The Soave Redlich-Kwong property method with modified Huron-Vidal mixing rule (SRKMHV2) is chosen here as it can reliably predict the thermodynamic properties at the supercritical water condition (Withag et al., 2012).

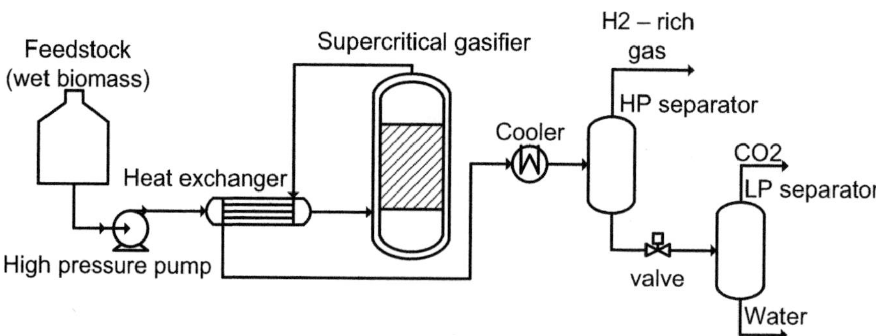

Figure 1. Biomass supercritical water gasification process.

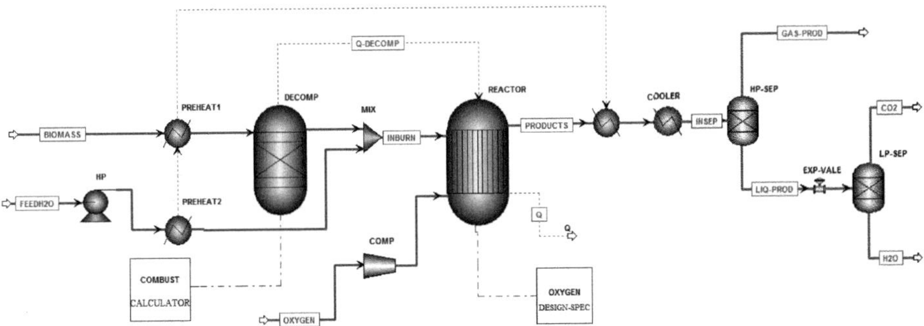

Figure 2. Simulation model of the biomass gasification in supercritical water.

Table 1. Comparison of the compositions of product gas from the supercritical water gasification

Gas composition	Experiment (Antal et al., 2000)	Model prediction
H_2	0.55	0.552
CO	0.03	0.027
CO_2	0.35	0.345
CH_4	0.06	0.076

2.1. Gasification process under energy self-sufficient condition

In this study, the gasification process is run under an energy self-sufficient condition, minimizing the external heat demand. Based on the energy balance, a total heat required for the gasification process is the sum of heat involving the decomposition and supercritical gasifier sections. Depending on the amount of air supply, the energy self-sufficient condition can be achieved by appropriate adjustment of operating parameters, such as biomass feedstock concentration, equivalence ratio (ER) and the gasifier temperature. It is noted that the ER is defined by the ratio of air fed into the gasifier to the stoichiometric amount of air required for the complete combustion.

2.2. Model validation

The simulation model of the supercritical water gasification is validated with experimental data of the cornstarch gasification in supercritical water reported by Antal et al. (2000). Input data for the experiment are as follows: feedstock concentration of 10.4 wt.%, gasifier temperature of 715 °C, operating pressure of 28 MPa. Table 1 compared the product gas compositions obtained from the experiment and the model prediction using the given input data. It is observed that the model prediction is in good agreement with the experimental data, especially for hydrogen, carbon monoxide and carbon dioxide.

3. Simulation results and discussion

This section presents a thermodynamic analysis of the supercritical water gasification process under an energy self-sufficient condition. Water Hyacinth is considered the biomass feedstock. The effect of key process parameters, i.e., supercritical gasifier temperature, feedstock concentration and pressure, on composition of the product gas is analyzed.

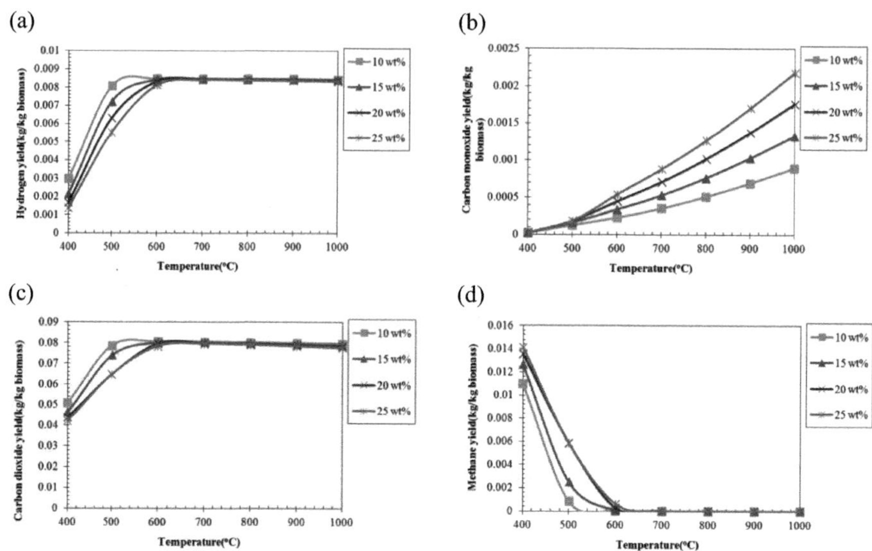

Figure 3. Product yields of the gasification process under different operating temperatures and feedstock concentrations: (a) hydrogen, (b) carbon monoxide, (c) carbon dioxide and (d) methane.

The gasifier temperature is a significant key operating parameter affecting the supercritical water gasification process. Figure 3 shows the product yields (dry basis) obtained from the gasifier run at temperatures ranging from 400-1000 °C and the feedstock concentration of 10-25 wt.%. Under the energy self-sufficient operation, the gasifier temperature considered for all the simulations is an adiabatic temperature, which the external heat flow equals to zero. The results show that the amount of oxygen fed into the gasification process is higher than that is needed for the biomass supply, resulting a complete combustion. This restrains the process of gasification. An increase in the gasification temperature raises the hydrogen yield as the water gas reaction is more pronounced at elevated temperatures. The maximal hydrogen yield of 0.0084 kg/kg biomass is obtained. From the viewpoint of thermodynamics, a further increase of the temperature is unnecessary as hydrogen is kept constant at the temperature higher than 600 °C. Figure 3(b) indicates that when the gasifier is run at high temperatures, carbon monoxide gradually increases. The yield of carbon dioxide also slowly increases with the increased temperature and remains constant at temperatures higher than 600 °C for all feedstock concentration (Figure 3(c)). In Figure 3(d), an increase in gasification temperatures decreases the yield of methane because the methanation reaction is unfavored at a higher temperature. The results shown in Figure 3 also indicate that hydrogen is highly generated when low-concentration feedstock is introduced to the gasifier at a temperature range of 400-600 °C. The hyacinth feedstock with less water drives the water gas reaction toward the product side. It can also be observed that an increase in the feedstock concentration increases the yield of carbon monoxide and methane. This observation can be explained by the shift reaction and steam reforming reaction.

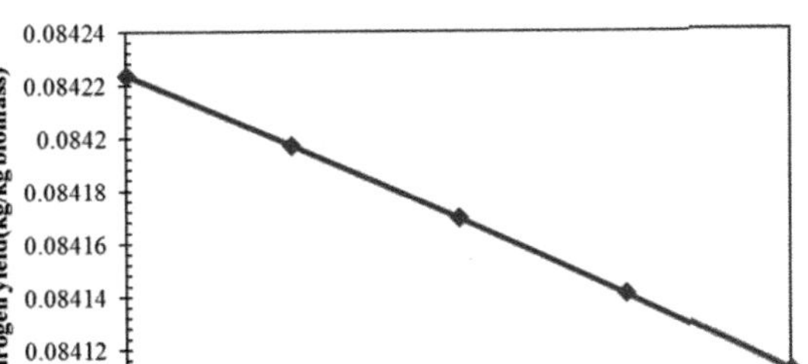

Figure 4. Effect of operating pressure on hydrogen yield (kg/kg biomass) (the feedstock concentration of 20 wt.% and temperature of 800 °C).

In general, operating pressure exhibits a complicated effect on the biomass gasification in supercritical water. The properties of water, such as density, static dielectric constant and ion product, change with pressure. As a result, the ion reaction rate increases and free-radical reaction is restrained with the increased pressure. The hydrolysis reaction presents a significant role in biomass gasification in supercritical water, but it requires the presence of H^+ or OH^-. When increasing the operating pressure, the ion product increases and thus the hydrolysis rate also increases. Moreover, a high pressure operation promotes the water-gas shift reaction, but reduces the decomposition reaction rate. Figure 4 shows a slight decrease in hydrogen when the gasification pressure is increased. It seems that the operating pressure in the studied range has no significant effect on the biomass gasification in supercritical water.

As the system energy consumption is significant, the thermodynamic efficiency of the hyacinth gasification is examined in order to find the optimum operating conditions that give the maximum yield of hydrogen with less energy consumption. The efficiency of the process is defined as follows:

$$\eta = \frac{n_{H_2} \times LHV_{H_2}}{n_{biomass} \times LHV_{biomass} + (Q_{gasifier} + \text{HP} + \text{Compressor})} \quad (1)$$

where n_i is the flow rate of component i (kg/hr), LHV_i is the lower heating value of component i (kJ/kg), $Q_{gasifier}$ is the heat requirement of gasifier (kJ/hr) and HP is the energy of high pressure pump (kJ/hr).

Figure 5(a) shows the effects of gasifier temperatures on the efficiency of the supercritical water gasification process fed by hyacinth with different concentrations. It is found that the increasing gasifier temperatures in a range of 400-700 °C increasingly improve the performance of the gasification process. The gasifier efficiency is also enhanced when high-concentration feedstock is applied. The optimum operating conditions for the supercritical water gasification of hyacinth at self-sufficient condition are at 600 °C with the inlet feedstock concentration of 20-25 wt.%. It is noted that the system energy is quite low due to the presence of water in the biomass feedstock. A comparison of the system efficiency based on different gasification technologies: conventional gasification, conventional gasification run at energy self-sufficient condition and supercritical water gasification at energy self-sufficient condition, is given in Figure 5(b). It is indicated that the supercritical water gasification technology is a suitable gasification technology to convert high-moisture content biomass (e.g., water

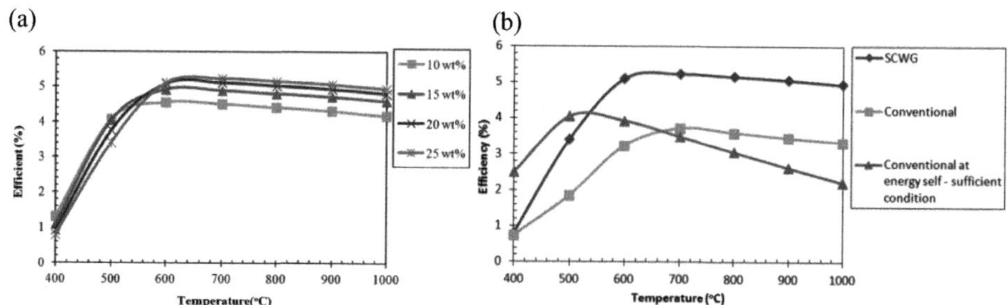

Figure 5. Gasification efficiency at different temperatures: impact of (a) feedstock concentration and (b) gasification technology

hyacinth). Based on the conventional gasification of biomass with high moisture, high energy is loss to dry out moisture before the thermal gasification reaction begins.

4. Conclusions

In this study, the supercritical water gasification of water hyacinth was studied. Modelling of the gasification process was performed using a flowsheet simulator and employed to investigate effects of key operating parameters on the gasification performances in terms of the syngas production and energy efficiency. The gasification operated at energy self-sufficient condition is considered to minimize an external heat supply. By comparing different gasification processes, the supercritical water gasification can produce the largest amount of hydrogen, resulting in higher system efficiency.

5. Acknowledgements

Support from the Ratchadaphiseksomphot Endowment Fund of Chulalongkorn University (RES560530067-EN) and the Thailand Research Fund is also gratefully acknowledged.

References

M.J. Antal, S.G Allen, D. Schulman, X. Xu, 2000, Biomass gasfication in supercritical water, Industrial and Engineering Chemistry Research, 39, 4040–4053.

Aspen Plus 2004.1, Getting Started: Building and Running a Process Model, Aspen Technology, Inc., Cambridge, USA

P. Basu, 2010, Biomass Gasification and Pyrolysis: Practical Design and Theory, Academic Press, MA, United States.

V. Maxim, C. Cormos, P.S. Agachi, 2011, Design of integrated gasification combined cycle plant with carbon capture and storage based on co-gasification of coal and biomass, Computer Aided Chemical Engineering, 29, 1904–1908.

N. Sadhwani, Z. Liu, M.R. Eden, S. Adhikari, 2013, Simulation, analysis, and assessment of CO_2 enhanced biomass gasification, Computer Aided Process Engineering, 32, 421–426.

J.A.M. Withag, J.R. Smeets, E.A. Bramer, G. Brem, 2012, System model for gasification of biomass model compounds in supercritical water – A thermodynamic analysis, Journal of Supercritical Fluids, 61, 157–166.

Jiří Jaromír Klemeš, Petar Sabev Varbanov and Peng Yen Liew (Editors)
Proceedings of the 24th European Symposium on Computer Aided Process Engineering – ESCAPE 24
June 15-18, 2014, Budapest, Hungary.

Fenske and Kremser Group Methods in the Design of Fully Thermally Coupled Distillation Column

Hosanna Uwitonze, Amit Goyal, Sejung Kim, Sungkwon Kim, Kyu Suk Hwang*

Department of Chemical Engineering, Pusan National University, San 30 Jangjeon-dong, Kumjeong-gu, Busan 609-735, Korea
kshwang@pusan.ac.kr

Abstract

The design of fully thermally distillation column is more complex than conventional arrangements due to greater number of degrees of freedom. This paper introduces a new structure design method to determine the structure of column system. The method combines approximate group method and Fenske equation for minimum equilibrium stage which is applied to three column model. The usefulness of the design method is explored using different feed systems. This design procedure gives an optimum structure for a given ternary separation. The method provides an initial design from which thermodynamic efficiency and optimal internal flow distribution are examined.

Keywords: Structural design, thermally coupled distillation, group method.

1. Introduction

Distillation, the most mature operation, is by far the most widely used method for fractionating liquid mixtures of chemical components. Unfortunately, distillation is a very energy–intensive technique (Seader and Henley, 1998); the 3 % of the world energy consumption is attributed to separation processes (Hewitt and Morell, 1999). However, improvement and heat integration of distillation columns are the potentials that can be good way for achieving large savings (Engelien and Skogestad, 2004). Conventionally, a distillation process battery separating more than two different components requires a series of binary-like distillation columns. The fully thermally coupled distillation column (known as Petlyuk column) has shown considerable energy savings in several cases; high thermodynamic efficiency of the column system has widely been recognized ever since it was introduced (Petlyuk et al., 1965); at the same time the design and operation concerns have peeped out.

Mention the comparative study of Annakou (Annakou and Miszey, 1996), carried on different energy integrated distillation schemes for the separation of a ternary mixture including the Petlyuk column and the heat-integrated two column scheme. Even though the fully thermally coupled distillation column (FTCDC) was introduced almost more than half a century ago, and many authors have predicted considerable savings in energy and capital cost with this design, relatively few practical applications of such columns have been documented in the literature to date (Rudd, 1992). The process industry's reluctance toward using this type of column system can, at least partly be attributed to concerns regarding potential control problems and the lack of design procedures. Both of these problems are related to many more degrees of freedom that the Petlyuk column has in comparison to conventional columns (Chavez et al., 1986).

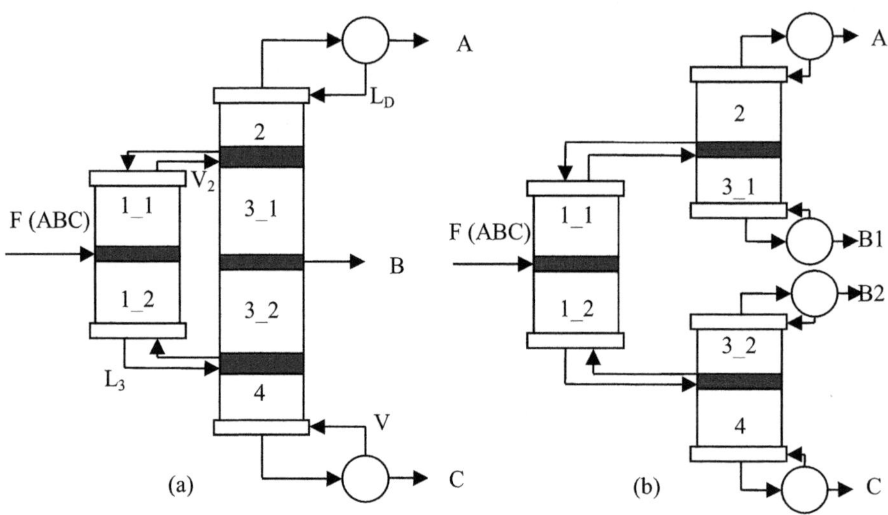

Figure 1. Schematic diagram of (a) FTCDC, (b) Three-column distillation system

2. Design assumptions

A design method is proposed to shape the column system, fixing the location of the feed tray, side-stream tray, interlinking trays and the total number of trays of column system. Trinatafyllou (Trinatafyllou and Smith, 1992), determined design degrees of freedom from two decision variables: recovery of A at the bottom of the prefractionator and the recovery of C at the top of the prefractionator. Lee (Lee et al, 2011) proposed a design method, from which internal sections of the column are divided into four separate sections and matched to the sloppy arrangement with three conventional simple columns. In this study, it is assumed that the net flow of species C at the top of prefractionator (Figure 1a) is equal to the flow of species C in the side draw; the net flow of species A at the bottom of prefractionator is equal to the flow of species A in the side draw, Chu (Chu et al, 2011). It is assumed that liquid compositions of component *i* on interlinking trays are equals. From feed and product purity specifications and assumptions, one can determine the composition of key components at the both ends of prefractionator.

3. Column system design procedure

3.1. Operating conditions

Wolff (Wolff and Skogestad, 1995) proved that no separation is achievable with some split of liquid flow between a main column and a prefractionator, the split for a given separation has upper and lower limits. The following equations are served to estimate the operating conditions of the prefractionator (Fidkowski and Królikowski, 1986).

$$L_P^{min} = \frac{\alpha_C F}{\alpha_A - \alpha_C} \tag{1}$$

$$V_P^{min} = \max\left[\frac{A\phi_2}{\alpha_A - \phi_2} + \frac{\alpha_B B}{\alpha_B - \phi_2}\beta\right] \tag{2}$$

where α's are relative volatilities and ø's are the solutions of Underwood equation for saturated liquid feed, β is the fraction of intermediate component at the top of prefractionator; minimum liquid flow rate and minimum vapor flow rate of the prefractionator are given by Eqs.(1) and (2). For initialization of rigorous design of FTCDC, minimum liquid flow rate in the main column is estimated from Eq. (3), this is total liquid flow rate of the main column and prefractionator. Vapor boil-up rate is found from the reflux flow rate and overhead product rate.

$$L^{min} = \max\left\{\frac{A\emptyset_1}{\alpha_A-\emptyset_1}, \frac{A\emptyset_2}{\alpha_A-\emptyset_2} + \frac{\alpha_B B}{\alpha_B-\emptyset_2}\right\} \quad (3)$$

3.2. Column system structure design

Structural design of column system is undertaken into two steps: the structure design of prefractionator is determined first; secondly the structure design of main column is made. The column system structure is shaped from three-column model (Figure 1b). For prefractionator, equations that relate compositions of multicomponent vapor and liquid streams are formulated, and solved to determine the numbers of stage needed.

3.2.1. Prefractionator structure design

Atop of section 1_1, material balance of heavy key component around the top stage is

$$V_{1\_1}y_{H,m+1} = L_{1\_1}K_H^{-1}y_{H,m} + V_t y_{H,m} \quad (4)$$

$$y_{H,m+1} = \frac{L_{1\_1}K_H^{-1}}{V_{1\_1}}y_{H,m} + \frac{V_{1\_1}-L_{1\_1}}{V_{1\_1}}y_{H,m} \quad (5)$$

Eq. (5) is vapor composition of heavy component atop top stage. Repeated use of this equation for N_{1_1} stages that make the column section gives the following formula

$$y_{H,N_{1\_1}} = a^{N_{1\_1}}y_{H,D1}\left[1 + \left(1-\frac{L_1}{V_1}\right)\left(\frac{1-a^{-N_{1\_1}}}{a-1}\right)\right] \quad (6)$$

N_{1_1} is the number of stages from the top to the bottom of the column section; $y_{H,D1}$ is vapor composition of heavy component atop of top stage of column section (accumulator), $y_{H,N1\_1}$ is vapor composition of heavy component entering through the bottom of column section. Likewise, at the bottom stage of section 1_2

$$L_{1\_2}x_{L,n+1} = V_{1\_2}K_L x_{L,n} + L_b x_{L,n} \quad (7)$$

$$x_{L,n+1} = \frac{V_{1\_2}K_L}{L_{1\_2}}x_{L,n} + \frac{L_{1\_2}-V_{1\_2}}{L_{1\_2}}x_{L,n} \quad (8)$$

Repeated use of Eq. (8) for N_{1_2} stages that make column section gives

$$x_{L,N_{1\_2}} = s^{N_{1\_2}}x_{L,B1}\left[1 + \left(1-\frac{V_2}{L_2}\right)\left(\frac{1-s^{-N_{1\_2}}}{s-1}\right)\right] \quad (9)$$

where $x_{L,B1}$ is light key component in bottom product, $x_{L,N1\_2}$ is liquid composition for light component entering the column section through the top; *s* and *a* are stripping and absorption factors respectively and are greater than unit. For evaluation of both absorption and stripping factors the K-values were assumed to be constant all along the respective column sections.

3.2.2. Location of feed tray

Absorber and stripper cascades have a common and shared tray "feed tray", the vapor leaving the feed tray goes in the absorber while the liquid goes into stripper section. Feed tray and tray numbers calculated from steps 1 and 2 are summed up and constitute total tray number for prefractionator. The design equations discussed in this section are easy and straightforward to compute the number of stages within a cascade once the operating conditions are known.

3.3. Main column structure design

From Figure 1a, sections 2 and 3_1 constitute a column section that separates the light component A from the middle component B and heavy component C which is sent in the main column through the top of prefractionator; sections 2 and 3_1 are combined when calculating the minimum tray number. Note that, these merged sections form a column section which mainly separates the light component A from middle component B. Likewise, sections 3_2 and 4 separate middle component B from heavy component C. Thence, Eqs (10) and (11) are served to compute the minimum number of trays wherein one can use the rule of thumb to calculate the actual tray numbers, by taking twice the minimum numbers.

$$\left(N_2 + N_{3\_1}\right)_{min} = \frac{\ln S_{2,3\_1}}{\ln \alpha_{ij}} i,j = \{A,B\} \tag{10}$$

$$\left(N_{3\_2} + N_4\right)_{min} = \frac{\ln S_{3\_2,4,}}{\ln \alpha_{ij}} i,j = \{B,C\} \tag{11}$$

3.3.1. Interlinking trays

The section column between upper interlinking stage and condenser is served to mainly separate light component A from middle component B, this sets the fate of the heavy component because it is automatically eliminated from the overhead product (distillate). For a column operating efficiently, section 2 mainly deals with separation of light component A from middle component B. A design equation is developed in similar manner as that of section 1_1 in prefractionator.

$$y_{H,N_2} = a^{N_2} y_{H,d}\left[1 + \left(1 - \frac{L_2}{V_2}\right)\left(\frac{1-a^{-N_2}}{a-1}\right)\right] \tag{12}$$

Section column between lower interlinking stage and reboiler is served to mainly separate middle component B from heavy component C. Design equation for the section is developed in similar manner as that of section 1_2, of prefractionator.

$$x_{B,N_4} = s^{N_4} x_{B,b1}\left[1 + \left(1 - \frac{V_4}{L_4}\right)\left(\frac{1-s^{-N_4}}{s-1}\right)\right] \tag{13}$$

Note that the interlinking stages may not be optimum, hence their optimization is necessary. The composition difference on interlinking trays of the prefractionator and main column has been made small as possible, this minimizes the mixing that can take place on the interlinking stage; otherwise the mixing lowers the efficiency of the column.

Table 1. Structure design results

Feed	Prefractionator	Main column	FT	UI	LI	SP
F1	19	69	7	11	57	33
F2	18	65	8	15	50	33
F3	21	66	7	12	56	33

Feed flow rate: 300 kmol/h, Pressure of the feed: 250 psia, Feed condition: saturated liquid, FT: Feed tray, UI: upper interlinking tray, LI: lower interlinking tray, SP: side product tray

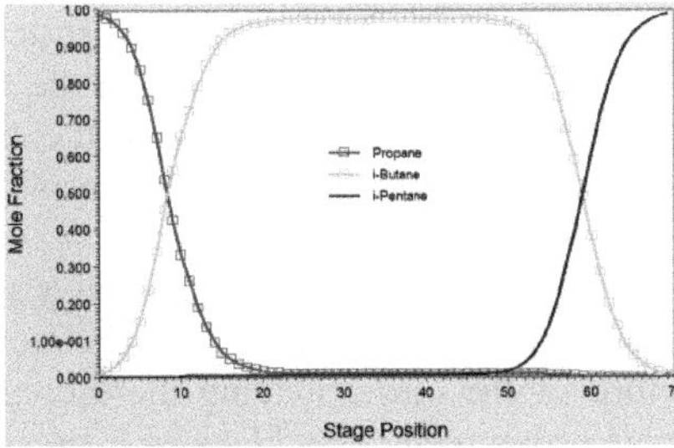

Figure 2. Composition profile of the main column of FTCDC

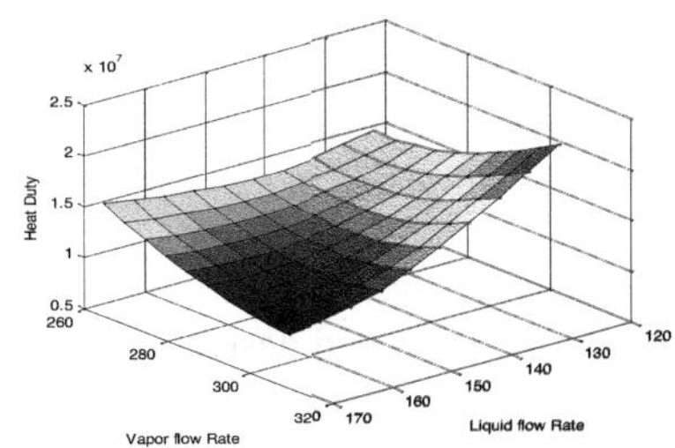

Figure 3. Effect of interlinking streams on the energy for F1

4. Example systems

The proposed design procedure is applied to multi-component feed systems in order to investigate its performance; feeds contain C3, i-C4, and i-C5, in particular 0.25/0.5/0.25 (F1), equimolar (F2) and 0.25/0.25/0.5 (F3). The design specification for the products for these examples is arbitrary set to 0.990 mol fraction of the lightest component in the overhead product, 0.98 mol fraction of intermediate component in side draw product, and 0.99 of the heaviest component in bottom product.

5. Results and discussion

The structural design and operating conditions results are used to initiate and perform rigorous simulation (Seader and Henley, 1998) of ternary systems, then analyzing and investigating the usefulness of the design method. Structural design results on the example systems using the proposed design procedure are summarized in Table 1. Column structure for feed system F1 includes 88 stages whose 19 stages are for prefractionator and 69 for main column; the top tray of prefractionator is interlinked to 11th tray while the bottom tray is interlinked to 57th tray of main column, side product draw is at 33rd tray. The feed system with high heavy component, its corresponding column has many stages in the prefractionator; that fact is many stages are needed to absorb heavy component. Figure 2 shows the composition profile for main column of the FTCDC system. From Figure 3, it is noticed that distribution of the internal liquid and vapor flows into prefractionator and main column is the most significant factor that affects the energy consumption. Many authors have also used response surface technique to optimize and analyze how the variables are interconnected; Long (Long and Lee, 2012), and Sangal (Sangal et al, 2013). The effect of product purity on energy consumption has shown that: as side product purity approaches unit the energy required increases drastically. On the other hand, energy variations for top and bottom products purity are almost constant.

6. Conclusions

This study emphasizes the design of fully thermally coupled distillation column structure on the basis of group method and Fenske equation. The method utilizes the three-column configuration equivalent to fully thermally coupled distillation column to find the proper structure in a simple manner. The search method for optimization is used to obtain the optimal interlinking flow rates of column system; even though this optimization technique does not provide true minimum values it gives a domain where the minimum values are located. Extensive simulation studies illustrate that the proposed method is suitable for fully thermally coupled distillation column structure design. The study carried out to investigate the effect of available energy on the side product compositions shown that purity of the side product has direct impact of energy consumption while the energy for top and bottom product purities is almost constant.

From the extensive simulation studies carried out, with a thorough analysis to investigate the proposed design method, it is noticed that near-optimal FTCDC structure can be reasonably determined from the structure of the corresponding there column configuration using a combination of approximate group method and Fenske expression.

References

J.D. Seader, E.J. Henley, 1998, Separation Process Principles, John Wiley & Sons, Inc., New York, pp 508-509, 531-538.

G. Hewitt, J. Quarini, M. Morell, 1999, More efficient distillation, Chem. Eng.

F.B. Petlyuk, V.M. Platonov, D.M. Slavinskii, 1965, Thermodynamically Optimal Method For Separating Multicomponent Mixtures, Int. Chem. Eng., 5, 555-561.

H.K. Engelien, S. Skogestad, 2004, Selecting control variables for a heat-integrated distillation system with prefractionator, Comput. Chem. Eng., 28, 683-691.

O. Annakou, P. Mizsey, 1996, Rigorous comparative study of energy integrated distillation schemes, Ind. Eng. Chem. Res., 35, 1877-1885.

I.J. Halvorsen, S. Skogestad, 2000, Distillation Theory, Norwegian University of Science and Technology, Norway.

H. Rudd, 1992, Thermal coupling for energy efficiency, Chem. Eng. (Distillation Supplement), S14-S15.

C.R. Chavez, J.D. Seader, T.L. Wayburn, 1986, Multiple steady-state solutions for interlinked separation systems, Ind. Eng. Chem. Fundam., 25, 566-576.

C. Triantafyllou, R. Smith, 1992, The design and optimization of fully thermally coupled distillation columns, Trans. Inst. Chem. Eng., 70, 118-132.

K. T. Chu, L. Cadoret, C. C Yu, J. D. Ward, 2011, A New Shortcut Design Method and Economic Analysis of Divided Wall Columns, Ind. Eng. Chem. Res., 50, 9221–9235.

S. H. Lee, M. Shamsuzzoha, M. Han, H. Y. Kim, M. Y. Lee, 2011, Study of the structural characteristics of a divided wall column using the sloppy distillation arrangement, Korean Journal of Chemical Engineering, 28, 348-356.

E. Wolff, S. Skogestad, 1995, Operation of Integrated Three-Product (Petlyuk) Distillation Columns, Ind. Eng. Chem. Res., 34, 2094-2103.

Z.T. Fidkowski, L. Królikowski, 1986, Thermally coupled system of distillation columns: Optimization procedure, AIChE J., 32, 537-546.

N.V.D. Long, M. Lee, 2012, Dividing wall column structure design using response surface methodology, Computers and Chemical Engineering, 37, 119-124.

V.K. Sangal, V. Kumar, I.M. Mishra, 2013, Optimization of divided wall column for the separation of C4-C6 normal paraffin mixture using box-Behnken design, Chemical Industry and Chemical Engineering Quarterly, 19, 107-119.

Jiří Jaromír Klemeš, Petar Sabev Varbanov and Peng Yen Liew (Editors)
Proceedings of the 24th European Symposium on Computer Aided Process Engineering – ESCAPE 24
June 15-18, 2014, Budapest, Hungary.

Dynamic Modelling and Solution Studies on Absorption of CO_2 in Rotated Packing Bed

Jia-Lin Kang[a], Kai Sun[b], David Shan-Hill Wong[a], Shi-Shang Jang[a]*, Chung-Sung Tan[a]

[a] *Department of Chemical Engineering, National Tsing Hua University, Hsinchu, 30013, Taiwan, ROC*

[b]*Department of Automation, Qilu University of Technology, Shandong, 250353, P.R. China*

ssjang@mx.nthu.edu.tw

Abstract

This study presented a model of the absorption of carbon dioxide by mono-ethanolamine solution in a rotating packed bed absorber using two-film theory for mass-transfer. It was found that temperature bulge can also be found in rotating packed bed if large amount of carbon dioxide was removed. Proper accounting of changes in liquid holdup is critical to accurate prediction of changes in capture efficiencies with gas and liquid flow rate. Moreover, use of a termolecular model for enhancement factor is necessary to predict experiment results using high amine concentrations. Since the model have been comprehensively validated using data provided by various authors in the literature with various gas-liquid flow rates, rotator speeds, and solvent conditions, it could be used as a tool for scale up studies.

Keywords: rotating packed bed; MEA; CO2; modelling; temperature bulge.

1. Introduction

Global warming is caused by high amounts of greenhouse gas emissions, mainly carbon dioxide, due to the use of fossil fuels. Carbon dioxide capture and storage may become an important solution of the global warming problem. Among many methods of capturing CO_2, absorption by chemical solvents, mainly aqueous amine solutions is one that closest to commercialization. One of the major challenges of carbon dioxide capture by chemical absorption is that the large volume of gas must be handled. Due to mass transfer limitation, if traditional separation equipment such as packed column are used, the equipment will be exceptionally huge and expensive. The rotating packed bed (RPB) was proposed to relax the mass-transfer limitation and intensify the process. The RPB utilizes centrifugal force to increase mass-transfer efficiency. The high rotator speed causes the liquid to disperse into droplets, which increases the gas-liquid interfacial area. Thus, RPB could effectively reduce the volume requirements of the equipment. In recent years a number of studies have investigated the feasibility of using RPB for CO_2 capture using various amine solutions (Jassim et al., 2007; Cheng and Tan, 2009; Cheng et al., 2010). There have also been a few studies in which models for predicting the performance of RPB for CO_2 capture. For example,Qian et al. (2009) developed a model of the absorption of absorption of CO_2 by aqueous N-methyldiethanolamine. The work focused on the modeling diffusion reaction process by Higbie's penetration theory. Qian et al. (2010) presented a followed up study on the selective absorption of hydrogen sulfide and CO_2 by MDEA.Sun et al. (2009) presented a model for absorption of

$CO_2$and ammonia into water in a RPB. Yi et al. (2009) presented studies of absorption of CO_2 into a Benfield solution (hot potassium carbonate promoted by DEA). One of the most commonly used amine for CO_2 capture is mono-ethanolamine (MEA). Recently, Yu et al. (2012) modeled the absorption of CO_2 by MEA by six stirred tanks in series followed by a gas–liquid contactor. Most of these studies assumed that the reaction is isothermal, and only mass transfer from gas to liquid phase was considered, i.e. vaporization of water was neglected. Therefore, the purpose of this work was to develop a comprehensive model based on two-film theory that could be applied to the absorption of carbon dioxide in a RPB model by MEA without using simplifying assumptions such as an isothermal reactor and no solvent vaporization. We shall demonstrate that accurate modeling of liquid holdup is critical to performance predictions and that a modified enhancement factor, proposed by Aboudheir et al. (2003), was necessary to improve prediction results for high MEA concentration situations.

2. Model Development

2.1. Material and energy balances

The gas and liquid material balances of the model are shown in Eq.(1) - (2):

$$\frac{dC_{g,i}}{dt} = -\frac{1}{2\pi rZ}\frac{\partial\left(C_{g,i}v_g\right)}{\partial r} - \varepsilon a_{gl}N_i \tag{1}$$

$$\frac{dC_{l,i}}{dt} = \frac{1}{2\pi rZ}\frac{\partial(C_{l,i}v_l)}{\partial r} + \varepsilon a_{gl}N_i + \varepsilon_L \times rxn_i \tag{2}$$

The components being considered in the gas phase are CO_2, water, MEA, and an inert gas (assumed to be nitrogen). The components being considered in the liquid phase are CO_2, MEA, H_2O,N_2, and the ionic species H_3O^+, OH^-, $MEAH^+$, $HCO_3^-$and $MEACOO^-$. The molar mass-transfer fluxes assumed that $N_{ionic\ species} = 0$ .Only N_{CO_2} , N_{MEA} , N_{H_2O} and N_{N_2} are nonzeros. The gas and liquid energy balances are shown in

$$\frac{dT_g}{dt} = \frac{1}{2\pi rZ}\frac{1}{C_g}\frac{d\left(C_gT_gv_g\right)}{dr} - \frac{\varepsilon a_{gl}}{C_gCp_g}h_{gl}\left(T_l - T_g\right) \tag{3}$$

$$\frac{dT_l}{dt} = -\frac{1}{2\pi rZ}\frac{1}{C_l}\frac{\partial(C_lT_lv_l)}{\partial r} + \frac{\varepsilon a_{gl}}{C_lC_{pl}}(h_{gl}\left(T_l - T_g\right) - \Delta H_{rxn}N_{CO2} - \Delta H_{vap}N_{H2O}) \tag{4}$$

2.2. Liquid phase reactions

Table 1 displays the reactions between CO_2, MEA and H_2Oconsidered in the liquid phase (Aspen, 2008).

2.3. Mass-transfer model

The mass-transfer model in this study was based on two film theory. The molar mass-transfer flux N_i was defined as:

$$N_i = k_{g,o,i}\left(P_{g,i} - P_i^{eq,*}\right) \tag{5}$$

The gas overall mass-transfer coefficient is shown as:

$$k_{g,o,i} = \frac{1}{\left(\frac{1}{k_{g,i}}\right)+\left(\frac{H_i}{k_{l,i}E_i}\right)} \tag{6}$$

Note that sinceMEA and H_2O are soluble in water, Eq. (7) should be simplified as:

$$k_{g,o,i} = \left(\frac{1}{k_{g,i}}\right) \quad for\ i = MEA, H_2O \tag{7}$$

Also, the equilibrium partial pressure for high solubility components and insoluble gases are expressed as follows:

$$P_i^{eq,*} = \gamma_i x_i P_i^{sat} \quad \text{for } i = \text{MEA}, \text{H}_2\text{O} \tag{8}$$

$$P_i^{eq,*} = H_i C_{l,i} \quad \text{for } i = \text{CO}_2, \text{N}_2 \tag{9}$$

Liquid phase non-idealities were described with the electrolyte non-random-two-liquid (electrolyte NRTL) model (Renon and Prausnitz, 1968).

2.4. Mass-transfer coefficients, interfacial area and liquid hold up

In this study, the mass transfer correlation is considered:Onda et al. (1968), Tung and Mah (1985) for gas and liquid phase mass transfer coefficients, with Onda et al. (1968) correlation for interfacial area. The correlation of liquid holdup use a Burns et al. (2000). note that the correlations of Burns et al. (2000) is developed specifically for RPB.

2.5. Enhancement factor and other parameters

The enhancement factor E in Eq. (10) is defined as the ratio of the liquid mass-transfer coefficients for absorption with and without a chemical reaction. This well-known equation is shown below:

$$E_{CO_2} = \frac{\sqrt{k_{app} D_{CO_2}}}{k_{l,CO2}} \tag{10}$$

The apparent reaction rate constant k_{app} was assumed to be a pseudo-first-order (Hikita et al., 1977).However, this widely used equation does not work well in cases of high MEA. In order to improve the agreements of this model and the experimental data, the formulation proposed by Aboudheir et al. (2003) of modelling the apparent reaction rate constant according to the tri-molecular reaction mechanism was adopted as follows:

$$k_{app} = k_{MEA}[MEA]^2 + k_{H2O}[H_2O][MEA] \tag{11}$$

Table 1. Reactions considered in the liquid phase

Name	Reactions
Protonation of MEA	$\text{MEAH}^+ + \text{H}_2\text{O} \leftrightarrow \text{MEA}+\text{H}_3\text{O}^+$
Water dissociation	$2\text{H}_2\text{O} \leftrightarrow \text{H}_3\text{O}^+ + \text{OH}^-$
Carbonate formation	$\text{HCO}_3^- + \text{H}_2\text{O} \leftrightarrow \text{CO}_3^{-2} + \text{H}_3\text{O}^+$
Carbamate formation	$\text{CO}_2 + \text{MEA} + \text{H}_2\text{O} \leftrightarrow \text{MEACOO}^- + \text{H}_3\text{O}^+$
Bicarbonate formation	$CO_2 + OH^- \leftrightarrow HCO_3^-$

3. Results and Discussion

3.1. Experimental data

In this section, the published data from previous works on MEA solutions byYu et al. (2012),and Jassim et al. (2007)were compared with the simulation data to validate the model developed in the previous section.

3.2. Effect of gas–liquid flow rates

Fig. 1 shows the agreements of the simulation and the experimental data. The results showed for predictions is within K_Ga and ±20 % for CO_2 removal.

3.3. Temperature Bulge

Fig. 2 (a)shows the liquid temperature profile in RPB using operating condition by Yu et al. (2012). This figure shows that a bulge of the liquid temperature in the RPB existed. It is well known (Kvamsdal and Rochelle, 2008) that a temperature bulge can be found near the bottom of a packed bed reactor. Fig. 2 (b) shows profiles of the heat transfer rate due to CO_2 absorption and water vaporization ($Q = -(\Delta H_{rxn} N_{CO2} + \Delta H_{vap} N_{H2O})$), and the temperature bulge also occurred at the point where the reaction heat of CO_2released is balanced by vaporization heat of water.

3.4. Effects of MEA concentrations

Fig. 3(a) and (b) compares results of the simulation and experimental data of Jassim et al. (2007) for 30, 55 and 75 wt% MEA with the enhancement factor calculated using the Hikita's pseudo first order kinetic constant and reaction rate constant by Aboudheir et al. (2003). Fig. 3 (a) shows that while model can predict the performance of RPB for 30 wt% MEA, it substantially under estimated $K_G a$. Aboudheir et al., 2003 showed that the problem could be resolved using termolecular reaction mechanism and an adjusted enhanced factor. Fig. 3 (b) shows that the predictions results for the 55 wt% and 75 wt% MEA can be substantially improved by this new equation. The performance of this new model for the 30 wt% MEA was maintained at an acceptable error range.

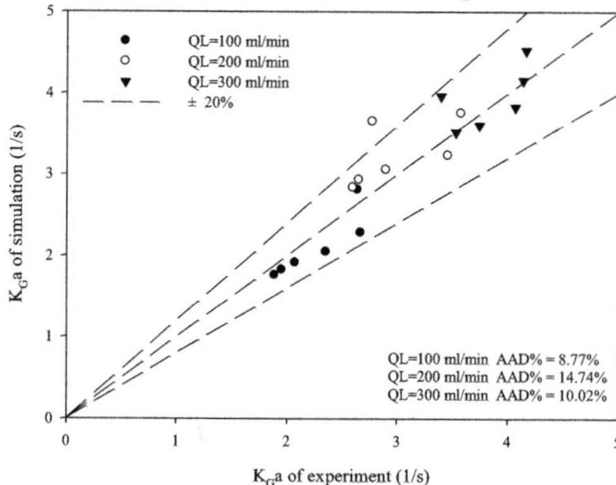

Figure1. The agreements of simulation and experimental of K_Ga for various liquid flow rates.

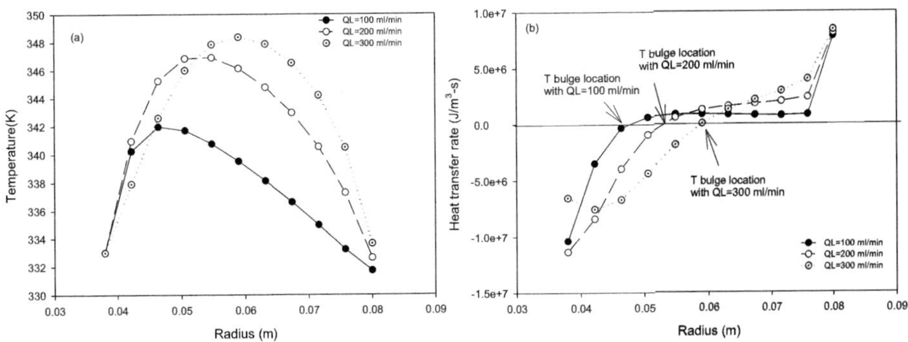

Figure 2. Liquid Temperature profiles and Interfacial heat transfer profiles with operation condition, Yu et al. (2012).

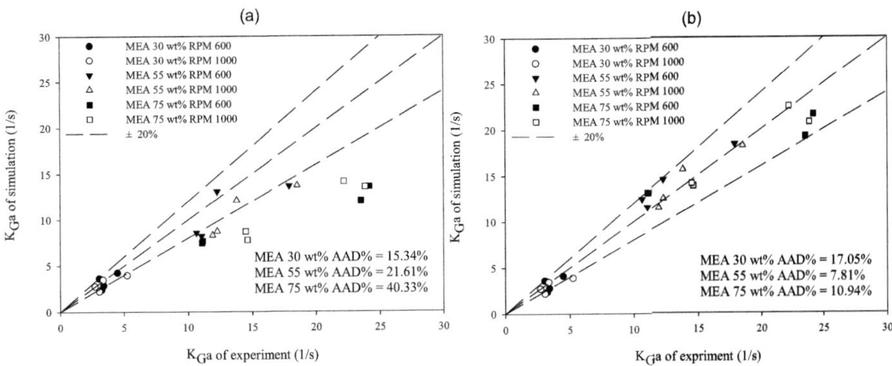

Figure 3. The agreements of simulation and experimental of with (a) pseudo first order kinetic constant and (b)reaction rate constant by Aboudheir et al. (2003)

4. Conclusion

This work presented a model of the absorption of CO_2 by mono-ethanolamine (MEA) in RPB using two-film theory for mass-transfer. The proposed model did not require the isothermal assumption and vaporization of water was considered. Temperature bulge can also be found in a RPB reactor if large amount of CO2 was removed. In the development of this model, it was found that the commonly employed correlations Onda et al. (1968) for liquid phase mass transfer coefficient and interfacial area, Tung and Mah (1985) for gas phase mass transfer coefficients and Burns et al. (2000) for liquid holdup is adequate to predict the effect of changes in gas and liquid flow rates. Proper accounting of changes in liquid-holdup is critical to accounting to the change in removal efficiency with liquid rate. It was also found that the frequently implemented pseudo first order kinetic enhancement model (Hikita et al., 1977) significantly underestimated the capture efficiency for experiments conducted with high concentrations of MEA. The termolecular reaction model proposed by Aboudheir et al. (2003) was able to correct such errors.

Acknowledgements

The authors acknowledged the financial support provided by Ministry of Economic Affairs through the grant 102-EC-17-A-09-S1-198, and National Science Council through the grant NSC 100-2221-E-007-058-MY2.

References

A. Aboudheir, P. Tontiwachwuthikul, A. Chakma, R. Idem, 2003, Kinetics of the reactive absorption of carbon dioxide in high CO2-loaded, concentrated aqueous monoethanolamine solutions, Chem Eng Sci, 58, 5195-5210.

Aspen, 2008, Rate-Based Model of the CO2 Capture Process by MEA using Aspen Plus, Aspen Technology Inc., Massachusetts, USA.

J.R. Burns, J.N. Jamil, C. Ramshaw, 2000, Process intensification: operating characteristics of rotating packed beds - determination of liquid hold-up for a high-voidage structured packing, Chem Eng Sci, 55, 2401-2415.

H.H. Cheng, J.F. Shen, C.S. Tan, 2010, CO2 capture from hot stove gas in steel making process, International Journal of Greenhouse Gas Control, 4, 525-531.

H.H. Cheng, C.S. Tan, 2009, Carbon dioxide capture by blended alkanolamines in rotating packed bed, Energy Procedia, 1, 925-932.

H. Hikita, S. Asai, H. Ishikawa, M. Honda, 1977, Kinetics of Reactions of Carbon-Dioxide with Monoethanolamine, Diethanolamine and Triethanolamine by a Rapid Mixing Method, Chem Eng J Bioch Eng, 13, 7-12.

M.S. Jassim, G. Rochelle, D. Eimer, C. Ramshaw, 2007, Carbon dioxide absorption and desorption in aqueous monoethanolamine solutions in a rotating packed bed, Ind Eng Chem Res, 46, 2823-2833.

H.M. Kvamsdal, G.T. Rochelle, 2008, Effects of the temperature bulge in CO2 absorption from flue gas by aqueous monoethanolamine, Ind Eng Chem Res, 47, 867-875.

K. Onda, H. Takeuchi, Y. Okumoto, 1968, Mass transfer coefficients between gas and liquid phases in packed columns, Journal of chemical engineering of Japan, 1, 56-62.

Z. Qian, L. Xu, H. Cao, K. Guo, 2009, Modeling Study on Absorption of CO2 by Aqueous Solutions of N-Methyldiethanolamine in Rotating Packed Bed, Ind Eng Chem Res, 48, 9261-9267.

Z. Qian, L.B. Xu, Z.H. Li, H. Li, K. Guo, 2010, Selective Absorption of H2S from a Gas Mixture with CO2 by Aqueous N-Methyldiethanolamine in a Rotating Packed Bed, Ind Eng Chem Res, 49, 6196-6203.

H. Renon, J.M. Prausnitz, 1968, Local compositions in thermodynamic excess functions for liquid mixtures, AIChE Journal, 14, 135-144.

B.C. Sun, X.M. Wang, J.M. Chen, G.W. Chu, J.F. Chen, L. Shao, 2009, Simultaneous Absorption of CO2 and NH3 into Water in a Rotating Packed Bed. Ind Eng Chem Res 48, 11175-11180.

H.-h. Tung, R.S.H. Mah, 1985, Modeling Liquid Mass-Transfer in Higee Separation Process, Chem Eng Commun, 39, 147-153.

F. Yi, H.K. Zou, G.W. Chu, L. Shao, J.F. Chen, 2009, Modeling and experimental studies on absorption of CO2 by Benfield solution in rotating packed bed, Chemical Engineering Journal, 145, 377-384.

C.H. Yu, H.H. Cheng, C.S. Tan, 2012, CO2 capture by alkanolamine solutions containing diethylenetriamine and piperazine in a rotating packed bed, International Journal of Greenhouse Gas Control, 9, 136-147.

Jiří Jaromír Klemeš, Petar Sabev Varbanov and Peng Yen Liew (Editors)
Proceedings of the 24th European Symposium on Computer Aided Process Engineering – ESCAPE 24
June 15-18, 2014, Budapest, Hungary.

Molecular Dynamics Study of Diffusion Behaviors of CO2 and N2 Confined to a Uni-directional Zeolite Structure

Kiwoong Kim, Won Bo Lee*

Department of Chemical and biomolecula Engineering, Sogang University, 35 Baekbeom-ro, Seoul, South Korea
wblee92@sogang.ac.kr

Abstract

A study of a molecular dynamic simulation was conducted to investigate the diffusion characteristics of the guest molecules, which diffuse into uni-directional zeolitic structures. Because of the complex and narrow micro-pore structures the zeolites possess, an observation of the anomalous diffusion behavior was reported. In particular, single-file diffusion occurs when the zeolites have an unconnected, narrow, single channel, which hinders the mutual passage of guest molecules. In this work, the diffusion behavior of the mixture consisting of CO_2 and N_2 in the zeolite of TON, which has an unconnected single channel, was investigated. Afterward, the change in diffusion behavior for TON anchored with the functional group selected as the amino group was also investigated.

Keywords: Single file diffusion, Molecular dynamics, Diffusion in zeolites

1. Introduction

Unlike bulk gas diffusion, diffusion behaviors in micro-pores exhibit various characteristics, depending on the subjected micro-pore structures. When pore size is smaller than the mean free path of gas particles, Knudsen diffusion is observed. At even smaller pore sizes, in the range of 20 Å, diffusion is shifted to a configurational diffusion in which the gas particles continuously diffuse into the micro-pore while feeling the interaction with the pore wall, indicating that the diffusion of gas particles is restrained by the surrounding wall. Diffusion in zeolite structures generally follows these Knudsen or configurational diffusions. An anomalous diffusion is known to occur when the zeolite structure has single and unconnected channels with dimensions that are comparable to gas particles (Hahn et al., 1996). In these narrow, unconnected channels, the mutual passage of adjacent particles is not allowed, and the anomalous diffusion is named “single file diffusion”.

When the particles freely diffuse, the normal Fickian diffusion holds, and the MSD (Mean Square Displacement) is proportional to time as in Eq. (1)

$$\lim_{t \to +\infty} < |\vec{r}(t) - \vec{r}(0)|^2 >= 6Dt. \quad (1)$$

However, when the particle diameter is larger than half of the zeolite diameter, mutual passage is forbidden, and Eq. (1) no longer holds. The MSD follows Eq. (2) so that MSD is instead proportional to the square root of time.

$$\lim_{t \to +\infty} \langle |\vec{r}_z(t) - \vec{r}_z(0)|^2 \rangle = 2F\sqrt{t}, \quad (2)$$

where D and F represent the self-diffusion constant and single file mobility, respectively.

Such zeolitic structures that could be the candidates for the occurrence of single file diffusion are plentiful. The single file system has been further investigated extensively using molecular simulation (Kim et al., 2013; Nelissen et al., 2007; Yang et al., 2009) and experimental techniques (Das et al., 2010).

In this work, the molecular dynamic simulations of an equimolar CO_2 and N_2 mixture were performed in the single channel zeolitic structure of TON. The diffusion behaviors in the chosen zeolitic structures were investigated for the mixture as well as pure CO_2 and N_2 molecules using the obtained MSD data and self-diffusion constants. Afterward, the effect of surface modification, using anchoring ammonia molecules to inner surface of TON structure, on diffusion behavior was discussed.

2. Model and Method

The pure silicalites that constituted by only silicon and oxygen atoms were chosen as the zeolites. The zeolite lattices are assumed to be rigid during the entire simulation time with the static Coulombic charges assigned as q_{Si}=+2.05 and q_O=-1.025 (Jaramillo and Auerbach, 1999).

The crystal structures of zeolite TON was obtained in IZA, which has 10-membered rings in the cross-sectional axis and the elliptical cross sections of 4.6 x 5.7 Å.

The CO_2 molecule was modeled as the linear, tri-atomic model with a linear and rigid C - O bond length of 1.16 Å, taken from the model of Harris and Yung. The N_2 molecules are modeled as a dumbbell with a rigid, inter-atomic N - N bond length of 1.098 Å. The partial charges of CO_2 and N_2 are distributed in the simulated model up to the quadrupole moments, which were realized by employing the virtual sites in CO_2 and N_2. The interaction energy of the system consisting of structured zeolite and guest molecules takes into account the Lennard - Jones 6 - 12 and Coulombic potentials. The force field parameters, such as Lennard-Jones parameters and partial charges, that we employed are derived from the work by García-Pérez et al (2007) and are summarized in Table 1 for clarity. The interaction between the zeolites and guest particles is dominated by dispersive forces that act between the oxygen atom in the zeolite and the guest particle. Therefore, the interaction with silicon is taken in account using the effective potential only with oxygen atoms.

The simulation box of 3 (in x-axis) x 3 (in y-axis) x 48 (in z-axis) was generated and, initially, equimolar amounts of CO_2 and N_2 molecules are placed inside the zeolite pore alternately with identical intervals.

The number of particles that are placed in the pore can be defined using the occupancy relationship as in Eq. (3).

Table 1. Lennard-Jones parameters and Coulombic partial charge for interactions of guest-guest and guest-host molecules, top left ε_{k_B} (K), and bottom right σ (Å).

	O_{zeo}	C	O_{CO2}	N	N_{NH3}
C	50.2 / 2.78	28.13 / 2.76	47.59 / 2.89	32.00 / 3.04	49.26 / 3.03
O_{CO2}	84.93 / 2.92	47.59 / 2.89	80.51 / 3.03	54.13 / 3.18	82.99 / 3.23
N	58.25 / 3.06	32.00 / 3.04	54.13 / 3.18	36.40 / 3.32	55.80 / 3.37
N_{NH3}	-	49.26 / 3.03	82.99 / 3.23	55.80 / 3.37	-
Charge [e^-]	-1.025	+0.6512	-0.3256	-0.40484	-1.02

$$\theta = \frac{N\sigma_s}{L} \tag{3}$$

N, σ_S and L represent the number of molecules in the mixture, diameter of the particle, and pore length, respectively. It is difficult to define the particle diameter, σ_S, for such a mixture and slender molecules. The effective diameter of the mixture will be obtained in the subsequent section using the concept of single file mobility. In the simulation, N/L was set to 0.74 per nm in the pore direction of the structure at initial state. The particles of CO_2 and N_2 are alternatively arranged in the direction of the pore length with random velocity and the occupancy for the initial condition.

The molecular dynamics simulation was performed using Gromacs 4.50 package (Berendsen et al., 1995; Lindahl et al., 2001). The leapfrog algorithm was used to integrate the equations of motion in time domain. The Nose-Hoover thermostat was employed to maintain the system at the desired temperature of 400 K. The molecular dynamic simulation of the NVT ensemble was run with fixed time intervals of 1 fs. The initial equilibration run during 1 ns was performed before the production run of 40 ns. The simulation results for the production run were equally divided into 10 blocks of which each block has the result of 4 ns to obtain the averaged ensemble results.

To elucidate the effect of surface modification with amino group, the TON impregnated with the amino group was generated as shown in Fig. 1. Three ammonia molecules were anchored per unit cell of TON. The ammonia molecule was treated as the rigid bond, as was the zeolite.

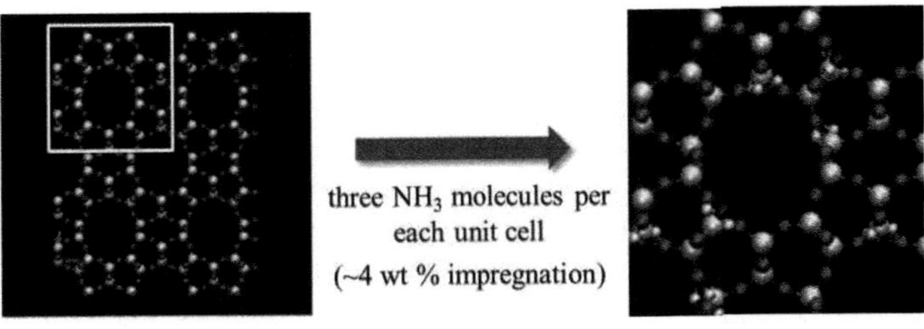

Figure 1. The crystal structures of (a) normal TON and (b) surface modified TON anchored with the functional group of ammonia molecule; red-oxygen (O), yellow-silicon (Si), blue-nitrogen atom (N), light gray-hydrogen atom (H).

The tetrahedral ammonia molecule was modeled by referring to Rizzo and Jorgensen (1999). The Lennard Jones parameters of ammonia with other particles are denoted in Table 1 with the corresponding electric charges. The ammonia hydrogen attached to the heteroatoms was considered to be a dummy particle that has a positive charge of 0.34.

3. Results and discussion

The diffusion characteristics of diffusing particles are evaluated using obtained through MSD data. MSD was calculated from the block averaged traveling data of the particles and MSD curve was regressed in the form of MSD $= \text{const} \times (time)^{\alpha}$. From the Einstein correlation, the self-diffusion constants were calculated from the block averaged MSD data from 3.5 ns to 4.5 ns to ensure the linear dependency of MSD with time.

3.1. The effects of inter-molecular interactions

The effective length of linear CO_2 is 4.96 Å, and the effective length of N_2 is much smaller than that of CO_2. Because CO_2 and N_2 particles alternate in the pore length direction, the zeolite diameter and CO_2 length determine the occurrence of single file diffusion.

That the maximum diameter of the TON structure is 5.71 Å infers that the particles that have a larger diameter than 2.85 Å cannot pass one another. However, because the CO_2 and N_2 molecules are slender, defining the particle diameter is difficult for these particles. When CO_2 aligns perpendicular to the channel axis, the diffusion of CO_2 would be single file. However, single file diffusion would not occur when CO_2 aligns parallel to the channel axis, as available room exists for molecules to pass one another. From a statistical perspective, the diffusion behavior of CO_2 in TON would converge on specific diffusion characteristics, which means that the effective particle diameter of CO_2 exists and can be obtained from the molecular dynamics.

The self-diffusion coefficient, obtained from the 3- dimensional trajectory of particles, was $0.9974 \times 10^{-5} cm^2/sec$. The MSD for only pore length direction was extracted from the 3-dimensional trajectory that the mixture traveled. The single file mobility was calculated using the correlation of Eq. (4) from the obtained MSD data between the interval from 0.1 to 0.3 ns in which the value of α is 0.565. The resulting single file mobility was $10.86 \times 10^{-10}\ cm^2/\sqrt{sec}$.

$$F = \frac{1-\theta}{\theta}\sigma_s\sqrt{\frac{D}{\pi}}, \tag{4}$$

where D is the diffusion coefficient.

Fig. 2 (a) shows the MSD profile of the system in which the mixture of CO_2 and N_2 diffuses in box 2 of TON. After the initial ballistic regime, the movement of particles becomes gradually suppressed due to the confining wall and adjacent neighbors. At approximately 0.3 ns, the regressed value of α is 0.554, which represents the system experiencing single file diffusion. As the time is extended, the atomic behavior becomes

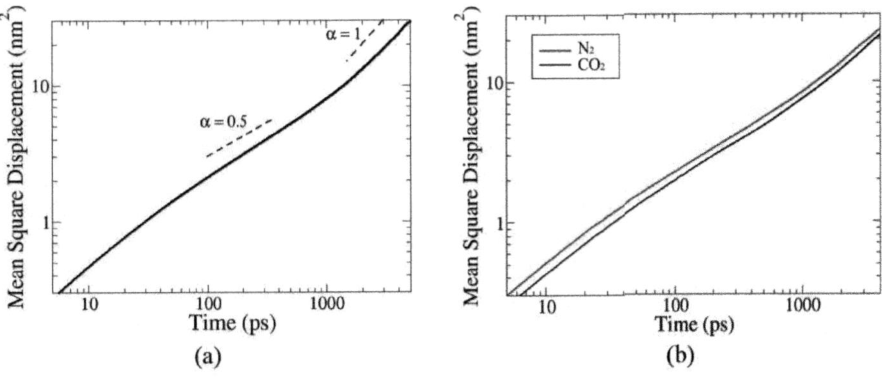

Figure 2. Diffusion behavior of (a) the mixture of CO_2 and N_2 and (b) the pure CO_2 and N_2 in TON.

relaxed, and the diffusion behavior finally follows the normal diffusion after some transient periods.

In Fig. 2 (b), the MSD profiles of pure CO_2 and N_2 in box 2 of TON structure are shown to compare the diffusion behaviors to those of the mixture. It can be seen that the strongly adsorbed species, CO_2, is slower than the less strongly adsorbed N_2, due to their inter-molecular interactions. That the diffusion behavior of the mixture follows that of the slower species, CO_2, can be extracted from the comparison of Fig. 2. The self-diffusion constants are computed as $0.8830 \times 10^{-5} cm^2/sec$ for pure CO_2 and $0.9542 \times 10^{-5} cm^2/sec$ for pure N_2.

3.2. The effect of anchoring ammonia on TON

The diffusion behavior of the mixture in TON anchored by ammonia was shown in Fig. 3 and compared to the diffusion behavior of mixture in only TON. The self-diffusion coefficient was obtained as $0.7016 \times 10^{-5} cm^2/sec$, which is much smaller than the self-diffusion coefficient of mixture in TON without ammonia. It could be deduced that anchoring the ammonia tends to detain the mixture due to the additional attractive force between the ammonia and the mixture because the ammonia is a weak base.

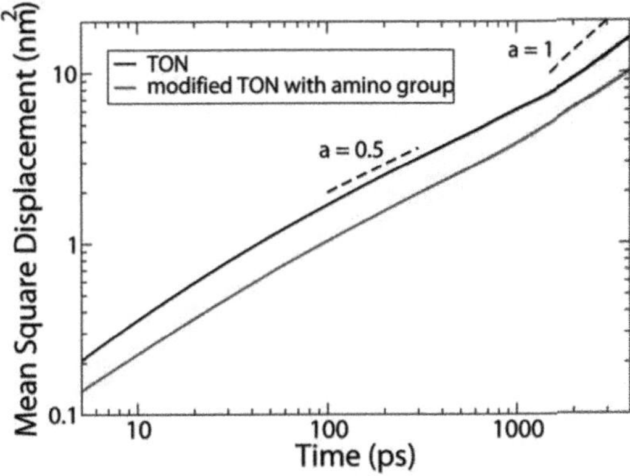

Figure 3. Diffusion behavior of the mixture in TON and TON anchored ammonia molecule.

4. Conclusion

A molecular dynamic study was conducted to investigate the diffusion characteristics of mixture of CO_2 and N_2 in the pure silicalite zeolite of TON as the host materials. From the block averaged MSD data, the diffusion behavior of the mixture shows SF diffusion around 0.3 ns and it approaches to the normal diffusion as time proceeds. The diffusion behaviors were quantitatively elucidated in terms of SF mobility and self-diffusion coefficient. Afterward, the diffusion behavior was compared in the normal TON and the modified TON with amino group. In the modified TON, the diffusion is more lagged by additional attractive potential between the amino group and CO_2. The diffusion behaviors of CO_2 and N_2 were evaluated in the normal TON and modified TON. In case of physi-sorption process, the slowest reaction rate corresponds to the intra-diffusion step where the gas diffuses into the adsorption surfaces. In this work, how the reaction rates are changed in the uni-directional zeolite and how it is varied according to the surface modification with amino group are investigated in quantitatively.

References

A. Das, S. Jayanthi, H.S.M.V. Deepak, K.V. Ramanathan, A. Kumar, C. Dasgupta, A.K. Sood, 2010, Single-File Diffusion of Confined Water Inside SWNTs: An NMR Study, ACS Nano, 4, 1687–1695.

E. García-Pérez, J.B. Parra, C.O. Ania, A. García-Sánchez, J.M. Van Baten, R. Krishna, D. Dubbeldam, S. Calero, 2007, A computational study of CO_2, N_2, and CH_4 adsorption in zeolites, Adsorption, 13, 469–476.

E. Jaramillo, S.M. Auerbach, 1999, New force field for Na cations in faujasite-type zeolites, The Journal of Physical Chemistry B, 103, 9589–9594.

E. Lindahl, B. Hess, D. Van Der Spoel, 2001, GROMACS 30: a package for molecular simulation and trajectory analysis, Journal of Molecular Modeling, 7, 306–317.

H.J.C. Berendsen, D. Van Der Spoel, R. van Drunen, 1995, GROMACS: A message-passing parallel molecular dynamics implementation, Computer Physics Communications, 91, 43–56.

K. Hahn, J. Karger, V. Kukla, 1996, Single-file diffusion observation, Physical Review Letters, 76, 2762–2765.

K. Kim, S. Lee, J.H. Ryu, K.S. Lee, W.B. Lee, 2013, An improved CO_2 adsorption efficiency for the zeolites impregnated with the amino group: A molcular simulation approach, International Journal of Greenhouse Gas Control, 19, 350–357.

K. Nelissen, V.R. Misko, F.M. Peeters, 2007, Single-file diffusion of interacting particles in a one-dimensional channel, EPL (Europhysics Letters), 80, 56004.

R.C. Rizzo, W.L. Jorgensen, 1999, Opls all-atom model for amines: Resolution of the amine hydration problem, Journal of the American Chemical Society, 121, 4827–4836.

X. Yang, M. Wu, Z. Qin, J. Wang, T. Wen, 2009, Molecular dynamics simulations on single-file diffusions: Effects of channel potential periods and particle-particle interactions, Journal of Applied Physics, 106, 084905.

Jiří Jaromír Klemeš, Petar Sabev Varbanov and Peng Yen Liew (Editors)
Proceedings of the 24th European Symposium on Computer Aided Process Engineering – ESCAPE 24
June 15-18, 2014, Budapest, Hungary.

Modelling, Simulation and Dynamic Analysis of the L-lysine Production Process

Teresa Lopez-Arenas,[a] Omar Anaya-Reza,[b] Rodolfo Quintero-Ramirez,[a] Mauricio Sales-Cruz[a*]

[a]*Departamento de Procesos y Tecnología, Universidad Autónoma Metropolitana-Cuajimalpa, Av. Vasco de Quirόga 4871, Mexico, D.F. 05348, Mexico*
[b]*Posgrado en Energía y Medio Ambiente, Universidad Autónoma Metropolitana-Iztapalapa, Av. San Rafael Atlixco 186,Mexico, D.F. 09430, Mexico*
asales@correo.cua.uam.mx

Abstract

L-Lysine is an essential amino acid which can be produced by chemical processes from fossil raw materials, as well as by microbial fermentation, the latter being a more economical procedure. In the present work the fermentation process of L-lysine from sugarcane molasses is studied, using modelling and dynamic simulation tools to compare batch and fed-batch process, as well as to determine feasible operating regions in terms of productivity, product yield and fermentation time. These results will be used in the future for economic analysis, optimization studies and environmental impact.

Keywords: Modelling, Simulation, Biorefinery.

1. Introduction

Biorefineries are facilities that integrate biomass conversion processes and equipment to produce fuels, power and commodity chemicals (Luo et al., 2010). These can be classified by a number of features, such as the type of raw materials like starch crops (i.e. wheat and corn), sugar crops (i.e. sugar beet and cane), lignocellulosic crops (i.e. firewood forest and short rotation coppice), lignocellulosic residues (i.e. bagasse and straw), oil crops (i.e. palm and rapeseed), aquatic biomass (i.e. algae and seaweed) and organic waste (i.e. industrial, commercial and post-consumer) (Jong et al., 2012). Some benefits of biorefineries are: compensation of the cost of biofuels, improvement of process economics, minimization of waste discharge, reduction of dependence on oil products, and also providing new economic opportunities for agriculture and chemical industry (Fitzpatrick et al., 2010).

Among the basic chemicals obtained through biorefineries are the amino acids, and among these is the L-lysine that cannot be synthesized by the body, and is of great importance in human and animal; so it must be supplied in sufficient quantities by the daily diet (Eggeling and Sahm, 1999). The worldwide production volume of L-lysine is 850,000 t/y. It is estimated that in the future there will be high competition in the fermentative production of L-Lysine. For example, the global market for L-lysine has increased more than 20 times in the past two decades. The estimates assume that the market is currently increasing by 10 % ± 15 % per year (Leuchtenberger et al., 2005).

During the last decades the efficiency of the industrial production of L-lysine has been progressively increased isolation of high producing mutant strains and the development of processes (Anastassiadis, 2007). Recently some studies about design, operation and sustainability have been report (Taras and Woinaroschy, 2012). However, optimization, monitoring, control activities including process engineering are still open research issues for this by-product. To carry out these studies is necessary to have a model and a dynamic analysis of the process. Moreover, the promotion of biotechnology and the (re) use of biomass have generated a broad field for the production of L-lysine from biomass.

The aim of this work is to study the production process of L-lysine from sugarcane molasses using modelling and dynamic simulation tools to compare batch and fed-batch process, as well as to determine feasible operating regions in terms of productivity, product yield and fermentation time. These results will be used in the future for optimization studies, economic analysis and environmental impact.

2. Process Model

The production process of L-lysine from glucose has been previously studied by Heinzle et al. (2007), where simulations were performed using an adaptable stoichiometric reaction based on the product yield and productivity. In the other hand, the kinetics and modelling of fermentation reactor for lysine has been reported by Büchs (1994). The production process has two sections: reaction section (which includes steps of pre-mixing, sterilization and fermentation) and purification section (which includes biomass filtration, water evaporation and product drying). In this work first the fermentation step of sugarcane molasses is studied, and then the complete production process is analyzed.

A dynamic model is developed based on mass and energy balances, describing the biological reaction activities and two types of fermentation operation (batch or fed-batch). Fermentation is carried out under aerobic conditions, using potassium phosphate (*KH_2PO4*) as phosphate source, ammonium hydroxide (*NH_4OH*) as a nitrogen source, *Corynebacterium glutamicum* as bacterium, and threonine is supplemented to the culture media in case of auxotrophic strains. The biological reaction is as follows:

$$\begin{aligned} &a\, C_6H_{12}O_6 + b\, KH_2PO_4 + c\, NH_4OH + d\, C_4H_9NO_3 + e\, O_2 \longrightarrow \\ &\quad f\, CH_{1.9}O_{0.3}N_{0.24}P_{0.02}K_{0.01} + g\, C_6H_{14}N_2O_2 + h\, H_2O + i\, CO_2 + j\, K \end{aligned} \tag{1}$$

The dynamic reactor model is given by the following six differential equations:

$$\frac{dc_s}{dt} = -\frac{1}{Y_{x/s}}\mu c_x - \frac{1}{Y_{p/s}} r_p c_x - m_s c_x + \frac{F}{V} c_{SF}, \quad \mu = \mu_{\max}\frac{c_s}{c_s + K_s}\cdot\frac{c_L}{c_L + K_o}\cdot\frac{c_{Thr}}{c_{Thr} + K_{Thr}} \tag{2}$$

$$\frac{dc_p}{dt} = r_p\, c_x, \qquad r_p = (\alpha_p \cdot \mu + \beta_p)\cdot\frac{C_S}{C_S + K_{ps}}\cdot\frac{C_L}{C_L + K_O} \tag{3}$$

$$\frac{dc_L}{dt} = -\frac{1}{Y_{x/o}}\mu\, c_x - \frac{1}{Y_{p/o}} r_p\, c_x - m_o\, c_x + OTR, \qquad OTR = k_{La}\left(L_{O2} p\, y_{O_2} - C_L\right) \tag{4}$$

$$\frac{dc_x}{dt} = (\mu - k_d)c_x; \qquad \frac{dc_{Thr}}{dt} = -\frac{1}{Y_{x/Thr}}\mu\, c_x; \qquad \frac{dV}{dt} = F \tag{5}$$

Table 1. Parameters for the dynamic model of L-lysine fermentation

Parameter	Value	Units	Parameter	Value	Units	Parameter	Value	Units
$Y_{x/s}$	0.52	g/g	k_d	0.0028	g/L	m_o	0.036	g/L
$Y_{p/s}$	0.6	g/g	K_o	6.4×10^{-6}	g/L	m_s	0.034	g/L
$Y_{x/Thr}$	0.33	g/g	K_s	0.01	g/L	α	0.2	g/g)
$Y_{p/o}$	4.11	g/g	K_{Thr}	0.01	g/L	β	0.043	g/g h
$Y_{x/o}$	1.29	g/g	K_{ps}	0.072	g/L	y_o	0.2095	mol/mol
μ_{max}	0.28	1/h	L_{O2}	0.00118	mol/L/bar			

Where c_S, c_{SF}, c_x, c_{Thr} ,c_L are concentrations of substrate in the reactor, substrate in the feed, biomass, threonine and oxygen in the reactor, respectively; μ is the specific growth rate, r_p is the rate of lysine production, m_s and m_o are specific consumption of substrate and oxygen for maintenance, respectively; $Y_{p/o}$, $Y_{p/s}$, $Y_{x/s}$, $Y_{x/o}$, $Y_{x/Thr}$ are the product and biomass yields; *OTR* is the oxygen transfer rate, V is the fermentation volume, and F is the feedflow. The corresponding parameter values are given in Table 1.

3. Simulation results for the fermentation section

As mentioned before, we are interested in the comparison of batch and fed-batch cases, and also in determining regions of operation leading to high product yields (equivalent to high product concentrations) and high productivities. For simulations purposes, the operation conditions were: $V_{reactor}$ = 300,000L, K_{La} = 1,000 s^{-1}, P = 1 atm. The initial conditions for batch operation mode were set at: $C_{S,0}$ = 200 g /L, $C_{P,0}$ = 0, $C_{L,0} = C_{L,max}$, $C_{x,0}$ = 0.1 g/L, $V_0 = V_{reactor}$. For fed-batch operation conditions were: $C_{S,0}$ = 35 g/L, $C_{P,0}$ = 0, $C_{L,0} = C_{L,max}$, $C_{x,0}$ = 0.1 g/L, $V_0 = 0.75V_{reactor}$ (the reactor is initially filled to 75% volume, then a glucose solution with C_{SF} = 700 g/L is added up to 100%). The initial threonine concentration (C_{Thr}) was varied in the range 0.6-2 g/L.

Some results are shown in Figure 1, where dynamic behaviour of concentrations for batch and fed-batch are compared using C_{Thr} = 1.6 g/L. The final fermentation time (θ_R) for batch operation was determined when product concentration achieved a maximum value. While for fed-batch operation, the reactor volume was constant (at 75 % filling) until the substrate (glucose) is exhausted, then a glucose solution is added until the reactor is filled to 100 % (this point defines θ_R). In both operation modes, the same amount of glucose was added, corresponding to a total glucose concentration of $C_{S,T}$ = 200 g/L. In Figure 1, it can be seen that the final Lysine concentrations, $C_P(\theta_R)$, are similar in both cases: 44 g/L for batch and 38.3 g/L for fed-batch; while θ_R are quite different: 35.3 h for batch and 62.5 h for fed-batch.

The overall product yield ($Y_{p/s}$) and the productivity (i.e. space time yield, STY) were calculated as: $Y_{p/s} = C_P(\theta_R)/C_{S,T}$ and STY = $C_P(\theta_R)/\theta_R$. Values of these two parameters are shown in Figure 2. Maximum productivity for batch operation (1.25 g $h^{-1}L^{-1}$) is achieved when C_{Thr} = 1.6 g/L, while fed-batch case achieves the maximum (0.87 g $h^{-1}L^{-1}$) at C_{Thr} = 1 g/L. However at the maximum point, the product yield for batch operation (0.218 g/g) is minor than fed-batch operation (0.31 g/g). This means that there is a trade-off between product yield and productivity.

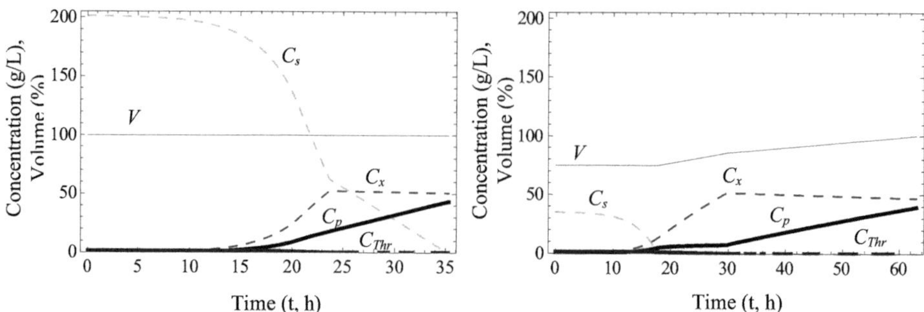

Figure 1. Dynamic behaviour of the fermentation reactor to produce L-lysine: (a) batch operation and (b) fed-batch operation, under similar conditions ($c_{Thr,0}$ = 1.6 g/L).

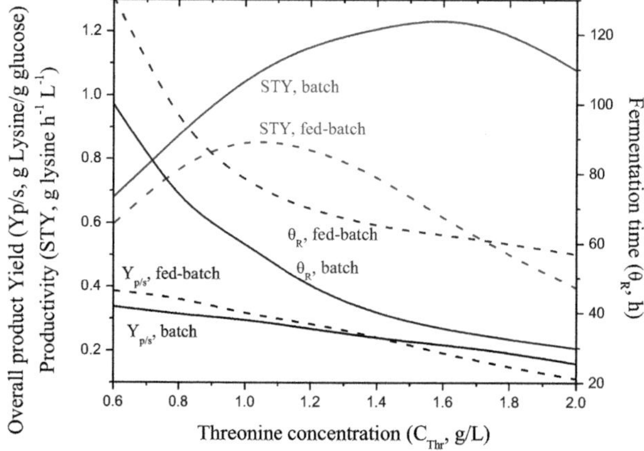

Figure 2. Overall product yield, productivity and reaction time for batch and fed-batch operations.

4. Simulation results for the production process

The production process was divided into four sections, as shown in Figure 3: (a) preparation of molasses, (b) preparation of the culture medium, (c) fermentation, and (d) purification. The process simulation was implemented in SuperPro Designer ®. In the first section, the molasses is diluted in water, then part of the impurities is removed by filtration and another is eliminated using a column of ion exchange chromatography. The resulting solution will be added to the reactor after being heat sterilized. In the section of the culture medium preparation, the nutrients are dissolved in water and heat sterilized. Then they are also transferred to the fermentation vessel. The fermentation time, yield and productivity depends on the strain of *Corynebacterium glutamicum* and threonine concentration, as shown in previous section. So that the stoichiometric reaction is derived for different values of C_{thr}, using the results obtained in by dynamic simulation. Molar stoichiometric coefficients of reaction (1) are given in Table 2 for some cases. The fermentation reaction is achieved at 35 °C, so that cooling water is used to remove heat from exothermic fermentation processes and to maintain a constant temperature. Once fermentation is complete, the broth is discharged into a tank acting as a buffer between the fermentation section and the purification section. Purification begins with the removal of the biomass by a rotary filter. The clarified liquor is then concentrated in an evaporator and cooled to 35 °C using a heat exchanger. This is then sent to a neutralization vessel and crystallization. There, the solution is neutralized with HCI solution and cooled to 15 °C in order to crystallize the L-lysine salt. The slurry solids are retained by a rotary vacuum filter and rinsed with water to remove remaining impurities. The wet crystals are dried, and the final product has about 99.8 % pure crystals of lysine-HCl.

From mass and energy balances, production rate and energy consumption was analyzed in order to understand the operation conditions. It is important to mention that due space limitations only some insights are presented. For instance, energy consumption in terms of utility amounts and costs are shown in Table 3, while Table 4 reports production rate, recipe time and energy cost. According these results, it can be seen that: (i) in a batch process, higher threonine concentrations requires minor energy, but also minor production rate (due to low product yields); (ii) a fed-batch operation requires more energy than a batch operation, and production rate is slightly higher. So that for these preliminary results, it can be concluded that the batch operation mode with C_{thr} = 1 g/L is the best case analyzed in terms of production rate and energy consumption.

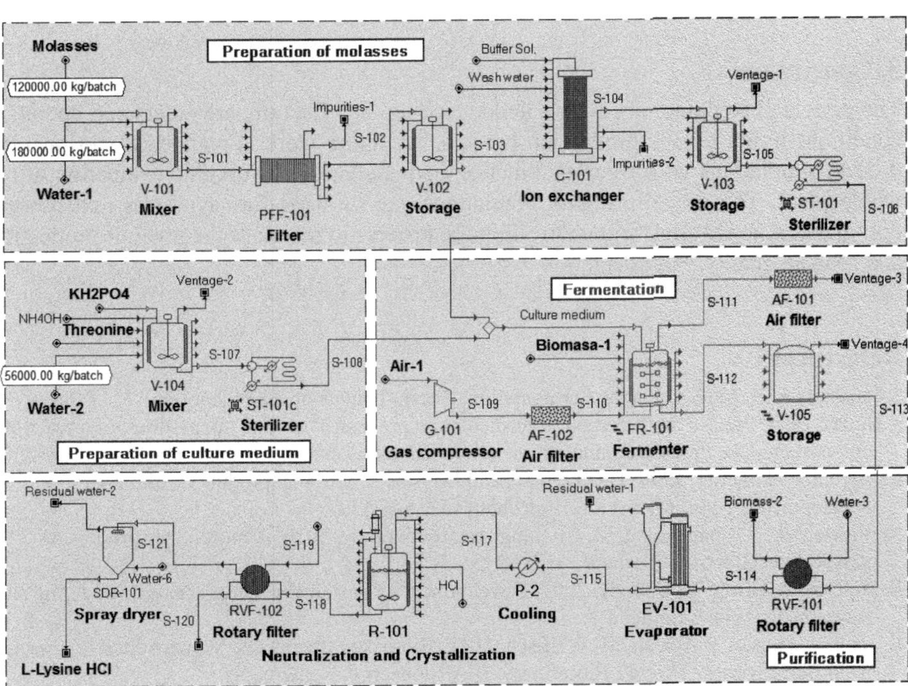

Figure 3. Flowsheet for the production process of L-lysine .

Table 2. Molar stoichiometric coefficients of fermentation reaction (1).

Operation mode	*a*	*b*	*c*	*d*	*e*	*f*	*g*	*h*	*i*	*j*
Batch (C_{Thr} = 1.6 g/L)	1.000	0.039	0.996	0.012	1.863	1.957	0.269	4.840	2.475	0.020
Batch (C_{Thr} = 1 g/L)	1.000	0.022	0.985	0.007	2.193	1.080	0.367	4.925	2.749	0.011
Fed-batch (C_{Thr} = 1 g/L)	1.000	0.020	1.013	0.007	2.116	1.025	0.387	4.902	2.683	0.010

Table 3. Energy consumption in terms of utility amounts and costs.

	Batch (C_{Thr} = 1.6 g/L)		Batch (C_{Thr} = 1 g/L)		Fed-batch (C_{Thr} = 1 g/L)	
Utility	Amount	Cost ($)	Amount	Cost ($)	Amount	Cost ($)
Standard Power	23,805 kW-h	2,380	40,326 kW-h	4,033	51,590 kW-h	5,159
Steam	632 MT	177	647 MT	181	647 MT	181
Chilled Water	156 MT	27	171 MT	30	173 MT	30
Cooled water	37,897 MT	947	39,535 MT	988	40,654 MT	1,016
TOTAL		3,532		5,232		6,387

Table 4. Production rate, recipe time and energy cost.

Operation mode	*Production rate (Kg/batch)*	*Recipe Time (h/batch)*	*Energy Cost ($/Kg)*
Batch (C_{Thr} = 1.6 g/L)	16,097	111.9	0.219
Batch (C_{Thr} = 1 g/L)	21,940	136.6	0.238
Fed-batch (C_{Thr} = 1 g/L)	23,161	153.6	0.276

5. Conclusions

The presented methodology allows understanding the effect of parameters and operating conditions in the Lysine production process. As future work is planned to perform the process simulations with rigorous kinetics, and analyze the economic evaluation of the whole plant. The modelling and simulations can be used for: synthesis and process optimization, monitoring and controlling the process to maintain the level of production and product quality, fault detection, etc.

References

S. Anastassiadis, 2007, L-Lysine Fermentation, Recent Patents on Biotechnology, 1, 11-24.

J. Büchs, 1994, Precise optimization of fermentation processes through integration of bioreaction and cost models, Process computations in biotechnology, McGraw-Hill, New Delhi, 194–237.

L. Eggeling, H. Sahm., 1999, L-Glutamate and L-lysine: traditional products with impetuous developments, Appl. Microbiol. Biotechnol., 52, 146-153.

M. Fitzpatrick, P. Champagne, M. Cunningham, R. Whitney, 2010, A biorefinery processing perspective, Bioresour Technol., 101, 8915-22,

E. Heinzle, A. Biwer, C. Cooney, 2007, Development of Sustainable Bioprocesses, Modeling and Assessment, Wiley, England.

E. Jong, A. Higson, P. Walsh, M. Wellisch, 2012, Bio-based Chemicals. Value Added Products from Biorefineries, Task 42 Biorefinery, IEA Bioenergy, Netherlands.

W. Leuchtenberger, K. Huthmacher, K. Drauz, 2005, Biotechnological production of amino acids and derivatives: current status and prospects, Appl. Microbiol. Biotechnol., 69, 1-8.

L. Luo, E. Voet, G. Huppes, 2010, Biorefining of lignocellulosic feedstock – Technical, economic and environmental considerations, Bioresource Technology, 101, 5023–5032.

S. Taras, A. Woinaroschy, 2012, An interactive multi-objective optimization framework for sustainable design of bioprocesses, Comput. Chem. Eng. 43, 10–22.

Jiří Jaromír Klemeš, Petar Sabev Varbanov and Peng Yen Liew (Editors)
Proceedings of the 24th European Symposium on Computer Aided Process Engineering – ESCAPE 24
June 15-18, 2014, Budapest, Hungary.

Capturing Uncertainties for Sustainable Operation of Autothermal Thermophilic Aerobic Digestion Systems

Natasha G. Vaklieva-Bancheva*, Elisaveta G. Kirilova, Raika K. Vladova

Institute of Chemical Engineering – BAS, Acad. G. Bontchev Street, Bl.103, 1113 Sofia, Bulgaria
vaklieva@bas.bg

Abstract

This study deals with a problem for the sustainable operation of Autothermal Thermophilic Aerobic Digestion (ATAD) systems. The problem is presented as a design of heat integrated batch processes under uncertainties. Heat integration framework is defined and a respective mathematical model is discussed. Two-stage stochastic optimization is formulated. A scenario decomposition concept and Genetic Algorithm are used for problem solution. Real sets of data are used to simulate the heat-integrated ATAD system and demonstrate the resulting sustainability of the operational temperatures in the bioreactors.

Keywords: ATAD systems, Uncertainties, Heat integration, Two-stage stochastic optimization, Genetic algorithm.

1. Introduction

Autothermal Thermophilic Aerobic Digestion processes use aerobic microorganisms with exothermic energy-metabolic exchange for the biochemical oxidation of organic substances in domestic wastewater. The processes are self-heating and allow to kill pathogens in operational conditions. The heat production and detainment is the basis of ATAD processes. Other advantages are their simplicity, high reaction rate and hence smaller sizes of bioreactors.

Conventional ATAD processes take place in parallel series of two batch bioreactors where the wastewater is treated at different temperatures with aeration and mixing for 20-24 hours. Once per day part of the treated sludge from the last bioreactors is discharged to "a product" storage. Then the partially treated wastewater from the previous stage is displaced to the next one and the system is fed with the fresh sludge from the feed tank. The required operational temperature for the bioreactors from the first stage is around 55°C, which is optimal for bacterial growth, while for the second one it is ~65°C – which is the best one for pasteurization. Nevertheless, both reactors usually operate below these temperatures. Systematic observations of ATAD facilities have found that after filling the bioreactors from the first stage with fresh sludge a sharp temperature drop occurs, which provokes a thermal shock (TSk) on the microorganisms in the bioreactors and affects the temperature conditions in both bioreactor stages due to impossibility to reach the operational temperature.

Many researchers have analyzed the opportunities to improve ATAD systems, in terms of their energy efficiency. Aiming to minimize the energy requirement in ATAD bioreactors, Rojas et al. (2010) and Rojas and Zhelev (2012) have created a dynamic model of ATAD reaction and have demonstrated that significant energy saving could be expected by appropriate altering of the operating conditions (OCs) while complying with the treatment objectives. Liu et al. (2012, 2013) have investigated the effect of temperature on the sludge stabilization in one stage ATAD systems and carried out heat balance analysis proving that the water evaporation and sludge discharged under thermophilic conditions are the two major sources which contribute to the heat loss.

Earlier, Layden et al. (2007) have indicated that recovering discharged heat would limit temperature fluctuations in the first stage reactors. This idea was further developed by Zhelev et al. (2008, 2009). We have proved that the energy potential of discharged heat is sufficient to be re-used trough energy integration for preheating the inflows to the bioreactors. We also have mentioned that ATAD facilities are subjected to daily uncertainties coming with the raw sludge flow, which parameters such as amounts, temperatures and compositions vary from day to day and affect the sustainable operation of the entire system. The goal of the present study is to continue these investigations on energy integrated ATAD systems, so as to deal with these uncertainties and to ensure more sustainable OCs of ATAD facilities.

2. Problem statement

Recovering and utilisation of this heat for conventional two stage ATAD facilities is obstructed by the batch processes and by the fact that the flows candidates for heat integration are shifted in time. The proposed heat integration framework is able to deal with this obstacle, Figure 1. It comprises one heat storage to store heat and cold at different time intervals, two heat exchangers for heating and cooling the respective flows when they appear and sludge and regular pumps, (Zhelev et al., 2008).

Additional specifics of the problem are the uncertainties in the estimation of the temperatures of the streams which are candidates for participation in the heat integration tasks. Consequently, to capture these uncertainties and ensure efficient heat recovery for sustainable operation of ATAD facilities, the design problem of heat integrated batch processes must be considered as a stochastic optimization problem.

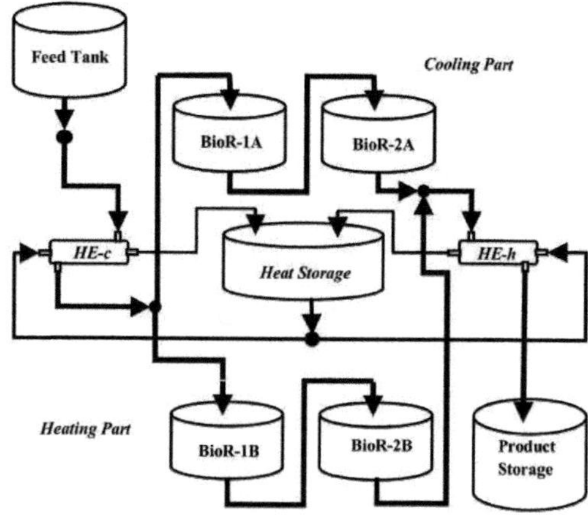

Figure 1. Heat integration framework.

3. Methodology

3.1. Mathematical model of the integration process

The energy storage tank and intermediate fluid offer a solution to the lag between the times at which cold and hot streams are available. During the cooling period the product leaving BioR 2-A(B) is cooled in *HE-h*, while in the heating period, *HE-c* is used for preheating the fresh cold sludge drawn from the Feed Tank. Water used as an intermediate fluid re-circulates between the heat tank and corresponding heat exchangers at predetermined time intervals and plays a role of a "cooling" or "heating" agent. The heat exchange is non-stationary. Neglecting heat losses, detailed mathematical description of the proposed heat-exchange frame is presented in our previous study, (Zhelev et al. 2008). It provides an opportunity to determine the target temperatures of the preheated sludge and the cooled product as functions of the main parameters of the heat integration scheme as mass of intermediate fluid, i.e. the volume of the heat storage, heat exchangers areas and fluids flowrates, respectively pumps power.

Due to heat integration, a rise in the operational temperatures in the bioreactors and TSk reduction is expected. It is proved that when the operating temperatures are very high, the activity of the microorganisms and the degradation rate decrease. To predict the expected operational temperature that could be reached in bioreactors, modeling of two-stage ATAD system is carried out by using ANN, (Kirilova and Vaklieva-Bancheva, 2013).

The model is complemented by technical and operational constraints for the units involved. Constraints following for a feasibility of the exchanged heat and restrictions for keeping the operation temperatures in bioreactors at the desired levels are also introduced.

3.2. Two-stage stochastic optimization

The mathematical model of energy integrated ATAD system developed above is used to formulate a two-stage stochastic optimization problem. Heat exchanger areas and volume of the heat storage are chosen as the first-stage variables, while flowrates presented through the required heating and cooling times, constitute the second-stage variables. Function accounting for the annualized units' costs and transferring costs of respective flows, is defined to be used as an optimization criterion.

The most common modeling technique used in stochastic programming is to convert the stochastic optimization problem to a deterministic multiscenario optimization problem. The latter could be done by replacing the point estimates with a finite number of scenarios for given stochastic data so as to represent possible stochastic situations, which appear with respective probabilities- p_s .

Mathematically, the optimization problem follows the below structure:

$$Min\ Z = C'(\mathbf{x}) + \sum_{s=1}^{S} p_s C''\left(\mathbf{x}, \mathbf{y}_s \overline{q_s}\right) \qquad (1)$$

subject to:

$$h_{s,i}(\mathbf{x},\mathbf{y_s}\overline{q_s}) = 0, \qquad s = 1,2,...,S, \quad i = 1,2,...I;$$

$$g_{s,j}\left(\mathbf{x},\mathbf{y_s}\overline{q_s}\right) \le 0, \qquad s = 1,2,...,S, \quad j = 1,2,...J;$$

$$X_{\min} \le \mathbf{x} \le X_{\max}, \quad Y_{\min} \le \mathbf{y_s} \le Y_{\max}, \quad Q_{\min} \le \overline{q_s} \le Q_{\max};$$

where $\mathbf{x}$ and $\mathbf{y_s}$ are vectors of the first and second stage decision variables and $\overline{q}_s$ is the vector of uncertain parameters in scenario s. The energy integration model is presented by the set of equations $h_{i,s}(.) = 0$ and inequalities $g_{j,s}(.) \le 0$. The objective function includes the costs- $C'(\mathbf{x})$ of the main units and the expectation costs- $C''\left(\mathbf{x},\mathbf{y_s}\overline{q_s}\right)$ for fluids transfer taken for each stochastic scenarios- s.

4. Solution approach

To solve the formulated stochastic optimization we have applied the scenario decomposition concept with Genetic Algorithm. It has provided the opportunity to solve simultaneously both stages of the formulated optimization problem. The solution approach follows the steps below.

4.1. Data analysis and Scenarios generation

Long term observations on a real ATAD facility have provided a large number of historical data sets registering values of the incoming sludge parameters and also the values of the temperatures in the first and second bioreactors stages. The data analysis carried out has shown that all data sets have a natural character and are subjected to the Normal distribution law. A confidence level of 0.95 is established to exclude the presence of noise from the data sets. Thus an original set of different scenarios is obtained.

Scenarios generation aims to select an appropriate reduced subset of scenarios from the original one that is able to approximate the optimal solution of the problem (1) as close as possible to the original one. For the purpose, we have applied a methodology proposed by Karuppiah at al (2010) with a criterion for selecting a minimal subset of scenarios from a given one, defined as relaxed Linear programming (LP). The data analysis already carried out is used to determine the probabilities associated with the uncertain parameters taken on some particular values. Then, relaxed LP is formulated and solved to obtain the subsets of scenarios for both,problem solution and verification.

4.2. Genetic Algorithm

BASIC GA is applied to solve the optimization problem (1), (Shopova and Vaklieva, 2006). Having in mind that the Genetic algorithms are direct methods dealing only with unconstrained problems, the optimization problem (1) is transformed to the unconstrained one by applying the dynamic penalty technique using distance-based penalty functions- $R_{s,k}(\mathbf{x},\mathbf{y_s},\overline{q_s},t)$:

$$R_{s,k}(\mathbf{x},\mathbf{y_s},\overline{q_s},t) = d_{s,k}(\mathbf{x},\mathbf{y_s},\overline{q_s}).sr_k(t).Cp_k, \tag{2}$$

where $d_{s,k}(\mathbf{x},\mathbf{y_s},\overline{q_s})$ is a distance metric of constraint k applied to the solution $(\mathbf{x},\mathbf{y_s},\overline{q_s})$:

$$d_{s,k}(\mathbf{x},\mathbf{y_s},\overline{q_s}) = \begin{cases} 0 \quad if \quad \left|h_{s,k}(\mathbf{x},\mathbf{y_s},\overline{q_s})\right| \le \Delta; \quad g_{s,k}(\mathbf{x},\mathbf{y_s},\overline{q_s}) \le 0 \\ \left|\left|h_{s,k}(\mathbf{x},\mathbf{y_s},\overline{q_s})\right|; \quad g_{s,k}(\mathbf{x},\mathbf{y_s},\overline{q_s}) \quad otherwise \end{cases} \qquad k = 1,2,3,...,I+J;$$

$sr_k(t) = 1 + B_k t,$, is a monotonic and nondecreased function depending on the number of current generation t, where $0 \le \text{Bk} \le 1$, and Cp_k is a penalty constant imposed for violation of the constraint k.

Thus, the multiscenario optimization problem (1) is transformed to:

$$Min\ Z' = C'(\mathbf{x}) + \sum_{s=1}^{S} p_s C''\left(\mathbf{x},\mathbf{y_s}\overline{q_s}\right) + \sum_{s=1}^{S}\sum_{k=1}^{I+J} R_{s,i}(\mathbf{x},\mathbf{y_s}\overline{q_s},t) \tag{3}$$

.

After that, an initial population with N individuals is generated randomly. Each individual n of the population is constituted in a way to provide one solution of problem (3) comprising both the vector of first-stage variables and the vectors of the second-stage variables for all scenarios from set S:

$$Individual(n) \Rightarrow \left[\mathbf{x}(n);\ \mathbf{y}(n)_1;\ \mathbf{y}(n)_2;\ \mathbf{y}(n)_3\ ;...;\ \mathbf{y}(n)_s;\ ...;\ \mathbf{y}(n)_S\right] \qquad n = 1,2,...,N\,. \tag{4}$$

Then GA is applied to approximate the optimal solution. Using initial population N the solutions of problem (3) are calculated and respective fitness functions are computed. Following predetermined evolutionary operators for selection, recombination and mutation the offspring is obtained and used for determining the population for the next generation. The procedure is repeated until the stop criterion (predetermined number of generations) is fulfilled.

5. Results

Using the created set of scenarios for a particular ATAD facility comprising bioreactors of 100 m^3, problem (3) is solved. The best obtained solutions with costs of 16900-17300 CU are analyzed in order to choose the pumps which are able to serve the entire ATAD system in different scenarios. The analysis and verification we carried out formed the basis of the decision for most appropriate design solution for the heat integrated ATAD system. The chosen solution comprises two heat exchangers of 33 and 57 m^2 for *HE-c* and *HE-h* respectively, heat storage with a volume of 35 m^3, two sludge pumps of 2.4 and 4.3 kW and one regular pump of 10.3 kW, to serve the heat storage.

Taking into account that discharging and charging of the real facility is carried out from Monday to Friday, simulation of the heat integrated ATAD system was carried out by using the chosen solution and real sets of weekly data for different seasons. During simulation we tracked the temperatures of the charged preheated raw sludge and levels of TSk and expected maximum temperatures in both bioreactors. Some of these results for one winter week are shown in Table 1.

From Table 1 it is seen that as a result of heat integration a considerable reduction of TSk up to 5-6 degrees is expected. Furthermore, more sustainable and close to required operational temperatures are obtained in both bioreactors.

Table 1. Comparison between measured (real) temperatures and calculated (calc) ones in simulation of heat integrated ATAD system.

		Feed		BioR-1				BioR-2			
	[m^3]	T [°C]		TSk [°C]		Tmax [°C]		TSk [°C]		Tmax [°C]	
		real	calc.	real	calc.	real	calc.	real	calc.	Real	calc.
M	17	9.1	18.5	49.1	49.2	50.1	51.6	58.0	61.8	62.7	63.2
T	15	9.5	19.9	48.1	49.8	50.2	53.6	60.9	62.3	61.5	63.3
W	15	9.6	20.0	47.1	50.5	49.2	55.1	54.1	62.3	54.6	63.1
T	15	9.0	19.5	46.4	51.9	48.6	55.9	56.6	62.2	60.8	63.1
F	16	5.6	16.2	46.2	51.7	48.9	55.8	59.1	62	62.3	63

6. Conclusions

The obtained results demonstrate partial suppression of the thermal shock up to 5-6 °C and more sustainable and close to the required operational temperatures in both stages of ATAD facilities, ~55 °C and ~63 °C, respectively. They prove that the daily uncertainties in the raw sludge could be captured trough application of the energy integration thus utilizing discharged heat. This work opens the prospect for further system's improvement.

Acknowledgement

This study is carried out with the financial support of the Grant scheme BG051PO001/3.3-05-001 "Science and business" under the OP "Human Resources Development" of the European Social Fund. We thank our colleagues from the University of Limerick, Ireland for providing real data scale of ATAD system.

References

E. Shopova, N. Vaklieva-Bancheva, 2006, BASIC – A Genetic Algorithm for Engineering Problems Solution, Comput. Chem. Eng, 30, 1293-1309.

E. Kirilova, N.Vaklieva-Bancheva, 2013, Modelling of two-stage ATAD bioreactor system by using Artificial Neural Network, <booksite.elsevier.com/9780444594310/downloads/ESC.58%20-20Modelling%20of%20two%20stage%20ATAD%20bioreactor%20system.pdf> accessed on 30/10/2013.

J. Rojas, T. Zhelev, 2012, Energy Efficiency Optimization of Wastewater Treatment – Study of ATAD, Comput. Chem. Eng, 38, 52-63.

J. Rojas, T. Zhelev, A. D. Bojarski, 2010, Modelling and Sensitivity Analysis of ATAD, Comput. Chem. Eng, 34, 802-811.

N. M. Layden, H. G. Kelly, D. S. Mavinic, R. Moles, J. Barlet, 2007, Autothermal thermophilic aerobic digestion (ATAD) - Part II: Review of research and full-scale operating experiences, J. Environ. Eng. Sci., 6, 679-690.

R. Karuppiah, M. Martin, I.E. Grossmann, 2010, A Simple Heuristic for Reducing the Number of Scenarios in Two-stage Stochastic Programming, Comput. Chem. Eng, 34, 1246-1256.

S. Liu, N. Zhu, P. Ning, L.I. Li, X. Gong, 2012, The one-stage autothermal thermophilic aerobic digestion for sewage sludge treatment: Effects of temperature on stabilization process and sludge properties, Chem. Eng. J, 197, 223-230.

S. Liu, P. Ning, N. Zhu, 2013, Heat balance analysis of one-stage autothermal the rmophilicaerobic digestion system, Fresenius Environmental Bulletin, 22, 1913-1918

T. Zhelev, N. Vaklieva-Bancheva, D. Jamniczky-Kaszás, 2008, About Energy Efficiency Improvement of Auto-thermal Thermophilic Aerobic Digestion Processes, ESCAPE'18, Computer Aided Chemical Engineering, 25.

T. Zhelev, N. Vaklieva-Bancheva, J. Rojas-Hernandes, T. Pembroke, 2009, "Smelly" Pinch, Computer Aided Chemical Engineering, 27, 933-938.

Jiří Jaromír Klemeš, Petar Sabev Varbanov and Peng Yen Liew (Editors)
Proceedings of the 24th European Symposium on Computer Aided Process Engineering – ESCAPE 24
June 15-18, 2014, Budapest, Hungary.

Thermodynamic Study of Hydrogen Production via Bioglycerol Steam Reforming

Zsolt Tasnadi-Asztalos,[a]* Arpad Imre-Lucaci,[a] Calin-Cristian Cormos,[a] Ana-Maria Cormos,[a] Mihaela-Diana Lazar,[b] Paul-Serban Agachi[a]

[a]*Babes-Bolyai University of Cluj-Napoca, Faculty of Chemistry and Chemical Engineering, Arany Janos 11, RO-400028 Cluj-Napoca, Romania*
[b] *National Institute for Research and Development of Isotopic and Molecular Technologies – INCDTIM, Donath 65-103, RO-400293 Cluj-Napoca, Romania*
t_a_zsolty@yahoo.com

Abstract

A thermodynamic analysis and experimental validation of bioglycerol catalytic steam reforming process using Ni/Al_2O_3 catalyst for hydrogen production is presented in this article. The thermodynamic study was performed by developing a mathematical model of the process using ChemCAD process simulator a well-known and widely used CAPE tool. All major reactions and major products (H_2, CO, CO_2, CH_4, C) obtained in the steam reforming of glycerol were considered in the thermodynamic analysis. For the validation of the simulation results, the results were compared with experimental data reported by literature. Following thermodynamic study the most important factors which influence the steam reforming of bioglycerol are the water/bioglycerol molar ratio and the temperature. The concentrations of the main product (H_2) at lower temperature are smaller than the ones at higher temperature due to by-products formation (methane). The maximum concentration of H_2 was obtained at 650 – 700 °C, 1 bar and molar ratio water/glycerol 10 : 1. The main by-products concentration (expressed in dry concentrations) where H_2 concentration is maximum, are the following: 0 % mol CH_4, 21.2 % mol CO, 9.7 % mol CO_2. The minimum formation of CH_4 and C was obtained at 1 bar, 1,000 °C and molar ratio water/glycerol 10 : 1.

Keywords: thermodynamic study, bioglycerol, hydrogen production, steam reforming of glycerol.

1. Introduction

A thermodynamic analysis and experimental literature date validation of bioglycerol catalytic steam reforming process using Ni/Al_2O_3 catalyst for hydrogen production is presented in this article.

Due to continuous increasing energy demand and low stocks of fossil fuels, new sources of energy and fuel are required to be developed. A solution for renewable fuels is based on biodiesel (Cormos et al., 2013). The main by-product of the process of biodiesel production is glycerol. With increasing production of biodiesel, a glut of glycerol ($C_3H_8O_3$) is expected in the world market and therefore it is essential to find useful applications for glycerol. Currently, glycerol is used in many applications including personal care, food, oral care, tobacco, polymer and pharmaceutical application (Adhikari et al., 2007). Bioglycerol is a newly proposed renewable energy carrier mainly produced from biomass. Reforming of bioglycerol provides a promising method for hydrogen production from renewable resources. The overall reaction for steam reforming of glycerol (SRG) is the following:

$$C_3H_8O_3 + 3H_2O \rightarrow 3CO_2 + 7H_2, \qquad \Delta H_{298}=128 \text{ kJ/mol} \qquad (1)$$

The thermodynamic study was performed by developing a mathematical model of the process using the ChemCAD process simulator a well-known and widely used CAPE tool. All major reactions (1, 3-7, 10-13) and major products (H_2, CO, CO_2, CH_4, C) obtained in the steam reforming of glycerol were considered in the thermodynamic analysis.

2. Materials and methods

A thermodynamic study of a process is very important, because process optimization, through sensitivity analysis study, leads to the optimal reaction conditions. According to Díaz Alvarado et al. (2012) and Castello et al. (2011) the most frequent methods for the thermodynamic analysis is based on the variation of Gibbs free energy (Eq. 2).

$$dG = \sum_{i=1}^{N} \mu_i dn_i \qquad (2)$$

The thermodynamic analysis was performed in ChemCAD processes simulator. The major secondary reactions which take place in parallel with steam reforming of glycerol are following (Pairojpiriyakul et al., 2010; Li et al., 2010):

Reactions where the major by-products are formated:

$$C_3H_8O_3 \leftrightarrow 4H_2 + 3CO \qquad (3)$$

$$CO_2 + CH_4 \leftrightarrow 2H_2 + 2CO \qquad (4)$$

$$CO + H_2O \leftrightarrow H_2 + CO_2 \qquad (5)$$

$$CO + 3H_2 \leftrightarrow CH_4 + H_2O \qquad (6)$$

$$CO_2 + 4H_2 \leftrightarrow CH_4 + 2H_2O \qquad (7)$$

$$C_3H_8O_3 \rightarrow C_3H_6O_2 + H_2O \qquad (8)$$

$$C_3H_8O_3 \rightarrow C_3H_6O_3 + H_2 \qquad (9)$$

The main reactions where carbon is formed are reported by Hajjaji et al. (2013):

$$2CO \rightarrow CO_2 + C \qquad (10)$$

$$CH_4 \rightarrow 2H_2 + C \qquad (11)$$

$$CO + H_2 \rightarrow H_2O + C \qquad (12)$$

$$CO_2 + 2H_2 \rightarrow 2H_2O + C \qquad (13)$$

$$C_2H_4 \rightarrow 2H_2 + 2C \qquad (14)$$

To simplify the thermodynamic analysis only the most important seven components which are presented in reactions (1, 3-7, 10-13) were used in the thermodynamic study. In total, three atoms (C, H, O) and seven compounds ($C_3H_8O_3$, H_2O, H_2, CO, CO_2, CH_4, C) were considered thermodynamically in the equilibrium system. In ChemCAD (CAPE simulator) the PSRK (Predictive Soave-Redlich-Kwong) thermodynamic model was set.

3. Results and discussion

The knowledge of the operational conditions promoting carbon formation is essential, because carbon deposition on the surface of the catalyst will result several undesirable reactions and products affecting the purity of the reformation products.

To perform the thermodynamic study it is essential to use a CAPE simulator (e.g. ChemCAD). A large domain for the water/bioglycerol molar ratio as well as for the temperature and medium pressure have been evaluated in the present work. The interval of investigated temperature was 100-1,000 °C, the pressure was in the range of 1-10 bar and the molar ratio of water/bioglycerol was between 1-10. The variations of gaseous species concentration e.g. H_2, CO, CO_2, CH_4 were analyzed.

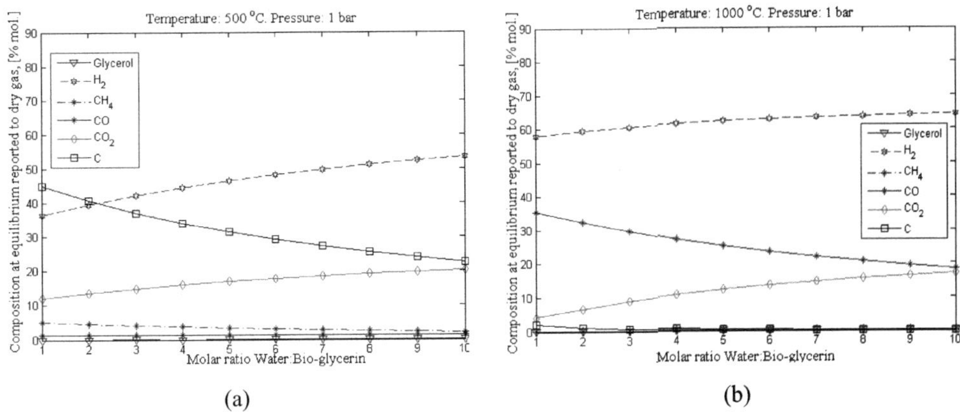

(a) (b)

Figure 1. Variation of major products concentration with molar ratio

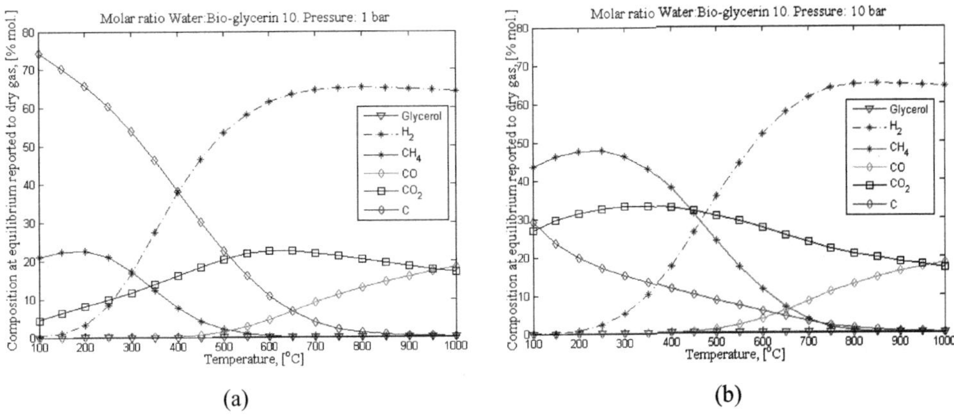

(a) (b)

Figure 2. Variation of major products concentration with temperature

The concentrations of the main components in the reaction mixture (obtained by simulation in ChemCAD) were represented in Figure 1 to Figure 3. Figure 1 present the variation of major components with reactants molar ratio. The most favourable molar ratio of water/glycerol and the trend of variation for major components with temperature can be observed in Figure 1.

The variation of major components concentrations as a function of temperature and pressure is shown in Figure 2. From Figure 1 and Figure 2 the most favourable conditions for steam reforming of glycerol: molar ratio water/glycerol 10 : 1, low pressure (1 bar) and range of temperature 650-700 °C can be observed.

The variation of H_2, C, CH_4, and CO_2 concentration with temperature and pressure at the molar ratio of water/glycerol, 10 : 1 is presented in Figure 3. Figure 3a shows that the maximum concentration of H_2 is reached at 1 bar in range 650 – 700 °C. The minimum carbon formation is obtained at high pressure and temperature (Figure 3b). Figure 3c presents the variation of concentration of CH_4 with temperature and pressure. The minimum CH_4 formation is obtained at low pressure and temperature. Figure 3d shows that the minimum concentration of CO_2 is reached at 1 bar and 100 °C.

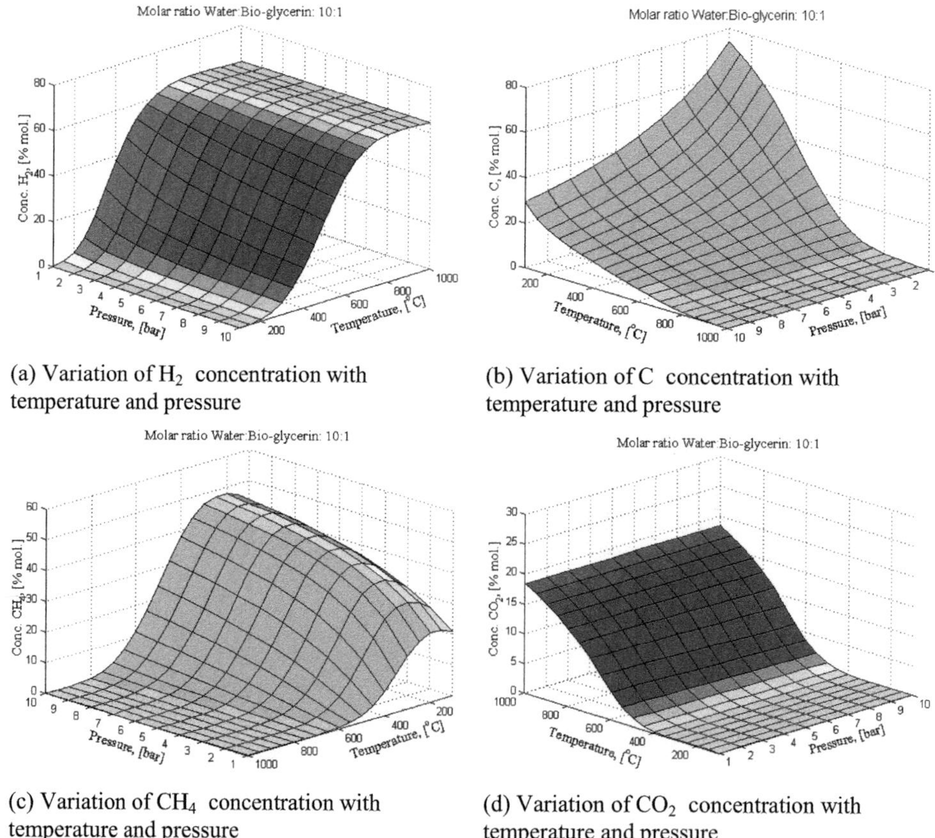

(a) Variation of H_2 concentration with temperature and pressure

(b) Variation of C concentration with temperature and pressure

(c) Variation of CH_4 concentration with temperature and pressure

(d) Variation of CO_2 concentration with temperature and pressure

Figure 3. Optimum conditions of the process of steam reforming of glycerol

Table 1. Experimental and calculated data for SRG where T = 450 °C and molar ratio water/glycerol 9:1 at different pressure value are reported by Cheng et al. (2012 and Chen et al. (2011)

Comp.	P= 1 bar		P= 2 bar		P= 3 bar		$\overline{\varepsilon_1}$	$\overline{\varepsilon_2}$
	Exp.	Calc.	Exp.	Calc.	Exp.	Calc.		
H_2	0.396	0.455	0.334	0.407	0.29	0.369	17.43	
CO_2	0.216	0.179	0.197	0.212	0.19	0.239	16.08	19.77
CH_4	0.06	0.044	0.094	0.110	0.119	0.162	25.81	

Table 2. Experimental and calculated data for SRG where T = 450 °C and p = 1 bar at different molar ratio water/glycerol are reported by Cheng et al. (2012) and Chen et al. (2011)

Comp.	5		7		9		$\overline{\varepsilon_1}$	$\overline{\varepsilon_2}$
	Exp.	Calc.	Exp.	Calc.	Exp.	Calc.		
H_2	0.254	0.392	0.342	0.426	0.396	0.455	22.62	
CO_2	0.16	0.153	0.187	0.167	0.216	0.179	10.54	18.44
CH_4	0.07	0.061	0.06	0.052	0.06	0.044	22.16	

The experimental data from literature and the data obtained using the from the thermodynamic study are presented in Table 1 and Table 2. The comparison of these data is requested in order to validate the thermodynamic study for the catalytic steam reforming of bioglycerol. This comparison was performed using Eqs. (15) and (16):

$$\overline{\varepsilon_1} = \frac{\sum \left| \frac{n_{exp\,i,j} - n_{calc\,i,j}}{n_{calc\,i,j}} \right|}{no.of\ exp.} * 100 \tag{15}$$

$$\overline{\varepsilon_2} = \frac{\sum \overline{\varepsilon_1}}{no.of\ comp.} * 100 \tag{16}$$

The results of the thermodynamic study of steam reforming of glycerol were compared to the experimental data reported in the literature by Cheng et al. (2012) and Chen et al. (2011) and the outcome of this comparisons is as the values of H_2, C, CO and CO_2 concentrations at different values of bioglycerol/water molar ratio, temperature and pressure are similar.

4. Conclusions

A thermodynamic analysis and literature validation of bioglycerol catalytic steam reforming using Ni/Al_2O_3 catalyst for hydrogen production is presented in this article. The paper presents the results of a detailed thermodynamic analysis, for a complete overview of the chemical process. Following thermodynamic study the most important factors which influence the steam reforming of bioglycerol are the water/bioglycerol molar ratio and the temperature.

The concentrations of the main product (H_2) at lower temperature are smaller than the ones at higher temperature due to by-products formation (methane). The concentration of H_2 obtained in the process using water/bioglycerol molar ratio of 10 (higher than the stoichiometric ratio) is higher than the one at water/bioglycerol molar ratio of 3. At lower pressures, the hydrogen concentration decreases slowly but the CO_2 concentration and C formation increase to a maximum value. The maximum concentration of H_2 was obtained at 1 bar, at a range of temperature 650 - 700 °C and the water/bioglycerol molar ratio 10. The main byproducts concentrations (expressed as dry conditions) where H_2 concentration is maximum are the following: 0 % molCH_4, 21.2 % mol CO, 9.7 % molCO_2. The minimum formation of CH_4 and C was obtained at 1 bar, 1,000 °C and molar ratio water/glycerol 10:1.

Acknowledgement

This work was supported by a grant of the Romanian National Authority for Scientific Research, CNCS – UEFISCDI, project ID PN-II-PT-PCCA-2011-3.2-0452: "Hydrogen production from hydroxylic compounds resulted as biomass processing wastes".

Nomenclature

G – Gibbs free energy
N – total number of species
i – number of component
n – molar number
μ – chemical potential
$\overline{\varepsilon_1}$ – average error for component i
$\overline{\varepsilon_2}$ – average error
$n_{exp\ i,j}$ – mol percent for component i and experiment j
$n_{calc\ i,j}$ – mol percent for component i and experiment j

References

C.C. Cormos, A. Imre-Lucaci, A.M. Cormos, Zs. Tasnadi-Asztalos, M. D. Lazar, 2013, Conceptual design of hydrogen production process from bioethanol reforming, Computer Aided Chemical Engineering, 32, 19-24.

S. Adhikari, S. Fernando, S.R. Gwaltney, S.D. Filip To, R.M. Bricka, P.H. Steele, A. Haryanto, 2007, A thermodynamic analysis of hydrogen production by steam reforming of glycerol, Int J Hydrogen Energy, 32, 2875-2880.

F. Díaz Alvarado, F. Gracia, 2012, Oxidative steam reforming of glycerol for hydrogen production: Thermodynamic analysis including different carbon deposits representation and CO_2 adsorption, Int J Hydrogen Energy, 37, 14820-14830.

D. Castello, L. Fiori, 2011, Supercritical water gasification o biomass: Thermodynamic constraints, Bioresource Technol, 102, 7574-7582.

T. Pairojpiriyakul, W. Kiatkittipong, W. Wiyaratn, A. Soottitantawat, A. Arpornwichanop, N. Laosiripojana, E. Croiset, S. Assabumrungrat, 2010, Effect of mode of operation on hydrogen production from glycerol at thermal neutral conditions: Thermodynamic analysis, Int J Hydrogen Energy, 35, 10257-10270.

Y. Li,W. Wang, B. Chen, Y. Cao, 2010, Thermodynamic analysis of hydrogen production via glycerol steam reforming with CO_2 adsorption, Int J Hydrogen Energy, 35, 7768-7777.

N. Hajjaji, M.N. Pons, 2013, Hydrogen production via steam and autothermal reforming of beef tallow: A thermodynamic investigation, Int J Hydrogen Energy, 38, 2199-2211.

C. K. Cheng, S. Y. Foo, A.A. Adesina, 2012, Thermodynamic analysis of glycerol-steam reforming in the presence of CO_2 or H_2 as carbon gasifying angent, Int J Hydrogen Energy, 37, 10101-10110.

H. Chen, Y. Ding, N.T. Cong, B. Dou, V. Dupont, M. Ghadiri, P.T. Williams, 2011, A comparative study on hydrogen production from steam-glycerol reforming: thermodynamics and experimental, Renew Energ, 36, 779-788.

Jiří Jaromír Klemeš, Petar Sabev Varbanov and Peng Yen Liew (Editors)
Proceedings of the 24th European Symposium on Computer Aided Process Engineering – ESCAPE 24
June 15-18, 2014, Budapest, Hungary.

Integrated Model Based Framework for Calculation of Geometry Changes in Leaching Process

Attila Egedy[a]*, Szabolcs Fogarasi[b], Tamás Varga[a], Árpád Imre-Lucaci[b] , Tibor Chován[a]

[a]*University of Pannonia, Department of Process Engineering, Egyetem Str. 10, H-8200 Veszprém, Hungary,*

[b]*Babes-Bolyai University, Faculty of Chemistry and Chemical Engineering : Arany János Str. 11, RO-400028, Cluj Napoca, Romania,*

egedya@fmt.uni-pannon.hu

Abstract

In this study an integrated framework is introduced for calculating the geometry changes during the leaching of precious metals from waste printed circuit boards (WPCB). The developed simulator applies hydrodynamic simulation based on a CFD model, while part of the component mass balances and the inducted changes in geometry were calculated in MATLAB. Using a COMSOL Multiphysics-MATLAB interface the two parts were integrated in one framework to calculate the geometry changes. The method and the developed simulator were validated against direct length measurements, and image processing based measurements during a copper solving experiment. The proposed method can be applied for calculating geometric changes of the solid mass.

Keywords: copper leaching, CFD simulator, geometry changes

1. Introduction

Waste electrical and electronic equipment (WEEE) recycling became a good way to create raw material for new devices, contributing this way to the preservation of natural resources. Printed circuit boards and computer parts such as memory, motherboard or other part contains large amount of alloys containing precious materials such as Au, Ag, Pt, etc. With a proper chemical treatment these materials can be efficiently extracted and selectively recovered from WEEE (Fogarasi et al., 2013).

Recovering the metals from WEEE became a pressing issue, due to the constant development in computer technology which leads to more and more waste to be processed (Oguchi et al., 2012). With the proper chemical treatment the precious metals can be recovered from the waste printed circuit boards (WPCBs), environmental and production costs can be avoided (Behnamfard et al. 2013). For the leaching step a specially designed leaching reactor containing rotating parts can be used (Fogarasi et al., 2012). There are many advantages of the rotating drum leaching reactor for example: intensified phase contact, easy operational parameter change and easy reagent or leached material changes. Different oxidants can be used for metal leaching, for example different acids, sulfates, and other redox agents (metal ions, etc.) (Muniyandi et al., 2013). The kinetic of these processes is very complex due to the multiple reactions, and because most of the reagents are not capable of selective leaching (Rubin et al.,

2013). The sufficient phase contact is very important in order to achieve adequate leaching, thus the hydrodynamic conditions will be crucial too. The circuit board often contains elements with different geometry and composition. Most of the studies apply simple description of the reactions, and do not calculate with the exact geometrical changes because it can be very complex. Using Computational Fluid Dynamics the exact geometries of the solid can be defined, and flow fields can be calculated even in 3D. Hence, the flow around the elements of the WPCB can be determined, and applied to model the leaching and geometrical changes besides the operational parameters. Most of the studies in the field of metal leaching discuss a detailed examination of global parameters (reagent concentration, acidity, revolution speed) but provide little attention to the geometry changes calculation (Souza et al. 2007).

The dissolution process involves important geometry changes of the leached materials which can affect the hydrodynamics of the process. Therefore the examination of these geometry changes is useful to understand the exact behavior of the dissolution processes, and obtain more adequate models. For calculating the changes of the component concentrations a basic kinetic model can be used using Arrhenius expressions to calculate the rate of the dissolution process. However, the shrinking core model is used in most of the cases with spherical solid particles, and considering an ash layer, which does not present in our case (Safari et al.. 2009). The shrinking core model calculates with one dimensional geometry change, and with chemical and diffusion controlled reaction steps (Nona et al. 2005). However most of the applied models (simple Arrhenius equations, shrinking core models) do not contain exact geometry changes instead uses averages or no geometry factors.

In this study copper leaching kinetics were applied to calculate the exact geometry changes of a copper wire leached by $Na_2S_2O_8$ reagent. The kinetic parameters of the dissolution process, identified in a previous research, were used this study.
The framework is based on a CFD part calculating the momentum balance, the developing flow field around the copper wire and the convective terms of component mass balances. Source terms and geometry changes were calculated outside the CFD environment in MATLAB. For CFD modeling COMSOL Multiphysics were used, and Livelink for MATLAB feature for connecting the two software.

2. Modelling and method

2.1. Modelling framework

The framework contain two different parts linked, the CFD part calculating the momentum balances and the convective term of the component balance, and the calculation of the source term, and the geometry changes. A metal leaching process was examined; a copper wire leaching process was used during the development. A 2D model approach was proposed, and the geometry changes were followed in two dimension. The first step was to define the initial conditions (initial wire geometry, initial concentrations). Then the momentum balance model was calculated using CFD software. Laminar regime equations (Navier-Stokes) were applied for the momentum balance calculation (Eq. (1)). The velocity field around the wire determined with the CFD model then applied in the component balance to calculate the convective term (Eq.(2)) within the CFD software. The source term, and the time dependence was calculate outside the CFD software.

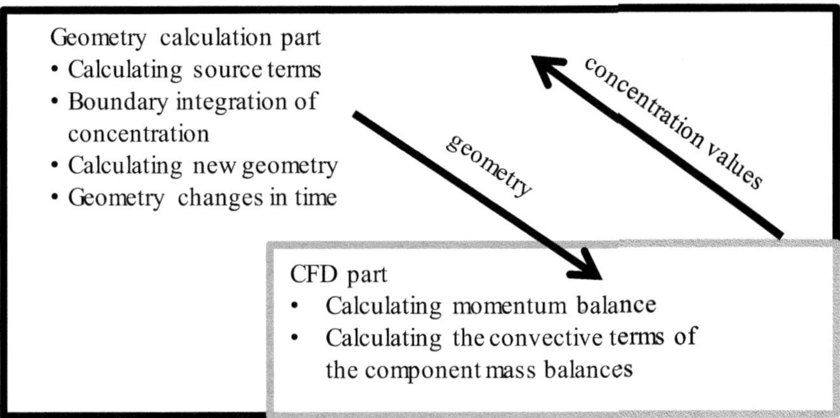

Figure 1. The structure of the proposed framework

Then we split the boundaries into smaller parts and calculate the integrated concentrations on the boundaries. The next step is the calculation the source term, the reaction at the boundaries. Table 1 shows the source terms, and the kinetic parameters, which were identified based on multiple measurements. A copper leaching reaction was used as main reaction without any side reactions. In the component balances the ions of the leached metal and the reagent was calculated. Figure 1 shows the structure of the proposed framework. With the calculated reactions we were able to calculate the boundary changes, and the new geometry. The geometry changes was detected in time, and calculated in a dynamic study using the framework, coupling CFD, differential and algebraic equations in a model of the process.

$$\rho(u \cdot \nabla) = \nabla \cdot \left[-p \cdot I + \mu\left(\nabla u + ((\nabla u)^T\right) - \frac{2}{3}\mu \cdot (\nabla u) \cdot I \right] + F \tag{1}$$

$$\frac{dc_i}{dt} = -\nabla \cdot (-D_i \nabla c_i) - u \cdot \nabla c_i + R_i \tag{2}$$

2.2. Experiments and image processing based validation

A four hour copper leaching experiment was conducted using copper wire and 100 ml reagent solution in a magnetically stirred vessel. The initial measures of the wire were d=0.27 cm, L=5.05 cm=2.37 g. An image processing based method was developed to follow the geometry changes during the experiment. Two different methods were applied to measure the wire one traditional validation technique, and one image processing based method. For the traditional method we measured the mass, diameter, and the length at every 15 min of the experiments. For the image processing based validation in every 15 min a picture was taken from the same distance and focal length, and processed. For the image processing the following steps were followed:

- Loading the picture to MATLAB using Image Processing Toolbox (a)
- Enhancing the picture
- Define the Region of Interest (ROI) automatically (b), based on the frames of the photograph
- Edge detection (finding the boundaries of the wire) for diameter calculation
- Diameter calculation based on the edges y coordinates

Table 1. The parameters for calculating the source term

Reaction *Source term*	k_0 $[mol \cdot m^{-2} \cdot s^{-1} \cdot m^3 \cdot mol^{-n}]$	E_A *[J/mol]*	n *[1]*
$Cu + S_2O_8^{\;2-} \rightarrow Cu^{2+} + 2SO_4^{\;2-}$ $r = k_0 \cdot \exp\left(\frac{-E_A}{RT}\right) \cdot (c_{Na_2S_2O_8})^n$	9528	52018	1

- Center line detection for the calculation of the length of the wire (c)
- Length coordinate based on the centerline

Figure 2 shows the steps of the image processing based validation method.

3. Results

After the framework was developed, we tested the operation based on a leaching experiment using $Na_2S_2O_8$ as a reagent. 200 mol/m^3 reagent concentration was used, and the changes of geometry was measured with two different measurement techniques (the image based measurement was validated by using a manual measurement). Figure 3 shows the results of the model validation with both validation techniques. Figure 3 shows normalized sizes for the easier comparability. Aside from a few points there are minimal differences between the measurement and image processing based validation methods. The simulated results have a good agreement to the two validation measurement results.

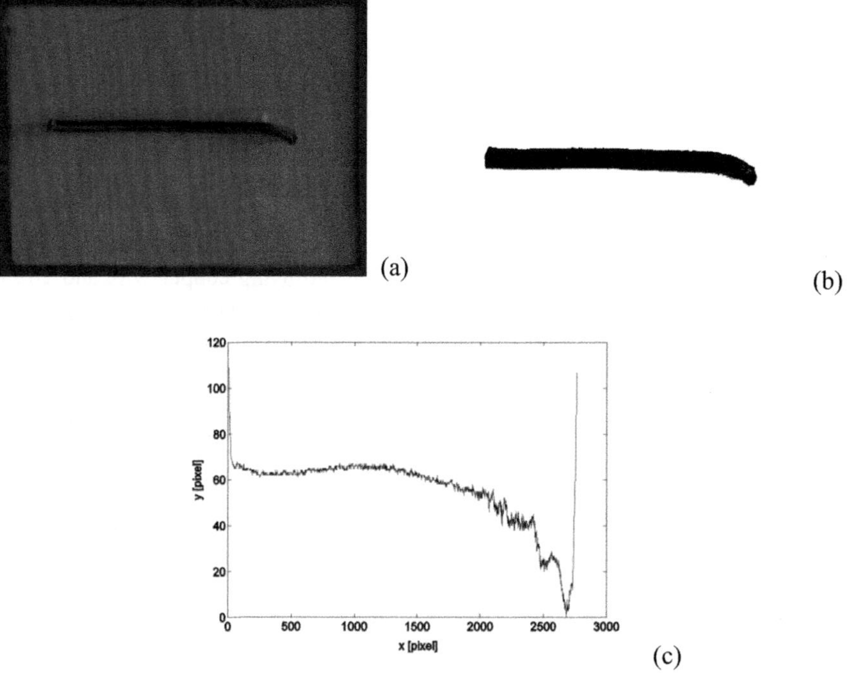

Figure 2. The steps of the image processing based validation method (a) raw picture, (b) enhanced picture, (c) the centerline

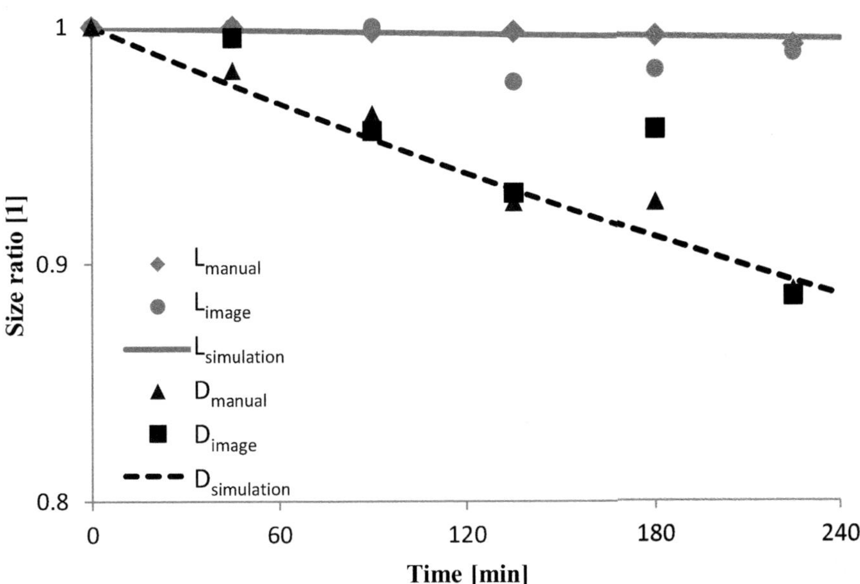

Figure 3. Results of the model validation with both validation techniques (L-length, D-diameter)

However, there are differences between the validation results mainly due to the fact, that in case of manual measurement, the diameter was measured only in one point, and with image analysis an average diameter was calculated for the whole wire.

4. Conclusion

An integrated framework was created to calculate the exact geometry changes during metal leaching from WEEE. The framework uses a CFD simulator to calculate the convective terms of the equations. The source term was calculated outside the CFD environment. With the framework the diameter and length changes can be calculated, applying boundary integration of the concentration values. An image processing validation program was also created to do automatic validation using phonographs of the wire during the leaching process.

The method was tested using a copper leaching reaction, where a copper wire was leached with $Na_2S_2O_8$ as a reagent. The measured and simulated lengths are in good agreement. However, in the future both the framework and the image processing method need further development. Besides we are planning to test the developed method using multiple reagents and multiple operational parameters and to use the developed image processing based validation technique to validate the exact geometry changes during leaching.

Acknowledgements

This work was supported by the Romanian-Hungarian Bilateral Program under project no. 673/2013, TET_12-RO-1-2013-0017 and by the European Union and the State of Hungary, co-financed by the European Social Fund in the framework of TÁMOP-4.2.2/A-11/1/KONV-2012-0071 project. Tamás Varga's research activity in this work was supported by the European Union and the State of Hungary, co-financed by the European Social Fund in the framework of TÁMOP-4.2.4.A/ 2-11/1-2012-0001 'National Excellence Program'.

Notation

q	density	kg/m^3
u	velocity	m/s
p	pressure	Pa
I	Identity matrix	1
μ	dynamic viscosity	Pas
F	other body forces	N
r	reaction rate	1/s
k_0	pre expontential constant	
E_A	Activation energy	J/mol
n	reaction order	1
d	diameter of the wire	cm
L	length of the wire	cm
m	mass of the wire	kg

References

A. Behnamfard, M. M. Salarirad, F. Veglio, 2013, Process development for recovery of copper and precious metals from waste printed circuit boards with emphasize palladium and gold leaching and precipitation, Waste Management, 33, 2354-2363

S. Fogarasi, F. Imre-Lucaci, P. Ilea, Á. Imre-Lucaci, 2013, The environmental assessment of two new copper recovery processes from Waste Printed Circuit Boards, Journal of Cleaner Production, 54, 264-269

S. Fogarasi, F. Imre-Lucaci, T.Varga, P. Ilea, 2012, Eco-friendly leaching of base metals from waste printed circuit boards: Experimental study and mathematical modeling, STUDIA UBB CHEMIA, LVII, 3, 91-100

S. K. Muniyandi, J. Sohaili, A. Hassan, 2013, Mechanical, thermal, morphological and leaching properties of nonmetallic printed circuit board waste in recycled HDPE composites, Journal of Cleaner Production 57, 327-334

K. Nona, C. Lidell, 2005, Shrinking core models in hydrometallurgy: What students are not being told about the pseudo-steady approximation, Hydrometallurgy, 79, 62-68

M. Oguchi, H. Sakanakura, A. Terazono, H. Takigami, 2012, Fate of metals contained in waste electrical and electronic equipment in a municipal waste treatment process, Waste Management, 32, 1, 96-103

R. S. Rubin, M:A:S:d. Castro, D. Brandão, V. Schalch, A.R. Ometto, 2014, Utilization of Life Cycle Assessment methodology to compare two strategies for recovery of copper from printed circuit board scrap, Journal of Cleaner Production, 64, 297-305

V. Safari, G. Arzpeyma, F. Rashchi, N. Mostoufi, 2009, A shrinking particle-shrinking core model for leaching of a zinc ore containing silica, International Journal of Mineral Process, 93, 79-83

A. D. Souza, P. S. Pina, V. A. Leao, C. A. Silva, P. F. Siqueira, 2007, The leaching kinetics of zinc sulphide concentrate in acid ferric sulphate, Hydrometallurgy, 89, 72-81

Jiří Jaromír Klemeš, Petar Sabev Varbanov and Peng Yen Liew (Editors)
Proceedings of the 24th European Symposium on Computer Aided Process Engineering – ESCAPE 24
June 15-18, 2014, Budapest, Hungary.

A Mathematical Programming Approach for the Optimal Synthesis of Nanofibers through Electrospinning Process

Julia Hernández-Vargas,[a] Jannett Betzabe González-Campos,[b*] Javier Lara-Romero,[a] José María Ponce-Ortega[a]

[a]*Chemical Engineering Department,* [b]*Institute of Chemical and Biological Researches, Universidad Michoacana de San Nicolás de Hidalgo, Morelia, 58060, México*

betzabe.gonzalez@yahoo.com.mx

Abstract

This paper presents a general mathematical programming formulation to determine the optimal operating conditions to synthesize nanofibers through the electrospinning process at the minimum cost. Several relationships based on experimental data for different polymers to determine the nanofiber diameter and cost are proposed. Also, a general optimization approach is proposed to trade off the relationships between cost and nanofiber diameter. A case study including the specific relationships for three polymers and five operating conditions is presented. The proposed approach is general and it can be applied to different cases.

Keywords: Optimization, electrospinning, nanofibers, minimum cost and diameter, disjunctive programming.

1. Introduction.

Research into polymer nanofibers synthetized by electrospinning technique has increased significantly over the last decade because they have potential applications in medicine, including artificial organ components, tissue engineering, implant materials, drug delivery and wound dressing (Agarwal et al., 2013). In the electrospinning process, an electric field is used to create a charged yet of polymer solution. The solvent is evaporated before reaching the collector and the final collected product is a mat composed of interconnected fibers of nanometer scale (see Figure 1). Some of the parameters influencing the electrospinning process are: polymer concentration, voltage, type of polymer, type of solvent, distance between electrodes, injection velocity, and temperature, between others. Sencadas et al. (2012) studied and analysed the effect of these parameters on quality, morphology and final diameter of nanofibers, which are key parameters for potential biomedical applications, in this regard Hong et al. (2013) developed nanofibers for a variety of biomedical applications. The most important physical property was the fiber diameter for every application (Khadka et al., 2012). With respect to empirical modelling, Kong et al. (2013) reported quantitative relationships between nanofiber diameter and some electrospinning parameters. However, none of them has considered the use of formal optimization approaches to determine the combination of parameters that allows yielding nanofibers with desirable characteristics and at the same time at the minimum possible cost. Therefore, in this paper is proposed a formal mathematical programming model to determine the combination of parameters (i.e. concentration, voltage, distance between electrodes, injection velocity and temperature)

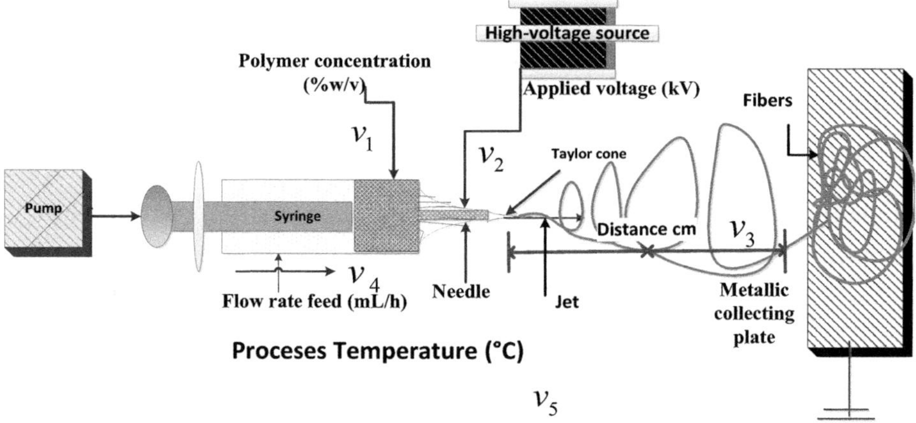

Figure 1. Schematic representation for the electrospinning process.

that yield polymer nanofibers with the desirable diameter at the minimum cost. This model formulation is based on experimental results for the electrospinning process.

2. Proposed Model Formulation.

Mathematical programming has been widely used in the optimization of processes (Raman and Grossmann, 1994), having the advantage that allows manipulating a lot of variables and constraints to determine the optimal solution of a given problem. Particularly, disjunctive programming formulations allow to easily representing a complex combinatorial problem and these formulations have been proven in several engineering applications (see Ponce-Ortega et al., 2009). This way, in the present paper, a general disjunctive programming formulation is proposed to determine the minimum cost associated to electrospun nanofibers production with specific characteristics. This disjunctive formulation must select the type of polymer used (*p*), the value for the variables (*V*) that includes the concentration, voltage, distance between electrodes, injection velocity and temperature, to determine the nanofibers required diameter (*Diam*) and satisfying specific constraints for the manipulated variables (*V*). This formulation includes relationships for each polymer for the cost ($f_p^{cost}(V_U)$) and diameter ($f_p^{Diam}(V_U)$) as a function of the manipulated variables (*V*). The proposed disjunctive formulation is stated as follows:

$$\bigvee_{p} \begin{bmatrix} Y_p \\ Cost = f_p^{cost}(V_U) \\ Diam = f_p^{Diam}(V_U) \\ V_{U,p}^{\min} \le V_U \le V_{U,p}^{\max} \quad \forall_U \in U \end{bmatrix}$$

In previous formulation, Y_p is a Boolean variable that is true when the polymer p is selected as the optimum one, and for this case the corresponding relationships for the cost and diameter are applied. In the case when the Boolean variable Y_p is false, the relationships are not considered. It should be noted that for each polymer there are specific relationships for the diameter and cost as well as limits for the involved variables. In addition, only one polymer must be selected as the optimal one. Then, previous disjunctive model must be reformulated as a set of algebraic relationships to be implemented as a formal mathematical programming formulation (Lee and Grossmann,

2000). The following reformulation is proposed in this paper. First the Boolean variables (Y_p) are transformed in binary variables (y_p); when the Boolean variable Y_p is true (i.e. the polymer is selected as the optimum one) then the corresponding binary variable y_p is 1; and when the Boolean variable Y_p is false (i.e. the corresponding polymer is not selected) the corresponding binary variable y_p is zero. Then, the relationships to determine the cost (*Cost*) for nanofibers must be stated only for the polymer *p* selected to be the optimum and the relationships to determine the diameter for the electrospun nanofibers depend on the type of polymer as follows:

$$Cost \leq f_p^{Cost}(V_U) + \mathrm{M}^{\mathrm{Cost}}(1 - y_p), \qquad \forall_p \in p \tag{1}$$

$$Cost \geq f_p^{Cost}(V_U) - \mathrm{M}^{\mathrm{Cost}}(1 - y_p), \qquad \forall_p \in p \tag{2}$$

$$Diam \leq f_p^{Diam}(V_U) + \mathrm{M}^{\mathrm{Diam}}(1 - y_p), \qquad \forall_p \in p \tag{3}$$

$$Diam \geq f_p^{Diam}(V_U) - \mathrm{M}^{\mathrm{Diam}}(1 - y_p), \qquad \forall_p \in p \tag{4}$$

where $\mathrm{M}^{\mathrm{cost}}$ and $\mathrm{M}^{\mathrm{diam}}$ are big M parameters used to activate the corresponding cost and diameter, respectively. This way, when the polymer *p* is selected, then the binary variable y_p is one and the last terms of relationships (1) and (2) are zero. Notice in the disjunction that the limits for the variables involved depend on the type of polymer selected, and because the type of polymer is an optimization variable then this is modeled as follows. First there are upper (V_U^{up}) and lower (V_U^{lo}) limits for the involved variables *U*; however, these limits are optimization variables that are determined depending on whether the polymer is selected or not.

This model is general, and it can be used for any number of polymers and considering different variables, only it is necessary to determine the relationships for the cost and diameter through a set of correlations from experimental data. Also notice that this can be a mixed-integer linear or nonlinear programming problem depending on whether these relationships are linear or nonlinear. The model was coded in the software GAMS) (Brooke et al., 2013) and a case study is presented in next section.

3. Case Study.

In this work three polymers were evaluated (collagen, gelatin and chitosan). These polymers were selected because of their biomedical applications have continuously increasing due to their excellent biocompatibility and biodegradability (Agarwal et al., 2013). The relationship between nanofiber diameter and electrospinning parameters is represented by equation (5):

$$Diam = f_p^{Diam}(v_1, v_2, v_3, v_4, v_5) \tag{5}$$

Where *Diam* is the average electrospun nanofibers diameter (nm), v_1, v_2, v_3, v_4 and v_5 are polymer concentration (% w/v), applied voltage (kV), distance (cm), flow rate feed (mL/h) and temperature (° C) respectively, and they are the electrospinning optimization variables *U* considered in this case. Based on experimental data previously reported for the synthesis of electrospun collagen, gelatin and chitosan nanofibers (Hong et al., 2013), a regression analysis was performed using the Statgraphics software to establish a quantitative relationship between fiber diameter and spinning parameters for each polymer. By multiple regression analysis a polynomial equation was found, it shows a relationship between the dependent variable (diameter) and independent variables (ν_1, ν_2, ν_3, ν_4 and ν_5 previously described). This equation is established after a series of regressions obtaining a 99 % of confidence interval. This polynomial equation was introduced into the mathematical model to represent the dependence of the fiber diameter versus electrospinning parameters. The relationships for the diameter are given for collagen, gelatin and chitosan in the equations (6-8).

$$\begin{aligned} Diam = & -3736.98 + 12.65 v_1^3 - 173.84 v_1^2 + 694.29 v_1 + 143.202 v_2 - 16.21 v_3^2 + \\ & 286.731 v_3 - 497.904 v_4 - 0.01 v_1^3 v_2^2 + 2.23 v_3^2 v_4 + v_1^2 v_5 \end{aligned} \tag{6}$$

$$\begin{aligned} Diam = & -7647.83 + 0.07 v_1^3 - 3.35 v_1^2 + 46.19 v_1 - 3.66 v_2^2 + 153.0 v_2 - 47.07 v_3^2 + \\ & 1048.3 v_3 - 465.71 v_4^3 + 1203.88 v_4^2 + v_1 v_4^2 + v_1 v_5 \end{aligned} \tag{7}$$

$$\begin{aligned} Diam = & 1089.67 - 0.45 v_1^2 + 32.26 v_1 - 0.94 v_2^2 + 31.29 v_2 + 4.19 v_3^2 - 180.26 v_3 - \\ & 180.89 v_4^2 + 478.72 v_4 + v_1 v_5 \end{aligned} \tag{8}$$

The correlation coefficients (R^2) for the experimental and calculated values obtained from the response surface equation were 0.975, 0.898 and 1.00, respectively. These values indicate a good correlation between process and solution parameters and nanofibers diameter.

To estimate the cost of one milligram of electrospun nanofibers produced through the electrospinning process, the following equation was considered:

$$TotCost = Cost^{polymer} + Cost^{solvent} + Cost^{electricity} \tag{9}$$

where *TotCost* is the total production cost of one milligram of nanofibers, $Cost^{polymer}$ is the cost associated to the polymer used in the production of one milligram nanofibers, $Cost^{solvent}$ is the cost of solvent used and $Cost^{electricity}$ is the cost associated to the electricity consumed for the production of one milligram of nanofibers with the specific characteristics indicated. The total production cost for collagen, gelatine and chitosan nanofibers are represented by equations (10-12).

$$TotCost = 50.31 + \frac{529.23}{v_1} + \frac{32.24}{v_1 v_4} + \frac{144 v_2}{v_1 v_4} \tag{10}$$

$$TotCost = 0.0012 + \frac{10.91}{v_1} + \frac{32.24}{v_1 v_4} + \frac{144 v_2}{v_1 v_4} \tag{11}$$

$$TotCost = 0.0018 + \frac{35.80}{v_1} + \frac{32.24}{v_1 v_4} + \frac{144 v_2}{v_1 v_4} \tag{12}$$

4. Results and Discussion.

4.1. Interaction between the involved variables.

From results, it is observed that for collagen nanofibers the most important parameter is the concentration. When the concentration and voltage are higher, nanofiber diameters are smaller. Whereas, when the distance decreases and the injection velocity increases the nanofiber diameter increases. The nanofibers diameter increases when the distance decreases and smaller nanofiber diameters are obtained at longer distance, lower concentrations and higher applied voltage. The influence of the different parameters on gelatine nanofibers diameter shows that when the concentration and voltage increase the nanofibers diameter obtained also increases, and when the distance decreases and the injection velocity increases the nanofibers diameter increases. Also, at longer distances, the nanofiber diameter decreases at low injection velocity. Smaller nanofiber diameters are obtained at longer distances; higher concentrations and higher applied voltage. Finally, in the case of chitosan nanofibers, the lower concentration and voltage, the lower nanofibers diameter, and when the concentration and voltage increase the diameter also increases. In addition, when the distance decreases and the injection velocity increases the fiber diameter decreases. Smaller nanofiber diameters are obtained at lower applied voltage, distances and concentrations.

4.2. Optimization results.

The optimum results obtained for the different polymers considered are shown in Table 1. It should be noticed that the best economic solution involves the use of gelatin; whereas the use of chitosan provides a solution with a moderate cost but with the minimum diameter. Collagen yields the worst economic scenario with a moderate diameter.

For collagen nanofibers diameters lower than ~10 nm, the production cost of nanofibers per milligram is $US 488.97, for diameters between ~10 nm and ~400 nm, the production cost per milligram is $US 107.08, whereas for diameters above ~400 nm the production cost per milligram is $US 106.96. When the diameters are low, the concentration of polymeric solution tends to ~1.3 (% w/v), the voltage to ~14.5 kV, the distance to ~10 cm, the injection velocity to ~0.885 mL/h and the temperature tends to ~23 °C. However, when the diameter is higher, the concentration tends to ~9.9 (% w/v), the voltage to ~22.5 kV, the injection velocity to ~0.10 mL/h, the temperature tends to ~26 °C and the distance is constant. With respect to gelatine nanofibers, for diameters below ~10 nm, the associated cost per milligram is $US 25.5. But for nanofibers diameters between ~10 and ~700 nm the associated cost per milligram of nanofiber is $US 1.46, whereas above ~700 nm nanofiber diameter the cost is $US 1.45. When the diameters are low the concentration of polymeric solution tends to ~2.12 (% w/v), the voltage to ~10.5 kV, the distance to ~10.5cm, the injection velocity to ~0.79 mL/h and the temperature tends to ~19 °C. However, when the diameter is higher the concentration tends to ~30 (% w/v), the voltage to ~25 kV, the injection velocity to ~0.10 mL/h, the temperature tends to ~27 °C and the distance is constant. Finally, for chitosan nanofibers diameters lower than ~50 nm the production cost per milligram is $US 15.23, for diameters between ~10 nm and 180 nm, the cost is $US 6.85, and for diameters greater than ~180 nm, the cost is $US 6.82. When the diameters are low the concentration of polymeric solution tends to ~4.5 (% w/v), the voltage to ~14 kV, the distance to ~12 cm, the injection velocity to ~0.05 mL/h and the temperature tends to ~20 °C. However, when the diameter is higher the concentration tends to ~10 (% w/v), the voltage to ~34 kV, and the distance, the injection velocity and the temperature are constant.

Table 1. Optimization results.

Concept/Polymer	Collagen	Gelatin	Chitosan
Cost ($/mg of nanofibers)	106.95	1.45	6.82
Diameter (nm)	400.75	748.29	184.38
Concentration (% w/v)	9.90	30.00	10.00
Voltage (kV)	22.50	25.00	34.00
Distance (cm)	11.00	10.00	10.00
Injection (mL/h)	0.100	0.100	0.050
Temperature (°C)	26.00	27.00	20.00

5. Conclusions

This paper proposed a set of relationships to determine the diameter and cost of nanofibers as a function of some independent variables involved in the electrospinning process; these relationships are integrated into a disjunctive programming formulation to determine the optimal conditions to yield the desired nanofibers diameter at the minimum cost. The proposed model was applied to a case study where the advantages of the proposed approach are highlighted. This approach can be useful to determine the minimum costs and operating conditions to yield a desirable nanofiber diameter. Finally, the proposed approach is general and it can be easily extended to analyse different polymers and other conditions.

6. References

A. Brooke, D. Kendrick, A. Meeruas, R. Raman, 2013, GAMS-Language Guide, GAMS Development Corporation, Washington, D.C..

D.B. Khadka, D.T. Haynie, 2012, Protein- and peptide-based electrospun nanofibers in medical biomaterials. Nanomedicine: Nanotechnology, Biology and Medicine, 8, 8, 1242 .

J.M. Ponce-Ortega, M. Serna-González, A. Jimenez-Gutierrez, 2009, A disjunctive programming model for simultaneous synthesis and detailed design of cooling networks, Industrial and Engineering Chemistry Research, 48, 6, 2991-3003.

L. Kong, G.R. Ziegler, 2013, Quantitative relationship between electrospinning parameters and starch fiber diameter, Carbohydrate Polymers, 92, 2, 1416– 1422.

N.K. Hong, A. Jiao, N.S Hwang, M. Sung, D. Hyun, 2013, Nanotopography-guided tissue engineering and regenerative medicine, Advanced Drug Delivery Reviews, 65, 4, 536 -558.

R. Raman, I.E. Grossmann, 1994, Modelling and computational techniques for logic based integer programming, Computers and Chemical Engineering. 18, 7, 563-578.

S. Lee, I.E. Grossmann, 2000, New algorithms for nonlinear generalized disjunctive programming, Computers and Chemical Engineering, 24, 9-10, 2125-2141.

S. Agarwal, A. Greiner, J.H. Wendorff, 2013, Functional materials by electrospinning of polymers, Progress in Polymer Science, 38, 6, 963– 991.

V.Sencadas, D.M. Correia, A. Areias, G. Botelho, A.M. Fonseca, I.C. Neves, J.L. Gomez-Ribelles, S. Lanceros-Mendez, 2012, Determination of the parameters affecting electrospun chitosan fiber size distribution and morphology, Carbohydrate Polymers, 87, 1, 1295– 1301.

Jiří Jaromír Klemeš, Petar Sabev Varbanov and Peng Yen Liew (Editors)
Proceedings of the 24th European Symposium on Computer Aided Process Engineering – ESCAPE 24
June 15-18, 2014, Budapest, Hungary.

Simulation and Optimization of an Integrated CO_2 Capture and Storage System

Sungho Kim[a], Seok Goo Lee[a], Taekyoon Park[a], Chonghun Han[a], Jae Wook Ko[b], Jong Min Lee[a]*

[a]*School of Chemical and Biological Engineering, Institute of Chemical Processes, Seoul National University, 1 Gwanak-ro, Gwanak-gu, Seoul 151-744, Republic of Korea*
[b]*Department of Chemical Engineering, Kwangwoon University, Seoul, 139-701, Republic of Korea*
Jongmin@snu.ac.kr

Abstract

Carbon dioxide capture and storage (CCS) system has been developed during several decades. However, most of studies about CCS system focus on a specific process, while a few does on the integrated CCS system. Further study about process design and optimization for the integrated CCS system is needed to deal with process consistency and decision making about choosing optimal design option of overall system. This study presents a bottom-up approach for designing an integrated CCS system. In first step, optimal design of each CCS unit process is proposed using previous researches and power plant operation data. Then all of designed process models are unified to construct a model of an integrated CCS system. Based on this model, proper integration and optimization study for designing whole CCS system is shown. Additionally, this study describes a list of design variables that have much influence on designing the integrated CCS process.

Keywords: Integrated process design, CO_2 Capture, Global warming

1. Introduction

In these days whole world heavily depends on fossil fuels. As more fossil fuels are burnt, carbon dioxide, a major greenhouse gas, is emitted into atmosphere. Increase of carbon dioxide amount in atmosphere is significantly effecting global warming of the earth.

Carbon dioxide capture and storage (CCS) system is a promising technology for accomplishing the desired green energy system. The system consists of CO_2 capture, liquefaction, transport, storage and other CO_2 application. A lot of researches and projects have been performed to study each process, and CCS projects are being operated in several regions such as United States and north Europe.

While technical demands for individual CCS processes are being satisfied successfully, a new technical challenge of integrating the whole chain of CCS processes into unified process in large scale has become the key for future of CCS technology. Dynamic modeling of individual CCS unit has made a remarkable progress such as developing a CO_2 capture model and validating it with expreimental results. For example, Posch (2013) used a rate based approach for dynamic modeling of CO_2 capture process and validated the result with experimental data from Dürnrohr power station in Austria.

Meanwhile, in modeling an integrated CCS chain, a top-down approach for designing an steady-state IGCC plant with pre-combustion CO_2 capture process was presented by Bhattacharyya (2011), and the study showed that the approach seem to be very useful and effective in process simulation environment for integrated CCS system. However, modeling a whole chain CCS process integrating the plant, capture, liquefaction and compression has not been presented before.

In this study, a bottom-up approach for design of integrated CCS model is shown. First, steam turbine for pulverized coal(PC) plant, CO_2 capture and liquefaction process are presented. Then an integrated model for CCS system is shown by connecting those models. Important process variables which have significant impact on whole process are listed.

2. Design of unit process models.

To build models of unit process, commercial process simulators ASPEN PLUS® and ASPEN HYSYS® is used in this section. Whole CCS chain is divided into power plant, CO_2 capture process and CO_2 liquefaction process for pipe transport. Simulation results from preceding process are used as a feed stream in following process.

2.1. Steam turbine cycle for purvurized coal (PC) plant.

Steam turbine is used to generate power from heated steam. It consists of turbines for power generation, stream splitters and heat exchangers for feedwater heater (FWH) system. First, water is heated by boiler to form steam with high pressure and temperature. The steam is used to operate two turbines which called high-pressure (HP) turbine. In this model, HP turbines generate about 31.5 % of demanded power. Used steam is sent to a reheater in the boiler to be reheated while small amount of the steam is splitted and used for FWH system. Reheated steam is sent to intermediate-pressure (IP) and low-pressure (LP) turbine to generate more electricity. For each turbine, a little of steam is splitted and sent FWH system as in HP turbine. Two turbines for IP and five turbines for LP are used in this model, and 29.8 %, 38.7 % of demanded electricity is generated each.

Optimal operating points such as pressure drop ratio of turbines and split ratio to FWH system were determined to maximize performance of steam cycle, which is indicated by the amount of required heat from boiler to achieve designated electricity generation.

Steam turbine model does not include flue gas stream from the boiler, but it is very necessary to find relation between power demand and operating condition of boiler. The operating condition of boiler directly effects condition of flue gas and it is most important property which connects plant model and CO_2 capture model. In Fig. 1 detailed configuration of the steam turbine cycle is described. Material flows(solid line) indicate steam flows and dotted lines means the energy flows which include heat transfer from a boiler and heat exchangers in FWH system. Generated electricity is gathered at the top of the PFD.

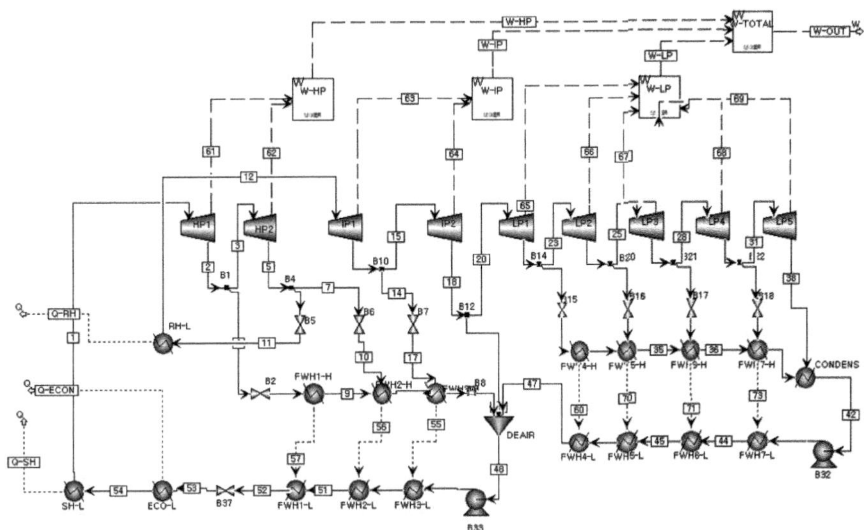

Figure 1. PFD of steam turbine cycle in power plant model

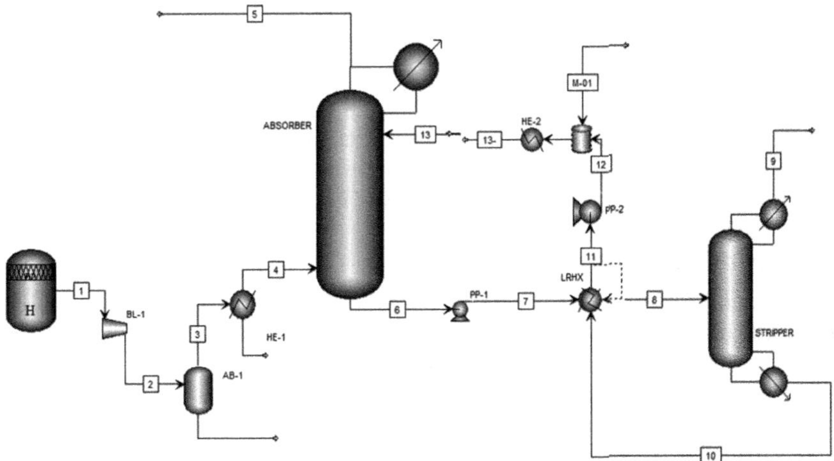

Figure 2. PFD of CO_2 capture process

2.2. CO_2 capture process

For modeling CO_2 capture process, a capture model which uses 30 wt % monoethanolamine (MEA) as solvent to separate CO_2 is chosen. Using actual data from a reference PC plant, condition of flue gas from a boiler is defined. Capture process simulation model is designed to satisfy desired goal of CO_2 capture which separates 90 % of CO_2 from flue gas. E-NRTL model is used for calculation of state equilibrium in absorber and stripper. Using rate-based distillation module in process simulator to describe both units.

In case of CO_2 capture process, process optimization means minimizing regeneration energy duty at the stripper unit. Optimal operating conditions were found to reduce the heat duty.

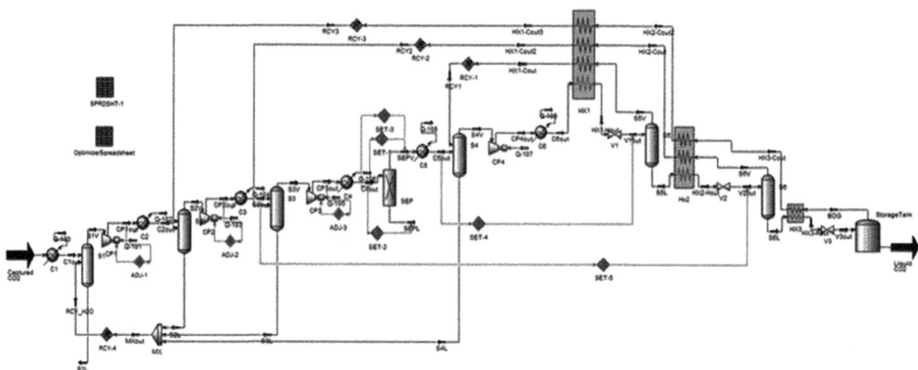

Figure 3. PFD of CO_2 liquefaction process

Purity of captured CO_2 is about 95 mol %. Required regeneration energy of solvent is approximately 3.9 GJ per /tCO_2. Fig. 2 shows the CO_2 capture process which consists of an absorber, a stripper, a heat exchanger between two columns and MEA loading system.

2.3. CO_2 liquefaction process

In case of compression and liquefaction of CO_2, the process consists of multi-stage compressors, dehydration unit using triethylene glycol (TEG), and additional cooling process to satisfy desired temperature condition of final product. A small amount of compressed CO_2 is used as coolant for heat exchangers at earlier compression stages. Soave-Redlich-Kwong (SRK) equation of state is used for this system. Required energy in this process is approximately 105 kWh/ tCO_2. Fig 3 shows detailed process design.

3. Integration of unit models

By connecting those models, an integrated process model is built using PRO/II. Fig 4 shows PFD of the entire process. This PFD

Process variables such as process materials(coal, solvent, utility etc.), operating condition and product specification goal are same as each individual model. This integrated model showed similar simulation results to the results from simulations of independent process model. The model would provide a comprehensive understanding of both every element of CCS chain and whole system.

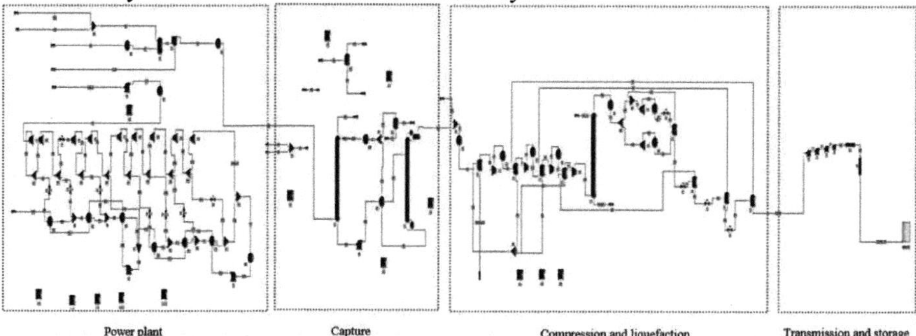

Figure 4. PFD of an integrated process model

3.1. Results of power plant model in the integrated process model.
The plant model is designed to use Illinois No.6 coal to generate 500 MW of electricity. Simulation results of steam cycle part came out to be same as the result from individual steam cycle model. Composition of the flue gas from power plant is listed below in Table 1. Since this plant uses air to burn coal, flue gas contains much of nitrogen gas. This result is used as input data for CO_2 capture part in the integrated model.

3.2. Results of CO_2 capture process in the integrated process model
CO_2 capture process which follows power plant is also designed simultaneously. Absorber column consists of 9 equilibrium stages and operated in 1bar. Regeneration column consists of 23 stages and operated in 1.30bar at top stage and 1.48bar in bottom stage. CO_2 capture plant spend 3.92 GJ/tCO_2. Results of CO_2 capture is shown at Table 2.

3.3. Results of CO_2 liquefaction process in the integrated process model
In liquefaction process, captured CO_2 is compressed to 7 bar, -49 °C for ship transport. Also, H_2O composition is decreased below 100 vppm. Required liquefaction energy came out to be 105 kWh/tCO_2. Efficiency of the power plant including CO_2 capture and liquefaction process came out to be 37.04 %, decreased from 46.4 % without CCS system attached.

4. Impact of process variables on integrated process model

Considering all of the results and relations, some variables are found to be have more impact on the entire system than others. These could be found by swinging variables by hand and observing the entire process.

Table 1. Composition of flue gas in integrated model.

Composition	Value	Units
Ar	0.0083	mol%
CO_2	0.1354	mol%
H_2O	0.1508	mol%
N_2	0.6815	mol%
O_2	0.0240	mol%

Table 2. Composition of captured CO_2

Composition	Value	Units
CO_2	0.9255	mol%
H_2O	0.0738	mol%
N_2	5.7E-04	mol%
O_2	1.2E-04	mol%

Table 3. Composition of liquefied CO_2 stream.

Composition	Value	Units
CO_2	0.9993	mol%
H_2O	5.9E-07	mol%
N_2	6.1E-04	mol%

In the power plant model, type of the power plant and rapid change of electricity demand greatly affected the later process results, especially composition of flue gas from plant.

Change of flowrate of the solvent (MEA) was most crucial factor to determine efficiency of capture plant. Other major process variables such as flue gas composition, desired capture ratio and pressure of each column was also important. Especially pressure change could directly change configuration of following CO_2 liquefaction process since if initial condition of the liquefaction process is changed then compression route of gas would be affected and compression units should be reorganized.

5. Conclusion

This study presented designing an integrated process model of carbon dioxide capture process using bottom-up based approach. In this approach, optimal process design of each CCS unit process were made, then the unit processes are unified to form an integrated process model for entire CCS chain which handles from a power plant to the CO_2 liquefaction process for transport. Much reasonable process design and its specification can be made using the integrated model rather than respective unit models.

Another advantage of this integration study is the possibility to offer a method to evaluate impact of process variables on entire CCS chain. A process designer who wants to design a whole-chain CCS model can determine detailed structure and process specification easily if he would already have knowledge about with important process variables such as electricity demand, desired CO_2 capture ratio, transport method, etc. Also this would help the designer to design a control strategy for the entire CCS chain.

References

S. Posch, M. Haider, 2013, Dynamic Modeling of CO_2 Absorption from Coal-Fired Power Plants into an Aqueous Monoethanolamine Solution, Chemical Engineering Research and Design, 91, 977-987

D. Bhattacharyya, R. Turton, S. E. Zitney, 2011, Steady-State Simulation and Optimization of an Integrated Gasification Combined Cycle Power Plant with CO_2 Capture, Ind. Eng. Chem. Res. 50, 1674–1690.

J. Xiong, H. Zhao, M. Chen, C. Zheng, 2011, Simulation Study of an 800MW Oxy-combustion Pulverized-Coal-Fired Power Plant, Energy and Fuels, 25, 5, 2405-2415.

D.M. Austgen, G.T. Rochelle, X. Peng, C.-C. Chen, 1998, A Model of Vapor-Liquid Equilibria in the Aqueous Acid Gas-Alkanolamine System Using the Electrolyte-NRTL Equation, AIChE Meeting, New Orleans, US.

F.-Y. Jou, A.E. Mather, F.D. Otto, 1995, The Solubility of CO_2 in a 30 Mass Percent Monoethanolamine Solution, The Canadian Journal of Chemical Engineering, 73, 140-147.

R. Brasington, H. Herzog, 2012, Dynamic Response of Monoethanolamine (MEA) CO_2 Capture Units, Carbon Management Technology Conference, 290.

A. Aspelund, K. Jordal, 2007, Gas conditioning—The interface between CO_2 capture and transport, International Journal of Greenhouse Gas Control, 1, 3, 343-354.

Jiří Jaromír Klemeš, Petar Sabev Varbanov and Peng Yen Liew (Editors)
Proceedings of the 24th European Symposium on Computer Aided Process Engineering – ESCAPE 24
June 15-18, 2014, Budapest, Hungary.

Optimization of Microalgal Bioreactor Oil Production via Run-to-run Control

Jung Hun Kim[a], Sung Jin Yoo[a], Dong Hwi Jeong[a], Gibaek Lee[b], Jong Min Lee[a,]*

[a]*School of Chemical and Biological Engineering, Institute of Chemical Processes, Seoul National University, Gwanak-ro, Gwanak-gu, Seoul 151-744, Republic of Korea*
[b]*Department of Chemical and Biological Engineering, Korea National University of Transportation, Chungju, 380-702 Republic of Korea*
jongmin@snu.ac.kr

Abstract

The oil production of microalgal bioreactor is optimized using Run-to-Run optimization. After a preliminary run, transfer functions of the model are gained by linearization at the three different time instants during the batch. Using these transfer function models, the input of the batch were calculated so as to handle the traditional optimizing task and at the same time, to consider the error of the previous run to compensate process-model mismatch. Inputs have been successively improved by taking into account the 'error' after each batch run. It is shown that the oil production rate was increased about 30% after five iterations.

Keywords: microalgae, bioreactor, run-to-run control, optimization

1. Introduction

The optimizing control problem of bioreactors has been receiving interest both from industry and academia for decades. While various attempts have been made to solve this problem, there still exists a gap between academia and industrial practice. One reason is that many researchers haven't put 'practical situations' into consideration in their studies (Banholzer et al., 2013). In industrial practice, the effects coming from unknown disturbances, unknown side reactions, and the lack of accurate state measurements are critical. These effects can be so big that they can literally leave most of the studies based on unrealistic assumptions nothing but academic values.

As a mean to bridge this discrepancy between the theory and the practice, iteration learning-based control method has been suggested and studied (Choi et al., 1996). The strong point of this method is that it enables the operators to meet operational conditions with minimal understanding of the process. A generally used algorithm is given below.

$$U^{k+1} = U^k + G_L(Y^d - Y^k) \tag{1}$$

U and Y are vectors which stand for input and output of the system, and G is the learning gain. Superscript k is the batch number. At the k-th run, the input U^k is given to the process to produce the output Y^k. If the desired output was Y^d, by calculating U^{k+1} as in Eq.(1) with appropriately chosen G_L, Y^k will converge to Y^d as k increases.
Since the term $(Y^d\text{-}Y^k)$ represents an error on the previous run, one can interpret Eq.(1) as an algorithm with a capacity to compensate for this error. If the learning matrix G_L is

provided as an inverse of a process model, i.e. $G_L = (G_P)^{-1}$, the provided scheme can achieve dead-beat control after just one iteration. However, since there rarely exists an accurate process model, G_L is chosen so that it can guarantee the convergence of Y^k to Y^d as k goes to infinity. A limitation of this approach is that the desired trajectory Y^d has to be determined beforehand. In other words, It doesn't have a capacity to determine which trajectory to follow by itself. So it is reasonable to conclude that we need a combined control scheme of these two, to handle practical situations.

2. Problem Statement

The problem is to find a time-varying input profile that maximizes the objective function, i.e., oil production. The original problem is a multi-input and multi-output (MIMO) system, and also a nonlinear system. Since it is very complex to deal with this problem directly, cautious assumptions have to be made to simplify the problem. There are two important simplifications used to solve this problem.

First, the original ODE model describing a bioreactor has been linearized around three different time instants. Linearization is a common method used in iterative learning control approaches. However, we cannot perform linearization around one nominal operation point. This is because biological systems have dynamics that differ severely by time. A common way to divert this problem is to perform linearization on every sampling points. For example, suppose there is a bioreactor with 360 working hours, and the sampling is done at every 24 h. Then one can have 360/24 = 15 different linearized models for each time period. One drawback of this is that the output of the linearized model in the previous time instant has to be consistent with the input of the next time instant. This can cause harsh computational constraints, affecting the reliability of the algorithm. A compromise between the two can be sought to avoid aforementioned issues. By setting a few 'characteristic time instants' during the batch, linearizations can be done by segments. In this study, the segmentation has been done into three parts: initial feeding period, growing period, and ending period. This way of segmentation can be qualitatively validated by the well-known observation of cell growth - cell population goes through the exponential growth phase, static phase, and dying-out phase. Thus it is reasonable to assume that the behaviour of the microbial in our bioreactor can be represented by three distinct linear models.

Second, it is assumed that the input profiles are piecewise constant. This form is assumed because this type of input is most commonly used in industrial practice. Also, it makes the optimizing calculations much easier. p_1^k , p_2^k will be used to denote the parameter set describing the first and the second feed input respectively, as indicated in Eq.(2) through Eq.(5), Subscript denotes the type of input and the superscript k denotes the iteration number.

$$\boldsymbol{p_1^k} = (p_{11}^k \ p_{12}^k \ p_{13}^k)^T \tag{2}$$

$$\boldsymbol{p_2^k} = (p_{21}^k \ p_{22}^k \ p_{23}^k)^T \tag{3}$$

$$f_1^k(t) = p_{11}^k(T_1 \le t < T_2),\ p_{12}^k(T_2 \le t < T_3), p\,_{12}^k(T_3 \le t \le T_f) \tag{4}$$

$$f_2^k(t) = p_{21}^k(T_1 \le t < T_2),\ p_{22}^k(T_2 \le t < T_3), p\,_{22}^k(T_3 \le t \le T_f) \tag{5}$$

3. Methodology

Before the iterative runs, a preliminary run has been conducted to gain data for linearization. Initial input profiles have been chosen from prior knowledge of a process. Using the data gained from this preliminary run, linearizations have been conducted at the middle of each time segments, namely $(T_1+T_2)/2$, $(T_2+T_3)/2$, $(T_3+T_f)/2$. As a result, 6 different transfer functions connecting 2 inputs to the output at three different periods are collected.

For the first run, the optimal feed profile was calculated using the linear transfer function model. The objective function to be maximized is

$$\boldsymbol{p}_1^1 = argmax_{\boldsymbol{p}_1}[Product(\boldsymbol{p}_1) - \lambda\ ||\boldsymbol{p}_1||] \tag{6}$$

Product prediction given $\mathbf{p}_1$ can be easily calculated using the linearized transfer functions. The second term prevents too abrupt a change of input profiles from the previous input profile. Normalized values of parameters are used in calculations. λ is an weighting factor to even the scale between two terms of the objective function. Its value can be flexibly chosen according to the user's preference. Once the calculation is done, we can implement this input to the first batch, along with the second feed profile which is still same as that of the preliminary run. This 'one input calculation at one time' policy is chosen to avoid getting entangled in the possible nonlinearity problem. During the first batch, samples of the product are measured from center times of each three time segments. The difference between the predicted output calculated from the model and the actually observed value are saved in the memory to be used in later steps. Before the second run, the second input is calculated exactly the same way as in the first step. Second input is calculated exactly the same way as in step one. This input is implemented with the first input which is calculated at the former step. The error between the model-predicted value and the actual value is again memorized.

It is from the third input calculation that begins using the prediction-measurement mismatch information. In addition to the input calculated with the same optimizing method as in previous steps (Eq.(7)), an error correction term is added and combined together to give the final result. (Eq.(8))

$$\boldsymbol{p}_{1}^3, opt = argmax_{\boldsymbol{p}_1}[Product(\boldsymbol{p}_1) - \lambda\ ||\boldsymbol{p}_1||] \tag{7}$$

$$\boldsymbol{p}_1^3 = \boldsymbol{p}_{1}^3, opt +\ \omega G^{-1}(Y_1^d - Y_1^1) \tag{8}$$

ω is another weighting factor that can be chosen between $0<\omega<1$. Bigger value of ω indicates putting more emphasis on correcting the model mismatch. After implementation, the difference between the linear model-predicted output and the actual output is memorized as usual. The scheme is repeated until the termination criteria is satisfied. The overall scheme is summarized in Figure 1.

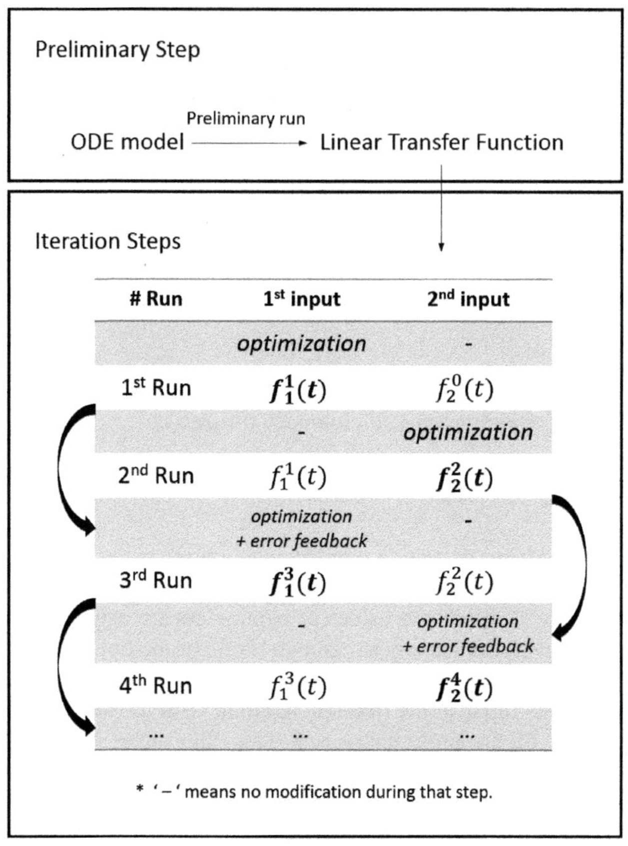

Figure 1. Overall scheme for Run-to-run optimization

4. Case Study : Microalgal Fed-batch Bioreactor

To demonstrate the proposed scheme, microalgal fed-batch bioreactor model proposed by Surisetty(2010) has been used. Model equations are given below:

$$\frac{dx}{dt} = \mu x - x\frac{f_0}{V} - x\left(f_1^i + f_2^i - f_0\right)\frac{1}{V} \tag{9}$$

$$\frac{dS_1}{dt} = -\rho x + S_1^i\frac{f_1^i}{V} - S_1\frac{f_0}{V} - S_1\left(f_1^i + f_2^i - f_0\right)\frac{1}{V} \tag{10}$$

$$\frac{dS_2}{dt} = -\frac{1}{Y_{xs}}\mu x + S_2^i\frac{f_2^i}{V} - S_2\frac{f_0}{V} - k_m x - \frac{1}{Y_{ps}}\pi x - S_2\left(f_1^i + f_2^i - f_0\right)\frac{1}{V} \tag{11}$$

$$\frac{dQ}{dt} = \rho x - \frac{1}{Y_{xq}}\mu x - Q\frac{f_0}{V} - Q\left(f_1^i + f_2^i - f_0\right)\frac{1}{V} \tag{12}$$

$$\frac{dI_p}{dt} = \pi x - I_p \frac{f_0}{V} - Ip(f_1^i + f_2^i - f_0)\frac{1}{V} \tag{13}$$

$$\frac{dV}{dt} = f_1^i + f_2^i - f_0 \tag{14}$$

$$q = Q/(x + I_p + Q) \tag{15}$$

$$\mu = \mu_m(\frac{q-q_m}{K_q+q})(\frac{S_2}{K_s+S_2}) \tag{16}$$

$$\rho = \rho_m(1 - \frac{S_0}{S_1})^{1+\varepsilon} \tag{17}$$

$$\pi = \pi_m(\frac{S_2}{K_\pi+S_2})(1 - \frac{I_p}{X}) \tag{18}$$

The model consists of 6 state variables and 12 parameters, and there are 2 input variables to be optimized : f_1^i (nitrogen source feed) and f_2^i (carbon source feed). 360 h Batch time was assumed. Time segments for piecewise linearization were proposed to be 24 h – 72 h, 72 – 264 h, and 264 – 360 h. For initial input feeds, $\mathbf{p_1^0} = [0.3\ 0.1\ 0.1]^T(ml/h)$, $\mathbf{p_2^0} = [5\ 5\ 5]^T(ml/h)$ were used. For the adjustable parameters, λ and ω from Eq.(6) and Eq.(8) were chosen as $3*10^{-4}$ and 0.2. All the calculations and *in silico* experiments were done in MATLAB R2013a and MATLAB optimization toolbox™.

5. Results

The transition of input parameters and improvement of total production as a function of iteration steps is given in Figure 2 and Figure 3. Computational time require for calculation of each steps in 2.93GHz CPU and 4.00GB RAM were lesser than 1 minute.

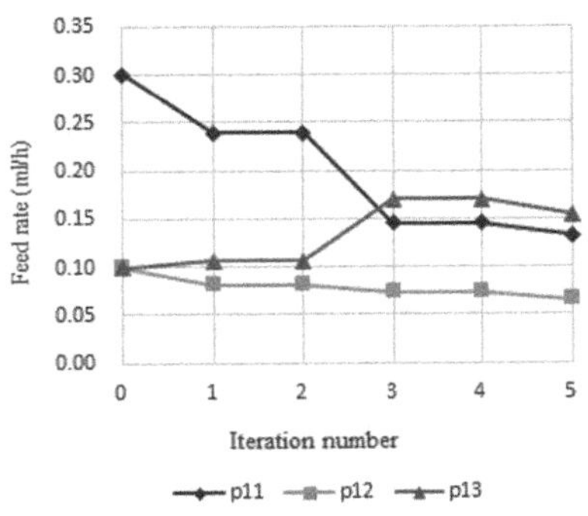

Figure 2. Feed 1 parameter transition

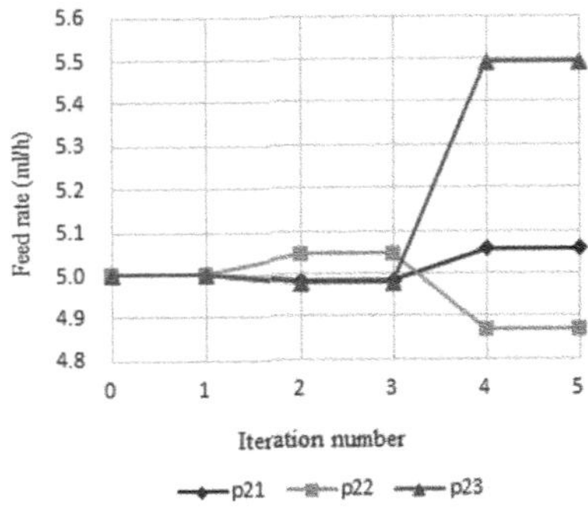

Figure 3. Feed 2 parameter transition

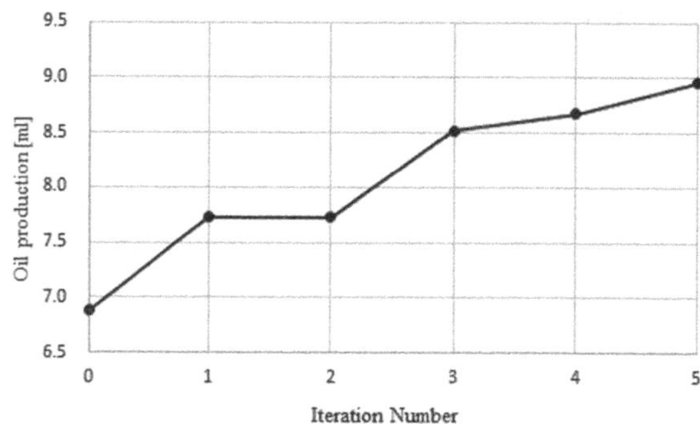

Figure 4. Increase of oil production through iterations

In Figure 4, it is shown that the productivity of the reactor has improved as iteration number increases. After five runs, the oil production of the reactor has increased about 30% of its original value. Note that most of the process improvement was made at odd-numbered iterations. This is due to the fact that the production rate is much more sensitive to the nitrogen feed (feed 1) than the carbon feed (feed 2).

6. Conclusions and future work

In this work, a combined strategy of optimizing control and learning control for computing optimal inputs has been presented. The method makes use of the conventional optimization techniques combined with the iterative learning-based control scheme in order to perform the optimization and error tracking at once. The capabilities of this methodology have been demonstrated with a microalgal bioreactor model and showed 30 % increase of production rate after five iterations. One drawback of this method is that the choice of initial points for linearization is crucial for successful implementation. A novel way to make it less sensitive to initial linearization is being studied.

Acknowledgements

This work is supported by Korea Ministry of Environment as Projects for Developing Eco-Innovation Technologies.(GT-11-G-02-001-5). This work was supported by the Advanced Biomass R&D Center (ABC) of Global Frontier Project funded by the Ministry of Education, Science and Technology (ABC-2012M3A6A2053881).

References

W. F. Banholzer, M. E. Jones, 2013, Chemical Engineers Must Focus on Practical Solutions, AIChE Journal, 59, 2708-2720.

J. W. Choi, H.G. Choi, K.S. Lee, W.H. Lee, 1996, Control of Ethanol Concentration in a Fed-batch cultivation of Acinetobacter calcoaceticus RAG-1 Using a Feedback-assisted Iterative Learning Algorithm, Journal of Biotechnology, 49, 29-43.

K. Surisetty, H. Siegler, W.C. McCafrey, A.Ben-Zvi, 2010, Model Re-parameterization and Output Prediction for a Bioreactor System, Chemical Engineering Science, 65, 4535-4547.

Jiří Jaromír Klemeš, Petar Sabev Varbanov and Peng Yen Liew (Editors)
Proceedings of the 24th European Symposium on Computer Aided Process Engineering – ESCAPE 24
June 15-18, 2014, Budapest, Hungary.

Dynamic Modelling of Particle Formulation in Horizontal Fluidized Beds

Katja Meyer*, Andreas Bück, Evangelos Tsotsas

Thermal Process Engineering, Otto-von-Guericke University Magdeburg, Universitätsplatz 2, 39106 Magdeburg, Germany
katja.meyer@ovgu.de

Abstract

A generic multi-compartment, multi-zone population balance model (PBE) is developed. The model considers particle properties as well as the geometric coordinates (apparatus length). Further features of the presented model are the possibility to include different transport mechanisms from one process chamber to the next, the possibility of arbitrary positions of particle recycle as well as different operating conditions in each chamber. By parametric studies the influence of important process parameters on the product quality is investigated. It is the aim of this work to link product properties, in particular the particle size distribution, to a multi-zone model that can be readily applied in an industrial environment for process design and optimization.

Keywords: fluidized bed, spray granulation, population balance model, particle formulation

1. Introduction

Particle formation is an important step in many production processes, especially in chemical, pharmaceutical and food industry. The product quality is closely linked to the particle properties in these processes, so in order achieve a high-quality product a thorough understanding of (a) the underlying particle formation process and (b) the complex interaction of matter and energy streams with the particles is required. Important particle formation processes in use are, e.g. crystallization, spray drying, mechanical granulation, and fluidized bed layering granulation or agglomeration. The formation processes are influenced by (1) apparatus design, (2) material properties and (3) the mode of operation (batch-wise, continuously) and the process parameters. This work will focus on continuous fluidized bed processes; however the following reasoning can be applied to other particle formation processes as well.

Usually, continuous fluidized bed processes are implemented using single-stage cylindrical apparatuses applying top or bottom spray and internal classification (Heinrich et al., 2002). Moreover, horizontal fluidized beds with a number of internal chambers are applied (Bertin et al., 2011), allowing to realize several process steps in one apparatus, for instance spraying followed by drying and cooling. The main advantage of continuously operated fluidized bed processes is the possibility to operate in steady-state, i.e. a constant product flow with constant properties can be achieved (Teunou and Poncelet, 2002). As a disadvantage one has to consider the residence time distribution of particles at the outlet (Fries et al., 2011).The main aim is to remedy this disadvantage by an improved process design, which necessitates the model-based analysis of the influences stated above on the particle properties.

In recent years, modelling of solids processes has been applied to different processes and apparatuses. To model the particle size distribution in fluidized bed spray granulation, a quite general formulation of the PBE was used by Vreman et al. (2009) to obtain information about stable and unstable process behaviour. In Hede et al.(2009), a dynamic heat and mass transfer model for the top-spray batch fluidized bed coating process was presented, which is based on one-dimensional discretization of the fluid bed into a number of well mixed vessels. Balaji et al.(2010) showed results for growth and aggregation of silicon particles in a continuous fluidized bed reactor using population balances in a multi-scale model. The evolution of the PSD during maltodextrin agglomeration in a pilot batch fluidized bed was modelled using PBE by Turchiuli et al. (2011) obtaining good agreement with experimental data. Li et al. (2012) described a compartment-based model to obtain the 2-D coating distribution on different seed particles in a paddle mixer. A mathematical model for ice crystallization in a scraped surface heat exchanger was coupled with PBE and product residence time distribution by Arellano et al. (2013). Bertin et al. (2013) developed a steady-state model of a multi-chamber fluidized-bed granulator used for urea production, validated and include pure coating or the combined mechanisms of coating and elutriation. In order to predict the process dynamics of a continuous Wurster coating process, a macroscopic PBM was developed by Hampel et al. (2013), considering particle growth. Various mechanisms such as aggregation, drying/rewetting and consolidation were taken into account by combination of heat and mass transfer models with a 3-D PBE of a fluid bed granulation process by Chaudhury et al.(2013).Population balance modelling was used recently to optimize granule quality in a batch fluidized bed spray granulation process (Niu et al., 2014).

The present work concerns spray layering granulation in a horizontal fluidized bed granulator consisting of different process chambers which are linked by weirs (Figure 1, left). In some of the chambers a solution or suspension is sprayed onto an already existing powder bed that is fluidized with air. The droplets hit the particles present in a specific zone created by the nozzle, the spraying zone. The rest of the process chamber is made up by a drying zone, where the particles do not receive new spray, but the applied solution dries, leaving the solid material and creating a new solid layer that increases the particle size. The exchange rates between the zones and the different chambers depend on the process conditions and on the weir configuration (number, type) and may depend on particle properties, i.e. a classifying effect – preferring some particles over others – results. The situation is further complicated by the possible occurrence of external solid flow, for instance recycle flows. As they may have a significant influence on process stability and product quality, the number and position of recycle flows have to considered design variables.

The generic multi-compartment, multi-zone model presented in the next section considers these possible effects, thus allowing the study of the influence of the process parameters and the apparatus design on the product quality.

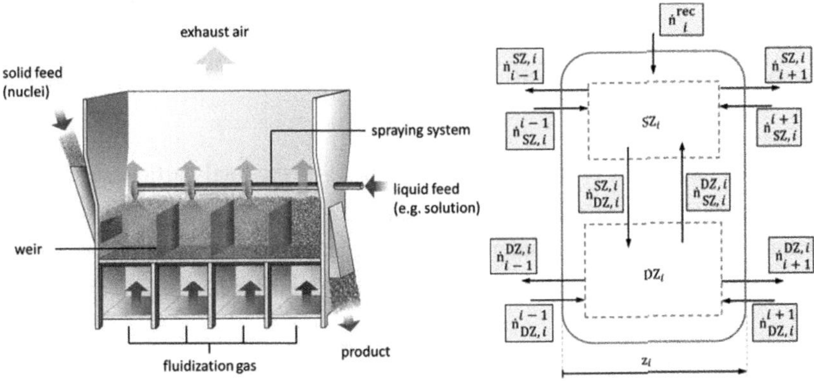

Figure 1. (left) Horizontal fluidized bed in top-spray configuration (Glatt Ingenieurtechnik GmbH, Germany); (right) Schematic of internal and external interconnection of solid flows.

2. Process modelling

In order to study the process dynamics, a dynamic model is derived describing the particle property distribution in the apparatus. The model considers the spatial dimension of the apparatus as well as the particle size. Figure 1, right, illustrates the balance scheme for one process chamber. As motivated in the Introduction, the chambers are virtually divided into two zones: the spraying zone (SZ) and the drying zone (DZ). It is assumed in the following, that particles in each compartment are perfectly mixed, so that particle properties may change from compartment to compartment, but in one specific compartment no spatial dependencies occur. Furthermore, it is assumed that all sprayed solution is deposited on the particles without premature droplet drying, and that the liquid is uniformly spread on all particles in the spraying zone.

Utilizing the population balance approach (Ramkrishna, 2000) to describe the change in particle size with respect to time and position in the apparatus, a number density function is defined, $n = n(t, z, \xi)$, where z denotes the spatial position and ξ the particle size as an equivalent particle diameter. Assuming that neither breakage nor agglomeration takes place the following population balance equation for $n(t, z, \xi)$ can be derived:

$$\frac{\partial n}{\partial t} = -\frac{\partial (Gn)}{\partial \xi} - \frac{\partial (wn)}{\partial z} + \dot{n}_{in} - \dot{n}_{out} \tag{1}$$

where G denotes the growth rate of particles and w the local convective velocity of particles in the apparatus which may depend on the particle properties. The quantities $\dot{n}_{in}$ and $\dot{n}_{out}$ denote the incoming and outgoing particle fluxes, respectively.

The growth rate G is modelled by a surface-proportional law, assuming a spherical particle shape(Heinrich, 2003):

$$G(t,z) = \frac{2\dot{M}_s(t,z)}{\rho_s A_p(t,z)}, \; A_p = \pi \int_{\xi_0}^{\infty} \xi^2 n(t,z,\xi)\,d\xi, \qquad (2)$$

where $\dot{M}_s$ is the mass flow rate of solid sprayed and A_p the total particle surface area. The exchange rates between the drying zone and the spraying zone and between the compartments are given by the residence times of the zones, $\tau_{1-\alpha}$ and τ_α, and can be related to the relative sizes $1-\alpha$ and α (Börner et al., 2011; Fries et al., 2011):

$$\dot{n}_{DZ}^{SZ} = \frac{n_{SZ}}{\tau_\alpha}, \quad \dot{n}_{SZ}^{DZ} = \frac{n_{DZ}}{\tau_{1-\alpha}}, \quad \text{etc.} \qquad (3)$$

In order to calculate the influence of the weirs, the number density fluxes of particles leaving the compartment (or entering from the neighbouring compartments) are determined by separation functions T, which model the selectivity of the weirs. This selectivity depends on the geometry of the weir and the particle properties. In the model a function according to Molerus and Hoffmann (1969) is used:

$$T(\xi) = \left\{ 1 + \left(\frac{\xi_c}{\xi}\right)^2 \exp\left[k_c \left(1 - \left(\frac{\xi}{\xi_c}\right)^2\right)\right]\right\}^{-1} \qquad (4)$$

where ξ_c is the critical separation diameter, which means that particles of larger size are conveyed in the next chamber, and incorporates the influence of the process parameters on the separation efficiency.

The equations for the two zones in compartment i then read:

$$\frac{\partial n^{SZ}_i}{\partial t} = -\frac{\partial (G n^{SZ}_i)}{\partial \xi} - \frac{\partial (w_i n^{SZ}_i)}{\partial z} - \dot{n}_{DZ,i}^{SZ,i} T^{SZ,i}_{DZ,i} + \dot{n}_{SZ,i}^{DZ,i} T^{DZ,i}_{SZ,i} - \dot{n}_{i-1}^{SZ,i} T^{SZ,i}_{i-1} - \dot{n}_{i+1}^{SZ,i} T^{SZ,i}_{i+1} + \dot{n}_{SZ,i}^{i-1} T^{i-1}_{SZ,i} + \dot{n}_{SZ,i}^{i+1} T^{i+1}_{SZ,i} + \dot{n}_{SZ,i}^{rec,i} \qquad (5)$$

$$\frac{\partial n^{DZ}_i}{\partial t} = -\frac{\partial (w_i n^{DZ}_i)}{\partial z} + \dot{n}_{DZ,i}^{SZ,i} T^{SZ,i}_{DZ,i} - \dot{n}_{SZ,i}^{DZ,i} T^{DZ,i}_{SZ,i} - \dot{n}_{i-1}^{DZ,i} T^{DZ,i}_{i-1} - \dot{n}_{i+1}^{DZ,i} T^{DZ,i}_{i+1} + \dot{n}_{DZ,i}^{i-1} T^{i-1}_{DZ,i} + \dot{n}_{DZ,i}^{i+1} T^{i+1}_{DZ,i} + \dot{n}_{DZ,i}^{rec,i} \qquad (6)$$

This set of equations allows calculating the particle size distribution in each process chamber and each process zone.

3. Results and discussion

The partial differential equations were implemented in Matlab (MathWorks, R2012b) as a set of ordinary differential equations after discretisation with respect to the position and particle size by the finite volume method (Heinrich et al., 2002). The equations were solvedusing the integration routine ode15s for the parameters given in Table 1.

Table 1. Model parameters

Parameter	Symbol	Values	Unit
Length of apparatus	L	4	[m]
Length of one chamber	z	1	[m]
Initial bed mass	M_{bed}	20	[kg]
Mass flow rate nuclei	$\dot{M}_{nuc}$	7/3600	[kgs^{-1}]
Mass flow of solid sprayed	$\dot{M}_{s}$	18/3600	[kgs^{-1}]
Solid density	ρ_S	1440	[kgm^{-3}]
Relative size of SZ	α	10	[%]
Residence time in SZ	τ_α	0.3	[s]
Transport velocity	w	0.001	[ms^{-1}]
Critical separation coefficient	k_c	2	[-]
Process time	t_{end}	7200	[s]

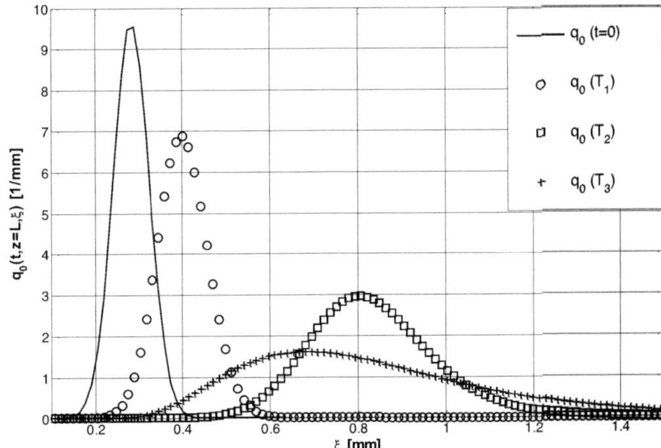

Figure 2. Normalized particle density distributions q_0 (t,z=L, ξ) for the three different separation functions for overflow weirs. In cases 1 and 2 the critical diameters in the compartments are: ξ_{c1} = 0.5mm, ξ_{c2} = 0.6mm, ξ_{c3} = 0.7mm, ξ_{c4} = 0.8mm.

In Figure 2 the results for the outlet particle size distribution for different separation functions T_i are presented. Three different settings were considered: (1) ideal, (2) real and (3) without separation, i.e. ideal separation with critical diameter zero. It can be seen that the weir configuration can have significant influence on the product size distribution. This offers the opportunity of a product design by specifying the weir configuration and fluidization regime.

4. Conclusions and outlook

In this work a multi-compartment, multi-zone model for particle formulation in horizontal fluidized bed processes was presented which considers the complex internal particle flow, the apparatus design and arbitrary position of the recycle flow. The model allows studying the influence of process conditions and apparatus design, e.g. weir configuration, on the particle size distribution which is an important measure for product quality and thus can be used to improve this type of process.

In future work, the heat and mass transfer in particle formulation has to be considered explicitly, allowing for drying or heating and cooling sections in the apparatus. Further work is required to establish and verify relations for the separation functions used to model the exchange rates between the zones and compartments, for instance by particle-tracking (PT) experiments or discrete particle model (DPM) simulations.

Acknowledgments

The authors gratefully acknowledge the funding of this work by the German Research Foundation (DFG) as part of the priority programme SPP 1679.

References

M. Arellano, H. Benkhelifa, G. Alvarez, D. Flick, 2013, Coupling population balance and residence time distribution for the ice crystallization modeling in a scraped surface heat exchanger, Chemical Engineering Science, 102, 502-513.

S. Balaji, J. Du, C.M. White, B.E. Ydstie, 2010, Multi-scale modeling and control of fluidized beds for the production of solar grade silicon, Powder Techn., 199, 23-31.

D.E. Bertin, I.M. Cotabarren, V. Bucalá, J. Pina, 2011, Analysis of product granulometry, temperature and mass flow of industrial multichamberfluidized bed urea granulator, Powder Techn., 206, 122-131.

D.E. Bertin, I. Cotabarren, J. Pina, V. Bucalá, 2013, Granule size distribution for multi-chamber fluidized-bed melt granulator: Modeling and validation using process measurement data, Chemical Engineering Science, 104, 319-329.

M. Börner, M. Peglow, E. Tsotsas, 2011, Particle residence times in fluidized bed granulation equipment, Chemical Engineering Technol., 34, 7, 1116-1122.

A. Chaudhury, A.Niziolek, R. Ramachandran, 2013, Multi-dimensional mechanistic modeling of fluid bed granulation processes: An integrated approach, Advanced Powder Techn., 24, 113-131.

L. Fries, S. Antonyuk, S. Heinrich, S. Palzer, 2011, DEM-CFD modelling of a fluidized bed spray granulator, Chemical Engineering Science,66, 2340-2355.

N. Hampel, A. Bück, M. Peglow, E. Tsotsas, 2013, Continuous Pellet Coating for the Wurster fluidized bed, Chemical Engineering Science, 86, 87-98.

P.D. Hede, P. Bach, A.J. Jensen, 2009, Batch top-spray fluid bed coating: Scale-up insight using dynamic heat- and mass-transfer modelling, Chemical Engineering Science, 64, 1293-1317.

S. Heinrich, M. Peglow, M. Ihlow, M. Henneberg, L. Mörl, 2002, Analysis of the start-up process in continuous fluidized bed spray granulation by population balance modelling, Chemical Engineering Science, 57, 4369-4390.

J. Li, B. Freireich, C. Wassgren, J.D. Litster, 2012, A General Compartment-Based Population Balance Model for Particle Coating and Layered Granulation, AIChE Journal, 58, 5,1397-408.

O. Molerus, H. Hoffmann, 1969, Darstellung von Windsichterkurven durch ein stochastisches Modell, Chemical Engineering Technol., 45, 340-344.

D. Niu, M. Li, F. Wang, 2014, Optimization of fluidized bed spray granulation process based on a multiphase hybrid model, Chemometrics and Intelligent Laboratory Systems, 131, 7-15.

D. Ramkrishna, 2000, Population Balances: Theory and Applications to Particulate Systems in Engineering, Academic Press, San Diego, USA.

E. Teunou, D. Poncelet, 2002, Batch and continuous fluidised bed coating – review and state of the art, Journal of Food Engineering, 53, 325-340.

C. Turchiuli, T. Jimenez, E. Dumoulin, 2011, Identification of thermal zones and population balance modelling of fluidized bed spray granulation, Powder Techn., 208, 542-552.

A.W. Vreman, C.E. van Lare, M.J. Hounslow, 2009, A basic population balance model for fluid bed spray granulation, Chemical Engineering Science, 64, 4389-4398.

Jiří Jaromír Klemeš, Petar Sabev Varbanov and Peng Yen Liew (Editors)
Proceedings of the 24th European Symposium on Computer Aided Process Engineering – ESCAPE 24
June 15-18, 2014, Budapest, Hungary.

Multivariate Hammerstein Structures: A Qualitative Accuracy Comparison to New Input-State Block Structure

Omar Naeem[a*], Adire. E. Huesman[b]

[a] *Department of Electrical Engineering, TU Eindhoven, P.O. Box 513, 5600 MB Eindhoven, the Netherlands.*

[b] *Delft Center for Systems & Control (DCSC), 3ME, TU Delft, 2628 CD, Delft, the Netherlands.*

naeemomer@gmail.com; o.naeem@tue.nl

Abstract

Multivariate Hammerstein structures have been used specifically for the identification of process systems, but never been developed and used exclusively for model reduction purposes in the past. We recently developed a new block-structure for model reduction purposes, which not only approximates the rigorous Non-Linear (NL) process/model, but also reduces large complex models. This block-structure is named Input-State (IS) Hammerstein structure. It is so-named because it exhibits properties of Hammerstein structure. In this paper, IS-Hammerstein block-structure is compared in terms of accuracy and computational time with existing multivariate Hammerstein models. The results show that the IS-Hammerstein structure preserves the fundamental characteristics of multivariate block-structures by implementation on complex chemical process (Catalytic Cracker) and the full order IS-Hammerstein model outperforms all other methodologies showing accuracy improvement of at least 85 % for the considered case. The reduced order IS-Hammerstein structure maintains the accuracy of the approximation along with reduction in simulation time by a factor of 2.60 compared to full order identified model.

Keywords: Nonlinear model identification, Input State Hammerstein model, nonlinear model order reduction, Multivariate Hammerstein block structures, Fluid Catalytic Cracker

1. Introduction

Almost all the process systems have nonlinearity in dynamic behavior. Nonlinear behavior in dynamic behavior of process is not an exception, rather it is generally known as "rule". Mostly chemical processes are very complex and it is hard to fully understand the nonlinearity characteristics. One approach to understand the nonlinear behavior is from the mathematical model of the process. Generally, there are two widely used approaches to achieve the mathematical model for process; a) rigorous modeling based on first principles, b) data based modeling (black box, gray box modeling). While each methodology has its pros and cons, in this paper though, the focus is on data based model development and identification techniques. Data based approach of modeling uses the process data such as inputs and outputs, to understand the process characteristics and model development. Even another approach to develop a process model is model development by combining fundamental process knowledge and process measured data (input-output-state). Such type of modeling is known as gray box modeling approach. Irrespective of the modeling approach, model structure plays an important role in process modeling, specifically for identification based modeling methods. Model structure is important because it helps to identify the process with less model parameters involved to be estimated, thus representing the nonlinear process behavior sufficiently well within desired operational window. Block structure models have been used extensively for the representation of NL processes, survey of which has been reported by Billings (1980). Block structure models have been used for the identification purposes (Eskinat et al., 1991; Norquay et al., 1999; Harnischmacher and Marquardt, 2007 etc.). Though block structure models have been used for the identification purposes, they have never been used for the model reduction exclusively.

In this paper, a block structure, IS-Hammerstein model, developed recently for the model reduction purposes Naeem and Huesman (2011) has been compared in context of identification accuracy and computational time to existing multivariate Hammerstein block structure models. Mulitvariate Hammerstein block structures are discussed in next section while the section IS-Hammerstein model discusses properties of a new model structure. Furthermore, it is shown that IS Hammerstein model exhibits the characteristics of multivariate block structure models i.e., ease of identification, input coupling and representation of input directional dynamics. The paper ends with comparison of results for the implementation of different Hammerstein structures on a fluid catalytic cracker.

2. Block-Structure Models

The survey in section 1 shows that the identification problem for the nonlinear model is simplified by using combination of linear dynamic and static NL blocks. For such block structure models, mainly two kinds of structures are used. Depending on the location of the static NL element, the block structure is either Wiener model (Wiener, 1958) or Hammerstein structure (Hammerstein, 1930). In this paper, Hammerstein model structures are considered. The Hammerstein model structure consists of a nonlinear static and linear dynamic block as shown in Figure 1(a). Hammerstein structures have been widely used for the identification of nonlinear processes in the past, for instance by Rollins, 2004 and Westwick, 2004. It is because of one major reason; ease of identification (Harnischmacher and Marquardt, 2007; Pearson, 2003). Mathematically, Hammerstein structure in continuous time is given as follows (for p inputs, q outputs, n state variables):

$$\dot{x} = \boldsymbol{A}x + G(\boldsymbol{u}) \qquad (1)$$

$$y = \boldsymbol{C}x$$

$\boldsymbol{A}$ - state matrix ($\dim[A] = n * n$); x - state vector ($x(t) \in \mathbb{R}^n$); G(**u**) - nonlinear static mapping, ($u(t) \in \mathbb{R}^p$); Steady-state gain vector (G) ($\in \mathbb{R}^n$); $\boldsymbol{C}$ is the output matrix ($\dim[C] = q * n$) and y is the output of the system ($y(t) \in \mathbb{R}^q$). In order to identify NL process, Hammerstein block-structure must exhibit the fundamental properties, i.e., a) must be able to represent the static multivariate nonlinearity of the system, b) must exhibit the input-directional dynamics (for the MIMO/MISO processes) and c) should provide the ease of identification of nonlinear and large processes. The SISO Hammerstein structure (shown in 1(a)) can be extended to MISO Hammerstein model by using vector valued input signal **u**.

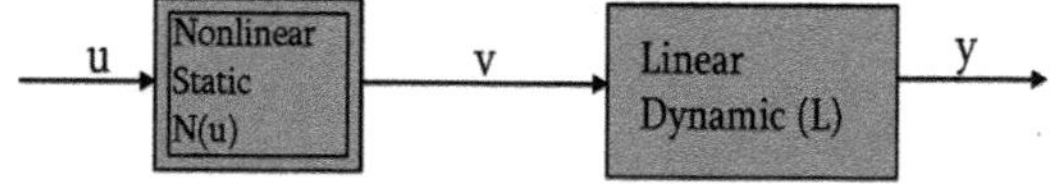

Figure 1(a): Classical Hammerstein structure, considered by RB

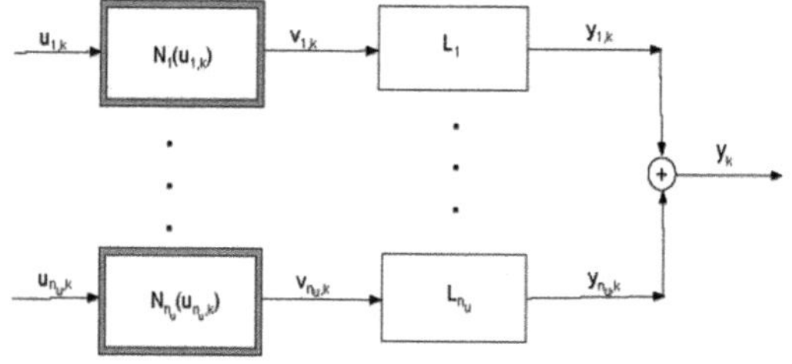

Figure 1(b): KU Hammerstein structure

Rollins and Bhandari (2004) used this simple Hammerstein structure for process identification. It will be called RB model in this paper. RB-model was not able to approximate NL processes sufficiently well, because the dynamic block consists of "average" linear model, which can only represent limited dynamics of the original system for all the input combinations. The issue here is not the nonlinearity of the process but is a "multivariate input directionality" issue which cannot be represented by RB model. The simple definition of input-directional dynamics is given as the response of one output to the input (Harnischmacher and Marquardt, 2007). Kortmann and Unbehauen (1987) developed a Hammerstein structure to take into account the input-directional dynamics of complex systems as shown in Figure 1(b), referred as the KU model in this paper. This specific model consists of a set of scalar Hammerstein models, containing scalar nonlinear maps and driven by scalar inputs. The final output is the sum of outputs from each scalar block. KU model can represent the input-directional dynamics for almost all the processes through the linear systems differing for each channel. The model structure also offers ease of identification, because of scalar channels, but it cannot represent the nonlinear coupling among the inputs, which is the fundamental and a vital property of MIMO systems which limits the use of KU model structure for nonlinear systems which was realized by Eskinat et al. (1991). Consequently Eskinat proposed Hammerstein structure based on combined nonlinearity principle which addressed the problems and limitations of RB and KU Hammerstein models. The proposed model structure by Eskinat is based on combining static nonlinearity for the nonlinear element and separate linear channels for the dynamic element, hence it is capable of representing nonlinear coupling of input variables and thus produced much better results for the processes studied by Eskinat. Though Eskinat structure exhibits modeling flexibility, model parameters identification is complex and difficult, since the nonlinear block cannot be identified separately from the linear element (Su and McAvoy, 1993). Eskinat model lacks an important characteristic of Hammerstein model; the ease of identification.

Not long ago, Harnischmacher and Marquardt (2007) developed a new multivariate Hammerstein structure to overcome the problems of previously developed Hammerstein structures, referred as HM-model in this paper. Like classical Hammerstein model, HM-model structure consists of a two blocks, a) the NL block which calculates the static multivariate nonlinearities by nonlinear mapping, b) the linear element supplements the system dynamics by the superposition principle, i.e., by adding the response of numerous parallel linear blocks. The mathematical symbols are self-explicable as depicted in Figure 2. Alike previous models, HM-model is derived from MIMO Hammerstein and is modified to overcome the deficiencies of former multivariate Hammerstein models, thereby resulting in HM-model. It has limited number of parameters to be identified and hence is useful with the constraint of limited access to process data. The nonlinear element on each branch is parameterized by full input vector u, thus allowing to model static multivariate nonlinearity, while the dynamic element on each branch j is excited by the signal in the direction of the input u_j. Each parallel branch represents the system's response in single input direction. The

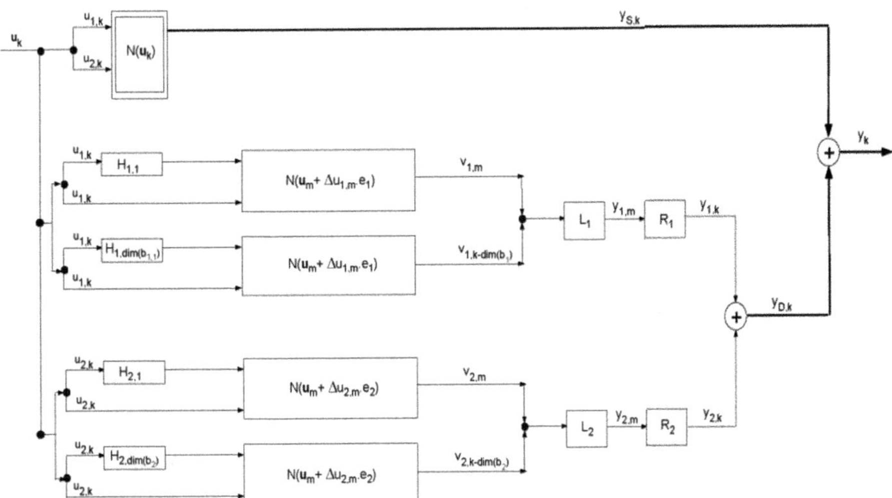

Figure 2. HM-Hammerstein structure

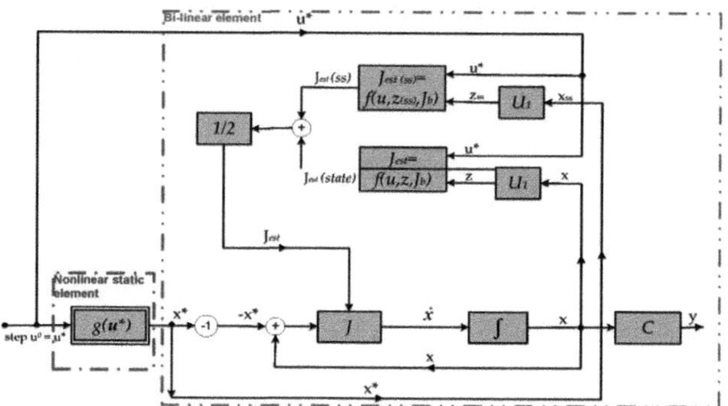

Figure 3. Approximation model (IS-Hammerstein); higher order approximation

branches are independent and hence can be identified easily since linear and nonlinear elements can be identified separately. The input-directionality is represented by superposition principle. HM-model is based on black box modeling approach, which means the intermediate variables $v_{i,j}$) do not have any physical meaning. HM-model is not capable of representing the highly nonlinear dynamics. Even though HM model structure can represent the static nonlinearity (input-directionality) because of the unrestricted and unlimited structure of the nonlinear element, the dynamic block has linear time invariant structure which limits the capability of HM-model to represent process nonlinearity.

2.1. IS-Hammerstein Structure

Recently, we developed a new multivariate Hammerstein structure with the intention for model reduction for large scale chemical process systems (Naeem et. al., 2011). This specific Hammerstein structure is named as Input-State (IS) Hammerstein structure and will be referred to IS-Hammerstein structure in this article. For detailed derivation of IS-Hammerstein, reader is referred to Naeem et. al., (2011). In this paper, only brief introduction to IS-Hammerstein model is given. IS-Hammerstein model is derived by expanding differential algebraic equation (DAE) of a system using Taylor series. Simplification of DAE model to an ordinary differential equation (ODE) considering trivial assumptions results in IS-Hammerstein structure. The nonlinear block in IS-Hammerstein model maps the static nonlinearity, i.e., performs input to state multivariate nonlinear mapping (by lookup table, neural network etc.). The linear element in this case consists of a bilinear approximation, thereby allowing for approximation of high NL systems accurately. Furthermore, IS-Hammerstein structure preserves the basic properties of Hammerstein block-structure; multivariate nonlinearity approximation and input-directional linear model, because of independence in identification between nonlinear and linear blocks. In this paper, the comparison of IS-Hammerstein with existing block-structures is based on accuracy and computational time, rather than comparison based on identification, since the objective of each developed block structure is different (e.g., black-box or grey box identification, model reduction etc.) though IS-Hammerstein model parameters are approximated by identification using process data. IS-Hammerstein is shown in Figure 3 which as two blocks: NL static block to map static process nonlinearity, followed by a linear dynamic block which is driven by difference between the future steady state 'x_{ss}' and the current state 'x'. Mathematical representation of IS-Hammerstein model is given as follows (for p inputs, q outputs, n state variables):

$$\dot{x} = \boldsymbol{J}(x - x_{ss}) + G(\boldsymbol{u}) \tag{2}$$

$$y = \boldsymbol{C}x$$

J(t)- Jacobian matrix (or state matrix ($\dim[J] = n * n$).

The approximation accuracy of IS-Hammerstein is improved by using higher order terms in Taylor series expansion of $\dot{x} = f(x)$. For the complete derivation, the reader is referred to Naeem et al. (2009, 2011). The final structure of the IS-Hammerstein model including higher order dynamic structure is shown in Figure 3. As shown in the figure, the dynamic block Jacobian (J_{est})

is estimated by input (u), reduced (current & steady) state (z, z_{ss}) and (orthogonal) basis functions (J_b). U_1 is the orthogonal basis function to achieve reduced order state vector (z) from full order state vector (x) by a linear function.

3. Chemical Process Engineering Example

Multivariate Hammerstein block-structures have been implemented on fluid catalytic cracker (FCC) which shows complex nonlinear dynamic behavior (Denn,1986). The process is simulated by rigorous, dynamic model, developed in gPROMS. Two inputs, the air flow rate R_{ai} and the catalyst recirculation rate R_{rc} are considered, while the riser outlet temperature T_{ra} is considered as output variable. The operation window, known as input domain is limited to $R_{ai} \in [390; 420]\, Mlb/h$ and $R_{rc} \in [40; 44]\, t/min$ and it is ensured that the stable steady-state points exist for all input combinations. The process is approximated by all the multivariate Hammerstein structures discussed in this paper (HM, RB, KU, IS-Hammerstein). These model structures (apart from IS-Hammerstein) are identified with polynomial nonlinear maps to assess their suitability for the identifying the dynamic behavior of the system. The nonlinear element is identified from a measured steady-state data set by solving the optimization problem. The model accuracy is tested by sequence of 5,000 time intervals with many random steps in operating domain (including the test signals at the boundaries of the operating domain). The case-study is identified by multivariate block-structures (RB model, KU model, HM model) and a part of this implementation is shown in Figure 4 (IS-Hammerstein model is not shown in this figure since it is not a discrete time model but continuous time). Figure 4 shows that HM model structure approximates and identifies the system better than all other multivariate Hammerstein structures. RB-Hammerstein structure does not perform well which is because of the limitation of dynamic (linear) block of this specific structure. The approximation error for KU-Hammerstein model is larger than HM & RB model structure, which is because of the lack of nonlinear coupling among the inputs in KU model structure. Both, IS-Hammerstein full and reduced order models are used identify the process, part of results are shown in Figture 5. The NL static block of the IS-Hammerstein full order model consists of NL steady-states, mapping as function of input, $x_{ss} = G(u)$. The Jacobian basis J_b and transformation matrix U_1 are achieved by singular value decomposition (SVD) analysis of data obtained from nonlinear rigorous model. The reduced order IS-Hammerstein model is achieved by state order reduction using SVD which results in reduction of 5 states to 3 states, there by resulting in reduction in Jacobian matrix from 25X25 to 9X9 and resulting in decrease in the simulation time by factor 2.6. IS-Hammerstein models (full and reduced order) outperform major existing multivariate block-structures, as far as accuracy and approximation are concerned. Satisfactorily accurate estimation of

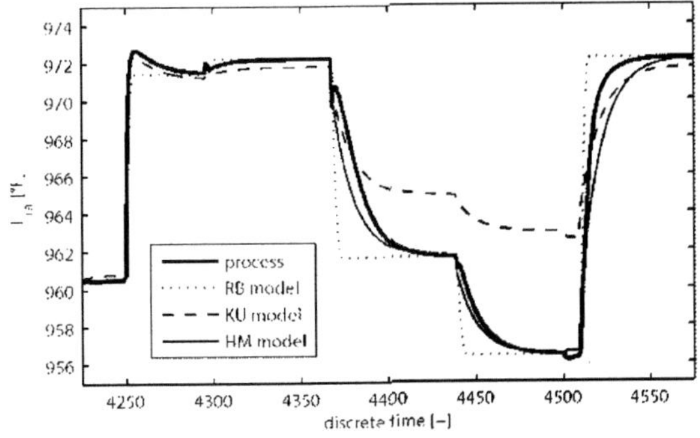

Figure 4. Multivariate Hammerstein structures approximation (Harnischmacher and Marquardt, 2007)

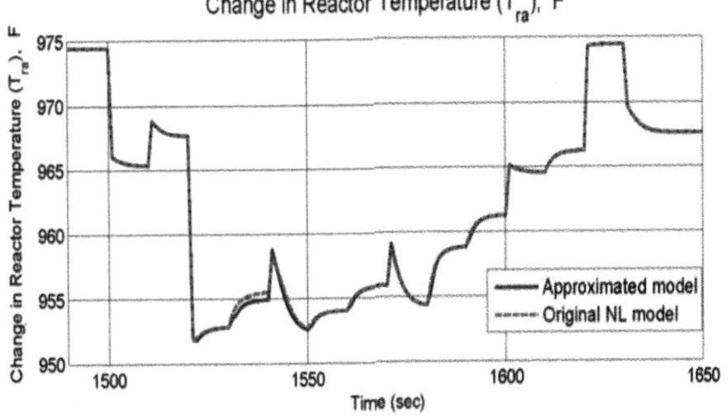

Figure 5. Full order IS-Hammerstein model's approximation of FCC

Table 1. Accuracy and simulation time comparison of methodologies

Methodology / Block-structure	Prediction Error, (°F)	Simulation time, (sec)
Original model - states 5, Jacobian matrix 25X25	-	7.9
KU Hammerstein model	1.21	5.1
RB Hammerstein model	1.10	5.03
HM Hammerstein model	0.43	5.0
IS-Hammerstein model (Full order) - 5 states - Jacobian - 25x25	0.0632	4.11
IS-Hammerstein model (reduced) – 3 states - Jacobian - 9x9	0.0854	1.58

multivariate, input directional and complex NL process shows that new IS-Hammerstein structure holds the basic properties of multivariate Hammerstein model (i.e.; it exhibits the multivariate static nonlinearity, input-directional dynamics and ease of identification). Table 1 shows an overview of qualitative comparison of different methodologies in terms of accuracy and simulation time. The simulations are performed on 1.8 GHz PC with MATLAB version 7.2. Table 1 shows the comparison of all multivariate Hammerstein models in context of accuracy and prediction error.

4. Conclusions

A new multivariate NL Hammerstein (full and reduced order) model, proposed recently has been tested and compared in the context of precision with the other multivariate block-structures from the literature. The model structure preserves the fundamental characteristics of the multivariate Hammerstein model i.e., it preserves the input-directionality property for multivariate processes, ease of identification, and the input coupling property. Moreover, it has been shown in this research work that full and reduced order IS-Hammerstein models are superior to previously developed multivariate Hammerstein models in the context of accuracy and low prediction-error.

References

A. Hammerstein, 1930, Nichtlineare integralgleichungen nebst anwendungen, Acta Mathematica, 54, 1, 117-176.

D. Rollins, N. Bhandari, 2004, Constrained MIMO dynamic discrete-time modeling exploiting optimal experimental design, Journal of Process Control, 14,6, 671-683.

E. Eskinat, S. Johnson, W. Luyben, 1991, Use of Hammerstein models in identification of nonlinear systems, American Journal for Chemical Engineering, 37, 2, 255-268.

G. Harnischmacher, W. Marquardt, 2007, A multi-variate Hammerstein model for processes with input directionality, Journal of Process Control, 17, 539-550.

H. Su, T. McAvoy, 1993, Integration of multilayer perceptron networks and linear dynamic models: A Hammerstein modeling approach, Industrial Engineering and Chemistry Research, 32, 9, 1927-1936.

M. M. Denn, 1986, Process Modeling, Pitman Publishing, Marshfield, USA.

M. Kortmann, H. Unbehauen, 1987, Identification methods for nonlinear MISO systems, Proceedings of IFAC World Congress, 225-230.

N. Wiener, 1958, Nonlinear problems in random theory, MIT Press, Cambridge, USA.

O. Naeem, A. Huesman, O. Bosgra, 2009, Non-linear model order reduction using input to state Hammerstein structures, In the proceedings of ADCHEM 2009 Symposium.

O. Naeem, A. E. Huesman, 2011, Non-linear model approximation & reduction by new input-state Hammerstein block structure, Computer and Chemical Engineering, 35, 5, 758-773.

R. Pearson, 2003, Selecting nonlinear model structures for computer control, Journal of Process Control, 13, 1-26.

T. Westwick, E. Demsey, 2004, Identification of Hammerstein models with cubic spline nonlinearities, IEEE Transaction on Biomedical Engineering, 51, 2, 237-245.

S. Billings, 1980, Identification of nonlinear systems - A survey, IEE Proc. Pt.D 127, 272-280.

Jiří Jaromír Klemeš, Petar Sabev Varbanov and Peng Yen Liew (Editors)
Proceedings of the 24th European Symposium on Computer Aided Process Engineering – ESCAPE 24
June 15-18, 2014, Budapest, Hungary.

Process Design and Economics for Bioethanol Production Process from Palm Empty Fruit Bunch (EFB)

Truong Xuan Do[a], Young-il Lim[a]*, Sungsoo Jang[b], Hwa-Jee Chung[b], Yong-Wook Lee[b]

[a]*Lab. FACS, Dept. Chemical Engineering, Hankyong National University, Anseong 456-749 Korea*

[b]*GenDocs, Inc., A-209 Migun Technoworld 2, Daejeon 305-500 Korea*

[b]*Sungsoo Jang (ssjang@gendocs.co.kr), Hwa-Jee Chung (hwajee@gendocs.co.kr)*

limyi@hknu.ac.kr

Abstract

Approximately one million metric ton of empty fruit bunch (EFB), which is a waste of the palm oil industry are discharged every year mainly in Malaysia and Indonesia. It is one of the most recent renewable energy resources and promises high yield in bioethanol productions. The objectives of this study are to conceptually design and economically analyze a whole bioethanol plant using eletrolyzed-reduced water (ERW) as the pretreatment method. To achieve the first objective, a comprehensive model of the bioethanol production plant is developed employing a process simulator on the basis of an experimental study in a pilot plant. The bioethanol production plant consists of five main areas: feed handling, pretreatment & conditioning, saccharification & co-fermentation, product purification, and wastewater treatment. For the second objective, the total capital investment (TCI) is estimated for 100 kton-dry EFB/yr plant. The economic analysis is performed in terms of the payback period (PBP), return on investment (ROI) and the product value (PV). The sensitivity of key variables is analyzed to find the potential reduction of PV.

Keywords: Empty fruit bunch (EFB), bioethanol, economic analysis, process design, process simulation.

1. Introduction and research objectives

The palm oil of 43×10^6 MT (metric ton) was produced in 2008 that formed 27% in the world vegetable oil market. The by-products of palm oil production are mainly palm oil mill effluent (POME) and empty fruit bunch (EFB), where 10 wt% of fresh fruit bunch (FFB) is POME, and 20 wt% is EFB. In 2008, the world-wide EFB production is reported in Table 1. The chemical composition of EFB is different with age and location, as illustrated in Table 2.

Kazi (2010) performed a techno-economic study comparing several process technologies for the production of ethanol from corn stover (Kazi et al., 2010). The dilute-acid pretreatment process has the lowest PV among all process scenarios, which is estimated to be \$ 1.36 /L of gasoline equivalent. While Tao (2011) economically compared six biomass pretreatment processes to convert switchgrass to fermentable sugars and ultimately to cellulosic ethanol (Tao et al., 2011). This study showed limited differentiation between the projected economic performances of the pretreatment optio-

Table 1. World-wide EFB production from FFB in 2008.

	Palm oil (MT)*		FFB (MT)	EFB (MT)
World-wide	43×10^6	100%	195×10^6	43×10^6
Malaysia	18×10^6	41%	82×10^6	18×10^6
Indonesia	19×10^6	45%	86×10^6	19×10^6
Others	6×10^6	14%	27×10^6	6×10^6

*MT=metric ton

Table 2. Chemical composition of oil palm EFB.

Reference	Hemicellulose (%)	Cellulose (%)	Lignin (%)	Others (%)	Total (%)	Location
(Hill and Abdul Khalil, 2000)	22	48	25	5	100	Malaysia
Rozman et al. (2005)	17	48	25	10	100	Malaysia
(Baharuddin et al., 2011)	26.1	50.3	18.0	5.6	100	Malaysia (Selangor)
(Abdullah and Bridgwater, 2006)	22.1	59.7	18.1	0.1	100	Malaysia
(Mohammed et al., 2011)	35.3	38.3	22.1	4.3	100	Malaysia

ns, except for processes that exhibit significantly lower monomer sugar and resulting ethanol yields. Fornell (2012) analyzed techno-economic of a kraft pulp mill converted to an ethanol production plant (Fornell et al., 2012).

This study aims to evaluate economic feasibility of the bioethanol production process from EFB using a new pretreatment method, where hot EWR (electrolyzed-reduced water) is used. To achieve the objective, the following subjects are investigated: (1) process simulation for bioethanol production process, (2) economic analysis of the bioethanol plant, and (3) a sensitivity analysis on bioethanol PV.

2. Process description for bioethanol production from EFB

The whole industrial bioethanol plant from EFB includes five areas: feed handing (A100), pretreatment and conditioning (A200), saccharification and co-fermentation (A300), product purification (A400), and wastewater treatment (A500). The conceptual process flow diagram (PFD) of the bioethanol plant is shown in Figure 1.

EFB is delivered to the feed handing area (A100) for storage, size reduction and homogenization. From there the shredded EFB is conveyed to the pretreatment & conditioning area (A200). In this area, EFB is treated by hot ERW at a temperature of 180 °C in 60 mins to resolve almost hemicellulose and form a hydrolyzate slurry. Enzyme and the rest detoxified hydrolyzate slurry are pumped to the saccharification & co-fermentation area (A300) and treated in continuous hydrolysis tank and anaerobic fermentation tanks in series. After two days of fermentation, the most of sugars such as glucose and xylose are converted to ethanol resulting in beer product. The beer product is distilled in two consequence columns, beer and rectification distillation columns, to raise the ethanol concentration to about 92.5 wt% in the purification area (A400). The ethanol product is dehydrated by a molecular sieve adsorption system to produce the commercial ethanol of 99.5 wt%. All the wastewater is sent to the wastewater treatment area (A500), and recycled a part to the process.

3. Methodologies of economic analysis

Cost analysis is necessary prior to the construction of a plant. Techno-economic analysis starts from the estimation of the total capital investment (TCI) based on Perter and Timmerhaus investment factors (Peters et al., 2003). The profitability of the plant is determined with regard to the payback period (PBP), return on investment (ROI), and product value (PV).

3.1. Estimation of TCI (total capital investment)

There are several methods to estimate the capital cost of chemical process plants. This study uses the factorial method. The contribution of each item to the TCI is obtained from the sum of multiplying TPEC (total purchased equipment cost) by an appropriate factor. The hierarchy for estimating TCI is depicted in Figure 2, where the Peters and Timmerhaus investment factors (Peters et al., 2003) are indicated.

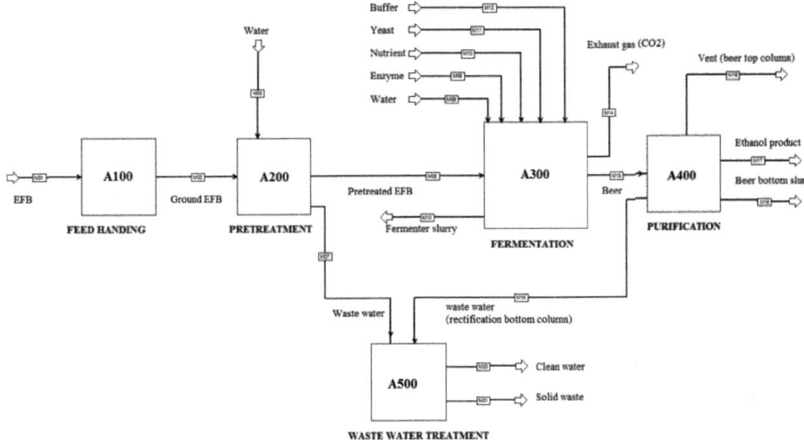

Figure 1. Conceptual PFD of bioethanol production plant from palm empty fruit bunch

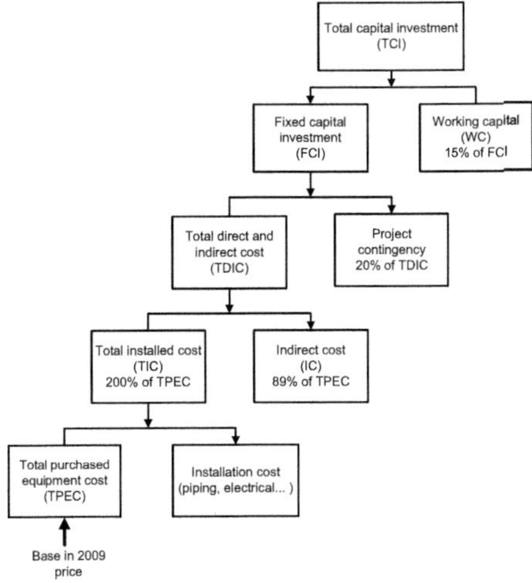

Figure 2. Hierarchy for estimating the total capital investment.

3.2. Economic assumptions and criteria

The plant is considered as 100 % owned capital. The working time is 8000 hours per year, which is equivalent to 91 % of the annual plant capacity. The construction time is assumed to be one year. The startup period is 4 months due to the medium plant sizes. During this period, 50 % production is achieved with an expenditure of 100% in both variable and fixed expenses. The project life is assumed to be 20 years, which has been often used for the small and medium plant sizes (Swanson et al., 2010; Zhu et al., 2012). The electricity and industrial water costs were set to be 0.098 \$/kWh and 0.31 \$/m^3, respectively. The depreciation period was set to be 10 y. An corporate income tax rate of 22 % of gross profit was used. To determine the PV, 10% of ROI is applied.

3.3. Parameters for sensitive analysis

The sensitive analysis was performed to identify parameters that have a significant impact on PV over the expected range of parameters variation. Typical parameters to be investigated and the range of variation are shown in Table 3.

4. Results and Discussion

Economic analysis key results are summarized in Table 4 for the 100 kton-dry EFB plant. The TIC and TPC estimated are about 34 M\$ and 8 M\$/yr, respectively. The PBP is approximate 5 y and ROI is 13 % at the bioethanol market price of 1.1 \$/kg. If the expected ROI is 10 %, the estimated bioethanol PV is 1.05 \$/kg.

Figure 3 shows the contribution of six factors to bioethanol PV. Feedstock is the biggest contribution to PV, about one third of 1.05 \$.kg. The second contributions are ROI and fixed costs, where each takes above 20% of PV, about 0.23 \$/kg and 0.21 \$/kg. The

Table 3. Optimistic and pessimistic values of sensitivity parameters.

Parameters	Optimistic	Baseline	Pessimistic
Bioethanol yield (based on dried EFB) (wt%)	16	13	10
EFB price (\$/ton-dried EFB)	30	50	70
Total capital investment (% of baseline)	70	100	130
ROI (%)	5	10	15
Corporate income tax (%)	15	22	30

Table 4. Economic analysis results of 100 kton-dry EFB plant.

Economic parameters	value
Total purchased equipment cost (TPEC, M\$)	8.27
Total installed cost (TIC, M\$)	17.36
Indirect cost (IC, M\$)	7.36
Total direct and indirect cost (TDIC, M\$)	24.72
Project contingency (PC, M\$)	4.94
Fixed capital investment (FCI, M\$)	29.66
Working capital (WC, M\$)	4.45
Total capital investment (TCI, M\$)	34.11
Total Raw Materials Cost (M\$/yr)	5.00
Total Utilities Cost (M\$/year)	0.28
Fixed cost (M\$/year)	2.73
Total Production cost (TPC) (M\$/yr)	8.01
Annual sale revenue (ASR, M\$)	15.60
Payback period (PBP, yr)	4.68
Return on investment (ROI, %)	13.15
Product value (PV, \$/kg)	1.05

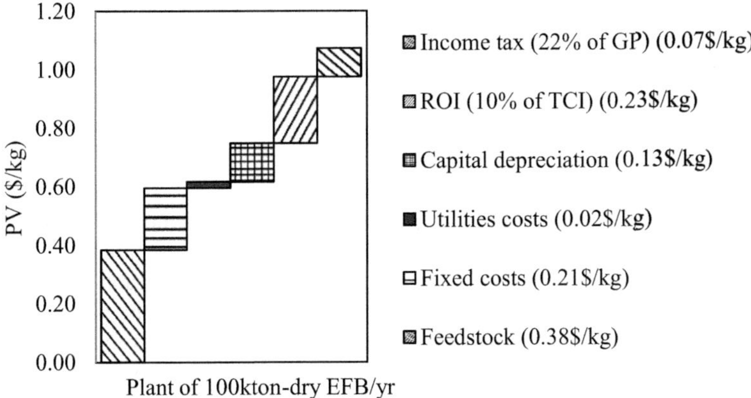

Figure 3. Contribution of six expenses to ethanol PV (product value)

remaining factors including capital depreciation, corporation income tax, and utilities cost contribute totally about 20 % of PV.

The plot of sensitivity (PoS) on PV is shown in Figure 4 according to the perturbation of the five economic parameters listed in Table 3. The bioethanol yield has the most influence on PV. Good plant operation can increase the yield to 16 wt% resulting in the decreasing PV to 0.85 $/kg. On the other hand, poor operation can reduce the yield to 10 wt% pushing PV to 1.36 $/kg, which is higher than the market ethanol price of 1.1 $/kg. Feedstock contributes one third of PV, therefore it has a significant impact on PV. The EFB cost changes PV to 0.9 $/kg and 1.2 $/kg for optimistic and pessimistic scenarios, respectively. Others parameters have slight impacts on PV.

5. Conclusion

This study explored the economic feasibility of the bioethanol production plant from EFB (empty fruit bunches) using ERW (electrolyzed-reduced water) pretremeant method. The process model of the plant was developed using the commercial process simulator. The total capital investment (TCI) was estimated by the factorial method, starting from the purchased equipment cost without delivery cost. The economic criteria in terms of PBP (payback period), ROI (return on investment), and PV (product value)

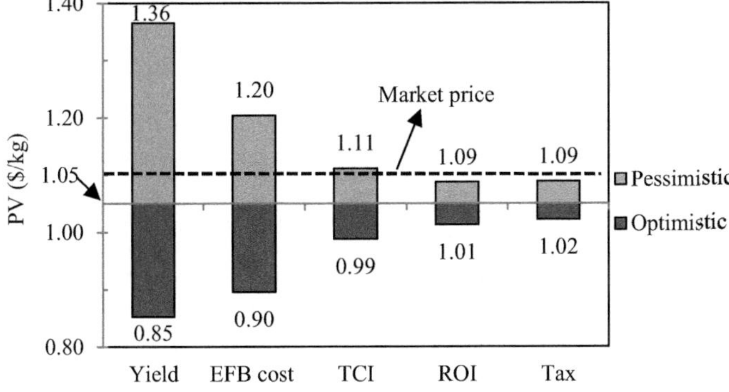

Figure 4. Plot of sensitivity (PoS) on product value (PV) (Baseline: 13 wt% yield; 50$/t EFB price; 100% TCI; 10% ROI; 22% corporation income tax).

were evaluated for the plant size of 100 kton/y of dry EFB. The sensitivity analysis of several key parameters such as bioethanol yield, EFB purchasing cost, TCI, ROI, and corporation income tax on PV was performed. The 100 kton/y dry EFB plant has a profitability at ROI of 13 % and PBP of 4.7 y. Feedstock, fixed costs, and ROI are main contributions to PV. It is confirmed in the sensitive analysis that bioethanol yield and EFB purchasing cost have a key impact on PV.

The bioethanol production from EFB is still in its infancy. Bioethanol yield using the ERW pretreament method is 13 wt% of dry EFB which is low compared to others . Various challenges need to be addressed so that this technology can reach the level of commercialization. It is expected that economic analysis considering the present value over the plant life with a given interest rate is useful to evaluate a more realistic GP (gross profit) and CF (cash flow). Further studies on both the process synthesis and the optimization of operating conditions could shed light on reducing PV.

Acknowledgements

This work was financially supported by Gendocs in 2013 in the framework of Cooperative R&D between Industry and Academy.

References

N. Abdullah, A. V. Bridgwater, 2006, Pyrolysis Liquid Derived from Oil Palm Empty Fruit Bunches, Journal of physical science, 17, 2, 117-129.

A. S. Baharuddin, N. A. A. Rahman, U. K. M. Shah, M. A. Hassan, M. Wakisaka, Y. Shirai, 2011, Evaluation of pressed shredded empty fruit bunch (EFB)-palm oil mill effluent (POME) anaerobic sludge based compost using Fourier transform infrared (FTIR) and nuclear magnetic resonance (NMR) analysis, African Journal of Biotechnology, 10, 41, 8082-8089.

R. Fornell, T. Berntsson, A. Åsblad, 2012, Process integration study of a kraft pulp mill converted to an ethanol production plant – part B: Techno-economic analysis, Appl. Therm. Eng., 42, 179-190.

C. A. S. Hill, H. P. S. Abdul Khalil, 2000, Effect of fiber treatments on mechanical properties of coir or oil palm fiber reinforced polyester composites, J. Appl. Polym. Sci., 78, 9, 1685-1697.

F. K. Kazi, J. A. Fortman, R. P. Anex, D. D. Hsu, A. Aden, A. Dutta, G. Kothandaraman, 2010, Techno-economic comparison of process technologies for biochemical ethanol production from corn stover, Fuel, 89, Supplement 1, S20-S28.

M. A. A. Mohammed, A. Salmiaton, W. A. K. G. Wan Azlina, M. S. Mohammad Amran, A. Fakhru'l-Razi, Y. H. Taufiq-Yap, 2011, Hydrogen rich gas from oil palm biomass as a potential source of renewable energy in Malaysia, Renewable and Sustainable Energy Reviews, 15, 2, 1258-1270.

M. S. Peters, K. D. Timmerhaus, R. E. West, 2003, Plant design and economics for chemical engineers, McGraw-Hill, New York, US.

R. M. Swanson, J. A. Satrio, R. C. Brown, A. Platon, D. D. Hsu, 2010, Techno-economic analysis of biofuels production based on gasification, National Renewable Energy Laboratory, Colorado, US.

L. Tao, A. Aden, R. T. Elander, V. R. Pallapolu, Y. Y. Lee, R. J. Garlock, V. Balan, B. E. Dale, Y. Kim, N. S. Mosier, M. R. Ladisch, M. Falls, M. T. Holtzapple, R. Sierra, J. Shi, M. A. Ebrik, T. Redmond, B. Yang, C. E. Wyman, B. Hames, S. Thomas, R. E. Warner, 2011, Process and technoeconomic analysis of leading pretreatment technologies for lignocellulosic ethanol production using switchgrass, Bioresour. Technol., 102, 24, 11105-11114.

Jiří Jaromír Klemeš, Petar Sabev Varbanov and Peng Yen Liew (Editors)
Proceedings of the 24th European Symposium on Computer Aided Process Engineering – ESCAPE 24
June 15-18, 2014, Budapest, Hungary.

Automatic Generation of Process Operating Window - Tracking Vortex Birth Inside Coating Flow

Jaewook Nam*

School of chemical engineering, Sungkyunkwan University, Suwon and 440-746, Republic of Korea
jaewooknam@skku.edu

Abstract

To avoid undesired effects from vortices in many industrial flow processes, it is important to know the set of operating parameters at which the flow does not have recirculation. The map of these conditions in the parameter space is called vortex-free operating window, especially for coating process. We propose an efficient way to construct such window automatically without expensively checking every possible flow states. The proposed technique is based on tracking a path in the parameter space at which the local kinematic condition at a stagnation point for vortex birth is satisfied. Solving an augmented Navier–Stokes system, performs this multi-parameter continuation. In the augmented system, the birth condition and the governing equations were represented in Galerkin's finite element context. We used the proposed method in two important coating flows with free surfaces: single-layer slot coating and forward roll coating.

Keywords: slot coating process, vortex birth, Galerkin finite element method

1. Introduction

The presence of vortices or recirculations in flows can lead to undesired effects in many industrial processes. In liquid coating, for example, the flow near the region where the liquid meets the moving substrate can develop microscopic gyres that are intense and typically extend across the entire coating bead. These were found in experiments by Coyle et al. (1986), Schweizer (1988), Sartor (1990) and others, as shown in Figure 1. They tend to centrifuge denser particles, to desorb dissolved gas, to collect and discharge bubbles, to hold formulations long enough for unwanted flocculation or polymerization, and to become nodular along their length and thereby detract from cross-wise coating uniformity. Therefore the set of operating parameters at which the flow does not present vortices are preferred in order to avoid the problems listed above. It is crucial to map these conditions in the parameter space, and construct the so called vortex-free operating window. This vortex-free window in the parameter space can be obtained by simply post-processing a large number of steady state solutions at different flow conditions, covering the range of interest in all the flow parameters. This procedure can be called vortex birth capturing and it is extremely expensive, the number of solutions needed to construct the window can easily reach 1,000 and post-processing each of these solutions can be very tedious. We propose an alternative efficient way to construct the vortex-free window of a flow. The event of vortex birth, or death, is signalized by changes in the eigenvalues and eigenvectors of the linear term of the Taylor series expansion of the velocity field around a stagnation point. Three types of vortex birth – inside the flow, from free surface, and from wall – are examined, and local birth conditions are defined in terms of kinematic variables. Vortex birth conditions are local flow features evaluated at stagnation points in the flow. In order to determine the set of flow parameters at which a vortex is born (or disappears), we need to find at which flow conditions the local flow feature that defines a vortex birth occurs, i.e. the local flow condition near stagnation points need to be coupled with the global flow parameters. In this study, we construct the vortex-free window by tracking the global flow conditions at which a recirculation appears (or disappears). This is done by performing a multi-parameter continuation, as described by Keller (1977) to obtain solutions only at the set of conditions at which the local vortex birth condition at stagnation points is satisfied. Therefore, the line (or surface) in the parameter space that defines the boundary of the vortex-free window is constructed automatically.

2. Vortex birth conditions

With the proper choice of the frame of reference, the description of a fluid particle motion inside a flow can be decomposed into two independent parts — deformation and rotation. In this frame of reference, a flow recirculation is characterized by closed streamlines, and the axis of rotation of the vortex, the *vortex center*, is at rest relative to the observer. As mentioned before, the birth of a vortex is characterized by a dramatic change in the structure of pathlines around an existing stagnation points. In order to identify a vortex birth, characteristics of stagnation points must be analyzed and classified, as discussed by Bakker (1991). The birth of a new vortex can be depicted as the splitting of a stagnation point into two or three stagnation points, including the center of the new vortex, as the flow parameters change. A new vortex can be born from inside the flow, from a free surface or from a solid wall. In all these three scenarios, the vortex birth conditions can be expressed in terms of local kinematic variables. They are summarized in Table below.

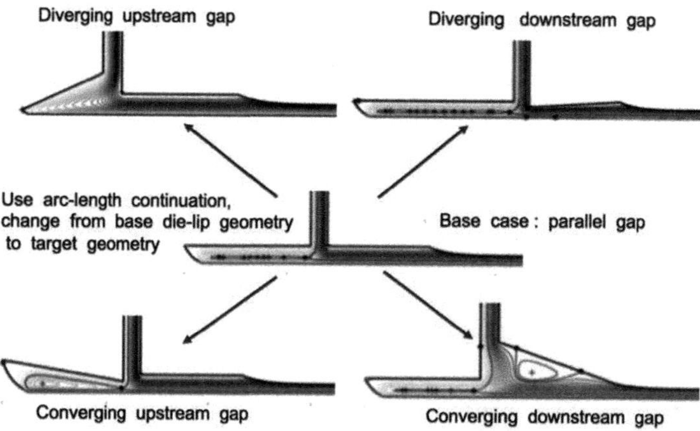

Figure 1. Various vortices in slot coating flows

Table 1. Vortex birth condition

Location	Vortex birth condition
Inside flow	$\mathbf{u}=0, \det(\nabla\mathbf{u})=0$
From free surface	$u_t=0, \tau_{tt}=0$
From solid surface	$\tau_{tn}=0, \partial\tau_{tn}/\partial s_t=0$

3. Automated tracking of vortex birth in flows

The multiparameter continuation described previously was done by augmenting the Navier–Stokes equation by equations that describe the vortex-birth condition. The solution of this augmented system was obtained by Galerkin's finite element method. The formulation and solution method for the multiparameter continuation is described in this section.

3.1. Navier-Stokes system for viscous free surface flows

The velocity and pressure fields of incompressible pressure fields of two-dimensional, steady state flow of a Newtonian liquid are governed by the continuity and momentum equations:

$$\nabla\cdot\mathbf{u}=0,\quad \rho\mathbf{u}\cdot\nabla\mathbf{u}=\nabla\cdot\boldsymbol{T}, \tag{1}$$

where ρ is the liquid density and T is stress tensor. For Newtonian liquid, it is given by $-\boldsymbol{T}=-p\boldsymbol{I}+\mu\left[\nabla\mathbf{u}+(\nabla\mathbf{u})^T\right]$, where p is the pressure and μ is the liquid viscosity. Flows with free surface give rise to a *free boundary problem*. The flow domain is unknown *a priori* and it is part of the solution. To solve a free boundary problem by means of standard techniques for boundary value problems, the set of differential equations and boundary conditions posed in the unknown physical domain have to be transformed to an equivalent set defined in a known, fixed computational domain (Kistler and Scriven, 1984). Here, this transformation is made by a mapping $x = x(\xi)$ that connects the two domains. The physical domain is parameterized by the position vector $x = (x, y)$, and the reference domain, by $\xi = (\xi, \eta)$. The mapping used here is the one described by de Santos (1989). The inverse mapping is governed by a system of elliptic differential equations identical to those encountered in the dilute regime of diffusional transport:

$$\nabla\cdot D_\xi(\xi,\eta)\nabla\xi=0,\quad \nabla\cdot D_\eta(\xi,\eta)\nabla\eta=0. \tag{2}$$

D_ξ and D_η are mesh diffusivities which control the steepness of gradients in the node spacing by adjusting the potentials ξ and η. Curves of constant ξ and η define the boundaries of elements used to describe the domain. The cross point of these curves of sets the position of a node. Boundary conditions are needed to solve the second-order differential equations (2). The discrete version of the mapping equations is generally referred to as mesh generation equations. Detailed procedure and boundary conditions for mesh equations are discussed in de Santos (1989).

3.2. Solution of the Navier-Stokes system for free surface flow by GFEM

Galerkin finite element method is used to solve the Navier–Stokes system coupled with the mesh generation equation, Eqs. (1) and (3). Each independent variable, velocity, pressure and position, is approximated by a linear combination of a finite number of basis functions. The basis function coefficients are the unknowns of the discretized problem. The velocity and nodal position are represented in terms of Lagrangian biquadratic function and the pressure in terms of linear discontinuous basis function. The weak form of Eqs. (1) and (3) are obtained by multiplying each equation by weighting functions, integrating over the physical domain, and applying the divergence theorem to the appropriate terms with divergence. In Galerkin's method, the weighting and basis functions are the same. In sum, the Galerkin finite element method reduces the Navier–Stokes and mesh generation differential equations to a set of nonlinear algebraic equations on the basis functions coefficients.

$$\mathbf{R}(\mathbf{z}, \lambda) = 0 \tag{3}$$

where z is the solution vector which consist of velocity u, pressure P and position x, and λ is a vector that contains the M parameters on which the system depends. Equation (3) is solved iteratively by Newton's method:

$$\begin{aligned} \boldsymbol{J}^{(i)}(\mathbf{z}^{(i)}, \boldsymbol{\lambda})\, \delta\mathbf{z}^{(i)} &= -\mathbf{R}^{(i)}(\mathbf{z}^{(i)}, \boldsymbol{\lambda}), \\ \mathbf{z}^{(i+1)} &= \mathbf{z}^{(i)} + \delta\mathbf{z}^{(i)}, \end{aligned} \tag{4}$$

The iteration continues until $\|R^{(i)}\|_2 < \varepsilon$. Here we choose 10^{-8} as ε.

3.3. Augmented Navier-Stokes system

The augmented system of algebraic equations consists of the algebraic equations that relate the finite element coefficients of the unknown fields and the conditions of vortex birth. The set of unknowns is also augmented by the number of algebraic equations that define the vortex birth condition, three in the case of vortex birth inside the flow and two in the case of vortex birth at a free surface or solid wall. The extra unknowns are the position of the stagnation point at which a vortex is born from and one of the flow parameters λ_1 that is not fixed. Actually, the solution of the augmented system will give the value of this parameter at which the vortex birth occurs. For a birth inside a flow, two coordinates (x^*, y^*) are required to locate the stagnation point. For a birth attached to a flow boundary, either solid surface or free surface; only one coordinate is enough to locate the birth point. The augmented system of equation can be

$$\begin{cases} \mathbf{R}(\mathbf{z}, \boldsymbol{\lambda}, \mathbf{p}) &= 0 \\ \mathbf{A}(\mathbf{z}, \boldsymbol{\lambda}, \mathbf{p}) &= 0 \end{cases}, \tag{5}$$

where z and λ are the vectors that contain the finite element coefficients and fixed flow parameters, as defined in Eq. (5), and p is a vector that contains the extra set of unknowns of the augmented problem, e.g $p = (x^*, \lambda_1)$. A is the set of algebraic equations that defines the vortex birth condition. This non-linear system is solved by Newton's method, which requires the evaluation of the Jacobian matrix of the system:

$$\left[\begin{array}{c|c} \frac{\partial \mathbf{R}}{\partial \mathbf{z}} & \frac{\partial \mathbf{R}}{\partial \mathbf{p}} \\ \hline \frac{\partial \mathbf{A}}{\partial \mathbf{z}} & \frac{\partial \mathbf{A}}{\partial \mathbf{p}} \end{array}\right] \left[\begin{array}{c} \delta\mathbf{z} \\ \hline \delta\mathbf{p} \end{array}\right] = -\left[\begin{array}{c} \mathbf{R} \\ \hline \mathbf{A} \end{array}\right] \tag{6}$$

where $\partial R/\partial p$ are the sensitivity of the residual equations to the extra unknowns, $\partial A/\partial z$ and $\partial A/\partial p$ are the sensitivity of the vortex birth conditions to the flow field (finite element coefficients) and extra unknowns. $\partial R/\partial z$ is the Jacobian matrix of the original problem. Because the new three blocks are usually small sub-matrices that are generally densely populated, the fill structure of the new matrix is that of an arrow head, which destroys the benefit of most direct sparse linear solver. Employing the bordering algorithm (Keller, 1977), the matrix-vector equations can be decomposed and solve them sequentially. Using the augmented Navier–Stokes system and the solution strategy discussed before, one can perform "direct tracking of vortex birth": an automated vortex birth tracking algorithm. Multiparameter continuation is the heart of this algorithm. The algorithm is shown in Figure 2. α and β stand for chosen operating or design parameters from the parameter space that define a plane at which a vortex-free window will be constructed. This plane is a cut on a multi-dimensional parameter space. Specifically, α is the parameter which will remain part of the solution of the augmented Navier–Stokes system, and β is the control variable, which is changed by a user-defined rule during continuation.

4. Example: slot coating flow

The slot coating is a high-precision coating method used to deposit a thin liquid film onto a moving substrate. It is a pre-metered coating method, where film thickness is directly controlled by the flow rate and web speed. However, the liquid flow in the application region, so called the coating bead, is strongly affected by operating parameters, liquid properties, and design parameters; such as web speed, surface tension, and geometry of the coating die. Here, we focused on the vortex birth inside coating bead and tracked it using direct tracking. Converging downstream die lip geometry expands operating ranges of vacuum pressure and coating speed. But adverse pressure gradient created inside the cannel can induce a flow detachment at the downstream die lip, which leads to a vortex formation, as illustrated in Figure 3. The presence of vortex may limit the operating ranges when coating quality is important.

5. Final remarks

Vortices in flow can cause undesired effects in many industrial processes, especially for continuous liquid coating on moving substrate. It is important to know the region of the operating parameters space at which vortices are not present in the coating flow, so these set of parameters can be avoided during operation. These regions are called vortex-free operating window.

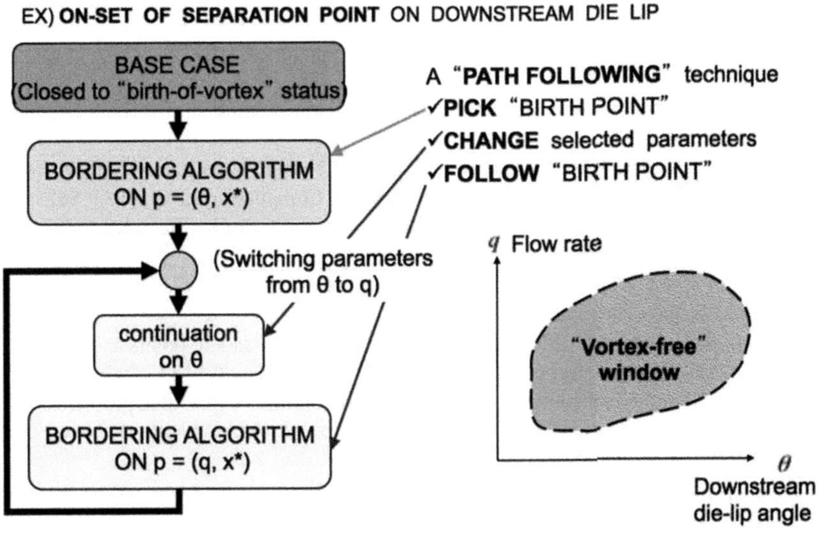

Figure 2. Direct tracking algorithm

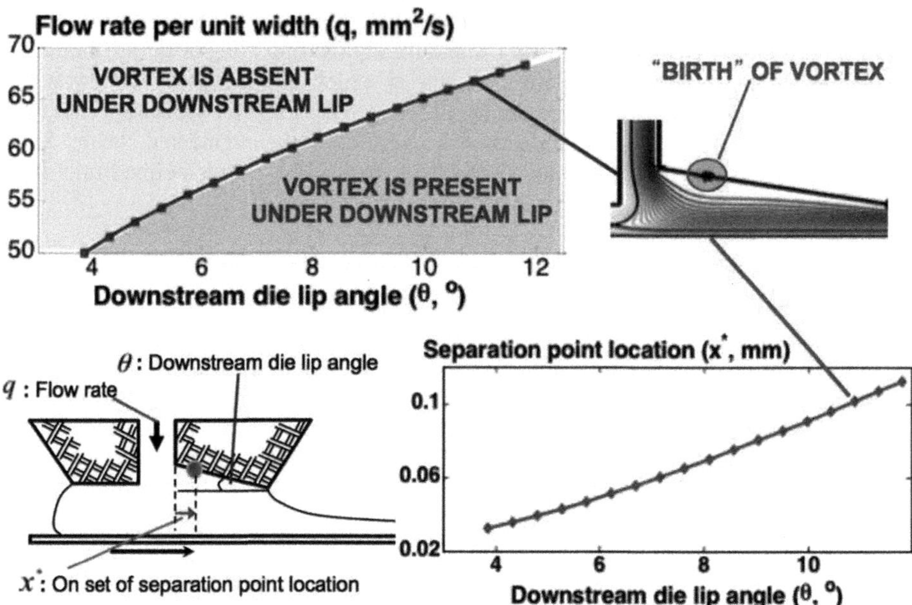

Figure 3. Example of on-set of separation point on downstream die lip

In computer-aided analysis and design, the most effective way to construct these is not to check a large set of solutions *a posteriori*, but to delineate the range of design parameters and operating conditions that define the boundary of the vortex-free window. This means tracking the birth (of death) of vortices. A way of doing this is to solve the Navier–Stokes or related governing equations, after augmenting the system with one or more equations that describe the local kinematic conditions at vortex birth and with an equal number of design parameters or operating conditions as new unknowns.

References

P.G. Bakker, 1991, Bifurcations in flow patterns, Kluwer Academic publishers, Dordrecht, The Netherlands.

M.S. Carvalho, L.E. Scriven, 1999, Three-Dimensional Stability Analysis of Free Surface Flows: Application to Forward Deformable Roll Coating, J. Comput. Phys., 151, 534–562.

D.J. Coyle, C.W. Macosko, L. E. Scriven, 1986, Film-splitting flows in forward roll coating, J. Fluid Mech., 171,539–571.

J. M. de Santos, 1989, Two-phase cocurrent downflow through constricted passage, PhD thesis, Univ. of Minnesota, Minneapolis, US.

P.H. Gaskell, M.D. Savage, H.M. Thompson, 1998, Stagnation-saddle points and flow patterns in Stokes flow between contra-rotating cylinders, J. Fluid Mech., 370, 221–247.

H. Keller, 1977, Numerical solution of bifurcation and nonlinear eignevalue problems, Applications of Bifurcation Theory, P. H. Rabinowitz, ed., Academic Press, New York, USA, 359–384.

S.F. Kistler, L.E. Scriven, 1984, Coating flow theory by finite element and asymptotic analysis of the Navier–Stokes system, Int. J. Numer. Methods Fluids, 4, 207–229.

L. Sartor, 1990, Slot coating: Fluid mechanics and Die design, PhD thesis, Univ. of Minnesota, Minneapolis, USA.

P.M. Schweizer, 1988, Visualization of coating flows, J. Fluid Mech., 193, 285–302.

Jiří Jaromír Klemeš, Petar Sabev Varbanov and Peng Yen Liew (Editors)
Proceedings of the 24th European Symposium on Computer Aided Process Engineering – ESCAPE 24
June 15-18, 2014, Budapest, Hungary.

EFENIS: Efficient Energy Integrated Solutions for Manufacturing Industries. European Context

Robin Smith[a], Nan Zhang[a], Simon Perry[a], Igor Bulatov[a,*], Wulf Dietrich[b], Daniela Koelsch[b], Jiří J Klemeš[c], Petar S Varbanov[c]

[a]*Centre for Process Integration, CEAS, The University of Manchester, Oxford Road, Manchester, M13 9PL, United Kingdom*

[b]*Bayer Technology Services GmbH, Kaiser-Wilhelm-Allee, Leverkusen, 51368, Germany*

[c]*Centre for Process Integration and Intensification – CPI^2, Research Institute of Chemical and Process Engineering – MÜKKI, Faculty of Information Technology, University of Pannonia, Egyetem utca 10, 8200 Veszprém, Hungary*

Abstract

Nearly one-third of the world's energy consumption and 36% of its carbon dioxide (CO_2) emissions are attributable to manufacturing industries. The adoption of advanced technologies could provide technical energy savings in industry of 27–41 EJ (Extra J), along with a reduction in CO_2 emissions of 2.2–3.2 GT/y, about 7–12% of today's global CO_2 emissions. The paper describes the activities within European EFENIS project (which stands for Efficient Energy Integrated Solutions for Manufacturing Industries) aimed at demonstrating the benefits of novel site-level energy saving technologies and their contribution to EU policies in the area of energy efficiency. It also covers scientific and technological as well as non-scientific barriers which the project targets, the methodology and structure of the project, its intermediate and expected final outcomes and impacts as the contribution to European strategy towards low carbon and energy efficient economy.

Keywords: Total Site, Energy Efficiency, European Energy Policy

1. Introduction

The EU has adopted a whole set of political and legislative documents in recent years aimed at mitigation of environmental impacts of industrial production, transport and domestic activities. One of the cornerstones of the EU's Energy and Climate Change Policy is the "20-20-20" target to "reduce greenhouse gas emissions by at least 20 % compared to 1990 levels or by 30 %, if the conditions are right; increase the share of renewable energy sources in our final energy consumption to 20 %; and a 20 % increase in energy efficiency" (Europe 2020 Strategy, 2010)

As part of those activities, EFENIS Project was launched by a consortium of leading European industrial and academic partners in 2012. The project funded by the European Union within FP7-ENERGY-2011-2, grant number 296003 directly promotes the key principles of Green Paper on Energy Efficiency (2006), which sets out the "20-20-20" targets thereby contributing to reducing Europe's dependence on oil and gas imports; identifies the quickest and most cost-effective manner to reduce greenhouse gas emissions and help the EU meet its commitments under the Kyoto and post-Kyoto framework agreements. In this context, the increase in energy efficiency in manufacturing processes would deliver significant benefits to security of energy supply as well as reduction of greenhouse gas emissions while reducing the cost of the manufactured goods. Also within the context of EU energy policy objectives, EFENIS provides technological solutions for implementation of the Action Plan for Energy Efficiency: Realising the Potential (2006), Energy Efficiency Plan (2011) and Directive on energy efficiency (2012). As energy-intensive industries account for large proportions of total, final energy consumption, efficiency gains here are crucial.

One of Europe 2020 Strategy's "seven flagship initiatives"Resource efficient Europe" is aimed to help decouple economic growth from the use of resources, support the shift towards a low carbon economy, increase the use of renewable energy sources, modernise our transport sector and promote energy efficiency"(Europe 2020 Strategy, 2010).In a concerted effort to reach those objectives a number of European research and demonstration projects have been dedicated to various aspects of energy efficiency, CORDIS (2013).

The main distinction of EFENIS project is the focus on the much deeper total site energy integration and its extension beyond the fence. Being a demonstration project, EFENIS is primarily focused on demonstrating benefits of the systematic approach to integrating energy flows at site and beyond-the-site levels. The main objective of EFENIS is to facilitate and accelerate a move to low carbon manufacturing processes and site management by deployment and demonstration of innovative energy management systems and enabling efficiency technologies, which extend the scope of energy management outside the boundaries of a single plant to total site and then beyond the total site to district heating/cooling systems. The potential is demonstrated across a selection of the EU's most energy-intensive sectors– thereby enabling integration across industries and processes while at the same time ensuring wide-spread deployment post-project.

To enable demonstration of the proposed solutions, targeted pre-demonstration research is being carried to generate deeper knowledge about conceptual targeting and design methods with the aim of systematically integrating energy profiles of a total site and identifying realistic and achievable energy savings, subject to carbon footprint. In addition, the project aims to build a detailed scientific understanding of viable systematic frameworks for multi-objective optimisation under uncertainty and variability of demands and supplies in order to empower and enable optimal decision on structures and operating conditions of site energy infrastructure and to perform rigorous economic trade-offs.

2. The challenges

For manufacturing industry, the overall potential [of energy savings] is estimated to be around 25% by 2020 (Action Plan for Energy Efficiency, 2006). However there are considerable barriers in achieving those potential energy savings. From EFENIS point of view, those scientific, technological and non-technical barriers are as follows.

2.1. Scientific and Technological Barriers

Traditionally energy studies in manufacturing industry have been limited mainly to the management of energy infrastructure within a single plant boundary, in which the layer of heat exchanger network within a process onion diagram is optimised using the pinch analysis to maximise the heat recovery within each plant. However, the interactions among reaction, separation, heat recovery and utilities have not been systematically exploited for improving the overall energy efficiency.

More recent developments cover the total site energy management where a number of plants are combined and energy consumption of the whole site is being minimised. Directive 2012/27/EU on energy efficiency (2012) outlines that "high-efficiency cogeneration should be defined by the energy savings obtained by combined production instead of separate production of heat and electricity. To maximise energy savings and avoid energy saving opportunities being missed, the greatest attention should be paid to the operating conditions of cogeneration units." However in practical applications, the state-of-the-art technologies fall short to consider sufficiently full appreciation of Combined Heat and Power (CHP) implementation as well as the retrofit issues, carbon capture, operability, RAM (reliability, availability and maintainability) issues, renewables and integration with district heating systems. There have been some attempts of such integration. However at present, no systematic approach integrating CHP and Energy Management Systems (EMS) across multiple sites has been demonstrated or deployed.

On the other hand, research in the area of local or urban energy systems mainly highlights the design and optimisation of distributed energy systems itself, not systematically integrating it with industrial energy and utility systems.

Besides the emphasis on cogeneration of steam and power in total site management, another important aspect in site utility systems is cooling requirement, which is typically satisfied by cooling water systems. The development of systematic design approaches of cooling water systems has been a subject of research in recent years. However, the developed methods deal with cooling water systems in isolation from other site utilities, missing important interactions with steam and power systems and individual processes. A typical example is the performance of condensing turbines acting as either power generators or process drivers, which links the conditions of cooling water in corresponding condensers with energy efficiencies for both total sites and individual processes. Therefore, there is a strong need to exploit the synergy among cooling water systems, other site utilities, and individual processes.

2.2. Non-technical Barriers

The Commission appreciates that "obstacles like the lack of information, lack of access to capital, and short term pressures of the business environment should also be addressed. Overcoming these obstacles would reduce energy bills and improve competitiveness" (Energy Efficiency Plan, 2011). Increasing the efficiency of industrial processes in manufacturing industries is considered to be a slow transformation process that will take decades. Whether a new technology is taken up by the market depends to a large extent on the economics. Cost-effective technologies are essential to achieving substantial emission reductions. With respect to new technology and concepts, progress from the laboratory to full market deployment is very slow because of barriers such as standards and regulations and the lifespan of the existing capital equipment stock. Therefore, options need to be demonstrated now to have a substantial impact on the attainment of the 2020 targets.

An often encountered non-technical barrier for the implementation of energy integration potentials that have been identified during site optimisation studies is related to different timelines for modifications in infrastructure and production plants. Typically production plants undergo structural changes much faster than utility generation systems because market demand and resulting production capacity are increasingly difficult to predict and increased global competition requires rapid reactions on market changes. Therefore, very often the structural data basis for a site optimisation is outdated before the structural improvement measures could have been implemented. Similarly, if changes for a production unit are planned often no up-to-date total-site study is available and often not feasible to include within the scope of a single revamping project. This situation leads to local adaptations of the utility systems that are mostly inefficient from a total site perspective. In order to eliminate this barrier Total Site optimisation frameworks have to be complemented with new tools to track changes in the plant design and ensure that an up-to-date Heat Integration design is always available. What is missing is an efficient workflow and appropriate interfaces that allow rapid updating or recalculation of an existing Total Site analysis. Furthermore, if an efficient interface for updating Total Site studies is available, this could also provide the basis to include regular screenings of the site energy integration status into a continuous improvement process for energy efficiency, thereby allowing to track and document energy savings.

3. What is EFENIS?

In its Energy Efficiency Plan (2011), the Commission emphasises that it "will continue to foster the development, testing and deployment of new energy-efficient technologies, ..., in order reduce the costs and improve the performance of energy efficient technologies". To achieve the stated technological objectives, as well as to overcome scientific and technical barriers, EFENIS, as an integrated, industry-driven and multi-disciplinary project has been formulated for reliable and sustainable management of energy generation, supply and distribution, under the Total Site Integration concept. Technical themes will be explored in the project, namely, i) wider-scope Total Site Integration methodology, ii) computer-aided optimisation framework, iii) intensified heat transfer iv) waste heat recovery, iv) district heating energy integration with renewables sources, vi) Total Site-wide carbon management and decarbonised energy (Figure 1). vii) The most important step beyond state-of-the-art in this project is implementation of a series of unprecedented simultaneous activities at a number of key industrial companies from different sectors with the aim of demonstrating the benefits of the technology proposed.

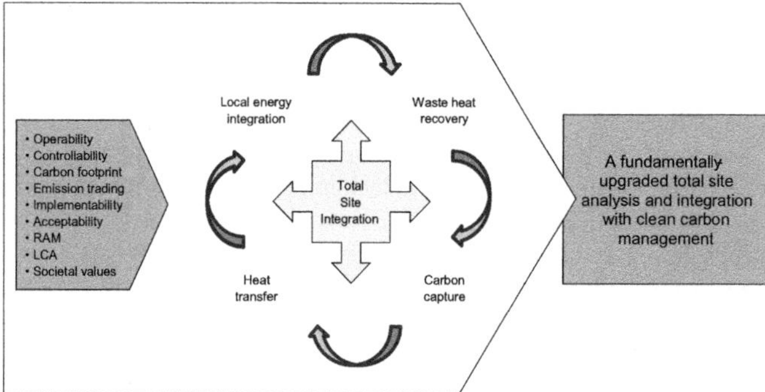

Figure 1. Overview of EFENIS project topics

The idea and concept builds on the anticipated capability of the consortium, which is composed of five big industrial companies, two SMEs and ten research organisations and universities which are centres of excellence in their fields.

3.1. Scientific and Technological Development

Main scientific and technological activities within the Project are listed below along with just a fraction (due to space considerations) of the latest research results generated by EFENIS are indicated as references.

- Improvement of understanding of overall process integration of reaction, separation, heat recovery and utilities, and site-wide (and "beyond the boundary") management – of heat (steam) and power (electricity) as well as development of guidelines for design and operation of utility system. (Nemet et al., 2013; Liew et al., 2013)
- Development of a procedure for efficient and reliable energy demand calculation by quantifying uncertainty and development of a framework for energy/GHG optimisation using multi-criteria optimisation (Koltsaklis et al., 2013)
- Measures for improvement of site-wide CO_2 management and decarbonised energy
- Improvement of understanding of total site heat transfer intensification - including systematic identification of implementable and operable engineering solutions (Arsenyeva et al., 2013)
- Identification of waste heat recovery and CHP potentials in general and of demonstration sites which is fully in line with Directive 2012/27/EU on energy efficiency (2012): High-efficiency cogeneration and district heating and cooling has significant potential for saving primary energy, which is largely untapped in the Union. Member States should carry out a comprehensive assessment of the potential for high-efficiency cogeneration and district heating and cooling."
- Improvement of understanding and develop guidelines of integrated cooling water systems in total site analysis
- Identification of the possibilities and barriers for strategic integration with local district energy systems
- Defining a workflow for continuously updating total site optimisation based on efficient interfaces between state-of-the-art process simulations and Total Site optimisation and management

3.2. Demonstration

Energy Efficiency Plan (2011) states that "For large companies the Commission will propose to make regular energy audits mandatory. It will recommend that Member States should develop incentives for companies to introduce an energy management system. EFENIS project provides the industry with demonstration case studies which

Table 1. EFENIS projected energy savings

Demonstration sites	Savings - BAT application (%)	Savings - EFENIS derived* (%)
Bayer	10	7.5
IPLOM	10	15
MOL	5	5
ENN	10	7.5

**The suggested advanced Total Site Integration is a novel technology so no BAT is available. It means the savings are in addition to BAT. The technology implementation is envisaged by the end of the project so the savings should be observed the first year after the end of the project*

show how adoption of the novel technologies can help companies in their energy audits. EFENIS will demonstrate and obtain reductions of primary energy use, CO_2 emissions and significant cost benefits from Total Site management and the application of enabling measures in the energy intensive industries, the expected energy savings are shown in Table 1.

4. Conclusions

European project EFENIS has been launched to demonstrate and promote the beyond state-of-the-art technologies which contribute to implementation of the EU energy policy, to achieving its global aims ("20-20-20") on part of the manufacturing sector and especially its main actors – big industrial companies. The project scientific, technological and non-technical results are systematically presented in numerous publications and deliverable reports. The complete set of public reports and the list of publications is available at EFENIS project (2013) website.

Acknowledgement

Financial support from FP7-ENERGY-2011-2 EFENIS-296003 EC Project, is gratefully acknowledged.

References

Action Plan for Energy Efficiency: Realising the Potential, 2006, <ec.europa.eu/energy/action _plan_energy_efficiency/doc/com_2006_0545_en.pdf> accessed on 14/09/2013

CORDIS, 2013, <cordis.europa.eu/projects/index.cfm?fuseaction=app.search&TXT=&FRM=1&STP=10&SIC=&PGA=FP7-ENERGY&CCY=&PCY=&SRC=&LNG=en&REF= > accessed on 14/09/2013

Directive 2012/27/EU on energy efficiency, 2012, Directive 2012/27/EU of The European Parlimentand ofthe Council of 25 October 2012 on energy efficiency, amending Directives 2009/125/EC and 2010/30/EU and repealing Directives 2004/8/EC and 2006/32/EC <eur-lex.europa. eu/LexUriServ/LexUriServ.do?uri=OJ:L:2012:315:FULL:EN:PDF> accessed 14/09/2013

EFENIS Project, 2013, <www.efenis.eu > accessed on 14/09/2013

Energy Efficiency Plan, 2011, <eur-lex.europa.eu/LexUriServ/LexUriServ.do?uri=CELEX:52011 DC0109:EN:NOT> accessed on 14/09/2013

EUROPE 2020 Strategy, 2010, A European strategy for smart, sustainable and inclusive growth <ec.europa.eu/eu2020/pdf/COMPLET%20EN%20BARROSO%20%20%20007%20-%20Europe%202020%20-%20EN%20version.pdf > accessed on 14/09/2014.

Green Paper - A European Strategy for Sustainable, Competitive and Secure Energy {SEC(2006) 317}, 2006, <eur-lex.europa.eu/smartapi/cgi/sga_doc?smartapi!celexplus!prod!DocNumber &lg=en&type_doc=COMfinal&an_doc=2006&nu_doc=105> accessed on 14/09/2013.

N.E. Koltsaklis, A.S. Dagoumas, G.M. Kopanos, E.N. Pistikopoulos, M.C. Georgiadis, 2013, A spatial multi-period long-term energy planning model: A case study of the Greek power system, Applied Energy, 115, 456–482.

P.Y. Liew, S.R. Wan Alwi, P.S. Varbanov, Z.A. Manan, J.J. Klemeš, 2013, Centralised utility system planning for a Total Site Heat Integration network, Comput. Chem. Eng., 57, 104-111.

A. Nemet, J.J. Klemeš, Z. Kravanja, 2013, Designing Total Site for Entire Lifetime Under Fluctuating Utility Prices, SDEWES 2013 Conference Proceedings, SDEWES2013-0561

O.P. Arsenyeva, R. Smith, I. Bulatov, L. Tovazhnyanskyy, O. Kapustenko, G. Khavin, 2013, Estimation of enhanced heat transfer area targets in process industries, Computer Aided Chemical Engineering, 32, 355-360.

Jiří Jaromír Klemeš, Petar Sabev Varbanov and Peng Yen Liew (Editors)
Proceedings of the 24th European Symposium on Computer Aided Process Engineering – ESCAPE 24
June 15-18, 2014, Budapest, Hungary.

Mathematical Programming Approach to Total Site Heat Integration

Andreja Nemet[a], Jiří Jaromír Klemeš[b], Zdravko Kravanja[a*]

[a]*Faculty of Chemistry and Chemical Engineering, University of Maribor, Maribor, Slovenia*

[b]*Centre for Process Integration and Intensification-CPI[2], Research Institute of Chemical and Process Engineering- MÜKKI, Faculty of Information Technology, University of Pannonia, Veszprém, Hungary*

zdravko.kravanja@um.si

Abstract

Heat Integration is one of frequently used methods for decreasing utility consumption. Originally it was developed for integration at the process level and gradually extended to heat recovery between various processes. In this current work a mixed-integer nonlinear programming (MINLP) model has been enhanced to evaluate the rate of heat recovery between those various processes and also to obtain the optimal temperature for the intermediate utility. This is achieved by considering: i) Heat losses during the transporting of steam through the pipeline, ii) Increased investment into heat exchangers and pipelines due to higher pressures and iii) Optimising the areas of heat the exchangers not only at the process level but also for those heat exchanger areas for heat transfer between process stream and intermediate utilities. A created superstructure considers that processes are connected to each other through various intermediate utilities, the temperature of which vary within their temperature intervals. Two different strategies for obtaining Total Site Heat Exchanger networks of a Total Site have been applied: a sequential and a simultaneous one. According to the first strategy Heat Integration is first obtained at the process level and then at the Total Site level from the resulting utility requirements obtained from the first step. In the second strategy the heat recovery is achieved simultaneously at the process and the Total Site levels. Both strategies were compared in order to evaluate, which one performs better.

Keywords: Total Site, Mathematical programming, Sequential strategy, Simultaneous strategy

1. Introduction

Further optimisation of heat integrated processes and sites can significantly contribute to the profitability of the processes. It can be performed for individual processes or at a wider scope – Total Site Heat Integration can be considered. In the latter case the complexity of the problem increases, especially, when even the residential and service sector units are integrated (Varbanov and Klemeš, 2012). An enhancement of the economic performance of units included in the Total Site can be obtained compared to the process level optimisation (Nemet et al. 2012).

So far Pinch Analysis (PA) has attracted a considerable industrial interest and number of applications (Klemeš, 2013). An example of planning the centralised utility system for Total Site Heat Integration network applying thermodynamic approach is presented in Liew et al. (2013). They are also many mathematical programming (MP) models available that with the

Heat Integration at the process level. On a Total Site level a usual approach is to optimise the steam turbine network, which serves the units with heat demand, e.g. Mavromatis and Kokossis, 1998. A more detailed review on Pinch Analysis and mathematical programming approach for heat integration history can be found in Klemeš and Kravanja (2013). An effective approach was proposed by developing a synergetic hybrid solution combining both PA and MP approaches (Klemeš et al, 2013). There is also a potential for applying the P-Graph (Halasz et al, 2002) optimisation approach – see e.g. Lam (2013).

Laukkanen et al. (2012), based on Yee and Grossmann' model (1990), developed a model for heat exchanger network synthesis for direct and indirect heat transfer inside and between processes. This model is in many respects simplified as e.g. it considers piping cost only as an increased fixed investment, heat losses during heat transportation between processes are neglected, and the investment increase due to higher pressures of intermediate utilities is neglected. Furthermore, it does not consider the possibility of optimising the pressures and temperatures of intermediate utilities in order to enable better heat recovery. In this presented work an upgraded mixed-integer nonlinear programming model for a Total Site Heat Integration Network has been developed after considering the previously mentioned drawbacks. A different Total Site superstructure has been generated that allows for different temperatures and within the pipes by connecting them in order to achieve optimal Total Site Profiles of the Source and Sink Sides. As the model of an individual process is based on the Yee and Grossmann' model (1990), the overall Total Site model exhibits similar features to those of the basic one – but it does not rely on the assumptions regarding the pinch temperature and minimum approach temperature, but all the temperature driven forces are treated as optimisation variables, thus enabling the obtaining of appropriate trade-offs between utility consumption and investment.

Two different strategies for the synthesis of Total Site have been used. In the first sequential approach, heat integration optimisation is obtained at the process level first and the resulting utility requirements serve as a basis for Total Site integration. In the second approach the whole Total Site is synthesised simultaneously.

2. Methodology

2.1. Scheme of Total Site

There are two main strategies for obtaining Total Site Heat Exchanger Design. The usual way of obtaining heat recovery is the sequential approach, where the heat recovery is done at a process level first and afterwards at a Total Site level. However, determining heat recovery at both levels simultaneously can be more beneficial. The superstructure of the sequential approach is shown in Figure 1 and the simultaneous one in Figure 2. Note that intermediate utilities are presented in the superstructures as additional cold and hot streams. They are produced at the Source Side from the residual heat, supplied by the process hot streams, and consumed at the Sink Side as intermediate hot utilities by the process cold streams.

2.1.1. The sequential Total Site Heat Integration.

The synthesis applying the sequential approach is completed over two steps. In the first step, Heat Integration at the process levels within each process is achieved. For this purpose, only the hot process-cold process matches in the middle stages ($k \in kp(k)$) and the process stream-utility matches at the extreme ends of the superstructure are allowed for heat exchange, whilst matches between process streams and intermediate utility streams are forbidden.

The residual parts of the hot and cold streams that represent Source and Sink Sides are identified this way for each process. Then, the integration of those matches between residual parts of process streams on the one side and intermediate utilities on the other side is performed ($k \in kh(k)$ and $k \in kc(k)$) during the second step.

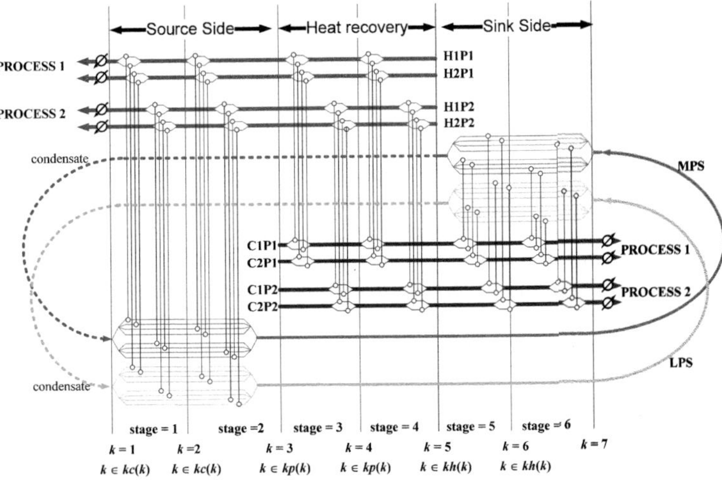

Figure 1. HEN superstructure for sequential Total Site Heat Integration for two processes, each with a pair of hot and cold process streams, and two intermediate utilities

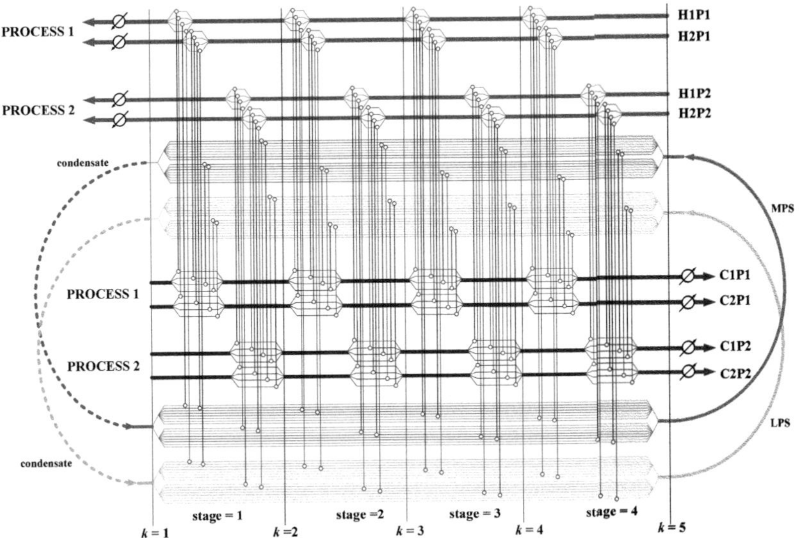

Figure 2. HEN superstructure for simultaneous Total Site Heat Integration for two processes, each with a pair of hot and cold process streams, and two intermediate utilities

2.1.2. The Total Site Heat Integration

In this approach heat integration is done at both the process and the Total Site levels simultaneously (Figure 2). All possible matches between hot and cold process streams within each process as well as between the hot process and the cold intermediate streams, and hot intermediate and cold process streams are proposed within each stage in the simultaneous superstructure.The objective for both strategies is minimisation of Total Annual Cost (*TAC*). Issues such as heat losses, piping cost and investment that increase due to higher pressures and temperatures were also considered in the model.

3. Illustrative case study

Input data for Total Site included the supply T_S and target T_T temperature, heat capacity flow rate *FC*, and the heat transfer coefficients of each stream (Table 1). Two types of heat exchangers were considered. A double pipe heat exchanger was used for the heat exchange between the process stream and the external utility having a fixed-charge coefficient of 121.4 k€ and a variable-charge coefficient of 0.193 k€/m^2, whilst for matches between the process streams and between the process streams and the intermediate utilities a fixed-plate shell and tube heat exchanger with a fixed-charge coefficient of 46.0 k€ and a variable-charge coefficient of 2.742 k€/m^2 were used. The data was taken from 2008, however updated to 2012 prices by applying the Chemical Engineering Plant Cost Index – CEPCI .The distance between the two processes was 0.3 km. The depreciation was determined for 15 years. The heat losses was assumed to be 1 %/km of pipeline (Kapil et al, 2012) and the cost of piping 1,000 k€/km.

Three intermediate utilities were considered: i) high pressure-, ii) medium pressure-, and ii) low pressure steam. The temperature range for each intermediate utility is presented in Table 2. After performing Heat Integration, the additional heating/ cooling requirements were supplied by hot oil and cooling water as external utilities (Table 2).

Table 1. Streams of each process in the Total Site

Process	Stream/ Type	T_S/°C	T_T/°C	FC / kW °C^{-1}	h/ kW (m^2 °C)$^{-1}$
Process A	1 /hot	450	300	5	0.33
	2/ hot	400	50	25	0.35
	3/ cold	40	180	45	0.45
	4/ cold	50	60	15	0.34
Process B	1/ hot	150	80	16	0.4
	2/ hot	130	90	12	0.36
	3/ cold	100	250	25	0.38
	4/ cold	80	320	20	0.42

Table 2. Intermediate and external utilities

Utility	Type	T_{lo}/°C	T_{up}/°C	h/ kW (m^2 °C)$^{-1}$
Intermediate	Low pressure steam	120	148	10
Intermediate	Medium pressure steam	148	208	10.5
Intermediate	High pressure steam	208	252	11
		T_{in}/°C	T_{out}/°C	
External	Hot oil	340	340	0.8
External	Cooling water	20	25	0.8

The price of hot oil was 0.161 €/kWh and the one for cooling water 0.020 €/kWh. Investment for heat exchangers was modified by a factor for increased steam pressure. 10 % and 15 % higher investment for piping was assumed for medium pressure steam and high pressure steam. The results were obtained for both the sequential and the simultaneous strategies. The comparison is presented in Table 3. As can be seen the *TAC* obtained with the simultaneous strategy was significantly lower compared to the results obtained with the sequential strategy (7,324 k€ vs. 9,940 k€). This was achieved due to significantly lower consumption of external utilities - by 25.8 % for hot utility requirement Q^{HU} and 95.0 % for cold utility requirement Q^{CU}. The external utility consumption decreased as a consequence of increased heat recovery on a Total Site level Q^{REC_TS} (269 %) for which higher investment of 6.6 % was needed. The rate of heat recovery on process level Q^{REC} was constant during both optimisations. Better Total Site heat recovery was obtained by more efficient arrangement within the Total Site Heat Exchanger Network (Figure 3).

By applying the simultaneous strategy additional options for integration can be explored, as can be seen from this illustrative case study. It enables to exchange heat between process streams and intermediate utilities (if profitable) prior to the heat exchange between process streams at the process level.

Table 3. Comparison of results obtained for both the sequential and the simultaneous strategies.

Optimisation	*TAC*/ k€	Q^{HU}/ kW	Q^{CU}/ kW	Q^{REC}/ kW	Q^{REC_TS}/ kW	T^{HU}/ °C	*D*/ k€
Simultaneous	7,324	4,782	116	P1: 6,450 P2:1,485 total:7,934	P1:3,050 P2:2,284	207	760
Sequential	9,940	6,448	2,341	P1: 6,450 P2:1,485 total:7,934	P1:826 P2:618	139	713
Difference	-2,616	-1,666	-2,225	0	P1:2,225 P2:1,666	68	47
Difference /%	-26.3	-25.8	-95.0	0	P1:269 P2:269	49	6.6

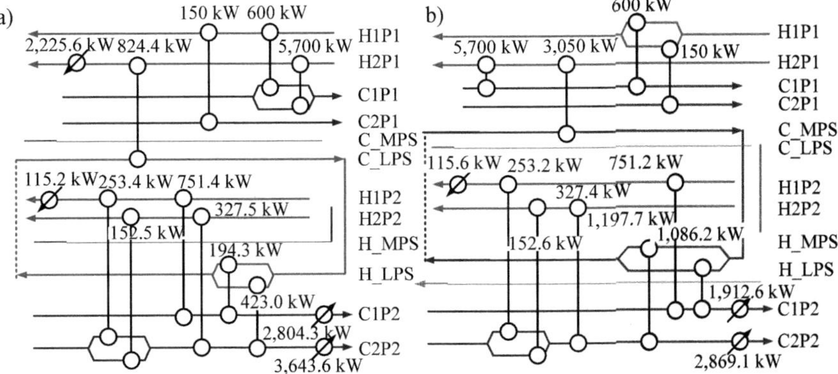

Figure 3. Results of optimisation obtained by a) sequential approach and b) simultaneous strategy

This leads to networks, where more intermediate utilities are produced at higher temperatures of Source Side making intermediate utilities reaching higher temperatures, which can potentially cover higher heat demands at higher temperatures on the Sink Side. Note that in this case study a medium pressure steam at 207 °C was produced rather than at 139 °C.

4. Conclusions

Two strategies both applying mixed integer nonlinear programming model have been presented for the optimisation of Total Site Heat Integration Network. It addresses couple of issues of Total Site synthesis, presented by Chew et al., 2013. The sequential model employing a two-step approach, determining heat integration on process level first and afterwards on the Total Site scale, followed the traditional way of performing Total Site heat integration. The second way of obtaining results was by applying the simultaneous optimisation on both the process and the Total Site levels. Applying the latter approach can lead to a significantly better result with lower Total Annual Cost - by 26.3 % in the case study presented. However, applying the simultaneous model on large-scale problems might be very hard or even impossible since the complexity as the problem increases rapidly with the number of processes and process streams included in the analysis. In these cases the sequential approach would be more useful.

Acknowledgement

The authors acknowledge the financial support from EC FP7 project ENER/FP7/296003/EFENIS 'Efficient Energy Integrated Solutions for Manufacturing Industries – EFENIS' and Slovenian Research Agency (Program No. P2-0032).

References

K.H. Chew, J.J. Klemeš, S.R. Wan Alwi, Z.A. Manan, 2013, Industrial implementation issues of Total Site Heat Integration, Applied Thermal Engineering, 61, 1, 17-25.

L. Halasz, A.B. Nagy, T. Ivicz, F. Friedler, L.T. Fan, 2002, Optimal retrofit design and operation of the steam-supply system of a chemical complex, Applied Thermal Engng, 22, 8, 939-947.

A. Kapil, I. Bulatov, R. Smith, J.-K. Kim, 2012, Site-wide low-grade heat recovery with a new cogeneration targeting method, Chemical Engineering Research and Design, 90, 5, 677-689.

J.J. Klemeš, Z. Kravanja, Forty years of Heat Integration: Pinch Analysis (PA) and Mathematical Programming (MP), Current Opinion in Chemical Engineering, 2, 4, 461-474.

J.J. Klemeš, P.S. Varbanov, Z. Kravanja, 2013, Recent Developments in Process Integration, Chemical Engineering Research and Design, 91, 10, 2037-2053.

H.L Lam, 2013, Extended P-Graph Applications in Supply Chain and Process Network Synthesis, Current Opinion in Chemical Engineering, 2, 4, 475-486.

T. Laukkanen, T.-M. Tveit, C.-J. Fogelholm, 2012, Simultaneous heat exchanger network synthesis for direct and indirect heat transfer inside and between processes, Chemical Engineering Research and Design, 90, 9, 1129-1140.

P.Y. Liew, S.R. Wan Alwi, P.S. Varbanov, Z.A. Manan, J.J. Klemeš, 2013, Centralised utility system planning for a Total Site Heat Integration network, Computers and Chemical Engineering, 57, 104-111.

S.P. Mavromatis, A.C.Kokossis, 1998, Conceptual optimisation of utility networks for operational variations — II. Network development and optimization. Chem Eng Sci, 53, 8, 1609–1630.

A. Nemet, P.S. Varbanov, P. Kapustenko, A. Durgutović, J.J. Klemeš, 2012, Capital Cost Targeting of Total Site Heat Recovery, Chemical Engineering Transactions, 26, 231-236.

P.S. Varbanov, J.J. Klemeš, 2011, Integration and management of renewables into Total Sites with variable supply and demand. Computers and Chemical Engineering, 35, 9,1815-1826

T. Yee, I. Grossmann, 1990, Simultaneous optimization models for heat integration II. Heat exchanger network synthesis, Computers and Chemical Engineering, 14, 10, 1165-1184.

Jiří Jaromír Klemeš, Petar Sabev Varbanov and Peng Yen Liew (Editors)
Proceedings of the 24th European Symposium on Computer Aided Process Engineering – ESCAPE 24
June 15-18, 2014, Budapest, Hungary.

Total Site Heat Integration Targeting Algorithm Incorporating Plant Layout Issues

Peng Yen Liew[a,b*],Sharifah Rafidah Wan Alwi[b], Jiří Jaromír Klemeš[a]

[a]*Centre for Process Integration and Intensification – CPI², Research Institute of Chemical and Process Engineering - MŰKKI, Faculty of Information Technology, University of Pannonia, Egyetem u. 10, H-8200 Veszprém, Hungary.*

[b]*Process Systems Engineering Centre (PROSPECT), Faculty of Chemical Engineering, Universiti Teknologi Malaysia, 81310 UTM Johor Bahru, Johor, Malaysia.*

pengyenliew@cpi.uni-pannon.hu

Abstract

Energy Efficiency has gained concern in the process industry due to the high energy consumption. Process Integration using Pinch Analysis plays an important role in enhancing the sustainability and the profitability margin of industrial processes. Total Site Heat Integration (TSHI) is one of the main branches of Process Integration based on Pinch Analysis technique, which is an industrial energy conservation strategy across individual process boundary. However, the pressure drop and heat loss on the steam mains have not been well discussed in the existing TS targeting methodologies. In this paper, an extended numerical algorithm is proposed for addressing the effects of plant layout to the minimum multiple utility targets. The extended tools are able to assist the designer to perform a preliminary assessment of the retrofit options for a steam system. This enhanced methodology improves the accuracy of the existing TS targeting methodology by considering the effects of plant layout in a TS system. The proposed methodology is demonstrated with an illustrative case study.

Keywords: Total Site Heat Integration; Problem Table Algorithm; Pinch Analysis; pressure drop; heat loss

1. Introduction

Sustainable development has been widely discussed around the world. Industries, as one of the core world energy users, has a responsibility to reduce their energy consumption by increasing energy efficiency and utilising renewable energy (Varbanov et al., 2004). Process Integration has been used for grassroots and retrofit design of Heat Exchanger Network (HEN) in the industry as an energy conservation initiative. Pinch Analysis is one of the most widely used techniques in Process Integration (Klemeš and Varbanov, 2013) for targeting the minimum energy consumption of industrial processes for more than 40 years (Klemeš et al., 2013). The technique was initially designed for individual process energy saving. Pinch Analysis has been extended to a Total Site (TS) concept by Dhole and Linnhoff (1993), where inter-plants or inter-processes energy conservation is implemented via utility system (Velasco-García et al., 2011). Total Site Heat Integration (TSHI) is mainly based on graphical methodologies, which are Total Site Profiles - TSP, Site Composite Curves - SCC, and Site Utility Grand Composite Curve - SUGCC (Klemeš et al., 1997). Liew et al. (2012) recently introduced a new series of analogous numerical algorithm for the TS targeting, including Multiple Utility Problem Table Algorithm (MU-PTA), Total Site Problem Table Algorithm (TS-PTA) and Total Site Utility Distribution (TSUD) Table. Further improvements of TSHI includes for the consideration of process modification (Hackl et al., 2011), process specific minimum temperature difference (Varbanov et al., 2012), effects of plant shutdown (Liew et al., 2013), capital cost (Boldyryev et al., 2013) and water sensible heat (Liew et al., 2014). Chew et al. (2013) inspected the main industrial implementation issues of TSHI. The main issues pointed out in the paper are layout, communication risk, pressure, fluid characteristic and undesired phase change. Wang et al. (2013) proposed a new graphical TS targeting methodology considering the horizontal distance between the heat sources and sinks in the TS region. However, the methodology should also consider pressure drop in the utility piping that affects the steam quality due to undesired phase change in the piping system.

In this paper, a novel numerical methodology for Heat Integration across Total Site processes considering different layout problem in the TS system has been developed. This methodology would be able to assist designers/engineers in representing the actual utility system performance for a TS utility system. The proposed algorithm is an extension of the existing numerical TSHI algorithm. This work helps in foreseeing the effect of pressure drops and heat losses in the utility system. The proposed methodology is generally an improvement of the existing TS targeting methodologies to achieve more accurate results, towards representing the real plant situation.

2. Methodology

The TS utility requirement targeting considering pressure drops and heat losses is performed based on the following steps:

2.1. Target the theoretical minimum utility requirement

In the first step, the theoretical utility requirement for the TS system without considering pressure drop and heat loss is targeted by using numerical energy cascade algorithm introduced by Liew et al. (2013), i.e. MU-PTA followed by TS-PTA. The distribution of process heat sources for generating steam and process heat sinks that requires steam are identified by using TSUD.

2.2. Estimate the pressure drop and heat losses

In the next step, the horizontal distance between the processes and the site utility are identified. In real situations, there is a pressure drop and heat losses for transferring the steam in the pipelines from one location to the other. The pressure drop and heat losses have to be considered in order to determine the minimum utility requirement of the TS as close to the real values.

2.2.1. Steam saturated temperature calculation based on pressure drop effect

It is assumed that the current utilities pressure have already considered the pressure drop effect that satisfies the pressure of the farthest downstream process from the utility site. Considering this pressure as P_f, the pressure for the nearer processes (P_n) could be evaluated using Eq.(1). The pressure drop (ΔP) is estimated by Darcy-Weisbach Equation - Eq.(2), where ΔP is the pressure loss (N/m^2), f is the friction coefficient, L is the length of the pipe (m), D is the diameter of the pipe and v is the average velocity of fluid (m/s). The temperature for the steam headers are changed to the saturated temperature at the calculated pressure.

$$P_n = P_f - \Delta P \quad (1)$$

$$\Delta P = f(L/D)(v/2) \quad (2)$$

2.2.2. Heat loss calculation

For heat loss calculation, Eq.(3) is used for estimating the heat losses via conductive and convective heat transfer in the piping system, where T is temperature (°C), h is the convective coefficient, W/(m^2.K), k is the mean thermal conductivity of a material W/(m.K), r is radius (m), L is the pipe length (m), indexes mean o outside, i inside, 1 denotes pipes, and 2 thermal insulations.

$$q_{loss} = \frac{T_o - T_i}{\frac{1}{2\pi h_{1,i} r_{1,i} L} + \frac{\ln(r_{1,o}/r_{1,i})}{2\pi k_1 L} + \frac{\ln(r_{2,o}/r_{2,i})}{2\pi k_2 L} + \frac{1}{2\pi h_{2,o} r_{2,o} L}} \tag{3}$$

The degree of steam superheat (ΔT_{sh}) is calculated by dividing heat loss by the heat capacity flow – CP (kW/°C) using Eq.(4). The ΔT_{sh} is added to the saturated temperature of the steam at pressure calculated in Step 2.1.

$$\Delta T_{sh} = q_{loss} / CP \tag{4}$$

2.3. Target the minimum utility requirement considering pressure drop and heat loss

Step 2.1 is repeated by using the new calculated steam temperature levels in Step 2.2. A new column is added in TS-PTA for the heat losses calculated. The net heat available is deducted by the heat losses. The methodology continues with the multiple utility requirements targeting.

3. Illustrative Case Study

The proposed methodology is illustrated by a Case Study. Table 1 shows the stream data for the case study. The minimum allowable utility to process temperature difference ($\Delta T_{min,up}$) is assumed 10 °C. The utilities available on site are High Pressure Steam (HPS) at 270 °C, Medium Pressure Steam (MPS) at 180 °C, Low Pressure Steam (LPS) at 133.5 °C and Cooling Water (CW) at 10 - 20 °C. As described previously, the first step is to calculate the theoretical TS minimum utility target without considering pressure drop and heat. Table 2 and 3 shows the TS-PTA and TSUD Table (Liew et al., 2012). The targeting results show that the utility requirements are 7,000 kW of HPS, 4,372 kW of LPS and 7,302 kW of CW. The MPS steam header is taken out from the study since there is no heat sink available at this utility level.

Table 1. Stream data for Illustrative Case Study (Liew et al., 2012)

Stream	T_s (°C)	T_t (°C)	ΔH (MW)	CP (kW/°C)	Stream	T_s (°C)	T_t (°C)	ΔH (MW)	CP (kW/°C)
Process A($\Delta T_{min,pp}$= 20 °C)					Process B($\Delta T_{min,pp}$= 10 °C)				
H1A	200	100	20.0	200	H1B	200	50	04.50	30
H2A	150	60	36.0	400	H2B	240	100	02.10	15
C1A	50	120	49.0	700	H3B	200	119	18.63	230
C2A	50	220	25.5	150	C1B	30	200	06.80	40
					C2B	50	250	04.00	20

Table 2. Total Site Problem Table Algorithm without considering pressure and heat losses (Liew et al., 2012).

Utility	Utility Temp. (°C)	Net Heat Source (kW)	Net Heat Sink (kW)	Net Heat Required (kW)	Initial Heat Cascade (kW)	Final Heat Cascade (kW)	Multiple Utility Heat Cascade (kW)	External Utility Required (kW)
					0	11,372	0	
HPS	270	0	7,000	-7,000				7,000
					-7,000	4,372	0	
MPS	180	2,165	0	2,165				0
					-4,835	6,537	2,165	
LPS	133.5	9,963	16,500	-6,537				4,372
					-11,372	0	0	(Pinch)
CW	15-20	7,302	0	7,302				-7,302
					-4,070	7,302	0	

Table 3. Total Site Utility Distribution (TSUD) Table without considering pressure and heat losses (Liew et al., 2012).

Utility	Heat Source (kW)			Heat Sink (kW)		
	Plant A	Plant B	Site Utility	Plant A	Plant B	Site Utility
HPS			7,000	6,000	1,000	
MPS		2,165				
LPS		9,963	4,372	16,500		
CW	4,000	3302				7,302

For Step b, the horizontal distances from utility site to Process B and Process A are 200 m and 500 m. The pipes inner diameters for transporting HPS and LPS from the utility plant to both processes are 202 mm and 314.67 mm for transporting LPS from Process B to A. Both pipes have 25 mm insulation. The mean thermal conductivity of the metal is assumed at 45 W/m.K and 0.064 W/m.K for the insulation. The steam saturated temperatures considering pressure loss are calculated by using Eqs.(1) and (2). The heat losses (q_{loss}) and degree of steam superheating (ΔT_{sh}) are calculated by using Eqs.(3) and (4). Table 4 shows the new steam pressure and temperature at different locations.

As the steam temperatures have now changed, TS-PTA (see Table 5) is performed again to determine the new minimum TS utility target. A new column for heat loss is added in the TS-PTA, which is the amount of heat that is deducted from the net heat available in the TS system. The TSUD Table (Table 6) is also redrawn to illustrate the energy flow between processes and site utility, as well as heat losses.

The heat recovery via indirect heat transfer has reduced to 9,993 kW, which is equivalent to 17.60 % of the targeted amount of heat recovery opportunity. The final targeted total hot utility requirement is calculated at 7,446 kW of HPS and 6,703 kW of MPS, while cooling requirement is 9,437 kW, which is also equivalent to the increment of 6.37 %, 53.31 %, and 29.24 % from the targeting result using the existing approach.

Table 4. Steam Pressure and Temperature for the case study

		Existing method	Proposed Method		
			Site Utility	Process B	Process A
HPS	Pressure (barg)	55.03	55.77	55.07	55.03
	Sat. Temperature (°C)	270.00	270.85	270.05	270.00
	Heat losses (kW)	-	178	268	-
	Temperature (°C)	270.00	278.80	284.05	270.00
LPS	Pressure (barg)	3.00	4.03	3.72	3.00
	Sat.Temperature (°C)	133.60	143.88	141.01	133.60
	Heat losses (kW)	-	84	112	-
	Temperature (°C)	133.60	151.41	143.52	133.60

Table 5. Total Site Problem Table Algorithm considering plant layout issues for the case study.

Utility	Net Heat Source (kW)	Net Heat Sink (kW)	Heat Loss (kW)	Net Heat Required (kW)	Initial Heat Cascade (kW)	Final Heat Cascade (kW)	Multiple Utility Heat Cascade (kW)	External Utility Required (kW)
					0	14,149	0	
HPS	0	7,000	446	-7,446				7,446
					-7,446	6,703	0	
LPS	9,993	16,500	196	-6,703				6,703
					-14,149	0	0	(PINCH)
CW	9,437	0		9,437				-9,437
					-4,712	9,437	0	

Table 6. Total Site Utility Distribution (TSUD) Table considering plant layout issues for the case study.

Utility	Heat Source (kW)			Heat Sink (kW)			Heat Loss (kW)
	Plant A	Plant B	Site Utility	Plant A	Plant B	Site Utility	
HPS			7,446	6,000	1,000		446
LPS		9,993	6,703	16,500			196
CW	4,000	5,437				9,437	

4. Conclusion

This work introduces an improved heat cascade algorithm for targeting the TS minimum utilities target considering pressure drop and heat losses in the utility system. The pressure drop affects the utility temperature at different locations. The degree of steam superheat is calculated in this methodology to ensure the steam supplied to the heat sink is in fully vapour state. This methodology is tested with an illustrative case study, which the indirect heat transfer via utility system is overestimated by 18 % using the existing methodology. The targeting result from the new methodology deviated for 6.37 % (HPS), 53.31 % (LPS), 29.24 % (CW) from the existing methodology. In future research the heat loss for the direct heat transfer HEN should be included and the economic potential is worth to be explored.

Acknowledgement

The authors would like to thank the EC-supported project Energy - 2011-8-1 Efficient Energy Integrated Solutions for Manufacturing Industries (EFENIS) – ENER/FP7/296003/EFENIS and the Universiti Teknologi Malaysia (UTM) for providing the research funding for this project under Vote No. Q.J130000.7125.03H44. The first author also appreciates the financial support from the Ministry of Education Malaysia through providing Ph.D. scholarship.

References

S. Boldyryev, P.S. Varbanov, A. Nemet, J.J. Klemeš, P. Kapustenko, 2013, Capital Cost Assessment for Total Site Power Cogeneration, Comput. Aided Chem. Eng., 32, 361-366.

K.H. Chew, J.J. Klemeš, S.R. Wan Alwi, Z. Abdul Manan, 2013, Industrial implementation issues of Total Site Heat Integration, Appl. Therm. Eng., 61, 17-25.

V.R. Dhole, B. Linnhoff, 1993, Total site targets for fuel, co-generation, emissions, and cooling, Comput. Chem. Eng., 17, 101-109.

R. Hackl, E. Andersson, S. Harvey, 2011, Targeting for energy efficiency and improved energy collaboration between different companies using total site analysis (TSA), Energy, 36, 4609-4615.

J. Klemeš, V.R. Dhole, K. Raissi, S.J. Perry, L. Puigjaner, 1997, Targeting and design methodology for reduction of fuel, power and CO_2 on total sites, Appl. Therm. Eng., 17, 993-1003.

J.J. Klemeš, P.S. Varbanov, 2013, Process Intensification and Integration: an assessment, Clean Technologies and Environmental Policy, 15, 417-422.

J.J. Klemeš, P.S. Varbanov, Z. Kravanja, 2013, Recent Developments in Process Integration, Chem. Eng. Res. Des., 91, 2037-2053.

P.Y. Liew, S.R. Wan Alwi, J.S. Lim, P.S. Varbanov, J.J. Klemeš, Z. Abdul Manan, 2014, Total Site Heat Integration incorporating the water sensible heat, J. Clean. Prod., DOI: 10.1016/j.jclepro.2013.12.047

P.Y. Liew, S.R. Wan Alwi, P.S. Varbanov, Z.A. Manan, J.J. Klemeš, 2012, A numerical technique for Total Site sensitivity analysis, Appl. Therm. Eng., 40, 397-408.

P.Y. Liew, S.R. Wan Alwi, P.S. Varbanov, Z.A. Manan, J.J. Klemeš, 2013, Centralised Utility System Planning for a Total Site Heat Integration Network, Comput. Chem. Eng., 57, 104-111.

P.S. Varbanov, S. Doyle, R. Smith, 2004, Modelling and Optimization of Utility Systems, Chem. Eng. Res. Des., 82, 561-578.

P.S. Varbanov, Z. Fodor, J.J. Klemeš, 2012, Total Site targeting with process specific minimum temperature difference (ΔTmin), Energy, 44, 20-28.

P. Velasco-Garcia, P.S. Varbanov, H. Arellano-Garcia, G. Wozny, 2011, Utility systems operation: Optimisation-based decision making, Appl. Therm. Eng., 31, 3196-3205.

Y. Wang, W. Wang, X. Feng, 2013, Heat integration across plants considering distance factor, Chem. Eng. Trans., 35, 25-30.

Jiří Jaromír Klemeš, Petar Sabev Varbanov and Peng Yen Liew (Editors)
Proceedings of the 24th European Symposium on Computer Aided Process Engineering – ESCAPE 24
June 15-18, 2014, Budapest, Hungary.

New Multiple Time Grid Continuous-Time Formulation for the Cyclic Scheduling of an Industrial Batch Plant

Djêide Rodrigues[a,b], Pedro M. Castro[a,*], Henrique A. Matos[b]

[a]*Laboratório Nacional de Energia e Geologia, Lisboa 1649-038, Portugal*
[b]*Centro de Processos Químicos, DEQ, Instituto Superior Técnico, Avenida Rovisco Pais, 1, Lisboa 1049-001, Portugal*
pedro.castro@lneg.pt

Abstract

In this paper, a cyclic scheduling problem from a batch pulp plant is used to test a new continuous-time, multiple time grid formulation. It can be employed in multistage multiproduct batch plants with a single unit per stage and complex interactions between immediate orders, which in this case take the form of integrated heating tasks. The results show that the solution of a real life problem can be obtained in under a second, which is some orders of magnitude faster than previous single grid discrete and continuous-time formulations based on the Resource Task Network (RTN). The new formulation is also considerably simpler, allowing to perform capacity expansion studies resulting from the addition of more parallel units. In particular, it is shown that steam availability is a major bottleneck, leading to a much lower productivity increase than the value expected from the increase in capacity.

Keywords: Multiple time grid, continuous-time, scheduling, energy efficiency, pulp.

1. Introduction

In the chemical industry, scheduling plays an important role wherever there is competition among tasks for limited resources over time. While traditionally, production scheduling has been done manually by trained individuals, the additional complexity resulting from a larger product portfolio, volatile customer orders and high pressure to save on production and energy costs, has made manual scheduling extremely challenging Harjunkoski et al. (2013). This has focused attention on optimization models and algorithms that can help the decision-making process and a variety of approaches has appeared in the literature. Key aspects of the production environment that influence the choice of the mathematical formulation are the plant topology and production recipe data. Mathematical models can either rely on a discrete- or continuous-time representation.

Several authors published works about optimization methods concerning pulp mill production and involving shared and/or limited resources. For instance, Hvala et al. (1993) proposed a solution procedure based on a heuristic algorithm combining a neighborhood search technique and linear programming in order to determine the most suitable digester sequence. Later, Castro et al. (2002) developed two RTN short-term approaches: discrete and continuous-time, where the objective was to minimize the makespan for a given number of cycles. The same authors also considered a periodic mode of operation employing the wrap-around concept Castro et al. (2003). Recently,

(Shaik and Bhat, 2013) proposed a discrete-time formulation applying the State-Task Network representation to model the short-term scheduling problem of displacement batch digesters. They tested different objective functions and settings of critical parameters of the MILP formulation to prove robustness of their formulation.

2. Problem definition

In this work, we consider a scheduling problem arising in the cooking section of a sulphite pulp plant. The process consists of a sequence of processing tasks that are executed inside four parallel digesters. The sequence starts with wood and chemicals filling and ends with pulp blowing into a storage reservoir. The resources (wood-chips conveyer (M1), acid-filling pump (M2), steam line (M3), high-and low-pressure degas tanks (M5 and M6), and blow tank (M7)) required by the tasks are shared among the digesters. Thus, with the exception of the steam line, two digesters cannot use any of these resources simultaneously. Total steam availability is limited and frequent waiting periods are observed, meaning that the heating stage is the process bottleneck. In order to use this resource efficiently, there is the possibility of heating two digesters simultaneously, if strict constraints on the production recipe are met, which are related to the heating rates between certain key temperatures. Given that the digesters have different capacities and the larger the digester, the longer it takes to reach a specified temperature set point, the digester sequence affects the duration of the heating stage and hence the cycle time.

Figure 1 is a generic representation of the sequential multistage multiproduct plant. Each task K_i is associated to unit/stage M_i, with $m \in M$, for every digester I_i, with $i \in I$. The set M comprises two types of units: shared equipment resources and virtual units (M4), $m \in M^{VU}$. The virtual units represent the cooking (reaction) stage, where the digester is the only equipment required. Cooking tasks of different digesters can occur simultaneously.

3. New multiple time grid continuous-time formulation

A new multiple time grid continuous-time formulation is proposed to address the periodic scheduling problem of the batch plant. Since the number of tasks that needs to be processed by each unit m is known a priori, the number of time slots required to find the global optimal solution is equal to the number of digesters (Castro and Grossmann, 2005), $|T| = |I|$. The novel aspect is related to the integrated heating tasks, which are modeled through variable processing times that are a function of the digester sequence.

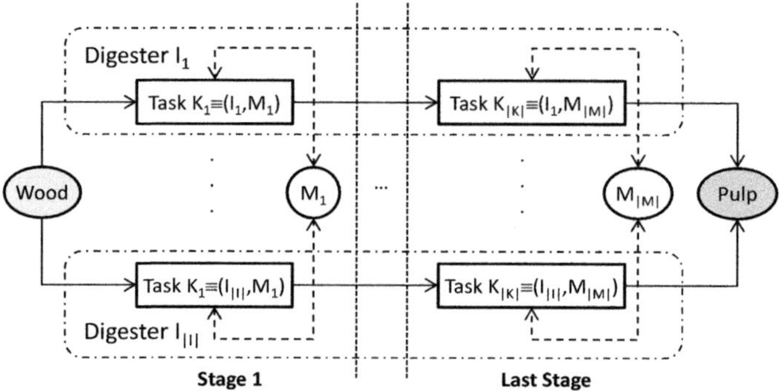

Figure 1. Generic representation of sequential multistage batch plant with a single unit per stage.

For modeling the continuity of operations between cycles, we use constraints first proposed in (Wu and Ierapetritou, 2004) that involve the wrap-around operator Shah et al. (1993).

The model uses two sets of binary variables: (i) digester-slot assignment variables $Y_{i,t}$; (ii) digester interaction variables $Z_{i,i',t}$, and four sets of nonnegative continuous variables representing: (a) the starting time of slot t in unit m, $Ts_{t,m}$; (b) its ending time $Te_{t,m}$; (c) the starting time of the second part of the heating task $Ts^{90}_{t,m}$, which takes the digester from 90 °C to the cooking temperature; (d) the cycle time H.

The wrap-around operator Ω defined in Eq.(1) allows for forward and backward wrap-around and can be used for indices t and m. In stages that require only the digester as resource (virtual units), tasks are allowed to overlap. In contrast, this behavior is not allowed for tasks executed in shared equipment units, see Eq.(2). In order to ensure that tasks within a certain digester follow the correct sequence of processing stages, we consider Eqs.(3-4). The former applies to units under zero-wait policy,$m \in M^{ZW}$.

$$\Omega(t) = \begin{cases} t + |T| \ ,t < 1 \\ t \ ,1 \leq t \leq |T| \\ t - |T|, t > |T| \end{cases} \tag{1}$$

$$Ts_{\Omega(t+1),m} \geq Te_{t,m} - H|_{t=|T|} \forall m \notin M^{VU}, t \in T \tag{2}$$

$$Ts_{t,\Omega(m+1)} = Te_{t,m} - H|_{m=|M|} \ \forall m \in M^{ZW}, t \in T \tag{3}$$

$$Ts_{t,\Omega(m+1)} \geq Te_{t,m} - H|_{m=|M|} \ \forall m \notin M^{ZW}, t \in T \tag{4}$$

Eq.(5) states that the difference between the ending and starting times of slot t in unit m is equal to the processing time $p_{i,m}$ of the digester assigned to slot t and applies to all but the heating stage. Eqs.(6-7) ensure that there is a 1:1 correspondence between digesters and slots.

$$Te_{t,m} = Ts_{t,m} + \textstyle\sum_{i \in I} (p_{i,m} \cdot Y_{i,t}) \ \forall m \notin M^{SL}, t \in T \tag{5}$$

$$\textstyle\sum_{i \in I} Y_{i,t} = 1 \ \forall t \in T \tag{6}$$

$$\textstyle\sum_{t \in T} Y_{i,t} = 1 \ \forall i \in I \tag{7}$$

The heating stage $m \in M^{SL}$ may involve a complex interaction between a digester and the ones immediately preceding and succeeding it, and so other types of constraints are needed. Eq.(8) is the constraint for the second part of the heating task and is conceptually similar to Eq.(5). Eq.(9) determines the time of occurrence of the 90°C state as the sum of the starting time of the first part of the heating task and its duration, which in turn is a function of the digester i' interacting with i (note that case i'=i handles the no interaction case). If the digester i is indeed interacting with further ahead digester i' at slot t, then the time available between the end of the previous stage and the start of m should be equal to $p_{i',m}$, see Eq.(10). Furthermore, digester i' must be assigned to slot t-1, see Eq.(11). If they are not interacting, Eq.(10) is relaxed to $Te_{t,m-1} \leq Ts_{t,m}$, becoming Eq.(4). Clearly, only if the digester i is assigned to slot t ($Y_{i,t}$) can it interact with the other digesters ($Z_{i,i',t}$), see Eq.(12).

$$Te_{t,m} = Ts_{t,m}^{90} + \sum_{i \in I} (p_{i,m} \cdot Y_{i,t}) \ \forall m \in M^{SL}, t \in T \tag{8}$$

$$Ts_{t,m}^{90} = Ts_{t,m} + \sum_{i \in I} \sum_{i' \in I} (p_{i,i'}^{H0} \cdot Z_{i,i',t}) \ \forall m \in M^{SL}, t \in T \tag{9}$$

$$Te_{t,m-1} \leq Ts_{t,m} + \sum_{i \in I} \sum_{\substack{i' \in I \\ i' \neq i}} (p_{i',m} \cdot Z_{i,i',t}) \ \forall m \in M^{SL}, t \in T \tag{10}$$

$$Y_{i,t} \geq \sum_{\substack{i' \in I \\ i' \neq i}} Z_{i',i,\Omega(t+1)} \ \forall i \in I, t \in T \tag{11}$$

$$Y_{i,t} = \sum_{i' \in I} Z_{i,i',t} \ \forall i \in I, t \in T \tag{12}$$

The cycle time of the system must be greater than the time required to conclude one batch of the four digesters. In Eq.(13), we use the lower bound on the duration of the steam sharing subtask H0, which for digester i is given by $p_{i,i}^{H0}$.

$$p_{i,i}^{H0} + \sum_{m \in M} p_{i,m} \leq H \ \forall i \in I \tag{13}$$

Finally, the goal is to minimize the cycle time H, Eq. (14).

$$min\ H \tag{14}$$

4. Results

In this section, we compare the performance of the new mathematical formulation with that of the discrete and continuous-time formulations proposed by Castro et al. (2003). All formulations give rise to mixed-integer linear programming (MILP) problems and were implemented in GAMS and solved by CPLEX 12.5 using a single thread and default options up to a relative optimality tolerance = 10^{-6}. The hardware consisted of a desktop with an Intel Core i7-3770 (3.40 GHz) CPU, 8 GB of RAM and running Windows 7. We consider two scenarios of constant steam availability:$F_{steam}^{total} = 13$ t/h and $F_{steam}^{total} = 14$ t/h. The plant consists of $|I| = 4$parallel batch digesters of different capacitiesand the duration of the processing tasks can be found in Castro et al. (2002).

The results in Table 1 show that the problem size is significantly different from one formulation to another. The smallest size is obtained by the new multiple time grid continuous formulation, which performs three orders of magnitude faster than the second best, the discrete-time model. Nevertheless, the latter is still able to find the optimal cycle time for an accurate representation of problem data with 1 min slots. In contrast, the single grid continuous-time model returns suboptimal solutions, either because the standard heuristic search procedure terminates after two consecutive iterations with the same cycle time (13 t/h), or the problem is becoming intractable (14 t/h). Another explanation for the excellent performance of the new multiple time grid formulation comes from the very low integrality gap (2 %).

The optimal schedule obtained from the multiple grid continuous-time formulation features the same digester sequence for both scenarios: I3-I5-I6-I4. In Figure 2, we show the Gantt chart for total steam availability of 14 t/h. Notice that in heating stage M3, the digester I4 is sharing steam with I3 and I3 is sharing steam with I6. These

Table 1. Comparison of different scheduling formulations.

Formulation	Discrete-time[(a)]		Continuous-time[(b)]			
			Single Grid		Multiple Grid	
F_{steam}^{total} (t/h)	13	14	13	14	13	14
Slot size (min)[(a)]/ Number of slots[(b)]	1	1	12	16	-	-
Cycle time H (min)	594	564	606	571	594	564
Integer variables	33263	31583	2688	3584	79	79
Total variables	64154	60914	3327	4435	141	141
Constraints	30932	29372	3331	4435	132	132
Obj. relaxed MILP ([(a)]t/h or [(b)]min)	109.8	115.64	121.58	71.56	583.26	552.03
Total CPU (s)	563	217	538	39371	0.11	0.21

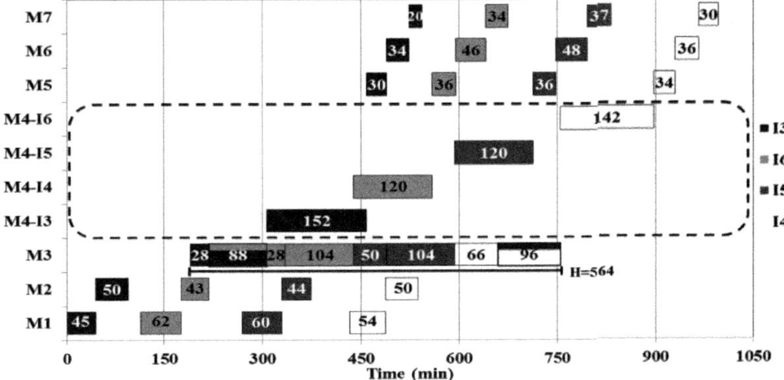

Figure 2. Optimal schedule for total steam availability = 14 t/h.

steam sharing tasks are represented using a horizontal gradient fill, featuring the shades of both digesters. It should be highlighted that I3 and I6 are not waiting after M2, because they are receiving the remaining steam respectively from I4 and I3. Indeed, the heating stage is the process bottleneck, since the optimal cycle found corresponds to the total time the digesters take to reach the cooking temperature. Note also that tasks belonging to the cooking stage M4 can overlap in time (I3 and I6).

At the time of the study, the company was planning a capacity expansion while keeping the steam generation system unchanged. This seemed awkward considering that the heating stage is the bottleneck. The versatility of the proposed model allows us to estimate the impact on productivity (P) of adding another parallel digester D_I*. To implement the model modifications it is only required to increase the size of set I and add the processing time. This value for each digester is given using a simulation of a digester dynamic model, similar to the existing ones. The results in Table 2 show that the increase in productivity for the new scenario (δ_{NS}) is roughly one tenth of the expected value (δ_{EV}) for 13 t/h, which are calculated using the total capacities (Q). The values improve by a factor of two for a steam availability of 14 t/h, with a cycle time of half an hour less than the first case, $F_{steam}^{total} = 13$ t/h.

Table 2. Effect of adding an extra digester on productivity

Digester sequence	Q (t)	F_{steam}^{total} = 13 t/h				F_{steam}^{total} = 14 t/h			
		H(min)	P (t/h)	$\delta_{NS.}$ (%)	$\delta_{EV.}$ (%)	H(min)	P (t/h)	$\delta_{NS.}$ (%)	$\delta_{EV.}$ (%)
D_3-D_6-D_5-D_4	1087	594	109.80	-	-	564	115.64	-	-
D_3-D_5-D_6-D_3*-D_4	1295	693	112.12	2.1	19.1	644	120.65	4.3	19.1
D_3-D_4*-D_6-D_5-D_4	1359	734	111.09	1.2	25.0	665	122.62	6.0	25.0
D_3-D_5*-D_6-D_5-D_4	1388	737	113.00	2.9	27.7	683	121.93	5.4	27.7
D_3-D_6-D_5-D_6*-D_4	1393	740	112.95	2.9	28.2	684	122.19	5.7	28.2

5. Conclusions

A real industrial problem of a batch plant constrained by insufficient steam availability was addressed by a new multiple grid continuous-time formulation in less than a second of computational time. This is at least three orders of magnitude faster than single grid discrete and continuous-time formulations taken from the literature. The proposed formulation remains tractable when additional digesters are incorporated. This formulation can handle variable processing times and has the potential to handle non-constant profiles for the heating utility, which will be the subject of future work.

6. Acknowledgement

Financial support from FEDER (Programa Operacional Factores de Competitividade – COMPETE) and Fundação para a Ciência e Tecnologia through project FCOMP-01-0124-FEDER-020764.

References

P. Castro, H. Matos, A.P.F.D. Barbosa-Póvoa, 2002, Dynamic Modelling and Scheduling of an Industrial Batch System, Comput. Chem. Eng., 26, 4-5, 671–686.

P.M. Castro, A.P. Barbosa-Póvoa, H.A. Matos, 2003, Optimal Periodic Scheduling of Batch Plants Using RTN-Based Discrete and Continuous-Time Formulations: A Case Study Approach, Ind. Eng. Chem. Res., 42, 14, 3346–3360.

P.M. Castro, I.E. Grossmann, 2005, New Continuous-Time MILP Model for the Short-Term Scheduling of Multistage Batch Plants, Ind. Eng. Chem. Res., 44, 24, 9175–9190.

I. Harjunkoski, C.T. Maravelias, P. Bongers, P.M. Castro, S. Engell, I.E. Grossmann, J. Hooker, C. Méndez, G. Sand, J. Wassick, 2013, Scope for Industrial Applications of Production Scheduling Models and Solution Methods, Comput. Chem. Eng., DOI:10.1016/j.compchemeng.2013.12.001

N. Hvala, S. Strmčnik, J. Černetič, 1993, Scheduling of Batch Digesters According to Different Control Targets and Servicing Limitations, Comput. Chem. Eng., 17, 7, 739–750.

N. Shah, C.C. Pantelides, R.W.H. Sargent, 1993, Optimal Periodic Scheduling of Multipurpose Batch Plants, Annals of Operations Research, 42, 193–228.

M. Shaik, S. Bhat, 2013, Scheduling of Displacement Batch Digesters Using Discrete Time Formulation, Chemical Engineering Research and Design, DOI:10.1016/j.cherd.2013.07.026.

D. Wu, M. Ierapetritou, 2004, Cyclic Short-Term Scheduling of Multiproduct Batch Plants Using Continuous-Time Representation, Comput. Chem. Eng., 28, 11, 2271–2286.

Jiří Jaromír Klemeš, Petar Sabev Varbanov and Peng Yen Liew (Editors)
Proceedings of the 24th European Symposium on Computer Aided Process Engineering – ESCAPE 24
June 15-18, 2014, Budapest, Hungary.

Process Utility Systems Conceptual Design by Graphical Methods

Li Sun, Steve Doyle, Robin Smith*

Centre for Process Integration, CEAS, The University of Manchester, Oxford Road, Manchester, M13 9PL, United Kingdom

Abstract

Previous graphical methods for utility system targeting have been developed to address the targets achieved only when the steam is saturated. This work has developed new graphical methods to improve the accuracy of the targeting by including important practical considerations. Steam Composite Profiles are constructed firstly including boiler feedwater (BFW) preheating, steam generation at the saturation temperature, and steam superheating for steam generation. Site Source-Sink Profiles and Site Grand Composite Curves are plotted to target realistic boiler steam demand, the desuperheated steam for process heating, steam generation from the process heat recovery, and steam saving due to process indirect heat recovery through steam mains. These new energy targeting have been applied to overcome the shortcomings of previous methods ignoring the heat of BFW preheating and steam superheating in steam generation, and allows practical quantitative analysis combined with conceptual insights.

Keywords: Superheating, desuperheating, preheating, utility targeting

1. Introduction

Utility systems provide energy and power to various site processes. Site utility systems are complex with many potential interactions, and analysis must include site processes as well as the utility system itself. Utility system analysis includes process utility demands, process heat recovery through steam mains, fuel combustion for steam and power generation, steam distribution to meet process heating at different steam mains, and potential power generation by steam expansion.

Graphical methods based on Pinch Analysis have been developed as a visualization tool for utility system conceptual design and optimization. Site Source-Sink Profiles (Dhole and Linnhoff, 1993) of the overall site utility system provide quantification of process heating and cooling targets, and implement process and utility system integration. Site Composite Curves (Linnhoff et al., 1982) address process heat recovery through steam mains to save utility VHP demand from fuel consumption in boilers and gas turbines with heat recovery for steam generation. The minimum site VHP steam demand and the cooling demand of the utility system can also be obtained in the Site Composite Curves (Smith, 2005). Site Utility Grand Composite Curves (Raissi, 1994) allow visualization of the steam cascade in the system. Shaft power potential by steam expansion in steam turbines can be calculated based on Site Utility Grand Composite Curves based on the Temperature- Enthalpy (T-H) model (Raissi, 1994).

The graphical methods have been extended and applied in simultaneous optimization of production processes and total site utility systems for reduction of fuel, power and CO_2 (Klemeš et al., 1997), process intensification and integration (Klemeš and Varbanov,

2013), site-wide heat and power analysis and cogeneration improvements (Sun et al., 2013), renewable energy sources analysis (Perry et al., 2008), hybrid renewable energy systems (Makwana et al., 1998), hybrid power systems (Wan Alwi et al., 2012), CO_2 emissions reduction analysis (Crilly and Zhelev, 2010), electricity system analysis (Krishna Priya and Bandyopadhyay, 2013), waste heat recovery system (Hackl et al., 2011), concentration and property-based resource conservation networks (Saw et al., 2011). Varbanov and Klemeš (2010) set time slices into site profiles and site composite curves to integrate renewables into the corresponding total site combined heat and power systems. Abbood et al. (2012) introduced a stream temperature and enthalpy plot technique to represent continuous individual hot and cold streams. Varbanov et al. (2012) specified process minimum temperature differences to obtain more realistic utility and heat recovery targets.

However, these graphical methods did not include many practical considerations, such as boiler feedwater (BFW) preheating and steam superheating for steam generation, and steam desuperheating for process heating. The targets based on these methods can only be achieved if steam is saturated. This is not realistic.

To be practical, steam superheating rather than saturated steam should be considered in the system analysis. Manassaldi et al. (2011) examined the effect of steam including both latent heating and superheating on the heat recovery steam generation design. Botros and Brisson (2011) designed steam power islands allowing for steam reheating before turbine expansion.

In this work, new site profiles and site composite curves are developed to overcome problems of no allowance for BFW preheating and steam superheating during steam generation in previous graphical methods. Steam desuperheating for process heating is common in reality, and is included in the utility steam targeting methodology. Condensate heat recovery included in the graphical methods can provide more accurate and realistic steam targets. The application of these targeting methods in process integration with utility systems can achieve thermodynamically possible and practical targets, and give quantitative insights of their interaction.

2. Graphical methodology development and site energy targets

Steam is generated from BFW to the superheat temperature. The heat load for BFW preheating and steam superheating should be included in graphical methods to address realistic steam targets.

2.1. New Steam Composite Profiles

Steam Composite Curves in Figure 1 are built by the combination of BFW preheating and steam superheating (SH) at certain temperature interval on a temperature-enthalpy (T-H) diagram. For example, the heat load between the medium pressure (MP) to the low pressure (LP) in the steam composite curves contains the steam superheating of the LP and BFW preheating of the MP steam generation. The Steam Composite Curves are the basis of graphical targeting method.

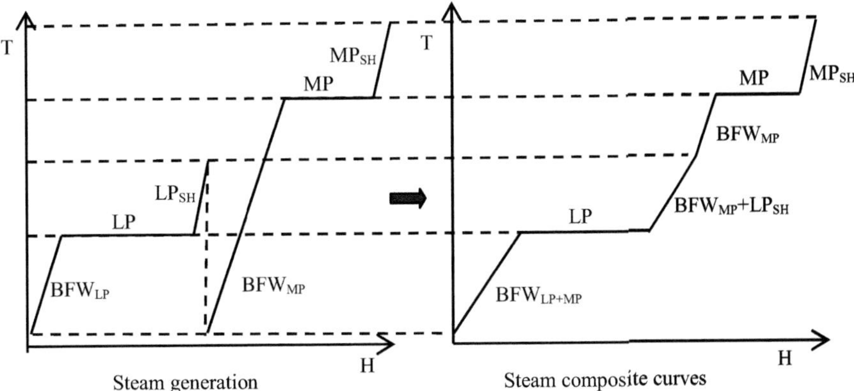

Figure 1. Steam Composite Curves

2.2. Site Source - Sink Profiles

Site Source-Sink Profiles of the overall site utility systems are constructed by the combination of the grand composite curves of different processes on the site. Heating and cooling targeting based on steam mains at saturation temperature alone limits its practical application.

The proposed steam composite profiles overcome the shortcoming of no allowance for BFW preheating and steam superheating during steam generation in the previous methods. Figure 2 addresses site source profile and steam generation from process heat recovery. Steam is generated from BFW to steam superheat temperature. Steam usage from the superheated steam to the saturated condensate for process heating is identified in the site sink profile. However, there are some issues with the Site Profile and source profile for more realistic steam targeting methodology.

2.3. BFW preheating and site profiles

Normally, process high temperature heat for BFW preheating is not economic. In the graphical method, BFW preheating as process cold streams, is removed from the site source profile and added to the site sink profile. Figure 3 shows the Site Source Profile and steam generation from the saturation temperature to the superheating temperature, and Figure 4 gives the construction of the site sink profile including BFW preheating.

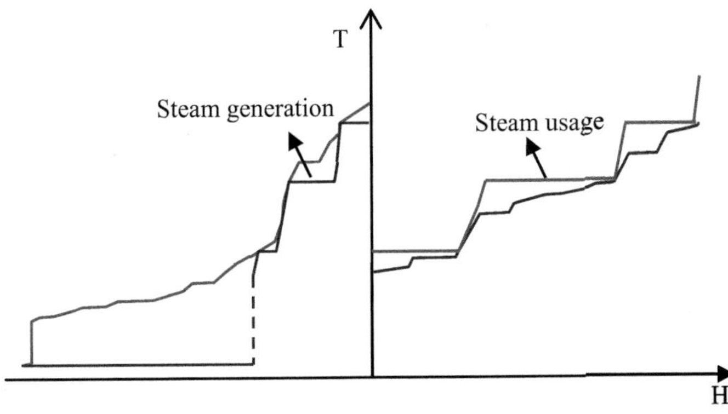

Figure 2. Site Source - Sink Profiles and steam targets

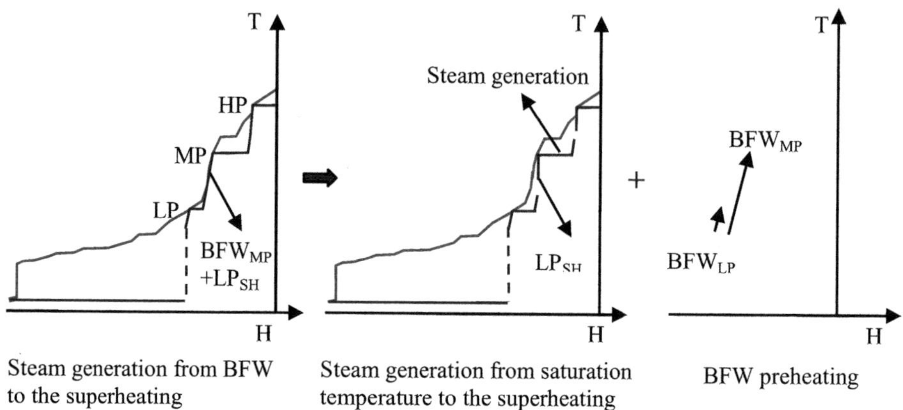

Figure 3. BFW preheating removed from the Site Source Profile

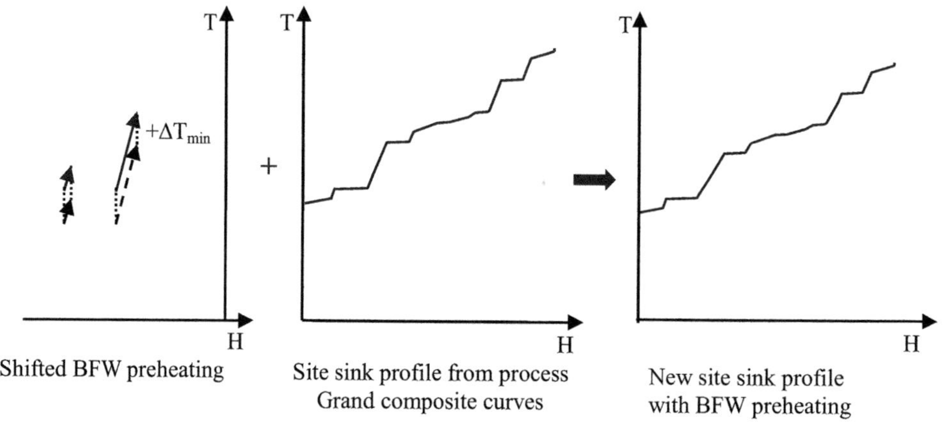

Figure 4. BFW preheating added to the Site Sink Profile

To account for the feasible heat transfer in exchangers, the BFW preheating has shifted temperature by adding the minimum temperature difference (ΔT_{min}) in the new Site Sink Profile.

2.4. Steam desuperheating

Actual steam mains are superheated. However, the steam supplied for process heating normally is desuperheated. BFW added to the superheated steam is a common desuperheating method. Figure 5 illustrates the target for the desuperheated steam for process heating in the Site Sink Profile.

2.5. Utility targeting

Process steam generation and the desuperheated steam for process heating are plotted in The Site Source - Sink Profiles. Site Composite Curves can be used for the site utility targeting. Site Composite Curves are constructed following the zero approach between the utility loads based on the Site Source - Sink Profiles.

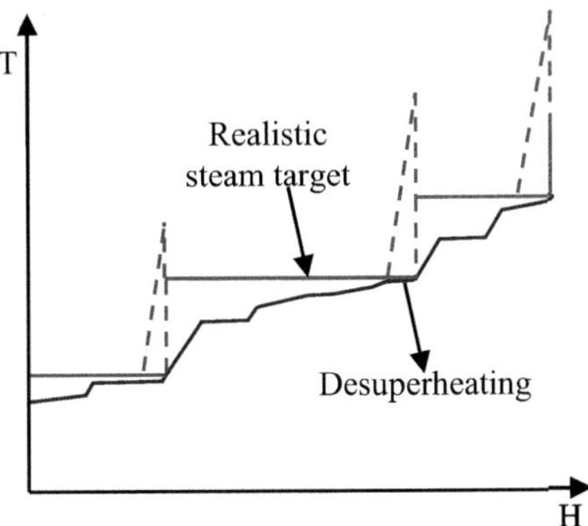

Figure 5. Desuperheated steam for process heating

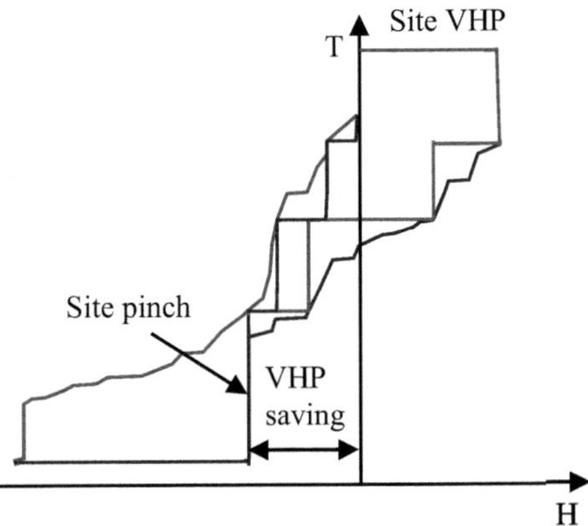

Figure 6. Site Composite Curves and utility targeting

As shown in Figure 6, the maximum site VHP saving due to process indirect heat recovery through steam mains are addressed in the Site Composite Curves. The minimum site VHP steam target is the difference between process total steam demand and the site VHP saving. Fuel consumption in boilers and gas turbines with heat recovery for VHP steam generation can be calculated from the Site Composite Curves. The site pinch is addressed in the site composite curves as well. It represents a bottleneck in the system indirect heat recovery.

3. Conclusions

A new graphical methodology for utility system energy targeting has been developed in this work, accounting for BFW preheating /steam superheating /desuperheating /condensate recycle and condensate cooling. The proposed graphical methods provide better matching of heat transfer between process streams and the utility, and lead to accurate and realistic steam targets. Furthermore, the graphical energy targeting methodology can be applied for the conceptual design and optimization as a visualization tool to better understand the integration of processes and utility systems with more realistic constraints.

Acknowledgement

The support of EC Project EFENIS (contract ENER /FP7 /296003 /EFENIS) is sincerely acknowledged.

References

N. Abbood, Z.A. Manan, S.R. Wan Alwi, 2012, A combined numerical and visualization tool for utility targeting and heat exchanger network retrofitting, Journal of Cleaner Production, 23, 1-7.

B.B. Botros, J.G. Brisson, 2011, Targeting the optimum steam system for power generation with increased flexibility in the steam power island design, Energy, 36, 8, 4625- 4632.

D. Crilly, T. Zhelev, 2010, Further emissions and energy targeting: an application of CO_2 emissions pinch analysis (CEPA) to the Irish electricity generation sector, Clean Technologies and Environmental Policy, 12, 177- 189.

V.R. Dhole, B. Linnhoff, 1993, Total site targets for fuel, co-generation, emissions and cooling, Computers and Chemical Engineering, 17(Suppl.), 101-109.

R. Hackl, E. Andersson, S. Harvey, 2011, Targeting for Energy Efficiency and Improved Energy Collaboration Between Different Companies Using Total Site Analysis (TSA), Energy, 36, 4609- 4615.

J.J. Klemeš, V.R. Dhole, K. Raissi, S.J. Perry, L. Puigjaner, 1997, Targeting and design methodology for reduction of fuel, power and CO_2 on total sites, Applied Thermal Engineering, 7, 993-1003.

J.J. Klemeš, P. Varbanov, 2013, Process Intensification and Integration: an assessment, Clean Technologies and Environmental Policy, 15, 417- 422.

G.S. Krishna Priya, S. Bandyopadhyay, 2013, Emission constrained power system planning: a Pinch Analysis based study of Indian electricity sector, Clean Technologies and Environmental Policy, 15, 5, 771-782.

B. Linnhoff, D.W. Townsend, D. Boland, G.F. Hewitt, B.E.A. Thomas, A.R. Guy, R.H. Marsland, 1982, A user guide on process integration for the efficient use of energy, The Institution of Chemical Engineers, Rugby, UK [last updated edition 1994].

Y. Makwana, R. Smith, X.X. Zhu, 1998, A novel approach for retrofit and operation management of existing total sites, Computer and Chemical Engineering, 22, Suppl., 793-796.

J.I. Manassaldi, S.F. Mussati, N.J. Scenna, 2011, Optimal synthesis and design of Heat Recovery Steam Generation (HRSG) via mathematical programming, Energy, 36, 475- 485.

K. Raissi, 1994, Total Site Integration, Ph.D. Thesis, UMIST, Manchester, UK.

L. Sun, S. Doyle, R. Smith, 2013, Cogeneration improvement based on steam cascade analysis, Chemical Engineering Transactions, 35, 13-18.

S. Perry, J.J. Klemeš, I. Bulatov, 2008, Integrating waste and renewable energy to reduce the carbon footprint of locally integrated energy sectors, Energy, 33, 10, 1489 -1497.

S. Saw, L. Lee, M. Lim, D. Foo, I. Chew, R. Tan, J.J. Klemeš, 2011, An extended graphical targeting technique for direct reuse/recycle in concentration and property-based resource conservation networks, Clean Technologies and Environmental Policy, 13, 2, 347- 357.

R. Smith, 2005, Chemical Process Design and Integration. John Wiley & Sons Ltd, Chichester, England.

P. Varbanov, J.J. Klemeš, 2010, Total sites integrating renewables with extended heat transfer and recovery, Heat Transfer Engineering, 31, 9, 733- 741.

P. Varbanov, Z. Fodor, J.J. Klemeš, 2012, Total Site targeting with process specific minimum temperature difference (ΔTmin), Energy, 44, 1, 20- 28.

S.R. Wan Alwi, N.E. Mohammad Rozali, Z. Abdul-Manan, J.J. Klemeš, 2012, A process integration targeting method for hybrid power systems, Energy, 44, 1, 6- 10.

Jiří Jaromír Klemeš, Petar Sabev Varbanov and Peng Yen Liew (Editors)
Proceedings of the 24th European Symposium on Computer Aided Process Engineering – ESCAPE 24
June 15-18, 2014, Budapest, Hungary.

Energy Integration Manager: A Workflow for Long Term Validity of Total Site Analysis and Heat Recovery Strategies

Timo Bohnenstaedt[a*], Christopher Brandt[a], Georg Fieg[a], Wulf Dietrich[b]

[a]*Institute of Process and Plant Engineering, Hamburg University of Technology, Schwarzenbergstraße 95, D-21071 Hamburg, Germany*

[b]*Bayer Technology Services GmbH, D-51368 Leverkusen, Germany*

timo.bohnenstaedt@tuhh.de

Abstract

The data basis for a Total Site study is only valid for a static snapshot of the whole industry Site. Changes to single process units throughout the design phase of new industrial solutions as well as subsequent process modifications to existing plants necessitate an actualization of the Total Site analysis. Previously identified potentials to increase the energy efficiency may have become outdated or infeasible.

As a first step in the development of an Energy Integration Manager, a conceptual approach for the implementation of an interface to an existing heat exchanger network (HEN) synthesis tool is proposed. Certain improvements to the HEN synthesis tool according to heuristic rules are described for enabling a suitable workflow.

Keywords: Total Site analysis, heat recovery, genetic algorithm

1. Introduction

In the state-of-the-art engineering workflow for investment projects in case of structural planning or modification of individual process units, simulating and updating of adequate computer-aided process models is obligatory. Very often these models include all heating and cooling stream data, the local utility system as well as all transfer streams to the super ordinated side-wide utility system. In fact, there is mostly no other alternative to close all mass and enthalpy balances without the simulation of missing measured data with the help of process models.

Using these process models as the data basis for consequent up to date Total Site energy analysis is most promising. The development of a conceptual workflow to determine the required work effort and the required amount of data will be the starting point in the development of an automated Total Site update procedure.

2. Conceptual structure of an Energy Integration Manager

To establish a comprehensive framework for updating Site-wide energy studies, several software tools have to be connected via interfaces. As mentioned in the introduction, the most promising way of retrieving process data is the usage of computer-aided process models, but for the simulation of former long term plant behavior the use of recorded data from plant control systems might be interesting as well. The overall software architecture is shown in Figure 1. The highlighted modules of the Data Interface and the HEN Optimisation Framework will be of further interest in this context.

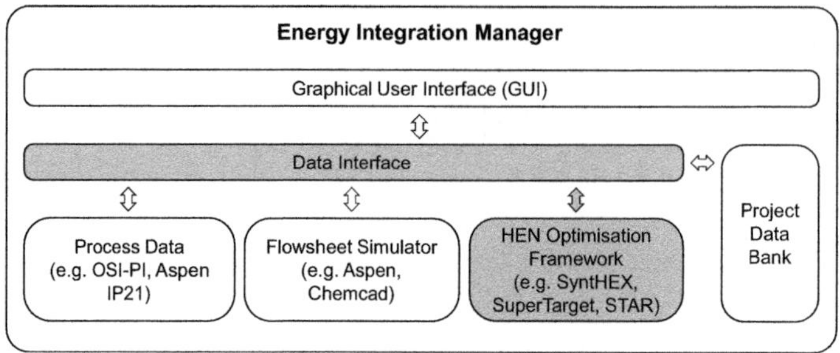

Figure 1. Structure of Energy Integration Manager

There are some advantages to start the design of the Energy Integration Manager with the embedment of a HEN synthesis tool using genetic algorithms instead of a synthesis tool which relies on the pinch technology. The mayor criterion is the complexity of the generated HEN solution. A high amount of heat exchanger sub-networks on the consideration level of a single process simplifies to track down the influence of a single process change to the super ordinated utility system. Furthermore the effectiveness of Mixed Integer Non Linear Programming (MINLP) methods such as genetic algorithms has already been demonstrated in recent papers (Escobar and Trierweiler 2013). Due to these reasons an existing software tool called SyntHEX was advanced by the incorporation of selected heuristic rules to improve the amount of sub-networks as well as the capability of finding the global optimum.

3. HEN synthesis using genetic algorithms

3.1. Data Interface: Input data set

A typical characterization of a HEN optimization task is described by Table 1. There are a number of hot process streams N_h and a number of cold process streams N_c which have to be cooled down or heated up, respectively. This data has to be provide by the Data Interface, as presented in Figure 1.

3.2. HEN Optimization: Objective function

The objective function is employed to generate a HEN solution with the least total annual costs for a given data set, as described in chapter 3.1. To achieve this each utility stream is linked to a specific cost factor c_{cu} in order to calculate the operating costs. Apart from the utility consumption no other operation costs are considered. The annualized investment costs are based on an empirical approach. There are two investment costs segments: The fix costs a and the area depending costs bA^c. The objective function can be formulated as follows:

$$C_{TAC} = \sum_{n=1}^{N_u} \left(c_{cu,n} \cdot \dot{Q}_{u,n}\right) + N_{HX} \cdot a + \sum_{n=1}^{N_{HX}} (b \cdot A_n^c) \tag{1}$$

Table 1: Characterization of optimization task

Name []	Inlet temp. T_{in} [°C]	Outlet temp. T_{out} [°C]	Heat transfer coefficient h [W/(m²·K)]	Heat capacity flowrate $\dot{W}$ [W/K]	Cost factor c_{cu} (utilities) [$/(W·h)]
⋮	⋮	⋮	⋮	⋮	⋮

In Eq.(1) N_U is the number of available utility streams and N_{HX} is the number of heat exchangers (HXs) present in the respective HEN. For the calculation of the heat exchanging area an ideal counter current heat exchanger is assumed. Due to minor influences of the thermal resistance of the apparatus partition wall only heat exchange coefficients are used to calculate the thermal transmittance.

3.3. HEN Optimization: The genetic algorithm

A brief overview for the mathematical background of the genetic algorithm used for this work will be presented. A deeper insight can be acquired with the help of the publication by Luo et al. (2009).

For representation of a HEN a stage-wise superstructure (Yee et al., 1983) is adopted. In each stage i of this superstructure every hot process stream j is connected to every cold process stream k. The index ijk of a HX can be calculated as follows:

$$ijk = (i-1) \cdot N_h N_c + (j-1) \cdot N_C + k \qquad (2)$$

Summarized, a HEN is defined by the heat exchangers which build up the structure. For these HX it is sufficient to specify the heat transfer area A_{ijk} and the heat capacity flow rates $W_{h,ijk}$ and $W_{c,ijk}$ through the HX. The temperatures within a HEN can then be calculated analytically or by a sequential iterative procedure.

For the genetic algorithm the key operations are selection, crossover and mutation. At first, an initial population of solution candidates, called individuals, are generated. In each generation the genetic operations are applied in order to build a new population. The better an individual is fitted to the objective function the higher are its chances to be selected for the crossover operations or to be sent directly into the next generation.

The quality of an individual is therefore expressed by its fitness value.

$$f = \frac{C_{TAC}^{-1} - C_{TAC,avg}^{-1}}{C_{TAC,min}^{-1} - C_{TAC,avg}^{-1}} \qquad (3)$$

In Eq.(3) $C_{TAC,min}$ represents the minimum total annual costs within the current population and $C_{TAC,avg}$ represents the average total annual costs of this population.

4. Incorporation of heuristic rules

4.1. Concept and motivation

Even though genetic algorithms do have advantages compared to heuristic procedures like the pinch technology, there are also mentionable drawbacks. The HEN synthesis is carried out for a fixed formulation of a given task, strictly mathematical. Because of the huge amount of binary variables in the problem formulation and their stochastic character these algorithms can be trapped into a local optimum. Conventional genetic algorithms do not possess methods for neglecting selected heat exchangers apart from the entirely stochastic methods of mutation and recombination. The possibilities to simplify complex HEN structures which may have been agglomerated during the optimization are limited.

4.2. Heuristic rules: Breaking of Loops & Recalculation of paths

As an iterative way to improve given HEN solutions the identification of loops and paths inside a network structure is well known and widely used The standard procedure

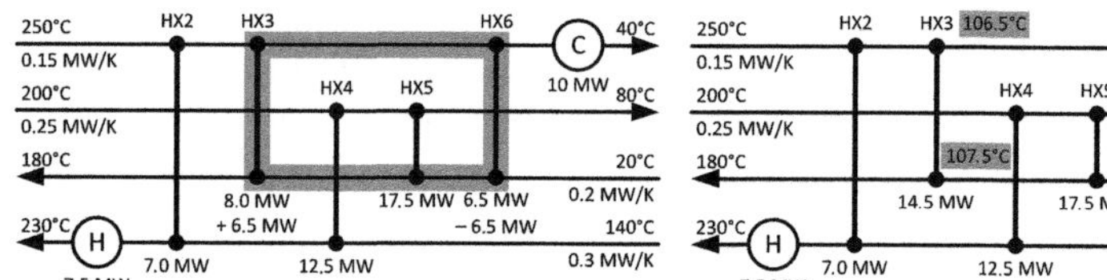

Figure 2. Identified loop and reallocation of heat load

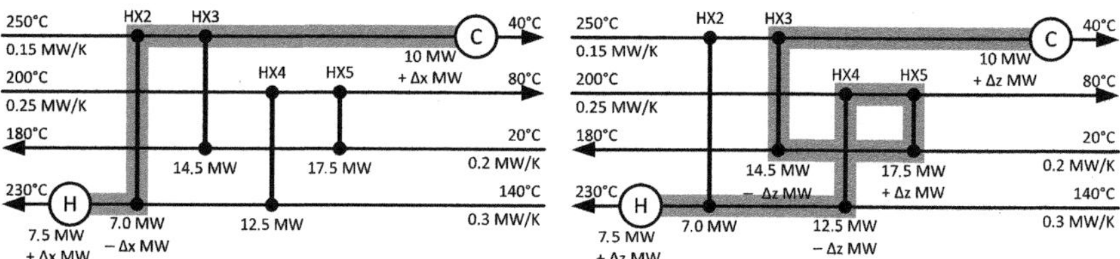

Figure 3. Identified paths and feasible solutions

is as follows: Identify existing loops within the HEN. Reallocate the heat duty of the heat exchanger with the smallest heat exchanging area.

Identify and exploit paths to ensure feasible temperature differences and the best compromise between utility cost and investment cost. These heuristic rules are visualized in Figure 2 and Figure 3 by using a small example. The embedment of loop breaking and path analysis into the evolutionary workflow of a genetic algorithm as astochastically applied procedure instead of an iterative procedure following to the actual HEN design is a new development approach. The implementation of a loop breaking algorithm has already been described in recent work (Brandt et al., 2011). This will now be extended by a procedure for path identification and optimization.

As in the example shown the temperature difference adjacent to HX3, after the removal of the loop, violates the second law of thermodynamics. Exploiting an existing path and shifting of heat duties along this path will solve this issue. Figure 3 demonstrates different solutions depending on the length of the chosen path. If all HXs should have a minimum temperature difference of 10°C adjacent to them, it would be $\Delta x = 1.6\ MW$ or $\Delta z = 6.5\ MW$.To determine the most favorable solution both alternatives have to be calculated. Depending on the underlying costs functions, the right choice is not always obvious.

4.3. Degree and identification of paths

Similar to the definition of a degree (or level) of a loop (Su and Motard, 1984), which is used to point out the amount of heat exchangers in the loop structure, a degree g_P for path structures can be defined. Assuming that the identified paths do not include loops along their track through the network, g_P can be calculated as follows:

$$g_P = (2 \cdot \min\{N_h, N_c\}) - 1 \tag{4}$$

Therefore the amount of hot and cold streams inside a path structure ($N_{h,P}$, $N_{c.P}$) for a given degree is always:

$$N_{h,P} = N_{c,P} = \frac{(g_P + 1)}{2} \tag{5}$$

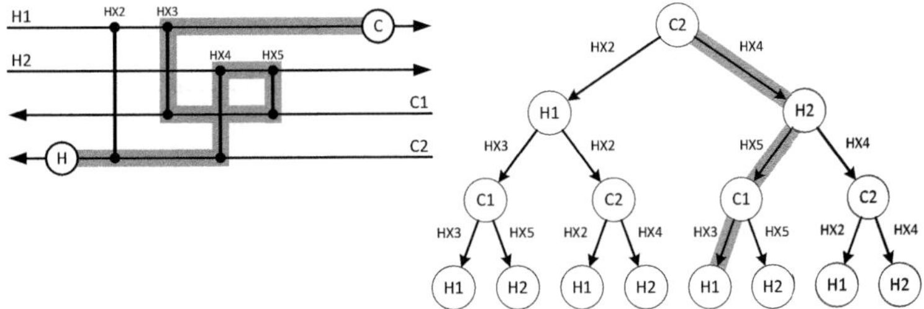

Figure 4. Binary search tree for path identification

For the identification of paths it is reasonable to use the prerequisites of paths namely the HXs which are connected to the supplied utilities as starting and ending points.

In this case the identification algorithm was developed "from left to right", which means it starts with HXs using the hot utility and advances through the structure towards the HXs using cold utility. The identification can be visualized as a binary search tree as shown in Figure 4. Detected paths will be optimized by numerical analysis regarding the objective function.

5. Application of improved genetic algorithm

To demonstrate the effectiveness of the enhanced HEN synthesis method a literature case was chosen (Luo et al., 2009). The problem definition is given in Table 2. Investment costs for heat exchanging units are calculated according to Equation 6.

$$C_{inv} = 8000 + 800 \cdot A^{0.8} \; (A \text{ in } m^2) \quad (6)$$

Table 2. Problem data according to Luo et al. (2009)

Name []	T_{in} [°C]	T_{out} [°C]	h [W/(m²·K)]	$\dot{W}$ [W/K]	Name []	T_{in} [°C]	T_{out} [°C]	h [W/(m²·K)]	$\dot{W}$ [W/K]
H1	180	75	2.0	30	C1	40	230	1.5	20
H2	280	120	0.6	15	C2	120	260	2.0	35
H3	180	75	0.3	30	C3	40	190	1.5	35
H4	140	45	2.0	30	C4	50	190	2.0	30
H5	220	120	0.08	25	C5	50	250	2.0	20
H6	180	55	0.02	10	C6	40	150	0.06	10
H7	170	45	2.0	30	C7	40	150	0.4	20
H8	180	50	1.5	30	C8	120	210	1.5	35
H9	280	90	1.0	15	C9	40	130	1.0	35
H10	180	60	2.0	30	C10	60	120	0.7	30
HU	325	325	1.0		CU	25	40	2.0	
Annual cost of hot utility: 70 $/(kW·a)					Annual cost of cold utility: 10 $/(kW·a)				

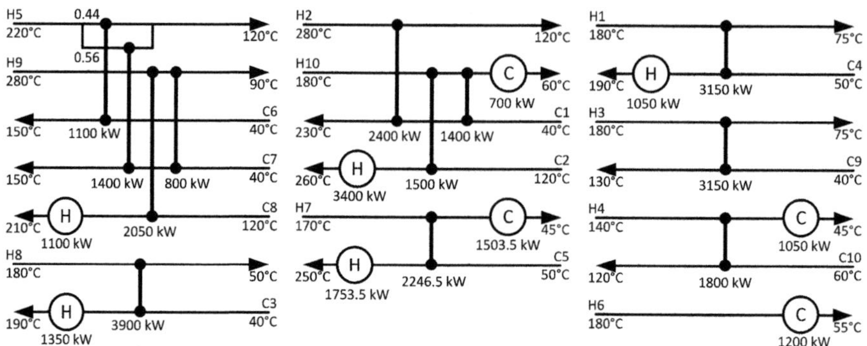

Figure 5. HEN solution for the example case

Compared to the solution published by Luo et al. (1,753,271 \$/a) the solution shown in Figure 5, which was generated by the new HEN synthesis method, is characterized by 2.1% lower annualized costs (1,717,295 \$/a). Remarkable is the total amount of heat transferring units, which has been reduced from 26 to 21. A reduced amount of paths inside the HEN structure (from 5 to 2) as well as a reduced amount of utility heat exchangers (from 15 to 9) state the effectiveness of the new path analyzing method.

6. Conclusions

To extent the exclusively mathematical approach of genetic algorithms, a new optimization procedure was suggested and successfully applied. This new optimization method implements the advantages of certain heuristic strategies while maintaining the capability of synthesizing low complexity HEN solutions due to the high amount of sub networks or respectively the low amount of loops and paths. The reduction of the amount of heat transferring units is in many cases of major industrial relevance. Summarized quantitatively these HEN solutions are mostly cheaper and easier to control regarding temperature or mass flow uncertainties. Single changes to the overall process have a smaller impact on other unchanged process units. The initial objective to establish a basis for an energy integration management system was achieved.

Acknowledgement

The authors acknowledge the financial support from EC FP7 project ENER/FP7/296003 'Efficient Energy Integrated Solutions for Manufacturing Industries – EFENIS'.

• References

M. Escobar, J. O. Trierweiler, 2013, Optimal heat exchanger network synthesis: A case study comparison, Applied Thermal Engineering, 51, 1-2, 801-826.

C. Brandt, G. Fieg, X. Luo, 2011, Efficient synthesis of heat exchanger networks combining heuristic approaches with genetic algorithm, Heat Mass Transfer, 47, 8, 1019-1026.

X. Luo, Q.-Y. Wen, G. Fieg, 2009, A hybrid genetic algorithm for synthesis of heat exchanger networks, Computers and Chemical Engineering, 33, 1169-1181.

J. L.Su, R. L. Montard, 1984, Evolutionary Synthesis of Heat-Exchanger Networks, Computers and Chemical Engineering, 8, 2, 67-80

T. F. Yee, I. E. Grossmann, Z. Kravanja, 1983, Simultaneous optimization models for heat integration-I. General framework and MER optimal synthesis, Chemical Engineering Science, 38, 5, 745-763

Jiří Jaromír Klemeš, Petar Sabev Varbanov and Peng Yen Liew (Editors)
Proceedings of the 24th European Symposium on Computer Aided Process Engineering – ESCAPE 24
June 15-18, 2014, Budapest, Hungary.

Design and Operational Planning of an Urban Energy Network based on Combined Heat and Power Generators

Nikolaos E. Koltsaklis[a], Georgios M. Kopanos[b], Dimitrios Konstantinidis[c], Michael C. Georgiadis[a,*]

[a]*Department of Chemical Engineering, Aristotle University of Thessaloniki, University Campus,Thessaloniki, 54124, Greece*
[b]*Imperial College London, Department of Chemical Engineering, Centre for Process Systems Engineering, SW7 2AZ London, UK*
[c]*ESTIA Consulting and Engineering, Thessaloniki-Thermi 57001, Greece*
mgeorg@auth.gr

Abstract

This work presents an optimization approach for the optimal design and operational planning of an urban energy network based on combined heat and power generators. The model is formulated as linear Mixed Integer Programming (MIP) and solved to optimality using standard branch-and-bound techniques. Optimality is assessed in terms of total system cost, while the applicability of the proposed model is illustrated using an illustrative example.

Keywords: Urban energy network; Optimal design; Operational planning; linear MIP;

1. Introduction

Nowadays, the development of high efficiency energy generation technologies is of top priority at an international level due to the volatility and the rising costs of energy resources, the depletion of fossil fuel resources and the severe environmental pollution. Because of the increasing concern regarding the environmental issues and the ratification of the Kyoto Protocol, co-generation receives more attention as a way to contribute to more efficient energy use and carbon mitigation (Streimikiene and Baležentis, 2013). Co-generation, also known as combined heat and power (CHP) generation is an approach to produce simultaneously electricity and useful heat from a single source. The main benefit of this production type is that its total efficiency could reach as much as 85-90 %, being around doubled when compared to that of single electricity production (40-45 %) (Monteiro et al., 2009). This fact implies lower energy generation costs with a more environmentally friendly production profile. Additionally, CHP plants are able to serve electricity markets with lower investments in the transmission infrastructure and with lower energy losses during transmission (Kopanos et al., 2013). In this context, micro-grid is defined as a low voltage distribution network with combination of distributed generators, energy storage devices, and controllable loads which could operate islanded or connected to central power grid. Liu et al. (2013) presented a review and an energy systems engineering approach to the modelling and optimisation of micro-grids for residential applications. Ren and Gao (2010) developed an MILP model for the integrated plan and evaluation of distributed energy systems by determining the optimal system configuration and operational strategies. Mehleri et al. (2012) introduced an MILP model for the optimal design and planning of distributed energy resources (DER) system by determining the optimal combination and allocation of DER technologies along with a heating pipeline network. Bracco et al. (2013) proposed an MILP model to optimally design and operate a combined heat and power distributed generation system applied to an urban area. To the best of our knowledge, few works address simultaneously the design and operational planning problem incorporating the whole range of the operational characteristics of the CHPs, such as minimum running time, off-time, start-ups as well as partial and full load conditions. This work presents a new MILP framework to address simultaneously the design and operational characteristics of an urban energy network based on CHP generators.

2. Problem description

This work deals with the design and planning problem of an urban energy network that may involve several energy generation systems. More specifically, the studied area is divided into a number of sections, each of which is characterized by a specific heat and electricity demand. The technologies to be installed in each section include: an energy generation technology, i.e., a CHP unit or a gas burner, and a heat buffer tank. Electricity interchange can take place among the sections of the network, which is connected to the main power grid for potential power interchange with it. There is also the option of an external heat source, constituting an alternative heat supplier to the network's sectors. The minimization of total cost under full heat and electricity demand satisfaction comprises the objective function of this study. The key decisions to be made by the administrator of the network are: (i) the selection of the technology unit types to be installed, (ii) the operating status for every installed energy generator, (iii) the heat generation level and electricity produced by each installed energy generator, and (iv) the heat provided from the external heat source to the heat buffer tank of each sector.

3. Mathematical formulation

In this section, a linear MIP framework is presented for the problem described above. The problem under consideration is formally defined in terms of the following items: A given time horizon is divided into a set of uniform time periods $t \in T$ and an urban area is divided into a finite number of sectors $s \in S$. A set of technology types $i \in I$ are available to be installed in the sectors $s \in S_i$, including: (i) CHP units $i \in I^{CHP}$, (ii) heat generation units $i \in I^{HG}$, and (iii) heat buffer tanks $i \in I^{HBT}$, each of which is characterized by a specific investment cost (ω_{si}). Every energy generator type $i \in I^{GEN}$:= ($i \in I^{CHP} \cup I^{HG}$) is characterized by: a minimum (maximum) thermal capacity $\theta_i^{min}(\theta_i^{max})$, a known power to heat generation ratio ρ_i, a given start-up cost φ_{si}, and a minimum running (γ_i) and shutdown time (δ_i). For heat generation units $i \in I^{HG}$, notice that: (i) $\rho_i = 0$, and (ii) minimum running and shutdown times are often negligible. Heat buffer tanks $i \in I^{HBT}$ have a known heat loss rate η_{si}, and a maximum (minimum) heat storage capacity $\beta_i^{max}(\beta_i^{min})$. Each sector $s \in S$ is characterized by a given aggregated heat, ζ_{st}^h , and electricity demand, ζ_{st}^e , at each time period *t*. There is an external heat source that has a certain heat capacity α_t that could be supplied to the sectors of the network with a specific cost, (σ_t). Parameter μ_{st} represents the heat losses percentage for providing heat from the external source to sector *s*. Minimum/maximum ($\varepsilon_t^{min}, \varepsilon_t^{max}$) total electricity generation levels for the urban energy network during each time period *t* are also given. The variable operating cost includes the fuel cost ξ_{sit} for operating the generators $i \in I^{GEN}$ of each sector $s \in S_i$ at time period *t*. The sectors can interchange electricity among them. In addition, electricity could be acquired from the main electrical grid in a given purchase tariff ψ_t. Finally, electricity could be exported to external networks in given selling tariff v_t. With regard to heat generation, the continuous variables used in the model involve the heat generation level for energy generation technology $i \in I^{GEN}$ of sector $s \in S_i$ in time period t ($\tilde{Q}_{sit}$), the real heat generation (including heat losses in start-up periods) by the energy generation technology $i \in I^{GEN}$ of sector $s \in S_i$ in time period t (Q_{sit}), and the heat generated by the energy generation technology $i \in I^{GEN}$ of sector $s \in S_i$ that is delivered to its heat buffer tank $i \in I^{HBT}$ in time period t ($\bar{Q}_{sit}$). Concerning the interaction with the power grid, electricity acquired from external networks in time period t is represented by the continuous variable P_t, while W_t denotes the electricity exported to external networks in time period t. Furthermore, B_{sit} represents the heat storage level in the heat buffer tank $i \in I^{HBT}$ of sector $s \in S_i$ at the end of time period t, and R_{sit} denotes the heat transferred from the external heat source to the heat buffer tank $i \in I^{HBT}$ of sector $s \in S_i$ in time period t. Binary variables are also introduced in the model representing both design and operational issues. Y_{si} equals 1 if the technology unit type $i \in I$ is installed in sector $s \in S_i$, X_{sit} represents the decision whether the energy generation technology $i \in I^{GEN}$, installed in sector $s \in S_i$, is operating at the beginning of time period t ($X_{sit} = 1$) or not, L_{sit} if the energy generation technology $i \in I^{GEN}$, installed in sector $s \in S_i$, starts operating at time point t (i.e., $X_{si,t-1} = 0$ and $X_{si,t} = 1$), and finally, F_{sit} determines if the energy generation technology $i \in I^{GEN}$, installed in sector $s \in S_i$, stops operating at time point t (i.e., $X_{si,t-1} = 1$ and $X_{si,t} = 0$). The objective function to be optimized concerns the minimization of the total annualized system cost, including the annualised capital cost, energy generations technologies' start-up cost, cost for purchasing heat from the external heat sources, fuel costs, and electricity trade cost, as expressed by Eq.(1):

$$\min \overbrace{\sum_{s\in S}\sum_{i\in I_s}\omega_{si}Y_{si}}^{\text{capital cost}} + \overbrace{\sum_{s\in S}\sum_{i\in(I^{GEN}\cap I_s)}\sum_{t\in T}\varphi_{si}L_{sit}}^{\text{start-up cost}} + \overbrace{\sum_{s\in S}\sum_{i\in(I^{HBT}\cap I_s)}\sum_{t\in T}\sigma_t R_{sit}}^{\text{heat purchase cost}} + \overbrace{\sum_{s\in S}\sum_{i\in(I^{GEN}\cap I_s)}\sum_{t\in T}\xi_{sit}\tilde{Q}_{sit}}^{\text{variable operating cost}} + \overbrace{\sum_{t\in T}(\psi_t P_t - v_t W_t)}^{\text{electricity trade cost}} \quad (1)$$

According to constraints (2) and (3), exactly one heat buffer tank and one energy generation technology must be installed in every sector $s \in S_i$.

$$\sum_{i\in(I^{HBT}\cap I_s)} Y_{si} = 1 \quad \forall s \in S \quad (2)$$

$$\sum_{i\in(I^{GEN}\cap I_s)} Y_{si} = 1 \quad \forall s \in S \quad (3)$$

Constraints (4) and (5) model the start-up and shutdown of energy generation units:

$$L_{sit} - F_{sit} = X_{sit} - X_{si,t-1} \qquad \forall s \in S, i \in (I^{GEN} \cap I_s), t \in T \quad (4)$$

$$L_{sit} + F_{sit} \le 1 \qquad \forall s \in S, i \in (I^{GEN} \cap I_s), t \in T \quad (5)$$

Minimum running and shutdown time for each generation unit $i \in I^{GEN}$ are modelled by constraints (6) and (7), respectively:

$$X_{sit} \geq \sum_{t'=\max\{1,t-\gamma_i+1\}}^{t} L_{sit'} \quad \forall s \in S, i \in (I^{GEN} \cap I_s), t \in T: \gamma_i > 1 \tag{6}$$

$$1 - X_{sit} \geq \sum_{t'=\max\{1,t-\delta_i+1\}}^{t} F_{sit'} \quad \forall s \in S, i \in (I^{GEN} \cap I_s), t \in T: \delta_i > 1 \tag{7}$$

Constraints (8) correlate design and operating decisions as follows:

$$X_{sit} \leq Y_{si} \quad \forall s \in S, i \in (I^{GEN} \cap I_s), t \in T \tag{8}$$

Heat generation limits for each energy generator $i \in I^{GEN}$ are imposed by constraints (9), Constraints (10) define the actual heat generated by the energy generation technologies $i \in I^{GEN}$ considering heat losses during the start-up period (λ_i):

$$\theta_i^{min} X_{sit} \leq \tilde{Q}_{sit} \leq \theta_i^{max} X_{sit} \quad \forall s \in S, i \in (I^{GEN} \cap I_s), t \in T \tag{9}$$

$$Q_{sit} = \tilde{Q}_{sit} - \lambda_i L_{sit} \quad \forall s \in S, i \in (I^{GEN} \cap I_s), t \in T \tag{10}$$

For each time period and sector, constraints (11) and (12) model the heat transferred to the heat buffer tank of the sector ($\bar{Q}_{sit}$). Note that M is a suitable big number.

$$\sum_{i' \in (I^{GEN} \cap I_s)} Q_{si't} - M(1 - Y_{is}) \leq \bar{Q}_{sit} \leq \sum_{i' \in (I^{GEN} \cap I_s)} Q_{si't} + M(1 - Y_{is}) \quad \forall s \in S, i \in (I^{HBT} \cap I_s), t \in T \tag{11}$$

$$\bar{Q}_{sit} \leq M Y_{is} \quad \forall s \in S, i \in (I^{HBT} \cap I_s), t \in T \tag{12}$$

Constraints (13) specify the energy balance in the heat buffer tank for each sector s at each time period t. Heat is extracted from the heat buffer tank to accommodate the heat demand (ζ_{st}^h), while heat is supplied to the heat buffer tank by the installed energy generation technology ($\bar{Q}_{sit}$) and/or the heat received (R_{sit}) from external sources. Heat storage capacity limits for each heat buffer tank are given by constraints (14).

$$B_{sit} = (1 - \eta_{si}) B_{si,t-1} + \bar{Q}_{sit} + (1 - \mu_{st}) R_{sit} - \zeta_{st}^h Y_{si} \quad \forall s \in S, i \in (I^{HBT} \cap I_s), t \in T \tag{13}$$

$$\beta_i^{min} Y_{si} \leq B_{sit} \leq \beta_i^{max} Y_{si} \quad \forall s \in S, i \in (I^{HBT} \cap I_s), t \in T \tag{14}$$

The available heat from the external heat source in time period t is given by Eq.(15):

$$\sum_{s \in S} \sum_{i \in (I^{HBT} \cap I_s)} R_{sit} \leq a_t \quad \forall t \in T \tag{15}$$

Constraints (16) describe the electricity balance at each time period t, while constraints (17) represent the bounds of total energy generation from the urban energy network.

$$P_t + \sum_{s \in S} \sum_{i \in (I^{CHP} \cap I_s)} \rho_i Q_{sit} = W_t + \sum_{s \in S} \zeta_{st}^e \quad \forall t \in T \tag{16}$$

$$\varepsilon_t^{min} \leq \sum_{s \in S} \sum_{i \in (I^{CHP} \cap I_s)} \rho_i Q_{sit} \leq \varepsilon_t^{max} \quad \forall t \in T \tag{17}$$

4. Description of case study

An urban energy network consisted of 4 sectors has been considered, including a City Hall (CH), a School (SC), a public Swimming Pool (SP), and a Residential Complex (RC). Four different seasons have been considered, i.e., Autumn (Aut), Summer (Smr), Spring (Spr), and Winter (Wtr) and one representative day type for each season. The main technical characteristics of all candidate technologies are presented in Table 1. Note that P_e and P_{th} represent the electric and heat capacity, as well as η_e and η_{th} the electric and thermal efficiency of each technology. HER denotes the heat to power ratio of each CHP technology. Heat demand during summer is considered negligible. External heat is assumed to be supplied by a refinery with a heat capacity of 500 kW_{th}.

5. Results and discussion

The total annualised cost of the design and operational planning of the urban energy network amounts to 537,758 €. When considering only the net cost components, i.e., excluding revenues from electricity sales, the largest share of the total net cost is set to be taken by fuel cost, accounting for 64 % of the total, followed by the capital cost (21 %), electricity purchases cost (13 %), heat purchases cost (2 %), while the start-up cost (1 %) is almost negligible. With regard to the installed technologies, the results indicate that the optimal solution includes three micro-gas turbines (MGT) of 50 kW_e in the CH, in the SC, and in the SP, as well as a reciprocating engine (RE) of 1 MW_e in the RC. Concerning heat buffer tanks, only large ones (HBUF2) with a heat capacity of 300 kW_{th} are selected. As illustrated in Figure 1, heat transfers from the refinery make up a significant share of the heat demand satisfaction in all sectors. This is expected due to the fact that the cost for purchasing refinery's heat is quite lower when compared to that of onsite heat production from the installed CHPs. It can be also noticed that in the first two sectors, i.e., CH and SC, local heat generation exceeds the heat acquired from the refinery, while in the other two sectors, SP and RC, characterized by higher heat demand, refinery's heat supply is greater than their onsite generation. This trend can be explained by the fact that CH and SC operate their CHPs up to levels that are necessary to cover their electrical loads, and sell to the grid some additional amounts of electricity produced. Figure 1 also highlights that the amount of available external heat supply is of great significance for the optimal design of an urban energy system.

Table 1. Main technical characteristics of all the candidate technologies

Type of CHP technology	P_e (kW_e)	P_{th} (kW_{th})	η_e	η_{th}	HER
Gas Engine (GE)	100	130	0.36	0.47	1.30
Gas Turbine 1 (GT)	65	112	0.29	0.50	1.72
Gas Turbine 2 (MGT)	50	55	0.43	0.47	1.10
Gas Turbine 3 (GGT)	5,000	5,701.3	0.41	0.46	1.14
Reciprocating Engine 1 (RE)	1,000	1,145.5	0.42	0.48	1.15
Reciprocating Engine 2 (GRE)	1,000	1,148.1	0.38	0.43	1.15
Micro-Turbine (MIT)	200	218.1	0.32	0.35	1.09
Fuel cell (FC)	400	230	0.35	0.20	0.58
Gas Burner 1 (GB1)	-	200	-	0.80	-
Gas Burner 2 (GB2)	-	400	-	0.80	-
Heat Buffer Tank 1 (HBUF1)	-	150	-	0.99	-
Heat Buffer Tank 2 (HBUF2)	-	300	-	0.99	-

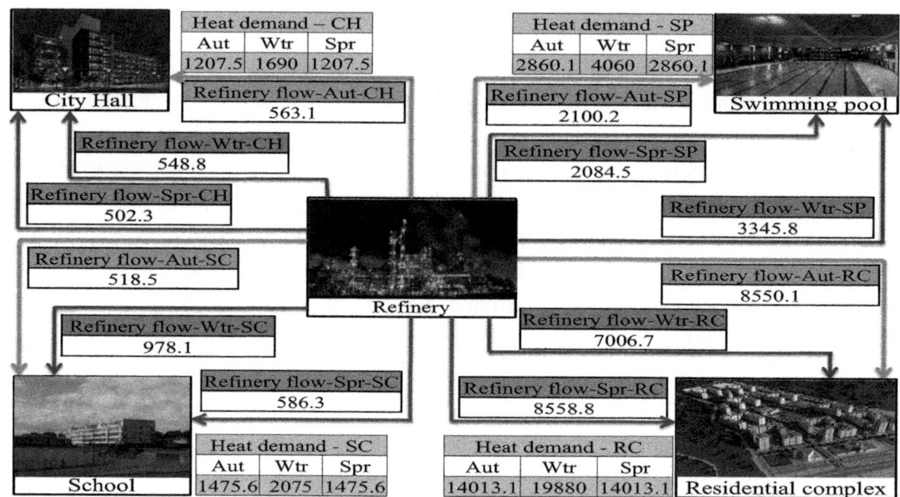

Figure 1. Heat flows in each sector for the heat demand satisfaction (kWh_{th})

6. Conclusions

This work introduces a new MILP formulation addressing simultaneously the design and operational planning of an urban energy network based on CHP units. It is demonstrated that heat demand constitutes the main driver of the technology selection and operational strategy of the studied network. Moreover, the availability of the external heat supply comprises an equally crucial factor for the decision making of this kind of problems.

Acknowledgements

Financial support from the European Commission's FP7 EFENIS project (Contract No: ENER/FP7/296003) "Efficient Energy Integrated Solutions for Manufacturing Industries" is gratefully acknowledged.

References

S. Bracco, G. Dentici, S. Siri, 2013, Economic and environmental optimization model for the design and the operation of a combined heat and power distributed generation system in an urban area, Energy, 55, 1014-1024.

G. M. Kopanos, M.C. Georgiadis, E.N. Pistikopoulos, 2013, Energy production planning of a network of micro combined heat and power generators, Applied Energy, 102, 1522-1534.

P. Liu, M.C. Georgiadis, E.N. Pistikopoulos, 2013, An energy systems engineering approach for the design and operation of microgrids in residential applications, Chemical Engineering Research and Design, 91, 2054-2069.

E.D. Mehleri, H. Sarimveis, N.C. Markatos, L.G. Papageorgiou, 2012, A mathematical programming approach for optimal design of distributed energy systems at the neighbourhood level, Energy, 44, 96-104.

E. Monteiro, N.A. Moreira, S. Ferreira, 2009, Planning of micro-combined heat and power systems in the Portuguese scenario, Applied Energy, 86, 290-298.

H. Ren, W. Gao, 2010, A MILP model for integrated plan and evaluation of distributed energy systems, Applied Energy, 87, 1001-1014.

D. Streimikiene, T. Baležentis, 2013, Multi-criteria assessment of small scale CHP technologies in buildings, Renewable and Sustainable Energy Reviews, 26, 183-189.

Jiří Jaromír Klemeš, Petar Sabev Varbanov and Peng Yen Liew (Editors)
Proceedings of the 24th European Symposium on Computer Aided Process Engineering – ESCAPE 24
June 15-18, 2014, Budapest, Hungary.

Trilateral Flash Cycle for Recovery of Power from a Finite Low-Grade Heat Source

Habeeb A. Ajimotokan*, Ilai Sher, Chechet Biliyok, Hoi Yeung

Process Systems Engineering Group, Cranfield University, Cranfield, MK43 0AL, UK.
h.a.ajimotokan@cranfield.ac.uk

Abstract

The trilateral flash cycle (TFC) among the heat recovery-to-power technologies presents a great potential for development. Unlike the Rankine cycle, the proposed TFC does not evaporate its working fluid during the heating phase; instead expands it, from the saturated liquid condition, as a two-phase mixture bypassing the isothermal boiling phase. This paper examines the feasibility of interfacing the TFC system for low-grade heat recovery-to-power generation using thermal energy from hot produced water at constant flow rate from a gas well. The corresponding thermodynamic processes of the TFC thermal power plant were thermodynamically modelled and implemented. The results depict that the thermal efficiency of the proposed TFC employing isobutane as the working fluid is 13.6 - 17.1 % over the examined cycle high temperatures of 363 - 393 K, which is 30 - 40 % improvement over organic Rankine cycle and the cycle exergy efficiency is 81.1 %.

Keywords: Heat recovery-to-power, trilateral flash cycle, process-oriented modelling.

1. Introduction

The need of innovative energy conversion technologies is significant for sustainable power generation premised on the consideration of Earth's limited fossil fuel reserves (Smith 1993), rising cost of energy prices in the global market (Sanjay 2011), high demand for electricity by teeming world population and effect of greenhouse gas emissions (Khennich and Galanis 2012). Amid these, heat recovery-to-power technologies present a great potential for development.

Amidst heat recovery-to-power cycles, the organic Rankine cycles (ORCs) have been broadly employed to generate electrical power from low and moderate temperatures due to their efficiency and simplicity in configuration (Chen et al., 2011). But a crucial drawback of ORCs is the 'isothermal boiling' particularly with pure fluids; creating poor thermal match during heat transfer from the heat source to the working fluid because of 'pinch point' and causing a huge irreversibility (Chen et al., 2011). Distinct from the variants of Rankine cycles, the proposed trilateral flash cycle (TFC) does not evaporate its working fluid during the heating phase; instead expands it, from the saturated liquid condition, bypassing the isothermal boiling phase. This feat permits better thermal matching during the heat transfer from the heat source or even sensible heat source (i.e. of variable temperature) to the working fluid (Chan et al., 2013), minimizing exergy destruction and improving process performance. While the ORC process is employed in some of the existing power stations, the TFC is a novel concept for technical development. It has become a new research direction due to its promising advantages in system efficiency, simplicity of configuration and thermal march during the heat transfer from the heat source to the working fluid (Smith et al., 2005).

The choice of suitable working fluid for given application, the feasible operating conditions/ parameters and the system design, is one of the utmost essential features of any thermal system design (Sahin et al., 2013). With the application of suitable working fluid in the thermodynamic cycle of the TFC, TFC power system could recover and convert low-grade heat efficiently from renewable thermal sources as well as from the by-product (waste heat) of numerous non-renewable sources into electrical power.

Numerous oil and gas wells produce hot water in addition to their hydrocarbon output, which annually equate to several billions barrels of produced water (Dahlheim and Pike, 2012). The thermal energy of this produced water could be recovered and employed as energy source for sustainable power generation in the tune of several GW. The electrical power generated from produced water would not only increase the much needed electricity but also lead to a more energy efficient oil and gas production, extending the life of most of these wells and producing more oil and gas.

The challenges associated with the development of a methodology for conceptual design of a novel TFC system and it application are numerous, thus, the great need for research to improve the understanding of its operation, behaviour and performance for different applications.

2. System Description

The system comprises four key components: feed pump, heater, expander and condenser. Though, the major consideration in the application of the TFC is the two-phase expander: a technically most challenging component; which may be a variable phase turbine, a scroll expander, a screw expander or a reciprocating engine (Fischer, 2011). Such an expander must be able to operate at a high efficiency to make the system viable. A screw expander has been proposed as suitable for the TFC application, as it can reach isentropic efficiency of over 75 % (Smith et al., 2001). Expanders available from a good number of OEM (Kaupert et al., 2013), used for LNG applications involving two phase fluids and can attain isentropic efficiencies of 85 %.

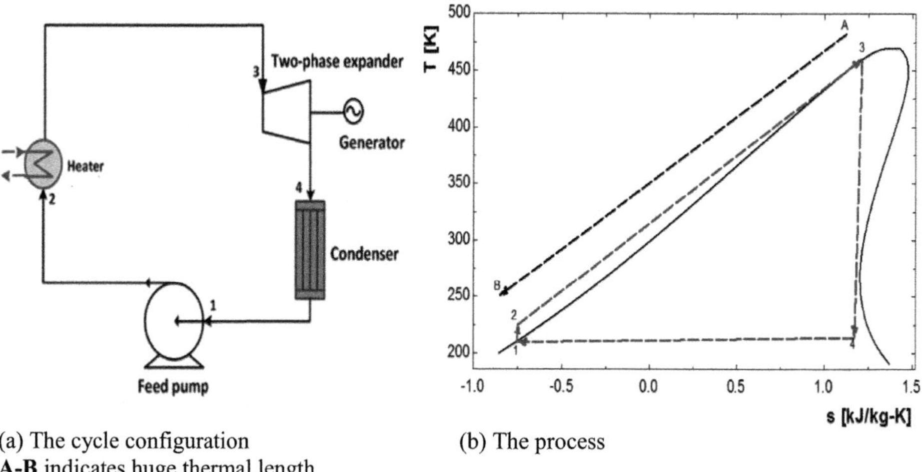

(a) The cycle configuration
A-B indicates huge thermal length

(b) The process

Figure 1. The trilateral flash cycle, showing the schematic cycle configuration in (a) and the T–s diagram of its thermodynamic process in (b)

Figure 1 depicts the TFC schematic cycle configuration and the temperature–entropy (T–s) diagram of its thermodynamic process. Similar to the Rankine cycles, the working fluid at ambient (reference) temperature and pressure (state 1) is pressurized (state 1 - 2), afterward heated just to its saturated temperature (boiling point) (state 2 - 3) and is being injected into the expander; where shaft work is produced (state 3 - 4), driving a generator to produce power. Subsequently, the new cycle is started by condensing the resulting vapour–liquid content to liquid (state 4 - 1).

2.1. *Process Modelling*

Based on the working conditions of the TFC thermal power plant coupled to a finite heat source of hot produced water at 393 K, accompanied by the thermo-physical requirements of the TFC system, a thermodynamic process-oriented modelling that permits the analyses of the behaviour and prediction of the performance of the trilateral flash cycle (TFC) was carried out. The assumptions for the thermodynamic modelling made are:

i) The cycle and its components operates at steady-state steady-flow conditions;
ii) Variations of kinetic and potential energies of the heat transfer fluid and working fluid in the cycle is negligible;
iii) Heat loss and pressure drop in the system (heat exchanger and connecting pipes) are negligible
iv) Expander inlet pressure 3 MPa; and
v) Average condensing temperature 310 K.

Isobutane with critical temperature of 407.9 K and critical pressure of 3.648 MPa is adopted as the working fluid. Governing equations of the TFC power plant, corresponding to its thermodynamic processes are modelled and implemented employing EES (engineering equation solver). Thermodynamic simulations using the system parameters (Table 1) and parametric analyses of the performance parameters of the cycle and ancillary components under various conditions are implemented, and results are obtained. The output power, thermal and exergy efficiencies of the cycle are evaluated using the inlet pressure of 2 - 3 MPa and expander isentropic efficiency of 0.5 - 0.85 respectively at cycle high temperature of 363 - 393 K.

2.2. *Thermodynamic Analysis*

The energy efficiency of the cycle η_{th} is:

$$\eta_{th} = \frac{\dot{W}_{net}}{\dot{Q}_{in}} = \frac{\dot{W}_{exp} - \dot{W}_p}{\dot{Q}_{in}} \tag{1}$$

Table 1. System configuration parameters

Parameters	Values [Units]
Pump isentropic efficiency	95 [%]
Expander isentropic efficiency	85 [%]
Reference temperature, T_o	298.15 [K]
Average condensing temperature, T_{con}	310 [K]
Feed pump pressure, P_p	3 [MPa]

Where $\dot{W}_{net}$ denotes the network output; $\dot{W}_{exp}$ is the work output of the expander, which is expressed as:

$$\dot{W}_{exp} = \dot{m}_{wf}\left(h_{exp}^{in} - h_{exp}^{out}\right) = \dot{m}_{wf}\left(h_{exp}^{in} - h_{\mathrm{exp}\_is}^{out}\right)\eta_{exp} \tag{2}$$

$\dot{W}_p$ is the work done by the pump, expressed as:

$$\dot{W}_p = \dot{m}_{wf}\left(h_p^{out} - h_p^{in}\right) = \dot{m}_{wf}\left(h_{p\_is}^{out} - h_p^{in}\right)/\eta_p \tag{3}$$

$\dot{Q}_{in}$ is the total energy input by the heater, expressed as:

$$\dot{Q}_{in} = \dot{m}_{wf}\left(h_{hx}^{out} - h_{hx}^{in}\right) \tag{4}$$

and $\dot{Q}_{in}$ is the total energy desipated by the condenser, expressed as:

$$\dot{Q}_{out} = \dot{m}_{wf}\left(h_{con}^{in} - h_{con}^{\mathrm{out}}\right) \tag{5}$$

Where $\dot{m}_{wf}$ denotes the working fluid mass flow rate, h_{exp}^{in} and h_{exp}^{out} are the specific enthalpies at the expander inlet and outlet respectively, $h_{\mathrm{exp}\_is}^{out}$ is the expander isentropic efficiency at expander outlet, h_p^{in} and h_p^{out} are the specific enthalpies at the pump inlet and outlet respectively, $h_{p\_is}^{out}$ is the pump isentropic efficiency at pump outlet, η_{exp} and η_p are the expander and pump isentropic efficiencies, h_{hx}^{in} and h_{hx}^{out} are the specific enthalpies at the heat exchange inlet and outlet respectively, and h_{exp}^{in} and h_{exp}^{out} are the specific enthalpies at the expander inlet and outlet respectively.

The exergy efficiency of the cycle η_{II} is expressed as:

$$\eta_{II} = \frac{\eta_{th}}{\eta_{th,rev}} \tag{6}$$

Where $\eta_{th,rev}$ denotes the reversible thermal efficiency (Carnot equivalent), which can be determined as follows:

$$\eta_{th,rev} = \left(1 - \frac{T_L}{T_H}\right) \tag{7}$$

Where T_L and T_H denote temperatures of heat source and heat sink, respectively. Hence, using Eq. (6), the exergy efficiency η_{II} of the proposed cycle is computed to be 81.11 %.

3. Results and Discussion

The thermodynamic simulations results of isobutane based TFC are computed based on the inlet pressure of 3 MPa (critical pressure 3.648 MPa), and 95 % and 85 % isentropic efficiencies for both pump and expander respectively, at cycle high temperature of 393 K (critical temperature 407.9 K). The analyses of the behaviour and prediction of the performance of the trilateral flash cycle (TFC) was carried out by variations of inlet pressures, cycle temperatures and expander isentropic efficiency values respectively. Figure 2 depicts the variation of thermal efficiency with inlet pressure. The resulting thermal efficiency increases as the inlet pressure is increased from 2 - 3 MPa because the quantities of heat added increases almost proportionately with the inlet pressure. The thermal efficiency of the TFC increases from 13.6 - 17.13 %. Figure 3 depicts the variation of network output with cycle high temperature. The resulting network output increases as the cycle high temperature is increased. The network output per unit mass of the working increases from 35.03 - 60.96 kW, when the cycle high temperature is increased from 363 - 393 K. Figure 4 depicts the variation of thermal efficiency with the expander isentropic efficiency. The resulting thermal efficiency increases as the expander isentropic efficiency values is increased. The thermal efficiency increases from 7.46 - 17.13 %, when the expander isentropic efficiency values is increased from 0.5 - 0.85. There is an increase in the thermal efficiency because as the expander isentropic efficiency increases, expander power output equally increases.

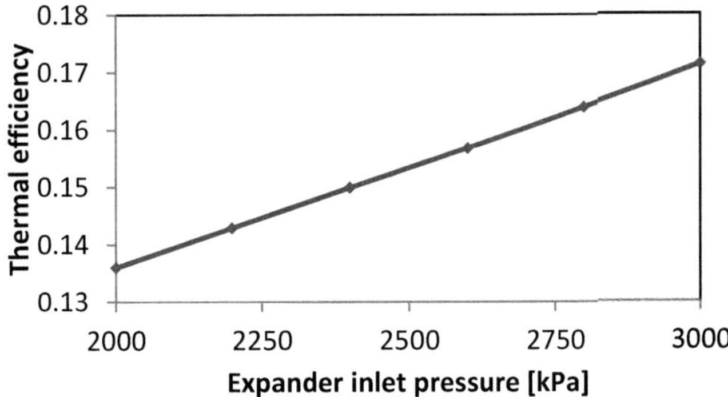

Figure 2. Variation of thermal efficiency with expander inlet pressure

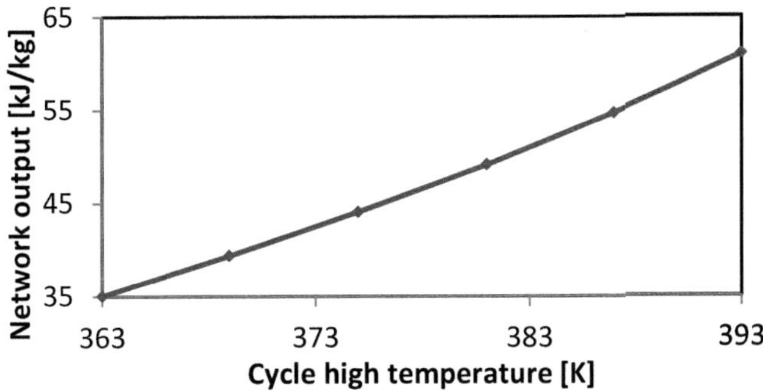

Figure 3. Variation of network output with cycle high temperature

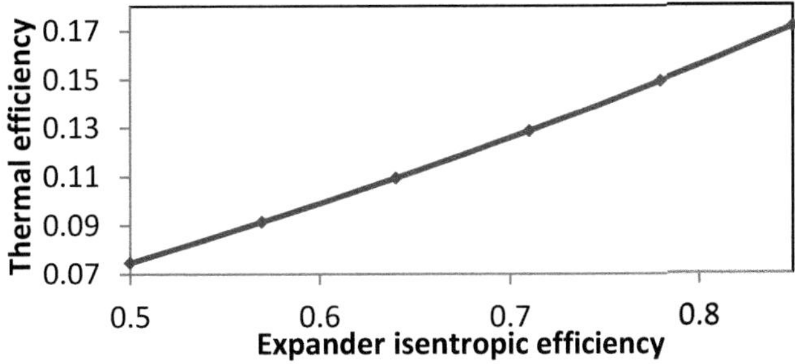

Figure 4. Variation of thermal efficiency with expander isentropic efficiency

4. Conclusions

The trilateral flash cycle (TFC) has been proposed and its thermodynamic feasibility studied for low-grade heat recovery-to-power generation using thermal energy from hot produced water; employing isobutane as the working fluid. The proposed cycle performance is examined and it is observed that the TFC can attain thermal efficiency of 13.6 - 17.1 % over the examined cycle high temperatures of 363 - 393 K, while the cycle exergy efficiency is computed to be 81.11 %. This study demonstrates the feasibility of implementing the TFC for heat recovery-to-power. Simulations and analyses are carried out to assess the performance of the cycle and its realistic predictions of behaviour to guide conceptual design and measurements, and application of TFC system for waste heat recovery-to-power.

References

C.W. Chan, J. Ling-Chin, A.P. Roskilly, 2013, A review of chemical heat pumps, thermodynamic cycles and thermal energy storage technologies for low grade heat utilisation, Applied Thermal Engineering, 50, 1257-1273.

H. Chen, D.Y. Goswami, M. Rahman, E.K. Stefanakos, 2011, A supercritical Rankine cycle using zeotropic mixture working fluids for the conversion of low-grade heat into power, Energy, 36, 549-555.

R. Dahlheim, W.J. Pike, 2012, Generating electricity from produced water, Journal of Petroleum Technology, 64, 30-32.

J. Fischer, 2011, Comparison of trilateral cycles and organic Rankine cycles, Energy, 36, 6208-6219.

K. Kaupert, S. Gandhi, C. Kaehler, Flashing liquid expanders for LNG liquefaction trains, 17th International Conference & Exhibition on Liquefied Natural Gas, <www.gastechnology.org/Training/Documents/LNG17-proceedings/Mach-2-Kevin_Kaupert.pdf>, acessed 04/11/2013.

M. Khennich, N. Galanis, 2012, Thermodynamic analysis and optimization of power cycles using a finite low-temperature heat source, International Journal of Energy Research, 36, 871-885.

A.Z. Sahin, E.M. Mokheimer, H.M. Bahaidarah, M.A. Antar, P. Gandhidasan, R. Ben-Mansour, S. Al-Dini, S. Rehman, A. Bejan, M.A., Al-Nimr, H.F. Oztop, L. Chen, A. Midilli, J. Lawrence, 2013, Special issue: Thermodynamic optimization, exergy analysis, and constructal design, Arabian Journal for Science and Engineering, 38, 219.

R. Sanjay 2011, Investigation of effect of variation of cycle parameters on thermodynamic performance of gas-steam combined cycle, Energy, 36, 157-167.

I.K. Smith, 1993, Development of the trilateral flash cycle system Part 1: fundamental consideration, Proceedings of the Institution of Mechanical Engineers, Part A: Journal of Power and Energy, 207, 179-194.

I.K. Smith, N. Stosic, A. Kovacevic, 2001, Power recovery from low cost two-phase expanders, Transaction-Geothermal Resources Council, 601-606.

I.K. Smith, N. Stosic, A. Kovacevic, 2005, Screw expanders increase output and decrease the cost of geothermal binary power plant systems, Geothermal Resources Council, 29, 787-801.

Jiří Jaromír Klemeš, Petar Sabev Varbanov and Peng Yen Liew (Editors)
Proceedings of the 24th European Symposium on Computer Aided Process Engineering – ESCAPE 24
June 15-18, 2014, Budapest, Hungary.

Sustainable Development – Challenges for the European CAPE Community

Michael Narodoslawsky*
GrazUniversity of Technology, Inffeldgasse 13/3, A 8010 Graz, Austria
narodoslawsky@tugraz.at

Abstract

The European Federation of Chemical Engineering (EFCE) is taking up the challenge of sustainable development by installing a special Sustainability Section to discuss the wide ranging implications of this development concept. Sustainable development will require a thorough re-structuring of chemical industry within the next decades and a fundamental re-orientation of the way chemical engineers pursue their research, technological development and design work as well. This poses new and formidable challenges to the European CAPE community.

Three challenges require new CAPE solutions in particular

- The integration of life cycle assessment into chemical engineering design;
- A change towards renewable resources for energy provision and raw materials for industrial processes;
- A systemic approach to integrating chemical industry sustainably into supply chains while providing energy services to society at the same time.

The re-orientation of chemical engineering research and design is already visible in the efforts of young chemical engineering researchers. Interdisciplinary research as well as tackling the tasks linked to the new role of chemical engineering within sustainable development is more and more defining the work of young chemical engineers. This has been particularly visible in the CAPE Forum 2013, that brought together an interdisciplinary group of researchers from 13 European countries to discuss these challenges of sustainable development and that fostered the discourse between young researchers and experienced scientists and practitioners. The paper will link the results of the 32 contributions to the CAPE Forum 2013 and the on-going initiatives in the Sustainability Section of the EFCE to generate a picture of the future role of the CAPE community with regard to sustainable development.

Keywords: sustainable process industry, CAPE Forum, sustainable energy systems.

1. Introduction

Chemical engineering is arguably the engineering discipline most directly concerned with the challenges of sustainable development. After all, chemical engineers design most industrial processes that convert primary resources (be they of fossil, mineral or biogenic nature) into materials that then form the base for any further production. In addition to that they are also in charge of most environmental technologies. This makes chemical engineers responsible for a large part of human society's metabolism, at least on the same footing as agro-engineering. From this crucial position comes a particular obligation to meet the challenges of sustainable development. This has been recognized by the European Federation of Chemical Engineers (EFCE) in the establishment of its Sustainability Section (see EFCE, 2013):

Within the chemical engineering discipline the sector of Computer Aided Process Engineering (CAPE) has become a major source of methods and tools supporting chemical engineering design tasks. Meeting new challenges therefore requires innovation within the CAPE community. There are three particular challenges for which new CAPE solutions have to be developed quickly (Narodoslawsky, 2013), namely:

- The integration of life cycle assessment into chemical engineering design;
- A change towards renewable resources for energy provision and raw materials for industrial processes;
- A systemic approach to integrating chemical industry sustainably into supply chains while providing energy services to society at the same time.

An interesting vantage point for estimating progress of chemical engineering research in meeting its innovation challenges is the analysis of conferences where new ideas are presented to the scientific community. This is particularly true for conferences where young scientists and PhD students congregate since these events usually provide insight into the latest scientific efforts in a certain field. The CAPE Forum held in Graz/ Austria from April 8-10, 2013 was such an event, dedicated to the new sustainability challenges in chemical and process engineering as well as innovation regarding sustainable energy systems.

2. The CAPE Forum 2013

The CAPE Forum 2013 brought together researchers from 13 countries and offered 32 interdisciplinary lectures. The main purpose of this event was to provide a platform for young scientists to discuss their work on CAPE applications for sustainable development with more experienced researchers as well as with researchers outside the field of process engineering. The range of topics was framed by the two introductory lectures: Glavic (2013) presented an overview on history, structure and future challenges of process system engineering while Visa (2013) went outside the confinement of process engineering, opening the horizon to CAPE applications for buildings.

3. Simulation and optimization for sustainable processes and technologies

A major scientific effort in process engineering is dedicated to simulation and optimization. In the CAPE Forum 2013 optimization was treated from the level of the supply chain to the support of management on the firm level to the level of single processes.

Regarding optimisation on the level of the supply chain, focus was laid on the application of process synthesis approaches to wider systems. Friedler (2013) discussed the application of P-Graph synthesis methods to various supply chains with special emphasis on the weighing profitability and sustainability. Kravanja (2013) discussed multi-objective LCA based MINLP to supply chain optimisation and pleaded for proper accounting of both, burdening and unburdening of the environment. Both contributions clearly indicated the importance of looking at the context of the supply chain when pursuing sustainability of industrial processes. They also critically analysed the complex interrelation between profit and ecological impact and highlighted the importance of LCA for future chemical engineering design tasks.

A number of contributions tackled sustainability on the level of processes. Novak Pintarič (2013) discussed trade-offs between economic, operational and environmental effects during flow sheet optimization. Dolinski (2013) concentrated on the development of practical decision support tools for management based in part on the Sustainable Process Index (SPI) that should help to identify eco-innovation on the firm level. Both contributions specifically addressed the importance of translating sustainability issues into the economic context of process design while retaining the claim of encompassing optimisation. Gourmelon (2013) provided another approach to integrating sustainable development issues into process engineering design by using exergy analysis within process simulation.

On the level of particular processes Benkö (2013) provided an LCA comparison of utilisation options for used tyres. Nagy (2013) discussed post combustion carbon dioxide capture with mono-ethanolamine. All contributions that dealt with sustainability issues on the firm and process level highlighted the importance of including sustainability metrics right into the modelling of processes.

Besides modelling supply chains and processes from the view point of sustainability, progress in key technologies as well as new approaches to model unit operations are required to meet the challenges ahead. Within the CAPE Forum 2013 particular focus was laid on heat exchange as a key step for more sustainable chemical processes as well as energy systems in general. Many contributions focussed on plate heat exchangers (PHE). Kapustenko (2013) discussed their application in buildings, indicating the increasing importance of chemical engineering know how for other sectors relevant to a change towards sustainable energy systems. Stogianis et al. (2013) modelled turbulent flow and heat exchange in PHE channels and Demirskiyet al. investigated the thermal and hydraulic performance of industrial PHE. The contributions showed the power of modelling flows in complex geometries to optimise heat exchange as well as to choose the right equipment.

Still another group of contributions was dedicated to modelling important steps and phenomena within sustainable processes. Conversion of carbon monoxide in porous catalysts was modelled by Ved et al. (2013). Triebl (2013) looked into the conversion of 5-Hydroxymethyl-furfuralto 2,5-Furandicarboxylic acid as a basic step from renewable resources to bulk chemicals, also investigating the economic potential of this conversion. Muntean (2013) presented a model for precipitation of calcium phosphate particles by using population balances. Nagy et al. investigated membrane separation process regarding their overall mass transfer as a base for innovative gas separation processes. The increasing importance of modelling the behaviour of granular material for many processes relevant to sustainable industrial production (e.g. drying or thermal conversion but also pharmaceutical engineering processes etc.) was highlighted by Peters (2013) who discussed an extended discrete element method and its application to granular material. These contributions presented strong evidence of the strong role CAPE methods will play in the development of future technologies that will be crucial to make process industry sustainable.

4. The challenge of utilising biogenic resources

CAPE Forum 2013 was evidence to the vivid research effort aimed at developing innovative processes based on biogenic resources that are currently going on globally. Again, contributions ranged from systemic approaches to detailed process development using CAPE methods. Friedl (2013) provided an overview on bio-refinery systems and the CAPE methods of choice in their development. He showed that for most engineering tasks, from process optimisation with flow sheet programs to LCA to economic analysis down to the design of optimal heat exchanger networks, reliable CAPE methods are already available. Lassmann et al. (2013) took this argument into more detail, modelling the down-stream process of a lingo-cellulose based ethanol production with existing flow sheet programs and HEN optimisation routines. Hegedüs and Nagy (2013) presented another aspect of second generation bio-refineries by looking at cellulase and hemicellulaseenzymaticnano particle degradation. Bongards (2013) raised the issue of control and automation in processes based on biogenic resources and provided examples for the application of IT solutions in biogas plants as well as pellets furnaces. Steinmüller (2013) analysed the situation of biogas production in Austria and employed LCA to identify optimal solutions for the management of agricultural residues. Corkery (2013) went even further in the link between CAPE and agriculture, presenting innovative applications of IT solutions in agricultural praxis.

Besides development on the level of processes and technologies, contributions to the CAPE Forum also looked at biogenic resource utilisation from a strategic point of view. Klemes et al. (2013) presented a comprehensive overview on global resource and energy flows and discussed the implications of impacts exerted by the utilisation of resources on the environment. They also analysed requirements for linking material and energy flows from the view point of sustainable development. Arentsen (2013) brought the regional and social dimension of a transition towards a bio-based economy in Europe into the discourse, highlighting its requirement as well as the chances for collaboration this transition entails.

All lectures in this field provided evidence of the complexity of development as well as implementation of technologies based on biogenic resources. They also pointed towards the chances that CAPE approaches may offer in the development towards a bio-based economy.

5. Energy systems as a key for the change towards sustainability

The energy system is arguably the most relevant technology sector for a change towards sustainable development. CAPE solutions may become crucial elements for transforming this sector as many energy technologies either utilise chemical engineering unit operations (e.g. thermal conversions) or profit from chemical engineering know how and methods. This fact also influenced the topics of contributions to the CAPE Forum.

Duic (2013) defined the playing field in an overview on the development of Europe's energy system in the first half of the 21st century. He pointed towards the changes currently under way in the electricity system, transforming Europe's electricity sector from a baseline production mode towards a sector that will have to deal with intermittent energy sources like wind and solar radiation. He also analysed the chances for material energy carriers, in particular biomass and biomass derived energy forms in a future energy market. Shifting the focus away from Europe, Novosel et al. (2013) analysed the situation in Jordan, looking in particular at chances of market penetration for renewable energy sources. Frits et al. (2013) discussed a novel tool to optimise regional renewable resource utilisation and energy supply applying Process Network Synthesis know how from chemical engineering. On the level of a firm, Kiraly (2013) showed the potential of applying CAPE methods to achieve energy efficiency and reduce ecological impact of its energy system.

A further line of contributions was dedicated to applying CAPE methods to sectors outside process industry, in particular the building sector. Comsit and Visa (2013) applied CAPE models to optimising PV systems in buildings of a university campus, Moldovan and Visa (2013) broke this approach down to the level of a single building.

6. Conclusions

The CAPE Forum 2013 presented a cross section of research efforts currently under way for promoting sustainable development by applying CAPE approaches. The focus on young scientists ensured that the contributions mirrored the most recent efforts in this field. CAPE approaches presented at the Forum showed the broad potential of chemical engineering know how in sustainable development: from classical process optimisation to innovative processes based on renewable sources to changing regional energy systems and the way we build and operate houses and settlements as well as agricultural problems, all benefit from CAPE solutions. The Forum however also showed that chemical engineering has to take the general societal development as well as knowledge from other disciplines, most notably social sciences, into account in order to succeed as a key discipline in sustainable development.

References

M. Arentsen, 2013, Biobased transition in regions-A multidisciplinary challenge of collaboration, Plenary Lecture Nr. 22, CAPE Forum 2013, April 8-10, 2013, Graz/Austria.

T. Benkö, Evaluation and comparison of used tyre utilization options withlife cycle assessment, Lecture Nr. 8, CAPE Forum 2013, April 8-10, 2013, Graz/Austria.

M. Bongards, 2013, Intelligent Automation and IT for the Optimization of Renewable Energy Processes, Plenary Lecture Nr. 14, CAPE Forum 2013, April 8-10, 2013, Graz/Austria.

M. Comsit, I. Visa, 2013, Computer Aided Process Engineering of a tracked PV testing platform integrated in the built environment in Trasilvania University Brasov-Colina campus, Lecture Nr. 27, CAPE Forum 2013, April 8-10, 2013, Graz/Austria.

G. Corkery, 2013, Smart Systems in Agriculture with an emphasis on Poultry Production, Plenary Lecture Nr. 25, CAPE Forum 2013, April 8-10, 2013, Graz/Austria.

O. Demirskiy, O. Arsenyeva, L. Tovazhnyanskyy, A. Yuzbashyan, 2013, Computer aided identification of industrial plate heat exchangers thermal and hydraulic performance, Lecture Nr. 13, CAPE Forum 2013, April 8-10, 2013, Graz/Austria.

M. Dolinski, 2013, Managerial decision support tools or sustainable actions, Lecture Nr. 4, CAPE Forum 2013, April 8-10, 2013, Graz/Austria.

N. Duic, 2013, Issues to solve on the way to 100 % RES energysystems, Plenary Lecture Nr. 29, CAPE Forum 2013, April 8-10, 2013, Graz/Austria.

EFCE, 2013, <www.efce.info/Sections/Sustainability.html>, accessed on 07/02/2014.

A. Friedl, 2013, Optimizing biorefinery concepts using simulation tools, Plenary Lecture Nr. 18, CAPE Forum 2013, April 8-10, 2013, Graz/Austria.

F. Friedler, 2013, Supply Chain Management: Sustainability vs. Profitability, Plenary Lecture 6, CAPE Forum 2013, April 8-10, 2013, Graz/Austria.

M. Frits, N. Niemetz, I. Heckl, A. Szlama, M. Narodoslawsky, 2013,Region Optimizer (RegiOpt): a framework for the synthesis of sustainable supply chain by the P-graph methodology, Lecture, CAPE Forum 2013, April 8-10, 2013, Graz/Austria.
P. Glavic, 2013, Process Systems Engineering and Sustainable Development, Plenary Lecture, CAPE Forum 2013, April 8-10, 2013, Graz/Austria.
St. Gourmelon, 2013, Exergy analysis within Process Simulation Software: a tool forprocess optimization, Lecture, CAPE Forum 2013, April 8-10, 2013, Graz/Austria.
I. Hegedüs, E. Nagy, 2013, Cellulase and hemicellulase degradation using single enzyme nanoparticles, Lecture, CAPE Forum 2013, April 8-10, 2013, Graz/Austria.
P. Kapustenko, The use and Integration and plate heat exchangersfor energy saving in buildings, Plenary Lecture, CAPE Forum 2013, April 8-10, 2013, Graz/Austria.
A. Kiraly, 2013, Improving company's environmental impacts by integratingrenewables, Lecture, CAPE Forum 2013, April 8-10, 2013, Graz/Austria.
J.J. Klemeš, P.S. Varbanov, A. Nemet, 2013, Integration of Energy and Resource Flows, Plenary Lecture, CAPE Forum 2013, April 8-10, 2013, Graz/Austria.
Z. Kravanja, Sustainable synthesis of chemical supply chains, Plenary Lecture, CAPE Forum 2013, April 8-10, 2013, Graz/Austria.
T. Lassmann, P. Kravanja, A. Friedl, 2013, Simulation of the downstream processing in the ethanol production from lignocellulosic biomasswith ASPEN PLUS and IPSE Pro, Lecture, CAPE Forum 2013, April 8-10, 2013, Graz/Austria.
M. Moldovan, I. Visa, 2013, Sustainable built environment - a case study for a solar house, Lecture, CAPE Forum 2013, April 8-10, 2013, Graz/Austria.
N. Muntean, 2013, Modelling the precipitation of amorphous calcium phosphate asprecursor of hydroxyapatite by population balance models, Lecture, CAPE Forum 2013, April 8-10, 2013, Graz/Austria.
T. Nagy, Modelling of post combustion carbon-dioxide capture withmonoethanolamine, Lecture, CAPE Forum 2013, April 8-10, 2013, Graz/Austria.
E. Nagy, R. Nagy, J. Dudás, 2013, Overall mass transport during membrane gas separation, Lecture, CAPE Forum 2013, April 8-10, 2013, Graz/Austria.
M. Narodoslawsky, 2013, Chemical engineering in a sustainable economy, J. Chem. Eng. Res. Des., DOI: 10.1016/j.cherd.2013.06.022.
Z. Novak Pintarič, 2013, Trade-offs between economic, operational andenvironmental efficiencies during the process flow sheetoptimization, Plenary Lecture, CAPE Forum 2013, April 8-10, 2013, Graz/Austria.
T. Novosel, B. Ćosić, G. Krajačić, N. Duić, M.S. Mohsen, M.S. Ashhab, A. K. Ababneh, Potential for the penetration of renewable energy sources in Jordan's energy system, Lecture, CAPE Forum 2013, April 8-10, 2013, Graz/Austria.
B. Peters, 2013, Application of the extended discrete element method (XDEM) incomputer-aided process engineering, Lecture, CAPE Forum 2013, April 8-10, 2013, Graz/Austria.
I.A. Stogiannis, S.V. Paras, O. Arsenyeva, P. Kapustenko, 2013, CFD Modelling of turbulent hydrodynamics and heat transfer:application for PHE Channels, Lecture, CAPE Forum 2013, April 8-10, 2013, Graz/Austria.
Ch. Triebl, 2013, Simulation and Economic Analysis of 5-Hydroxymethyl-furfuralconversion to 2,5-Furandicarboxylic Acid, Lecture, CAPE Forum 2013, April 8-10, 2013, Graz/Austria.
O. Ved, V. Ved, L. Tovagnansky, 2013, Mathematical model of coversion of carbon monoxid in porous catalyst, Lecture, CAPE Forum 2013, April 8-10, 2013, Graz/Austria.
I. Visa, 2013, Energy efficiency, energy saving and urban acceptance of facade integrated solar thermal collectors, Plenary Lecture, CAPE Forum 2013, April 8-10, 2013, Graz/Austria.

Jiří Jaromír Klemeš, Petar Sabev Varbanov and Peng Yen Liew (Editors)
Proceedings of the 24th European Symposium on Computer Aided Process Engineering – ESCAPE 24
June 15-18, 2014, Budapest, Hungary.

Synthesis of Water, Wastewater Treatment, and Heat-Exchanger Networks

Nidret Ibrić,[a] Elvis Ahmetović,[a,*] Zdravko Kravanja[b]

[a]*University of Tuzla, Faculty of Technology, Univerzitetska 8, 75000 Tuzla, Bosnia and Herzegovina*

[b]*University of Maribor, Faculty of Chemistry and Chemical Engineering, Smetanova ulica 17, 2000 Maribor, Slovenia*

elvis.ahmetovic@untz.ba

Abstract

This contribution describes a general methodology for the synthesis of water networks of different complexities, ranging from simple water networks up to combined water, wastewater treatment and heat exchanger networks. The overall network model is formulated as a mixed-integer nonlinear programming (MINLP) problem. The methodology is illustrated and implemented on a case study. In the first step we present a base case of water network design without water reuse and determine freshwater consumption. Then an optimal water network design with the minimum freshwater usage and wastewater generation is synthesized. In the next step, an integrated water-using and wastewater treatment network is synthesized. Finally, the water and wastewater networks are combined with the heat exchanger network (HEN), and solved simultaneously. The obtained results show that the methodology can be used both for the synthesis of isothermal and non-isothermal water and wastewater networks.

Keywords: superstructure, heat-integrated water networks, simultaneous optimization.

1. Introduction

Water and energy are key resources within the process industries. The profitability and sustainability of industrial processes depend on efficient usages of water and energy, thus represent one of the important current and future issues. In order to simultaneously reduce water and energy consumption, systematic methods have been developed, namely, pinch technology and mathematical programming. The reader is referred to review paper (Klemeš, 2012) related to water networks (WNs) as well as to recent developments in process integration (Klemeš et al., 2013), simultaneous optimisation of processes and HENs (Drobež et al., 2012) and heat and water integration within processes (Yang and Grossmann, 2012).

The first studies regarding the synthesis of water and wastewater networks focused on water-reuse, regeneration, and recycling (Wang and Smith, 1994). WNs were studied in order to minimize freshwater consumption by following with wastewater network synthesis (Galan and Grossmann, 1998). Later, water and wastewater networks were considered as an integrated network and solved simultaneously (Ahmetović and Grossmann, 2011). In order to obtain more practical solutions, temperature constraints within WNs were incorporated within the synthesis problem and combined WNs and HENs were studied using pinch (Savulescu et al., 2005), mathematical programming by applying sequential (Bagajewicz et al., 2002), and simultaneous approaches (Ahmetović and Kravanja, 2013). It is worth pointing out that only a simultaneous approach can explore strong interactions within the overall network in order to obtain appropriate trade-offs between freshwater and utilities consumption, and investment (Ahmetović and Kravanja, 2014). To the best of our knowledge, only a few studies have considered the synthesis problem of non-isothermal water and wastewater networks. This problem was simultaneously solved by Dong et al. (2008) using state-space superstructure, and Bogataj and Bagajewicz (2008) using superstructure including the mixing of water streams within the HEN. Also, Chen et al. (2010) proposed sequential strategy for solving the same synthesis problem. The goal of this paper is to present the methodology for solving both isothermal and non-isothermal water and wastewater networks. The proposed superstructure and solution strategy of non-isothermal water and wastewater networks are different compared to the previous works enabling additional heat integration opportunities and producing the improved solutions.

2. Problem statement

Given is a set of freshwater sources, a set of process water-using units and a set of wastewater treatment units. The objective of this study was to determine an optimal design for a combination of water-usage, wastewater treatment, and HENs, thus minimizing the total annual cost (TAC). Temperature constraints were provided for process water using units (PUs), treatment units (TUs), as well as for the effluent stream discharged into the environment. Also, the temperature and the contaminants' concentrations were given for freshwater. The specific heat-capacities of the water streams were assumed to be constant.

3. Superstructure

The recently proposed superstructure (Ibrić et al., 2013) was extended by wastewater TUs (Figure 1). This superstructure consists of freshwater heating stages, PUs, wastewater cooling stages, TUs, and a final wastewater mixer. The freshwater heating stages allow for the gradual heating and splitting of the freshwater stream while the wastewater cooling stages are designed as cooling stages between PUs and TUs, thus allowing both direct and indirect cooling of the wastewater streams. Multiple choice mixers and splitters are used before and after PUs and TUs in order to include additional opportunities for heat-integration between water streams.

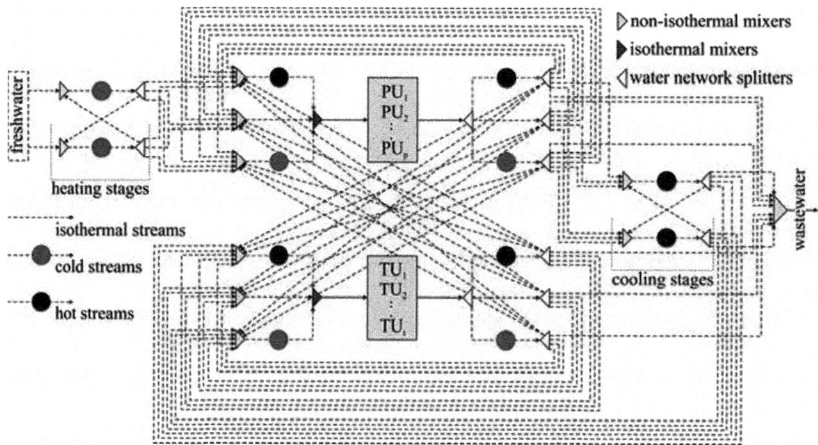

Figure 1. Superstructure of integrated water, wastewater treatment, and heat exchanger networks

4. Model and solution strategy

An isothermal WN model consists of mass and contaminants balance equations with the objective function minimizing TAC including freshwater cost and TUs operating and investment costs. The problem is formulated as a nonlinear programing (NLP) model and solved using the global optimization solver BARON. The same synthesis problem can be formulated as an MINLP model and solved to the global optimum. For the synthesis of non-isothermal water, wastewater treatment and HENs, the overall model consists of two sub-models. The first one is a NLP model consisting of a WN model and a simultaneous optimization and heat integration model (Duran and Grossmann, 1986). The second model is an MINLP model consisting of a modified WN model combined with modified HEN model (Yee and Grossmann, 1990).

The two-step solution strategy proposed by (Ibrić et al., 2013) was slightly modified in order to solve non-isothermal water, wastewater treatment and HENs. In the first synthesis step the NLP model was solved in order to minimize freshwater and utility consumption, and the operating costs of TUs. The solution of this model was used as an initialization point during the second synthesis step. In addition, the values for freshwater and utility consumption as well as total wastewater flow rate through TUs, (obtained for a given value of heat recovery approach temperature (HRAT)) were set as rigorous constraints when solving the MINLP model in the second synthesis step. The objective function of the MINLP model was to minimize the TAC of the network including operating cost (freshwater, utilities and TU operating cost) and the investment costs for HEs and TUs. A set of good locally optimal solutions was obtained by using different initial points for HRAT (1-20 °C) during the first synthesis step, and the best one with minimum TAC was chosen from amongst them. A problem was modeled in GAMS (Rosenthal, 2008). The NLP model was solved using AlphaECP and the MINLP model using a SBB solver. The advantage of the proposed solution strategy is that the rigorous bounds on water and utilities can be defined. Also, one can obtain a set of good locally optimal solutions. However, for generating multiple solutions the model has to be solved several times for different HRAT values during the initialization step.

5. Case study

In order to illustrate the proposed approach, a small multi-contaminant problem was studied and solved (Bogataj and Bagajewicz, 2008). Freshwater was supplied free of contaminants at a temperature of 20 °C and wastewater discharged into the environment at a temperature of 30 °C. The hot utility was steam at a temperature of 126 °C. The inlet and outlet temperatures of the cold utility were 15 and 20 °C. The freshwater price was assumed to be 2.5 \$/t and the prices for the hot and cold utilities were 260 and 150 \$/(kW·y). The total heat transfer coefficient was assumed to be 0.5 kW/(m^2·K) for the HEs and coolers, and 0.833 kW/(m^2·K) for the heaters. The annualized investment costs for the shell and tube HEs were estimated by the equation: $10{,}000+860\cdot(\text{Area})^{0.75}$. The plant operated continuously at 8,322 h/y. The specific heat capacity of the water streams was assumed to be 4.186 kJ/(kg·°C). Operating data for PUs and TU were given in Table 1. The capital cost (\$/y) for TU were given by equation $10{,}000\cdot(\text{Flow rate})^{0.78}$, while the operating cost (\$/t) was calculated using equation 0.95·(Flow rate). Removal ratio for the contaminants A, B and C in the TU were 75, 90, and 90 %. The inlet and outlet operating temperatures of the TU were 40 and 37 °C. It should be noted that the maximum concentration of the contaminants in the effluent stream discharged into the environment was not imposed in this case study.

Table 1. Operating data for the case study (Bogataj and Bagajewicz, 2008)

PU/ contaminants		Mass load (kg/h)	Maximum inlet concentration (ppm)	Maximum outlet concentration (ppm)	Temperature (°C)	
	A	6	5	50	In	Out
1	B	3	150	200	25	35
	C	4	100	200		
	A	5	150	300	In	Out
2	B	8	120	150	100	85
	C	1	60	300		

5.1. Base case

In the conventional WN the freshwater feeds all the PUs (Figure 2). In PUs the freshwater is contaminated and then collected and discharged into the environment. Using limiting contaminant concentrations (Table 1) and mass load of contaminants minimum flow rates of freshwater through PUs (120 t/h for PU_1 and 53.333 t/h for PU_2), and minimum freshwater consumption (173.333 t/h) can be determined. However, PUs requires water at specific temperatures. Freshwater at a temperature of 20 °C requires heating in order to achieve the targeted temperatures of the PUs. The outlet water streams from the PUs require cooling in order to satisfy the effluent temperature constraint (30 °C). In the conventional network each cold and hot stream requires a heater and a cooler (see Figure 2b). Investment cost for HEs is 102,943.8 and TAC of the conventional network of 4,584,162.2 $/y.

5.2. Water and heat-exchanger networks

Freshwater is used in the PUs of the conventional network, which requires large amounts of freshwater and utilities. In order to reduce freshwater and utilities consumption, water can be reused between PUs. Firstly, an isothermal WN is optimized with the objective of minimizing freshwater cost and an optimal WN design is presented in Figure 3a.

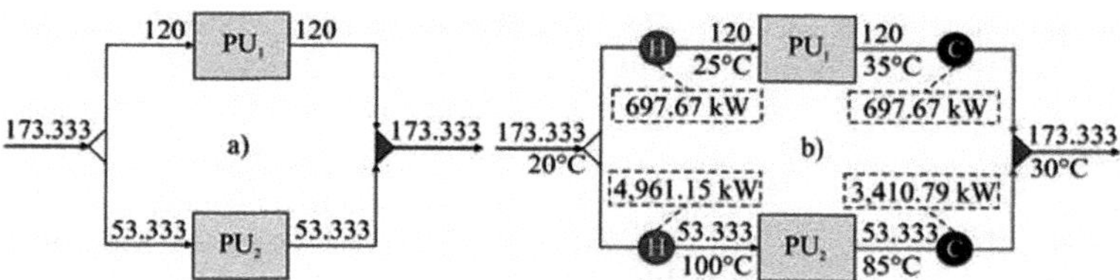

Figure 2. A base case (freshwater is used in all PUs) a) isothermal, b) non-isothermal design

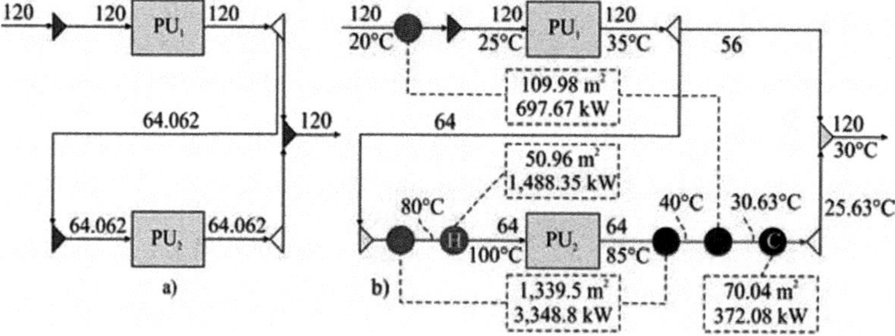

Figure 3. Optimal network design a) isothermal, b) non-isothermal

Water leaving PU_1 is partially reused ($PU_1 \rightarrow PU_2$), and freshwater consumption and wastewater generation is thus reduced (120 vs. 173.333 t/h). Secondly, a non-isothermal WN is synthesized using the two-step solution strategy. The optimal network design (Figure 3b) exhibited minimum freshwater consumption. The network consists of two HEs, one heater, and one cooler with investment cost for HEs of 296,855.4 $/y. The TAC of the network is reduced to 3,236,240 $/y.

5.3. Water, wastewater treatment and heat exchanger networks

In the next step of the methodology, an integrated WN was considered which would consist of PUs and TUs. Firstly, an isothermal WN was solved. The corresponding optimal design exhibited minimal freshwater consumption (80 t/h) (see Figure 4a). Wastewater from the PU_1 was partially reused (PU_2), regenerated and recycled (PU_1). Annualized operating and investment costs for TU are 377,264 and 444,722 $/y. TAC of the isothermal network was 2,486,386 $/y. Finally, a non-isothermal network, consisting of PUs, TUs, and HEs, was solved. It is worth pointing out that the optimal network design obtained in our case, when the TU was included within the superstructure, was similar to the solution presented in Figure 3b with the same TAC. However, in Figure 4b we presented a solution selected from a set of locally optimal solutions similar to the one reported by Bogataj and Bagajewicz (2008). This network design exhibited the minimum freshwater usage and consumption of hot (1,558.5 kW) and cold utility (891.2 kW). Its HEN consisted of two HEs, two coolers, and one heater. The TAC of the network was 3,386,558.9 $/y. Note that Bogataj and Bagajewicz (2008) presented a design with the same freshwater usage (80 t/h), the same number of HEs, and the same investment and operating costs for TUs. However their network design had a higher consumption of hot (1,602 vs. 1,558.5 kW) and cold utilities (933 kW vs. 891.2 kW), and somewhat higher TAC (3,410,588.4 $/y) due to higher investment costs for HEs (323,352.8 vs. 316,618.4 $/y) and higher utility cost.

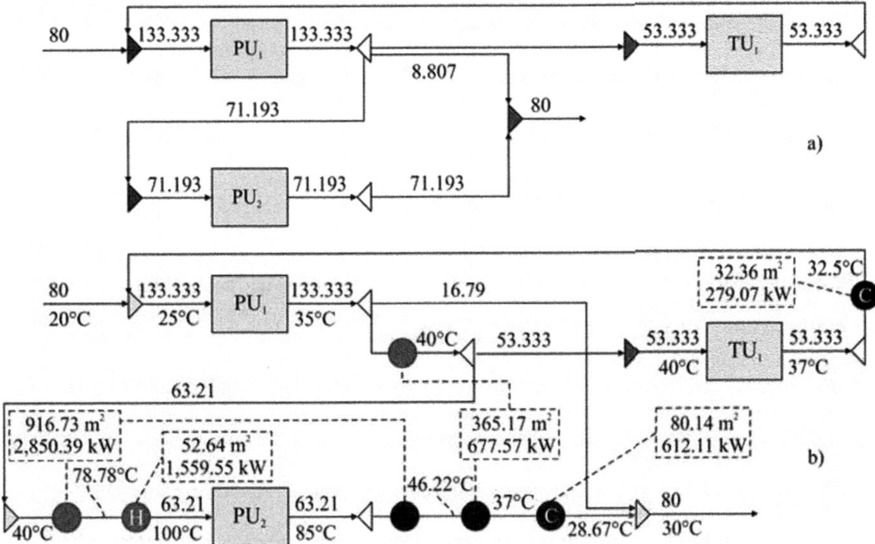

Figure 4. Optimal network design for integrated WNs a) isothermal, b) non-isothermal

6. Conclusions

This work presented a methodology for the synthesis of water, wastewater treatment and HENs. WNs without wastewater regeneration were firstly synthesized followed by water, wastewater treatment and HENs synthesis. A two-step strategy was used for non-isothermal WNs model solving, whilst isothermal WNs model was directly solved using BARON. A case study was used to demonstrate the methodology, and the obtained solutions were in good agreement with the reported results.

Acknowledgement

The support from bilateral project between Bosnia and Herzegovina and Slovenia, and the Slovenian Research Agency (Program No. P2-0032) is gratefully acknowledged.

References

E. Ahmetović, I. E. Grossmann, 2011, Global superstructure optimization for the design of integrated process water networks, AIChE Journal, 57, 434-457.

E. Ahmetović, Z. Kravanja, 2013, Simultaneous synthesis of process water and heat exchanger networks, Energy, 57, 236-250.

E. Ahmetović, Z. Kravanja, 2014, Simultaneous optimization of heat-integrated water networks involving process-to-process streams for heat integration, Applied Thermal Engineering, 62, 302-317.

M. Bagajewicz, H. Rodera, M. Savelski, 2002, Energy efficient water utilization systems in process plants, Computers and Chemical Engineering, 26, 59-79.

M. Bogataj, M. J. Bagajewicz, 2008, Synthesis of non-isothermal heat integrated water networks in chemical processes, Computers and Chemical Engineering, 32, 3130-3142.

C.-L. Chen, H.-L. Liao, X.-P. Jia, Y.-J. Ciou, J.-Y. Lee, 2010, Synthesis of heat-integrated water-using networks in process plants, Journal of the Taiwan Institute of Chemical Engineers, 41, 512-521.

H.-G. Dong, C.-Y. Lin, C.-T. Chang, 2008, Simultaneous optimization approach for integrated water-allocation and heat-exchange networks, Chemical Engineering Science, 63, 3664-3678.

R. Drobež, Z. N. Pintarič, B. Pahor, Z. Kravanja, 2012, Simultaneous synthesis of a biogas process and heat exchanger network, Applied Thermal Engineering, 43, 91-100.

M. A. Duran, I. E. Grossmann, 1986, Simultaneous optimization and heat integration of chemical processes, AIChE Journal, 32, 123-138.

B. Galan, I. E. Grossmann, 1998, Optimal Design of Distributed Wastewater Treatment Networks, Industrial and Engineering Chemistry Research, 37, 4036-4048.

N. Ibrić, E. Ahmetović, Z. Kravanja, 2013, A two-step solution strategy for the synthesis of pinched and threshold heat-integrated process water networks, Chemical Engineering Transactions, 35.

J. J. Klemeš, 2012, Industrial water recycle/reuse, Current Opinion in Chemical Engineering, 1, 238-245.

J. J. Klemeš, P. S. Varbanov, Z. Kravanja, 2013, Recent developments in Process Integration, Chemical Engineering Research and Design, 91, 2037-2053.

R. E. Rosenthal, 2008, GAMS: A User's Guide, GAMS Development Corporation, Washington, US.

L. Savulescu, J.-K. Kim, R. Smith, 2005, Studies on simultaneous energy and water minimisation—Part I: Systems with no water re-use, Chemical Engineering Science, 60, 3279-3290.

Y. P. Wang, R. Smith, 1994, Wastewater minimisation, Chemical Engineering Science, 49, 981-1006.

L. Yang, I. E. Grossmann, 2012, Water Targeting Models for Simultaneous Flowsheet Optimization, Industrial and Engineering Chemistry Research, 52, 3209-3224.

T. F. Yee, I. E. Grossmann, 1990, Simultaneous optimization models for heat integration—II. Heat exchanger network synthesis, Computers and Chemical Engineering, 14, 1165-1184.

Jiří Jaromír Klemeš, Petar Sabev Varbanov and Peng Yen Liew (Editors)
Proceedings of the 24th European Symposium on Computer Aided Process Engineering – ESCAPE 24
June 15-18, 2014, Budapest, Hungary.

Optimal Renewable Energy Systems for Smart Cities

Stephan Maier *, Michael Narodoslawsky

Institute for Process and Particle Engineering, Graz University of Technology, Inffeldgasse13/3, A-8010 Graz/Austria,
stephan.maier@tugraz.at

Abstract

Energy systems for smart cities will require on the one hand a much higher share of renewable energy sources for heat and electricity and on the other hand a high standard of integration of industry and utilities supplying households and business. New technological options such as passive buildings, bio-methane injection into grids, small scale CHP with heat storage and PV driven heat pumps for heat provision alter common strategies to supply larger settlements.

As energy options become more diverse, heat integration of industry into cities becomes important from economic and ecological considerations. Stabilising distribution grids in the face of diverging supply and demand profiles will further complicate planning of smart city projects. In the face of these challenges, innovative planning tools will gain importance.

This paper will discuss using the P-Graph method in its application to sustainable technology systems. This method will be used to generate optimal energy systems linking industry to smart cities and to integrate innovative energy technologies into such systems. The Sustainable Process Index will be used to evaluate these systems from the ecological sustainability point of view. This sustainability measure is particularly well suited to differentiate between conventional fossil based and renewable source based energy systems.

A real life case study of the application of these methods to the challenge of designing the optimal energy system for a smart city will be discussed in the paper. The case study deals with a green field development in a medium sized city in Austria (Graz). This project includes different energy provision sources (e.g. excess heat from industry, ground water energy), low energy buildings and innovative storage and energy provision technologies.

Keywords: Optimal Energy Systems, Smart Cities, Process Network Synthesis, Sustainable Process Index

1. Introduction

The integration of different renewable energy systems into an urban energy system and the optimisation of that system are challenging planning tasks. Process Network Synthesis (PNS) is a valuable tool to attend to this challenge executing an optimisation of a whole regional or urban energy system (Stoeglehner et al., 2011). In order to create holistic statements to achieve sustainable and integrated Regional Optimisation (RegiOpt) of urban areas the localisation of a series of parameters is crucial. Main component of these studies is the optimisation of technology networks, process chains and efficient use of capacities of on-site renewable energy to cover energy demand (Kettl et al., 2011). Process Network Synthesis (PNS) constantly used in different projects of regional and urban development and research of optimum energy technology networks (Maier, 2012) and various studies of sustainable energy supply chains (Vance et al., 2013) lead to basic knowledge and new insights in the field of optimisation of urban energy systems. In a case study the urban redevelopment of a brown-field of a former brewery is analysed (Reininghaus, city of Graz/Austria).

2. Methodology

2.1. Process Network Synthesis (PNS)

Process Network Synthesis (PNS) is a method to optimise systems of material- and energy flows. Methodical background is the p-graph method using combinatorial rules (Friedler et al., 1995). For urban and regional planning the software tool PNS Studio is used to find sustainable technology systems (Narodoslawsky et al., 2008).

Starting point of a PNS analysis is to set up a maximum structure as shown in Figure 1. Hereby all available raw materials and resources (including waste heat flows) can be defined as well as the technology network which can convert them either to intermediates which can be used in other processes or to products which can be sold on the market. Capacities of technologies as well as availability, amount and quality structure of materials are user-defined. Moreover time bound availabilities of resources, the specific demand of products, all included mass- and energy flows, investment and operating costs of the whole infrastructure, cost of raw materials, transport and selling prices for products must be defined.

Out of the maximum structure the programme creates an optimum structure. The optimum structure contains the optimal technology network. For this application the generation of the economically most feasible technology network was in the centre of consideration by setting the revenue for the whole system as target value.

2.2. Sustainable Process Index (SPI)

Energy- and material flows from PNS were steadily evaluated using the Sustainable Process Index (SPI), a member of the family of ecological footprints (Narodoslawsky and Niederl, 2006). The SPI uses life cycle impact assessment (LCIA) and evaluates human activities according to the area necessary to embed them sustainably into the ecosphere. It uses only natural references and life cycle inventory data for this evaluation. It is a helpful method to evaluate the ecological footprint of networks of technologies, evaluating resource use as well as emissions with their respective ecological impacts (Krotscheck and Narodoslawsky, 1996). To execute SPI the method has been integrated in a table based programme and different projects have been in use of the evaluation tool called SPIonExcel (Sandholzer and Narodoslawsky, 2007).

Since the tool has been developed further the determination of the ecological footprint is executable with the online tool SPI on Web (Kettl and Narodoslawsky, 2013). In the sense of open science research the web tool is freely accessible on web.

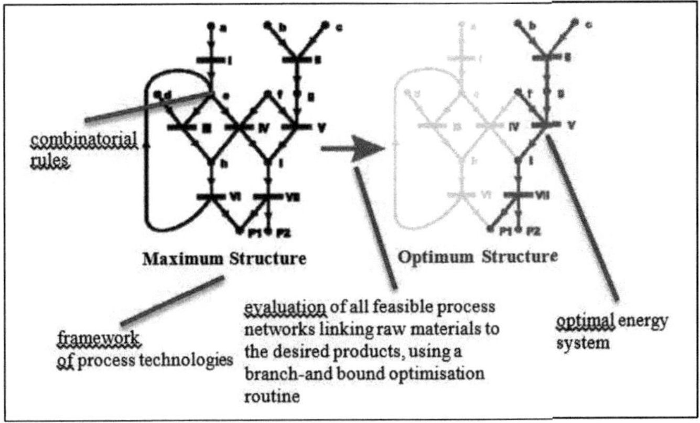

Figure 1. Maximum structure and Optimum structure of a technology network

3. Smart Urban Energy System (SUES)

For the case study technological pathways to Smart Urban Energy Systems have been selected. Findings in good-practice examples (Maier et al., 2013) showed that it is better to consider a broad portfolio of technologies instead of concentrating on single solution pathways (e.g. geothermal energy only). Figure 2 shows technological pathways to supply energy within an urban area used in this work. PNS maximum structure was constructed including specific boundary conditions for the area under consideration.

3.1. Energy demand of planned quarters

During the project of the case study the brown-field area was divided into 25 quarters which were aggregated to 20 groups with similar requirements. Passive house standard multi-storey buildings are planned to be built on an area of around 270,000 m² with an assumed gross floor area of nearly 1,000,000 m². In a first step the energy supply and demand situation was examined. Therefore the estimated energy demand of the planned buildings was used. The heat demand of the buildings is 30 $kWh{\cdot}m^{-2}{\cdot}y^{-1}$, so the total energy demand is 29,600 $MWh{\cdot}y^{-1}$. The electricity demand is 25 $kWh{\cdot}m^{-2}{\cdot}y^{-1}$, so the total electricity demand is 24,700 $MWh{\cdot}y^{-1}$. The cooling demand is 15 $kWh{\cdot}m^{-2}{\cdot}y^{-1}$, so the total cooling demand is $7{,}600{\cdot}y^{-1}$. The full energy demand was divided into three periods winter, midterm, summer as shown in Table 1.

Table 1. Energy demand by period and type in kWh

Month	**Heating water**	**Hot water**	**Electricity**	**Cooling**
January	Heating water	Hot water	Electricity	Cooling
February	5,497,156	1,234,192	2,056,986	0
March	1,854,623	1,234,192	2,056,986	0
April	260,181	1,234,192	2,056,986	0
May	6,671	1,234,192	2,056,986	74,239
June	0	1,234,192	2,056,986	445,434
July	0	1,234,192	2,056,986	1,781,735
August	0	1,234,192	2,056,986	2,227,169
August	0	1,234,192	2,056,986	1,781,735
October	0	1,234,192	2,056,986	1,262,062
October	33,357	1,234,192	2,056,986	74,239
December	2,114,804	1,234,192	2,056,986	0
Year	**5,043,507**	**1,234,192**	**2,056,986**	**0**

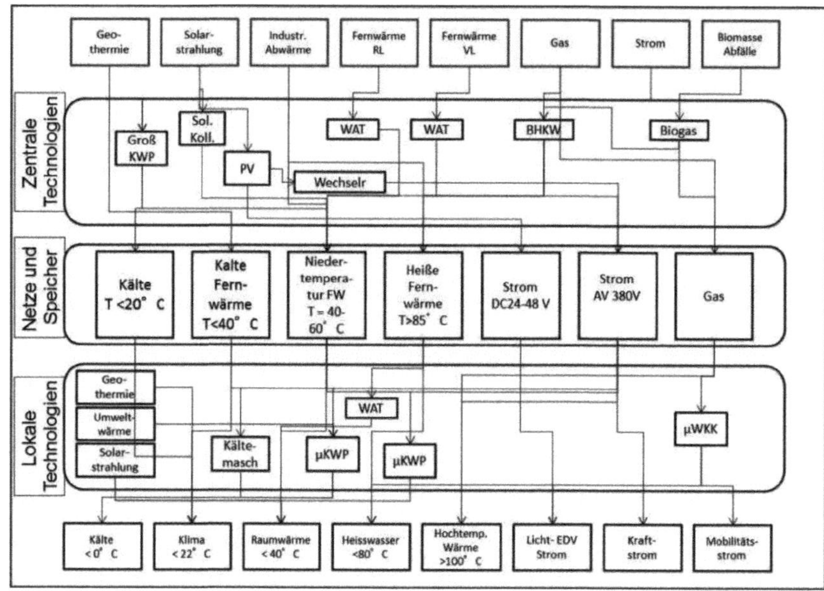

Figure 2. Technological pathways in an urban energy system

The quarter groups are located between a dense net of an already installed system of gas- and heat mains. Furthermore there is a high potential of unused hot and cold energy flows. These possible energy sources were set linked to central and decentralised energy technology systems. To recreate a significant energy supply system in a maximum structure of possible technological options it was important to define quarter groups, unused energy sources and distances to possible injection points as shown in Figure 3.

Distances for possible gas-, cold- and heat energy transport pipes between energy suppliers and quarter groups were crucial to calculate the cost for the respective construction and installation of the pipes and grouped separately in supply areas determined as "knot nord-west, knot nord-east and knot-south".

4. Process Network Synthesis

For PNS-maximum structure technologies were allowed which can use renewable resources or waste heat or cold flows to supply the quarters. These were on the one hand decentralised technologies like solar heat, gas burner, CHP, PV, air conditioner, geothermal energy, heat exchanger and heat pumps which can be positioned directly at the location of the supplied buildings. On the other hand centralised technologies are considered (gas burner, CHP, heat pumps and heat exchanger on district heating or micro net scale) to supply cold energy, heat and electricity. The use of industrial waste heat and deep wells (industry: Marienhütte, Lindegas, Stamag), as shown in Figure 4 was also considered.

The structuring started with pipes, industrial heat, cold energy, centralised technologies taking into account limitations concerning available resources and demand of products and energy. Decentralised technologies were made for a first quarter group (N) which contains quarters 11 und 11b. This group has demand of all kinds of defined technologies of the defined technology network (e.g. not all quarters need cooling).

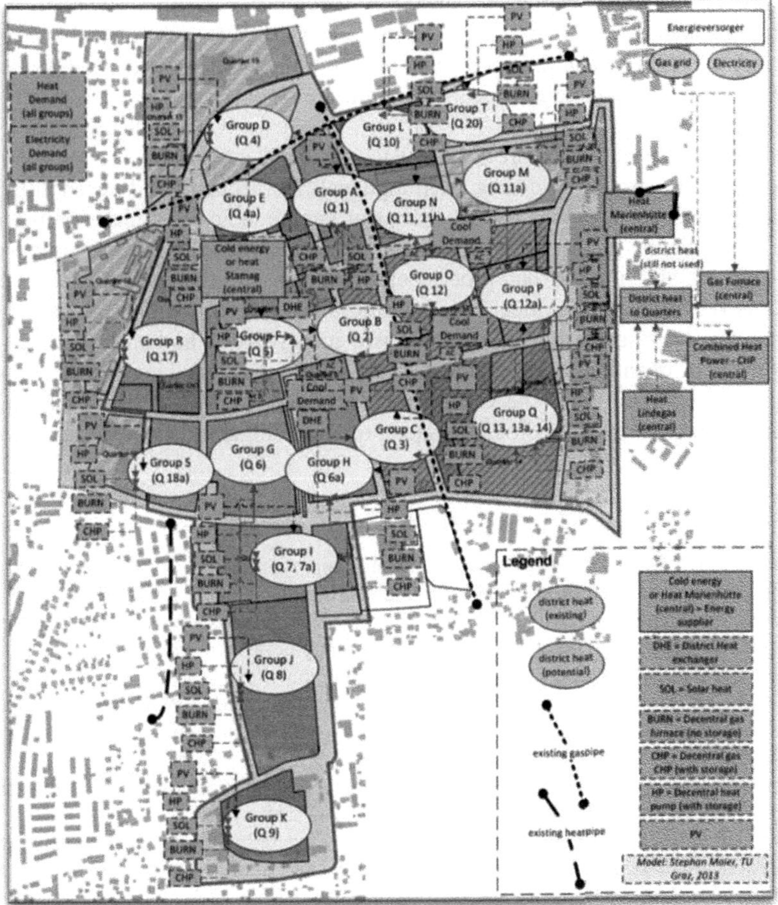

Figure 3. Quarter groups and energy structure

The next steps will be a testing and a redevelopment of the current maximum structure and finally an extensive structuring of the other 19 Quarter groups (from A to T) and optimisation and the creation of scenarios.

The maximum structure can be supplemented by different scenarios by manipulating copies of the basic maximum structure. Options are dependent on specific boundary conditions ranging from changing of costs and prices up to structural enlargements and resource/technological limitations. Hence this gives an overview of different variants to develop the observed brownfield in a maximum practicability.

5. Conclusions

In this work the evaluation of an optimum energy system is embedded in the ongoing process of the redevelopment of a district of a growing middle-sized city (Graz/Austria). Different aspects of sustainable urban development (e.g. external energy demands, external energy grids, economical demand, geographical optimum transport situation etc.) are under consideration. The energy system as a whole must be integrated in the local context. Interdisciplinary planning becomes essential (spatial planning, construction planning, energy engineering, infrastructure planning). The energetic evaluation of different building scenarios of electricity-, cold energy- and heat supply is evaluated with thermal and electrical balancing.

Use of renewable energy sources (e.g. PV) for local use shows the grade of energy autonomy of the brown-field area (Reininghaus). An efficient and decentralised urban self-supply and an optimum use of the local energy helps to reduce emissions (e.g. CO_2). This newly determined knowledge is essential to influence future projects concerning Smart Cities. Urban process optimisation with the help of Process Network Synthesis (PNS) provides valuable information for decision making processes such as the optimum use of available resources (waste energy flows) and urban energy network. To extend the quantitative assessment of the PNS analysis the energy- and material flows of the scenarios will be ecologically evaluated with SPI. This allows making conclusions regarding the ecological impact of technological pathways suggested by the PNS-scenarios.

References

F. Friedler, J. B. Varga, L. T. Fan, 1995, Decision-mapping: a tool for consistent and complete decisions in process synthesis, Chemical Engineering Science, 50, 1755-1768.

K. H. Kettl, N. Niemetz, N. Sandor, M. Eder, I. Heckl, M. Narodoslawsky, 2011, Regional Optimizer (RegiOpt) – Sustainable energy technology network solutions for regions, Computer Aided Chemical Engineering, 29, 1959-1963.

K.-H. Kettl, M. Narodoslawsky, 2013, SPIonWeb – Dynamic Life Cycle Impact Assessment (LCIA) process modelling based on Sustainable Process Index (Ecological Footprint), Journal of Environmental Accounting and Management, 1, 1, 1-5.

C. Krotscheck, M. Narodoslawsky, 1996, The Sustainable Process Index - A new dimension in ecological evaluation, Ecological Engineering, 6, 241-258.

S. Maier, 2013, Regionale Energieoptimierung in St. Margarethen an der Raab mittels Prozess-Netzwerk-Synthese und RegiOpt-Datenbank, MSc Dissertation, <www.zuerst-energie.at/fileadmin/media/ZUERST/Das_ist_ZUERST/ Magisterarbeit_Regionale_Energieoptimierung_in_St_Margarethen.pdf>, Accessed on 27/01/2014.

S. Maier, A. Gemenetzi, M. Eder, M. Narodoslawsky, 2013, Optimal Renewable Energy Systems for Industries in Rural Regions, Conference on Sustainable Development of Energy, Water and Environment Systems – SDEWES, Dubrovnik.

M. Narodoslawsky, A. Niederl, 2006, Renewable-Based Technology: Sustainability Assessment, Chapter 10: The Sustainable Process Index (SPI), Chapter 10, Renewables-Based Technology: Sustainability Assessment, 159-172, Wiley, Chichester, UK.

M. Narodoslawsky, A. Niederl, L. Halasz, 2008, Utilising renewable resources economically: new challenges and chances for process development, Journal of Cleaner Production, 16, 2, 164-170.

PNS Software Version 3.0.4, 2011, <www.p-graph.com>, accessed on 10/01/2014.

D. Sandholzer, M. Narodoslawsky, 2007, SPIonExcel—Fast and easy calculation of the Sustainable Process Index via computer, Resources, Conservation and Recycling, 50, 2, 130-142.

G. Stoeglehner, N. Nora Niemetz, K. H. Kettl, 2011, Spatial dimensions of sustainable energy systems: new visions for integrated spatial and energy planning, Energy, Sustainability and Society, 1, 1, 2.

L. Vance, H. Cabezas, I. Heckl, B. Bertok, F. Friedler, 2013, Synthesis of Sustainable Energy Supply Chain by the P-graph Framework, Ind. Eng. Chem. Res., 52, 1, 266–274.

Jiří Jaromír Klemeš, Petar Sabev Varbanov and Peng Yen Liew (Editors)
Proceedings of the 24th European Symposium on Computer Aided Process Engineering – ESCAPE 24
June 15-18, 2014, Budapest, Hungary.

New Energy Planning Software for Analysis of Island Energy Systems and Microgrid Operations – H2RES Software as a Tool to 100% Renewable Energy System

Goran Gašparović,[a,*] Goran Krajačić,[a] Neven Duić,[a] Mato Baotić[b]

[a]*University of Zagreb, Faculty of Mechanical Engineering and Naval Architecture, Croatia*

[b]*University of Zagreb, Faculty of Computer Engineering, Croatia*

goran.gasparovic@fsb.hr

Abstract

H2RES energy planning software was created for optimization of microgrid components sizing. Requirements taken into the account during optimization are: local loads, the level of microgrid autonomy from the utility grid, technical characteristics and cost of components, lifetime of equipment, available area and space, impact on the environment. The optimization resides on the past meteorological data for the specific location (wind speed and solar insulation). Procedures for selecting, dimensioning and placing of renewable energy systems (RES) for location-specific microgrids in urban environments are assessed with weather forecasting.

The problem of storage systems is the increase in cost of distributed RES, making them, in market terms, less economically viable. This storage characteristic is even more highlighted in microgrids that need sophisticated and costly power electronics and communication systems to manage power flows from various sources to different controllable and uncontrollable loads. It is essential for further deployment of microgrids to ensure its optimal planning and sizing in order to avoid unnecessary costs on one side and on the other to ensure acceptable level of energy supply autonomy.

Keywords: H2RES, microgrid, EV, storage, planning

1. Introduction

There is a considerable number of energy software in existence. One common occurrence amongst these is the complexity of use. As stated by nearly all providers of software, it requires a minimum of several weeks of training for obtaining even a moderate level of skill and ability to command a given tool, and thus, generate meaningful results from it. To that effect, H2RES energy planning software (Fig.1) was used for planning and optimization of future microgrids. The aim of H2RES is to facilitate as much as possible the input/output, manipulation and presentation of the results used for simulating and optimizing an energy case. To ease the use and shorten the time needed to learn the usage, intuitive graphical user interface (GUI) was created. As investigated by Connolly et al. (2010), a number of existing energy planning software exists, and H2RES energy planning software was originally developed by Duić et al. (2008) to create a framework for island energy scenarios implementing high share of RES generation.

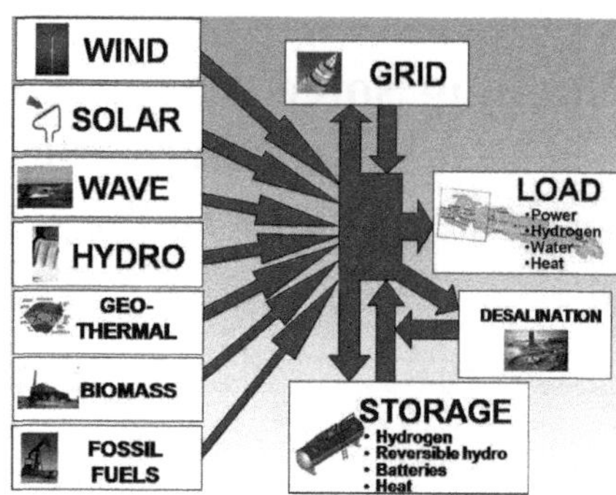

Figure 1. General layout of H2RES hourly energy planning software

Options for energy storage and integration of energy and resource flows that could help solve intermittency problems in the islanded energy systems (IES) were proposed using the RenewIslands methodology, included in work by Krajačić et al. (2009). To achieve 100 % RES target, the most likely candidate for transition to RES is the transport sector, examined by Lund et al. (2011) and Mathiesen et al. (2011) and further explained in Mathiesen et al. (2012). Further cases of 100 % RES penetration microgrid environments with storage as arbitration energy medium were examined by Stadler (2009). Similar approach was applied for island environments by Segurado et al. (2011), based on prior application as presented by Krajačić et al. (2008). Optimal sizing of microgrids is investigated by Zhou et al. (2010) and further by Hafez and Bhattacharya (2012). The inclusion of battery electric vehicles (BEV) or plug-in hybrid electric vehicles (PHEV) creates an opportunity for economic benefits, stated by Stadler et al. (2011). Since the path to 100 % RES will not happen instantaneously, it is necessary to plan in the short and medium-term for combined operations with non-RES generation by Erdinc and Uzunoglu (2012). Housing sector, along with transportation will be the major contributor to demand shift in the future, as envisaged by Duić et al. (2013). Flexible storage with high RES input and observation of demand increase is described by Mathiesen et al. (2012).

2. H2RES energy planning software

H2RES is designed to take the user hierarchically through steps in creating an energy scenario. The user inputs are executed in the upper left menu of the GUI (Fig. 2).

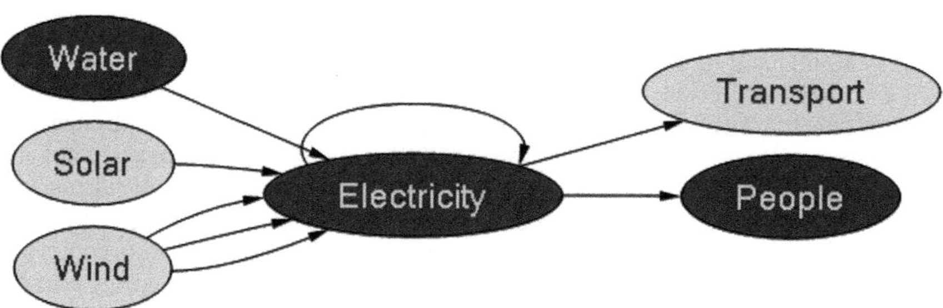

Figure 2. General overview of Bus Nodes in H2RES main screen

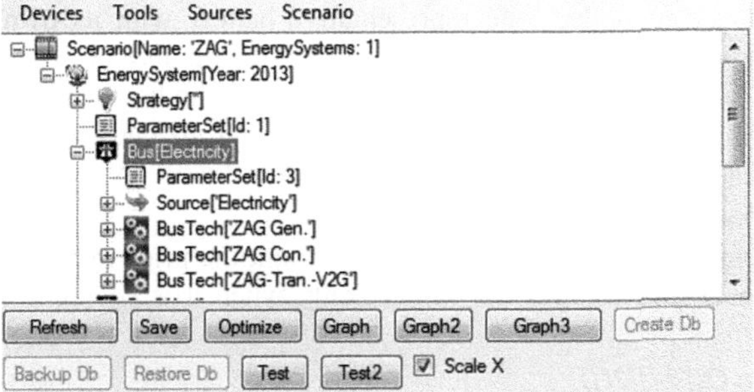

Figure 3. General H2RES Scenario GUI window

Initial step is to create a "Scenario" (SC) (Fig. 3). SC contains all the data for all the generation, demand and storage components, with all the energy carriers, for the entire period of energy planning, usually in the period of 10-50 years.

"Energy System" (ES) contains the same data from SC for only one year. In general, not all years are modelled specifically, and for time steps of approximately 5-10 years, a specific year is looked into in detail to provide insight for trends and to account for specifics such as phase-out of major power generating capacity or a change in demand.

"Energy Bus" (EB) is a representation of an energy carrier or vector, such as electricity, heating, cooling or other forms of energy.

"Bus Tech" (BT) encompasses logically the segments of the ES such as generators, consumers or storages.

"Bus Node" (BN) is the logical connection point for actual devices that are a part of the ES. A parameter of "Discount Rate" (DR) which is tied to the project costs and not the actual devices is also part of the BN.

"Device" (DEV) represents the physical device ranging from power plants, wind turbine generators, solar panels, to storages and electric vehicles. Each device is represented with parameters such as:Unique identifiers; Installed power and capacity; Lifetime; Economic parameters; Investment price and operation and maintenance costs which are DEV specific.

2.1. Example of H2RES modular architecture – Electric Vehicle module description

Electric Vehicles (EV) in H2RES are a part of the "Storage" (STO) segment of the system, and are considered equally in the calculations as other DEV such as pumped hydro storage (PHS), batteries (BAT) or hydrogen storage (HS). There are certain specifics which were addressed during the modelling of the EV module which will be detailed further in the next paragraph. Modes of charging and discharging of EV batteries in H2RES are as follows:

2.1.1. Dump Charge (DC)

A simple model of an electric vehicle designed to be charged automatically when plugged into an outlet, while disregarding the time of day and tariffs. This mode is only able to charge the vehicle. Whether the EV will be modelled as an aggregate battery model or a single EV for micro-grids is left for the user to determine. H2RES supports both modes for the purposes of calculations. If the energy scenario plans for a single type of EV's to be modelled, one representative battery with its own Power Curve, Transformation and demand is required. To change the number of EV's in a scenario, a property in the GUI window "Number of installations" can be changed. Along with the number increase or decrease, the battery capacity and all battery parameters will be calculated appropriately. The same mechanism applies for all EV modes described.

2.1.2. Smart Charge (SC)

Another charge-only mode, which takes into account the price rates, state of charge of battery, peak loads and charges the vehicle only when it is economical or absolutely necessary.

2.1.3. Vehicle to Grid (V2G)

Most complex of all, this mode is able to return the energy back into the grid if necessary and economically favourable. Parameters considered for this activity are time of day, future probability of vehicle use, state of charge of battery, price rates for electricity, peak load values and feasibility of discharge. The last parameter is crucial in determining the amount of energy available to be discharged into the grid. This number depends on the number of cars that are in traffic, and thus unavailable for grid connection, the number of stationary cars that are connected to the grid (as some cars could be parked, but not connected to a grid, e.g. an employee's car on a company parking not connected to the grid), and finally the number of connected cars that are able to discharge.

Firstly, an EV module within the ES (Figure 4) is a composite object consisting of a consumer (the electric motors) and storage (the on-board batteries). The consumer part of the EV is defined by the demand for electrical energy that is a direct result of user demand, or driving. The input for consumption is expressed as demand in kWh for every hour in one year, or 8760h. To enable such input, a structure called "Transformation" (TR) is used to input time-series of 8760 points (equivalent to hours in one year). The method for obtaining actual demand data is not part of the H2RES software and is generally derived from outputs of other tools such as the Four-Step Model (FSM), used in transportation planning.

The second component of the composite EV object is the battery (Figure 5). It is defined by parameters of maximum and minimum capacity, charge and discharge power, and charge and discharge efficiency. The actual number of EVs within a system is also defined in the BN "EVBattery" since the BN is the H2RES representation of real-world number of EVs.

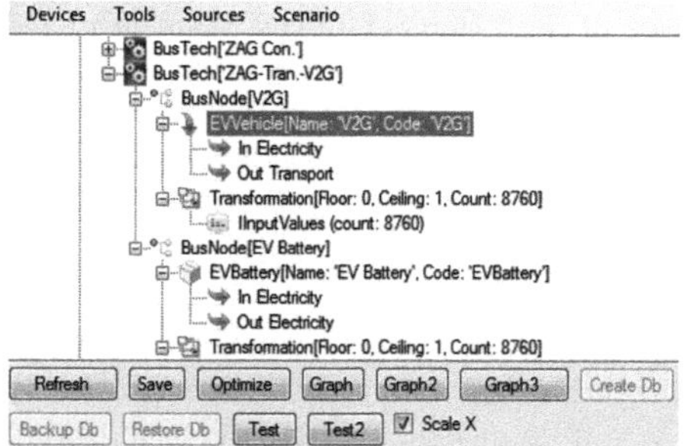

Figure 4. BT EVBattery view

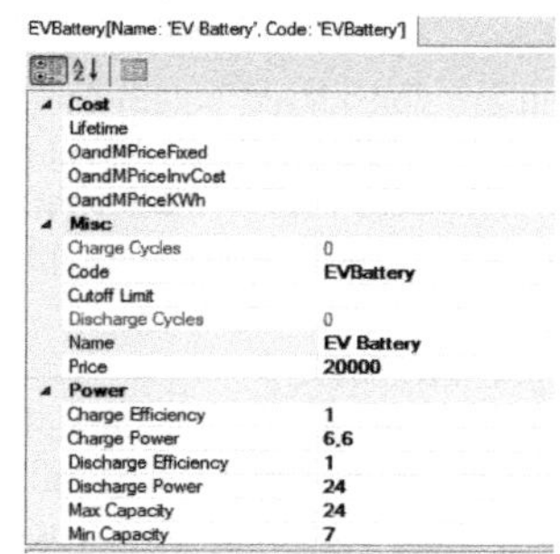

Figure 5. Properties of EVBattery

Within the total number of EVs in the system, there is a need to distinguish which EVs are at any one hour: Driving; Parked and connected to the grid; Parked and not connected to the grid.

With that information, it is possible to calculate the exact amount of EV battery capacity that is available for the system to manage. Another TR is used that has the following characteristics. Its time-series input is the amount of capacity of EV batteries connected to the grid at any hour. As the output from traffic planning models gives an exact of vehicles currently driving, that number is subtracted from the total number of EVs in the system. The capacity of vehicles driving at a given hour cannot be used by the system since these vehicles are not connected. Further, as user input, the ratio of EVs parked and connected to the grid versus those parked and not connected to the grid is taken into account. After calculating and rounding up the number of EVs parked and not connected the number is also subtracted from the total number of EVs in the system. The final number of EVs available for charging is finally multiplied by the capacity of EV battery in kWh to obtain the available capacity in kWh for 8760h shown in Eq. (1).

$$Capacity = \left(N(EV_{total}) - N(EV_{driving}) - N(EV_{not\ connected}) \right) * Capacity(EV_{battery}) \quad (1)$$

3. Economic aspects of H2RES energy planning software

Implementation of economic model in H2RES is in support of calculating the profitability of energy scenarios. Towards that goal, several parameters were implemented regarding economics. First parameter looks into the Investment Costs (IC) of a scenario. These involve the funds to purchase the equipment. The equipment has a Lifetime (LT), over which the costs need to be amortized. Each new piece of equipment in the SC is considered to be purchased via a loan or credit; therefore, a Discount Rate (DR) is attached to each new BN after the starting year. Additionally, Operations and Maintenance Costs (O&M) are taken into consideration, which are expressed either by a fixed amount per year, a percentage of the IC or in cost per unit of generated energy. These parameters can be divided into fixed and marginal costs of energy. The fixed cost involves IC, while the marginal cost considers O&M and fuel costs if the generating equipment is of a non-RES type. Prices of fuel can be specified separately in a fixed manner, defined for each hour of the year to simulate market prices, or left specified as free to account for RES sources. All the parameters combined with LT define the Levelised Cost of Energy (LCoE) metric expressed in cost per unit of energy.

4. Conclusion

In order to create a 100 % RES it is necessary to take into account the changing nature of energy systems in the future. Microgrids consisting of EVs frequently used for peak-load shedding, RES providing energy for zero-energy buildings and with added smart grid capabilities demand-side management will be a common occurrence. H2RES provides a flexible and modular software framework for optimal generation and storage component sizing for the long-term planning. Future work consists of implementing the updated H2RES to a test-case consisting of solar PV, EV/PHEV and grid connection setup and development of an optimization algorithm for microgrid management. Meteorological forecasting for RES will have to be improved in order to better understand the dynamic of daily, weekly and seasonal changes in weather and RES generation. Storage management needs from daily cycles to seasonal accumulation.

• Acknowledgement

The authors would like to thank the Croatian Science Foundation for funding of the Microgrids project, Grant No. I-4463-2011, project leaders, and all the members of the research groups involved.

• References

D. Connolly, H. Lund, B. V. Mathiesen, M. Leahy, 2010, A review of computer tools foranalysing the integration of renewable energy into various energy systems, Appl. Energy, 87, 4, 1059–1082.

N. Duic, G. Krajačić, M. da G. Carvalho, 2008, RenewIslands methodology for sustainable energy and resource planning for islands, Renew. Sustain. Energy Rev., 12, 4, 1032–1062.

G. Krajačić, N. Duić, M. da G. Carvalho, 2009, H2RES, Energy planning tool forisland energy systems – The case of the Island of Mljet, Int. J. Hydrogen Energy, 34, 16,7015–7026.

H. Lund, P. A. Østergaard, I. Stadler, 2011, Towards 100% renewable energy systems, Appl. Energy, 88, 2, 419–421.

B. V. Mathiesen, H. Lund, K. Karlsson, P. Alberg Østergaard, I. Stadler, 2011, 100 % Renewable energy systems, climate mitigation and economic growth, Appl. Energy, 88, 2, 488–501.

B. V. Mathiesen, I. Stadler, G. Rizzo, Z. Guzović, B. Ćosić, G. Krajačić, N. Duić,2012, A 100 % renewable energy system in the year 2050: The case of Macedonia, Energy, 48, 1, 80–87.

M. Stadler, C. Marnay, A. Siddiqui, J. Lai, B. Coffey, H. Aki, 2009, Effect of Heat and Electricity Storage and Reliability on MicrogridViability: A Study of Commercial Buildings in California and New York States, Lawrence Berkeley National Laboratory (LBNL), Berkeley, California, USA.

R. Segurado, G. Krajačić, N. Duić, L. Alves, 2011,Increasing the penetration ofrenewable energy resources in S. Vicente, Cape Verde, Appl. Energy, 88, 2, 466-472.

G. Krajačić, R. Martins, A. Busuttil, N. Duić, M. da G. Carvalho, 2008, Hydrogen asan energy vector in the islands' energy supply, Int. J. Hydrogen Energy, 33, 4, 1091-1103.

W. Zhou, C. Lou, Z. Li, L. Lu, H. Yang, 2010, Current status of research on optimumsizing of stand-alone hybrid solar–wind power generation systems, Appl. Energy, 87, 2,380–389.

O. Hafez, K. Bhattacharya, 2012, Optimal planning and design of a renewable energybased supply system for microgrids, Renew. Energy, 45, 7–15.

M. Stadler, C. Marnay, R. Sharma, G. Mendes, M. Kloess, G. Cardoso, O. Megel, A.Siddiqui,2011, Modeling electric vehicle benefits connected to smart grids, IEEEVehicle Power and Propulsion Conference, 1–8.

O. Erdinc, M. Uzunoglu, 2012,Optimum design of hybrid renewable energy systems:Overview of different approaches, Renew. Sustain. Energy Rev., 16, 3, 1412–1425.

N. Duić, Z. Guzović, V. Kafarov, J. J. Klemeš, B. vad Mathiessen, J. Yan, T. Pukšec, B. VadMathiesen,2013,Potentials for energy savings and long term energy demand ofCroatian households sector, Appl. Energy, 101, 15–25.

B. V. Mathiesen, N. Duić, I. Stadler, G. Rizzo, Z. Guzović, M. Metz, C. Doetsch, 2012,Electric vehicles as flexible loads – A simulation approach using empirical mobility data, Energy, 48, 1, 369–374.

Jiří Jaromír Klemeš, Petar Sabev Varbanov and Peng Yen Liew (Editors)
Proceedings of the 24th European Symposium on Computer Aided Process Engineering – ESCAPE 24
June 15-18, 2014, Budapest, Hungary.

Sustainability Analysis of Copper Extraction and Processing using Life Cycle Analysis Methods: a Case Study in the North of Chile

Julio Castro-Molinare, Anna Korre*, Sevket Durucan

Department of Earth Science and Engineering, Royal School of Mines Imperial College London, SW7 2AZ, London, UK
a.korre@imperial.ac.uk

Abstract

Although life cycle of mining and mineral processing systems, including copper production, have been carried out since the mid to late 1990s; these studies are limited to the ore extraction and mineral processing, not considering waste management, which is the most important part of metal production systems when assessing their environmental performance. In addition, the low level of detail in mineral production systems included in conventional LCA tools (not accounting for emission at unit process level) lead to oversimplifications and underestimation of true impacts. This paper presents the life cycle assessment model developed by the authors to assess the impacts of copper extraction and processing, including waste management. The model is designed at unit process level and accounts for emissions to the different environmental compartments (air, water, soil).The model functionality is illustrated through a case study of a Chilean mining and mineral processing operation. The sensitivity of the LCA impact category indicator scores to the variation of input parameters, such as the copper ore grade, mine stripping ratio, metal recovery efficiency and electricity source mix are also evaluated and presented.

Keywords: mining, mineral processing, life cycle assessment, copper, waste management

1. Introduction

The concept of sustainability on the one hand and the extraction and processing of primary resources on the other, at first glance, appear to be in conflict, since the production processes deplete resources that are strictly considered finite. In addition these processes inevitably disturb the environment. This is especially true in copper production considering this is a metal with a high global demand, currently mined at increasingly low grades. The life cycle thinking approach, when assessing the sustainability of products, systems or activities, goes beyond the traditional focus on production site and manufacturing processes. Essentially, it includes the environmental, economic, and social impacts of a product over its entire life cycle. The Life Cycle Assessment (LCA) is an established method to assess the sustainability profile of products, processes and systems that has become important in recent years through the establishment of the ISO 14040 series of standards.

Despite the important efforts that have been made towards understanding and using LCA in mineral extraction and processing, there are still important gaps in the implementation of life cycle approaches in this field. One difficulty is that LCA practitioners can use variable goal and scope definitions when utilising the standards (e.g. variable process system, spatial and temporal boundaries). Secondly, due to the absence of spatial and temporal differentiation in the life cycle impact assessment (LCIA) methodologies used, prediction of environmental concentrations becomes difficult. Specific to mineral and metal production life cycle studies is a lack of integration between the ore extraction and mineral processing with the subsequent waste handling and an oversimplification of the waste management stage. In most mineral production LCA studies, solid wastes are considered as a direct emission to the environment without accounting for the process of waste management. The model presented in this paper aims to resolve these issues. The innovative aspects of the project, presented on this paper, relate to the development of a methodology that supports optimal use and management of copper resources taking into account the mineral, water and land resources, as well as the waste generated and environmental impacts, throughout the life cycle of a project. The approach taken considers the extraction and mineral processing stages, and the waste management associated with these at high level of detail.

2. Copper extraction and processing LCA model development

2.1. Life cycle model goal and scope definition

In order to develop a complete LCA framework for the "cradle-to-gate" assessment of alternative copper exploitation technologies and a comprehensive and quantitative Life Cycle Inventory (LCI) database, the Copper extraction and processing LCA system boundaries used include the mining, mineral processing and waste management, considering both the process life and the operations life, as illustrated in Figure 1.

In terms of temporal boundaries for the LCI model developed, besides the operational stages of the Copper exploitation and production operations, the construction and closure life cycle phases are also considered. The functional unit used for the estimation of the final emissions and life cycle environmental impacts is one tonne of refined copper cathode. There are several time horizons involved in the LCA of copper mining and extraction. The operational life cycles of mines, processing plants, smelters and waste storage facilities are normally quite different. In addition, production lines can include more than one mine, concentration plants, smelters and waste storage facilities. In order to account for these different time horizons, the impacts of different sub-system processes have been normalised to the lifetime of the mineral processing sub-system.

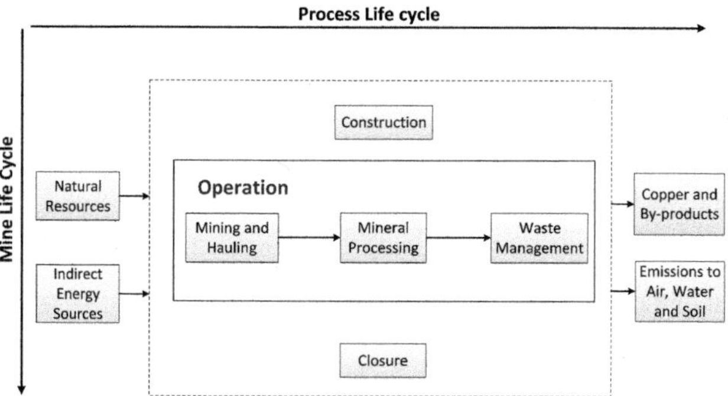

Figure 1. System boundaries of LCA of Copper mining and mineral processing

2.2. Life Cycle Inventory modelling and impact assessment

A copper extraction and mineral processing system comprises of a set of inter-related component unit processes. In the LCA model developed by the authors, the system is broken down or modularised into manageable sub-systems connected by flows of intermediate products or emissions. The modularisation is implemented for both the process and mine life cycles. The data that used to populate the LCI models consists of all inputs, outputs and intermediate flows that are part of the copper production processes, including: energy, materials, intermediate products, wastes and emissions. In order to account for these emissions to different environmental compartments, emission and control efficiency factors from literature, along with mass conservation and engineering calculations are used.

Air pollutant emissions factors and control method efficiency factors were mainly obtained from the USEPA AP-42 (USEPA, 2009a) and the Australian NPI mining related documents (NPI, 2012).The USEPA Nonroad2008a model was used (USEPA, 2009b) for the machinery and non-road vehicle related air emissions. In order to account for water flows throughout the copper extraction and mineral processing operations from their point of entry to the system, their partitioning in sub-systems and unit processes and the final emission (effluent disposal), the fraction of solids and water contents of intermediate flows (e.g. milled ore, concentrates and tailings, etc.) is accounted for throughout the system. Substances of environmental concern, which are abundant in copper ores and run of mines (e.g. sulphur, arsenic, other heavy metals and trace elements), are accounted for in different process, either directly or are estimated through emissions factors related to the level of activity of input resources or intermediate products.

Four different LCIA methods are used and compared in order to compare the results and complement some of the gaps present in individual LCIA impact indicator categories, such as those relating to water depletion, fuel depletion and land occupation impact indicators. The IMPACT 2002+ (Jolliet et al., 2003) and ReCiPe (Goedkoop et al., 2013) LCIA methods are used in the results reported in this paper. A number of scenarios were evaluated for some of the key parameters which affect significantly LCA impact category scores. These include the ore Copper grade, extraction strip ratio, concentrate transport distances, emission control efficiency parameters and power grid mix characterisation. The purposes of this scenario analysis and sensitivity studies are: to evaluate likely outcomes of the case study impacts in relation to the aforementioned parameters; establish how sensitive the different LCIA indicators are to these parameters; and assess the relative importance of the parameters in the evaluation of sustainability of copper extraction and production systems. In addition, a Monte Carlo based sensitivity analysis has been carried out on some of the key parameters to assess the effect of data and parameter uncertainty and variability on the life cycle inventory and the estimated life cycle impact indicator scores.

3. LCA model implementation for a Chilean copper extraction and processing facilities

The mining site and mineral processing on which this case study is based are located in the north of Chile. Due to confidentiality, the name of the study site is referred to as "Cerro Bonito". Figure 2 illustrates the high level life cycle inventory model structure as configured in the Gabi 6 LCA modelling environment.

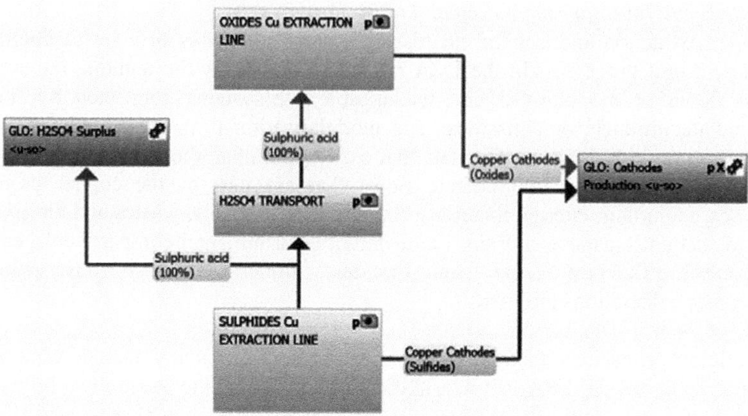

Figure 2. Copper extraction and processing LCI model in Gabi 6

Detailed production data for the year 2010 has been used to populate the inventory model for the copper ore extraction, and both the copper oxide and sulphides ore processing. For the few unit processes, where specific data for the "Cerro Bonito" facilities has not been available, the relevant information was estimated from other non-confidential data sources. Smelting facilities are external to "Cerro Bonito" operations. This company actually sells its concentrate from the sulphide ore to different copper smelting companies around the world. The smelting process LCI was created using the Codelco El Teniente smelter data from a USGS report (Goonan, 2004). In other words, the model assumes that all the smelting facilities that receive copper sulphide concentrates from "Cerro Bonito" have the characteristics and configuration of the El Teniente smelter.

Scenarios for past or future year production are estimated using the model developed and accounting for the specific year average copper ores grade, stripping ratio etc. parameters. A lifetime scenario for the copper extraction and mineral processing facilities is subsequently created using lifetime yearly average values for the above parameters. A small sample of the LCA model results for the normalised and weighted ReCiPe damage categories for the Cu extraction and processing per tonne of Cu cathode produced is shown in Figure 3.

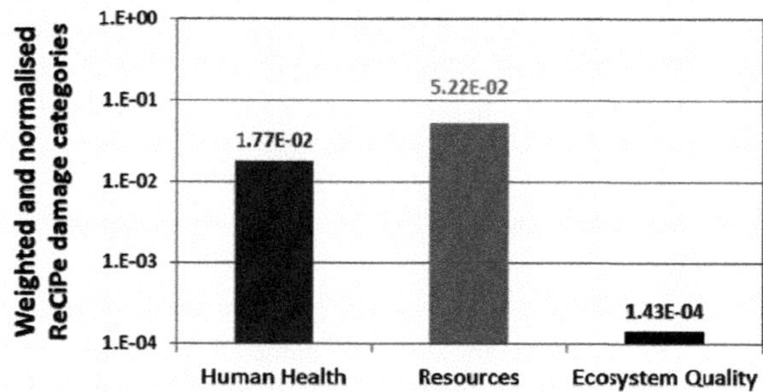

Figure 3. Normalised and weighted ReCiPe damage categories for the Cu mining and extraction process per tonne of Cu cathode

These results show that the highest normalised and weighted damage score corresponds to the resources category, accounting for both metal and fossil fuels depletion midpoint impact categories, which have relatively higher scores with respect to the other impact categories. The second highest damage category corresponds to human health, followed by a much lower ecosystem quality damage category. Four power supply variant scenarios have been compared for the two Chilean grid systems (SING and SIC): (1) a "solar power scenario", representing a 10 % increase of the solar based power generation share in the supply of electricity from SING, (2) a "wind power 1 scenario", representing an increase of 10 % of the wind power generation share in the SIC grid, (3) a "wind power 2 scenario", increase of 5 % each of the wind based power generation share in both SING and the SIC power-grids and (4) a "natural gas scenario", representing an increase of 6.7 % and 3.3 % of natural gas fuelled power generation share in the SING and SIC power-grids.

Table 1 shows an example of the parameter sensitivity analysis illustrating that a stripping ratio value of 0.89 would be needed, instead of the original strip ratio of four, to compensate for the Global Warming Potential (GWP) impact increase introduced by a 1 % reduction in the Cu ore grade. The table also shows that the solar power scenario is the most effective to compensate the mentioned Cu ore grade reduction related GWP impact increase. An extra share of 11.79 % of solar based power generation in the SING power-grid would be needed to compensate the same GWP impact.

4. Chilean case study results and conclusions

The LCA model results for the Chilean copper extraction and processing case study demonstrate that nearly all environmental emissions from the activities occur during the operational stage of the mine and mineral processing facilities. For the ReCiPe LCIA method, in the case of Global warming potential and fossil fuel depletion, the life-cycle environmental impacts are dominated by the emissions from the most energy intensive processes, which are part of the comminution-beneficiation process.

Human toxicity, marine ecotoxicity, ozone depletion, particulate matter formation, photochemical oxidant formation, terrestrial acidification and terrestrial ecotoxicity impact categories are dominated by emissions to the air from the smelting-converting process, mainly due to heavy metal and sulphur dioxide emissions to the air.

The freshwater ecotoxicity impact category is dominated by heavy metal emissions to the freshwater from the comminution-beneficiation process and phosphorus associated with the water treatment processes resulting from the comminution-beneficiation process. The water depletion impact category is dominated by internal water consumption of the comminution-beneficiation process, and then by the external energy consumption required for the same process.

Table 1. Changes needed to compensate the GWP impact of 1% of Cu grade reduction in the sulphide ore

Compensations in GWP (ReCiPe)	Stripping Ratio	Solar Power [%]	Wind Power 1 [%]	Wind Power 2 [%]	Natural Gas [%]
1 % Cu ore grade reduction	0.890	11.79	77.71	16.74	33.30

The land occupation impact category is dominated by the mineral extraction and waste storage, followed by the tailings storage facilities from the comminution-beneficiation process. Finally, the metal depletion impact category is dominated by the extraction operation due to the copper depletion. The power grid configuration changes investigated in the scenario analysis show that incremental increases of solar, wind and natural gas fuelled power generation shares produce positive changes in almost all the impact indicators, especially in the global warming potential, fossil fuels depletion and water depletion impact indicators. Clearly, one of the best options, in terms of impact reductions, is the increase in solar power generation in the SING system, which is the power grid system located in the north of Chile. This is a very important option to take into account, because the north of Chile boasts one of the best conditions in the world for harvesting solar energy.

Great differences were found between the ReCiPe and the Impact2002+ LCIA methods results, especially in the case of the impacts categories under the ecosystem quality and resources damage categories. Impact categories under the human toxicity damage category present lesser differences. The ecotoxicity impact categories were the most difficult ones to compare, showing the most significant differences between the ReCiPe, IMPACT 2002+ and Traci 2.1 LCIA methods. Land-use and water depletion categories from the ReCiPe method were used as no equivalent exists in the other three methods used in this research. In the case of the GWP, the different methods were compared and no substantial differences were found.

The research reported in this paper accomplished the development of a complete LCA framework for the "cradle-to-gate" assessment of copper extraction and processing making possible to: (1) compare alternative copper production technologies and commodity chains in terms of LCA, waste production and water resource consumption; (2) identify opportunities which can reduce environmental impacts and wastes produced in a life-cycle perspective; (3) evaluate the effect of key operational parameters, such as Cu grade and mine stripping ratio, on environmental impacts, resources efficiency and production. The development of the LCI models for copper production at component unit process level and the use of fundamental physical and chemical principles, have improved significantly the capacity of the LCI model developed to handle complexity and reduced model uncertainty, as compared with other available approaches.

References

M.J. Goedkoop, R. Heijungs, M. Huijbregts, A. De Schryver, J. Struijs, R. Van Zelm, 2013, ReCiPi 2008: A life cycle impact assessment method which comprises harmonised category indicators at the midpoint and the endpoint level, Report I: Characterisation, <www.lcia-recipe.net> accessed on 31/01/2014.

T.G. Goonan, 2004, Flows of selected materials associated with world copper smelting, U.S. Geological Survey Open-File Report 2004-1395, pubs.usgs.gov/of/2004/1395/2004-1395.pdf.

O. Jolliet, M. Margini, R. Charles, S. Humbert, J. Payet, G. Rebitzer, R. Rosenbaum, 2003, IMPACT 2002+: A new life cycle impact assessment methodology, The International Journal of Life Cycle Assessment, DOI: 10.1007/BF02978505.

NPI, 2012, Emission Estimation Technique Manual for Mining Version 3.1, Australian Government, ISBN: 0 642 54700 9.

USEPA, 2009a, Compilation of Air Pollutant Emission Factors, AP-42, 5th Edition, <www.epa.gov/ttnchie1/ap42> accessed on 31/01/2014.

USEPA, 2009b, NONROAD Model (nonroad engines, equipment, and vehicles), <www.epa.gov/otaq/nonrdmdl.htm> accessed on 31/01/2014.

Jiří Jaromír Klemeš, Petar Sabev Varbanov and Peng Yen Liew (Editors)
Proceedings of the 24th European Symposium on Computer Aided Process Engineering – ESCAPE 24
June 15-18, 2014, Budapest, Hungary.

Economic Viability and Environmental Impact of Centralized Biogas Plants in Croatia

Tomislav Novosel*, Tomislav Pukšec, Neven Duić

University of Zagreb Faculty of Mechanical Engineering and Naval Architecture, Department of Energy, Power Engineering and Environment; Ivana Lučića 5; 10002 Zagreb; Croatia
tomislav.novosel@fsb.hr

Abstract

Biogas plants are an established technology and their benefit is well recognized but they are still underutilized in Croatia, mostly due to the specific state of its agricultural sector. They can reduce the environmental impact of a farm, help with manure management and can also be an extra source of income to the owner. The biggest problem for Croatian farms is their small size and because of that, the supply of the plant with the necessary substrate. The utilization of centralized biogas plants is a possible solution to this problem. There are several factors that can influence the economic viability of a biogas plant ranging from its size to the modes of transport used to supply it with raw material. Because of this, the design of the plant and its operation has to be carefully planned in order to guaranty its economic viability. The goal of this work is to analyze the impact of the transportation distances on the economic viability of biogas plants and the resulting reduction of greenhouse gas emissions. Three hypothetical centralized biogas plants with installed electrical powers of 250 kW, 500 kW and 1 MW have been analyzed. Different transportation distances and different transport efficiencies have been taken into account.

Keywords: biogas, renewable energy, feasibility, CO_2 emissions

1. Introduction

The utilization of biogas can have a significant and positive effect on the reduction of CO_2 emissions of the energy and agricultural sector. One of the most important issues that the European energy sector is facing is the security of supply and greenhouse gas (GHG) emissions (Ćosić et al., 2011). The need for the reduction of GHG emissions is not important only for the energy sector but is also an important issue for other sectors such as industry (Mikulčić et al., 2013; Gharaie et al., 2012), households (Pukšec et al., 2013b), transport (Pukšec et al., 2013a) and agriculture (Robaina-Alves and Moutinho, 2014). Biogas plants can help with both issues. They can help with the decrease of the GHG emissions trough energy production from sustainable sources (Čuček et al., 2011) as well as the reduction of the release of methane in the atmosphere and they also represent a local source of energy that can reduce the dependence on energy import and provide a source of income for the owner (Sanchez, 2011).

Biogas plants are an established and widespread technology in Europe and their potential for energy production from waste is widely recognized (Oppong et al., 2012). There are currently over 7,500 biogas plants in operation in Germany (Lorenz et al., 2013). There are currently only 14 biogas plants in operation in Croatia (HROTE, n.d.) even though there is a potential for their wider use (Pukšec and Duić, 2011). The reason for such a low utilization of biogas in Croatia is the small size of the average farm. Small family farms are usually not able to support a biogas plant by themselves because they don't produce enough organic waste that can be used as a substrate. Larger centralized biogas plants that are supplied by multiple smaller farms could be a solution.

The goal of this work is to evaluate the impact of the transportation distance on the economic viability and CO_2 emission reduction of centralized biogas plants in Croatia. Multiple scenarios with different installed capacities, manure content in the substrate, transport distances and transport efficiencies have been compared.

2. Methodology

In order to analyze and compare the effect of different parameters on the economic viability and environmental aspects of centralized biogas plants in Croatia, an MS Excel based model has been developed. The model is used to calculate the IRR of the different scenarios and CO_2 emissions and savings used for the comparison. Three different centralized biogas plants with an installed electrical power of 250 kW, 500 kW and 1 MW have been analyzed. For every plant three different transport distances of 10 km, 30 km and 60 km as well as two different transport efficiencies, Croatian average and a lower efficiency, have been taken into account. The amount of manure used as substrate has also been taken into account. Each scenario has been tested with manure content in the substrate of 20 %, 50 % and 80 %.

The investment cost for the three different biogas plants were taken from the JRC (JRC, 2011) and the DEA (DEA, 2010). An electric efficiency of 40 % and a thermal efficiency of 38 %, as well as an availability of 90 % have been presumed for all three plants. The specific energy derived from the different substrates used in the analysis has been taken from the KTBL (KTBL, n.d.). The price of maize silage of 32 €/t was used in this paper. The transport efficiency has been calculated using the data obtained from CBS (2011), EIHP (2010) and EIHP (n.d.). The average efficiency of freight transportation using trucks and light transport vehicles has been calculated to be approximately 0.09 L/tkm (ton kilometers). A less efficient alternative of approximately 0.11 L/tkm has also been compared. The fuel consumption has been calculated using Eq. ((1).

$$AFE = \frac{TEC \cdot 10^{12} \cdot SFT}{FT \cdot Hd_d \cdot 3600} \quad (1)$$

AFE – average fuel efficiency [L/tkm]
TEC – total energy consumption of the road transport [PJ/y]
SFT – share of freight transport in total road transport [%]
FT – total freight transport achieved [tkm/y]
Hd_d – lower heating value of diesel [kWh/L]

The price of fuel has been taken from (INA, n.d.).The feed in tariff for biogas plants in Croatia depends on the installed electrical power of the plant. The tariff for a plant with a power up to 300 kWel is 1.42 kn/kWh, which is 0.19 €/kWh, and the tariff for biogas plants up to 1,000 kWel is 1.2 kn/kWh or 0.16 €/kWh (HROTE, n.d.). The feed in tariff is valid for a period of 14 years (HIDRA, n.d.) and the operator of the distribution system is obliged to take in all of the electricity produced from renewable sources or cogeneration. The CO_2 content of diesel has been taken from (Ćosić et al., 2012). The CO_2 savings have been calculated using Eq. (2). The total CO_2 emission savings, including emissions from transport, have been calculated using Eq. (3).

$$CO_2S = ElP \cdot fCO_2 + PBG \cdot CCH_4 \cdot \rho_{CH_4} \cdot GWP_{CH_4} \tag{2}$$

CO_2S – CO_2 savings [t/y]
ElP – electricity production [kWh/y]
fCO_2 – CO_2 emission factor for the Croatian electrical grid [tCO_2/kWh]
PBG – production of biogas [m^3/y]
CCH_4 – content of methane in biogas [%]
ρ_{CH4} – density of methane [kg/m^3]
GWP_{CH4} – global warming potential of methane [-]

$$TCO_2S = CO_2S - AFE \cdot TD \cdot TDCO_2D \tag{3}$$

TCO_2S – total CO_2 savings [t/y]
TD – transport distance [km/y]
CO_2D – CO_2 content of diesel [tCO_2/l]

3. Results

The results of the preformed analysis are presented in this chapter. Figure 1, Figure 2 and Figure 3 present the internal rate of return (IRR) for the analyzed biogas plants. It can be seen that the scenarios which incorporate the largest biogas plant, 1 MW, are the most economically feasible. The scenarios with a biogas plant with an installed electrical power of 500 kW have a lower IRR than the ones with 250 kW. This is due to the feed in tariff being higher for plants with a power up to 300 kW. It can also be seen that the transport distance have a significant impact on the economic feasibility of the project as well as the manure content in the substrate.

The IRR, for the scenarios with an average efficiency, varies from a value of only 6.61 % for the scenario that includes a 500 kW plant with a transport distance of 60 km and 20 % manure content to 26.33 % for a 1,000 kW plant, 10 km transport distance and manure content of 80 %

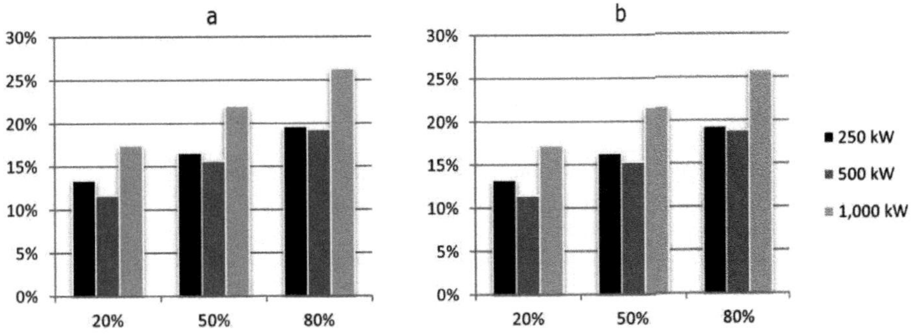

Figure 1. IRR for transport distance of 10 km, average efficiency (a) low efficiency (b)

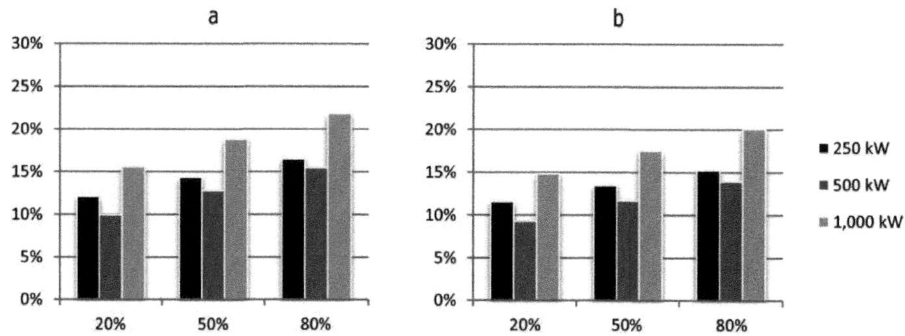

Figure 2. IRR for transport distance of 30 km, average efficiency (a) low efficiency (b)

The IRR, for the scenarios with a lower efficiency, varies from a value of only 5.92 % for the scenario that includes a 500 kW plant with a transport distance of 60 km and 20 % manure content to 25.78 % for a 1,000 kW plant, 10 km transport distance and manure content of 80 %.

Table 1 presents the CO_2 emission savings achieved from the utilization of a biogas plant because of the burning of methane and the production of electricity. The emission reductions due to the burning of methane are achieved because methane has a greater global warming potential than CO_2. The emission savings from electricity production are due to the fact that the electricity is produced from a sustainable source. The average emission Croatian emission factor of 0.376 $kgCO_2/kWh$ has been used.

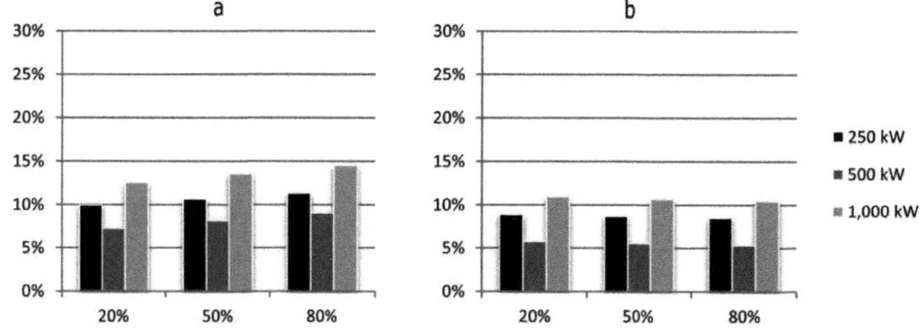

Figure 3. IRR for transport distance of 60 km, average efficiency (a) low efficiency (b)

Table 1. CO_2 emission savings

Unit	Electricity production [kWh/y]	Emission savings [tCO2/y]	Produced biogas [m3/y]	Emission savings [tCO2/y]	Total [tCO2/y]
250 kW	1,971,000	741	885,179	7,450	8,191
500 kW	3,942,000	1482	1,770,359	14,900	16,382
1,000 kW	7,884,000	2,964	3,540,718	29,801	32,765

Table 2. CO_2 emissions from transport and total emission savings for 80 % manure

Unit	Transport distance	Emissions avg. efficiency [tCO_2/y]	Emissions low efficiency [tCO_2/y]	Savings avg. efficiency [tCO_2/y]	Savings low efficiency [tCO_2/y]
250 kW	10 km	58	71	8,133	8,120
	30 km	175	214	8,016	7,977
	60 km	351	429	7,841	7,763
500 kW	10 km	117	143	16,266	16,240
	30 km	351	429	16,032	15,954
	60 km	702	858	15,681	15,525
1000 kW	10 km	234	286	32,532	32,480
	30 km	702	858	32,064	31,908
	60 km	1,403	1,715	31,362	31,051

Table 2 presents the CO_2 emissions from transport for both the scenarios with the average and low transport efficiency and for a manure content of 80 % and the total emission savings from all sources with transport taken into account.

It can be seen that that the added emissions from the transportation of the substrate has a small influence on the ecological aspect of a biogas plant within the parameters of the analysis conducted in this work. If the case of a 1 MW plant is observed the difference in emissions between the case of a 10 km transport distance with an average efficiency and a 60 km trip with a low efficiency is approximately 3 %.

4. Conclusion

Biogas plants, if designed and implemented properly, have a potential to be economically very viable in Croatia, as well as provide a great ecological benefit for the owner and the surrounding.

The IRR of larger centralized biogas plants with an installed power of 1 MW can be above 20 % if enough manure can be procured to reduce the need for the purchase of maize silage even for transport distances of 30 km. For a distance of 60 km the IRR drops to around 15 %. Smaller biogas plants with a power of 250 kW can also be economically viable with an adequate supply of manure.

From an environmental aspect all configurations have a great potential for CO_2 emission reduction with values ranging from 8,120 to 31,362 t of CO_2 annually.

Acknowledgement

Financial support from the European Commission's Intelligent Energy Europe Programme "Focussed Strategy for Enabling European Farmers to Tap into Biogas Opportunities – GERONIMO II" Grant agreement IEE/10/228 is gratefully acknowledged.

References

CBS, 2011. Statistical Yearbook of the Republic of Croatia, Croatian Bureau of Statistics, Zagreb, Croatia.

L. Čuček, R. Drobež, B. Pahor, Z. Kravanja, 2011, Sustainable LCA-based MIP Synthesis of Biogas Processes, Computer Aided Chemical Engineering, 29, 1999–2003.

B. Ćosić, N. Markovska, G. Krajačić, V. Taseska, N. Duić, 2012, Environmental and economic aspects of higher RES penetration into Macedonian power system, Applied Thermal Engineering, 43, 158-162.

B. Ćosić, N. Markovska, V. Taseska, G. Krajačić, N. Duić, 2011, The Potential of GHG Emissions Reduction in Macedonia by Renewable Electricity, Chemical Engineering Transactions, 25, 57-62.

DEA, 2010, Technology Data for Energy Plants, Danish Energy Agency, Denmark.

EIHP, 2010, Annual Energy Report Energy in Croatia, Energy Institute HrvojePožar, Zagreb.

EIHP, n.d., Energy Institute HrvojePožar. <www.eihp.hr/english> Accessed 06/07/2013.

HIDRA, n.d., Tarifni sustav za proizvodnju električne energije iz obnovljivih izvora energije I kogeneracije (NN 063/2012), <hidra.srce.hr/arhiva/263/33319/041464.htm> Accessed on 01/08/2013.

HROTE, n.d., HROTE, <www.hrote.hr> Accessed on 10/06/2013.

M. Gharaie, M. Jobson, M. H. Panjeshahi, N. Zhang, 2012, Energy Management Strategies for Process Site CO2 Emissions Reduction, Computer Aided Chemical Engineering, 30, 352–356.

INA, n.d., INA industija nafte d.d. <www.ina.hr> Accessed 25 August 2013].

JRC, 2011, Technology Map of the European Strategic Energy Technology Plan, Publications Office of the European Union, Luxembourg.

KTBL, n.d., Das KuratoriumfürTechnik und Bauwesen in der Landwirtschaft, <www.ktbl.de> Accessed on 05/06/2013.

H. Lorenz, P. Fischer, B. Schumacher, P. Adler, 2013, Current EU-27 technical potential of organic waste streams for biogas and energy production, Waste Management, 33, 11, 2434–2448.

H. Mikulčić, M. Vujanović, N. Markovska, R. V. Filkoski, M. Ban, N. Duić, 2013, CO2 Emission Reduction in the Cement Industry, Chemical Engineering Transactions, 25, 703-708.

G. Oppong, M. O'Brien, M. McEwan, E. B. Martin, G. A. Montague, 2012, Advanced Control for Anaerobic Digestion Processes: Volatile Solids Soft Sensor Development, Computer Aided Chemical Engineering, 30, 967–971.

A. Sanchez, 2011, Co-production of ethanol, hydrogen and biogas using agro-wastes. Conceptual plant design and NPV analysis for mid-size agricultural sectors, Computer Aided Chemical Engineering, 29, 1884–1888.

T. Pukšec, N. Duić, 2011, Geographic Distribution and Economic Potential of Biogas from Croatian Farming Sector, Chemical Engineering Transactions, 25.

T. Pukšec, G. Krajačić, Z. Lulić, B. V. Mathiesen, N. Duić, 2013a, Forecasting long-term energy demand of Croatian transport sector, Energy, 57, 169-176.

T. Pukšec, B. V. Mathiesen, N. Duic, 2013b, Potentials for energy savings and long term energy demand of Croatian households sector, Applied Energy, 101, 15-25.

M. Robaina-Alves, V. Moutinho, 2014, Decomposition of energy-related GHG emissions in agriculture over 1995–2008 for European countries, Applied Energy, 114, 949–957.

Jiří Jaromír Klemeš, Petar Sabev Varbanov and Peng Yen Liew (Editors)
Proceedings of the 24th European Symposium on Computer Aided Process Engineering – ESCAPE 24
June 15-18, 2014, Budapest, Hungary.

Identification of Process Integration Options for Carbon Capture

Peng Yen Liew[a], Petar Sabev Varbanov[a,*], Igor Bulatov[b], Simon John Perry[b], Mona Gharaie[b], Nan Zhang[b], Euan Fenelon[c], Aggelos Doukelis[d], Georgios Dimitriadis[e]

[a]*Centre for Process Integration and Intensification –CPI[2], Research Institute of Chemical and Process Engineering, Faculty of Information Technology, University of Pannonia, Egyetem utca 10, 8200 Veszprém, Hungary*

[b]*Centre for Process Integration, School of Chemical Engineering and Analytical Science, The University of Manchester, Manchester, United Kingdom*

[c]*Scottish Power Generation Ltd., Alloa, United Kingdom*

[d]*Laboratory of Steam Boilers and Thermal Plants, National Technical University of Athens, Athens, Greece*

[e]*CaO Hellas Macedonian Lime SA, Thessaloniki, Greece*

varbanov@cpi.uni-pannon.hu

Abstract

Many industrial sites consume vast amounts of fossil fuels and it is likely that they will continue to do so for the foreseeable future. The reasons for this are of various types, but the main ones are related to the convenience of using fuels as easily manipulated degrees of freedom in operating the plants. One of the options for reducing the emissions of greenhouse gases and most notably CO_2 is the CO_2 capture and its following sequestration. The present work aims at the optimisation of the performance of the power plants with CO_2 capture, examining all possible options for heat integration – including utilisation of low-grade waste heat. The identification of streams containing low-grade or low-value heat are performed in this regard, combined with potential waste streams suitable for generating additional energy. The integration of the capture process into the power plants will also consider the use of fans, coolers, gas polishing and CO_2 capture equipment. In power plants the steam extraction from the power train will be targeted for optimisation together with the recirculation of high grade heat. This allows identifying targets for energy recovery potentials and provides a sound design basis for cogeneration systems.

Keywords: Process Integration; Power Plant; Carbon Capture; Pinch analysis.

1. Introduction

The energy consumption of a process plant directly affects the greenhouse gases emission and further increases the load for the Post-combustion Carbon Capture (PCC) facility. Huge amount of energy is required to operate the PCC hardware, which creates energy penalty. This penalty is frequently defined as the increase of energy requirement for a power plant to maintain the energy output after considering the PCC facility (Harkin et al., 2010).

Process Integration and its subset Heat Integration (HI) is a established strategy for enhancing the process efficiency, reducing the resources consumption and reducing the emissions (Klemeš et al., 2010). Pinch Analysis is one of the proven methodologies in analysing the Process Integration opportunities within chemical process for more than 40 years (Klemeš and Kravanja, 2013). The process integration with Pinch Analysis is started with Heat Integration (HI) for single process (Linnhoff et al., 1982), which deals with the heat recovery using the Heat Exchanger Networks (HEN). HI methodology works well in reducing the energy consumption of a process and energy source intake.

1.1. Natural Gas Power Plant and Post-combustion Carbon Capture

There is a lot research done on renewable energy for fulfilling the increase of world energy demand and environmental awareness. Until the renewable energy become the more considerable portion of the power generation, the existing natural gas or fossil fuel based processes have to work with the maximum possible efficiency (Bass et al., 2011). In order to increase the efficiency of power generation process, Combined Cycle Gas Turbine (CCGT) plants have the benefits in greenhouse gas emissions, environmental impacts and cost (Silveira et al., 2007).

A natural gas power plant is usually using CCGT concept. The CCGT power plant consists of gas turbine, heat recovery steam generator (HRSG) and steam turbines. Fig 1 shows a natural gas CCGT power plant with amine based PCC facility attached for flue gas cleaning. In order to reduce the emission from the power generation process, carbon capture facility is frequently suggested to integrated to CCGT power plant (Biliyok and Yeung, 2013). However, PCC facility has high energy consumption which reduces the net power generation from the plant.

A CCGT power plant has great degree of freedom for heat and power generation in HRSG facility. Optimisation on the steam levels is required for increasing the performance of the whole power plant (Valdés and Rapún, 2001).

In this work, the HI options are identified for power plant with CC facility. The integration strategies can reduce the energy consumption and further decrease the energy penalty due to the operation of PCC facility. This work aimed for identifying wider range of HI options from single process to TS system, for reducing the energy penalty due to the CC facility operation.

2. Pinch Analysis

Pinch Analysis is a series of methodologies for resources conservation. HI is based on Pinch Analysis as an energy saving tool. Besides grassroots HEN design for new processes, the HI methodology has been developed for retrofitting the existing chemical

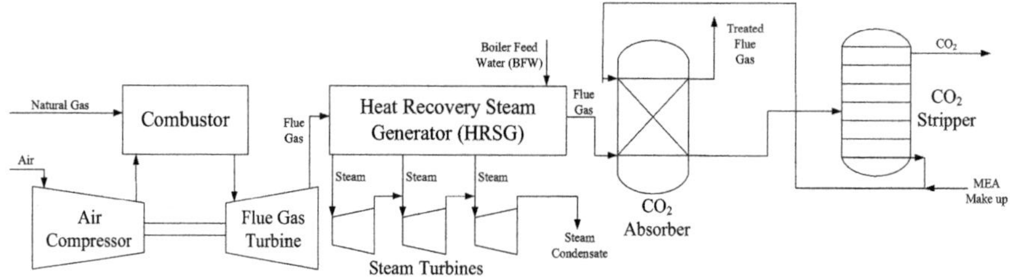

Figure 1. CCGT plant with amine based PCC facility.

processes, which the HEN design is restricted by the existing heat exchangers (Tjoe and Linnhoff, 1986).

Several tools are used for targeting the energy requirement of a process in Pinch Analysis. Composite Curves (CC), Grand Composite Curve (GCC), Balance Composite Curve (BCC) and Problem Table Algorithm (PTA) are the most common used techniques. The energy targeting methodology using Pinch Analysis is listed below (Klemeš and Varbanov, 2010):

I. Data extraction
II. Hot and Cold Composite Curves (CC) construction
III. Grand Composite Curve (GCC) construction
IV. Process modification options determination
V. Effects of process modification evaluation

There are some established concepts in process modification through Pinch Analysis, which are keep cool streams cold, keep hot streams hot, Plus-minus Principle, and appropriate utility placement. The energy penalty minimisation for PCC facility and power plant is investigated by various researchers. Pinch Analysis is frequently used to analyse the HI opportunities between power plant and PCC facility (Romeo et al., 2008). A combined Pinch analysis and linear programming methodology has been introduced for target the energy penalty (Harkin et al., 2010). Harkin et al. (2012) introduced a methodology for assisting the retrofit of power plant to introduce PCC facility. This methodology also incorporated the trade-off between power generation and energy requirement.

3. Process Modification Opportunity for a CCGT Power Plant

In this study, HI opportunities for a given optimised CCGT power plant are required to be identified. The processes streams are examined using Pinch Analysis. Figure 2 shows the GCC of the power plant with PCC facility, the Pinch located at 97 °C, while the hot and cold utility requirements are 171.7 MW and 277.0 MW.

3.1. Condensing Steam Turbine and Regenerative Solvent

Based on Figure 2, the hot utility is required to satisfy the energy deficit for the regenerative solvent at temperature between 102 °C and 120 °C. The condenser after LPS turbine is operating at temperature 33 °C, which 242.4 MW of cooling utility is re-

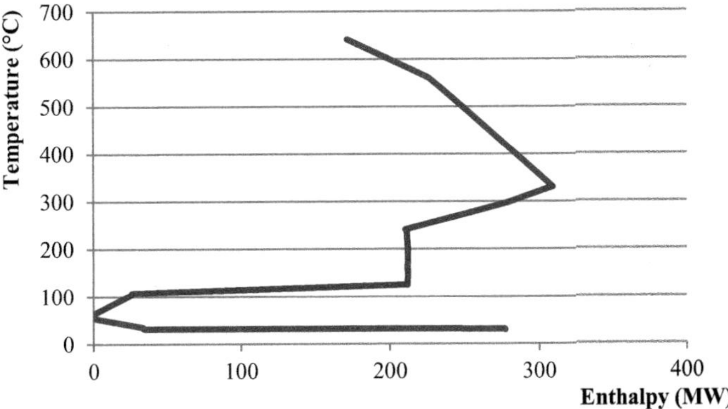

Figure 2. Initial Grand Composite Curve (GCC)

quired. It is suggested to optimise the exhaust pressure of steam turbine for recovering heat from condensation process for regenerative solvent process.

The exhaust pressure of the steam turbine can be optimised in order to increase the temperature of the heat available for heat recovery between the exhaust of steam turbine and the regenerative solvent. A trade-off analysis between the opportunity for heat recovery and power penalty is done for getting the optimum exhaust pressure at steam turbine. The analysis is divided to two parts, which is exhaust pressure from 4. 798 bar to 2.298 bar and 2.298 bar to 0.048 bar. This is due to the exhaust temperature would be higher than the required temperature for heat recovery at higher exhaust pressure. With exhaust pressure higher than 2.298 bar, the steam discharge temperature is higher, which can be directly use to heat up the heat sink (cold stream). For exhaust pressure lower than 2.298 bar, the steam exits steam turbine at low temperature, which heater is required for increasing the hot stream temperature. The heat exchangers arrangements in the trade-off analysis could be found in Figure 3.

The result of the trade-off analysis is shown in Figure 4. Power penalty increased exponentially with the increase of turbine exhaust pressure. There is a sharp increment of heat recovery opportunity and sharp decrease of condenser duty for exhaust pressure of 1.248 bar. This is due to the condensation process happens above the minimum temperature for heat recovery. At this point, a small amount of energy is required to operate heater, low cooler load and high energy recovery opportunity.

Figure 5 showed the GCC of the process after process modification on the steam turbine exhaust. As a result, the hot utility required by the site is 0 MW, reduced 100 % from the initial targeting result, and the cold utility reduced by 128.5 MW (53 % of the initial target).

3.2. Other Process Modification Options

Based on the Figure 2, the operation condition of the condensing steam turbine can be synchronised with the regenerative solvent. The temperature of the regenerative solvent can be optimised with the exhaust pressure of the condensing turbine. It would be ideal if the feasible heat exchange can happen in between the existing temperature. The CO_2 removal efficiency would decrease to a reasonable level due to the changes in operating condition of the stripper. There are pressure stations or compressor station in every defined distance of natural gas transportation pipeline. In order to maintain the pressure in the pipeline, the pressure stations are separating the condensed natural gas and the gas is compressed to continue the transportation. A small portion of the natural gas is

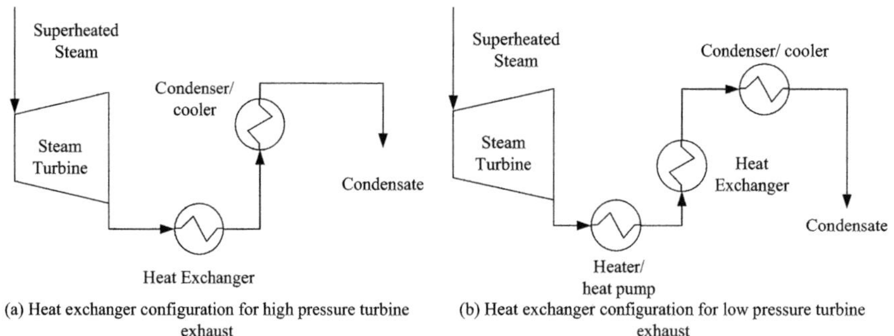

(a) Heat exchanger configuration for high pressure turbine exhaust

(b) Heat exchanger configuration for low pressure turbine exhaust

Figure 3. Process modification options

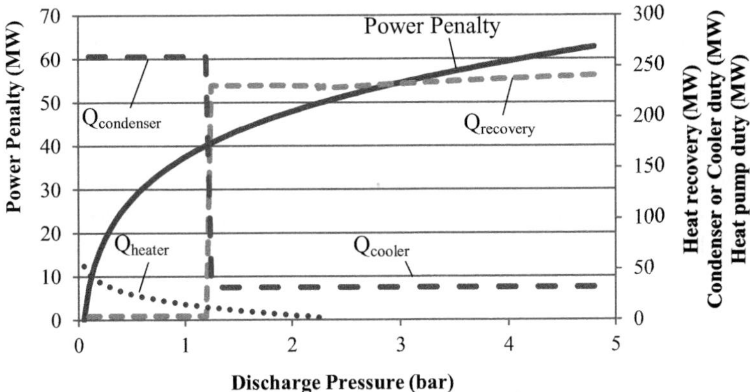

Figure 4. Trade-off analysis

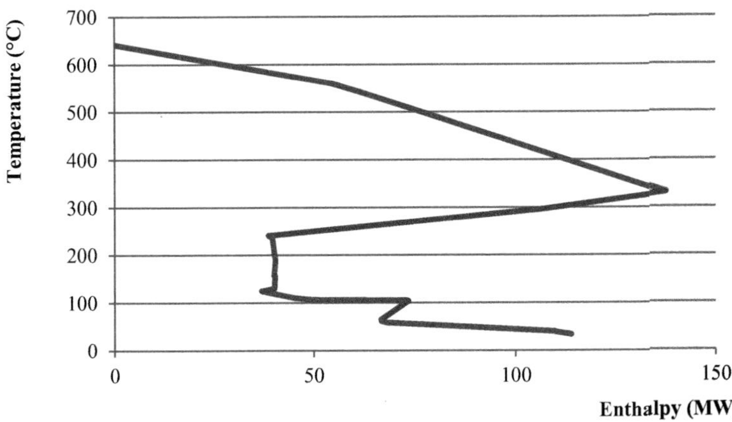

Figure 5. The GCC after process modification

used for powering the compressor. The fuel burning system can be assisted with a Combined Heat and Power (CHP) system, which produced low grade heat and to be utilised in the power plant. The effect of integrating the low grade heat sources from compressor station to the power plant are worth to be explored.

4. Conclusion

Power plants with PCC facility are essential in the market for addressing environment impacts of the industry. However, the PCC facility creates high power penalty to the power generation process. Energy analysis on an existing optimised natural gas CCGT power plant has been performed for obtaining the optimum solution for recovering heat between the power generation and PCC process. It has been found that the exhaust pressure of the condensing turbine could be optimised for recovering energy with the regenerative solvent. The optimum exhaust pressure is 1.248 bar. The power penalty is 41 MW and 231 MW of energy could be recovered through the condensation process. At this condition, cooler and heater energy consumption are 32 MW and 12 MW. The overall hot and cold utility consumption after process modification are 0 MW and 128 MW. There are several heat sources options for HI in future research, e.g. low grade heat from pressure station and intercooler in CO_2 compression. The key environment footprints (Čuček et al., 2012b) and also GHG and Nitrogen footprints (Čuček et al., 2012a) from these process modification options should also being considered in the trade-off analysis.

Acknowledgement

The financial support is gratefully acknowledged from the EC FP7 project "Design Technologies for Multi-scale Innovation and Integration in Post-Combustion CO2 Capture: From Molecules to Unit Operations and Integrated Plants" – CAPSOL, Grant No. 282789.

References

R.J. Bass, W. Malalasekera, P. Willmot, H.K. Versteeg, 2011, The impact of variable demand upon the performance of a combined cycle gas turbine (CCGT) power plant, Energy, 36, 1956-1965.

C. Biliyok, H. Yeung, 2013, Evaluation of natural gas combined cycle power plant for post-combustion CO2 capture integration, International Journal of Greenhouse Gas Control, 19, 396-405.

L. Čuček, J.J. Klemeš, Z. Kravanja, 2012a, Carbon and nitrogen trade-offs in biomass energy production, Clean Technologies and Environmental Policy, 14, 389-397.

L. Čuček, P.S. Varbanov, J.J. Klemeš, Z. Kravanja, 2012b, Potential of total site process integration for balancing and decreasing the key environmental footprints, Chemical Engineering Transactions, 29, 61-66.

T. Harkin, A. Hoadley, B. Hooper, 2010, Reducing the energy penalty of CO2 capture and compression using pinch analysis, Journal of Cleaner Production, 18, 857-866.

T. Harkin, A. Hoadley, B. Hooper, 2012, Optimisation of power stations with carbon capture plants – the trade-off between costs and net power, Journal of Cleaner Production, 34, 98-109.

J. Klemeš, F. Friedler, I. Bulatov, P. Varbanov 2010. Sustainability in the Process Industry: Integration and Optimization, New York, McGraw-Hill, USA.

J.J. Klemeš, Z. Kravanja, 2013, Forty years of Heat Integration: Pinch Analysis (PA) and Mathematical Programming (MP), Current Opinion in Chemical Engineering, 2, 461-474.

J.J. Klemeš, P.S. Varbanov, 2010, Process Integration - Successful Implementation and Possible Pitfalls, Chemical Engineering Transactions, 21, 1369-1374.

B. Linnhoff, D.W. Townsend, D. Boland, G.F. Hewitt, B.E.A. Thomas, A.R. Guy, R.H. Marsland 1982. User guide on process integration for the efficient use of energy., Rugby, U.K., The Institution of Chemical Engineers.

L.M. Romeo, I. Bolea, J.M. Escosa, 2008, Integration of power plant and amine scrubbing to reduce CO2 capture costs, Applied Thermal Engineering, 28, 1039-1046.

J.L. Silveira, J.A. De Carvalho Jr, I.A. De Castro Villela, 2007, Combined cycle versus one thousand diesel power plants: pollutant emissions, ecological efficiency and economic analysis, Renewable and Sustainable Energy Reviews, 11, 524-535.

T.N. Tjoe, B. Linnhoff, 1986, Using Pinch Technology for Process Retrofit, Chemical Engineering (New York), 93, 47-60.

M. Valdés, J.L. Rapún, 2001, Optimization of heat recovery steam generators for combined cycle gas turbine power plants, Applied Thermal Engineering, 21, 1149-1159.

Jiří Jaromír Klemeš, Petar Sabev Varbanov and Peng Yen Liew (Editors)
Proceedings of the 24th European Symposium on Computer Aided Process Engineering – ESCAPE 24
June 15-18, 2014, Budapest, Hungary.

Footprints Evaluation of China's Coal Supply Chains

Yuli Shan,[a*] Lidija Čuček,[b] Petar S. Varbanov,[b] Jiři J. Klemeš,[b] Kexi Pan,[a] Hanxiong Zhu[a]

[a]*School of Social Development and Public Policy, Fudan University, 220 Handan Road, Shanghai, 200433, People's Republic of China*
[b]*Centre for Process Integration and Intensification – CPI2, Research Institute of Chemical and Process Engineering, MŰKKI, Faculty of Information Technology, University of Pannonia, Egyetem utca 10, Veszprém, Hungary*
shanyuli1990@gmail.com

Abstract

This work presents the China's coal supply chains and environmental and social footprints associated with them. Those impacts are based on a life cycle of coal from cradle-to-gate. Several environmental footprints are considered, such as carbon, water, nitrogen, sulphur and other, as well as social footprints including number of accidents and radioactivity footprints. At last, several currently used footprints prevention steps are analysed within China, such as CO_2 sequestration, desulphurisation and denitration.

Keywords: Coal Supply Chains, Environmental Footprints, Social Footprints, Footprints Abatement Options, China

1. Introduction

Coal is currently the fastest-growing fossil fuel, with China currently the largest coal producer and consumer in the world (BP, 2013). Coal provides 75 % of electric power, 60 % of chemical industry fuel, and 80 % of the industrial fuel in China (Watson and Zhao, 2007).Coal is the most important fuel resource in China industry. Therefore, coal's production and consumption rose for several times during last decades (Yu and Wei, 2012) in China, as shown in Figure 1.

With increased coal use, also the coal-related emissions increased (Pan et al, 2013). Since it has enormous consumption, which is 1,873.3 Mtoe in 2012 (BP, 2013), has relatively low-cost and can be replaced probably only partially with other fuels, its environmental and social footprints are important. This contribution therefore presents China's coal supply chains and discusses environmental and social footprints, whilst suggests abatement options for footprints reduction.

2. China's Coal Supply Chain

Coal supply chain is comprised of mining and pre-treatment, processing, and usage and final consumption including transportation. China's coal supply chain can be seen in Figure 2.

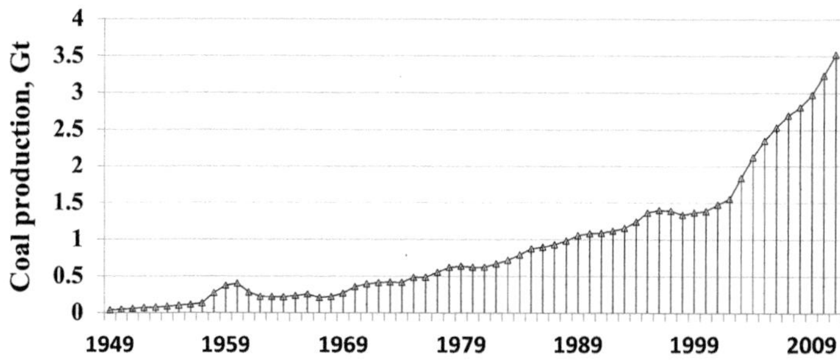

Figure 1. Coal production in China, 1949-2011 (China Energy Statistical Yearbook, 2012)

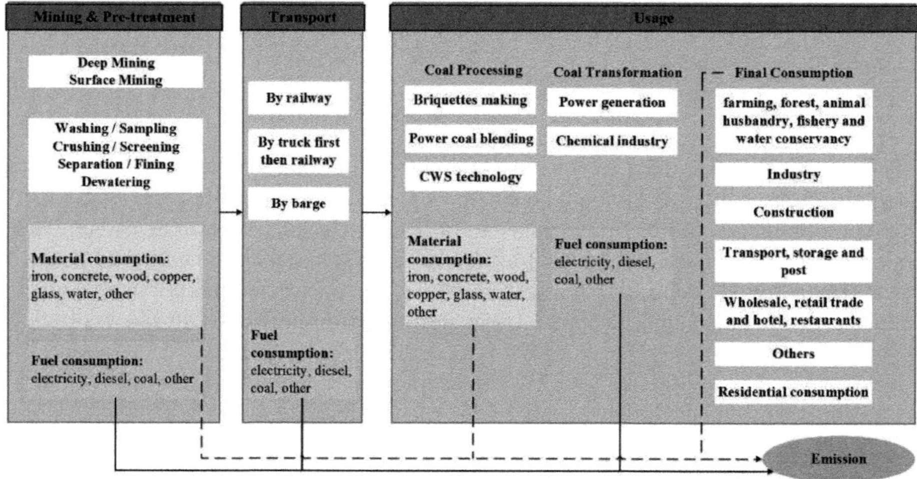

Figure 2. China's coal supply chain

2.1. Coal Mining

There are two different methods of coal mining, surface and underground mining. The process of coal mining in China contains the following several parts: coal mine development, mining tunnelling (only for underground mining) and supporting, extraction process (coal mining craft, including underground mining and surface mining), mine ventilation and mine coal transportation.

2.2. Coal pre-treatment

Coal pre-treatment refers to a series of coal-treating processes after mining. It contains the following parts: washing, sampling, crushing, screening, gravity separation, fining, dewatering and so on. Among them, coal washing is the most important part and is widely used in the whole country. There are four washing methods widely used in China: physical, chemical, physicochemical, microorganism washing. By washing, some impurities are removed such as sulphur, and the full use of coal is made. Among the four methods, physical and physicochemical washing are currently the most common in China.

2.3. Coal Transportation

After pre-treatment, coal is transported to different locations for usage in process industries, power plants, households and other sectors. There are three main ways to transport the coal in China. In China in 2010, the percentage of the coal transported by different modes is the following: by railway (46.2 %), by truck and railway (36.7 %), by barge (0.9 %), and other modes (16 %).

2.4. Coal usage

2.4.1. Coal processing

In order to make full use of coal, such as e.g. getting as much heat as possible when burning it, it usually requires some processingbefore utilization. The following three processing technologies are widely used in China.

Briquettes making: the pulverised coal is processed into different briquettes according the requirement of application.

Power coal blending: different coal types are mixed together in order to meet the equipment and environmental requirement. This can improve the thermal efficiency in coal utilization and make full use of the resource, especially for the low-quality coal.

CWS (coal-water slurry) technology: CWS is made of coal (about 60%), water (27%-35%) and chemical additives (about 1%) (Ma, 2007). Using this process, the incombustible and polluting components in coal are filtered-out, such as sulphur and ash. The CWS has the character of high density, high liquidity and it is easy to store.

2.4.2. Coal transformation

Coal istransformed into different products, such as power and chemical products.Coal could be burned within power plants in order to generate the power, where the generated heat could be used for district heating.Also, coal could be transformed into chemical products, such as aromatics, ammonia, olefins, and other.

2.5. Coal final consumption

The China's final coal consumption is divided into several sectors (China Energy Statistical Yearbook, 2011): in industry, construction, residential consumption and other. Almost 95 % of coal is consumed within industry, shown in Table 1.

3. Footprints Originating from Coal Supply Chain

3.1. Footprints included

Sustainability, especially environmental sustainability, has emerged as a key issue amongst governments, policymakers, researchers, and the public (Čuček et al., 2012). In China, as it is shown above in Fig. 1, the coal is important energy resource and will be in the further several decades. Coal is therefore an important raw material that influenc-

Table 1. Coal use within the Chinese industrial sectors for 2010 (Minchener, 2013)

Sector	Coal use (Mt)	Proportion of coal use (%)
Power generation	1,765	54.8
Iron and steel	515	16.0
Building materials	515	16.0
Chemicals	171	5.3
Others	245	7.6
Exports	10	0.3

es the sustainability in China. For this reason, it is important to consider the coal environmental and social footprints. In this research, both environmental and social footprints of China's coal supply chain are assessed.

3.2. Environmental footprints

The following four environmental footprints are evaluated: carbon (CF), water (WF), nitrogen (NF) and sulphur footprints (SF). Those footprints are regarded as the main footprints relating to coal usage.

Carbon footprint: Amongst the environmental footprints, the CF has become one of the most important environmental protection indicator (Lam et al., 2010). The combustion of coal is the largest contributor to the human-made increase of CO_2 in the atmosphere.

Water footprint: Water is widely used in the procedure of coal washing, coal chemical industry and other processes in the coal supply chain. A WF of coal industry evaluates the water utilization during the whole process of coal industry in China.

Nitrogen footprint: Coal contains significant share of nitrogen, about 0.5% to 2%. When it is combusted, NO_x are emitted into the atmosphere. NF is a measurement of the amount of reactive nitrogen (Leach et al., 2013), and mainly covers the following emissions: NO_x, N_2O, NO_3^-, and NH_3 (Galloway et al., 2003).

Sulphur footprint: Coal usually contains less than 2% of sulphur; however several types of coal, such as anthracite contains 8% to 10% sulphur(Wu et al., 2003). During pre-treatment, such as coal washing, most of sulphur in the coal is removed; however, there is still some residual sulphur. After combustion, the sulphur turns into SO_2 and SO_3, and it is emitted to the atmosphere.

3.3. Social footprints

In regards to social footprints, the following two footprints of the coal supply chain in China are involved: radioactivity footprint (RF) and number of accidents.

Radioactivity footprint: Coal utilization leads to radioactive contamination due radioactive uranium, thorium and fly ash. The radioactivity level near power plants and coal chemical industrial plants is quite high.

Number of accidents: Death rate due to mining accidents is a critical issue (He and Song, 2012). The safety should be the most important in mining activities. In this research, the number of accidents is focused along the coal supply chain.

Table 2 shows the different levels of these environmental and social footprints along the supply chain. It can be seen that most footprints are significant during processing and transformation of coal, especially carbon footprint. During mining, there is large negative social footprint – the number of accidents. During pre-treatment the water footprint is the largest. It can be seen also from Table 2 that transport and final consumption brings to mostly negligible and small footprints.

4. Footprints Abatement Options for Coal Supply Chains

Under the sustainability pressure, especially environmental one, several compulsory and stringent emission control policies are being carried on in China. These measures include: replacement of small, inefficient electric power generating units with larger and more efficient ones,installation of flue gas desulfurization (FGD) systems for all new thermal power units since 2005 (Zhao et al., 2008), and Carbon Capture and Storage (CCS) technology (Li et al., 2011)

Table 2. Footprints along the coal supply chain

Footprints	Mining	Pre-treatment	Transport	Usage	
				Processing & transformation	Final consumption
Carbon	Medium	Small	Medium	Large	Small
Water	Small	Large	Negligible	Medium	Small
Nitrogen	Small	Medium	Negligible	Medium	Small
Sulphur	Small	Medium	Negligible	Small	Negligible
Radioactivity	Negligible	Negligible	Negligible	Small	Negligible
Accidents	Large	Small	Small	Negligible	Negligible

Replacement of small, inefficient electric power generating units with larger and more efficient ones and installation of flue gas desulfurization (FGD) systems for all new thermal power units: Due to low combustion efficiency and poor emission control technology, the energy consumption and pollutant emissions of small units were extremely high. Also, FGD system can only be applied within large power units (Zhao et al., 2008). Facing this huge challenge more stringent regulations for small units are, or will be, taking effect.

CCS technology: As for the footprints abatement technology, CCS is seen as an important and strategic technology for China to reduce its CO_2 emissions. China has begun work on CCS demonstration in recent years, and had moved forward quickly in these pursuits. Several CCS demonstration projects in China are active or under construction (Li et al., 2011).

5. Conclusions and Future Work

The current contribution presented the China's coal supply chains and environmental and social footprints related to them. The most important environmental footprints related to coal are carbon, water, nitrogen and sulphur footprints, and social footprint are radioactivity footprint and the number of accidents. The contribution of each footprint along the coal supply chain was identified.

In the future, footprints relating to coal will be evaluated in more details along the China's supply chain from cradle-to-gate. For this purpose commercial life-cycle analysis software package, and the Ecoinvent database (Frischknecht et al., 2007) will be used. Also, footprints will be evaluated using Environmental Performance Strategy Map (De Benedetto and Klemeš, 2009).

Acknowledgments

The authors acknowledge the financial support from the following projects: EC FP7 project ENER/FP7/296003 'Efficient Energy Integrated Solutions for Manufacturing Industries – EFENIS', EC FP7 project FP7-PEOPLE-2011-IRSES 'Energy Systems Engineering – ESE', project No. 294987, and Fudan University 985 project 'The adjustment of EU economic and social and political framework, as well as the response of China in post-crisis era', project No. 2012SHKXYB010.

References

BP (British Petroleum), 2013, BP Statistical Review of World Energy, <www.bp.com/content/dam/bp/pdf/statistical-review/statistical_review_of_world_energy_2013.pdf> Accessed on 01/09/2013.

L. De Benedetto, J. Klemeš, 2009, The Environmental Performance Strategy Map: an integrated LCA approach to support the strategic decision-making process, Journal of Cleaner Production, 17, 900-906.

L. Čuček, J. J. Klemeš, Z. Kravanja, 2012, A review of footprint analysis tools for monitoring impacts on sustainability, Journal of Cleaner Production, 34, 9-25.

M. Fang, C. K. Chan, X. Yao, 2009, Managing air quality in a rapidly developing nation: China, Atmospheric Environment, 43, 79-86.

R. Frischknecht, N. Jungbluth, H. J. Althaus, G. Doka, T. Heck, S. Hellweg, R. Hischier, T. Nemecek, G. Rebitzer, M. Spielmann, G. Wernet, 2007, Overview and methodology, ecoinvent report no. 1, Swiss Centre for life cycle inventories, Dübendorf, Switzerland

J. N. Galloway, J. D. Aber, J. W. Erisman, S. P. Seitzinger, R. W. Howarth, E. B. Cowling, B. J. Cosby, 2003. The nitrogen cascade, Bioscience, 53, 4, 341–356.

X. He, L. Song, 2012.Status and future tasks of coal mining safety in China. Safety Science, 50, 894-898.

H. L. Lam, P. S. Varbanov, J. J. Klemeš, 2010, Minimising carbon footprints of regional biomass supply chains, Resources, Conservation and Recycling, 54, 303-309.

A. M. Leach, J. N. Galloway, A. Bleeker, J. W. Erisman, R. Kohn, J. Kitzes, 2012, A nitrogen footprint model to help consumers understand their role in nitrogen losses to the environment, Environmental Development, 1, 40-66.

Z. Li, D. Zhang, L. Ma, L. West, W. Ni, 2011, The necessity of and policy suggestions for implementing a limited number of large scale, fully integrated CCS demonstrations in China, Energy Policy, 39, 5347-5355.

J. Ma, 2007, Promotion with effort of the development of Chinese coal processing (in Chinese), Coal Processing & Comprehensive Utilization, 5, 5-9.

A. J. Minchener, 2013, Gasification based CCS challenges and opportunities for China, Fuel, doi: 10.1016/j.fuel.2013.02.046.

X. Ou, Y. Xiaoyu, X. Zhang, 2011, Life-cycle energy consumption and greenhouse gas emissions for electricity generation and supply in China, Applied Energy, 88, 289-297

K.-X. Pan, H.-X.Zhu, Z. Chang, K.-H.Wu, Y.-L.Shan, Z.-X. Liu, 2013, Estimation of coal-related CO_2 emissions: The case of China, Energy and Environment, 24, 7-8, 1309-1322.

J. Watson, Z. Zhao (Eds.), 2007, Committee on Energy Futures and Air Pollution in Urban China and the United States, Energy Futures and Urban Air Pollution: Challenges for China and the United States, National Academies Press, Washington, DC, US.

L. Wu, G. Cheng, Z. Yu, C. Ning, X. Lv, 2003, The obstacles in the development of coal washing process and policy recommendation (in Chinese), 5, 18-21.

S. Wu, 2009, Development of Chinese coal preparation in past 30 years (in Chinese), Coal Processing and Comprehensive Utilization, 5, 1-4.

S. Yu, T.-m. Wei, 2012, Prediction of China's coal production-environmental pollution based on a hybrid genetic algorithm-system dynamics model, Energy Policy, 42, 521-529.

Y. Zhao, M. B. Mcelroy, J. Xing, L. Duan, C. P. Nielsen, Y. Lei, J. Hao, 2011, Multiple effects and uncertainties of emission control policies in China: Implications for public health, soil acidification, and global temperature, Science of the Total Environment, 409, 5177-5187.

Y. Zhao, S. Wang, L. Duan, Y. Lei, P. Cao, J. Hao, 2008, Primary air pollutant emission of coal-fired power plants in China: current status and future prediction, Atmospheric Environment, 42, 8442-8452.

M. Zhang, Y. Guo, 2013, Process simulations of NH_3 abatement system for large-scale CO_2 capture using aqueous ammonia solution, International Journal of Greenhouse Gas Control, 18, 114-127.

X. Zhuang, K. Jiang, 2009, Energy consumption assessment of coal products from well to user (in Chinese), China Energy, 31, 30-35.

Jiří Jaromír Klemeš, Petar Sabev Varbanov and Peng Yen Liew (Editors)
Proceedings of the 24th European Symposium on Computer Aided Process Engineering – ESCAPE 24
June 15-18, 2014, Budapest, Hungary.

Process Disturbances Detection via Spectral Graph Analysis

Estanislao Musulin

CIFASIS-CONICET, Ocampo y Esmeralda, 2000, Rosario, Argentina
Universidad Nacional de Rosario. FCEyA, Pellegrini 250,2000, Rosario, Argentina
musulin@cifasis-conicet.gov.ar

Abstract

In this work, Spectral Graph Analysis Monitoring (SGAM) is introduced as a method for process disturbance detection. It is shown that processes can be monitored by analysing the spectral properties of a properly defined weighted graph. The developed technique can be used as an alternative or complement to PCA, LPP and other on-line statistical monitoring approaches. SGAM has been illustrated in an autocorrelated synthetic case, where several types of process disturbances have been evaluated, including steps, drifts and random variations.

Keywords: Process Monitoring, Spectral Graph Analysis, Data Driven

1. Introduction

In complex modern processes, the interest on monitoring systems has increased following the demand of better management of the plants according to more restrictive economic and environmental conditions. In the last years, many process monitoring methods have been developed to timely detect process disturbances. In particular, data driven techniques have attracted the greatest interest due to the high availability of on-line data.

Many process monitoring applications rely on dimensionality reduction techniques; process measurements are projected into a low-dimension space where most of the normal data variability is contained. Therefore, the monitoring performance is directly influenced by the quality of the projection model. The most widespread of these techniques are the Principal Components Analysis (PCA) and its extensions (Nomikos and MacGregor, 1995). PCA examines the measurements covariance and selects a new orthogonal base of reduced dimensionality that explains most of the data variance. Thus, PCA can be considered as a globality-based data projection method that does not consider the local structure of data. That is, data neighbourhood can be altered after projection.

Recently, several methods of dimensionality reduction where proposed in the pattern recognition area (Von Luxburg, 2007). As opposed to PCA, those methods, known as manifold learning, are based on the local structure of data. Moreover, most of these approaches are non-linear and computationally expensive. Between them, Locality Preserving Projections (LPP) (Niyogi, 2004) is of particular interest; LPP is a linear technique that defines the neighbourhood relationship between data samples and finds the projection that preserves the intrinsic geometry structure of the dataset. However, the outer shape of the dataset can be modified, and therefore the global data structure can be distorted. Lately, Global-Local Structure Analysis (GLSA) (Zhang et al., 2011) and Local and Global PCA (LGPCA) (Yu, 2012) were proposed as compromise solutions. They construct dual objective functions aiming to preserve both local and global dataset structure.

In this work, SGAM is introduced as an alternative method for process disturbance detection. It is shown that processes can be monitored by analyzing the spectral properties of a properly defined weighted graph. Many real-world situations can conveniently be represented by a diagram consisting of a set of vertices joined by a set of edges, therefore configuring graphs. A graph can be represented by its adjacency matrix A; the analysis of A based on eigenvalues and eigenvectors is called the theory of graph spectra. Spectral graph theory has acquired great relevance in the last decade, particularly in the computer science area (Cvetković and Simić, 2011). The paper is organized as follows. Section 2 gives some insight into spectral graph theory. In section 3 the new monitoring methodology is presented. Experimental results are shown in section 4. Finally in section 5 conclusions are given and some future works are proposed.

2. Spectral Graph Analysis

Let $G=(V,w)$ be a finite undirected weighted graph of order n without loops or multiple edges, and suppose that its vertices are labeled $1,2,\dots,n$. If vertices i and j are joined by an edge, it is said that i and j are adjacent and write $i\sim j$. Since the graph is weighted and undirected, it is assumed that each edge carries a non-zero symmetric weight ($w_{ij} = w_{ji}$). The elements of the *weighted adjacency matrix* $\mathbf{A}_w$ of the weighted graph G are defined as

$$a_{ij} = \begin{cases} w_{ij} \neq 0 & \text{if } i \sim j \\ 0 & \text{otherwise} \end{cases} \tag{1}$$

Under this definition, A_w is a real symmetric matrix with zero diagonal.

2.1. Graph Energy

Let $\lambda_1,\dots,\lambda_n$ be the eigenvalues of $\mathbf{A}_w$. Then, the energy of G is defined as,

$$\mathbb{E}(G) = \sum_{i=1}^{n} |\lambda_i| \tag{2}$$

This quantity is well known in chemical applications; since in some cases the energy defined in this way corresponds to the energy of a molecule (Gutman, 2005). However, the graph invariant $\mathbb{E}(G)$ can be considered for any graph independently of the chemical context, recently much work on graph energy appeared also in the pure mathematics literature (Nikiforov, 2007; Gutman and Shao, 2011). This new perspective provided new generally valid mathematical properties for (G).

2.2. Algebraic connectivity

Given $\mathbf{A}_w$, the discrete Laplacian matrix L is defined as $\mathbf{L}= \mathbf{A}_w\text{-}\mathbf{D}$, where $\mathbf{D}$ is the diagonal matrix of vertex degrees $\mathbf{D} = diag(a_i)$, and $[\mathbf{D}]_{ii} = a_i = \sum^{n}_{j=1} = a_{ij}$. $\mathbf{L}$ is a positive semi-definite matrix and so all its eigenvalues are no negative. The second smallest eigenvalue of $\mathbf{L}$ is usually called algebraic connectivity of G and it is denoted by $a(G)$.

Although a simple eigenvalue is not enough to describe the graph structure, the algebraic connectivity has some important relations with several graph metrics. As a consequence, it has been used in separation, metric and isoperimetric problems (Cvetković et al., 2010). In particular, *a(G)* is related with the graph isoperimetric number or conductance by,

$$i(G) = \min_{0<|S|<=n/2} \frac{|\delta S|}{|S|} \tag{3}$$

where S is a subset of vertices of G, δS is the edge boundary of S and $|S|$ is the number of vertices in S. If *i(G)* is small, then a relative big number of vertices can be separated from the graph by removing relatively few edges (Note that $i(G)=0 <=> G$ is disconnected). Therefore, *i(G)* (and so *a(G)*) can be considered as a numerical measure of the graph conductance, and consequently as a measure of connectivity.

3. Use of SGA in process monitoring

To perform on-line monitoring based on the spectral graph features, it is proposed the construction of a graph G in which each vertex represents a process measurement vector $\mathbf{x}_m(k) \in \Re^m$. If the normal process measurements are analysed in groups of n samples, each group can be characterized as a graph of n disconnected vertices each one of dimension m. To establish connections, the graph adjacency matrix $\mathbf{A}_w$ can be determined by calculating the Euclidean distances between vertices and applying a heat kernel as a measure of neighbourhood. Note that $\mathbf{A}_w$ results of dimension nxn independently of the dimension of the measurement vector m.

To establish data groups, the Normal Operation Conditions (NOC) dataset is studied using a moving window ($TW_{nxm}(k) = [\mathbf{x}_m(k-n),...,\mathbf{x}_m(k)]$), thus obtaining a series of graphs represented by their corresponding adjacency matrix Aw . (G) and *a(G)* are calculated for each Aw as explained in section 2. The obtained (G) and *a(G)* sequences are considered as normal and disturbed only by common cause variance, so limits of normality can be estimated from them. This procedure is formally stated in Table 1. Using the obtained normality limits, two control charts are built: the EG-control chart and the *aG-control chart* to monitor (G) and *a(G)*. Then, on-line monitoring is performed by analysing the last n measurements in a sliding window, building G, calculating (G) and *a(G)* and comparing the obtained values with the established normality limits in the control charts. See Table 2 for a step by step explanation.

4. Case study: Five variables autocorrelated process

In this section, SGAM has been applied in the following multivariate system, introduced by Ku et al. (1995) and modified by Yu (2012),

$$z(k) = \begin{bmatrix} 0.118 & -0.191 & 0.287 \\ 0.847 & 0.264 & 0.943 \\ -0.333 & 0.514 & -0.217 \end{bmatrix} z(k-1) + \begin{bmatrix} 1 & 2 \\ 3 & -4 \\ -2 & 1 \end{bmatrix} u(k-1) \tag{4}$$

$$y(k) = z(k) + v(k) \tag{5}$$

where u is the correlated input:

$$u(k) = \begin{bmatrix} 0.811 & -0.226 \\ 0.477 & 0.415 \end{bmatrix} u(k-1) + \begin{bmatrix} 0.193 & 0.689 \\ -0.320 & -0.749 \end{bmatrix} w(k-1) \tag{6}$$

and w is a two variables random vector with distribution $\mathcal{U}(-2,2)$. The measurement vector under analysis is defined as $x(k) = [y'(k),u'(k)] \in \Re^5$. This is an interesting process, since it introduces dynamics and therefore autocorrelation into process variables. The process was simulated for 300 samples, generating a normal (under control) dataset. The normal dataset was auto-scaled and used to implement PCA, three principal components has been selected to retain most (≅90 %) of the common cause variability. SGAM was also applied to this example using the procedure depicted on Table 1. Since data is auto-scaled (zero mean and unit variance), the neighborhood parameter was set to σ=1, meaning that points at a distance > 4σ will be almost disconnected. The maximum response time of this system is about 15 samples. Therefore, n is set to 80, which is enough to have a graph that comprises the process dynamics and most of the common cause variability. To examine the monitoring performance, four disturbances of different type have been introduced in the input variable w1. Each disturbance was introduced at sample 101 (see Table 3). Figure 1a and 1b show the monitoring results for the step disturbance IDV(1). PCA detects the fault at time 107 (three consecutive T2 samples out of the 99 % limit). The spectral detection is produced at the same time, but it is much clearer, showing a decrement in the graph energy and in the algebraic connectivity. Note that after the step, the spectral features return to normal values. IDV(2) (see Figures 1c and 1d) is a small drift disturbance, which is detected by the T2 statistic intermittently at samples 138, 178, 185 and more clearly after sample 197.

Table 1. SGAM process characterization stage. Build graphs and set limits for (*G*) and *a(G)*

Consider an auto-scaled (zero mean, unit variance) normal data matrix **X** consisting of *N* samples of *m* variables, an so $\mathbf{X} = [\mathbf{x}_m(1),\mathbf{x}_m(2),...,\mathbf{x}_m(N)]$, with $\mathbf{x}_m(k) \in \Re^m$.

1. Take a time windows *TW(n)* consisting on the first *n* samples of X (i.e. $TW(n) = [\mathbf{x}_m(1),\mathbf{x}_m(2),...,\mathbf{x}_m(n)]$), where $n < N$.

   1a. Construct a weighted graph to represent *TW(n)*: Let *G* denote a graph with *n* vertices. Build a fully connected graph by simply connecting all points with positive similarity with each other. Weights are assigned to graph edges computing the Gaussian kernel function, leading to a matrix $\mathbf{A}_w$ with entries $w_{ij} = e^{\frac{\|x_i - x_j\|^2}{2\sigma^2}}$.

   1b. Calculate the energy of *G* as $\mathbb{E}(G) = \sum_{i=1}^{n} |\lambda_i|$, where λ i are the eigenvalues of $\mathbf{A}_w$. Note that with this definition, *G* is a connected graph and so only the first Laplacian eigenvalue will be null with multiplicity one. (Von Luxburg (2007))

   2b. Calculate the graph algebraic connectivity *a(G)* as explained in section 2.2. It requires to compute the graph Laplacian matrix $\mathbf{L} = \mathbf{A}_w\text{-}\mathbf{D}$ of dimension *nxn* and the calculation of its second smallest eigenvalue.

2. Take a new time window $TW(n+1) = [\mathbf{x}_m(2),...,\mathbf{x}_m(N+1)]$. To analyze *TW(n+1)* it is not necessary to rebuild all the graph, only the following steps are required,

   2a. Remove the first column of Aw corresponding to the older point $\mathbf{x}_m(1)$.

   2b. Add $\mathbf{x}_m(n+1)$ to the graph by calculating the weighted distance to the other graph vertices, and update $\mathbf{A}_w$.

   2c. Recalculate (*G*) and *a(G)*.

3. Continue the procedure from step 2 until the complete normal dataset has been processed.

Table 2. SGAM on-line monitoring stage. Compute (*G*) and *a(G)* and compare with normality.

1. Initialize Aw

   1a. Take the last n measurements $TW(k)=[\mathbf{x}_m(k-n),\ldots,\mathbf{x}_m(k)]$.

   1b. Build the weighted graph $\mathbf{A}_w$ with entries $w_{ij} = e^{\frac{\|x_m(i)-x_m(j)\|^2}{2\sigma^2}}$.

   1c. Calculate (*G*) and *a(G)*, plot them in their corresponding control graph and compare with the normality limits.

2. Until each new measurement $\mathbf{x}_m(k+1)$ Do:

   2a. Remove the first column of $\mathbf{A}_w$ corresponding to the older point $\mathbf{x}_m(k-n)$.

   2b. Add $\mathbf{x}_m(k+1)$ to the graph by calculating the weighted distance to the other graph vertices, and update $\mathbf{A}_w$.

   2c. Recalculate (*G*) and *a(G)*, plot them in their corresponding control graph and compare with the normality limits.

Table 3: Five variables autocorrelated process: Disturbances and faults introduced in w1.

Disturbance	Description
IDV(1)	Step of size = +3 at sample = 101
IDV(2)	Drift fault, of slope = 0.03 at sample = 101
IDV(3)	Noise increased by 50 % at sample = 101
IDV(4)	Noise reduced by 20 % at time = 101

Using SGAM, the disturbance is distinctly detected in the aG-control chart from sample 137. Since the system does not return to a steady state, the spectral features do not completely return to the normality limits. IDV(3) and IDV(4) (see Figures 1e, 1f, 1g and 1h) correspond to increments and decrements in the noise levels. IDV(3) is detected by PCA at sample 126, and again and with more clarity at sample 190. Detection using the aG-control chart is faster and sharper at sample 105.

Note that since the noise level is kept higher than normal, the SGAM charts do not return to its normal values. Regarding IDV(4), although the reduction of noise causes a reduction in the values of its statistics (See Figure 1g) this disturbance cannot be detected by PCA. On the other hand, IDV(4) causes an increment in the graph energy (the graph vertices are more concentrated) that can be observed in the EG-control chart from sample 132 (see Figure1h).

5. Conclusions and future work

In this work Spectral Graph Analysis Monitoring (SGAM) has been presented. SGAM is a new process monitoring technique, based on the spectral graph analysis theory, which does not require dimensionality reduction. The developed technique can be used as an alternative or complement to PCA, LPP and other on-line statistical monitoring methods. SGAM has been illustrated in an autocorrelated synthetic case, several types of process disturbances have been evaluated, including steps, drifts and random variations. As a future work, SGAM will be extended to more complex processes, further investigating its potentialities as a fault diagnosis tool.

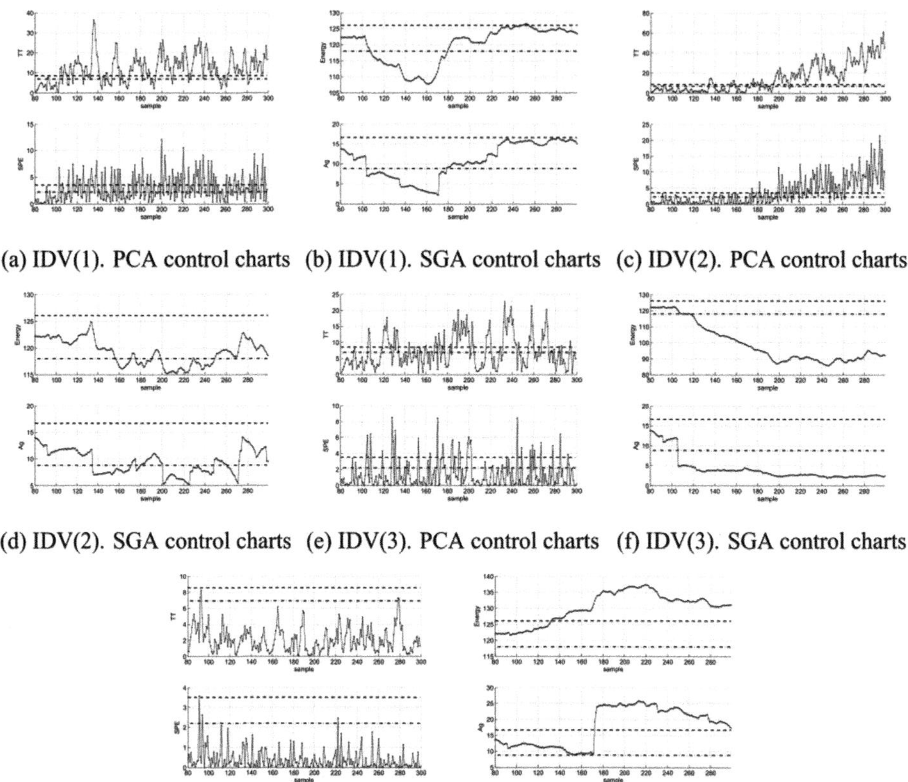

(a) IDV(1). PCA control charts (b) IDV(1). SGA control charts (c) IDV(2). PCA control charts

(d) IDV(2). SGA control charts (e) IDV(3). PCA control charts (f) IDV(3). SGA control charts

(g) IDV(4). PCA control charts (h) IDV(4). SGA control charts

Figure 1: Five variables autocorrelated process. PCA and SGA Control charts. Disturbances introduced at sample 101.

References

D. Cvetković, S. Simić, 2011, Graph spectra in computer science, Linear Algebra and its Applications 434, 1545-1562.

D. Cvetković, P. Rowlinson, S. Simić, 2010, An introduction to the theory of graph spectra, Cambridge University Press, Cambridge, England.

I. Gutman, 2005, Topology and stability of conjugated hydrocarbons. the dependence of total pi-electron energy on molecular topology, J. Serb. Chem. Soc., 70, 3, 441-456.

I. Gutman, J. Shao, 2011, The energy change of weighted graphs, Linear Algebra and its Applications, 435, 2425-2431.

W. Ku, R.H. Storer, C. Georgakis, 1995, Disturance detection and isolation by dynamic principal component analysis, Chemometrics and Intelligent Laboratory Systems, 30, 179-196.

V. Nikiforov, 2007, The energy of graphs and matrices, J. Math. Anal. and Appl., 326, 1472-1475.

X. Niyogi, 2004, Locality preserving projections, Neural Inf. Proc. Syst., 16, 153-160.

P. Nomikos, J. MacGregor, 1995, Multivariate SPC charts for monitoring batch processes, Technometrics, 37, 1, 41-59.

U. Von Luxburg, 2007, A tutorial on spectral clustering, Statistics & computing, 17, 4, 395-416.

J. Yu, 2012. Local and global principal component analysis for process monitoring, Journal of Process Control, 22, 7, 1358-1373.

M. Zhang, Z. Ge, Z. Song, R. Fu, 2011, Global local structure analysis model and its application for fault detection and identification, I&E Chemistry Research, 50, 11, 6837-6848.

Jiří Jaromír Klemeš, Petar Sabev Varbanov and Peng Yen Liew (Editors)
Proceedings of the 24th European Symposium on Computer Aided Process Engineering – ESCAPE 24
June 15-18, 2014, Budapest, Hungary.

An Ontology-based Framework to Support Multivariate Qualitative Data Analysis

Fernando Roda[a]*, Estanislao Musulin[a,b]

[a]*CIFASIS-CONICET, Ocampo y Esmeralda, 2000, Rosario, Argentina*
[b]*Universidad Nacional de Rosario. FCEyA, Pellegrini 250,2000, Rosario, Argentina*
roda@conicet-cifasis.gov.ar

Abstract

In this work, an ontology-based Intelligent Data Analyses (IDA) framework is presented. The proposed approach facilitates a complete quantitative-qualitative data analyses, ranging from simple outliers detection to the identification of qualitative multivariate temporal patterns. A novel ontology has been developed to represent Temporal Abstractions. Two major elements have been considered: a consistent modelling of time series and a proper scheme to operate over temporal relations.

Keywords: Intelligent Data Analysis, Qualitative reasoning, Temporal reasoning

1. Introduction

The improvement of sensing and communication technologies and the continuous decrease in storage prices have enable modern plant information systems to collect, store and share a huge amount of data. In the last decades becomes evident the need of computer-aided systems that perform Intelligent Data Analyses (IDA) over the obtained data streams. Lavrac et al. (2000) define intelligent IDA as: "encompassing statistical, pattern recognition, machine learning, data abstraction and visualization tools to support the analysis of data and discovery of principles that are encoded within the data". Using IDA, a data series is segmented into contiguous episodes associated to its underlying trends. The success of an IDA framework for arriving at accurate and timely data interpretation depends on two important requirements, 1) a proper time series representation and, 2) an efficient management of domain knowledge.

In a chemical plant, the overwhelming amount of information makes quantitative methods of limited use. The data stream modelling provided by Temporal Abstraction (TA) has proven to be an excellent practice to embrace such complexity. A TA technique takes either raw or pre-processed data as input and produces a qualitative interval based representations (i.e. Episodes). Qualitative representation is a straightforward technique for data stream analysis. It leads to more efficient processing as it uses abstracted views of signal behaviour (tendencies, alarms, degree of transient states, etc.) instead of the numeric time series given by the data acquisition systems. Many researchers have work in this general area (Stacey and McGregor, 2007; Villez et al., 2013). Most of these works analyse the optimal extraction of qualitative episodes and presents methods to estimate qualitative trends similarities.
However, there are two important aspects that were not discussed in detail in the bibliography, the multivariate qualitative analysis and the proper management of domain knowledge. Ontologies and knowledge modelling technologies can improve software interoperability and integration, as well as facilitate reasoning (Musulin et al., 2013), so they are key for enabling modern IDA systems.

In this work, an ontology-based framework to support multivariate dynamic analysis of time series is presented. It makes use of semantic technologies to provide a powerful and transparent inference mechanism that is capable to formally justify the obtained conclusions.

2. Ontology-based framework for trend analysis

Knowledge based systems involves a knowledge base (KB), an inference engine or reasoner and some interfaces to other computer systems and/or to human users. In the proposed framework the KB is composed by: 1) The classes, properties and constraint that define the domain concepts, 2) A set of ontological assertion axioms that describe the instances for particular applications, 3) A set of if-then rules to infer new facts. The ontological statement of the KB was implemented in OWL2 (Web Ontology Language). It is a sound and complete language with a formal semantic based in SROIQ Description logic (DL). Since rules expressed as OWL axioms are limited by the SROIQ constraints, Semantic Web Rule Language (SWRL) has been considered to formulate the KB rules. SWRL allows the use of OWL terms and built-in functions that are valuable for dynamic data analysis. Regarding the inference engine, any off-the-shelf DL reasoner can be used to process OWL axioms. However, SWRL expressions require a SWRL-enabled reasoner like Pellet or Kaon, or the addition of a rule engine such as Jess or Drool. Finally, the Semantic Query Web Rule Language (SQWRL) is proposed as the interface for knowledge extraction. It is a SQL-like language that let client agents to perform queries about the measurement and qualitative representation of the process dynamic.

3. Ontological Modelling

With regards to the knowledge model, three fundamental requirements have been identified to support IDA tasks, 1) A scheme to capture the quantitative raw data produced by sensing tasks. In this regard, it is useful to consider the established standards to share measurements and sensor data. 2) A scheme for temporal modelling and reasoning. It must deal with the representation of temporal entities (e.g. time instants, periods, duration, etc.) and with the interpretation and processing of temporal relations (e.g. before, after, during, etc.). 3) A scheme to store and manage temporal abstractions. Several conceptualizations that partially contemplate the previous issues have been studied. As a result, three ontologies have been reused, Semantic Sensor Network ontology (SSN) (Compton et al., 2012), Descriptive Ontology for Linguistic and Cognitive Engineering (DOLCE) (Masolo et al., 2002) and SWRL Temporal Ontology (SWRLTO) (O'Connor and Das, 2011). The following section presents a brief description of the reused conceptualizations and explains how they were aligned in a novel ontology.

3.1. Sensor measurements modelling

The Semantic Sensor Network (SSN) ontology (Compton et al., 2012) (See Figure 1) targets at the formal and machine-processable representation of sensor capabilities, properties, observations and measurement processes. *Observation* is a key concept of SSN, it is defined as “a Situation in which a Sensing method has been used to estimate or calculate a value of a Property of a Feature of Interest”. The class "ssn:Observation" provides the structure to represent a single observation; hence it is related to a single measurement (i.e. ssn:SensorOutput) and attributed to a single property (i.e. Classes "ssn:Property" and "ssn:Feature Of Interest") and to a particular Sensor. The result of the sensing process is modelled by the class "ssn:SensorOutput".

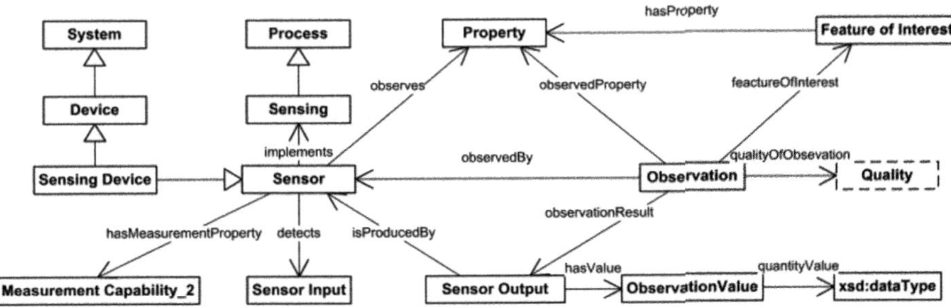

Figure 1. Partial overview of the SSN conceptualization (UML diagram)

Information about observation time is represented by means of the object properties "ssn:observationSamplingTime" and/or "ssn:observationResultTime". However, it should be noted that the SSN ontology does not prescribe a format for the representation of time.

3.2. Temporal modeling and reasoning

To manage temporal information, the SWRL Temporal Ontology (SWRLTO) (O'Connor andDas, 2011) has been considered (See Fig. 2). SWRLTO is based on the simple and expressive valid-time temporal model. Temporal entities are modelled by the class "swrlto:ValidTime" which can be a time instant (swrlto:ValidInstant) or a time interval (swrlto:ValidPeriod). Additionally, SWRLTO provides a set of SWRL built-in predicates to handle temporal relations (including the 13 Allem operations (Allen, 1983)).

3.3. Temporal Abstraction (TA) modelling

In this section, a DL-based ontology to formally represent the semantic of temporal abstractions is proposed (TA onto). Fig. 3 shows an overview of its structure and the semantic alignment with SSN and DOLCE Ultra Lite (DUL). A qualitative representation is the description of a time series by means of contiguous episodes. The class "Episode" models a TA of a set of time stamped data obtained by a heuristic or formal method. An "Episode" is formally defined as a set of two elements: a time interval (i.e. a temporal extent) and a qualitative context, providing the temporal extension with significance. In the ontology, the temporal extent is given by a "swrlto:ValidTime" while the qualitative context is given by a "Primitive". In terms of DOLCE, Primitives are quality regions that describe a state or condition of an observed Property. A primitive is usually associated to an alphabetic character or symbol. By definition, an episode is characterized by a single primitive and a primitive has no sense without a reference to the method used in the representation. (See the relation "usePrimitive" from "Representation Method" to "Primitive"). In order to trace the abstraction process, each episode is associated to the agent that was responsible of its creation (i.e. "Representation Agent"). This is not limited to software agents and it can

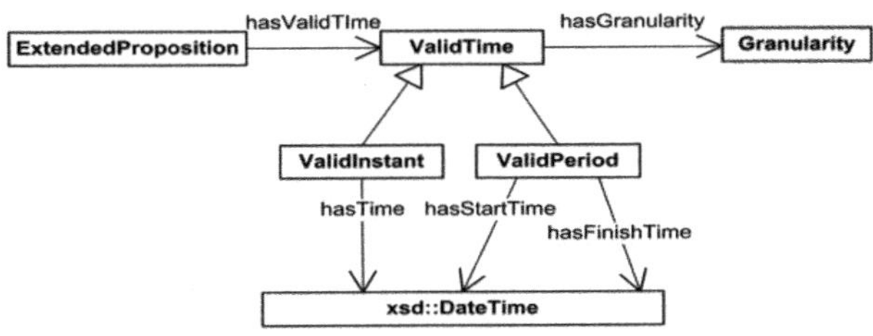

Figure 2. SWRL Temporal Ontology.

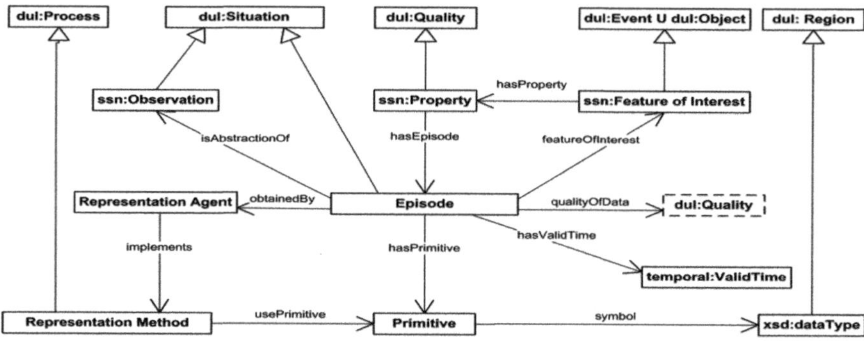

Figure 3. Temporal Abstraction Ontology

also be a human expert performing a heuristic analysis. Some object properties have been defined to link these classes to SSN entities ("isAbstractionOf", "hasEpisode", "featureOfInterest"). It is important to note that the formulation of "isAbstractionOf" enables an episode be defined as a temporal abstraction of a set of other episodes in a lower abstraction level, thus forming a multilayer abstraction hierarchy. Finally, note that with a proper instantiation, the proposed conceptualization enables different representation approaches such as the Triangular Episodes of Cheung and Stephanopoulos (1990) or Symbolic Aggregate Approximations of Lin et al. (2003). These representations can be stored in the same KB as alternative views of the process under study.

4. Illustrative Example

The following example illustrates how measurements are managed in the knowledge base. Consider the observations realized by a temperature sensor (T1) located in a given CSTR reactor. T1 is sampled each minute; Figure 4 shows an interpolated view of three samples of T1 together with its qualitative representation (i.e. the primitive "A"). In the KB, this information is represented as a set of interconnected instances, which are distributed through the four aligned ontologies. HermiT DL reasoner is used to analyze the information, check consistency and infer new facts.

Observations T_O1, T_O2 and T_O3 correspond to the sensor outputs T_SO1, T_SO2 and T_SO3 respectively. Measured values are represented by instances of the class "TemperatureValue" (a ssn:ObservationValue subclass). "T_episode001" represents the signal slice that has been abstracted as the "A" primitive. This episode has been identified and instantiated by an external software agent (QRPT_Agent) that implements the "Qualitative Representation of Process Trends" (QRPT_Method) due to Cheung and Stephanopoulos (1990). Since in QRPT the primitives are identified with the signs of the first and second derivatives, "A_primitive" is described by XML literals that store these signs and the symbol ("A"). Note that this primitive must be linked by the property "usePrimitive" with the method used to extract the episode. Otherwise the reasoning results in a logic inconsistency.

The relation "isAbstractionOf" is used to link the individual observations with their correspondent qualitative representation, and can be inferred by the DL reasoner through the time and the involved property. In the case that these relations be provided by the external agent, the DL reasoner checks their consistency. Moreover, both observations and its qualitative representations must be associated to the same

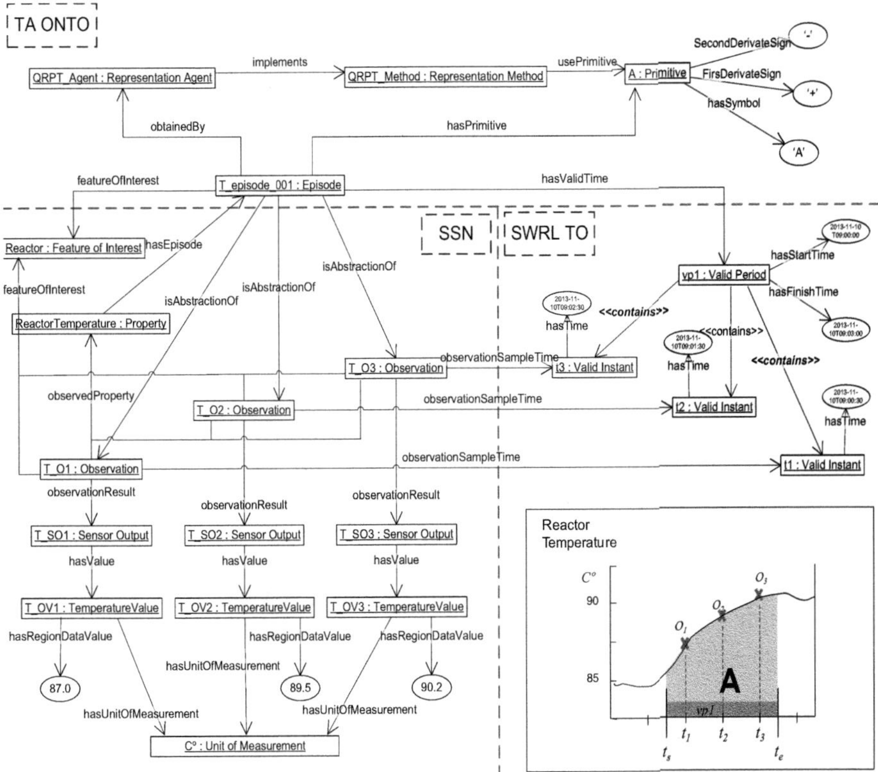

Figure 4. Ontology instantiation to represent a qualitative episode in the Reactor Temperature.

"Property" (i.e. ReactorTemperature) and to the same "Feature of interest" (i.e. Reactor) to be consistent. All temporal references are represented by instances of SWRLTO. "T_episode001" spans over the time interval (vp1) starting at 09:00 and finishing at 09:03. Likewise, each observation (T_O1, T_O2 and T_O3) is associated with the time instants of sensing (t1, t2 and t3) by the property "ssn:observationSampleTime".

Next, some examples are included to demonstrate how temporal reasoning joined to the qualitative representation of trends improves the expressiveness of rules and queries to support IDA. For instance, consider that we are interested in analysing the dynamic of the reactor temperature T1 in periods of "High" concentration of A in the effluent F (i.e. High X). The query is formulated using SQWRL as follows,

```
hasEpisode(ta:effluentConcentration, ?ce)^hasPrimitive(?ce,ta:x_Hight)^
hasEpisode(ta:reactorTemperature,?te)^obtainedBy(?te, ta:qrtp_agent)^during(?te,?ce)^
hasPrimitive(?te,?tp)^hasStartTime(?te,?teS)^hasFinishTime(?te, teF?)^hasSymbol(?tp,?s)
->select(?s,?teS,?teF)
```

This query returns the symbols (?s) and their temporal location (?teS and ?teF) corresponding to the QRPT episodes of T1. Multivariate temporal reasoning is also valuable to infer a process condition. Figure 5 shows an example of a rule expression that states a fault condition based in the observed dynamic. Here, a particular combination of episodes must be found on T1 and in the concentration (X) in the same time interval *w*. As it is shown in the T1 search pattern, a flexible formulation is allowed, since any symbol could be placed between A and C.

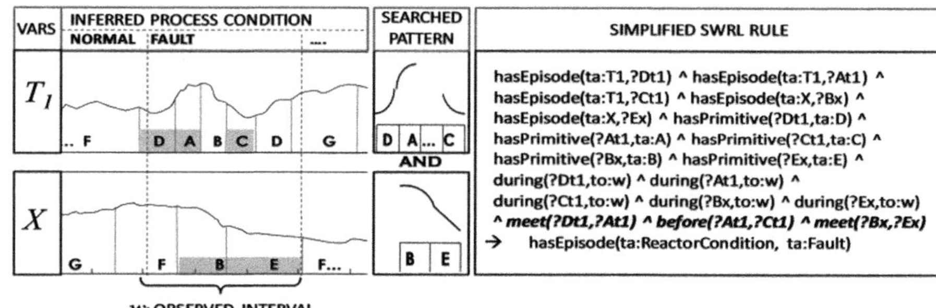

Figure 5. Multivariate qualitative temporal reasoning example.

5. Conclusions

In this work, an ontology-based Intelligent Data Analyses (IDA) framework has been presented. The proposed approach facilitates a complete data analyses, ranging from simple outliers detection to the identification of qualitative multivariate temporal patterns. To support reasoning, a novel ontology for temporal abstractions representation (TA onto) has been developed and aligned with SSN and SWRLTO and DUL. The ontology are able to store and manage alternative views of the process under study through different representation schemes. Complex temporal patterns are easily formulated and searched using Allen temporal operators in rules and queries.

References

J. F. Allen, 1983, Maintaining knowledge about temporal intervals, Communications of the ACM, 26, 11, 832-843.

J. Cheung, G. Stephanopoulos, 1990, Representation of process trends-part I. A formal representation framework, Computers and Chemical Engineering, 14, 4-5, 495-510.

M. Compton, P. Barnaghi, L. Bermudez, R. García-Castro, O. Corcho, S. Cox, J. Graybeal, M. Hauswirth, C. Henson, A. Herzog, V. Huang, K. Janowicz, W. D. Kelsey, D. L. Phuoc, L. Lefort, M. Leggieri, H. Neuhaus, A. Nikolov, K. Page, A. Passant, A. Sheth, K. Taylor, 2012, The ssn ontology of the w3c semantic sensor network incubator group, Web Semantics: Science, Services and Agents on the World Wide Web, 17, 25-32.

N. Lavrac, E. Keravnou, B. Zupan, 2000, Intelligent data analysis in medicine, Encyclopedia of computer science andtechnology, 42, 9, 113-157.

J. Lin, E. Keogh, S. Lonardi, B. Chiu, 2003, A symbolic representation of time series, with implications for streamingalgorithms, Proceedings of the 8th ACM SIGMOD workshop on Research issues in data mining and knowledgediscovery, ACM, 2-11.

C. Masolo, S. Borgo, A. Gangemi, N. Guarino, A. Oltramari, R. Oltramari, L. Schneider, L. P. Istc-cnr, I. Horrocks, 2002, The wonderweb library of foundational ontologies and the dolce ontology, Report, Wonderweb Deliverable D17, ISTC-CNR, Trento, Italy.

E. Musulin, F. Roda, M. Basualdo, 2013, A knowledge-driven approach for process supervision in chemical plants, Computers and Chemical Engineering, 59, 164-177.

M. J. O'Connor, A. K. Das, 2011, A method for representing and querying temporal information in owl, Biomedicalengineering systems and technologies, 127, 97-110.

M. Stacey, C. McGregor, 2007, Temporal abstraction in intelligent clinical data analysis: A survey, Artificial Intelligence in Medicine, 39, 1, 1-24.

K. Villez, C. Rosén, F. Anctil, C. Duchesne, P. A. Vanrolleghem, 2013, Qualitative representation of trends(QRT): Extended method for identification of consecutive inflection points, Compututer and Chemical Engineering, 48, 187-199.

Jiří Jaromír Klemeš, Petar Sabev Varbanov and Peng Yen Liew (Editors)
Proceedings of the 24th European Symposium on Computer Aided Process Engineering – ESCAPE 24
June 15-18, 2014, Budapest, Hungary.

Diagnosing Process/Model Mismatch in First-Principles Models by Latent Variable Modeling

Natascia Meneghetti, Pierantonio Facco, Fabrizio Bezzo, Massimiliano Barolo*

CAPE-Lab – Computer-Aided Process Engineering Laboratory, Department of Industrial Engineering, University of Padova, via Marzolo 9, 35131 Padova PD (Italy)
max.barolo@unipd.it

Abstract

A methodology is proposed to diagnose the causes for the process/model mismatch (PMM) that may arise when a process is simulated using a first-principles (FP) model. To this purpose, a latent variable model is used to assess the consistency between the correlation structure of a historical operation dataset and that of a similar dataset generated using the FP model. Inconsistencies between the two correlation structures are analyzed by means of diagnostic indices. Engineering judgment is then used to pinpoint which equations or parameters of the FP model are mostly responsible for the observed PMM. The proposed methodology is tested on two simulated case studies, and it is shown to provide clear indications on where the mismatch originates from.

Keywords: process/model mismatch; model diagnosis, PCA

1. Introduction

Process modeling is an essential tool to support several engineering activities, such as process design, process optimization, product design, and process control. First-principles (FP) models are often preferred to data-based (DB) ones, because they rely on a physical understanding on the system under investigation and allow some extrapolation (Pantelides and Renfro, 2013).

An FP model is made by equations and parameters. The equations represent the available knowledge on the underlying general mechanisms driving the process, whereas the parameter values inform on how the general mechanisms are tuned to the actual process. Process/model mismatch (PMM) occurs when the model results does not match the experimental evidence to a desired accuracy. The occurrence of PMM may be a critical issue if the model is used within a design, optimization or control activity. Model-based design of experiments (MBDoE) techniques (Franceschini and Macchietto, 2008) can be used both for model discrimination among alternative set of equations, and for parameter identification from a given set of equations. However, these techniques may be very demanding if one does not know in advance which equations or parameters are most responsible for the observed mismatch. Therefore, to improve the model performance when PMM is detected, it would be very useful if one were able to assess whether the observed mismatch is due to an inappropriate set of equations (structural mismatch) or to inaccurate estimation of some parameters (parametric mismatch).

In this study, a methodology is proposed to diagnose the causes for the PMM originating from the use of an FP model. Despite the importance of diagnosing PMM, this issue has been addressed mainly with respect to DB models used in process monitoring and control applications (Wang et al., 2012; Badwe et al., 2009), but has been somewhat overlooked with respect to FP models. In order to pinpoint which model equations or model parameters are most responsible for the observed PMM, we propose to use a set of historical operation data to design a DB model of the process, and to use this model to analyze the performance of the FP model. Note that we are not interested in improving the FP model performance by complementing the FP model with a DB model section, as done for example in hybrid modeling (Hosseini et al., 2013). Rather, we would like to provide the modeler with a tool that can help him/her to detect which sections of the FP model are not performing well, thus targeting subsequent research efforts (for example through an MBDoE study). The proposed methodology is tested on two simulated systems: a jacket-cooled chemical reactor and a solids milling unit.

2. Proposed methodology

We assume that an FP model describing the process is available, and that a PMM has been observed by comparing the model results to a set of available historical measurements (steady state process inputs and outputs). The rationale of the proposed diagnosing methodology is the following. First, a DB model (namely, a latent variable model) is developed to model the correlation structure of appropriate combinations of the simulated process variables, these combinations being suggested by the FP model structure. Then, it is assessed whether the combinations of the same variables, but calculated from the historical measurements, conform to this correlation structure. Finally, from the analysis of some model diagnostics, engineering knowledge is used pinpoint the FP model sections that are mostly responsible for the observed PMM.

2.1. Principal component analysis

Principal component analysis (PCA; Jackson, 1991) is used to build the DB model. PCA is a multivariate statistical correlative method that allows summarizing the information embedded in a matrix $\mathbf{X}$ $[N\times M]$, where N is the number of available samples (experiments), and M the number of correlated variables to be analyzed. PCA captures the variability of the data and the correlation among the original variables by projecting the data onto a system of latent orthogonal variables, called principal components (PCs). PCA decomposes $\mathbf{X}$ as the sum of A scores $\mathbf{t}_i$ and A loadings $\mathbf{p}_i$, where A is the number of PCs that describe an adequate percentage of variability of the dataset (Valle et al., 1999):

$$\mathbf{X} = \mathbf{t}_1\mathbf{p}_1 + \mathbf{t}_2\mathbf{p}_2 + \cdots + \mathbf{t}_A\mathbf{p}_A + \mathbf{E} \quad \text{so} \quad \mathbf{X} = \mathbf{T}\mathbf{P}^{\mathrm{T}} + \mathbf{E} \quad . \tag{1}$$

The $\mathbf{p}_i$'s and $\mathbf{t}_i$'s contain information on how variables and samples relate to each other,. $\mathbf{E}$ is the residuals matrix, which reflects the data variability that is not captured by the model (and that is expected to be non-deterministic if A is appropriate).

2.2. General procedure to diagnose process/model mismatch

The proposed methodology for PMM diagnosis consists of the following steps, where subscripts Π and M refer to the process and to the model.

1. Auxiliary variable designation. FP model simulations are carried out using the same sets of inputs available in the historical dataset (one simulation for each of the N available samples), and estimations of the measured outputs are obtained. For each sample, the inputs, outputs and parameters are combined to obtain two sets of V auxiliary variables: one set refers to the combinations obtained using the simulated measurements, the other one to the same combinations, but using the measured

variables. As will be clarified later, how the variables should be combined is suggested by the FP model structure. The auxiliary variables are then organized to form the columns of $\mathbf{X}_{\mathrm{M}}$ $[N \times V]$ and $\mathbf{X}_{\Pi}$ $[N \times V]$, which are the model matrix and the process matrix. Due to the existence of PMM, the correlation structure in $\mathbf{X}_{\Pi}$ is expected to be different from that in $\mathbf{X}_{\mathrm{M}}$.

2. DB model development. Both $\mathbf{X}_{\mathrm{M}}$ and $\mathbf{X}_{\Pi}$ are autoscaled (Eriksson et al., 2001) on the mean and standard deviation of $\mathbf{X}_{\mathrm{M}}$. A PCA model is then built from $\mathbf{X}_{\mathrm{M}}$, and the residuals matrix $\mathbf{E}_{\mathrm{M}}$ is calculated from:

$$\hat{\mathbf{X}}_{\mathrm{M}} = \mathbf{T}_{\mathrm{M}}\mathbf{P}_{\mathrm{M}}^{\mathrm{T}}, \quad \mathbf{E}_{\mathrm{M}} = \mathbf{X}_{\mathrm{M}} - \hat{\mathbf{X}}_{\mathrm{M}} \tag{2}$$

3. Process matrix projection. $\mathbf{X}_{\Pi}$ is projected onto the PCA model space:

$$\hat{\mathbf{X}}_{\Pi} = \mathbf{T}_{\Pi}\mathbf{P}_{\mathrm{M}}^{\mathrm{T}}, \quad \mathbf{T}_{\Pi} = \mathbf{X}_{\Pi}\mathbf{P}_{\mathrm{M}}, \quad \mathbf{E}_{\Pi} = \mathbf{X}_{\Pi} - \hat{\mathbf{X}}_{\Pi} \tag{3}$$

4. Residuals analysis. Once the normality of the distribution of the residuals (i.e., columns of $\mathbf{E}_{\mathrm{M}}$ and $\mathbf{E}_{\Pi}$) has been checked, the two residuals matrices are compared to identify the auxiliary variables that are most responsible for the inconsistency in the correlation structures of $\mathbf{X}_{\mathrm{M}}$ and $\mathbf{X}_{\Pi}$. These auxiliary variables, together with engineering judgment, are used to pinpoint which model sections are most responsible for the observed PMM. Note that $\mathbf{E}_{\Pi}$ does not reflect only the mismatch between $\mathbf{X}_{\Pi}$ and $\mathbf{X}_{\mathrm{M}}$, but also the fraction of data variability not described by the PCA model. In order account for the contribution due to the PMM only, the contribution related to the un-modeled variability should be removed from $\mathbf{E}_{\Pi}$. For this reason, the residuals analysis results are expressed as the difference of the sum of squares of the residuals for each column c ($DSSR_c$):

$$DSSR_c = \sum_{n=1}^{N}(e_{\Pi,n,c})^2 - \sum_{n=1}^{N}(e_{\mathrm{M},n,c})^2 \tag{4}$$

3. Case studies and results

The proposed procedure is applied to two simulated case studies: a jacketed continuous stirred tank reactor (CSTR), and a continuous solids milling process.

3.1. Case study 1: CSTR

The system consists of a CSTR equipped with a cooling jacket. It is assumed that two consecutive exothermic reactions occur in the reactor:

$$\begin{aligned} &\text{reaction1: } \mathrm{A+B \rightarrow 2C} \quad ; \quad \Delta H_1 < 0 \quad ; \quad R_{\Pi,1} = k_1 C_A C_B \\ &\text{reaction2: } \mathrm{C \rightarrow D} \quad ; \quad \Delta H_2 < 0 \quad ; \quad R_{\Pi,2} = k_2 C_C \end{aligned} \tag{5}$$

where A and B are the reactants, C is the desired product, D is the byproduct, C_i is the molar concentration of species i, and R_r, k_r and ΔH_r are the rate, kinetic constant and enthalpy of reaction r. The system is described by the following model (Luyben, 2007):

$$
\begin{aligned}
&C_i^{out} - C_i^{in} - \sum_{r=1}^{2}\left(\nu_{i,r}\cdot R_r\right)\cdot\theta = 0 \quad , \qquad i = \mathrm{A,B,C,D} \\
&\rho\cdot c_P\cdot\left(T^{out} - T^{in}\right) - \left(-Q_R - Q_{dot}/V\right)\cdot\theta = 0 \\
&\rho_w\cdot c_{P,w}\cdot\left(T_j^{\,out} - T_j^{\,in}\right) - \left(Q_{dot}/F_j\right) = 0 \\
&Q_{dot} = UA\left(T^{out} - T_j^{\,out}\right)
\end{aligned}
\quad , \qquad (6)
$$

where subscripts *in* and *out* refer to inlet and outlet conditions, subscript j refers to the jacket, subscript w refers to the cooling water, v is the stoichiometric coefficient, V is the reactor volume, θ is the residence time, c_P is the specific heat, ρ is the density, Q_R the heat of reaction, T stands for temperature, F stands for flowrate, Q_{dot} is the heat exchange between the reactor and the external jacket, U is the heat transfer coefficient, and A the total area available for the exchange.

The historical dataset consists of 15 different steady states, with different values of the following measured variables: C_i (in and out), T and T_j (in and out), θ and F_j. Eq. (5) represents the true (hence, unknown) process kinetics, which was used in (6) to generate the historical dataset. PMM was enforced by erroneously modeling the kinetics of the first reaction as $R_{\mathrm{M},1} = k_1 C_A^{2/3} C_B^{4/3}$, and using this reaction rate in (6) instead of $R_{\Pi,1}$; $R_{\mathrm{M},2} = R_{\Pi,2}$ was set instead. The reasons of the observed PMM could not be diagnosed by simple comparison of the simulated and historical outputs.

3.1.1. Results

Following the assumed FP model structure, 14 auxiliary variables are defined:

$$
\begin{aligned}
&x_1 = C_A^{out} - C_A^{in} && x_5 = -\nu_A\cdot R_{\mathrm{M},1}\cdot\theta && x_{10} = \rho\cdot c_P\cdot\left(T^{out} - T^{in}\right) \\
&x_2 = C_B^{out} - C_B^{in} && x_6 = -\nu_B\cdot R_{\mathrm{M},1}\cdot\theta && x_{11} = \theta\cdot\left(-Q_R\right) \\
&x_3 = C_C^{out} - C_C^{in} && x_7 = -\nu_C\cdot R_{\mathrm{M},1}\cdot\theta && x_{12} = -\theta\cdot\left(-Q_{dot}/V\right) \\
&x_4 = C_D^{out} - C_D^{in} && x_8 = -\nu_C\cdot R_{\mathrm{M},2}\cdot\theta && x_{13} = \rho_w\cdot c_{P,w}\cdot\left(T_j^{out} - T_j^{in}\right) \\
& && x_9 = -\nu_D\cdot R_{\mathrm{M},2}\cdot\theta && x_{14} = -Q_{dot}\cdot F_j
\end{aligned}
\quad , \qquad (7)
$$

and $\mathbf{X}_\mathrm{M}$ and $\mathbf{X}_\Pi$ are built from them. Note that the auxiliary variables represent portions of the assumed FP model structure.

Once the PCA model is built from $\mathbf{X}_\mathrm{M}$ (step 2), $\mathbf{X}_\Pi$ is projected onto this model (step 3). Due to the existence of PMM, the PCs that optimally describe the variability of $\mathbf{X}_\mathrm{M}$ are not able to reliably represent the correlation structure in $\mathbf{X}_\Pi$. Analysis of the residuals (step 4) shows that the largest values of $DSSR_c$ is encountered for auxiliary variables x_5, x_6 and x_7 (Figure 1*a*). Hence, these variables mostly contribute to the observed PMM. From (7), one can see that $x_{5\text{-}7}$ all depend on $R_{\mathrm{M},1}$. Therefore, it can be concluded that the observed PMM is most probably due to a mismatch on the modeling of the kinetics of the first reaction. This conclusion is further supported by the large $DSSR_c$ shown by $x_{1\text{-}2.}$ In fact, both these variables include measurements of reactant concentrations involved in R_1. Also other auxiliary variables show relatively large $DSSR_c$ values, and this is due again to their correlation with R_1.

3.2. Case study 2: milling process

The milling process refers to the size reduction of a granulated polymer. The FP model includes mass and population balances of the solid distributed phase. The population balance equation on mass basis for phase p is (Vogel and Peukert, 2005):

$$\frac{\partial M_p(y,t)}{\partial y} = \int_0^{y_{\max}} P_{B,p}(z) b_p(y,z) M_p(z,t) dz - P_{B,p}(y) M_p(y,t) \quad , \tag{8}$$

where the change of the particle mass M_p of a certain size y is given by the mass leaving the size band as fragments (second addendum on the right term in (8)) and the mass entering the size band as fragments from larger size (z) (integral term in (8)). Two key quantities are considered: the grinding rate selection function $P_{B,p}$ and the breakage function b_p. Different empirical formulations for the breakage and selection functions are available in the literature. The one suggested by Vogel and Peukert (2005) was used:

$$\begin{aligned} &B_p = \left(\frac{z}{y}\right)^q \frac{1}{2}\left(1+\tanh\left(\frac{y-y'}{y'}\right)\right), \quad \frac{\partial B_p(z,y)}{\partial y} = b_p(z,y) \quad , \\ &P_{B,p} = 1-\exp\left(-f_{\mathrm{Mat}} zk\left(W_{m,\mathrm{kin}} - W_{m,\min}\right)\right) \end{aligned} \tag{9}$$

where $P_{B,p}$ and b_p depend on several parameters (f_{Mat}, $W_{m,\mathrm{kin}}$, $W_{m,\min}$, q, k) specific of the type of material involved (namely, PMMA-G55 polymer). Details on the model parameters and on the solution of the population balances are reported by Vogel and Peukert (2005). The original values of the parameters were used to obtain the results for the process, and gSOLIDS 3.0 (2013) was used as a simulation tool.

The historical dataset consists of 15 different steady states, with different values of the following measured variables: mass flowrate W, mean particle diameter D_{in} and standard deviation σ_{in} of the particle size distribution (PSD_{in}) of the inlet material, bulk density ρ_{bulk}, rotational velocity of the mill v, and final PSD (PSD_{out}). Note that the only measured output is the final PSD. Parametric mismatch was enforced by altering the values of several parameters in the model. The results obtained by modifying (from q_Π to q_M) the value of parameter q, related to the rotational velocity of the milling, are reported in the next section.

3.2.1. Results

Based on the FP model structure, 12 auxiliary variables were defined as:

$$\begin{array}{lll} x_1 = f_1(P_{B,p}) & x_5 = f_5(B_p, P_{B,p}, PSD, \rho) & x_9 = W_{m,\mathrm{kin}} \\ x_2 = f_2(PSD) & x_6 = f_6(P_{B,p}, PSD, \rho) & x_{10} = W_{m,\min} \\ x_3 = f_3(B_p) & x_7 = f_7(PSD_{out}) & x_{11} = k \\ x_4 = f_4(B_p, P_{B,p}) & x_8 = f_{\mathrm{Mat}} & x_{12} = q_\mathrm{M} \end{array} \quad , \tag{10}$$

where, for the sake of simplicity, notation $f_n(\cdot)$ has been used to indicate the function of variable $(\cdot)$ resulting from the model structure. Note that, since PSD_{out} is the only measured output, $\mathbf{X}_\mathrm{M}$ and $\mathbf{X}_\Pi$ turn out to be equal except for column x_7 (which changed as a result of the modification of q). Hence, due to output measurement deficiency, this case study is tougher than the previous one.

After projection of $\mathbf{X}_\Pi$, the results in Figure 1*b* are obtained. The very large $DSSR_c$ value associated to x_7 is due to the PSD_{out} differences in the two matrices. The fact that

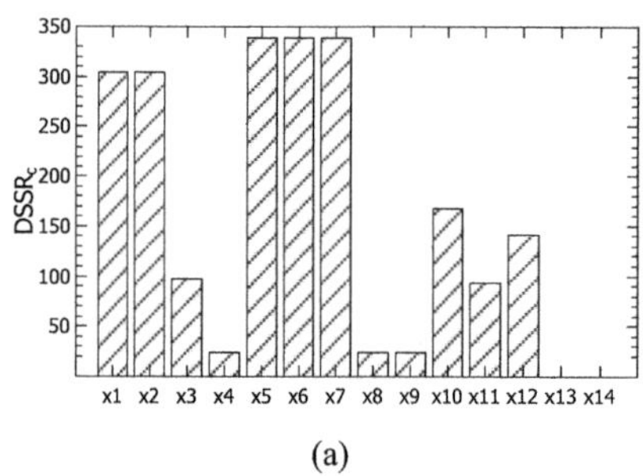

(a)

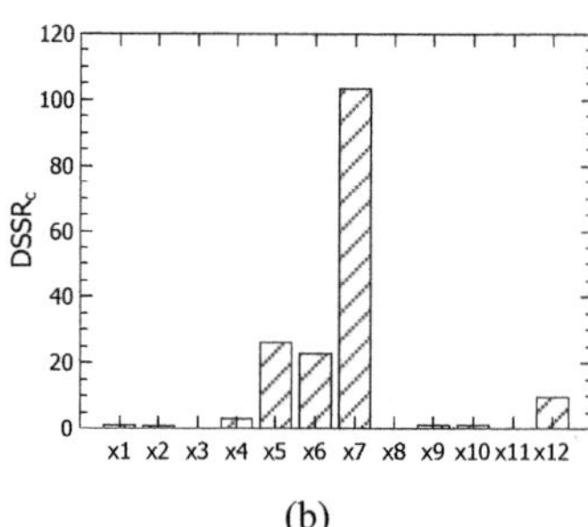

(b)

Figure 1. Results of the analysis in terms of $DSSR_c$ for each auxiliary variable for (*a*) Case study 1 (4 PCs were used) and (*b*) Case study 2 (4 PCs were used). About 90 % of the data variability was explained in both case studies.

also x_5, x_6 and x_{12} show relatively large values of $DSSR_c$ suggests that the FP model cannot describe parameter q adequately. In fact, q affects x_{12} directly, but it also affects x_5 via B_p, where B_p is correlated to $P_{B,p}$, i.e. to x_6.

4. Conclusions

A methodology has been proposed to diagnose the causes of the PMM that may arise when a FP process model is developed. A DB model is used to assess the consistency between the correlation structure of a historical operation dataset and that of a similar dataset generated using the FP model. Diagnostic indices and engineering judgment are used to pinpoint which equations or parameters of the FP model are mostly responsible for the PMM. Two simulated case studies confirm the effectiveness of the proposed methodology.

References

A. S. Badwe, R. D. Gudi, R. S. Patwardhan, S. L. Shah, S., C. Patwardhan, 2009, Detection of model-plant mismatch in MPC applications, J. Process Contr., 19, 1305-1313.

L. Eriksson, E. Johansson, N. Ketteneh-Wold, S. Wold, 2001, Multi - and Megavariate Data Analysis, Principles and Application, Umetrics AB, Umeå, Sweden.

G. Franceschini, S. Macchietto, 2008, Model-based design of experiments for parameter precision: State of the art, Chem. Eng. Sci., 63, 4846-4872.

gSOLIDS, 2013, (version 3.0), Process Systems Enterprise Ltd., London, UK.

A. Hosseini, M. Oshaghi, S. Engell, 2013, Control of the particle size distribution in emulsion polymerization by mid-course correction using a hybrid model, Computer Aided Chemical Engineering, 32, 787-792.

J.E. Jackson, 1991, A User's Guide to Principal Components, John Wiley & Sons, New York, NJ.

W. L. Luyben, 2007, Chemical Reactor Design and Control, John Wiley & Sons, New York, NJ.

C.C. Pantelides, J. G. Renfro, 2013, The online use of first-principles models in process operations: Review, current status and future needs, Comput. Chem. Eng., 51, 136-148.

S. Valle, W. Li, S. J. Qin, 1999, Selection of the Number of Principal Components: The Variance of the Reconstruction Error Criterion with a Comparison to Other Methods, Ind. Eng. Chem. Res., 38, 4389-4401.

L. Vogel, W.Peukert, 2005, From single particle impact behavior to modelling of impact mills, Chem. Eng. Sci., 60, 5164-6176.

H. Wang , L. Xie, Z. Song, 2012, A Review for Model Plant Mismatch Measures in Process Monitoring, Chinese J. Chem. Eng., 20, 1039-1046.

Author Index

9780444634559